The Good Food Guide 2002

D0525559

WHICH? BOOKS

Which? Books is the book publishing arm of Consumers' Association, which was set up in 1957 to improve the standards of goods and services available to the public. Everything Which? publishes aims to help consumers, by giving them the independent information they need to make informed decisions. These publications, known throughout Britain for their quality, integrity and impartiality, have been held in high regard for four decades.

Independence does not come cheap: the guides carry no advertising, and no restaurant or hotel can buy an entry in our guides, or treat our inspectors to free meals or accommodation. This policy, and our practice of rigorously re-researching our guides for each edition, helps us to provide our readers with information of a standard and quality that cannot be surpassed.

The Good Food Guide 2002

Edited by

Jim Ainsworth

WHICH? BOOKS
CONSUMERS' ASSOCIATION

Which? Books are commissioned and researched by
Consumers' Association and published by
Which? Ltd, 2 Marylebone Road,
London NW1 4DF

Distributed by The Penguin Group:
Penguin Books Ltd, 27 Wrights Lane,
London W8 5TZ

Copyright © 2001 Which? Ltd

Base mapping © Map Marketing Ltd/
European Map Graphics 2001
Map information © Which? Ltd 2001

British Library Cataloguing in Publication Data
A catalogue record for this book is
available from the British Library

ISBN 0 85202 856 3

No part of this publication may be reproduced or transmitted in any form or by any means, electronically or mechanically, including photocopying, recording or any information storage or retrieval system, without prior permission in writing from the publisher, nor be otherwise circulated in any form of binding or cover other than that in which it is published and without a similar condition being imposed on the subsequent purchaser. This publication is not included under licences issued by the Copyright Agency.

The Good Food Guide is a registered trade mark of
Which? Ltd.

For a full list of Which? books, please write to:
Which? Books, Castlemead, Gascoyne Way,
Hertford X, SG14 1LH
or access our web site at http://www.which.net

Photoset by Tradespools Ltd, Frome, Somerset
Printed in England by Clays Ltd, St Ives plc

Cover design by Price Watkins Design Limited

Contents

Features

Main entries

The Good Food Guide voucher scheme (£5)

Again this year the Guide includes three £5 vouchers that readers will be able to redeem against the price of meals taken in participating restaurants. (Look for the (£5) symbol at the very end of entries to locate those participating.) Only one voucher may be used per booked table, for a minimum of two people. Remember that your intention to use the voucher MUST be mentioned at the time of booking. Some restaurants may restrict use of the voucher at some sessions or for some menus (usually 'special offer' or lower-cost set meals); it is best to ask when booking. Actual vouchers (not photocopies) must be presented. The vouchers will be valid from 1 October 2001 to 30 September 2002, and may not be used in conjunction with any other offers.

The Guide online

Internet users can find *The Good Food Guide* online at the Which? Online web site http://www.which.net. (You will need to be a Which? Online subscriber to make full use of the Guide online.) For a free CD that will give you more details about Which? Online and how to be connected to the Internet, phone 08459 830254.

Update service

Written details of restaurant sales, closures, chef changes and so on since this edition of the Guide was published will be available free of charge from 1 December 2001 to 1 May 2002. Readers should write to: FREEPOST, Update, *The Good Food Guide*, 2 Marylebone Road, London NW1 4DF (no stamp is required if you post your request in the UK). Alternatively, you may email *goodfoodguide@which.net* (remember to include your full name and address when you email), or phone 020-7770 7551. As always, readers who send in reports on meals will automatically be sent an Update Sheet.

How to use the Guide

FINDING A RESTAURANT

If you are seeking a restaurant in a particular area: *first go to the maps* at the centre of the book. Once you know the locality (or, for London, the restaurant name), go to the relevant section of the book to find the entry for the restaurant. The Guide's main entries are divided into seven sections: London, England, Scotland, Wales, Channel Islands, Northern Ireland, and Republic of Ireland. In the London section, restaurants are listed alphabetically by name; in all other sections, they are listed by locality (usually the name of the town or village).

In addition to the main entries are the Round-ups (a range of restaurants, cafés, bistros and pubs that are worth a visit but do not merit a full entry): those for London can be found just after the London main-entry section, and those for everywhere else are towards the back of the book just after the Republic of Ireland main-entry section.

If you know the name of the restaurant: *go to the index* at the back of the book, which lists both main and Round-up entries.

If you are seeking award-winning restaurants, those offering a particular cuisine, etc.: *make use of the lists* starting on page 11, which feature the top-rated restaurants, restaurants with outstanding wine cellars, restaurants of the year, new entries in the Guide, London restaurants by cuisine, budget eating and other helpful groupings.

HOW TO READ A GUIDE ENTRY

A sample entry is set out overleaf. At the top of the entry you will find the restaurant's name, map number, address, telephone and fax numbers, its email address and web site address if it has these, as well as any symbols that may apply to the establishment, (see inside front cover for what the symbols stand for). The cuisine style is also given; this is not meant to be a comprehensive assessment of cooking style, but rather to act as a helpful pointer and in many cases has been suggested by the restaurant itself. At the top of entries you will also find the mark, from 1 to 10, awarded by the editor for cooking (see next page for a full explanation of marks), and the cost range for one person having a three-course meal including wine (see page 9 for how that is worked out). The middle part of the entry describes food, wines, atmosphere and so on, while the final section gives a wealth of additional information (explained in greater detail on pages 9-10).

LOCALITY County map 4

▲ Restaurant Name £ **NEW ENTRY**

Address
TEL: (01234) 111111 FAX: (01234) 222222 COOKING **6**
EMAIL: restaurant@place.co.uk MODERN BRITISH
WEB SITE: www.restaurant.co.uk £15 to £100

This is where you will find information about the restaurant – cuisine, service, décor, wine list, and any other points of interest not covered by the details at the foot of the entry. Each entry in the Guide has been re-researched from scratch, and is based on information taken from readers' reports received over the past year, confirmed where necessary by anonymous inspection. In every case, readers and inspectors have been prepared to endorse the quality of the cooking. The text usually concludes with a description of the wines offered.

CHEFS: : John and Mary Smith PROPRIETOR: : Mary Smith OPEN: : Mon to Fri L 12 to 2, Mon to Sat D 7 to 10 CLOSED: : 25 and 26 Dec, Easter, 2 weeks July, bank hols · MEALS: : alc (main courses £9 to £15). Set D £16 (2 courses) to £20. Cover £1.50. Light L available. SERVICE: : not inc, card slips closed; 10% for parties of 6 or more CARDS: : Amex, Delta, Diners, MasterCard, Switch, Visa DETAILS: : 50 seats. 15 seats outside. Private parties: 25 main room, 15 private room. Car park. Vegetarian meals. Children's helpings. No children under 7. Jacket and tie. No smoking in dining-room. Wheelchair access (also WC). No music. Air-conditioned ACCOMMODATION: : 5 rooms, all with bath/shower. TV. Phone. B&B £35 to £80. Rooms for disabled. Baby facilities. Swimming pool. (*The Which? Hotel Guide*) (£5)

- For an explanation of symbols, see inside front cover.

Cooking mark

Marks are given out of 10, and are for cooking only, as perceived by the *Guide* and its readers. They signify the following:

1–2 COMPETENT COOKING Cafés, pubs, bistros and restaurants which offer sound, basic, capable cooking. Those scoring 2 use better ingredients, take fewer short-cuts, please more reporters, and make good neighbourhood restaurants.

3–4 COMPETENT TO GOOD COOKING These restaurants use fine ingredients and cook them appropriately, although some inconsistencies may be noted. They please reporters most of the time. Those scoring 4 show greater skill in handling materials, and are worthy of special note in the locality.

5–6 GOOD TO VERY GOOD COOKING These restaurants use high-quality ingredients, achieve consistently good results, and are enthusiastically reported. Those scoring 6 show a degree of flair, and are among the best in the region.

7–8 VERY GOOD TO EXCELLENT COOKING A high level of ambition and achievement means that the finest ingredients are consistently treated with skill and imagination. Those scoring 8 are worth a special effort to visit.

9–10 **The best** These are the top restaurants in the country. They are few in number, and can be expensive, but are highly individual and display impressive artistry. Those scoring 10 are the A-team, and can comfortably stand comparison with the stiffest international competition.

Cost

The price range given is based on the cost of a three-course meal (lunch and/or dinner) for one person, including coffee, house wine, service and cover charge where applicable, according to information supplied by the restaurant. The lower figure is the least you are likely to pay, from either á la carte or set-price menus, and may apply only to lunch. The higher figure indicates a probable maximum cost, sometimes based on a set-price meal of more than three courses, if that is what is offered. This figure is inflated by 20 per cent to reflect the fact that some people may order more expensive wine, extra drinks and some higher-priced 'special' dishes, and that price rises may come into effect during the life-time of this edition of the Guide.

Meals

At the bottom of entries information on the types of meals offered is given, with any variations for lunch (L) and dinner (D), and details of availability. An á la carte menu is signified by the letters *alc*. This is followed by a range of prices for main courses, rounded up to the nearest 50p. *Set L* denotes a set-price lunch; *Set D* means set-price dinner. Set meals usually consist of three courses, but can include many more. If a set meal has fewer than three courses, this is stated. If there is a cover charge, this is also indicated. Brief details of other menus, such as light lunch or bar snacks, are also given. If there is a cover charge, that is also mentioned here.

Service

Net prices means that prices of food and wine are inclusive of service charge, and this is indicated clearly on the menu and bill; *not inc*, that service is not included and is left to the discretion of the customer; *10%*, that a fixed service charge of 10 per cent is automatically added to the bill; *10% (optional)*, that 10 per cent is added to the bill along with the word 'optional' or similar qualifier; and *none*, that no service charge is made or expected and that any money offered is refused. *Card slips closed* indicates that the total on the slips of credit cards is closed when handed over for signature.

Other details

Information is also given on *seating, outside seating* and *private parties*. We say *car park* if the restaurant provides free parking facilities for patrons (*small car park* if it has only a few spaces), and say *vegetarian meals* only if menus list at least one vegetarian option as a starter and one as a main course (if this is not noted, a restaurant may still be able to offer vegetarian options with prior notice – it is worth phoning to check). Any restrictions on children are given, such as *no children* or *no children under 6 after 8pm*; otherwise, it can be assumed that children are welcome. In addition, *children's helpings* are noted if smaller portions are available at a reduced price; *jacket and tie* if it is compulsory for men to wear a jacket and tie to the restaurant; *wheelchair access* if the proprietor has confirmed that the entrance is at least 80cm wide and passages at least 120cm wide in accordance with the Royal Association for Disability and Rehabilitation (RADAR) recommendations, and *also WC* if the proprietor has assured us that toilet facilities are suitable for disabled people (*not WC* means these are not available or the proprietor is not sure). *Music* indicates that live or recorded music is usually played in the dining-room; *occasional music* that it sometimes is; *no music* that it never is.

Accommodation

For establishments offering overnight accommodation, the number of rooms, along with facilities provided in the rooms (e.g. bath/shower, TV, phone), is set out. Prices are given usually for bed and breakfast (*B&B*). *D,B&B* indicates that the price also includes dinner. The first figure given is the lowest price for one person in a single room, or single occupancy of a double, the second is the most expensive price for two people in a double room or suite. *Rooms for disabled* means the establishment has stated that its accommodation is suitable for wheelchair-users. Restrictions on children, and facilities for guests with babies, are indicated. *The Which? Hotel Guide* means the establishment is also listed in the 2001 edition of our sister guide to over 1,000 hotels in Britain.

Miscellaneous information

At the end of London entries, the nearest Underground station is given after the symbol ⊖. For restaurants that have elected to participate in the *Good Food Guide* £5 voucher scheme, a (£5) symbol appears at the very end of entries (see page 6 for further details).

The top-rated restaurants

(See pages 8-9 for explanation of marking system.)

Mark **9** for cooking

London

Gordon Ramsay, SW3

England

Le Manoir aux Quat' Saisons, Great Milton
Watcrside Inn, Bray
Winteringham Fields, Winteringham

Mark **8** for cooking

London

The Capital, SW3
cheznico, W1
Pied-à-Terre, W1
The Square, W1
La Tante Claire, SW1

England

Croque-en-Bouche, Malvern Wells
Fat Duck, Bray
Fischer's Baslow Hall, Baslow
Gidleigh Park, Chagford
Hambleton Hall, Hambleton
Lords of the Manor, Upper Slaughter
Merchant House, Ludlow

Restaurants with outstanding wine cellars

Marked in the text with a 🍷

London
Alloro, W1
Bibendum, SW3
Bleeding Heart, EC1
Cambio de Tercio, SW5
Chez Bruce, SW17
Clarke's, W8
Fifth Floor, SW1
John Burton-Race at the Landmark, NW1
Odette's, NW1
Oxo Tower, SE1
Pied-à-Terre, W1
Ransome's Dock Restaurant, SW11
RSJ, SE1
The Square, W1
Tate Gallery Restaurant, SW1

England
Birmingham, Hotel du Vin & Bistro
Bowness-on-Windermere, Porthole Eating House
Bray, Fat Duck
Bristol, Harveys
Bristol, Markwicks
Bristol, Hotel du Vin & Bistro
Chagford, Gidleigh Park
Chinnor, Sir Charles Napier
Corse Lawn, Corse Lawn House
Dedham, Le Talbooth
East Grinstead, Gravetye Manor
Faversham, Read's
Grasmere, Michaels Nook
Grasmere, White Moss House
Great Milton, Le Manoir aux Quat' Saisons
Hambleton, Hambleton Hall
Hetton, Angel Inn
Ilkley, Box Tree
Keyston, Pheasant Inn
Leeds, Leodis
Leeds, Sous le Nez en Ville
Lewdown, Lewtrenchard Manor
Little Bedwyn, Harrow Inn
Lyndhurst, Le Poussin at Parkhill
Madingley, Three Horseshoes
Malvern Wells, Croque-en-Bouche
Moulton, Black Bull Inn
Newton Longville, Crooked Billet
Norwich, Adlard's
Oxford, Cherwell Boathouse
Padstow, Seafood Restaurant
Romsey, Old Manor House
Ross-on-Wye, The Pheasant at Ross
Shepton Mallet, Bowlish House
Southwold, The Crown
Stockcross, Vineyard at Stockcross
Tunbridge Wells, Hotel du Vin & Bistro
Ullswater, Sharrow Bay
Waterhouses, Old Beams
Williton, White House
Winchester, Hotel du Vin & Bistro
Worfield, Old Vicarage

Scotland
Achiltibuie, Summer Isles Hotel
Anstruther, Cellar
Edinburgh, Valvona & Crolla Caffè Bar
Fort William, Inverlochy Castle
Glasgow, Ubiquitous Chip
Gullane, Greywalls
Kingussie, The Cross
Linlithgow, Champany Inn
Nairn, Clifton House
Peat Inn, Peat Inn

Wales
Aberdovey, Penhelig Arms Hotel
Llandudno, St Tudno Hotel
Llansanffraid Glan Conwy, Old Rectory Country House
Portmeirion, Hotel Portmeirion
Pwllheli, Plas Bodegroes
Reynoldston, Fairyhill
Talsarnau, Maes-y-Neuadd

Republic of Ireland
Dublin, Thornton's
Howth, King Sitric
Kenmare, Park Hotel Kenmare
Kenmare, Sheen Falls Lodge, La Cascade
Newport, Newport House

Restaurants of the year

This award does not necessarily go to the restaurants with the highest mark for cooking, but rather to ones which have shown particular merit or achievement during the year. It may go to an old favourite or to a new entry, but in either case the places listed below are worth visiting in their own right, and have enhanced the eating-out experience in some way. Although we have looked at all geographical areas, not all have been lucky enough to have such special achievers.

GFG 2002 RESTAURANT OF THE YEAR
Winteringham Fields, Winteringham, North Lincolnshire

REGIONAL RESTAURANTS OF THE YEAR

England
Devon: Carved Angel, Dartmouth
Yorkshire: Guellers, Leeds

Scotland
Braidwoods, Dalry

Wales
Tan-y-Foel, Capel Garmon

Channel Islands
Suma, Gorey

REGIONAL NEWCOMERS OF THE YEAR

London
La Trompette, W4

England
Dorset: Museum Inn, Farnham
Gloucestershire: Trouble House, Tetbury
Herefordshire: Lough Pool Inn, Sellack
Home Counties: Drakes, Abinger Hammer
Nottinghamshire: World Service, Nottingham

Scotland
Plumed Horse, Crossmichael

Wales
Seland Newydd, Pwllgloyw

COMMENDED RESTAURANTS

London
Cinnamon Club, SW1
Pétrus, SW1

England
Bedfordshire: Strawberry Tree, Milton Ernest
Devon: Percy's, Virginstow, and 22 Mill Street, Chagford
Gloucestershire: Lumière, Cheltenham
Greater Manchester: Ramsons, Ramsbottom, and White Hart, Lydgate
Northamptonshire: Roade House, Roade
Yorkshire: Mill Bank, Millbank, and Restaurant Martel, Gateforth

Scotland
Monachyle Mhor, Balquhidder

Wales
Dermott's, Swansea

London restaurants by cuisine

Boundaries between some national cuisines – British, French and Italian particularly – are not as marked as they used to be. Therefore, the restaurants listed below are classified by the predominant influence, although there may be some crossover. The headings are in many cases more generalised than the brief cuisine descriptions given at the tops of the entries themselves.

American
Christopher's, WC2
Utah, SW19

British
City Rhodes, EC4
Connaught, W1
French House Dining Room, W1
Greenhouse, W1
Popeseye, W14
Quality Chop House, EC1
Rhodes in the Square, SW1
Rules, WC2
St John, EC1
Smiths of Smithfield, EC1
Tate Gallery Restaurant, SW1
Wiltons, SW1

Chinese
Aroma II, W1
Four Seasons, W2
Fung Shing, WC2
Golden Dragon, W1
Hakkasan, W1
Mandarin Kitchen, W2
Mr Kong, WC2
Orient Restaurant, W1
Royal China, W1, W2 and NW8

Danish
Lundum's, SW7

Fish/Seafood
Back to Basics, W1
Bibendum Oyster Bar, SW3
Fish!, SE1
J. Sheekey, WC2
Livebait, SE1
Livebait's Café Fish, SW1
Lobster Pot, SE11
Lou Pescadou, SW5
One-O-One, SW1
Rasa Samudra, W1
Two Brothers, N3

French
Admiralty, WC2
Amandier, W2
Aubergine, SW10
Bleeding Heart, EC1
Brasserie St Quentin, SW3
Le Chardon, SE22
cheznico, W1
Club Gascon, EC1
Le Colombier, SW3
Le Coq d'Argent, EC2
Criterion Brasserie, W1
The Don, EC4
Drones, SW1
L'Escargot Marco Pierre White, W1
L'Estaminet, WC2
Gordon Ramsay, SW3
Le Gavroche, W1
Inter-Continental Hotel, Le Soufflé, W1
John Burton-Race at the Landmark, NW1
Mirabelle, W1
Mon Plaisir, WC2
Neat Restaurant, SE1
Oak Room Marco Pierre White, W1
L'Oranger, SW1
Pétrus, SW1
Pied-à-Terre, W1
Le Potiron Sauvage, SW6
Ritz, W1
Roussillon, SW1
Spread Eagle, SE10
La Tante Claire, SW1
La Trompette, W4

Greek
Real Greek, N1

Hungarian
Gay Hussar, W1

Indian/Pakistani
Babur Brasserie, SE23
Bar Zaika Bazaar, SW3
Café Spice Namaste, E1 and SW11
Chor Bizarre, W1
Chutney Mary, SW10
Cinnamon Club, SW1
ginger, W2
Haandi, SW3
Masala Zone, W1
Mela, WC2
Mem Saheb on Thames, E14
New Tayyabs, E1
Old Delhi, W2
Parsee, N19
Porte des Indes, W1
Radha Krishna Bhavan, SW17
Rasa Travancore, N16
Sarkhel's, SW18
Salloos, SW1
Soho Spice, W1
Tabla, E14
Tamarind, W1
Yatra, W1
Zaika, SW3

Indian vegetarian
Kastoori, SW17
Rani, N3
Rasa, N16 and Rasa W1
Sabras, NW10

Indonesian/Straits
Gourmet Garden, NW4
Singapore Garden, NW6

Italian
Al Duca, SW1
Alloro, W1
Al San Vincenzo, W2
Arancia, SE16
Assaggi, W2
Cecconi's, W1
Il Convivio, SW1
Del Buongustaio, SW15
Enoteca Turi, SW15
Il Forno, W1
Great Eastern Dining Room, EC2
Green Olive, W9
Ibla, W1
Isola, SW1
Metrogusto, N1 and SW8
Neal Street Restaurant, WC2
Olivo, SW11
Passione, W1
Red Pepper, W9
Riso, W4
Riva, SW13
River Café, W6
Rosmarino, NW8
Salusbury, NW6
Sartoria, W1
Spiga, W1
Teca, W1
Zafferano, SW1

Japanese/Sushi bars
Café Japan, NW11

Itsu, SW3 and Itsu (Soho), W1
Kiku, W1
K10, EC2
Kulu Kulu Sushi, W1
Moshi Moshi Sushi, EC2, EC4 and E14
Nobu, W1
Sushi-Say, NW2
Ubon, E14
Wagamama, WC1

North African/ Middle Eastern

Adams Café, W12
Al Hamra, W1
Azou, W6
Istanbul Iskembecisi, N16
Iznik, N5
Noura, SW1
Original Tagines, W1
Tas, SE1

Peruvian

Fina Estampa, SE1

Russian/ Eurasian

Little Georgia, E8

Spanish

Cambio de Tercio, SW5
Cigala, WC1
Gaudí, EC1
Lomo, SW10
Moro, EC1

Thai

Blue Elephant, SW6
Mantanah, SE25
Sri Siam Soho, W1
Thai Garden, E2

Vegetarian

Gate, NW3

London party bookings for 25 or more in private rooms

London

Alastair Little, W1
Amandier, W2
Aroma II, W1
Atlantic Bar and Grill, W1
Belair House, SE2
Bleeding Heart, EC1
Bluebird, SW3
Brackenbury, W6
Brown's Hotel, Restaurant 1837, W1
Chinon, W14
Chor Bizarre, W1
Christopher's, WC2
Chutney Mary, SW10
Cinnamon Club, SW1
Le Colombier, SW3
Cotto, W14
Del Buongustaio, SW15
Delfina Studio Café, SE1
L'Escargot Marco Pierre White, W1
Fina Estampa, SE1
First Floor, W11
Fung Shing, WC2
Gay Hussar, W1
Golden Dragon, W1
Green Olive, W9
Ibla, W1
Ivy, WC2
John Burton-Race at the Landmark, NW1
Kensington Place, W8
Launceston Place, W8
Lindsay House, W1
Lobster Pot, SE11
Maison Novelli, EC1
Mandarin Oriental Hyde Park, Foliage, SW1
Mash, W1
Mela, WC2
Mem Saheb on Thames, E14
Mezzo, W1
Mirabelle, W1
Montcalm Hotel, Crescent, W1
Neat Restaurant, SE1
Nobu, W1
Odette's, NW1
1 Lombard Street, EC3
Parade, W5
Le Potiron Sauvage, SW6
Quaglino's, SW1
Quo Vadis, W1
Rasa Samudra, W1
Ritz, W1
Roussillon, SW1
RSJ, SE1
Singapore Garden, NW6
Smiths of Smithfield, Top Floor, EC1
Soho Spice, W1
Spread Eagle, SE10
Sri Siam Soho, W1
Tabla, E1
Tas, SE1
Tentazioni, SE1
The Vale, W9
White Onion, N1
Yatra, W1

London restaurants with at least 1 no-smoking dining room

Data supplied by the restaurants themselves and in most cases (but not all) substantiated by reporters or inspectors. If you find any in this list that do not belong here, please let us know.

Chez Bruce, SW1
Gate, NW3
Gaudi, EC1
ginger, W2
Great Eastern Hotel, Aurora, EC2
Itsu, SW3
Itsu (Soho), W1
K10, EC2
Kulu Kulu Sushi, W1
Livebait, SE1
Livebait's Café Fish, W1
Masala Zone, W1
Mela, WC2
Mem Saheb on Thames, E14
Metrogusto Islington, N1
Montcalm Hotel, Crescent, W1
Moshi Moshi Sushi, EC2, EC4 and E14
National Gallery, Crivelli's Garden, WC2
National Portrait Gallery, Portrait, WC2
Neat Restaurant, SE1
Nobu, W1
No. 6 George Street, W1
One-O-One, SW1
Phoenix, SW15
Rani, N3
Rasa, N16 and W1
Rasa Samudra, W1
Rasa Travancore, N16
Rules, WC2
Spiga, W1
Stepping Stone, SW8
Sugar Club, W1
Sarkhel's, SW18
Tabla, E14
Tamarind, W1
Sugar Club, W1
Thai Garden, E2
The Vale, W9
Villandry, W1
Wagamama, WC1
Yatra, W1

Budget eating £

At the restaurants below, it is possible to have a three-course meal, including coffee, half a bottle of wine and service, for £25 or less per person, at any time the restaurant is open, i.e. at dinner as well as lunch. It may be possible to spend considerably more than this, but by choosing carefully you should find £25 or less achievable.

London

Adams Café, W12
Anglesea Arms, W6
Arancia, SE1
Aroma II, W1
Eagle, EC1
Gate, NW3
Gourmet Garden, NW4
Istanbul Iskembecisi, N16
Itsu (Soho), WC1
Kastoori, SW1
Kulu Kulu Sushi, W1
Little Georgia, E8
Masala Zone, W1
Mela, W2
Mem Saheb on Thames, E14
Mr Kong, W2
New Tayyabs, E1
Radha Krishna Bhavan, SW17
Rani, N3
Rasa, N16 and W1
Tas, SE1
Thai Garden, E2
Two Brothers, N3
The Vale, W9
Wagamama, W1

England

Aldeburgh, Lighthouse
Aldeburgh, Regatta
Bath, Richmond Arms
Birmingham, Chung Ying
Bradford, Akbar's
Burnham Market, Hoste Arms
Carterway Heads, Manor House Inn
Chester, Brasserie 10/16
Colchester, Lemon Tree
Corscombe, Fox Inn
Dartmouth, Carved Angel Café
Exeter, Brazz
Foulsham, The Gamp
Frithsden, Alford Arms
Great Yeldham, White Hart
Harrogate, Drum and Monkey
Ipswich, Mortimer's on the Quay
Lavenham, Angel
Leeds, Salvo's
Liverpool, Tai Pan
Manchester, Great Wall
Manchester, Greens
Manchester, Koreana
Manchester, Kosmos Taverna
Manchester, Ocean Treasure
Manchester, Le Petit Blanc
Manchester, Tai Pan
Masham, Floodlite
Mill Bank, Millbank
Nantwich, Peppers
Oxford, Al-Shami
Paxford, Churchill Arms
Peter Tavy, Peter Tavy Inn
Ponteland, Café 21
Richmond, Chez Lindsay
Rye, Landgate Bistro
Sawley, Spread Eagle
Sellack, Lough Pool Inn
Sudbury, Red Onion Bistro
Wethersfield, Dicken's
Whitby, Magpie Café
Woodbridge, Captain's Table

Scotland

Auchmithie, But 'n' Ben
Blair Atholl, Loft
Cairndow, Loch Fyne Oyster Bar
Edinburgh, Kalpna
Glasgow, No. Sixteen
Glasgow, Café Gandolfi

Wales

Broad Haven, Druidstone
Cardiff, Izakaya Japanese Tavern
Dolgellau, Dylanwad Da
Llanarmon Dyffryn Ceiriog, West Arms
Swansea, La Braseria

Northern Ireland

Belfast, La Belle Epoque
Limavady, Lime Tree

Arguments will still rage about the best way to proceed with our farming industry, but the cumulative effect of a series of disasters over the years, from salmonella in eggs, via BSE, to FMD, has been to put a big question mark over the large-scale industrialisation of agriculture. If sheep had not been moved around the country so much, so the argument goes, then the spread of FMD would not have been as great. If cattle had not been fed an unnatural diet, we would not have had BSE. If poultry were properly kept in low densities with access to fields and open air, they would not need to be junkies, injected with antibiotics which travel up the food chain to us. And if we, the public, were not so hung up on buying cheap meat, but would be prepared to pay a fair price for humanely and sensibly reared animals, then none of this counter-intuitive agribusiness would be necessary. Cheap food, it is becoming apparent, is just about the most expensive food there is.

It is not such a neat, open-and-shut case, of course. But at least none of us now has an excuse to close our eyes to the issues that have been raised. At least it has focused attention on the conditions in which animals are kept when alive, the way they are transported and how they are slaughtered, and our sense of value of the meat produced. If the opportunities for small-scale food producers are enhanced as a result, it may even give us a real food heritage to be proud of.

It is a pity that it takes an outbreak of a devastating disease for those in power to act. Many commentators have alerted the world at large to food-industry problems well in advance of actual disaster, but have typically not been taken seriously by those in a position to do something about it. Environmental scientists are encountering similar problems in some quarters with their predictions about the effects of global warming. In the case of food, it will be interesting to see whether government response is limited to the specific after-effects of FMD, or whether it extends to concern for other aspects of food production. Fishing is an obvious example, a branch of the industry now in serious decline and torn between conflicting ideas and practices.

On the one hand, over-fishing in the wild has the potential to deplete stocks to the point of no return, so that whole coastal communities are threatened, and a generation may never know what cod or wild salmon tastes like. On the other hand, fish farming has brought its own difficulties, disease and pollution among them: it seems that intensive agriculture, no matter what species it is applied to, is not the easy answer its proponents claim. Once again, if we didn't insist on cheap food, we might not be in this pickle.

Inside this edition . . .

When it comes to buying up the relatively small supplies of top-quality home-grown material, restaurateurs are often at the front of the queue, although judging by the mantra that some of them trot out about using 'only local and organic ingredients' one could be forgiven for thinking that every last field and plot in the country was now devoted to organic agriculture. What they do with those ingredients has been the subject of this Guide since it first appeared in 1951/52, and we asked a long-standing friend, Professor of Cultural Studies Fred Inglis, to chart its progress from inception to the present day (see 'GFG: 50 years on', in the pages that follow).

We have also asked other friends to give us a view about how restaurants in Britain, particularly London, compare with some of the best around the world. We sent them on expenses-paid trips to four continents to gather information. Only kidding: the Guide doesn't have that kind of money. They are people who eat out regularly, here and abroad, and who are thus in a position to address that vexed question: is London really a world gastronomic capital, or are we just deluding ourselves? (See 'Far-flung food'.)

And wine lovers should note that, for this edition, instead of our two-yearly vintage chart, we thought it would be more reader-friendly to give a succinct rundown on how best to home in on the best-value and most interesting wines on restaurant lists. Food and wine writer Stuart Walton has done just that in 'A happy diversity'.

That the Guide has survived and prospered for half a century is thanks to you, the reader. You help us discover, assess, compare and analyse what the best of British kitchens prepare, day in, day out, for months on end, until it is time to begin the next edition (work on which, as usual, has already started by the time you read this). You tell us what you enjoy and what bugs you, you bring us the best and worst of your experiences, for which the Guide, and your fellow readers, are forever grateful.

What takes the edge off

Eating out has to be about enjoyment; otherwise we might as well all pack up and go home. And it is when the edge is taken off what should be a happy occasion that letters and reports tend to get longer and more incandescent. Just in case there are any restaurateurs reading this, you may wish to know how to make life more unpleasant for us. Here are ten tips:

1. As soon as you answer the telephone, say 'Can you hold?', but don't wait for a reply, just put the customer on hold anyway and leave them there until you have finished whatever it was you were doing.
2. Tell them that, if the booking is for six weeks hence, they can have a table for dinner at either 6pm or 11pm. Everybody knows that your restaurant will be half empty all evening, and that it doesn't matter two hoots what time they come, but where's the fun in that?
3. Then – most important this – ask for a faxed confirmation and credit card details. Remember, you are trying to make as much money as you can out of gullible punters, so you need them in a legal armlock. And by all means debit the card before the customer arrives to take up the booking, as you did to one of our inspectors.
4. Misplace at least some of your bookings every mealtime, so that you can greet customers with a blank look when they have travelled from Aberdeen to London for lunch. Be at your most vociferous in blaming them for the error when you have plenty of free tables and there is absolutely no need whatsoever to prevaricate.
5. Make sure children pay full price, to punish their parents for taking up valuable space in your dining room that could be occupied by bigger spenders: a bill for £48 for one course for a six-year old seems to be the current record, held by another inspector.
6. Insist on the telephone that you do vegetarian meals, even when you don't. They can always have an omelette.
7. Permit smoking everywhere in your restaurant. Customers are not there to savour the food or appreciate the wine, they are there to fill the till, and if you turned away smokers, where would you be?
8. Play loud Muzak to disguise the otherwise dreadfully dull atmosphere. There is nothing customers like more during a meal than to sing along with '70s pop music or Mario Lanza's greatest hits.
9. Never let customers serve their own wine. Always keep it well out of their reach and top it up as and when you feel like it. Nanny knows best.
10. As a general rule, make customers aware how much of a privilege it is for them to spend money in your restaurant. That way they will keep coming back for more.

You think I'm making this up? If the restaurateurs who behave this way only knew how they appear to their customers, to our readers and reporters. The worst of it is that the list could go on. The best is that the great majority of restaurants are not like that at all, at least not the great majority of the ones that appear in this book. We hope you enjoy it, make use of it, and agree, or disagree, strongly enough about what you find in its pages, and in the restaurants where you eat, to want to write to us. We have managed 50 years with your help; please keep the reports coming, and help us to make the next edition better still.

GFG: 50 years on

Fred Inglis, author, *Good Food Guide* inspector from the '60s through the '80s, and currently Professor of Cultural Studies at the University of Sheffield, offers a personal retrospective

The unmistakable initials are part of the unmistakable character. GFG: familiar, commanding, slightly clipped, a kind of password. Once you call it that, you're a member. If a stranger hears and recognises the initials, he or she is a friend. And of course that was how it all began: the Good Food Club was, and remains, the club you join when you contribute to its contents (see the back of the book for a list of current members).

In Britain in the immediate aftermath of World War II, the country was almost bankrupted; there wasn't enough fuel to go round, rationing was extended even though the war was over, and as Bloomsbury bluestocking Frances Partridge once put it, 'food was all-beige, starting with beige soup, followed by beige beans and beige potatoes, thin beige apple stew and a sort of skilly'.

Warfare, despite its horrors, had taught pretty well the whole of British society the enormous force in that old-fashioned concept, the common good. There was, however, a difficulty with this. It was that such a necessary ideal also taught a courteous acquiescence in what life brought you, since to complain might disrupt the common effort striving towards the common good, and there were still any number of people prepared to make as much money as they could out of the country's customary amiability, its refusal to complain about the cold, late trains, awful food.

They didn't know it then, but people stood at the hinge of a new political epoch. The democratic citizens of the 'great Labour victory' were set, very gradually and over a period of 30 or 40 years, to turn themselves into democratic consumers.

It was a sparkling new idea, and it found one of its first and best embodiments in *The Good Food Guide*. The people took off their uniforms and came back to everyday life and its dreadful food. They were consumers all right, but without a consumers' association. They were allowed to chuck away the last coupons in their ration books only in 1951. Fed up, they lined up behind a portly Labour historian, gentleman of letters and detective story-writer, wine connoisseur, sometime conscientious objector and subsequent lance-corporal of Dad's Army, to put the quality back in the dreary and tasteless equality of British restaurant food.

The Postgate years: laying down the fundamentals

Raymond Postgate was that sharp, genial and excellently public-spirited leader. He coined the phrase and created the actuality of *The Good Food Guide*, a phrase now repeated until it has become a cliché, transforming the instructions sent out on smudged and dog-eared typescripts together with handwritten reports and scribbled telephone messages sent back, into the stocky little pocket edition of the Guide which Cassell first published in 1951.

In 1962 Consumers' Association assumed publication, with Postgate still doing all the donkey-work. The absolute principle then and now was that all reporters must be unknown to the restaurants, all inspectors anonymous. 'You can corrupt one man, or a couple,' he wrote. 'You can't bribe an army.'

Inspectors were recruited on Postgate's hunches. He picked them out for punctuality, for spotting and nominating decent new restaurants, for being able to turn a nice phrase round a meal. He initiated the practice of contriving reports out of his own prose, plain and good as it was, flavoured with choice fragments of inspectors' insights. His noble declaration of independence from the tyranny of grim restaurants called his followers to 'report only on the quality and price of food and drink and upon the hospitality and courtesy of staff. . . .'

For many years, the only recognition inspectors and reporters received was the printing of their name or, in a little attack of discretion, their initials, below the reports concerned. No other touch could have so gratifyingly confirmed the faint, agreeable air of secret service with which the members went to work.

Scattered through the early editions you could find a future Chancellor of the Exchequer, three world-famous English conductors, a great painter, a socialist bishop and, respectively, the most famous military historian (Sir Basil Liddell Hart) and the most famous cricket commentator (John Arlott) of the 50 years of GFG longevity. You could also find a 1934 Chambertin for eighteen bob, a Château d'Yquem for 29/6, dinner at the Lygon Arms for 14/6, ham and eggs for tea in Great Langdale for 5/6, and the unforgettable injunction in a Castle Combe hotel that 'women are, by order of the management, forbidden to be served at the bar'.

Passing the baton

In 1970 Postgate handed over to Christopher Driver, a respected journalist by profession and by nature another non-conformist, music-loving social historian and classical scholar (as well as poet and keen cook). He took over just as the transfiguration of welfare-and-smokestack Britain into pop-and-fashion Britain really began to speed up. Instead of Postgate's terse specifics ('good, plain English food: eel soup 6/-' etc), Driver quickly devised a more technical, as well as a more leisurely and incisive idiom, a sane affirmative speech which encapsulated the pleasure of the table and the graces of abstinence. Dry understatement balances cadenced eulogy – 'Tinned pineapple au kirsch was a severe miscalculation, and the Northumberland climate does not encourage a herb garden'; 'remarkably fine calvados sauce' – and Driver's own words were judiciously punctuated with the best jokes from his inspectors' notes.

He saw the Guide through the '70s into the early '80s, and the house style – calm, assured, witty, moderate – stood up to those years; the sales swept up to 50,000, imitators began to hit the stands; and British middle-class consumerism started to go round the bend and over the top.

The Guide refused such excess. It had a *cause*, which was to speak up plainly for artistry on a plate, and honesty and fairness in a bill. Its staunch Driver kept the plain style speakable through his last edition in 1982, when he left for futher literary and journalistic challenges. By then the noov foodies, as novelist Angela Carter once put it, had had their hooves in the trough for a few years.

They were, one might argue, not entirely an attractive bunch, but their advent marks the coming of a quite new gastronomic era, the era of what Carter called 'gastro-porn', and its shameless conjunction of food, fashion and extravagance, the plateful as a sumptuous painting in the colourist manner.

By the time Drew Smith, an experienced food writer and Glenfiddich award-winner, took over at the Guide from the Postgate-Driver dynasty, this elaborate frame of feeling and eating was well established, and even nonconformist liberal newspapers had their wine and food sections.

Drew Smith knew his Onions all right, and matched a quite different prose and poise to the expectations of his audience. His two-page essay on Tante Claire in the 1983 edition shows him at his best; it is highly specific, technically very well informed, startling in its sensitivity to nuance and contrast as well as in the voluptuary holism with which a meal is comprehended:

> The smell of chocolate tinged the richness of the black meat with an earthy decadent taste brilliantly leavened by potatoes so light they were almost doing the work of a salad.

The coming of limitless credit and deferrable debt didn't last long. Tom Jaine's editorship restored a more level tone and a more candid recognition of the limits on plastic. He knew his way round the lavish style and *Gault Millau*, but he kept a drier tone than his predecessor: 'the business is Business', 'not just the feather-bedding of millionaires from abroad, but a genuine interest in everybody's welfare', 'her approach is charming and ingénue; some suggest too much so'. Jaine had a sharp eye for social change, and over the years of this decade he and his intelligent and witty successor in 1995, Jim Ainsworth, together chronicled the changes not only in the culture of restaurants but also of their consequence for taste and custom and ceremony in the everyday life of the eating-out classes. Supremely, they picked up from their inspectors the quite sudden and exhilarating extension of cuisine from a Continental reference (largely French with some Italian) to take in a much vaster world.

Of course, there had long been Chinese, Indian and Indonesian restaurants. (In fact, even in the '70s the Guide had been berated by various 'posh' restaurants when they found they had been excluded and various hitherto unknown 'ethnics' included instead.) But in the '80s and '90s, with the help of the supermarkets, a national re-education in culinary geography speeded up and the Guide was a prominent tutor in all this. Specialised menus were blended in a new globalism of cooking; the entire Mediterranean coastline, for example, could appear on one menu (with a fine tolerance which the countries involved would hardly be likely to show each other), and the Caribbean burst on to the table in a riot of colour – yellow fish, red vegetables, emerald fruit.

The cult of the chef

Jaine kept an appreciative but always ironic eye upon the chefs themselves as well, a tradition that Ainsworth has maintained. For these past 20-odd years, the chef has attained a quite unprecedented celebrity status. The grand, tutorial padrone is replaced by the big cheeses of chefdom and their gastronaut producers as they vie for the championship of screen cuisine.

Well, we all live in a celebrity culture, and we shall all do our gaping at them. But the Guide is rarely star-struck and always manfully egalitarian. Celebrated is as celebrated does, and though the celebrities may do you well, they may also do your credit card in.

At the end of Christopher Driver's excellent little history *The British at Table*, he lists a lineage of chef-restaurateurs who had been students at the hands of George Perry-Smith, who opened Bath's Hole in the Wall in 1952. This history marks out a line of classical cookery that had has its venerable prophet Elizabeth David, whose practitioners learned French first, Italian second, acquired the graces of a *nouvelle cuisine* without its parsimony, and who were open to but discriminatory about the torrent of new dishes flooding in from round the world.

These classic chef-restaurateurs also, I like to believe, eschew television celebrity and the ruin of talent which it inexorably causes. Their best representatives have something of the character of Kenneth Graham's Badger in that great novel *The Wind in the Willows*. They are a bit shy, a bit gruff, not easy to find, calm, authoritative, of absolute integrity. Their kitchen and their restaurant is of a piece with these attributes. It is plain, well-worn, homely; it is at once secluded and congenial. Its meals are repasts. Its dependable apotheosis in 2002, in my opinion, is Markwick's in Bristol, Chez Moi in London, Sharrow Bay in Ullswater, the Peat Inn, Fife; as for you, you'll make your own choices from these same pages.

When all the world is on the move, and people fret and chafe about its fearfulness and uncertainty, a fine restaurant is a reassurance that certain antique, necessary values may still be trusted: decent hospitality, good manners, a fair price, and of course the quality and enjoyability of the food.

These much cherished values would be in a much worse state had the GFG not done all it has to keep them strong and stout and of good report.

Far-flung food

As our culinary frontiers expand, we cook and eat ever more exotic food. But, unless we have been there ourselves, we don't know how Thai cooking in Thailand compares with Thai cooking in Britain, or whether Sydney restaurants are more exciting than our own, or just sunnier and friendlier. We asked four well-travelled friends of the Guide who live, work and eat in the UK, to give us a glimpse of what it's like to dine in some of the far-flung places that have contributed to the revolution in British cooking.

West Coast USA: a rich mix

By Andy Hayler

Ever since the gold rush, California has been a magnet for immigrants from around the world, a true land of opportunity. In fact, almost the whole West Coast is such a melting pot that it has the advantage of being able to offer a rich culinary mix: restaurants with cuisines from every land can be found in San Diego, Los Angeles, San Francisco and Seattle. Californian cuisine itself was pioneered by Alice Waters at Chez Panisse in Berkeley, San Francisco in the 1970s. Her idea of taking local ingredients and using fresh herbs and spices to mix in flavours from various cuisines was an antidote to the bland 'surf and turf' mentality that most restaurants had during that time.

Modern British cooking owes its roots in no small measure to the Californian approach. Indeed, chef/proprietor Sally Clarke brought her West Coast experience directly back to London, and still delivers this style of cooking to a high standard in her Kensington restaurant, Clarke's. Californian cuisine at its best is light, refreshing, with good ingredients and the excitement of flavour combinations from multiple origins, and nowhere does it better, in my opinion, than the French Laundry, in the tiny town of Yountville, Napa Valley, an hour's drive north from San Francisco.

It has a simple, rustic dining room, with bare walls and no distracting music, and its chef, Thomas Keller, revels in tasting-menus of many courses. Start perhaps with a pike mousse on a light pastry base. Next might be tuna tartare on a bed of radish and cucumber drizzled with aged Tamari soy sauce. Showing that the kitchen has a fine grasp of classical technique when it wants to, a Maine scallop comes topped with a mousse of foie gras in a ring of superb creamy mash, the whole arrangement sitting within a demi-glacé reduction.

Moreover, service is impeccable. I went there recently on two successive nights, and on the second we were welcomed with a different tasting-menu from the one we had the evening before, so that no dishes would overlap. Our waiter was able to quote the dishes we'd had the previous night from memory: impressive enough, I thought, but even more so when you realise that he was a *different waiter.*

Other fine restaurants to try are Aqua and Boulevard in San Francisco, and Cascadia and Campagne in Seattle. In general, though, there are very few places on the West Coast whose standards reach as high as, say, 5/10 in *Good Food Guide* terms. Many indulge in cramming far too many – often quite unsuitable – flavours on the plate, or show major technical deficiencies. At one top Los Angeles restaurant the chef managed to use star anise in absurd quantities in no fewer than three dishes in a single meal, including a dessert.

Many West Coast restaurants are more worried about the show than the food, with 'precious' maitre d's who seem to assume that they and the glitz of the place are the attraction. This is worst in Los Angeles, where eating at somewhere Julia Roberts was seen the night before may be the height of fashion but does not compensate for chowder that could have come from a packet and potatoes that a burger joint would have rejected.

Overall, London compares favourably as a culinary destination at the top end, but the West Coast remains a fascinating showcase of cooking from around the world – and as a bonus there is the Californian climate. Having lunch in the open air in San Diego on a sunny December day with the temperature at 22°C makes up quite a lot for the odd slip in the kitchen.

Japan: tradition and balance

By Brian Ma Siy

Japan is famously a society deeply rooted in its observations of codes and behaviour, and this carries over into the eating-out experience. The tea ceremony has been likened to a religious experience, where each movement of the tea-making is gracious, choreographed and profoundly traditional. Then, on a more expansive level, there is the Kaiseki dinner: eight or more courses meant to show off different cooking methods (raw, pickled, fried, steamed, grilled, etc.), with the intention of achieving 'balance'. Again, method and presentation often deliver more than does the food itself.

The ultimate all-in-one experience – and one certainly not likely to be found in Britain – is to stay at an onsen, a natural hot spring reputed to have healing powers, and where a Kaiseki dinner is offered. At the hedonistic and outrageously expensive (£1,000 per night for full board for two) Gora Kadan in the resort area of Kadone, Japanese service puts all UK – indeed, European – models to shame. After wallowing in the hot pools or meditating in the landscaped garden, you are taken by your own staff to your own private dining room to be seated on cushions placed on tatami mats before a garden view.

Visually striking dishes will then begin to arrive in orderly and precise succession. Sashimi is so dazzlingly fresh that it has no fish taste: only the colours and the textures give a clue as to which variety you might be tasting. Tofu comes in various guises: steamed to a junket-like consistency, perhaps, or deep-fried and left to cool so that its hardened casing counters the astringency of accompanying pickles. Hot dishes, usually plainly grilled, may include buttery and rich-tasting Kobi beef, and eel fillets in sweet syrupy marinade. Then there are the sea vegetables, with their slimey, foamy texture making them less easy for some Western palates to appreciate. The whole effect differs quite dramatically from a European meal, which is usually carefully structured around the main ingredient; instead it is like a series of gently intriguing surprises set to a leisurely rhythm, with the goal of achieving an ultimate balance of colour, taste and texture.

One criticism that has been levelled at Japanese food is its perceived one-dimensionality: a repetitiveness due to lack of variety, and an absence of spontaneity as a result of the always reverential service. (This applies to top-end Japanese restaurants in London, too, although not to sushi bars, where the range on offer can be considerable, and may include some modern 'fusions'.) To some extent, however, these 'faults' are compensated for by the veritable freshness of the food, and by the 'fun factor' of chefs cooking in front of you.

If you go to the sushi bar at the Ritz Carlton in Osaka (£100 to £200 per person for dinner), you will note that it takes only around 20 seconds to prepare a tuna sushi. But watching the deftness of the venerable old sushi master, as he holds and shapes the rice and glides his knife through the fish as though through silk, is a wonderfully entertaining thing to do. Or observe the tempura master whisk his batter to the right point of consistency and then fry the legs of a prawn to a delicate, perfect brittleness (you know if you breathe on them they'll blow off!). Sometimes, one suspects, it seems that the skill of the craftsman is valued more than the product itself.

For the Japanese, eating is only part of the dining process. A meal is the opportunity to appreciate the calmness of the setting, the formality of the service, and the expertise in the crafting of each dish to achieve a balance for eye, feel, and taste.

Hong Kong: search and you will find

By Brian Ma Siy

Chinese have a fixation about food. Almost from birth they are taught to quest for the clearest broth, the crispiest chicken skin, and the softest-textured tofu. Nowhere is this pursuit for perfection more evident than in Hong Kong, where this preoccupation is further nurtured by the greatest concentration of Chinese restaurants anywhere on the planet. However, the standard of cooking cannot be taken for granted any more because of the exodus of talented chefs to the west coasts of Canada and the USA to service the wealthy Chinese communities there (though, sadly, not usually to London: it is perhaps because the Chinese community is not as demanding about the standard of its food?).

Furthermore, fine-dining in Hong Kong is now very expensive, partly as a result of the influx of entrepreneurial mainland Chinese who fly over to Hong Kong with suitcases of Hong Kong dollar bills to monopolise the best restaurants. Top ingredients such as turtle, live fish, live lobster, dried abalone, and shark fin have reached astronomical prices because demand has become so high.

Even finding great dim sum can be tricky. One place where you will come across some of the best is Liu Gardens, a large, plush restaurant in Wanchai. Here dim sum have delicate, gossamer-like wrappings, and char siu is served 'whole' – i.e. in slices re-assembled to look like the whole roast tenderloin – and is resplendent with Chinese honey and an exceptional barbecue flavour. Desserts are good too: glutinous rice balls with black sesame are so light that the crunchiness of the individual sesame seeds is discernible.

Our search for the perfect bowl of won ton and beef brisket noodles came to a happy conclusion in the unassuming coffee-shop of the Furama Intercontinental Hotel in central Hong Kong. This is a bizarre place, straight out of the 1970s, but the beef brisket was light, meltingly soft, and came with a delicate broth, as opposed to the usual heavy gravy. It has just enough of a hint of star anise and tangy orange peel, plus lovely crunchy fresh noodles, with a definite bite: a dish far superior to what can be found in London's Soho or Bayswater.

On a more exuberant level, a banquet at Fu Ho Restaurant on Lockhart Road in Causeway Bay is a lesson in texture. (To the Western mind, to judge texture first and taste second may seem the wrong way around, but to the Chinese, texture is very important, and of course freshness is taken for granted.) Dinner may start with a plate of braised ducks webs, where the slightly rubbery but pliant skin contrasts beautifully with the glutinous jelly around the web bones. Then there is sea cucumber, like a grey slug with an even more rubbery texture, and next to that is a whole abalone, sliced thin to provide a flat opulent firmness, bordering on the crisp. Whole sea bass steamed with ginger and spring onion may be a familiar sight in Chinatowns all over the world, but here the bass is guaranteed to be astoundingly fresh – having been swimming around just minutes beforehand – and the dish is further distinguished by split-second timing that accentuates the fish's firm but springy texture, and by use of a distinctive soy sauce.

Also at the banquet you might find lotus-leaf-wrapped rice in the form of an enormous folded packet which the waiter ceremoniously cuts open with a knife, whereby the wonderful aroma of seafood rice steamed in the perfume of the leaf is released. It is a dramatic dish where rice is carefully cooked, but has absorbed the flavours of the prawns, egg and char siu, so tastes rich yet light. Once again, it is the texture of the rice, a humble commodity, with its crunchiness and just-cooked quality which spells out the technical wizardry of the kitchen and raises this dish above anything similar found in London restaurants.

Thailand: five myths about Thai food

By David Wolfe

Street food is superb. You can eat well at street stalls, but you can eat badly too. The best ones (2 or 3 out of 10 in *Good Food Guide* terms) tend to trade up, putting a few metal tables, plastic chairs and umbrellas on the pavement by the stall; some may even take over the shop behind and become simple eating-houses. But, in whatever guise, the stalls are remarkably cheap. Body and soul can be kept in contact for as little as £3 a day, with main dishes of rice or noodles plus curry or a stir-fry costing about 65 pence. At that price even the economically minded tourist can afford to make the occasional mistake. Mine was ordering what I thought was chicken curry which turned out to be curried chicken's feet. Although the Thais, unlike the Chinese, remove the bones from this delicacy, the resulting scraps of skin do not make a dish that every Westerner will enjoy.

Glamorous restaurants in big hotels should be avoided. The Bangkok Amari Boulevard Hotel's most luxurious restaurant is the Season, which is on a fifth-floor terrace surrounding a large pool. There is Thai dancing to enliven a comparatively expensive multi-course banquet, but early in the evening you can eat more cheaply: say £6.50 including service for fried fishcakes, curry, rice and a beer. The enormous Ambassador Hotel's street stalls occupy most of the square in front of the hotel. Inside is a seafood restaurant where you garner your fish, shellfish and vegetables from an eye-delighting iced counter. You take your choices, pay for them according to weight, then state in which of a dozen ways you want them cooked. While waiting in the large, comfortable restaurant for the result, you are offered sushi, sashimi and other Japanese snacks from a buffet (GFG score 4/10). The whole meal might cost £5 including beer if you choose cheaper ingredients such as clams and mussels; for £7 you can enjoy the cheapest 'river' prawns, while large prawns, crab or lobster could take you to the dizzying expense of £12: nearly a week's wages for an assistant chef.

Stick to the food of the country. But the food of the country in Bangkok, and the second city, Chiang Mai, is as likely to be Chinese as Thai. At a very long-standing but basic eating-house – which wouldn't even make a Round-up in the Guide – run by two Chinese female dragons of age immemorial, my lunch was disappointing. The low point was braised ox tongue: thickly and roughly sliced pieces of meat in a nondescript brown sauce on a plate with boiled potatoes and green beans.

Avoid large spectacular restaurants. The Rain Forest, in a suburb of Chiang Mai, and no relation to the London establishment of that name, has four hundred tables (Thai restaurateurs quote the number of tables, not the number of covers). It is a pavilion built around an enormous decorative pool. It was packed, with only a few non-Thais among the customers, and a magnificent feast for eight cost about £11 per head: easily 5/10 for cooking.

Thai food is blisteringly hot. Yes, I did see a Thai diner stir a heaped dessert spoon of hot chilli powder into a bowl of soup-noodles with vegetables, followed by the same amount of sugar. But at that Chiang Mai meal just described – actually a family banquet at which I was a guest – just one mildly spicy curry and one decidedly spicy salad featured among the ten courses. 'Did you order it specially mild for your children, and my Western taste?' I asked my host. 'No, it was a normal, balanced Thai dinner,' he replied. He should know, for he used to own one of London's best Thai restaurants, the Bahn Thai. He now operates a bright, cheerful sports café in Chiang Mai for Western expats, tourists and locals. Called the Easy Diner, it offers a British-American menu (chilli-spiced chips are one of its biggest sellers) with Thai daily specials. Philip Harris doesn't seem to miss Soho, though his voice sounds a trifle wistful when he says how much he enjoys welcoming his old Bahn Thai customers to Chiang Mai.

Australia: focus on Sydney

By Pat Fenn

Sydney, still on a post-Olympic high, just can't stop opening new restaurants. Many of them make good use of existing buildings, like the Victorian bank now housing award-winning 'Banc', or the basement of the old Post Office, economically dubbed 'Post', dishing up Modern Australian cooking. Level Five of the Customs House is reincarnated as Café Sydney, revelling in spectacular views over the harbour.

Claims of rival restaurants are as eagerly disputed as those of football teams here, and a table at the latest opening is as eagerly sought as tickets for a Premier League match. The transfer of a star chef is big news. The highly influential weekly food column in the *Sydney Morning Herald* is read by the whole family and discussed at the hairdresser's and the rowing club. Eating out is something everyone does regularly, and it never fails to generate excitement.

The affordability of a meal plays a large part in the habit of course. BYO (bring your own wine) helps to keep the cost down. (This is in contrast to restaurants in the UK, where BYO is rarely encouraged.) Many of the expensive trappings of a classy restaurant are dispensed with: the idea of waiters in starched shirts and black suits lifting synchronised silver domes would be laughable. But the young, informal staff are guaranteed to know their menu and are happy to discuss it with you.

With mouth-watering indigenous ingredients so plentiful, and emigrants from so many other cultures ready to share their experiences, Aussie chefs are half-way to their goal. A visit to the Sydney fish market (second biggest in the world) illustrates mouth-watering bounty. Few shackles of classic cuisine restrict experimentation. Confidence grows, culture-cringe is a thing of the apologetic past.

That confidence can sometimes appear misplaced. The menu at the currently hot 'Salt' restaurant posited yamba prawn raviolo with cauliflower cream, curry oil and garlic nougatine. Not that one can attribute this apparent mishmash to the locals. The chef in this case is Luke Mangan, late of the Waterside Inn and Kensington Place, clearly intoxicated with the possibilities.

Location is as important to a dinkum night out as is the cooking. On Balmoral beach stands the Bather's Pavilion, recently facelifted, now a gastro-landmark. Where in the UK can you dine, sand between your toes, on abalone matched with crisped pig's ear? The Kiosk on Shelly Beach, and the Tea Rooms on Shark Bay offer modern Australian cooking that belies their humble names, while fish and chips is what the inimitable Doyles-on-the-Beach does best, never skimping on freshness.

A decided trend is the extension of the culinary revolution to the suburbs. Modest neighbourhood bistros win reputations that pack 'em in to enjoy innovative cooking at prices that make it silly to stay at home. Their pavement tables make the most of the balmy climate. Many of Sydney's ethnic restaurants cluster together in their own 'burb, resisting the fusion fashion and resolutely cooking as their émigré predecessors taught them. Leichhart is the place to enjoy 'real' Italian cooking, in Marrickville it's all Greek, in Lakemba Lebanese, in Bondi Jewish, in Haymarket Chinese, while Cabramatta is generally known as Vietnamatta.

More than any other city in the world, Sydney looks to the future not the past for its culinary inspiration. Its four million gourmets are ready, willing and able to appreciate their new status as world-class players.

South of France: real Provençal cooking

By Brian Ma Siy

Take a seat on the left hand side as you fly to Nice airport. You will be treated to a surreal view of the luxury properties facing the sea with their pink roofs, swimming pools, and sparkling white yachts lounging in the harbour. Wealth has encouraged elaborate food, so simple Provençal cooking – which makes good use of seasonal produce, especially vegetables, gathered in the local market early in the morning – is not so easy nowadays to find without a little effort.

Two exponents of this genre share a common background: both have been head chefs at Hotel Negresco's Chantecler restaurant. Dominique Le Stanc left his two Michelin stars behind to cook in a tiny open kitchen, called Merenda, next to the market in old-town Nice at 4 rue Terrasse. He follows the repertoire of the previous owner, the extraordinary Jean Giusti, and serves beignets of courgette flowers deep-fried in fruity olive oil; stuffed sardines with golden breadcrumbs and herbs; and a no-nonsense home-made pasta with pesto. There is nothing refined about the food; it is home cooking, with robust flavours.

A more sophisticated approach can be found in Jacques Maximin's eponymous restaurant in the rolling hills outside Vence. Often overlooked and underrated, his cooking captures the essence of what Provence is all about. His vegetables taste divine. Something as humble as a flageolet bean, or some peas, is handled in such a way that freshness is unadulterated, just helped by a little stock or the juices of the accompanying fish. Dishes feature the lightest and most delicate artichokes, the crunchiest and sweetest purple asparagus (which puts any white or green variety in the shade), and plum tomatoes that have a wonderful aftertaste that goes on for ever. Maximin's handling of fish, usually just roasted or pan-fried, and baked lamb from the Sisteron hills, is top-notch. By contrast with many London restaurants offering this style of cooking, there is a total lack of embellishment, just a concentration on technique to allow the principal ingredients to shine through.

Where style and embellishment are essential, however, the South of France does not disappoint. The most lavish and over-the-top restaurant in these parts – indeed anywhere, perhaps – is Louis XV in Monte Carlo's Hotel de Paris. Here the dining room is of Versailles proportions, decorations are of the outrageous baroque and resplendent gold ilk, complete with oil paintings and deep, deep carpets: and service features more waiters than you'd find in the army of a minor republic. Yet somehow this is a wonderful place in which to eat. It does not matter that world-famed chef/patron Alain Ducasse is hardly there, because his brigade cooks brilliantly. Do not be distracted by the two dozen different bread rolls, the two different 500-gram slabs of butter, or the padded stool for handbags; what is delivered on the plate is marvellous.

Start with a melba toast sandwich with local goats' cheese, then creamy risottos with al dente rice, and proceed to wild, beautifully timed roasted sea bass. Finish with a mille-feuille of wild strawberries that features the lightest, butteriest, barely-held-together pastry, covering wonderfully scented wild strawberries, each set in a vertical position and bound with crème Chantilly: a classic combination of fruit, cream and pastry executed to perfection.

Afterwards, those wishing to depart in style might take the helicopter back to Nice airport: remember, of course, to sit on the right-hand side this time.

A happy diversity

Stuart Walton, wine and food writer, suggests what's exciting and good value on restaurant wine lists

It is of course still possible for diehard traditionalists to stick with the celebrated wines of France's classic regions – Bordeaux, Burgundy and Champagne – whenever they go out for a meal at a good restaurant. For some, an impeccably chilled young Chablis is the only thing to drink with grilled trout, and rack of lamb would be unthinkable without a reasonably mature bottle of classed-growth Médoc to accompany it.

Nowadays, however, the excitement, and very often better value, lies elsewhere. Largely as a result of the revolution in wine retailing over the past 20 years or so, restaurant wine lists have branched out into previously unexplored corners of the vinous universe in search of flavours that more accurately match the eclectic or fusion cooking (call it what you will) that is today's culinary Esperanto. And the good news is that the choice doesn't have to be Chardonnay or Cabernet, even though those varietals still comprise the backbones of many wine lists.

Viognier is a grape worth getting acquainted with. At its best, it marries the broad-beamed, fleshy tones of Chardonnay with something of the cinnamon spice of certain Alsace grapes. At one time restricted to the elusive wines of Condrieu in the northern Rhône, it now crops up in the Midi, in California and in Australia at prices that are considerably kinder on the bank balance. Australia's Yalumba operation makes a good one, as does Maurel-Vedeau in the Languedoc.

Pinot Gris, too, combines delicately musky aromatic personality with the richness of texture of good Chardonnay, without the producer necessarily having had to resort to oak. Look for examples from the Pacific Northwest of America (Washington State and Oregon), from New Zealand, or from central European countries such as Hungary. In Italy they call it Pinot Grigio. Araldica in Piedmont makes a crisply satisfying one, but too many Italian versions suffer from the blandness that afflicts other dry whites from that country.

Other white varietals worth investigating are **Albariño** from Galicia in the northwest of Spain (from denominations such as Rias Baixas), Italian **Arneis** from Piedmont (go for one from the Roero district, if you see it on the list), and the often overlooked **Riesling**. Germany is, alas, the forgotten country of modern restaurant wine lists, but there are fine dry Rieslings from regions such as the Clare Valley in South Australia and Alsace.

Among reds, possibly no regional varietal offers better value for money currently than **Merlot** made in Chile. Voluptuous plum fruit, well-integrated oak and a depth of flavour not often encountered outside the grape's original heartland in the Pomerol district of Bordeaux can be delivered to your palate at significantly less than £20 on many lists. The very best region for Chilean Merlot is the Rapel valley.

On the other side of the Andes, **Malbec** has become the hot varietal in Argentina's Mendoza region. The wines typically combine ripe damson fruit with a layer of light astringency that is best enjoyed when paired with densely textured red meat: think beef or venison. For the richest and densest style of red, Australian **Shiraz** is still hard to beat, and most up-to-the-minute wine lists will give a wide choice, but similarly sturdy wines from the southern Rhône appellation of Gigondas are worth considering too, particularly with vigorously spiced food.

Good-value **Pinot Noir** remains something of a Holy Grail. There are some fine New Zealand examples, but many are beginning to approach the price point of modest burgundy. A pretty ubiquitous buzz wine in recent years has been Firesteed's exemplary Pinot from Oregon, worth snapping up without hesitation for drinking with poultry dishes, light game or even salmon.

Italy remains an undiscovered treasure-house of food-friendly, characterful reds as long as you pass over most of the Chianti on offer. Head south for wines such as Puglia's creamy-smooth **Salice Salentino**, the hauntingly scented **Aglianico del Vulture** from Basilicata, Campania's spice-tinged **Taurasi**, or the lightly cherryish **Ciro** from Calabria. Remember too that **Montepulciano d'Abruzzo** from the Adriatic coast is a far more appealing proposition than most similarly priced Sangiovese-based Tuscan reds, and costs not much more than do many house wines.

And if you are in the market for an appetite-sharpener while you study the menus, ask to see the wine list first. Restaurants are considerably more geared up now than they were a generation ago when it comes to wine by the glass. A glass of bone-dry fino or manzanilla sherry is a fine aperitif when it is fresh and chilled – which, sadly, it often is not – but you may wish instead to look for crisp and fresh varietal wines from grapes such as **Sauvignon** or **Pinot Blanc**.

A sparkling wine is perhaps the best stimulant to the digestive juices of them all, but don't pay £8 a glass for some flavour-free champagne you've never heard of. Australia, California, New Zealand and South Africa are all producing fine sparklers by the traditional method, as England is too. **Nyetimber** and **Ridgeview**, both made in Sussex, are benchmark wines. You may have to eat out in Sussex to find them, but they are certainly worth trying if you do.

The happy diversity to be found on the best modern wine lists should be celebrated. It truly represents the protean possibilities of the contemporary wine scene, and reminds us that the wine map doesn't end at the French border.

London

Adams Café £ map 12

77 Askew Road, W12 9AH
TEL/FAX: (020) 8743 0572

COOKING **3**
NORTH AFRICAN
£22–£31

This green-painted Shepherds Bush oasis is a simple, pleasant eating house with a predictable (because wholly authentic) menu of Tunisian and Moroccan specialities that delighted a reporter with their impressive execution. The crisp, fan-shaped pastry envelope and delicate spicing of its egg and tuna filling makes brik irresistible to many fans of this cuisine. But, if not brik, try its seafood variation briouattes, or home-made soups: seafood or vegetarian harira with lentils and chickpeas. There are meatless dishes among tagines and couscous, but ravenous carnivores tend to choose couscous royal with two sorts of lamb, meatball, grilled chicken, and merguez sausage. Pickled lemon, dates, almonds, prunes and sultanas add distinctive flavours and textures to the tagines (dates and figs are also the bases of the recommended Tunisian digestifs). For those who drink deep, the short list of north African (or French) wines starts at £8.50, with only Château Musar exceeding £15; mint tea or Arabic coffee makes a temperate finish.

CHEF: Abdel Boukraa PROPRIETORS: Abdel and Frances Boukraa OPEN: Mon to Sat D 7 to 10.30 CLOSED: 1 week Christmas, bank hols, 1 weekend Aug MEALS: Set D £9.95 (1 course) to £14.95 SERVICE: not inc CARDS: Amex, Delta, Diners, MasterCard, Switch, Visa DETAILS: 60 seats. Private parties: 36 main room, 24 private room. Vegetarian meals. Wheelchair access (not WC). Music ⊖ Ravenscourt Park (£5)

Admiral Codrington map 14

17 Mossop Street, SW3 2LY
TEL: (020) 7581 0005 FAX: (020) 7589 2452

COOKING **4**
MODERN EUROPEAN
£32–£53

A quiet, leafy street off Draycott Avenue is the setting for this extended pub, where lunch may be taken in the bar or restaurant, and where the glass roof over the latter area slides back when the sun comes out. What you eat while you bask will very likely be fish because that is what Daniel Pederson's menus specialise in. The signature dish of herb-crusted cod with tomatoes and mushrooms is again well-reported this year, but you can ring the changes with sea bass served with caramelised red peppers and papaya in a herbed vinaigrette, or fillet of marlin with a lime-spiked sauce vierge. Ingredients are conscientiously sourced, as seems evident from the Caesar salad that is tricked out with roasted prosciutto and a soft-poached egg.

While fish preparations try out some novel combinations, most of the starters are pretty traditional (pea and mint soup, foie gras and chicken liver parfait, salmon tartare), and meat-eaters can get a grilled Scotch ribeye with onion rings and mushrooms if they wish. A wide variety of home-made ice creams comes on at dessert stage, but the 'rich and indulgent' constituency is also catered for with the likes of honey cheesecake and warm chocolate pot. 'Efficient and polite' staff help to ensure satisfaction. The core list of Berry Brothers wines opens with house Bordeaux at £11. It covers a fair amount of ground in itself, but those in more expansive mood should ask to see the fine wine list that supplements it.

CHEF: Daniel Pederson PROPRIETOR: Longshot Estates Ltd OPEN: all week 12 to 2.30 (3.30 Sat and Sun), 7 to 10.30 CLOSED: 24 to 26 Dec, 1 Jan MEALS: alc (main courses £10 to £14.50). Cover 50p at D. Bar menu available all week SERVICE: 12.5% (optional), card slips closed CARDS: Amex, Delta, MasterCard, Switch, Visa DETAILS: 56 seats. 16 seats outside. Vegetarian meals. Music. Air-conditioned ⊖ South Kensington, Sloane Square

Admiralty

map 13

Somerset House, Strand, WC2R 1LA — COOKING **3**
TEL: (020) 7845 4646 FAX: (020) 7845 4647 — FRENCH
EMAIL: theadmiralty@gruppo-events.co.uk — £38–£77

Within the striking setting of Somerset House, Admiralty is an agreeable place, despite its quirky décor, bare wooden tables and low illumination. Styling itself 'cuisine du terroir', the cooking runs to duck consommé (poured from a copper pan over a brunoise of tomatoes and cucumber), snail ravioli, and high-quality pot roast rack of lamb with minty herbs, served with poached garlic, olives and a balsamic jus. It takes itself rather seriously, with a lot of effort devoted to what some might consider non-essentials: the mushroom ravioli and artichoke soubise, for example, that partner lightly roasted Anjou squab pigeon breast on Puy lentils with a red wine jus.

This is also one of the few places that still applies elaborate spun sugar to desserts: a rather conventional dark chocolate moelleux with a decent pistachio crème anglaise, and a fine strawberry tartlet with lemon confit and cream. Smartly dressed and friendly staff spend time chatting amiably among themselves, but get the job done. High prices are not helped by a £4 charge for vegetables, nor by an all-French wine list that reaches for the sky. Look to the south for some relief, or try one of the 16 wines by the glass.

CHEF: Morgan Meunier PROPRIETOR: Gruppo Ltd OPEN: all week L 12 to 3, Mon to Sat D 6 to 10.45 CLOSED: 25 and 26 Dec MEALS: alc (main courses £16.50 to £18.50). Set L £27 to £39, Set D 6 to 9 £45, Set D £39 SERVICE: 12.5% (optional), card slips closed CARDS: Amex, Delta, Diners, MasterCard, Switch, Visa DETAILS: 65 seats. Private parties: 65 main room. Wheelchair access (also WC). No music Air-conditioned ⊖ Charing Cross

The Good Food Guide *is a registered trade mark of Which? Ltd.*

Alastair Little

map 15

49 Frith Street, W1D 5SG
TEL: (020) 7734 5183 FAX: (020) 7734 5206

COOKING **5**
MODERN EUROPEAN
£40–£58

Soho supports just about every kind of restaurant imaginable, many of them victims to fashion, but this – a ground-breaking restaurant when it opened back in 1985, and one of the first icons of the new British culinary wave – has not only stayed the course but undergone something of a rejuvenation. The modest frontage has had a lick of blue paint and, despite its lack of creature comforts, the dining room, with its maple-wood floor, artwork and cream walls, has been refreshed and brightened up. An Italian streak still runs through the open-to-view kitchen, in the shape of Tuscan fish casserole, and pizzetta bianca, but the net is cast wide enough to include tuna sashimi, home-cured loin of pork with choucroute, and calf's liver with fries and onion gravy.

It is a light, some might say healthy, style of cooking whose simplicity and clear flavours reflect well on the original aims: a handsome slice of convincingly fresh and crisp-skinned turbot in an impressively light nage of herby leeks and mussels, for example, or a chunky veal chop with roast potatoes and artichokes. There is nothing flashy about the presentation, no gimmicks, just prime materials confidently treated. Starters – a light, fluffy potato pancake with smoked eel and horseradish-dressed salad, or a fine, rich ballottine of foie gras with a well-made onion marmalade – seem to score better than desserts. Professional and friendly service encourages maximum relaxation with minimal fuss, and the shortish wine list covers a good range of styles and prices, starting with house Italian at £14.

CHEF: Edward Rugg PROPRIETORS: Alastair Little and Kirsten Pedersen OPEN: Mon to Fri L 12 to 3, Mon to Sat D 6 to 11 CLOSED: bank hols MEALS: Set L £16 (1 courses) to £27, Set D £18 (1 courses) to £35 SERVICE: not inc CARDS: Amex, Delta, Diners, MasterCard, Switch, Visa DETAILS: 65 seats. Private parties: 8 main room, 25 private room. Vegetarian meals. Children's helpings. No music. Air-conditioned ⊖ Tottenham Court Road

Alastair Little Lancaster Road

map 12

136A Lancaster Road, W11 1QU
TEL: (020) 7243 2220 FAX: (020) 7792 4535

COOKING **3**
MODERN ITALIAN
£32–£53

Next to the junction with Ladbroke Grove, Alastair Little's second restaurant is as near to the pulse of trendy west London as his original place (see above) is to that of Soho. Equally compact and equally plainly decorated, it offers a menu that changes with every session and nails its colours firmly to the new-wave Italian mast. Simplicity is still the watchword, and there is no sense of underselling in presenting a plate of seasonal leaves garnished with pear and shaved Parmesan and dressed in aged balsamic vinegar as a starter. Main courses tack to the lighter side of things too, with poached cod aïoli; brill with mash, spinach and hollandaise; and breast of corn-fed chicken with grilled Portobello mushrooms on offer on a spring menu. That should leave room for something like apple crumble tart, or chocolate marquise with espresso ice cream; or blood-orange sorbet for the calorie-counters. House wines from Italy's Montefiascone district at £14 a bottle head up the same list that the Frith Street branch operates.

CHEF: Tony Abarno PROPRIETORS: Mercedes André-Vega, Kirsten Pedersen and Alastair Little OPEN: all week L 12 (12.30 Sun) to 2.30 (3 Sat, 3.30 Sun), Mon to Sat D 6.30 to 11 CLOSED: bank hols MEALS: alc L (main courses £9 to £14.50). Set D £24.50 (2 courses) to £28.50 SERVICE: not inc, 12.5% for parties of 8 or more CARDS: Amex, Delta, Diners, MasterCard, Switch, Visa DETAILS: 40 seats. 10 seats outside. Private parties: 10 main room. Vegetarian meals. Children's helpings. No pipes in dining room. Wheelchair access (not WC). No music. Air-conditioned ⊖ Ladbroke Grove

Al Duca

map 15

4–5 Duke of York Street, SW1Y 6LA — COOKING **4**
TEL: (020) 7839 3090 FAX: (020) 7839 4050 — ITALIAN
WEB SITE: www.alduca-restaurant.co.uk — £32–£66

The absence of frills, immediately obvious from the simple, clean décor with its wooden tables and chairs, hints at what is to come: unpretentious food based on fine ingredients carefully handled. Subdued colours tone well with the grey suits that frequent this smart location, giving it the feel of an executive canteen at lunchtime, and the workmanlike menu (with a few price supplements) gets to grips with starters of baby squid salad with chickpeas and sweet chilli, and poached egg served with lemon-marinated asparagus, aromatic leaves and crispy Parmesan.

Pasta is a strong suit, some of it home-made, including crab ravioli with tomato consommé, and tagliatelle with wild mushrooms and summer truffle, and dishes are well designed, without distractions: roast cod comes with tomatoes, capers and soft polenta, for example, and chargrilled loin of pork with white beans and shallot vinaigrette. As well as the inevitable tiramisù and pannacotta, desserts might run to nougat parfait, and poached pears in red wine. The Italian wine list offers much of interest, and those free from financial constraints can have a most agreeable time, although there are some relatively affordable bottles too. House Chardonnay and Nero d'Avola are £14.

CHEF: Michele Franzolin PROPRIETOR: Claudio Pulze OPEN: Mon to Sat L 12 to 2.30 (12.30 to 3 Sat), all week D 6 to 10.30 (11 Thur to Sat, 10 Sun) MEALS: Set L £16.50 (2 courses) to £22.50, Set D £19 (2 courses) to £27 SERVICE: 12.5% (optional), card slips closed CARDS: Amex, Delta, MasterCard, Switch, Visa DETAILS: 60 seats. Private parties: 70 main room. No cigars/pipes in dining room. Wheelchair access (also women's WC). No music. Air-conditioned ⊖ Piccadilly Circus

Al Hamra

map 15

31–33 Shepherd Market, W1J 7PT — COOKING **5**
TEL: (020) 7493 1954/1044 FAX: (020) 7493 1044 — LEBANESE
£35–£61

The heated patio now seats 26, but this doesn't reduce the crush inside, where tables are so close that some touch. None the less, the waiters manage to give good service, and the corner location and bright décor make this a bright and lively venue. There are a few 'Continental dishes' in the otherwise classical

Lebanese menu, and one reader appreciated his 'beautifully grilled' Dover sole being presented off the bone. But the authentic hot and cold Lebanese hors d'oeuvres, and chargrilled lamb and chicken dishes in many variations, are what attract both those used to Middle Eastern cooking and those seeking gastronomic adventure: one intrepid reporter sampled beid ghanam (grilled lamb's testicles with a piquant lemon sauce) which he described as 'between kidney and sweetbreads'.

More-conventional tabbouleh, and grilled quails, are both dishes that have been commended for their freshness and crisp textures. The £2.50 cover charge brings olives, home-baked bread and the traditional salad that precedes every Middle Eastern meal. To finish there is fresh fruit, ice cream or Lebanese pastries. The vintage-free list is fully priced, with French and Lebanese house wines at £12.75 and £16.50 respectively. There are several sorts of arak, and a yoghurt drink makes another appetising aperitif.

CHEF: Mahir Abboud PROPRIETOR: Hassan Fansa OPEN: all week noon to 11.30 CLOSED: 24 Dec to 2 Jan MEALS: alc (main courses £10 to £20). Cover £2.50 SERVICE: not inc CARDS: Amex, Delta, Diners, MasterCard, Switch, Visa DETAILS: 70 seats. 26 seats outside. Private parties: 80 main room. Vegetarian meals. Wheelchair access (not WC). Music. Air-conditioned ⊖ Green Park (£5)

Alloro

NEW ENTRY **map 15**

19–20 Dover Street, W1S 4W
TEL: (020) 7495 4768 FAX: (020) 7629 5348

COOKING **4**
ITALIAN
£35–£54

In a swanky location just off Piccadilly near the Ritz, and under the same ownership as (Aubergine, L'Oranger, Rosmarino, Spiga, Teca and Zafferano; see entries), is a long dining room with dark wooden tables and chairs, a modern brown and yellow colour scheme, and low level background illumination. Michele Brogi, a Tuscan by birth, puts a canny London spin on some Italian ideas, so the food will appeal across a broad spectrum. Fixed-price menus (with a few supplements) allow the option of just two courses as well as four, at prices that are not unreasonable for the area. The food doesn't try to be too ambitious, which is invariably a good idea, and the kitchen functions effectively within its own limits, turning out simple compilations of charred vegetables (some better than others) with mozzarella, and another starter of ox tongue with a strong parsley and caper dressing.

Fresh, well-timed materials include cod with a crisp, salty skin, on a bed of earthy-tasting lentils, and gnocchi are well rendered: dark brown nuggets deeply flavoured with mushroom and black truffle, under a soft covering of fonduta. Cheese consists of a bit of several or a lot of one, according to preference, served with two slices of toasted raisin bread, one smeared with honey, the other with lemon jam. Or there may be a fresh, sharp, lightly bitter orange sorbet, resting in a sea of Campari. Polite service is delivered by smartly dressed Italian speakers, and a walk-in cellar houses a fine collection of Italian wines, with special selections from Tuscany and Piedmont. The wine list itself is helpfully organised by region, and effort has been made to feature the lighter styles under £20 as well as the more refined £100-and-over bottlings. Along with champagne, French styles also appear alongside a Chilean, as the house reds, whites and rosé, all at £14.50.

CHEF: Michele Brogi PROPRIETOR: A To Z Restaurants Ltd OPEN: Mon to Sat 12 to 2.45, 7 to 10.45 (11 Thur to Sat) CLOSED: Christmas, bank hols Easter MEALS: Set L £19.50 to £23.50, Set D £23 to £32 SERVICE: 12.5% (optional) CARDS: Amex, Delta, Diners, MasterCard, Switch, Visa DETAILS: 60 seats. Private parties: 90 main room, 20 private room. Vegetarian meals. No cigars/pipes in dining room. Occasional music. Air-conditioned

Al San Vincenzo

map 13

30 Connaught Street, W2 2AF
TEL: (020) 7262 9623

COOKING **3**
ITALIAN
£48–£63

Vincenzo Borgonzolo may appear to have canonised himself in the naming of his restaurant, but none the less manages to keep his feet firmly on the ground at this small but comfortable venue not far from the bustle of Edgware Road. Cream walls and wooden floors set a neutral context for the sturdy Italian cooking he specialises in. Prawns and squid flashed under the grill and bedded on tagliatelle dressed in a lemony cream sauce is an appetising way to start, or there may be eel fried with onions, lemon and chilli. Continue the maritime theme if you will with main courses of poached sea bass with salsa verde, or brill with mussels and saffron and potato purée, or get your teeth into roast pork fillet rolled in a crunchy coating of hazelnuts served with Savoy cabbage and truffled mash. Bread-and-butter pudding made with panettone, cantuccini served with vin santo, or a plate of Italian farmhouse cheeses keep the tricolore flying to the end, as does the wine list, where even the single entry under 'Champagne' turns out to come from Franciacorta. Mark-ups are a touch high, but house Chardonnay and Merlot are £15.

CHEF: Vincenzo Borgonzolo PROPRIETORS: Elaine and Vincenzo Borgonzolo OPEN: Mon to Fri L 12.15 to 1.30, Mon to Sat D 7.15 to 9.30 CLOSED: 26 Aug to 4 Sept MEALS: Set L and D £27.50 (2 courses) to £33.50 SERVICE: not inc, 12.5% for parties of 5 or more CARDS: Delta, MasterCard, Visa DETAILS: 24 seats. Private parties: 8 main room. Vegetarian meals. No children under 12. No cigars/pipes in dining room. Music ⊖ Marble Arch

Amandier

map 13

26 Sussex Place, W2 2TH
TEL: (020) 7262 6073 FAX: (020) 7723 8395

COOKING **3**
FRENCH/PROVENÇALE
£31–£58

Handy for Paddington Station, on a corner site with large green awnings, Amandier is a narrow room with green and gold furnishings, banquettes down either side, and just enough room for staff to navigate along the centre. The format is two- or three-course meals with half a dozen choices per course, the business French food with a Provençale accent, taking in goats' cheese and artichoke soufflé, or maybe a substantial crab ravioli in the shape of a pork pie, topped with a prawn beignet. Main courses of pink duck breast, or fresh, well-timed, crisp-skinned sea bass fillet tend to be accompanied by polenta (rather than potato) and either simple spinach, or more complicated vegetables such as aubergine soufflé or ratatouille. Desserts run to a fine apple tart served with a scoop of calvados ice cream melting over it, service is heavy-going French, and the wine list's patrician Gallic leanings are tempered by more affordable input from elsewhere, and house wines open at £12.95. If prices are a problem, bear in mind that the less expensive downstairs Bistro Daniel is serviced from the same kitchen.

CHEF: Daniel Gobet PROPRIETORS: M. Ahmed and Daniel Gobet OPEN: Mon to Fri L 12 to 2.30, Mon to Sat D 7 to 10.30 CLOSED: 25 Dec to 2 Jan, Easter, May bank hols MEALS: Set L £15 (2 courses) to £25.50 (2 courses), Set D £25.50 (2 courses) SERVICE: 12.5% (optional) CARDS: Amex, Delta, Diners, MasterCard, Switch, Visa DETAILS: 28 seats. 10 seats outside. Private parties: 30 main room, 65 private room. Vegetarian meals. Children's helpings. No cigars/pipes in dining room. Music. Air-conditioned ⊖ Lancaster Gate (£5)

Anglesea Arms £ — map 12

35 Wingate Road, W6 0UR — COOKING **4**
TEL: (020) 8749 1291 FAX: (020) 8749 1254 — MODERN EUROPEAN
£24–£39

This popular gastro-pub is a live and kicking place full of conversation and laughter, with an open layout and no real demarcation between bar and dining area. Done out in lots of wood and shades of brown, it has absolutely no pretensions, yet is serious about its food. Menu options are chalked up on a large blackboard at the far end of the room. Depending on the time of year, dishes may include crisp-battered stuffed courgette flowers au pistou with ricotta and basil, or the Basque-influenced pipérade tart with tomato salad.

Although most of the menu is decidedly modern British, some items, such as sashimi of line-caught tuna with samphire, soy, ginger, spring onions and very hot mustard, hint at broader horizons. Portions, as in a main course of seared sea bream with Mediterranean vegetable lasagne and sauce vierge, are generous, and the flavours finely tuned. Desserts are big on the comfort factor. A tart chibouste with raspberries is a creamy but light, almondy confection; Yankee dark and white chocolate truffle cake with chilled ginger and Bourbon anglaise is the kind of spectacular artery-clogging pudding that chocaholics dream about. The wine list, organised by price, has civilised mark-ups on wines from around the globe. Prices start at £10.25, and 15 come by the glass.

CHEFS: Dan Evans and Luke Smith PROPRIETORS: Dan and Fiona Evans OPEN: all week 12.30 to 2.45 (1 to 3.30 Sun), 7.30 to 10.45 (10.15 Sun) CLOSED: 24 to 31 Dec MEALS: alc (main courses £7 to £10) SERVICE: not inc CARDS: Delta, MasterCard, Switch, Visa DETAILS: 70 seats. 20 seats outside. Vegetarian meals. Children's helpings. Wheelchair access (not WC). No music. Air-conditioned ⊖ Ravenscourt Park, Goldhawk Road

Several sharp operators have tried to extort money from restaurateurs on the promise of an entry in a guidebook that has never appeared. The Good Food Guide *makes no charge for inclusion.*

See inside the front cover for an explanation of the symbols used at the tops of entries.

Arancia £ **map 12**

52 Southwark Park Road, SE16 3RS
TEL: (020) 7394 1751 FAX: (020) 7394 1044

COOKING **2**
MODERN ITALIAN
£22–£33

On a corner site in Camberwell, this is a popular neighbourhood Italian serving up a lively, modern version of country cooking. Its orange-painted dining room and bright, colourful crockery are suitably cheerful for the prevailing sense of informality, while paper table covers and plain white candles in holders emphasise the fact that this is not a posh place. Reporters have been generous with their praise, for starters of polenta and Swiss chard, salt-cod salad, and stuffed red pepper (filled with tomato, basil, anchovy paste and roast garlic), and for mains of 'well-herbed' octopus and rice salad, tuna fishcakes with tomato and rocket, and belly pork on cannellini beans. Finish perhaps with chocolate semifreddo, or ricotta cheesecake. A good-value varied pack of two dozen exclusively Italian wines opens with Arpeggio Bianco and Rosso at £8.

CHEF: Catherine O'Sullivan PROPRIETORS: A. Rossi and C. O'Sullivan OPEN: Wed to Sun L 12.30 to 2.30, all week D 7 to 11 CLOSED: 25 Dec to 3 Jan, bank hols MEALS: alc (main courses £9 to £9.50). Set L £7.50 (2 courses) to £10, Set D £10 SERVICE: not inc, card slips closed CARDS: Delta, MasterCard, Switch, Visa DETAILS: 40 seats. 20 seats outside. Private parties: 8 main room. Vegetarian meals. No cigars/pipes in dining room. Occasional music ⊖ Bermondsey (£5)

Aroma II £ **map 15**

118 Shaftesbury Avenue, W1D 5EP
TEL/FAX: (020) 7437 0377
EMAIL: booking@aromarestaurant.co.uk
WEB SITE: www.aromarestaurant.co.uk

COOKING **1**
CHINESE
£18–£86

The well-lit interior has bright yellow walls, an elderly carpet and a tropical fish tank. The vast menu encompasses Cantonese stir-fries, a few vegetarian pairings (such as aubergine in garlic sauce), banquet seafood dishes (braised abalone with oyster sauce) and, half-way through, some more interesting hotpots and texture foods (braised whole pork knuckle, sea cucumber with spring onion and shrimp roe). Among the more successful dishes at an inspection meal were baked soft-shell crab (crusted with salt and pepper and laced with chillies) and, to follow, steamed sea bass with ginger and spring onions (filleted at table by one of the attentive staff). The drinks list comprises cocktails, beers and Chinese spirits, plus a fair (but vintageless) choice of mostly French wines; house wines start at £8.50.

CHEF: David Tam PROPRIETOR: Goldrim Ltd OPEN: all week, noon to 11.30 (10.30 Sun) MEALS: alc (main courses £6 to £28). Pre-theatre all week 5 to 7 £9 (2 courses, min 2), Set L and D from £15 (min 2) SERVICE: 12.5% (optional) CARDS: Amex, Delta, Diners, MasterCard, Switch, Visa DETAILS: 120 seats. Private parties: 80 main room, 40 private room. Vegetarian meals. Children's helpings. Wheelchair access (also WC). Music. Air-conditioned ⊖ Leicester Square, Piccadilly Circus (£5)

Assaggi

map 13

The Chepstow, 39 Chepstow Place, W2 4TS
TEL: (020) 7792 5501

COOKING **3**
ITALIAN
£38–£64

Located upstairs from The Chepstow pub, in a row of perfect white houses, the restaurant would no doubt feel smaller if it weren't for the huge windows and simple décor: light wood tables, plain wood floors and no clutter. The menu, too, is straightforward, serving simple and enjoyable, if occasionally uneven, Italian cooking, though the high prices suggest something grander. Starters, preceded by thin, golden, salted Sardinian carta di musica bread, may include Italian standards such as grilled vegetables marinated in olive oil and herbs, or Pecorino cheese with rocket and ham. Although a main course of fegato di vitello has disappointed, a whole rack of spring lamb with pea purée has been splendidly flavourful. Desserts might include sharp lemon tart. The short wine list is all-Italian, and prices rise rapidly from Sardinian house wines at £11.95.

CHEF: Nino Sassu PROPRIETORS: Pietro Fraccari and Nino Sassu OPEN: Mon to Sat 12.30 (1 Sat) to 2.30, 7.30 to 11 CLOSED: 2 weeks Christmas, bank hols MEALS: alc (main courses £15 to £19) SERVICE: not inc, card slips closed CARDS: Amex, Delta, Diners, MasterCard, Switch, Visa DETAILS: 35 seats. Private parties: 6 main room. Vegetarian meals. Children's helpings. No cigars/pipes in dining room. No music. Air-conditioned ⊖ Notting Hill Gate

Atlantic Bar and Grill

map 15

20 Glasshouse Street, W1R 5RQ
TEL: (020) 7734 4888 FAX: (020) 7734 5400

COOKING **2**
MODERN ENGLISH-PLUS
£29–£68

This huge underground space – the basement of the former Regent Palace Hotel – has become something of an institution. Coffered ceilings, art deco fittings and marble columns provide a glimpse of 1930s grandeur, and Atlantic continues to be a place for hedonism, with much swilling of cocktails and champagne. Once past the doorman, diners make their way through the gargantuan bar, which is often packed.

Since the arrival of Stephen Carter, the menu has been revamped, favouring British cooking based on quality native produce. Expect to find starters such as Woodalls Cumbrian air-dried ham, Rosary goats' cheese and Cuan rock oysters. For main course, roast Telmara duck comes with thick-cut sweet potato chips and green pepper dressing, and wild sea bass is agreeably offset by saffron linguine and basil. Desserts such as white chocolate cheesecake with blueberries, or bread-and-butter pudding, aren't always as well executed, however. Top estates figure strongly on the wine list, but those bottles come at a price, and there is not much below £25. Value can be hunted out, though, and house wines kick off at £13.50 (£4.60 by the glass).

CHEF: Stephen Carter PROPRIETOR: Gruppo Ltd OPEN: Mon to Fri L 12 to 2.45, all week D 6 to 12 (7 to 10.30 Sun) MEALS: alc (main courses £11.50 to £18.50). Set L and pre-theatre D £14.50 (2 courses) to £16.50. Cover £1 SERVICE: 12.5% (optional), card slips closed CARDS: Amex, Delta, Diners, MasterCard, Switch, Visa DETAILS: 200 seats. Private parties: 75 private room. Vegetarian meals. Music. Air-conditioned ⊖ Piccadilly Circus (£5)

Aubergine

map 14

11 Park Walk, SW10 0AJ
TEL: (020) 7352 3449 FAX: (020) 7351 1770

COOKING **6**
FRENCH
£35–£130

A ragged yellow finish, contemporary landscapes and grand flower displays give the dining room both a cheery feel and an air of serious intent, and William Drabble's menu supplies plenty of luxury ingredients in support. Foie gras has appeared in three out of seven starters (as a terrine, a mousse, and in a salad with quail and sweetbreads), vying for attention with tortellini of lobster and truffles. Fish are prime species – high-quality, grilled red mullet given the escabèche treatment, for example – and shellfish is well handled too, in an unbeatable starter of first-class juicy scallops, wrapped in ventreche ham, on a bed of silky-smooth artichoke purée.

The cooking has reached high peaks, but has also dipped, and views diverge. The jury remains out on whether carefully sautéed duck foie gras paired with confit beetroot and a balsamic dressing makes a balanced partnership, and variability has affected main courses: 'dried-up' halibut at one meal, the same fish 'beautifully timed' with creamed leeks and chanterelles at another. Among meats, a 'stunning' pink duck breast has come on a potato galette with a creamy confit of cabbage.

Desserts, though not a highlight, have included a commendable lime parfait, an apple and raisin charlotte, and peaches roasted with Muscat de Beaumes de Venise and served with almond ice cream. Bookings require credit-card details and a faxed confirmation, children under 16 are no longer allowed in, and a dress-code warning is issued. Apart from those unfriendly practices, service by well-drilled, mostly French waiters is pleasant and unobtrusive. A wonderful wine list starts at £14, but is marred by high prices (even house wine is £22); for a £50 supplement seven glasses of wine accompany the seven-course 'menu gourmand'.

CHEF: William Drabble PROPRIETOR: A To Z Restaurants Ltd OPEN: Mon to Fri L 12 to 2.30, Mon to Sat D 7 to 10.30 CLOSED: 2 weeks Christmas, 2 weeks Aug, bank hols MEALS: Set L £20 (2 courses) to £25, Set D £48 to £115 (inc wine) SERVICE: 12.5%, card slips closed CARDS: Amex, Delta, Diners, MasterCard, Switch, Visa DETAILS: 50 seats. Private parties: 55 main room. No children under 16. Jacket and tie. No cigars/pipes in dining room. Wheelchair access (not WC). No music. Air-conditioned ⊖ South Kensington

Avenue 🍷

map 15

7–9 St James's Street, SW1A 1EE
TEL: (020) 7321 2111 FAX: (020) 7321 2500
EMAIL: avenue@egami.co.uk
WEB SITE: www.theavenue.co.uk

COOKING **4**
MODERN EUROPEAN
£33–£66

Decoration is minimal at this 'cavernous white box' of a dining room, its dimensions exaggerated by the massive plate mirrors at one end. The buzz is helped by a jazz piano at the door, and by the crowds that flock here. Dean Carr pays close attention to the quality of ingredients and applies a careful, understated cooking style to old favourites such as fishcake, Caesar salad, and crab mayonnaise. Seemingly simple dishes appear to work best – chilled asparagus soup, and exemplary tagliatelle alla carbonara – while fish fingers (pointedly not called goujons) use good-quality fish and come with a heap of leaves in a honeyed vinaigrette and a huge bowl of 'first-class' chips.

Desserts, such as pecan tart and fruit pavlova with vanilla ice cream, are equally unpretentious, if not always as successfully rendered as other dishes. Service is efficient, and a comprehensive spread of wine styles by the glass is listed on the lunch menu. The full list is well worth perusing, with around 150 bottles arranged by grape variety. Prices start at £14.50, and mark-ups at the top end are modest. For oenophiles, there is a short list of wines bought from Christie's auction house, which offers some unusual ones at very fair prices.

CHEF: Dean Carr PROPRIETOR: Christopher Bodker OPEN: all week 12 to 3, 5.45 to 12 (12.30 Fri and Sat, 10 Sun) CLOSED: Sat L Aug, 25 Dec MEALS: alc D (main courses £10.50 to £18). Set L £17.50 (2 courses) to £19.50, Set D 5.45 to 7.30 and 11 to 12 £14.50 (2 courses) to £16.50 SERVICE: 12.5% (optional), card slips closed CARDS: Amex, Delta, Diners, MasterCard, Switch, Visa DETAILS: 188 seats. Private parties: 250 main room. Vegetarian meals. Children's helpings. Wheelchair access (also WC). Music. Air-conditioned ⊖ Green Park

Azou

map 12

375 King Street, W6 9NJ
TEL: (020) 8563 7266 FAX: (020) 8748 1009

COOKING **2**
NORTH AFRICAN
£21–£41

Décor brightly evokes north Africa without overdoing it. The menu still lists main dishes according to their origins in Algeria, Morocco or Tunisia, but now also has a section headed 'Azou Specialities'. Three are tagines of Chris Benarab's devising, using herbs and spices from all three countries: Romanne is chicken in pomegranate sauce, with almonds, caramelised onions and raisins; Tefah is chicken breast with caramelised apples, raisins and almonds; while Constantine is 'very hot, spicy lamb with chilli and potatoes'. A fourth, Mechoui, needs ordering in advance: marinated, spiced, whole roast lamb at £280 for ten people. Starters include chermoula-marinated fried sardines, baba ganoush aubergine purée, and chakchouka, a North African version of ratatouille with merguez sausage. Minor but significant pleasures are couscous, Moroccan and Algerian bread, and olives marinated in harissa. House wines are £9.70; Moroccan red is £13.

CHEF/PROPRIETOR: Chris Benarab OPEN: all week D only 6 to 11 (occasionally open L; phone to check) MEALS: alc (main courses £7 to £13). Set D £14 (min 2) SERVICE: 12.5% (optional) CARDS: Delta, MasterCard, Switch, Visa DETAILS: 40 seats. Private parties: 40 main room. Vegetarian meals. Occasional music. Air-conditioned ⊖ Stamford Brook

Babur Brasserie

map 12

119 Brockley Rise, SE23 1JP
TEL: (020) 8291 2400 FAX: (020) 8291 4881
WEB SITE: www.babur-brasserie.com

COOKING **2**
INDIAN
£16–£46

The fascia, with its tiger's head, and the lively décor light up this corner of London, and the menu bears no resemblance to that of a curry house. Some regional dishes originate in Goa: calamari balchao (a starter of strips of squid stir-fried with a hot and sour sauce), and green curry of salmon. In some typically original twists, duck xacuti uses smoked breast of Barbary duck, and venison is pan-fried and finished in spicy orange, mushroom and Madeira sauce. A dozen vegetable side dishes range from black dhal (spinach and mushrooms) to Keralan avial (pumpkin, courgettes, green banana, dudi cucumber, yam and mooli in a yoghurt and coconut-milk sauce). Desserts extend beyond the usual rasmalai and kulfi to chocolate bread-and-butter pudding. Sunday lunch is a buffet. Modestly priced house wines are £8.95.

CHEF: Enam Rahman PROPRIETOR: Babur 1998 Ltd OPEN: Sat to Thur L 12.15 to 2 (2.30 Sun), all week D 6.15 to 11.15 CLOSED: 25 and 26 Dec MEALS: alc exc Sun L (main courses £7 to £12), Sun buffet L £8.95 SERVICE: not inc CARDS: Amex, Delta, Diners, MasterCard, Switch, Visa DETAILS: 56 seats. Private parties: 30 main room. Vegetarian meals. Children's helpings. Music. Air-conditioned (£5)

Back to Basics

map 15

21A Foley Street, W1W 6DS
TEL: (020) 7436 2181 FAX: (020) 7436 2180 — COOKING **3**
EMAIL: fishisthedish@aol.com — SEAFOOD
WEB SITE: www.backtobasics.uk.com — £26–£48

'A seafood lover's delight,' says the menu of this quirky restaurant. Fresh fish ('Today's Catch') encompasses about 14 choices – until some run out – that may include tuna loin steak and salad niçoise; fillet of wild sea bass with spring onions and ginger; and scallops with sweet chilli sauce and sour cream. If you want fish and chips, though, look elsewhere; here the potatoes are new, mashed or sautéed with onions. There are no expensive crustaceans, most seafood is grilled, and cold garnishes – such as salad with the tuna or couscous with monkfish – are quite usual. Vegetables of the day might be courgettes or broccoli.

Starters are also mainly fishy: for instance mussels steamed in white wine, home-made gravlax, or marinated herring fillets. Steak, lamb and chicken are offered as main-course specialities, and desserts take in chocolate mousse, bananas baked with rum, and a selection of cheeses and ice creams. The décor and style live up (but not down) to the restaurant's name, and the closeness of white-clothed tables and the friendliness of staff and customers create an agreeable ambience. House wines at £10.95 start the short list, but an 'Alternative Cellar' of over 30 French classics deserves consideration.

CHEFS: Stefan Pflaumer and Philip Banks PROPRIETOR: Stefan Pflaumer OPEN: Mon to Fri 12 to 10 CLOSED: 2 weeks Christmas, New Year, third and fourth week Aug, bank hols MEALS: alc (main courses £8 to £14.50) SERVICE: 10% (optional), card slips closed CARDS: Amex, Delta, Diners, MasterCard, Switch, Visa DETAILS: 40 seats. 40 seats outside. Private parties: 40 main room. Vegetarian meals. Children's helpings. Wheelchair access (not WC). Occasional music ⊖ Oxford Circus (£5)

'I spent the entire evening at about a foot's distance from staff sorting cutlery . . . and folding serviettes. The evening was a veritable crash course in folding serviettes. A serviette was folded to the accompaniment of my every mouthful.' (On eating in the West Country)

Bank Aldwych 🍷 map 13

1 Kingsway, WC2B 6XF
TEL: (020) 7379 9797 FAX: (020) 7240 7001 COOKING **4**
EMAIL: aldres@bankrestaurants.com MODERN EUROPEAN
WEB SITE: www.bankrestaurants.com £29–£65

Between City and theatre-land, this is one of the busiest parts of London, and the bar is usually bustling with City suits during the week. The huge dining room – down a corridor (mirrored on one side, the kitchen on display behind plate glass on the other) – has red leather seating and friendly, knowledgeable staff who usually cope well with the frenetic pace. French and Italian influences are most obvious on the extensive and wide-ranging menu, in starters of prosciutto with celeriac rémoulade and a soft-boiled egg, or a smooth, delicately creamy haddock and ricotta tart.

Main courses might bring good-quality, crisply grilled sea bass with mushrooms, salsify and lardons, or rack of lamb stacked on well-prepared fondant potato with spinach. Desserts, such as lemon tart with blackberry sorbet, seem less consistent. Simple style headings structure the unpretentious wine list; it is a highly individual collection, starting with house southern French at £12.90, and a fair number are under £20. The Bank Cellar selection offers something rarer and more serious. Two other Bank restaurants are in Birmingham and in Westminster (see entries).

CHEF: Lee Ward PROPRIETOR: Bank Restaurant Group plc OPEN: all week 12 to 3 (11.30 to 3.30 Sat and Sun), 5.30 to 11.30 (10 Sun) CLOSED: 25 Dec, bank hols MEALS: alc (main courses £9.50 to £19). Set L Mon to Fri £15.50 (2 courses) to £17.50, Set D 5.30 to 7.30 and 10 to 11.30 £15.50 (2 courses) to £17.50. Bar menu also available SERVICE: 12.5% (optional), card slips closed CARDS: Amex, Delta, Diners, MasterCard, Switch, Visa DETAILS: 200 seats. Private parties: 50 main room. Vegetarian meals. Children's helpings. Wheelchair access (also WC). No music. Air-conditioned ⊖ Holborn, Temple

Bank Westminster 🍷 NEW ENTRY map 13

45 Buckingham Gate, SW1E 6BS
TEL: (020) 7379 9797 FAX: (020) 7379 5070 COOKING **3**
EMAIL: westres@bankrestaurants.com MODERN EUROPEAN
WEB SITE: www.bankrestaurants.com £25–£65

Previously known as Zander, but now rebranded by the Bank family of restaurants (see entries above and Birmingham) this designer-led, brasserie-style restaurant-cum-bar is lodged in part of the St James Hotel. Behind the curvaceous stainless steel bar, one of Europe's longest, is a semicircular conservatory dining room, with yellow, blue and some plank walling, and deep-mauve Julyan Wickham-style chairs, overlooking the hotel's courtyard. Tables are set with white napery and attended by staff wearing black tunics, though service can prove rather uncertain.

The resolutely cosmopolitan menu describes dishes succinctly, and offers rock oysters, charcuterie from Spain, and black pudding with seared foie gras, fried egg and frisée. Crispy-skinned, flaky black bream has come with a provençale-style barigoule of artichokes, and pink, juicy and flavourful rump of lamb with confit garlic mash. A trio of chocolate, or sticky date pudding and marzipan ice cream round things off. The compact, global wine list runs by style with a fair few bottles under £20. Own-label house Chardonnay and Merlot are £12.90, and the Cellar selection is the place to find some serious stuff.

CHEF: Matt Dawson PROPRIETOR: Bank Restaurant Group plc OPEN: Sun to Fri L 12 (11.30 Sun) to 3, all week D 5.30 to 11.30 (10 Sun) CLOSED: 25 and 26 Dec, 1 Jan MEALS: alc (main courses £10.50 to £19.50). Set L and D 5.30 to 7 and 10 to 11.30 £13.50 (2 courses) to £15.50 SERVICE: 12.5% (optional), card slips closed CARDS: Amex, Delta, Diners, MasterCard, Switch, Visa DETAILS: 130 seats. 25 seats outside. Private parties: 300 main room, 20 private room. Vegetarian meals. Children's helpings. No-smoking area. Wheelchair access (also WC). Occasional music. Air-conditioned (£5)

Bar Zaika Bazaar

NEW ENTRY **map 14**

2A Pond Place, SW3 6DU
TEL/FAX: (020) 7584 6655
EMAIL: info@zaika-bazaar.co.uk

COOKING **3**
INDIAN
£31–£46

This combination bazaar and restaurant off the Fulham Road extends the concept of a restaurant-cum-art gallery selling pictures, to pottery, musical instruments, cushions and silks. Vineet Bhatia's menu offers a relaxed, informal version of his cooking at Zaika (see entry); chakna (Indian street food) is ordered as separate dishes or as platters. The tandoor supplies interestingly marinated lamb, chicken, quail and guinea fowl, plus Bhatia's signature dish of spiced, tandoori-smoked salmon, with its 'extra dimension, created by the zigzag of sambal and a line of mint chutney' on the plate. Chilli-garlic naan is also recommended (other variations include masala-cheese; chicken tikka and spring onion; and saffron, sesame and butter), and black lentils draw praise too. The wide-ranging menu also includes tava dishes (griddled with masala, cumin and tomato) and kathis: roti wrappers filled with various ingredients. The three 'large dishes' are chicken makhani (aka chicken tikka masala), aloo gosht (lamb with potatoes), and poached swordfish with an onion and coconut masala. The 50 skilfully selected wines, starting from £12 per bottle, include 16 by the glass, and, unusually for an Indian establishment, espresso coffee has been proclaimed good.

CHEF: Vineet Bhatia PROPRIETOR: Cuisine Collection OPEN: Mon to Fri, noon to 11 CLOSED: bank hols MEALS: alc (main courses £5.50 to £9) SERVICE: 12.5% (optional), card slips closed CARDS: Amex, Delta, MasterCard, Switch, Visa DETAILS: 70 seats. Private parties: 70 main room. Vegetarian meals. Music. Air-conditioned ⊖ South Kensington

Belair House

map 12

Gallery Road, SE21 7AB
TEL: (020) 8299 9788 FAX: (020) 8299 6793
EMAIL: belairhouse@aol.com
WEB SITE: www.belairhouse.co.uk

COOKING **4**
MODERN EUROPEAN
£36–£59

The setting alone would make this elegant white-painted Georgian villa in municipal Belair Park worth the visit, just a stone's throw from the Picture Gallery in leafy Dulwich. The dining room's high ceilings, perfect proportions and bold yellow walls strike a modern chord, well attuned to the cooking. A set-price menu, peppered with luxury ingredients, offers six choices at each level, and Zak El Hamdou (who used to cook at Chezmax in SW10; see entry) is putting his mark on the contemporary European repertoire. His classical French training is reflected in cep salad with truffles, a 'generous and well-flavoured' bouillabaisse, and in pot-au-feu of squab pigeon with ravioli of foie gras.

His less usual offerings, however, draw equal praise: for tea-smoked quail (in a salad with foie gras and Sauternes jelly), and in braised monkfish cheek (with mussels, girolles and broad beans). Finish with lemon tart with a crisp, caramelised brûlée topping, pear tarte Tatin with vanilla ice cream, or a trio of chocolate. Service is pleasant, efficient and friendly, while breads, amuse-gueules and rich, dark truffles with coffee add good support. The 80-strong, well-chosen wine list crosses the continents but shows a slight leaning towards the Old World. Prices start at £16 but soon accelerate above £20.

CHEF: Zak El Hamdou PROPRIETOR: Gary Cady OPEN: Tue to Sun L 12 to 2.30 (3 Sun), Tue to Sat D 7 to 10.30 MEALS: Set L £17.95 (2 courses) to £21.95, Set D £29.95 SERVICE: 12.5% (optional) CARDS: Amex, Delta, Diners, MasterCard, Switch, Visa DETAILS: 55 seats. 22 seats outside. Private parties: 85 main room, 45 private room. Car park. Children's helpings. No cigars/pipes in dining room. Wheelchair access (also WC). Music (£5)

Belvedere Marco Pierre White **map 13**

off Abbotsbury Road, Holland House, W8 6LU
TEL: (020) 7602 1238 COOKING **5**
FAX: (020) 7610 4382 MODERN BRITISH/MEDITERRANEAN
WEB SITE: www.whitestarline.org.uk £33–£86

The setting in pretty parkland remains as charming as ever: the restaurant is on two levels, with a few sought-after outdoor tables on the upper floor, while downstairs is a 'glorious' room with a vaulted ceiling and picture windows letting light flood in. Unsurprisingly, this is a popular summer venue. Matthew Brown has slipped easily into the recognisable Marco style, though the cooking is reckoned to be more ambitious than at other outposts of the empire, with one or two flourishes embroidering the assured blend of modern British and Mediterranean ideas.

Among starters, endives are given the tarte Tatin treatment and served with thyme-flavoured grilled scallops, and a combination of crab with Russian salad and mayonnaise is fashioned into a layered tower and surrounded by dollops of crab mayonnaise garnished with caviar. Highly refined execution is characteristic, whether applied to apparently straightforward dishes such as carefully cooked poulet noir (with chanterelles, black trumpet mushrooms and a generous helping of creamy mash), or to an earthy rendition of pigs' trotters 'aux saveurs de terroir'.

For dessert, a classic lemon tart with delicate pastry and a rich filling balanced with good acidity is embellished by the presence of a lemon soufflé and a refreshing lemon ice cream. The set-price lunch menu of three courses for £18 deserves mention as one of London's bargains, though the 'optional' 12.5 per cent added for service takes off a little of the shine. Wines are aggressively priced, the larger part of the list falling in the £40-plus bracket, though there are a few bottles under £20.

CHEF: Matthew Brown PROPRIETOR: Marco Pierre White OPEN: all week 12 to 2.30, 6 to 11 (5.30 during opera season) MEALS: alc (main courses £14.50 to £25). Set L £14.95 to £39, Set D £25 to £39 SERVICE: 12.5%, card slips closed CARDS: Amex, Delta, Diners, MasterCard, Switch, Visa DETAILS: 108 seats. 25 seats outside. Children's helpings. No pipes in dining room. Wheelchair access (not WC). No music. Air-conditioned ⊖ Holland Park, High Street Kensington

Bibendum 🍷 map 14

Michelin House, 81 Fulham Road, SW3 6RD
TEL: (020) 7581 5817 FAX: (020) 7823 7925 — COOKING **5**
EMAIL: manager@bibendum.co.uk — MODERN BRITISH
WEB SITE: www.bibendum.co.uk — £45–£105

What was, in the early part of the twentieth century, the Michelin Tyre Company's first permanent British headquarters, rescued and refurbished by Sir Terence Conran 15 years ago, is a place of unpretentious, nostalgic charm. Natural daylight contributes to the airy feel, pouring through windows etched with the Michelin man riding a bicycle, and street plans of French cities. It is a place to come for simple but well-prepared food that is at once up to date and yet as ageless as the surroundings. The menu contrives to comfort with familiarity, and yet to excite with novelty, turning up such dishes as spinach and truffled pecorino tart, ox tongue salad with beetroot and horseradish cream, and deep-fried fillet of plaice with chips and tartare sauce.

British dishes rub shoulders with simple French classics, and game and offal are among the kitchen's favourites: roast partridge with ceps, or one visitor's 'desert island dish' of grilled calf's kidney with roast tomato, chorizo, sherry and basil. The straightforwardness of the cooking is a big plus, yielding cream of leek soup perfumed with chervil, and a classic version of grilled asparagus with olive oil, Parmesan and balsamic. Cogency is also evident in, for example, poached salt-duck with lentils, given piquancy and sweetness by the accompanying mustard fruits and salsa verde.

Finish perhaps with a creamy, flavourful orange bavarois, or gâteau Opéra with its rich flavourings of chestnut, coffee and chocolate. An encyclopedic collection of traditional greats in mature vintages shares the wine list with modern classics. Prices can be unforgiving, but foraging for bottles under £25 will bring pleasant surprises from southern France and Portugal. House wines start at £15.95, and six wines are sold by the glass from £4.25.

CHEFS: Matthew Harris and Jamie Younger PROPRIETORS: Sir Terence Conran, Lord Hamlyn, Simon Hopkinson and Graham Williams OPEN: all week 12 to 2.30 (3 Sat and Sun), 7 to 11.30 (10.30 Sun) CLOSED: 25 and 26 Dec MEALS: alc D (main courses £15.50 to £26). Set L £24 (2 courses) to £28.50 SERVICE: 12.5% (optional), card slips closed CARDS: Amex, Delta, Diners, MasterCard, Switch, Visa DETAILS: 84 seats. Private parties: 100 main room. Children's helpings. Wheelchair access (also WC). No music. Air-conditioned ⊖ South Kensington (£5)

(£5) *indicates that the restaurant has elected to participate in the* Good Food Guide *voucher scheme. For full details, see page 6.*

Bibendum Oyster Bar

NEW ENTRY **map 14**

Michelin House, 81 Fulham Road, SW3 6RD
TEL: (020) 7589 1480 FAX: (020) 7823 7925
EMAIL: manager@bibendum.co.uk
WEB SITE: www.bibendum.co.uk

COOKING **4**
SEAFOOD
£29–£79

Downstairs from the main restaurant (see entry above), in the foyer of the former Michelin building, is the more informal – and slightly cheaper – oyster bar, which according to aficionados offers 'some sort of perfection, particularly when it comes to shellfish'. Four varieties of oyster appear on the menu along with a range of impressive seafood platters, while fish might appear as a cold roasted cod fillet with a compote of peppers and onions and an 'intense' salsa verde.

Most other tastes are catered for by the praiseworthy, modern brasserie-style cooking: chargrilled chicken breast on a bed of fried noodles, and 'very rare, tender and juicy' roast lamb on a purée of pimentos and minted yoghurt. The approach is seemingly casual and the range is limited, but behind it all is assiduous attention to detail that guarantees a high level of success; that also goes for service from a well-drilled young team. Wines understandably concentrate on whites, in a number of styles at moderate prices; try the Sauvignon de Touraine at £14.95. For a wider choice, a look at the full restaurant list can be requested.

CHEFS: Lewis Norman and Jamie Younger PROPRIETORS: Sir Terence Conran, Lord Hamlyn, Simon Hopkinson and Graham Williams OPEN: all week 12 to 10.30 (10 Sun) MEALS: alc (main courses £9 to £28.50) SERVICE: 12.5% (optional), card slips closed CARDS: Amex, Delta, Diners, MasterCard, Switch, Visa DETAILS: 45 seats. 12 seats outside. Vegetarian meals. Children's helpings. Wheelchair access (not WC). No music ⊖ South Kensington

Bleeding Heart

map 13

Bleeding Heart Yard, Greville St, EC1N 8SJ
TEL: (020) 7242 8238 FAX: (020) 7831 1402
WEB SITE: www.bleedingheart.co.uk

COOKING **4**
FRENCH
£33–£59

In Hatton Garden, good restaurants are rarer than diamonds, but this one is high-carat, not least for its responsive, knowledgeable and friendly service. From a secluded yard, a flowery terrace leads to the ground-floor bistro and downstairs restaurant. Despite its old-style, panelled, booked-lined 'clubby' rooms, the décor is upbeat and tasteful (barring a surfeit of bleeding heart stickers), lightened by mirrors and a garden behind a window. An à la carte menu is extended with the help of 'plats du jour' and luxurious, unpriced 'evening specials', and fine ingredients are cooked with a degree of skill.

The determinedly French approach shows in a marbled terrine of foie gras, duck and chicken livers (accompanied by well-timed fine beans and baby spinach), and in a full-flavoured double-baked Stilton soufflé with roasted pears. Subtle sauces link stars and supporting actors, in harmonious main courses such as pancetta-wrapped squab pigeon with juniper cabbage and red wine gravy. Cheeses are mainly French, but have also included an unusual Welsh Saval. 'Classic' crème caramel, and a rhubarb version of trifle have counted among happy dessert choices. The wine list highlights the proprietors' own vineyard, Trinity Hill in New Zealand (source of house wines from £14.95), but other stylish Antipodeans figure too. The majority of the list consists of great names from France, many in impressively mature vintages at expense-account prices. A new sister restaurant is The Don in EC4 (see entry).

CHEF: Andrew Barber PROPRIETORS: Robert and Robyn Wilson OPEN: Mon to Fri 12 to 2.30, 6 to 10.30 CLOSED: 10 days from 24 Dec, bank hols MEALS: alc (main courses £10 to £18). Bistro and tavern menus also available SERVICE: 12.5% (optional), card slips closed CARDS: Amex, Delta, Diners, MasterCard, Switch, Visa DETAILS: 110 seats. 30 seats outside. Private parties: 50 main room, 40 and 130 private rooms. Car park. Vegetarian meals. No children. No music. Air-conditioned ⊖ Farringdon, Chancery Lane

Bluebird

map 14

350 King's Road, SW3 5UU
TEL: (020) 7559 1000 FAX: (020) 7559 1111
WEB SITE: www.conran.com

COOKING **3**
MODERN EUROPEAN
£28–£77

The courtyard of this former garage houses the cook shop and food shop, which are worth a visit. Although no longer new, Bluebird still attracts crowds of glossy folk. But there are some changes; new head chef Blair Smethurst has increased the focus on shellfish, and his cooking is confident, assured and safe, though it doesn't come cheap. Weekday lunch and dinner seem more reliable than weekend brunch. Starters include three types of oyster (rock, fine de claire or native), potted shrimps and langoustines with mayonnaise, as well as steak tartare and foie gras with fig chutney. Humbler materials have included roast huss in prosciutto, and rabbit with bacon, while puddings take in old stagers such as crème brûlée and pavlova. Tables are close-set, and service can be rushed at busy times. Wines span Old World and New, with eight interesting house wines from £12.75 (£3.75 a glass), though prices quickly breach £20, peaking at £70 for Bordeaux, more for champagne.

CHEF: Blair Smethurst PROPRIETOR: Conran Restaurants Ltd OPEN: all week 12 to 3, 6 to 11 (10 Sun), Sat and Sun brunch 11 to 3.30 MEALS: alc D (main courses £11 to £21.50). Set L Mon to Fri £12.50 (2 courses) to £16.50. Brunch menu available Sat and Sun 11 to 4 SERVICE: 12.5% (optional), card slips closed CARDS: Amex, Delta, Diners, MasterCard, Switch, Visa DETAILS: 260 seats. 30 seats outside. Private parties: 32 main room, 48 private room. Vegetarian meals. Children's helpings. Wheelchair access (also WC). Music. Air-conditioned ⊖ South Kensington

Blue Elephant

map 12

3–6 Fulham Broadway, SW6 1AA
TEL: (020) 7385 6595 FAX: (020) 7386 7665
EMAIL: london@blueelephant.com
WEB SITE: www.blueelephant.com

COOKING **1**
THAI
£42–£76

There is no other interior quite like it: exotic and glamorous, it really does transport visitors to the land of a thousand temples. Drink at an ornate gilt-edged bar shaped like a dragon, as water cascades over rocks, and fish (including some handsome carp) swim in the ponds. Bridges and plants are everywhere, although the scale is tempered in the dining areas by clever use of screens. A long menu with flowery descriptions yields decent Thai fishcakes, vermicelli salad, chicken satay, yellow prawn curry, and prawn and chicken wrapped variously in rice paper or spring roll and deep-fried. Much of the food, though, is anglicised, with many primary Thai flavours quite muted in favour of a general and powerful sweetness. Desserts, however, include authentic-tasting jasmine cake, and ta ko (a jelly made with rice flour and water chestnuts topped with coconut cream). Drink beer.

CHEFS: Sir-Aim Surapol, Chaliew Plangsri and M. Suphanavong PROPRIETOR: Blue Elephant International plc OPEN: Sun to Fri L 12 to 2.30 (3 Sun), all week D 7 (6.30 Fri and Sat) to 12.30 (10.30 Sun) CLOSED: 24 to 27 Dec MEALS: alc (main courses £9.50 to £20). Set L and D £32 to £36. Cover £1.50 SERVICE: not inc CARDS: Amex, Delta, Diners, MasterCard, Switch, Visa DETAILS: 250 seats. Private parties: 100 main room. Vegetarian meals. Wheelchair access (also WC). Music. Air-conditioned ⊖ Fulham Broadway

Blue Print Café

map 13

Design Museum, Butlers Wharf, SE1 2YD
TEL: (020) 7378 7031 FAX: (020) 7357 8810
WEB SITE: www.conran.com

COOKING **4**
MODERN EUROPEAN
£35–£67

The white concrete box on the riverside that houses the Design Museum also accommodates this appropriately stylish restaurant, whose striking river views are a match for any along this stretch. The dining room has been enhanced by a refit, which has opened up the space, while the kitchen's emphasis remains on the best seasonal ingredients fashioned into imaginative modern European dishes. These range in scope from whole grilled mackerel with tabbouleh, and impressive grilled cuttlefish with tabil ('a pale green, garlicky, parsleyish purée'), to rabbit with barley and peas, and exemplary Middle White pork – 'with an outrageous amount of fat and wonderful crispy crackling' – served with fennel, olives and rosemary.

Successful desserts have included a classically rendered crème brûlée, and a crisp-pastried tart (like 'deconstructed Bakewell'), with an intensely almondy sponge filling, and a great dollop of Jersey cream on the side. Large inconsistencies have been noted, with some dishes a fitting testament to Jeremy Lee's undoubted talents, others not, but at its best this is genuinely top-notch cooking. Service is amiable, though prices on the wine list are hardly fitting for a café, starting at around £15 and rising quickly.

CHEF: Jeremy Lee PROPRIETOR: Conran Restaurants Ltd OPEN: all week L 12 to 3, Mon to Sat D 6 to 11 MEALS: alc D (main courses £11 to £17). Set L £19.50 (2 courses) to £22.50 SERVICE: 12.5% (optional), card slips closed CARDS: Amex, Delta, Diners, MasterCard, Switch, Visa DETAILS: 65 seats. 50 seats outside. Private parties: 110 main room. No music ⊖ Tower Hill, London Bridge

Not inc *in the details at the end of an entry indicates that no service charge is made and any tipping is at the discretion of the customer.*

London Round-ups listing additional restaurants that may be worth a visit can be found after the main London section.

Brackenbury

map 12

129–131 Brackenbury Road, W6 0BQ
TEL: (020)8748 0107 FAX: (020) 8741 0905

COOKING **4**
MODERN BRITISH
£22–£46

This is largely a quiet residential area, and the Brackenbury is very much the bistro-style neighbourhood local. Double-fronted, it consists of two small split-level rooms with boldly painted walls and ceiling, simple bare tables and blond-wood chairs. It is 'very relaxing and laid back' and can be noisy when crowded, so on summer days the pavement tables beckon. The menu, which changes daily for lunch and dinner, shows respect for ingredients and focuses on freshness and quality, giving a 'wonderfully honest feel to the food'. Marcia Chang Hong's modern British style is coloured by forays to the Mediterranean and beyond. Trademark omelettes feature as mains, perhaps Gruyère with chips and green salad, or, more adventurous, pan-fried John Dory with lentils and romescu sauce. Starters number excellent seared scallops and zingy guacamole, or Serrano ham with soft-boiled goose egg and truffle oil. For dessert, a strawberry tart has pleased, or perhaps try pannacotta with blueberries. A compact, globe-trotting wine list is simply laid out in ascending price order from Vins de Pays d'Oc at £10.

CHEF: Marcia Chang Hong PROPRIETOR: Christopher Bodker OPEN: Sun to Fri L 12.30 to 2.45, Mon to Sat D 7 to 10.45 CLOSED: Christmas MEALS: alc (main courses £8.50 to £15). Set L £10.50 (2 courses) to £12.50 SERVICE: not inc CARDS: Amex, Delta, Diners, MasterCard, Switch, Visa DETAILS: 60 seats. 20 seats outside. Private parties: 40 main room, 30 private room. Vegetarian meals. Children's helpings. No cigars in dining room. No music ⊖ Goldhawk Road

Bradleys

map 13

25 Winchester Road, NW3 3NR
TEL: (020) 7722 3457 FAX: (020) 7435 1392

COOKING **4**
ANGLO-FRENCH
£23–£56

Elegance and balance are keynotes in this light, airy, minimally decorated dining room, with its crisp-linen tablecloths and attentive service. The menu offers meat, vegetarian and fish main dishes (choose from one of each at weekday lunches, more at dinner). Fish might include pan-fried scallops (a favourite with reporters) in versions with onion sauce, with cauliflower purée and red wine sauce, and with pea sauce. Grilling is a favoured technique, applied to squid as a starter, to halibut and to marinated tuna as mains, while successful meat dishes have included loin of venison with shallot Tatin and horseradish mash. Start perhaps with a warm quail and watercress salad with rillettes and fried quail eggs, and finish with apple tart and its accompanying baked apple ice cream, or hot lemon and raspberry soufflé with custard. The wine list, too, is more balanced than before: for the first time European wines complement New World bottles. Chilean house selections are £13 but other prices soon exceed £20.

CHEF: Simon Bradley PROPRIETORS: Simon and Jolanta Bradley OPEN: Sun to Fri L 12 to 3, all week D 6 to 11 CLOSED: 25 and 26 Dec, 1 Jan MEALS: Set L Mon to Fri £10 (2 courses) to £14, Set L Sun £15 (2 courses) to £18, Set D £22 (2 courses) to £27 SERVICE: 12% (optional), card slips closed CARDS: Amex, Delta, MasterCard, Switch, Visa DETAILS: 60 seats. Private parties: 60 main room. Vegetarian meals. Children's helpings. No cigars/pipes in dining room. Wheelchair access (not WC). Music. Air-conditioned ⊖ Swiss Cottage (£5)

Brasserie St Quentin

map 14

243 Brompton Road, SW3 2EP
TEL: (020) 7589 8005

COOKING **2**
FRENCH
£28–£63

With its small, closely spaced tables, white damask tablecloths, copious chandeliers and large mirrors lining the walls, this brasserie has the look and feel of one in Paris, which seems to be the aim. Diners can start off with a decently rendered Kir while perusing the menu, which lists brasserie favourites such as French onion soup, or endive and frisée salad for starters, and Toulouse sausages with herb mash and shallot sauce, or grilled tuna niçoise for main courses. Finish off with a convincing and generous tarte Tatin and good coffee. The cooking might not be cutting-edge, and prices reflect the affluence of the neighbourhood, but service, from mainly Francophone staff, is polite and attentive. Although the mainly French wine list is hardly innovative, prices start at £10.95 and nine wines are available by the glass.

CHEF: Lionel Lemaitre PROPRIETOR: Groupe Chez Gérard OPEN: all week 11 to 11 (10.30 Sun) MEALS: alc (main courses £9.50 to £22) SERVICE: 12.5%, card slips closed CARDS: Amex, Delta, Diners, MasterCard, Switch, Visa DETAILS: 55 seats. Private parties: 16 main room, 17 private room. Music. Air-conditioned ⊖ South Kensington

▲ Brown's Hotel, Restaurant 1837 🍷

NEW ENTRY **map 15**

Albemarle Street, W1S 4BP
TEL: (020) 7493 602
EMAIL: 1837@brownshotel.com
WEB SITE: www.brownshotel.com

COOKING **4**
MODERN EUROPEAN
£42–£112

Named after the year in which the hotel was built, rather than Queen Victoria's year of accession, this plush Mayfair hotel has a determined air of bygone elegance, reinforced by wood panelling, a majestically camp floral display, and a wood-effect gas fire. Andrew Turner, who cut at least some of his teeth at Le Gavroche under Albert Roux, has given the menus a new lift. Seafood is a particularly strong suit: an open raviolo, on which is erected a tower of crabmeat, tomato, ink-black pasta and caviar, is an exercise in freshness and texture, while baked lobster has arrived in the shell with truffled mash, green summer vegetables and a smooth reduction of Muscat wine, cream and ginger.

Luxuries are equally conspicuous among meat dishes, encompassing a fillet of milk-fed veal served with morels, asparagus and Madeira sauce. Desserts at inspection failed to dazzle, as did the cheeseboard, but luckier customers might enjoy strawberry shortcake with basil essence, or the house crème brûlée. Service proceeds at a stately pace, which may come as welcome respite to many and be seriously irksome to others. A dream of a wine list supplies myriad smart bottles from France, Italy, Spain and beyond. A selection of 'wines on a budget', comprising distinct varietal styles from around the world, is an intelligent antidote to the more exclusive bottles, as are the house wines from south-west France at £18. The availability of 300 wines by the glass makes this one of the best places in town for wine lovers to experiment.

CHEF: Andrew Turner PROPRIETOR: Raffles International OPEN: Mon to Fri L 12 to 2.30, Mon to Sat D 7 to 10 CLOSED: 1 to 8 Jan, bank hols MEALS: alc (main courses £20 to £32). Set L £20 (2 courses) to £29, Set D £37 to £80 (inc wine). Bar menu available SERVICE: not inc CARDS: Amex, Delta, Diners, MasterCard, Switch, Visa DETAILS: 60 seats. Private parties: 70 main room, 2 to 100 private rooms. Children's helpings. No cigars/pipes in dining room. No music. Air-conditioned ACCOMMODATION: 118 rooms, all with bath/shower. TV. Phone. Room only £270 to £365. Rooms for disabled. Baby facilities ⊖ Green Park (£5)

Café du Jardin 🍷

map 15

28 Wellington Street, WC2E 7BD
TEL: (020) 7836 8769 and 8760
FAX: (020) 7836 4123
WEB SITE: www.lecafedujardin.com

COOKING **3**
MODERN BRITISH
£21–£53

The location, opposite the Royal Opera House, and rather higher ambitions than most nearby eating places, draw a mature clientèle and many tourists. They enjoy the civilised, but not too quiet, ambience of the ground floor and basement rooms, and approve the attention to detail in both food and service. There is a set-price lunch, and a set dinner before 7.30 or after 10pm, but the à la carte is also very fairly priced. As main dishes (or to precede one) Italian-style pasta and risottos are specialities, and a particularly successful risotto with an inspector's crab cake starter provided a fine balance of heat and delicacy. Artichoke heart filled with mushroom and served with a warm glazed poached egg has also been properly executed, while monkfish has been accompanied by a 'richly flavoured mild version of a Thai green curry' with lime-scented Basmati rice. The long wine list starts with house selections at £9.75, and there is a splendid 'fine and rare' supplement. Sister restaurant Le Deuxième, in nearby Long Acre, was due to open as the Guide went to press (tel (020) 7379 0033)

CHEF: Tony Howorth PROPRIETORS: Robert Seigler and Tony Howorth OPEN: Mon to Sat 12 to 3, 5.30 to 12, Sun 12 to 11 CLOSED: 24 to 25 Dec MEALS: alc (main courses £10.50 to £15.50). Set L and D Mon to Sat 5.30 to 7.30 and 10 to 12 £9.95 (2 courses) to £13.50 SERVICE: 15% (optional), card slips closed CARDS: Amex, Delta, Diners, MasterCard, Switch, Visa DETAILS: 100 seats. 16 seats outside. Private parties: 60 main room. Vegetarian meals. Wheelchair access (not WC). Music. Air-conditioned ⊖ Covent Garden

Café Japan

map 13

626 Finchley Road, NW11 7RR
TEL: (020) 8455 6854

COOKING **5**
JAPANESE
£20–£51

The décor has been tidied up, posters of specials have disappeared, and the walls now bear only an oft-repeated announcement that Tuesday night is sushi night. But sushi are not the peak of this restaurant's achievements. Mr Konnai has now resumed his role of chef, and turns out some notable weekly specials including an inside-out roll of crispy fried yellowtail, and gindara (grilled marinated black cod), whose price tag of £9.90 is perfectly justified by its elegant combining of the best white fish with the depth of flavour of an oily fish.

Among regular small dishes are orosho tori karaage (deep-fried marinated chicken with onion and lightly dressed leaves), and distinguished yakitori; these grilled, skewered nibbles include excellent shiitake mushrooms, and little pork meatballs rolled with the multi-flavoured herb shiso. Set meals from £8 (single dishes accompanied by rice, pickles and soup) are mostly based on salt-grilled fish, as austerely luxurious as a perfect oyster. Of three classic Japanese ice creams – maccha tea, kuri chestnut and azuki red bean – the last is outstanding. Ordinary saké is just that, so Japanese beer, especially the dry Asahi, makes a better accompaniment.

CHEF/PROPRIETOR: Koichi Konnai OPEN: Wed to Sun L 12 to 2, Tue to Sun D 6 to 10.30 CLOSED: Christmas, Easter, bank hols MEALS: alc D (main courses £9 to £14). Set L £5.90, Set D £19.50 SERVICE: not inc CARDS: Delta, MasterCard, Switch, Visa DETAILS: 40 seats. Private parties: 6 main room. Vegetarian meals. Music. Air-conditioned ⊖ Golders Green

Café Spice Namaste

maps 12 and 13

16 Prescot Street, E1 8AZ
TEL: (020) 7488 9242 FAX: (020) 7488 9339 — COOKING **4**
247 Lavender Hill, SW11 1JW — INDIAN
TEL: (020) 7738 1717 FAX: (020) 7738 1666 — £32–£58

The cliché that the vivid décor of Cyrus Todiwala's restaurants mirror the exciting flavours in his food is, like a lot of clichés, true. Many Indian regions are represented in the menus, and a few neighbouring countries. From southern India, seafood ullathiyad incorporates sauté scallops, king prawns, squid rings and green-lipped mussels. Punjabi makhanwala murg, or butter chicken, resembles chicken tikka masala, as the Lavender Hill menu notes. Goa contributes garlic-flavoured seafood salad, and chicken tikka piri-piri starters with authoritative pork vindaloo to follow.

But Cyrus's real passion is Parsee food from his Bombay home (see Parsee, main entry, London), such as chicken curry with puréed cashew nuts and coconut; whole pan-fried pomfret; and sweet and sour vegetable stew. Appetite-inducing prose poems in his menus explain Bombay snacks such as bhel poori, and papeta na pattis, a version of his mother's fried potato cakes filled with peas, coconut, nut and spices. Menus at the two branches are almost identical (although some dishes are differently named), but only at Prescot Street will you encounter the weekly special list of finds from the markets as well as exotic rarities such as ostrich or kangaroo. A short, reasonably priced list has house wines at £11.90, and Muree is new to the beer list.

CHEFS: Cyrus Todiwala and Angelo Collaco (both alternate between branches) PROPRIETOR: Cyrus Todiwala OPEN: Prescot Street: Mon to Fri 12 to 3, Mon to Sat 6.15 (6 Sat) to 10.30; Lavender Hill Sun L 12 to 3 and Tue to Sun D 6 11.30 (Sun 10.30) CLOSED: 25 Dec and 2 Jan, bank hols MEALS: Prescot Street: alc (main courses £8 to £15). Set L and D £22 to £35. Light L also available. Lavender Hill: alc (main courses £6 to £13). Set D £18 (2 courses) to £22. Light L also available SERVICE: 12.5% (optional), card slips closed CARDS: Amex, Delta, Diners, MasterCard, Switch, Visa DETAILS: Prescot Street 140 seats, Lavender Hill 92 seats, 16 outside. Private parties: Prescot Street 160 main room; Lavender Hill 120 main room. Vegetarian meals. Children's helpings. Wheelchair access (also men's WC). Music. Air-conditioned ⊖ Aldgate, Tower Hill (Prescot Street), Clapham Common (Lavender Hill)

Cambio de Tercio **map 14**

163 Old Brompton Road, SW5 0LJ
TEL: (020) 7244 8970 FAX: (020) 7373 8817

COOKING **3**
MODERN SPANISH
£38–£64

'A fun place, buzzing with life even on a Sunday evening,' enthuses a reader, who found it 'friendly, very Spanish', like its décor in the Spanish national colours. Ingredients other than fish are imported from Spain, and that includes the powerful, uncompromising jamón de Jabugo, which was 'worth every peseta'. Other starters include grilled vegetables with romescu sauce; a Basque stew of red tuna and potato; and accurately timed deep-fried squid with black ink and a 'very garlicky' white aïoli. Main dishes, equally divided between fish and meat, might include hake and clams in parsley and garlic sauce, or stewed quails with asparagus and rice. Spanish cheeses are 'a revelation', enhanced by an outstanding quince preserve. Cheerful service, and the encyclopaedic, 150-strong, Spanish wine list draw praise too, and guidance towards a red Jumilla (Carchelo Monastrell at £16.50) was appreciated by one visitor. Other styles range from a crisp Albariños from Galicia to full-bodied reds of Priorato. Prices are wide-ranging too, from fruit-driven offerings below £20, to rare £200-plus bottlings. Vintages are not listed in the main list, but a '50 Year List' gathers together 21 vintages ranging back to 1952 to give a taste of what traditional Spanish styles can achieve with extra bottle age. House wines start at £12.50.

CHEFS: Javier Jimenez and Ignacio Arce PROPRIETORS: Abel Lusa and David Rivero OPEN: all week 12.15 to 2.30, 7 to 11.30 CLOSED: 2 weeks at Christmas MEALS: alc (main courses £13.50 to £15.50) SERVICE: not inc, 12.5% for parties of 6 or more CARDS: Amex, Delta, MasterCard, Switch, Visa DETAILS: 45 seats. 6 seats outside. Private parties: 20 private room. Wheelchair access (not WC). Music ⊖ Gloucester Road

Cantaloupe **map 13**

35–42 Charlotte Road, EC2A 3PD
TEL: (020) 7613 4411 FAX: (020) 7613 4111
WEB SITE: www.cantaloupe.co.uk

COOKING **2**
MEDITERRANEAN
£24–£39

'Relaxed but with attitude' sums up the appeal of this Hoxton bar-restaurant that, in the words of owner Richard Bigg, 'becomes increasingly lively as the week progresses'. It has a 'comfortable industrial' feel, and the furniture is a mix of mismatching wooden tables, odd sofas and comfortable chairs, which all adds to the sense of informality. The cooking takes its cues from either side of the Mediterranean, particularly Spain and Morocco, with starters of chargrilled asparagus with tapénade, or fried salt-cod cake with a poached egg and aïoli, alongside a Moroccan salad of dates, oranges, carrots and almonds. Main courses show more of a fusion of styles, as in chargrilled tuna with tabbouleh and a honey, yoghurt and tahini sauce, or roast Barbary duck breast with roast pumpkin, chickpeas and a pomegranate and walnut dressing. At lunchtimes a tapas bar menu also operates. Wines are a well-chosen and good-value selection, opening at £9.50 and offering ten by the glass from £2.50.

CHEF: Henry Brereton PROPRIETORS: Richard Bigg and Nigel Foster OPEN: Mon to Sat L 12 to 3, Mon to Sat D 6 to 12 (7 Sat). Also open Sun brunch 12 to 4 CLOSED: 25 Dec, 16 Apr, 27 Aug MEALS: alc (main courses £8 to £12.50). Bar menu available L SERVICE: 12.5% (optional), card slips closed CARDS: Amex, Delta, MasterCard, Switch, Visa DETAILS: 50 seats. Private parties: 50 main room. Vegetarian meals. No children Thur to Sat D. Wheelchair access (also WC). Music. Air-conditioned ⊖ Old Street, Liverpool Street

▲ The Capital

map 14

22–24 Basil Street, SW3 1AT
TEL: (020) 7589 5171 FAX: (020) 7225 0011 — COOKING **8**
EMAIL: reservations@capitalhotel.co.uk — FRENCH
WEB SITE: www.capitalhotel.co.uk — £38–£91

Eric Chavot seems at last to have relaxed and found an environment where he can develop his own culinary style and extend his horizons. His theatre of operations is an intimate dining room in a fine hotel, its décor undistinguished apart from carefully arranged lighting and a few objets d'art attached to the mirrors. Success is down to a combination of near-faultless technique and a degree of innovation that eschews novelty in favour of simply putting interesting and complementary flavours together.

This may be a rather old-fashioned way to proceed, but it seems to work, for example in a starter of warm smoked haddock served on aïoli potatoes, accompanied by blinis and a salad of deep-fried quail's eggs. It is the ability to present concentrated flavours without distraction that lifts the cooking to a new realm, be it oxtail served simply with mashed potatoes, or 'dazzling' truffle-flecked turbot, surrounded by a fricassee of ceps and Jerusalem artichokes, some small gnocchi adding enough starch to offset the rich thyme-flavoured red wine reduction.

Vertical presentations are standard: for example, a base of first-class tomato risotto wrapped in smoked pork belly, topped with a brace of seared langoustines, then an accomplished langoustine raviolo, and finally a slice of deep-fried chorizo. Although this original dish may seem anything but simple, its different components work well together. French cheeses in generally good condition are served from a handsome covered silver trolley, and while desserts may not reach quite the heights of other departments, they have included a plate of lemon dishes (including little pancakes wrapped into cylinders containing lemon chibouste), and a chocolate and peppermint vacherin decorated with meringue 'paintbrushes'. Petits fours are about as good as petits fours get.

Service is a match for the food, combining friendliness and professionalism, and the sommelier is able to advise intelligently about wines to partner the food. His list is built around first-class vintages – both young and mature – from renowned estates (predominantly French), which explains the hefty price tags. But place has been found for value, particularly in southern France, and plenty are available by the glass. House Loire red and white are £14.50.

CHEF: Eric Crouillère-Chavot PROPRIETOR: David Levin OPEN: all week 12.30 to 2.15, 7 to 11.15 MEALS: alc (main courses £22). Set L £26.50, Set D £60 SERVICE: 12.5%, card slips closed CARDS: Amex, Delta, Diners, MasterCard, Switch, Visa DETAILS: 36 seats. Private parties: 8 main room, 10 and 22 private rooms. Car park. Jacket and tie. No cigars/pipes in dining room. No music. Air-conditioned ACCOMMODATION: 48 rooms, all with bath/shower. TV. Phone. Room only £180 to £245. Baby facilities (*The Which? Hotel Guide*) ⊖ Knightsbridge

Le Caprice

map 15

Arlington House, Arlington Street, SW1A 1RT
TEL: (020) 7629 2239 FAX: (020) 7493 9040

COOKING **4**
MODERN BRITISH
£35–£84

More than 20 years on, Le Caprice looks much as it has always done, with its timeless and elegant black furnishings. If anything the atmosphere seems 'even clubbier, with lots of tanned wealth lounging at familiar tables'. A simple, one-page carte (there are vegetarian and vegan menus too) lists the retro comfort food for which it is famous, and for which the famous return: from eggs Benedict to sauté foie gras with Sauternes jus, from a plum tomato and basil galette to deep-fried haddock with minted pea purée, chips and tartare sauce.

Staples of the repertoire, such as chopped steak Américaine, are balanced by a few more inventive options: Thai-baked sea bass with fragrant rice and soy dip, or corn-fed chicken breast with Szechuan vegetables and black bean sauce. For dessert, quince takes well to its caramelisation in a tarte Tatin, and Scandinavian iced berries with white chocolate sauce is a long standing favourite. The wine list, from £11.25, covers Old World and New and offers reasonable choice under £25; Californian selections are particularly good.

CHEFS: Kevin Gratton and Tim Hughes PROPRIETOR: Belgo Group plc OPEN: all week 12 to 3 (3.30 Sun), 5.30 (6 Sun) to 12 CLOSED: 25 and 26 Dec, 1 Jan, Aug bank hol MEALS: alc (main courses £10 to £28.50). Cover £1.50 (unless dining in bar). Brunch menu Sun SERVICE: not inc CARDS: Amex, Delta, Diners, MasterCard, Switch, Visa DETAILS: 80 seats. Private parties: 8 main room. Vegetarian meals. Wheelchair access (not WC). Music. Air-conditioned ⊖ Green Park

Cecconi's

NEW ENTRY **map 15**

5A Burlington Gardens, W1S 3EP
TEL: (020) 7434 1500 FAX: (020) 7494 2440

COOKING **3**
ITALIAN
£39–£62

In the middle of moneyed Mayfair, Cecconi's has epitomised extravagant Italian eating since 1978. In 2001 it was acquired by Hani Farsi, who co-opted Giorgio Locatelli, formerly of Zafferano (see entry), to revitalise the kitchen. Tasselled curtains, leather chairs and lighting seemingly from a 1950s cinema contribute to an air of decadence. But Nick Bell manages the Locatelli formula competently, producing main courses of delicately pink roast veal kidney with artichokes, lentils and bacon, or a fillet of John Dory with wild fennel, both incorporating first-rate ingredients. The presence of fegato alla veneziana suggests that not all is new-wave modernity. Starters were less impressive at inspection, but reporters have enjoyed summer minestrone, risotto primavera, and oxtail ravioli. A plainly served chocolate and hazelnut tart makes an admirable dessert, and there is tiramisù, or a trio of ice cream, sorbet and granita. The largely Italian wine list is something of a gem, harbouring flights of modern classics including Tignanello and Ornellaia, but you will need serious funds to enjoy them. The sommelier's selection opens at £15.75.

CHEF: Nick Bell PROPRIETOR: Hani Farsi OPEN: Mon to Sat 12 to 3, 7 to 11.30 CLOSED: Christmas, New Year MEALS: alc (main courses £12.50 to £16) SERVICE: 12.5% (optional), card slips closed CARDS: Amex, Delta, Diners, MasterCard, Switch, Visa DETAILS: 86 seats. Private parties: 10 main room. Wheelchair access (also WC). No music. Air-conditioned ⊖ Green Park

Le Chardon

map 12

65 Lordship Lane, SE22 8EP
TEL: (020) 8299 1921 FAX: 020 8480 1582

COOKING **2**
FRENCH
£21–£56

Unmistakably a French bistro, Le Chardon retains the décor of thistle-pattern tiles, net curtains and fairy lights it has had for years. Almost as long-running, the menu – supplemented by blackboard specials – offers plenty of choice, with some highlights. Fish soup, properly tricked out with rouille, croûtons and grated Swiss cheese, scored well at inspection, as did a venison rump steak with a tri-coloured peppercorn coating and a rich sauce. The rest ranges from caviar (Iranian beluga at £45 a shot) to fairly familiar international territory in the form of Thai fishcakes with sweet chilli and lime dressing, and wild mushroom risotto with garlic, thyme and parsley. Gratin dauphinois is worth the extra, though a platter of French cheeses may be a safer bet than dessert. Not surprisingly the wine list is all-French, opening at £9.90.

CHEFS: Didier Lemond and Didier Dixneuf PROPRIETOR: Robert Benayer OPEN: all week 12 to 11 CLOSED: bank hols MEALS: alc (main courses £10 to £14.50). Set L Mon to Sat 12 to 5 £6.95 to £9.95 (both 2 courses), Sun £13.50 SERVICE: 10% (optional) CARDS: Amex, Delta, Diners, MasterCard, Switch, Visa DETAILS: 50 seats. 30 seats outside. Private parties: 60 main room. Vegetarian meals. Children's helpings. Wheelchair access (not WC). Music. Air-conditioned (£5)

Chez Bruce

map 12

2 Bellevue Road, SW17 7EG
TEL: (020) 8672 0114 FAX: (020) 8767 6648

COOKING **6**
MODERN BRITISH
£35–£75

The crimson frontage, wrought-iron chandeliers and art-covered walls may have disappeared by the time you read this. As the Guide went to press the restaurant, in a suburban row of shops opposite Wandsworth Common, was due to close for refurbishment front-of-house and for the installation of a completely new kitchen. There are no indications that the cooking style is likely to change, though, as Bruce Poole produces an appealing slate of dishes that effortlessly combine traditional with more inventive ideas. A fine example of chateaubriand with first-class frites and béarnaise could hardly be more of a repertoire standard, and yet there may also be an onion risotto with snails and gizzards, or hot foie gras with an oxtail bouillon and ravioli.

The common thread running through all this is food that is unshowy, yet admirably light and deeply satisfying. Eating here can be 'an absolute pleasure', thanks not least to the underlying straightforwardness of, for example, roast cod with olive oil mash and gremolata, or partridge with stuffed cabbage. Mediterranean flavours come to the fore, meanwhile, in a tasty 'sandwich' of deep-fried sardine and tapénade, served with tomato salad and aïoli, and in rare grilled tuna with a noodle salad, tomato, pesto and tapénade. Indulgence is never far away, as the kitchen comforts with smoked haddock, served with creamed leeks and poached egg, or a gratin of figs with Marsala and ice cream that is 'worth the 15-minute wait'. Service is friendly and helpful. Wines are listed in price order, which highlights just how strong and broad the £16 to £25 selection is, from a southern French Marsanne to a new-style Sicilian red. Prices start at £14.

CHEF: Bruce Poole PROPRIETOR: Larkbrace OPEN: all week L 12 to 2 (12.30 to 3 Sun), Mon to Sat D 7 (6.30 Fri and Sat) to 10.30 CLOSED: 24 to 27 Dec, bank hol Mons MEALS: Set L Mon to Sat £21.50, Set L Sun £25, Set D £30 SERVICE: 12.5% (optional), card slips closed CARDS: Amex, Delta, Diners, MasterCard, Switch, Visa DETAILS: 70 seats. Private parties: 18 main room, 18 private room. Children's helpings. No smoking in 1 dining room. No cigars/pipes in dining room. No music. Air-conditioned ⊖ Clapham South, Balham

Chezmax

map 13

168 Ifield Road, SW10 9AF
TEL: (020) 7835 0874 FAX: (020) 7244 0618

COOKING **1**
FRENCH
£23–£82

French is the lingua franca at this neighbourhood restaurant. It isn't just the interior – dark red ceiling, parquet floor, and a digestif cabinet – which sets the scene. The menu, too, is entirely in French, which gives the proprietor ample opportunity to explain the construction and seasoning of dishes. Unlike at a French café, the cooking here is complex. Although there are a few simpler dishes, such as tournedos of beef with onion, garlic and morels, curious juxtapositions of flavours characterise most of the fare. Spiced crab may come with avocado and sesame-infused cream dressing, and sauces may combine honey and balsamic vinegar, or port and tarragon. While some combinations work surprisingly well, it is the simpler dishes that tend to show best. Desserts stick more closely to tradition, as in chocolate mousse with sablé biscuits, or apple and calvados crème brûlée. Service can be rather unhurried. France (particularly red and white burgundy and red Bordeaux) is the main focus of the wine list, with just a short list of 'wines from elsewhere'. House vins de pays are £13.50.

CHEF: Nick Reeves PROPRIETORS: Graham Thomson and Steven Smith OPEN: Mon to Sat D only 7 to 11 MEALS: alc (main courses £14.95 to £20.50). Set D £12.50 SERVICE: 12.5% (optional), card slips closed CARDS: Amex, Delta, Diners, MasterCard, Switch, Visa DETAILS: 50 seats. Private parties: 50 main room, 14 and 16 private rooms. Children's helpings. No cigars/pipes in dining room. Occasional music. Air-conditioned ⊖ West Brompton (£5)

indicates that smoking is either banned altogether or that a separate dining room (not just an area) is maintained for non-smokers.

If a restaurant is new to the Guide this year (did not appear as a main entry in the last edition), NEW ENTRY *appears opposite its name.*

Chez Moi

map 12

1 Addison Avenue, W11 4QS
TEL: (020) 7603 8267 FAX: (020) 7603 3898
EMAIL: chezmoi-rest@hotmail.com
WEB SITE: www.chezmoi-restaurant.co.uk

COOKING **4**
FRENCH-PLUS
£25–£57

Despite the imitation zebra-skin headrests, this is considered a quiet and calming place, with a deep pink and dark green colour scheme, and mirrors in ornate gold frames. People come here not for flair or originality but for a degree of consistency. 'We have never had a bad meal' is a typical summing up of the level of contentment that Richard Walton's cooking engenders in its 35th year. The menu's mix is an odd one, hardly cutting-edge, yet managing to combine disparate dishes such as bortsch, cod and salmon ceviche, chicken dhosa, Moroccan lamb tagine, and Thai chicken.

In all this it keeps a sense of balance: between a vegetable tart with pesto on the one hand, and more substantial stincotto, or a venison fillet with gnocchi, on the other. Desserts tend towards traditional crème brûlée or lemon tart. For best value, take the set price lunch. Sevice has variously been described as 'efficient', 'exemplary' and 'immaculate'. A largely French wine list manages to find some bottles under £20, including house wines from Australia and South Africa at £10.75.

CHEF: Richard Walton PROPRIETORS: Colin Smith and Richard Walton OPEN: Tue to Fri L 12.30 to 1.45, Mon to Sat D 7 to 10.45 CLOSED: bank hols MEALS: alc (main courses £13 to £17). Set L £15 SERVICE: not inc CARDS: Amex, Delta, Diners, MasterCard, Switch, Visa DETAILS: 45 seats. 16 seats outside. Private parties: 16 main room. Vegetarian meals. Children's helpings. No babies. No cigars/pipes in dining room. Wheelchair access (not WC). No music. Air-conditioned ⊖ Holland Park

cheznico

map 15

90 Park Lane, W1K 7TN
TEL: (020) 7409 1290 FAX: (020) 7355 4877

COOKING **8**
FRENCH
£63–£115

Those who ate here when Nico Ladenis was in charge like to spot what's changed and what hasn't. The setting is much as before: green-canopied walkway; plush reception area and courteous welcome; bright, spacious, hotel-style dining room with mirrored pillars (what it lacks in character it makes up for in comfort). The carte may not have quite the same range of complex or luxurious dishes as before, but several items remain: grilled Dover sole with tartare sauce, goats' cheese ravioli, and foie gras with orange among them. And if there is a penchant for less expensive ingredients, no corners are cut over technique or delivery.

The peaks of the gastronomic menu distinguish this kitchen from Incognico's (see entry), where the simpler dishes are handled well enough. Paul Rhodes maintains the lustre of grand cuisine, bringing balance and a light touch to his remarkably consistent output, for example in a tortellini of langoustines in a 'breathtaking' lobster bisque. The food, if not innovative or ground-breaking, is immaculately turned out, and, says one visitor, 'there cannot be many chefs who deliver such sophisticated cooking based around simple ingredients': from ham hock terrine, to cod with minted pea purée, to veal sweetbreads with morels. Simplicity can be deceptive, though, as in a single juicy scallop served with garlic butter, or a piece of sea bass with tiny girolles and a sweet baby leek. There is no attempt to dress things up – looking at some dishes, it is hard to anticipate out-of-the-ordinary tastes – but sheer excellence of materials and timing sets them apart, witness a herb-crusted saddle of lamb with 'world-class rösti' and provençale vegetables: a dish of subtle flavours and sensitive seasoning.

'Don't miss the cheeseboard,' recommended one who found it in prime condition, and, if the chocolate negus is no longer there, there is a chocolate tart to compensate, and the inimitable lemon tart with raspberry coulis, still delivered with impressively exact technique. Younger staff may be inexperienced, although the key players are first-rate. The wine list keeps an eye on newer areas, but France's mainstream regions are its mainstay. Prices start from £18, but there is little under £25, even among halves; six wines are offered by the glass from £6.

CHEF: Paul Rhodes PROPRIETORS: Nico and Dinah-Jane Ladenis OPEN: Mon to Fri L 12 to 2, Mon to Sat D 7 to 11 CLOSED: 10 days Christmas, 4 days Easter, bank hols MEALS: Set L £35 (2 courses) to £62, Set D £62 SERVICE: 12.5% (optional), card slips closed CARDS: Amex, Delta, Diners, MasterCard, Switch, Visa DETAILS: 90 seats. Private parties: 10 main room, 20 private room. No pipes in dining room. Wheelchair access (also women's WC). No music. Air-conditioned ⊖ Marble Arch, Hyde Park Corner

Chinon

map 12

23 Richmond Way, W14 0AS
TEL: (020) 7602 5968 FAX: (020) 7602 4082

COOKING **5**
FRENCH-PLUS
£38–£45

Chinon is a 'gem of a local restaurant' in an unassuming parade of shops in Shepherd's Bush. The décor is 'mildly eccentric', with a large picture window giving on to palms and other exotica; lighting is discreet, chairs are asymmetrical wrought-iron constructions, and the atmosphere is relaxed, apart from the Muzak. Dinner starts with a glass of Kir and is now £25 for four courses (one of them a careful assembly of top-quality soft French cheeses), and ambition runs to crab ravioli with shellfish bisque and rouille, and a deep-fried filo parcel of just-melting goats' cheese on a thick slice of sweet-sour aubergine, with a different relish at each of the four corners.

The food has a polished professionalism which shows in guinea fowl leg, chargrilled and juicy, sitting on white beans in a garlic cream sauce, with a 'miraculously light' crépinette of black pudding to one side, and in fillet of venison accompanied by a disc of red cabbage and one of mashed potato neatly wrapped in a cabbage leaf. Desserts appear to be the poor relation, although bread is highly rated, and Barbara Deane runs a tight ship. Around 50 wines, mostly French, are missing some important details; house wine is £16. As always, the restaurant has not provided any information so we cannot vouch for the accuracy of the following.

CHEF: Jonathon Hayes PROPRIETORS: Barbara Deane and Jonathon Hayes OPEN: Mon to Sat D only 7 to 10.45 MEALS: Set D £25 SERVICE: 12.5%, card slips closed CARDS: Amex, Delta, MasterCard, Switch, Visa DETAILS: 60 seats. 6 seats outside. Private parties: 30 main room, 30 private room. No children under 10. No cigars/pipes in dining room. Music ⊖ Shepherd's Bush

Chiswick

map 12

131 Chiswick High Road, W4 2ED
TEL: (020) 8994 6887 FAX: (020) 8994 5504

COOKING **3**
MODERN EUROPEAN
£21–£48

In summer, the doors at the front of this high-street venue are thrown open, with a few tables outside for al fresco dining. Inside, floors are covered in light brown carpet, the taupe walls hung with a few modern prints, and the ceiling accented with spotlights. As with its sister restaurant, Salt House (see entry), sensible modern British cooking at fair prices is the name of the game. For starters, think sardines with aubergine, rocket and sun-dried tomatoes, or a warm salad of chorizo, pork confit and fried bread.

Main courses might include Chinese-inspired steamed sea bass with pak choi, ginger and spring onion, or appealingly textured tagliatelle with tender artichokes and girolles. Puddings range from Tuscan-style roast white peaches with Amaretto cream, to Bakewell tart; or finish with well-looked-after Golden Cross goats' cheese. Good coffee is served with home-made chocolate chip shortbread. Service is casual and can be stretched at busy times. The wine list has around 40 bottles spanning the world fairly democratically. Most are over £20, but vins de pays kick off at £11.50.

CHEF: Jim Garvan PROPRIETORS: Adam and Katie Robinson OPEN: Sun to Fri L 12.30 (12 Sun) to 2.45 (3 Sun), 7 to 11 MEALS: alc (main courses £6.50 to £15). Set L and D 7 to 8 £9.50 (2 courses) to £12.95 SERVICE: 12.5% (optional), card slips closed CARDS: Amex, Delta, MasterCard, Switch, Visa DETAILS: 65 seats. 12 seats outside. Private parties: 64 main room. Vegetarian meals. Children's helpings. No-smoking area. No cigars/pipes in dining room. No music. Air-conditioned ⊖ Turnham Green (£5)

Chives

NEW ENTRY **map 14**

204 Fulham Road, SW10 2PJ
TEL/FAX: (020) 7351 4747

COOKING **5**
MEDITERRANEAN
£31–£45

This cool, cosmopolitan newcomer is part of the Red Pepper group, which has avoided the standardisation of other mini-chains. Warm cream-coloured walls, sap-green woodwork and a long, frosted-edged mirror on one wall make the ambience cheering, especially on a bright summer's day. Jun Tanaka's cooking meets the expectations raised by his training under Marco, Nico and Albert Roux. An open raviolo of caramelised foie gras with deep-fried quail's egg beignet is 'heart-stoppingly good', and the contemporary French touch shows also in a starter of confit pork belly with Toulouse sausage, white bean and truffle cassoulet.

Amid the homogenous cooking that besets much of London, it is refreshing to see food with a proper sense of identity, evident in a whole roast baby chicken ('an ample, bronzed beauty') with girolles, leeks and roast garlic cloves to give natural, pungent sweetness. Also sound (marred only by lukewarm temperature) has been a main course of sea bass with a tomato and avocado salsa and a tartlet of caramelised onions with olives and anchovies. After long waits for such painstakingly presented dishes, you may shirk the extra 15 to 20 minutes preparation time involved in chocolate fondant with vanilla ice cream, or raspberry soufflé; if so, try the crème brûlée, which may contain a trendy complement of rhubarb. Service is friendly and professional. France and Italy loom large in a short wine list that opens with southern French varietals at £14.50 but jumps beyond £20 before you can blink.

CHEF: Jun Tanaka PROPRIETOR: Red Pepper Group OPEN: Mon to Sat D only 7 to 10.30 CLOSED: Christmas, New year MEALS: alc (main courses £9.50 to £15) SERVICE: 12.5% (optional) CARDS: Amex, Diners, MasterCard, Switch, Visa DETAILS: 55 seats. 14 seats outside. Private parties: 50 main room, 20 private room. Vegetarian meals. No cigars/pipes in dining room. Wheelchair access (not WC). Music. Air-conditioned ⊖ South Kensington, Fulham Broadway

Chor Bizarre

map 15

16 Albemarle Street, W1S 4HW
TEL: (020) 7629 9802 FAX: (020) 7493 7756
EMAIL: chorbizarrelondon@oldworldhospitality.com
WEB SITE: www.chorbizarrerestaurant.com

COOKING **1**
INDIAN
£39–£66

The name is a pun (Chor Bazaar is the New Delhi thieves' market), but this place is also bizarre: something to savour alongside its serious cooking. It looks like a furniture-cum-bric-à-brac shop, with unmatching tables (one a four-poster bed, one silver-plated), chairs and decorations. From a mainly North Indian menu, tandoori chicken is delivered with assurance, and tak-a-taks sautéed on a metal tawa plate include 'very spicy, but equally lovely' crab meat with chilli and mustard seeds. Reporters have praised South Indian dishes, too: tender, moist quick-fried dakshini scallops, and chicken Chettinad. Thali set meals come on banana leaves or metal platters. Service could be improved, and credit-card slips are left open after 12.5% has already been added. Interesting wines from £12 have been chosen by Charles Metcalfe to match the food.

CHEF: Deepinder Singh Sondhi PROPRIETOR: India's Restaurant Ltd OPEN: all week 12 to 3, 6 to 11.30 (10. 30 Sun) CLOSED: 25 Dec, 1 Jan MEALS: alc (main courses £13 to £15) SERVICE: 12.5% (optional) CARDS: Amex, Delta, Diners, MasterCard, Switch, Visa DETAILS: 80 seats. Private parties: 80 main room, 30 private room. Vegetarian meals. Music. Air-conditioned ⊖ Green Park (£5)

The Guide relies on feedback from its readers. Especially welcome are reports on new restaurants appearing in the book for the first time. All letters to the Guide are acknowledged.

Christopher's

map 15

18 Wellington Street, WC2E 7DD
TEL: (020) 7240 4222 FAX: (020) 7836 3506
EMAIL: info@christophers.uk.net
WEB SITE: www.christophersgrill.com

COOKING **1**
CONTEMPORARY AMERICAN
£31–£79

This well-established Covent Garden venue, spread over three floors, continues to serve good-value pre- and post-theatre meals, and a wide-ranging American-style brunch menu at weekends. The main carte also has a transatlantic feel, with the likes of New England clam bake, 'Harry's Bar'-style beef carpaccio, and of course classic Caesar salad. Roasts, grills and steaks, the main-course meat options, take in simple Aberdeen Angus fillets alongside lamb chops with butternut squash and rosemary dauphinoise, plus chicken and duck. To finish, there's tiramisù mousse with Kahlua, or Texas buttermilk pie with rhubarb and raspberries. Over 30 wines are offered by the glass (from £3.50), and the list ranges wide in terms of both geography and price, starting at £14. A second branch, close to Victoria Station and located in the Thistle Victoria (tel (020) 7976 5522), takes the same route from east to west coasts.

CHEF: Adrian Searing PROPRIETOR: Christopher Gilmour OPEN: all week L 12 to 3 (4.30 Sat and Sun), Mon to Sat D 5 to 11.30 CLOSED: 25, 26 and 31 Dec MEALS: alc (main courses £12 to £28). Set D before 7 and after 10 £14.50 (2 courses) to £18.50. Cover 50p. Bar menu available SERVICE: 12.5%, card slips closed CARDS: Amex, Delta, Diners, MasterCard, Switch, Visa DETAILS: 160 seats. Private parties: 150 main room, 50 private room. Vegetarian meals. Children's helpings. No music. Air-conditioned ⊖ Covent Garden

Chutney Mary

map 12

535 King's Road, SW10 0SZ
TEL: (020) 7351 3113 FAX: (020) 7351 7694
EMAIL: action@realindianfood.com
WEB SITE: www.realindianfood.com

COOKING **1**
INDIAN
£25–£72

In this well-appointed basement and ground floor restaurant the coveted tables are in the conservatory. Opulent décor recalls the Raj, and the cooking, like the name Chutney Mary, was originally Anglo-Indian (now it is mainly regional Indian, but the links endure). Back on the menu is Country Captain chicken, its sauce made with caramelised onion, palm vinegar and hot spices. A new starter is baked crab, flaked, sautéed with fennel, ginger and chilli and returned to its shell. Regional seafood main dishes now include swordfish marinated in turmeric, lime and chilli with a Keralan curry sauce. Bengali, Hyderabadi and Chettinad lamb (old favourites), are joined by masala roast shank with a mixed thoran of dry vegetables. Also reflecting the Raj is bread-and-butter pudding; however, few of 50 world wines (including Indian) from £11.50, chosen to complement Indian food, would be familiar to pukka colonels.

CHEF: Murali Dharan PROPRIETORS: Ranjit Mathrani and Namita Panjabi OPEN: all week 12.30 to 2.30, 6.30 to 11.30 (10.30 Sun) MEALS: alc (main courses £9 to £17). Set L £11 (2 courses) to £15, Set D 6.30 to 7.15 and 10 to 11.30 (10.30 Sun) £11 (2 courses) to £14. Light L also available Mon to Sat. Cover £1.50 SERVICE: 12.5% (optional) CARDS: Amex, Diners, MasterCard,

Switch, Visa DETAILS: 150 seats. Private parties: 12 main room, 36 private room. Vegetarian meals. Children's helpings. No cigars/pipes in dining room. Wheelchair access (not WC). Music. Air-conditioned Fulham Broadway

Cigala

NEW ENTRY map 13

54 Lamb's Conduit Street, WC1N 3LW
TEL: (020) 7405 1717 FAX: (020) 7242 9949
WEB SITE: www.cigala.co.uk

COOKING **3**
SPANISH
£29–£65

On a corner site with windows all round (and tables on the pavement), Cigala captures so much daylight and street action that you hardly notice its bare walls. Service is helpful and efficient, and the kitchen is open to view, so a friendly and welcoming atmosphere pervades. Although Jake Hodges used to cook at Moro (see entry), he is less concerned with Moorish input than he is with plain, traditional Spanish cooking, much of it in either rustic or domestic mould: a 'roadside caff' dish of scrambled eggs with peppers and spring onions perhaps, or cocido Madrileño, a homely stew of chicken, salt-beef, morcilla, chorizo and chickpeas.

Salads, stews and grills enable the kitchen to keep a longish menu under control and to deliver plain, honest flavours, as in a ham and chestnut soup, a stuffed piquillo pepper, and a variation on moules marinière made with clams and manzanilla. Occasionally the food reaches impressive heights – a deeply flavoured seafood stew filled with fresh-tasting white fish and shellfish – and desserts have included a light, moist orange sponge on a thin pastry base. The wine list cleverly combines Spanish wines with others from around the world made from Spanish grape varieties (Australian Garnacha, Mexican Tempranillo), and leads with a handful of fine Valdespino sherries by the glass.

CHEF/PROPRIETOR: Jake Hodges OPEN: all week L 12 to 3 (12.30 to 3.30 Sat and Sun), Mon to Sat D 6 to 10.45 CLOSED: 22 Dec to 6 Jan, Easter MEALS: alc (main courses £11 to £25). Set L £15 (2 courses) to £18 SERVICE: 12.5% (optional), card slips closed CARDS: Amex, Delta, Diners, MasterCard, Switch, Visa DETAILS: 65 seats. 20 seats outside. Private parties: 12 main room. Vegetarian meals. Children's helpings. No cigars/pipes in dining room. Wheelchair access (not WC). No music

Cinnamon Club

NEW ENTRY map 13

Old Westminster Library,
Great Smith Street, SW1P 3BU
TEL: (020) 7222 2555 FAX: (020) 7222 1333
EMAIL: info@cinnamonclub.com
WEB SITE: www.cinnamonclub.com

LONDON GFG 2002 COMMENDED

COOKING **4**
MODERN INDIAN
£26–£62

Round the corner from Westminster Abbey, this politico-haunted converted Victorian library has a large airy bar, and dining rooms on ground floor and mezzanine above. Décor is modern English club style, with shelves of books, large, well-spaced, white-clothed tables, leather banquettes and high-backed, lavishly upholstered chairs in shades of brown. The cooking is as far from curry-house as you can get (and there are no poppadums), but neither is it 'fusion' cooking, rather a modern take on a traditional style, all the rage just now. Sandalwood, for example, is used to flavour tandoori chicken breast, and a wild boar chop is given the hot-and-sour treatment. Equally unusual has been loin of rabbit with cottage cheese and dried fruit, and chargrilled bream with pomegranate extract.

Tandoori dishes are a feature – of set menus, and of the carte and its dishes of the day – and might include a partnership of lambs' sweetbreads and kidneys with vegetable rice. Chilli hotness rarely threatens, and side dishes run to wild mushroom and spinach stir-fry, and mustard leaves with garlic and chilli. Imaginative desserts include dosa pancake with pepper ice cream, and cumin and saffron poached pears with cinnamon ice cream. A dozen wines by the glass, from a well-chosen list, include house selections at £3 (£13 a bottle).

CHEF: Vivek Singh PROPRIETOR: Iqbal Wahhab OPEN: Sun to Fri L 12 to 2.30, Mon to Sat D 6 to 11 CLOSED: bank hols MEALS: alc (main courses £11 to £22). Set L and D 6 to 7 £15 (2 courses) to £18 (Sun brunch £15 to £18). Bar menu available Mon to Fri L till 6 SERVICE: not inc, 12.5% for parties of 6 or more, card slips closed CARDS: Amex, Delta, Diners, MasterCard, Switch, Visa DETAILS: 180 seats. Private parties: 120 main room, 14 and 45 private rooms. Vegetarian meals. Children at Sunday brunch only. Wheelchair access (also WC). No music. Air-conditioned ⊖ Westminster

Circus **map 15**

1 Upper James Street, W1R 4BP
TEL: (020) 7534 4000 FAX: (020) 7534 4010 COOKING **4**
EMAIL: circus@egami.co.uk MODERN EUROPEAN/MEDITERRANEAN
WEB SITE: www.circusbar.co.uk £25–£62

The large, elegant and very modern dining room on a corner spot in a smart part of Soho has big windows to view – and be viewed by – passers-by on the street. Despite its minimalist décor it manages a feeling of intimacy, with chrome and glass cages for table candles and concealed lighting all making it easy on the eye. The main menu deals in fashionable and well-chosen ingredients, pairing seared scallops with crab cakes; grilled salmon with choi sum, tomatoes and cumin; and roast ostrich breast with red curry and rice.

An early-evening menu of Thai-spiced mackerel fillets, chicken chasseur with 'very smooth' puréed potatoes, and raspberry tart (a pastry case filled with raspberry mousse) was lauded by one reader for its excellent value, competence and attractive presentation. Desserts may seem like a trip down Memory Lane, but with interesting twists: Arctic roll is a citrus and chocolate version with Bailey's sauce, there's coffee sauce with the amaretto cheesecake, and toffee sauce with apple fritters. The varietally arranged wine list offers plenty to go at, but few concessions on price. The baseline is £14.50, though on the plus side there are 20 wines by the glass, including three dessert wines.

CHEF: Richard Lee PROPRIETOR: Mirror Image Restaurants OPEN: Mon to Fri L 2 to 3, Mon to Sat D 5.45 to 12 CLOSED: 24 to 26 Dec, 1 Jan MEALS: alc (main courses £11.50 to £18.50). Set L £10.50 (2 courses) to £19.50, Set D 5.45 to 7.15 and 10.30 to 12 £10.50 (2 courses) to £12.50. Bar meals SERVICE: 12.5% (optional), card slips closed CARDS: Amex, Delta, Diners, MasterCard, Switch, Visa DETAILS: 140 seats. Private parties: 150 main room, 16 private room. Vegetarian meals. Wheelchair access (not WC). No music. Air-conditioned ⊖ Piccadilly Circus

City Rhodes

map 13

1 New Street Square, EC4A 3BF
TEL: (020) 7583 1313 FAX: (020) 7353 1662

COOKING 6
MODERN BRITISH
£49–£86

This would hardly be worth its 'City' tag if a few deals weren't done behind the pale blinds of the sharp-suited dining room, with its royal-blue carpet, grey-checked seat coverings, and vividly coloured splashes of modern art. And for those who don't have a television there are plenty of reminders about the 'Rhodes' bit too, although Gary of that ilk presumably has his fingers in too many pies nowadays to take full credit for what goes on here. Adam Gray, however, has capably sustained the style of innovative combinations of top-quality ingredients cooked with demonstrable skill that the maestro himself set in motion.

Forget black pudding fritters and Waggon Wheels, though; this is grown-up food. Crab ravioli looks the part, a single large vessel stuffed to the gunwales with lemony-fresh shredded crab, surrounded by half a dozen baby leeks and a modest quantity of light, subtly flavoured sauce bouillabaisse. Luxurious touches run to a truffled veal stock for turbot and mash, and soft textures and a fair amount of cream are in evidence, not least when it comes to sumptuous desserts. Spiced poached rhubarb sandwiched between layers of wafer-thin puff pastry, with vanilla and lemon cream and a scoop of intensely flavoured rhubarb ice cream, is one such thrill. The thoroughly plutocratic wine list contains many bottles in three figures, but there are also Vin de Pays d'Oc Chardonnay and Syrah at £16.50, and a slate of 16 wines by the glass from £3.90 to £9.

CHEF: Adam Gray PROPRIETOR: Sodexho OPEN: Mon to Fri 12 to 2.30, 6 to 9 CLOSED: Christmas, bank hols MEALS: alc (main courses £14.50 to £23) SERVICE: 12.5% (optional), card slips closed CARDS: Amex, Delta, Diners, MasterCard, Switch, Visa DETAILS: 100 seats. Private parties: 24 main room, 12 private room. Vegetarian meals. No cigars/pipes in dining room. Music. Air-conditioned ⊖ Chancery Lane

Clarke's

map 13

124 Kensington Church Street, W8 4BH
TEL: (020) 7221 9225 FAX: (020) 7229 4564
EMAIL: restaurant@sallyclarke.com
WEB SITE: www.sallyclarke.com

COOKING 6
MODERN BRITISH
£38–£61

Sally Clarke's formula hasn't changed in 16 years. This low-lit basement restaurant, with open-plan kitchen and a smaller ground-floor room, still serves a no-choice, four-course evening menu displaying 'the underrated virtue of serving first-rate ingredients plainly'. Each year someone asks, 'Why pay this price for no choice when you can go elsewhere and choose?', yet its undiminished popularity shows the bedrock of trust it has built up. Lunch is a selection of four starters, three mains (all priced the same), and either cheese or pudding of the day.

In the evening the meal often starts with a salad – perhaps grilled squab with bitter leaves, celery, honey-baked shallots and a dressing of raisins in balsamic vinegar – or pasta: fresh ravioli with an 'arrestingly tasty' filling of ricotta, peas and mint, adorned with rocket and Parmesan. A typical week's main courses may be meat on two days, fish on three (a slab of Irish sea trout with a caper, lemon and chive mayonnaise has impressed). Vegetable accompaniments are usually imaginative and varied, and quantities carefully judged to leave room for cheese and oatmeal biscuits before dessert. This is often a lesser-known English dish, perhaps a 'gem' of soft meringue filled with mango and pineapple sorbet and topped with passion fruit cream. The wine list is Californian-influenced (and includes some stunning and pricey rarities) but also has fine French bottles and lively, great-value country wines starting from £14. There is also a characterful collection of wines by the glass.

CHEFS: Sally Clarke and Elizabeth Payne PROPRIETOR: Sally Clarke OPEN: Mon to Fri 12.30 to 2, 7 to 10 CLOSED: Christmas, Easter, 2 weeks Aug MEALS: alc L (main courses £14). Set D £44 SERVICE: net prices, card slips closed CARDS: Amex, Delta, Diners, MasterCard, Switch, Visa DETAILS: 90 seats. Private parties: 14 main room. No cigars/pipes at L; no smoking in dining room at D. Wheelchair access (not WC). No music. Air-conditioned ⊖ Notting Hill Gate

Club Gascon

map 13

57 West Smithfield, EC1A 9DS
TEL: (020) 7796 0600 FAX: (020) 7796 0601

COOKING **5**
FRENCH
£34–£81

There is nothing else quite like this. It is set on a corner plot (once a Lyons tea house) near Smithfield Market, and massive flower displays lend a bit of drama to the small square room's marbled walls and dark wooden floors. South-west France is Pascal Aussignac's inspiration, although a few items may stray over the Pyrenees: roast lobster basquaise, perhaps, or a 'plancha' of hot baby squid with tomato and fried herbs. The menu comes in half a dozen sections with a handful of dishes in each, although, since portion sizes are not related to price, it can be difficult to estimate how many dishes to order. But it is the combination of traditional regional materials with a degree of innovation that gives the cooking its vitality.

Strong but well-balanced flavours are characteristic, typified by a Tatin of duck foie gras paired with truffles and turnip, and by a cappuccino of black pudding and lobster. Other successful meat and seafood partnerships include rare seared tuna with andouille and a frothy chervil sauce, while a delight in textural contrast has produced a dish of smooth, cold foie gras and warm, crisp kombu seaweed. For those who simply can't get enough foie gras, there is a sweet version for dessert (with marron glacé and chocolate). Alternatively, there may be a crunchy chocolate and cherry emulsion. Male French staff are professional and friendly, but this is not a place to come to if you are in a hurry, nor indeed if you are counting the pennies, nor if you give up easily when trying to make a telephone booking, nor if you hate the wines of south-west France: Irouléguy and Marcillac feature, as well as Cahors, Madiran and Bordeaux. Otherwise it is 'a truly terrific' restaurant.

CHEF: Pascal Aussignac PROPRIETORS: Vincent Labeyrie and Pascal Aussignac OPEN: Mon to Fri L 12 to 2, Mon to Sat D 7 to 10 (11 Sat) CLOSED: 23 Dec to 6 Jan, bank hols MEALS: alc (main courses £7 to £23.50). Set L £30, Set D £30 to £50 (inc wine) SERVICE: 12.5% (optional), card slips closed CARDS: Amex, Delta, MasterCard, Switch, Visa DETAILS: 60 seats. Private parties: 60 main room. Vegetarian meals. Wheelchair access (not WC). Music. Air-conditioned ⊖ Barbican, Farringdon

Le Colombier

map 14

145 Dovehouse Street, SW3 6LB
TEL: (020) 7351 1155 FAX: (020) 7351 0077

COOKING **3**
FRENCH
£28–£61

Sporting a blue and white, terracotta-tiled terrace (covered when the weather dictates) as well as a big-windowed dining room, this former pub has a 'genuinely local' ambience and enough domesticity to make it feel like sitting round the table at home. The food marks out its Gallic territory with oeufs en meurette, snails in puff pastry, and crêpes suzette, although it also indulges in calf's liver and bacon, grilled Dover sole, and cottage pie, which suggest that Olivier Galeran is no purist. There is plenty for seafood lovers – fish soup, three kinds of oyster, sole goujons with tartare sauce – as well as simple grills of lamb cutlets or ribeye steak with béarnaise. Not all reporters have been equally happy with results, and prices are considered steep, but staff are friendly and relaxed. Wines are a traditionally French line-up, with ambitious prices to match, although a handful of wines by the glass offers some relief. House vins de pays varietals are £12.90 a bottle.

CHEF: Olivier Galeran PROPRIETOR: Didier Garnier OPEN: all week 12 to 3 (3.30 Sun), 6.30 to 11 (10 Sun) MEALS: alc (main courses £12 to £20). Set L Mon to Sat £13 (2 courses), Set L Sun £15 (2 courses), Set D 6.30 to 7.30 £13 (2 courses) SERVICE: 12.5% (optional), card slips closed CARDS: Amex, Delta, Diners, MasterCard, Switch, Visa DETAILS: 70 seats. 35 seats outside. Private parties: 40 main room, 40 private room. Wheelchair access (not WC). No music. Air-conditioned ⊖ South Kensington

▲ The Connaught

map 15

16 Carlos Place, W1K 2AL
TEL: (020) 7499 7070 FAX: (020) 7495 3262
EMAIL: info@the-connaught.co.uk
WEB SITE: www.savoy-group.com

COOKING **6**
ANGLO-FRENCH
£54–£162

Quite a few restaurants in the Guide style themselves Anglo-French, but this one is different. Were Toulouse-Lautrec to stroll in for a glass of absinthe, or the Prince of Wales (the one who gave his name to Edwardian England) to turn up for lunch with a lady on each arm, nobody would bat an eyelid. Although Michel Bourdin has been here since 1975, his style harks back to much earlier times. He is only the fifth French chef in a line stretching back to 1897, and is about to retire to Provence during the currency of the Guide. His replacement, premier sous-chef Jerome Ponchelle, joined the brigade in 1988, and must by now have the Bourdin style in his bones.

The wood-panelled setting is quite up to all this, with a flurry of formally dressed staff, trolleys and chafing dishes at the ready. Only the menu's admonition about mobile phones strikes a remotely contemporary note. It reminds us that there was once something called traditional hotel food, into which a chef could introduce his own specialities, and it knows which side its bread is buttered, naming them after royalty: consommé Prince of Wales to commemorate a visit by HRH to the kitchens in 1994; homard d'Ecosse Reine Elizabeth to honour the Queen Mum's hundredth birthday. Despite all the pomp, the length of the carte would put many a brasserie to shame, and it is possible to dine off kipper pâté and mixed grill just as easily as oysters Christian Dior, consommé en gelée Cole Porter, or galette Connaught Tuber Melanosporum. The wine list is a roll call of the most prestigious classics of the wine world, with prices matching their status and that of the establishment. Choosing from the varied house bottles starting at £23 or the by-the-glass selection from £5.50 may help ease the bill, although ordering by the glass is not always encouraged.

CHEF: Michel Bourdin PROPRIETOR: Blackstone OPEN: all week 12 to 2.45, 6.30 to 10.45 MEALS: alc (main courses £15 to £45). Set L £28.50, Set D £58 SERVICE: 15%, card slips closed CARDS: Amex, Diners, MasterCard, Switch, Visa DETAILS: 65 seats. Private parties: 22 main room, 12 and 22 private rooms. Vegetarian meals. Jacket and tie. Wheelchair access (also WC). No music. Air-conditioned ACCOMMODATION: 92 rooms, all with bath/shower. TV. Phone. Room only £329 to £582. Rooms for disabled. Baby facilities (*The Which? Hotel Guide*) ⊖ Bond Street, Green Park (£5)

Il Convivio

NEW ENTRY **map 13**

143 Ebury Street, SW1W 9QN — COOKING **2**
TEL: (020) 7730 4099 FAX: (020) 7730 4103 — ITALIAN
WEB SITE: www.etruscagroup.co.uk — £36–£69

There is a lot to like about this Italian restaurant in Belgravia. It occupies a neatly converted Georgian terraced house with a small bar, sympathetic lighting, a bright, spacious dining room (the inscriptions on walls and windows are from Dante) that does indeed feel convivial, and a courtyard at the back with an electric roof for al fresco eating. Prices are 'low enough to entice the butlers from nearby homes to dine here', and the food's pluses just about outweigh the minuses (one of which is variable seasoning), thanks not least to sound ingredients such as plump scallops, served with fennel purée, and tender quail marinated in sweet grape must.

First-rate pappardelle and black spaghetti are both better than their accompaniments, and among highlights are a handsome veal chop, precisely cooked, with fresh morels, and a wicked white espresso ice cream that is 'worth a visit on its own'. Friendly, willing and enthusiastic service adds to the pleasure, and the charming sommelier helps you to get the best from the short but interesting Italian wine list; prices start from £14.50.

CHEF: Lukas Pfaff PROPRIETORS: Enzo and Piero Quaradeghini OPEN: Mon to Sat 12 to 3, 7 to 11 CLOSED: 25 and 26 Dec, 1 Jan, Easter, bank hols MEALS: Set L £16 (2 courses) to £20, Set D £24.50 (2 courses) to £35.50 SERVICE: 12.5% (optional), card slips closed CARDS: Amex, Delta, Diners, MasterCard, Switch, Visa DETAILS: 65 seats. Private parties: 65 main room, 12 private room. Vegetarian meals. Music. Air-conditioned ⊖ Victoria

Restaurateurs justifiably resent no-shows. If you quote a credit card number when booking, you may be liable for the restaurant's lost profit margin if you don't turn up. Always phone to cancel.

Coq d'Argent 🍷 map 13

1 Poultry, EC2R 8EJ — COOKING **3**
TEL: (020) 7395 5000 FAX: (020) 7395 5050 — FRENCH
WEB SITE: www.conran.com — £34–£78

An undeniably spectacular rooftop setting makes the most of its opportunities, with a lawned garden and open-air bar, and a viewing gallery that looks out over the Oxo Tower, Mansion House and the City. Stone, glass, wooden panelling and well-judged lighting combine to make the large dining room as smart as can be, and the 'generic Conran' menu characteristically features a range of shellfish, from oysters to lobster to a convincingly fresh crab salad with rocket leaves, alongside archetypally French coq au vin, and frogs' legs provençale. Performance tends to be uneven, the highlight of an inspection meal being flavourful corn-fed chicken – four slices of breast and a single leg – with a few morels and a rich gravy, while desserts failed to live up to their promise. A hefty wine list is built around serious names with equally heavyweight prices, with most of its focus on France, in vintages ranging back to the 1940s. Do not overlook that country, though, in a search for character and good-value offerings – house French red and white are £13.50 a bottle – and the by-the-glass page starts at £3.50.

CHEF: Mickael Weiss PROPRIETOR: Conran Restaurants Ltd OPEN: Sun to Fri L 11.30 (11 Sun) to 3 (2.30 Sun), Mon to Sat D 6 (6.30 Sat) to 10 CLOSED: 22 to 31 Dec, 13 to 16 Apr, 7 and 28 May, 27 Aug MEALS: alc (main courses £10.50 to £21). Set L Sun £21.50 (2 courses) to £25 SERVICE: 12.5% (optional), card slips closed CARDS: Amex, Delta, Diners, MasterCard, Switch, Visa DETAILS: 148 seats. 66 seats outside. Private parties: 145 main room. Vegetarian meals. Wheelchair access (also WC). Occasional music ⊖ Bank

Cotto map 12

44 Blythe Road, W14 0HA — COOKING **4**
TEL: (020) 7602 9333 FAX: (020) 7602 5003 — MODERN EUROPEAN
EMAIL: bookings@cottorestaurant.co.uk — £29–£52

With its distinctive white exterior, Cotto is set on a corner site in the hinterland of Olympia. Its contemporary, minimalist edge is emphasised by off-white walls, colourful geometric abstracts, and black leather chairs; small, tightly packed tables fill the L-shaped room (there's additional dining downstairs), and floor-to-ceiling windows add to a sunny ambience. James Kirby has worked with Simon Hopkinson at Bibendum and with Richard Neat at Pied-à-Terre (now at Neat, see entry), and his modern British approach embraces French and Italian influences while displaying refined technique and attractive presentation.

Asparagus with a deep-fried poached egg is a commendable seasonal starter, while ballottine of quail has come with foie gras and onion marmalade. The food is neither showy nor exotic, happy to deal in simple classics such as navarin de veau printanière; pan-fried halibut with braised celery hearts, veal jus and gremolata; and pea, artichoke and pecorino tortellini. Finish with pistachio parfait with dark chocolate fondant, or raspberry muffin with mascarpone sorbet. Service is attentive from staff clad in dark outfits, while the ten-page user-friendly wine list travels the globe and offers six house selections from £12.50 (£3.30 a glass).

CHEF: James Kirby PROPRIETORS: James and Jane Kirby OPEN: Mon to Fri L 12.30 to 2.30, Mon to Sat D 7 to 10.30 CLOSED: Christmas, bank hols MEALS: alc (main courses £10 to £16). Set L £15.50 (2 courses) to £18 SERVICE: 12.5% (optional), card slips closed CARDS: Amex, Delta, MasterCard, Switch, Visa DETAILS: 65 seats. 16 seats outside. Private parties: 65 main room, 35 private room. Vegetarian meals. Children's helpings. No cigars/pipes in dining room. Wheelchair access (not WC). Music. Air-conditioned ⊖ Kensington Olympia

Cow Dining Room

map 13

89 Westbourne Park Road, W2 5QH
TEL: (020) 7221 0021 FAX: (020) 7727 8687
EMAIL: thecow@thecow.freeserve.co.uk

COOKING **4**
MODERN EUROPEAN
£30–£55

The dining room above a popular pub buzzes with vitality. Café chairs and a tiled floor keep it simple and relaxed, and the menu's challenge, 'Eat heartily and give the house a good name', is willingly taken up. Spanish and Italian modes, the kitchen's mainstays, are reflected in proper gazpacho, antipasto platters, and such delights as a rich, ochre-hued Tuscan fish stew of mussels, squid and white fish with toasted ciabatta. A main course serving of seared free-range chicken breast with girolles and stewed onions in a richly aromatic stock shows a clear understanding of earthy flavours. Even better was a brilliantly timed piece of yellow-fin tuna with 'strikingly colourful' cherry tomato salsa and guacamole, the latter's 'sappiness' counterpointing the rich meatiness of the grilled fish. Fig and almond tart comes as a generous wedge with a blob of mascarpone, or try textbook pannacotta with raspberries. Despite the odd lapse, service is helpful and willing. The concise wine list dips mainly into France and the southern hemisphere, but prices vault quickly past £20; house Vins de Pays d'Oc are £12.50.

CHEF: James Rix PROPRIETOR: Tom Conran OPEN: Sat and Sun L 12.30 to 3.30, all week D 7 to 11 (7.30 to 10.30 Sun) CLOSED: 25 Dec, 31 Dec to 1 Jan MEALS: alc (main courses £10 to £17) SERVICE: not inc CARDS: Amex, Delta, MasterCard, Switch, Visa DETAILS: 35 seats. Private parties: 35 main room. Vegetarian meals. No music ⊖ Westbourne Park, Royal Oak

Creelers

map 14

3 Bray Place, SW3 3LL
TEL/FAX: (020) 7838 0788
WEB SITE: www.creelers.co.uk

COOKING **2**
MODERN BRITISH
£25–£73

Two blocks back from the main King's Road hub, Creelers reels in the Chelsea smart set with its high-quality Scottish produce and West Coast seafood. Outside there are green marble pillars, inside a small but elegant dining room with blond-wood flooring and white walls hung with modern abstracts. The southern arm of two other outlets – the original on Arran and another in Edinburgh – it has a lengthy repertoire dominated by seafood. Smoked salmon, oysters, scallops, langoustine and fish soup all find a place; or start instead with lightly curried mussels with lemon grass and coriander. Try pan-fried hake with a roast tomato, aubergine and coriander dressing and okra tempura to follow, or roast monkfish with creamed salt-cod ravioli. Meatier options run the gamut of venison, duck breast and Aberdeen Angus fillet. Finish with steamed rhubarb and ginger pudding with clotted cream ice cream. The compact wine list displays a Francophile leaning, with five house bottles at £12.95 and £13.50.

CHEF: Victoria Hemming PROPRIETORS: Fran and Tim James, and Dieter Jurgensen OPEN: Mon to Sat 12 to 2.30 (3 Sat), 6 to 10.30 (11 Sat) CLOSED: 24 to 26 and 31 Dec, 1 Jan, Easter MEALS: alc (main courses £14.50 to £22.50). Set L £12 (2 courses) to £15 SERVICE: not inc, 15% for parties of 8 or more CARDS: Amex, Delta, MasterCard, Switch, Visa DETAILS: 45 seats. Private parties: 20 main room, 22 private room. Vegetarian meals. Children's helpings. Music ⊖ Sloane Square, South Kensington (£5)

Criterion Brasserie

map 15

224 Piccadilly, W1J 9HP
TEL: (020) 7930 0488 FAX: (020) 7930 8380

COOKING 4
FRENCH/MEDITERRANEAN
£31–£82

As monumental dining rooms go, this one is hard to beat, its high ceiling and gilt mosaic tiles giving it a distinct Byzantine feel, and rendering it every bit as stunning as reporters expect. Although chefs move around the Marco Pierre White empire (Peter Reffell was listed last year at Titanic), the 'very French, very classy' food here remains in 'up-market brasserie' mould. It is varied enough to take in an assiette of sashimi, and rougets served with couscous, although the broadly European strand is perhaps most representative: as in ravioli of snails in a garlic nage, or a dish of moist rabbit (saddle and two legs) with a thick, strongly flavoured mushroom gravy.

Despite a few disappointments, results are technically accomplished, producing a voluptuously creamy crab and pimento risotto topped with a scoop of white crabmeat, and two deep-fried parcels, one containing a barely discernible oyster, the other a fat, juicy scallop. Desserts are a highlight, judging by a saffron-poached pear in a deep pool of syrupy orange-flavoured eau-de-vie, and a wedge of two-layered mocha tart – one dense, one light and mousse-like – with a scoop of coffee-chocolate ice cream on top. Service has varied from 'faultless' to 'unreasonable, rude and unacceptable', with regimented time limits, wine service and general 'muddle' all contributing to reporters' frustrations. France and southern Europe get the greatest share of the wine list, although a Mexican Tempranillo gets a look in. The majority of bottles are over £20, although vins de pays are £15.

CHEF: Peter Reffell PROPRIETOR: Marco Pierre White OPEN: Mon to Sat L 12 to 2.30, all week D 5.30 to 11.30 (10.30 Sun and bank hols) CLOSED: D 24 Dec, 25 and 26 Dec, 1 Jan MEALS: alc (main courses £12.50 to £25.50). Set L and D 5.30 to 6.30 £14.95 (2 courses) to £17.95 SERVICE: 12.5% (optional), card slips closed CARDS: Amex, Delta, Diners, MasterCard, Switch, Visa DETAILS: 150 seats. Private parties: 150 main room. Vegetarian meals. Wheelchair access (also WC). No music ⊖ Piccadilly Circus

'All you can say politely about the sauce was "It was brown".'
(On eating in Yorkshire)

Crowthers

map 12

481 Upper Richmond Road West, SW14 7PU
TEL/FAX: (020) 8876 6372

COOKING **3**
MODERN BRITISH/FRENCH
£36–£43

A friendly, husband-and-wife team runs this neighbourhood restaurant, modest in size, and unpretentiously decorated with cream and deep red walls, yellow floral curtains and watercolours of fruit. Five starters on the set menu might include sweet potato and garlic cream soup, caramelised onion tart, Gruyère cheese ramekin, or shiitake mushrooms in filo pastry. Some main dishes are purely European: grilled ribeye steak with rösti and glazed shallots in red wine sauce, for example. Others incorporate oriental ingredients: roasted Barbary duck breast with lime and ginger, and grilled sea-bass fillet with crisp curly kale and Thai spices. Those who like simple flavours will appreciate tarte au citron to finish, more sensual ones might choose three-chocolate parfait with raspberry purée. Aperitifs are a speciality, with a range of fine sherries, as well as pineau des Charentes and six variations on the theme of kir. The 27 wines listed are mainly French, starting at £11.50.

CHEF: Philip Crowther PROPRIETORS: Philip and Shirley Crowther OPEN: L 12 to 2 (by prior arrangement only), Tue to Sat D 7 to 10 CLOSED: 1 week Christmas, 1 week Easter MEALS: Set D £19.75 (2 courses) to £24.75 SERVICE: not inc CARDS: Delta, MasterCard, Switch, Visa DETAILS: 32 seats. Private parties: 32 main room. Children's helpings. Wheelchair access (not WC). No music. Air-conditioned ⊖ Richmond

Cucina

map 13

45A South End Road, NW3 2QB
TEL: (020) 7435 7814 FAX: (020) 7435 7147
EMAIL: enquiries@cucina.uk.com

COOKING **2**
MODERN EUROPEAN
£24–£49

A shop now sells take-away food prepared on the premises, while the large, echoey, windowless dining room remains much the same as always, dominated by a large painting of Donald Duck. Few stones are left unturned in the search for novelty, given Szechaun-seared kangaroo with a lotus root and mizuna salad, for example, but ideas are well conceived. Among the good ones have been salmon and coriander won tons in a shellfishy sauce, and chargrilled ostrich fillet with grilled radicchio, broad beans and mostardo-like figs. Menuspeak can be a little odd – 'meatballs' to describe a vegetarian mix of beans and courgettes, served with zingy pilaff rice, or 'tacos' instead of the more accurate brandy-snaps to hold chocolate mousse and sorbet – and results do not always match ambition (an inspection meal found the cooking heavy-handed), but service is friendly, and a short, varied wine list keeps prices in check, starting with a couple of Vins de Pays d'Oc varietals at £11.95.

CHEF: Andrew Poole PROPRIETORS: Vernon Mascarenhas and Andrew Poole OPEN: all week 12 to 2.30 (3 Sat and Sun), 7 to 10.30 (11 Fri and Sat) MEALS: alc (main courses L £8, D £10.50 to £15). Set L Sun £13.95 (2 courses) to £16.95 SERVICE: not inc CARDS: Amex, Delta, MasterCard, Switch, Visa DETAILS: 85 seats. Private parties: 85 main room. Vegetarian meals. Children's helpings. No cigars/pipes in dining room. Occasional music. Air-conditioned ⊖ Belsize Park

Del Buongustaio

map 12

283–285 Putney Bridge Road, SW15 2PT
TEL/FAX: (020) 8780 9361
EMAIL: mail@theitalianrestaurant.net
WEB SITE: www.theitalianrestaurant.net

NEW CHEF
ITALIAN
£16–£53

The warm ambience owes much to the décor, depicting classical times, and might have been new any time these last 40 years. What is indisputably new is the arrival of Antonio Vinciguerra, just as the Guide went to press. He looks set to continue some of the historically accented cooking in which the restaurant has long specialised, including a Renaissance dish of pasta filled with duck, ricotta and Swiss chard, in a duck and pancetta ragoût, but is equally happy with more timeless ideas such as calarmari or tiger prawns cooked with garlic and chilli, or grilled lamb cutlets with a rosemary-flavoured pesto. Wines cover the country from Piedmont, Friuli and Veneto in the north to the southern regions of Basilicata, Puglia and Sicily, with a few token New World offerings for variety. Prices start at £10.95.

CHEF: Antonio Vinciguerra PROPRIETOR: Del Buongustaio Ltd OPEN: all week 12 to 3 (12.30 to 3.30 Sun), 6.30 to 11 MEALS: alc Mon to Sat (main courses £10 to £16). Set L Mon to Sat £7.95, Set L Sun £12.75, Set D £25.95, Set Mon to Sat D 25. Cover 90p. Light L menu also available SERVICE: not inc, card slips closed CARDS: Amex, Delta, MasterCard, Switch, Visa DETAILS: 150 seats. Private parties: 90 main room, 60, 90 private rooms. Vegetarian meals. Children's helpings. No cigars/pipes in dining room. Wheelchair access (also WC). Music. Air-conditioned ⊖ East Putney (£5)

Delfina Studio Café

map 13

50 Bermondsey Street, SE1 3UD
TEL: (020) 7357 0244 FAX: (020) 7357 0250
EMAIL: book@delfina.org.uk
WEB SITE: www.delfina.org.uk

COOKING **4**
GLOBAL
£28–£48

Art and food come together here, in an expansive white space not far from London Bridge station. A large gallery for displaying contemporary work forms the backdrop to a daylight-filled, buzzing lunch venue where Maria Elia produces some inspired modern dishes. Starter combinations are artfully conceived, be they fennel-studded salami with roasted wild asparagus, Parmesan and a soft-boiled egg, or chicken livers marinated in harissa with pomegranate and watercress salad and parsnip skordalia. You will need your culinary atlas to hand as you move on to chargrilled New Zealand lamb cutlets with Szechuan braised aubergines and herbed couscous, perhaps accompanied by green beans in chestnut pesto. At the end, there may be Cornish Yarg with oatcakes and apple chutney, or chocolate ravioli with mascarpone honey cream. It is all served with proficiency and dispatch, alongside an up-to-date wine list that delves into France and the New World, with house red and white from Rioja's Cosme Palacio estate at £12.50.

CHEF: Maria Elia PROPRIETORS: Digby Squires and Delfina Entrecanales OPEN: Mon to Fri L only 12 to 3 CLOSED: 22 Dec to 2 Jan MEALS: alc (main courses £9 to £14) SERVICE: 12.5% (optional), card slips closed CARDS: Amex, Delta, Diners, MasterCard, Switch, Visa DETAILS: 120 seats. Private parties: 600 main room, 5 to 600 private rooms. Vegetarian meals. Wheelchair access (also WC). No music ⊖ London Bridge (£5)

Ditto

map 12

55–57 East Hill, SW18 2QE
TEL: (020) 8877 0110 FAX: (020) 8875 0110
WEB SITE: www.doditto.co.uk

COOKING **4**
MODERN EUROPEAN
£28–£57

The name, in case you were wondering, reflects the stated aim of owners Giles Cooper and Christian Duffell of making visitors want to return again and again. In order to achieve this, they have created a comfortable, stylish environment where displays of exotic plants and modern artworks add colour to the mainly white décor, and drinkers are encouraged to linger in the plush sofas in the bar area. They have also employed the services of Calum Watson, who shows a keen awareness of what is fashionable and modern on a lively-sounding menu. Smoked haddock fishcake with chive butter, seared salmon with creamed cabbage, bacon and peas, and twice-cooked shank of lamb with basil mash are typically bold flavour combinations. To ensure that all needs are catered for, there are good-value set-price menus, as well as bar snacks and lighter dishes. A short list of wines keeps prices reasonable and offers good choice by the glass from £2.85. Bottle prices start at £11.50.

CHEF: Calum Watson PROPRIETORS: Giles Cooper and Christian Duffell OPEN: Sun to Fri L 12 to 3, Mon to Sat D 7 to 11 CLOSED: 25 to 27 Dec MEALS: alc (main courses £9.50 to £14). Set L Mon to Fri £10 (2 courses inc wine), Set D £14.50 (2 courses) to £18.50. Bar menu available Mon to Sat 12 to 3, Sun 6 to 9 SERVICE: not inc, 12.5% for parties of 6 or more CARDS: Delta, MasterCard, Switch, Visa DETAILS: 70 seats. Private parties: 24 private room. Vegetarian meals. Children's helpings. Wheelchair access (not WC). No music (£5)

The Don 🍷

NEW ENTRY **map 13**

The Courtyard, 20 St Swithin's Lane, EC4N 8AD
TEL: (020) 7626 2606 FAX: (020) 7626 2616
EMAIL: bookings@thedonrestaurant.co.uk

COOKING **2**
FRENCH
£30–£60

Neither academic nor mafioso, this Don – with black cape and sombrero – is the mark of Sandeman, the port and sherry house whose London headquarters was here from 1798 to 1969. Set in a courtyard, like its sister restaurant Bleeding Heart (see entry), The Don has many reminders of its past, including a deep, barrel-vaulted, brick-lined cellar that is now the bistro. The main restaurant, a very twenty-first-century rectangular room with abstract metal sculptures under its high ceiling, has colourful abstract blinds over large windows, and richly coloured seats. With the two- and three-course set meals one can chose three glasses of wine (from a dozen) for an extra £14.95.

The shortish à la carte offers well-presented modern dishes such as scallops baked en croûte with lime and vanilla, and an inspector's fine, flavourful loin of New Zealand venison, well complemented by roasted figs. The wine list pays homage to sherry (including less usual styles), then a page devoted to the proprietors' vineyard (Trinity Hill, Hawkes Bay, New Zealand) offers well-priced alternatives to the traditional French bottles that comprise the core of the list; sweeties and post-prandials listed at the back include notable ports and malt whiskies. House wines start at £14.25

CHEF: Matthew Burns PROPRIETORS: Robert and Robyn Wilson OPEN: Mon to Fri 12 to 2.30, 6 to 10 CLOSED: 22 Dec to 2 Jan MEALS: alc (main courses £12 to £19). Set D Jan to Nov £14.95 (2 courses) to £17.95 SERVICE: 12.5% (optional), card slips closed CARDS: Amex, Delta, Diners, MasterCard, Switch, Visa DETAILS: 45 seats. Private parties: 55 main room, 24 private room. Vegetarian meals. No music. Air-conditioned ⊖ Bank

Drones

NEW ENTRY map 14

1 Pont Street, SW1X 9EJ
TEL: (020) 7235 9555 FAX: (020) 7235 9566

COOKING **5**
FRENCH
£31–£88

Drones continues Marco Pierre White's ambition to revitalise notable restaurants of old (such as Quo Vadis and Mirabelle, see entries). The makeover by designer David Collins includes caramel-coloured walls hung with black and white photos to add a touch of glamour and catch the Woosterish allusion. Menu descriptions are in Franglais, and the back-combed and bouffant-haired diners are 'typical of the Belgravia set'.

The cooking is staunchly MPW, classic French dishes cohabiting with British favourites ('deceptively simple dishes with great craft' as one reporter put it), and mostly managing to stay the right side of formulaic. Expect pig's trotters, potted shrimps, braised oxtail en daube, and côte de veau. Simple and precise cooking has yielded a fine dish of grilled lemon sole with sauce tartare and pomme mousseline, and smoked haddock 'as good as it can get' (served with poached egg) has also produced a rave. Desserts, such as tart sablée of bitter chocolate, are decadent and satisfying, and predominantly French service is willing, if linguistically challenged on occasion.

The wine list is more adventurous than the cooking. Though not cheap, there are interesting bottles from good producers in Uruguay and South Africa, as well as the more predictable Bordeaux, Champagne and Burgundy. Prices start at £15.50, although there's not much choice below £20. Thirteen wines are available by the glass.

CHEF: Joseph Croan PROPRIETOR: White Star Line Restaurants Ltd OPEN: all week 12 to 2.30 (3.30 Sun), 6 to 11 (10.30 Sun) CLOSED: 25 and 26 Dec, 1 Jan MEALS: alc (main courses £15 to £25). Set L £14.95 (2 courses) to £17.95, Set L Sun £19.50 SERVICE: 12.5% (optional), card slips closed CARDS: Amex, Delta, Diners, MasterCard, Switch, Visa DETAILS: 100 seats. Private parties: 50 main room. Vegetarian meals. Children's helpings. No music. Air-conditioned ⊖ Knightsbridge, Sloane Square

The Guide office can quickly spot when a restaurateur is encouraging customers to write recommending inclusion. Such reports do not further a restaurant's cause. Please tell us if a restaurateur invites you to write to the Guide.

Eagle £

map 13

159 Farringdon Road, EC1R 3AL
TEL: (020) 7837 1353

COOKING **2**
MEDITERRANEAN
£21–£38

After singing in a performance of Handel's *Messiah*, one reader repaired to the Eagle for refreshment, then sang its praises to us. Undeterred by the noise level of this forever busy and crowded pub, and the 'somewhat raffish décor', he waited ten minutes for a table before tackling a grilled organic ribeye steak with black beans and chorizo salad that was 'tasty and cooked as ordered'. He also found the service very good. Iberia and Italy feature strongly in a menu that might offer Florentine pea soup, or a Catalan larder salad of new potatoes, beans, anchovies, olives, peppers, artichokes and boiled egg. Shoulder of lamb is 'en sofrito – chilli and caraway seeds – couscous with dried fruits and nuts', as the menu describes it, while poached ham hock comes with chickpeas, spinach and chives. Everything is a main course, barring the Portuguese custard tarts, or Sardinian ewes' milk cheese (with flatbread and marmalade), to finish. A blackboard lists a dozen wines by the glass or bottle from £10, and unusual draught and bottled beers. The Eagle now has a sister pub-restaurant, The Fox, in Shoreditch (28 Paul Street, tel (020) 7729 5708)

CHEF: Tom Norrington-Davies PROPRIETOR: Mike Belben OPEN: all week L 12.30 to 2.30 (3.30 Sat and Sun), Mon to Sat D 6.30 to 10.30 CLOSED: Christmas, bank hols MEALS: alc (main courses £4.50 to £12.50) SERVICE: none, card slips closed CARDS: Delta, Switch DETAILS: 60 seats. Vegetarian meals. Wheelchair access (not WC). Music ⊖ Farringdon

English Garden

map 14

10 Lincoln Street, SW3 2TS
TEL: (020) 7584 7272 FAX: (020) 7584 1961
EMAIL: english.garden@ukgateway.net

COOKING **5**
ANGLO-FRENCH
£33–£64

Under the same ownership as Lindsay House (see entry, London, where Malcolm Starmer worked with Richard Corrigan), and within walking distance of Sloane Square, the Garden has been praised for its clean, simple lines and colours, which make an appropriate backdrop for some thoughtful modern cooking. Ideas and materials are up to the minute (horseradish dumplings in the cep consommé, turnip choucroute with the roast duck) and intelligently assembled, producing starters of potato and Taleggio gnocchi with shin of veal for example, or red mullet on a salad of oranges flavoured with basil and saffron. Combinations may sometimes be unexpected but are invariably well handled and enjoyable: roast cod might come with salsify, Beaufort cheese and ceps, while leg of rabbit has been served with chorizo and aïoli. Menus change twice daily, presentation is attractive, and desserts are indulgent, taking in chocolate fondant with Baileys mousse, and toffee banana crumble with crème caramel. Wines are sharply chosen and pleasingly varied, with ten available by the glass (from £4.80).

CHEF: Malcom Starmer PROPRIETOR: Richard Corrigan OPEN: Tue to Sun L 12 to 2.45, all week D 6.30 to 10.45 (10.15 Sun) CLOSED: 26 to 29 Dec, 1 to 14 Aug MEALS: Set L £17.50 (2 courses) to £19.50, Set D £27.50 SERVICE: 12.5% (optional) CARDS: Amex, Delta, Diners, MasterCard, Switch, Visa DETAILS: 68 seats. Private parties: 32 main room, 8 and 20 private rooms. Children's helpings. Music. Air-conditioned ⊖ Sloane Square (£5)

Enoteca Turi 🍷 NEW ENTRY map 12

28 Putney High Street, SW15 1SQ — COOKING **2**
TEL: (020) 8785 4449 FAX: (020) 8780 5409 — ITALIAN
£27–£51

This refurbished Italian restaurant now has blond plank flooring, off-white walls, moulded chairs with leather seats, and terracotta-look pillars. A concise menu follows the Italian style – four courses, with pasta for the second – and juxtaposes classics such as bresaola (dressed with truffle oil and thickly shaved Parmesan) with trendier offerings including quickly seared scallops with smoked aubergine and pesto dressing. Colourful pastas include saffron and lemon linguine with fresh crab and chilli, and potato gnocchi comes with fresh broad bean pesto and Pecorino.

Mains may include fillet of sea bass with potato cake, endive and salsa verde, or perhaps plump breast of guinea fowl with a dark rich mushroom sauce. Chocolate fondant pudding is light, soft and warm, or there are Italian cheeses. Young service is efficient and skilled. Given the enoteca handle, it is no surprise that wines are taken seriously. A mainly Italian list of over 100 includes some great names, but there are many under £20 too, like house Sicilian at £10.50, plus some interesting halves and pudding wines. In addition, there is a recommended wine by the glass for each item on the menu.

CHEF: S. Busciglia PROPRIETOR: Giuseppe Turi OPEN: Mon to Fri L 12 to 2.30, Mon to Sat D 7 to 11 CLOSED: 25 and 26 Dec, 1 Jan, L only bank hol Mons MEALS: alc (main courses £9.50 to £16) SERVICE: 12.5% (optional), card slips closed CARDS: Amex, Delta, Diners, MasterCard, Switch, Visa DETAILS: 85 seats. Private parties: 28 main room. Vegetarian meals. Wheelchair access (also WC). Occasional music. Air-conditioned

L'Escargot Marco Pierre White map 15

48 Greek Street, W1D 4EF — *NEW CHEF*
TEL: (020) 7439 7474 FAX: (020) 7437 0790 — MODERN FRENCH
WEB SITE: www.whitestarline.org.uk — £31–£84

Marco Pierre White seems to have a thing about venerable London restaurants, judging by his interests in Criterion Brasserie, Mirabelle, Quo Vadis (see entries), and this period piece from the 1920s. Known for its displays of art by Miró, Chagall, Matisse, Hockney and Warhol, with an entire room devoted to Picasso, it was due to close for a David Collins make-over as the Guide went to press. Jeff Galvin joins from the Oak Room (see entry) to take an executive role over both dining rooms, with Alan Pickett cooking downstairs. Upstairs is due to take the Oak Room as its inspiration, while downstairs you can expect the brasserie-style dishes produced at the Belvedere and Drones (see entries). Reports please.

CHEFS: Jeff Galvin and Alan Pickett PROPRIETORS: Jimmy Lahoud and Marco Pierre White OPEN: Mon to Fri L 12.15 to 2.15, Mon to Sat D 6 to 11.30 CLOSED: 25 and 26 Dec, 1 Jan, bank hols MEALS: ground floor alc (main courses £13). Set L and D 6 to 7 £14.95 (2 courses) to £17.95. Picasso Room Set L £20.50 (2 courses) to £55, Set D £42 to £55 SERVICE: 12.5% (optional), card slips closed CARDS: Amex, Delta, Diners, MasterCard, Switch, Visa DETAILS: 80 seats. Private parties: 26 and 60 private rooms. Vegetarian meals. No cigars/pipes in dining room. Wheelchair access (also men's WC). Occasional music. Air-conditioned ⊖ Leicester Square, Tottenham Court Road

L'Estaminet

map 15

14 Garrick Street, WC2E 9BJ
TEL: (020) 7379 1432 FAX: (020) 7379 1530

COOKING **1**
FRENCH
£22–£59

Classic French bistro cooking in the heart of theatreland – with both menus and the unfailingly punctilious service geared accordingly – is the *raison d'être* of L'Estaminet. In the welcoming candlelit ambience of a more genteel era, choose from quiche of the day, marinated herrings with warm potato salad, or smoked salmon on pastry with horseradish dressing to start, and then main courses that range from fillet of cod grilled with herbs to knuckle of lamb cooked with honey and rosemary. A terrine of sole and salmon, and desserts that included a simple but impressively varied fruit salad and a very good tarte aux pommes, helped to make the evening of one theatre-bound pair. A textbook French wine list at rather lofty prices kicks off with vins de maison at £11.50.

CHEF: Philippe Tamet PROPRIETOR: Christian Bellone OPEN: Mon to Sat 12 to 2.30, 5.45 to 11.15 CLOSED: bank hols MEALS: alc (main courses £13 to £17). Set D Mon to Fri 5.45 to 7.30 £11.99, Set D Sat 5.45 to 7.30 £14.50 SERVICE: 12.5%, card slips closed CARDS: Amex, Delta, MasterCard, Switch, Visa DETAILS: Private parties: 16 main room, 16 private room. Children's helpings. No pipes in dining room. Wheelchair access (not WC). Music. Air-conditioned ⊖ Leicester Square, Covent Garden

Fifth Floor

map 14

Harvey Nichols,
109–125 Knightsbridge, SW1X 7RJ
TEL: (020) 7235 5250 FAX: (020) 7823 2207

COOKING **3**
MODERN BRITISH
£31–£82

Superficially, not much has changed since the departure of Henry Harris. The top-floor dining room sports the same Oxbridge-blue upholstered chairs and bright faux-naïf paintings, and has the same view into the bustling food market, café and deli. The food, meanwhile, aims to provide sustenance in the most comforting way, offering wild mushroom and truffle soup, halibut fillet with English asparagus and hollandaise, and ribeye of beef with horseradish ketchup.

The kitchen has turned out an impeccable saffron risotto, and well-timed dishes of Dover sole with shrimp and parsley beurre noisette, and veal chop with Roquefort and watercress butter. Portion control, however, is a bit wonky, and small helpings at these prices are simply not good value (added to which, vegetables are charged extra on the carte), although the lunchtime and early-evening set-price deals are comparatively worthwhile. To finish, there may be a plate of chocolate puddings, or caramelised raspberry custard tart: a 'sort of crème brûlée in pastry'. Service is polite, attentive and friendly. A plump wine list is packed with star producers from around the world, including some rare finds, which inevitably results in a few three-figure prices. A less daunting, though equally globe-trotting line-up is found on the one-page 'Little List', which ranges from cheery house French at £13.50 through zesty Clare Valley Riesling to fairly mature burgundies and clarets.

CHEF: Simon Shaw PROPRIETOR: Dickson Poon OPEN: all week L 12 to 3 (3.30 Sat and Sun), Mon to Sat D 6.30 to 11.30 MEALS: alc (main courses £19 to £24). Set L £21.50 (2 courses) to £25, Set D Mon to Sat 6.30 to 7.30 £18.50 SERVICE: 12.5% (optional) CARDS: Amex, Delta, Diners, MasterCard, Switch, Visa DETAILS: 130 seats. Private parties: 150 main room. Vegetarian meals. No-smoking area. No pipes in dining room. Wheelchair access (also WC). No music. Air-conditioned ⊖ Knightsbridge

Fina Estampa

map 13

150–152 Tooley Street, SE1 2TU
TEL/FAX: (020) 7403 1342

COOKING **2**
PERUVIAN
£24–£47

If you don't know carapulcra or lomo saltado, Fina Estampa can provide a Peruvian culinary adventure. The menu comes with explanations, but Richard Jones is out front to advise, while wife Bianca (from Lima) cooks her homeland's food with a personal touch. Potatoes, a recurring ingredient, appear in starters of papa a la huancaina (a national dish of fromage frais sauce made with mild Peruvian yellow chilli and served over new potatoes), and mains of pollo almendrado: chicken cooked in almond and pecan-nut sauce with sauté potatoes and parsley rice. Desserts generally consist of commercially available ice creams, sorbets and cakes, though cheesecake is home-made. The green-painted dining room (dark ceilings, light walls) is decorated with Peruvian photographs, plates, mirrors and artefacts, and the wine list runs to 11 Chilean and Argentinian bottles from £12.50.

CHEF: Bianca Jones PROPRIETORS: Richard and Bianca Jones OPEN: Mon to Fri L 12 to 2.30, Mon to Sat D 6.30 to 10.30 MEALS: alc (main courses £7.50 to £15) SERVICE: not inc, card slips closed CARDS: Amex, Delta, Diners, MasterCard, Switch, Visa DETAILS: 60 seats. Private parties: 66 main room, 50 private room. Vegetarian meals. Children's helpings. Occasional music ⊖ London Bridge (£5)

First Floor

map 13

186 Portobello Road, W11 1LA
TEL: (020) 7243 0072 FAX: (020) 7221 9440

COOKING **4**
MODERN ENGLISH
£23–£51

This upstairs room above a pub is filled with light and air and is a pleasure to eat in on a summer evening particularly. Andy Appleton may have toned down some of the more obviously way-out ideas of previous years, but productively so, and while the culinary gleanings can still take a magical mystery tour through three courses, an interpreter is no longer mandatory. You can even start with Caesar salad if you must. Gnocchi, risotto and pasta (perhaps crab ravioli with a sauce of smoked tomatoes and basil) may all be taken as either starters or mains, and the principal main courses run a gamut from sea bass (with herbed rice, baby pak choi and balsamic tomatoes) to slow-roast double cutlets of lamb (with roasted red onions and tabbouleh salad). Vegetables and side salads are charged extra. Good chocolate is shown off to its best advantage at dessert stage, and ice creams are well made. The short wine list is mostly French, with dips into the southern hemisphere here and there, and enough below £20 to maintain interest. House French is £10.50, and there are 11 wines by the glass, including champagne.

CHEF: Andy Appleton PROPRIETOR: Antony Harris OPEN: Tue to Sun L 12 to 3, Mon to Sat D 7 to 11.30 MEALS: alc (main courses £10.50 to £15.50). Set L £10.50 (2 courses) to £14 SERVICE: 12.5%, card slips closed CARDS: Amex, Delta, MasterCard, Switch, Visa DETAILS: 100 seats. Private parties: 70 main room, 28 and 42 private rooms. Vegetarian meals. Music ⊖ Ladbroke Grove

Fish! — map 13

Cathedral Street, SE1 9AL
TEL: (020) 7234 3333 FAX: (020) 7234 3343 — COOKING **1**
EMAIL: reservations@fish.plc.uk — SEAFOOD
WEB SITE: www.fishdiner.co.uk — £24–£46

The original outlet is now one of over 20 branches open or planned, from Battersea to Birmingham to Leeds. It is as noisy as ever, with sound reverberating off glass and steel; centralisation of everything from booking to supplies gives things a rather robotic feel, though the formula still works. 'They know how to cook fish properly,' maintains one visitor, and that is about the top and bottom of it. The place-mat is the menu: choose one of 23 fish (lemon sole, sea bass, plaice, tuna, skate, you name it), say whether you want it steamed or grilled, add a sauce, and away you go. There are no surprises (except, perhaps, that the chips aren't better). Vegetarians get a single 'vegetarian dish' in two sizes. To make up three courses, there are things like prawn cocktail and summer pudding, and a tiny wine list starts with house Loire Sauvignon Blanc at £9.90 (£2.50 a glass).

CHEF: Phil Goble PROPRIETOR: Fish plc OPEN: all week 11.30 (12 Sun) to 11pm (10.30 Sun) CLOSED: 25 and 26 Dec, 1 Jan, 26 Aug MEALS: alc (main courses £7 to £16) SERVICE: 10% (optional) CARDS: Amex, Delta, Diners, MasterCard, Switch, Visa DETAILS: 100 seats. 20 outside. Children's helpings. Music. Air-conditioned ⊖ London Bridge (£5)

Il Forno — map 15

63–64 Frith Street, W1V 5TA
TEL: (020) 7734 4545 FAX: (020) 7287 8624 — COOKING **2**
EMAIL: reservations@ilforno-restaurant.co.uk — MODERN ITALIAN
WEB SITE: www.ilforno-restaurant.co.uk — £25–£51

A sister establishment of Al Duca (see entry), this busy, buzzy restaurant can get warm and noisy; none the less, its professional, international staff cope remarkably well under pressure. The focus is on 'simple, clean flavours at fair prices', and much of the menu centres on straightforward pizza, pasta and polenta, with starters taking in perhaps grilled vegetables with basil, or chickpea soup with leeks, tomato and thyme. Linguine with mussels is served correctly al dente and 'enlivened by a little julienne of lemon zest and red chilli', while half a dozen meat or fish options – roasted cod with lentils, shallots, sun-dried tomatoes and chervil, for example, or chargrilled lamb steak with chicory, peppers, capers and olives – round out the main-course offerings. Among desserts might be a 'better than fair' nougat parfait, and on the all-Italian wine list, which starts at £12.50, are a decent number by the glass.

CHEF: Marco Stucchi PROPRIETOR: Cuisine Collection OPEN: Mon to Fri L 12 to 2.30, all week D 6 to 10.30 (10 Fri and Sat, 11 Sun) CLOSED: bank hols MEALS: alc (main courses £5 to £14.50) SERVICE: 12.5% (optional), card slips closed CARDS: Amex, Delta, MasterCard, Switch, Visa DETAILS: 70 seats. Private parties: 70 main room. Vegetarian meals. Occasional music. Air-conditioned ⊖ Tottenham Court Road

Four Seasons

map 13

84 Queensway, W2 3RL
TEL: (020) 7229 4320

COOKING **3**
CHINESE
£25–£45

Sophisticated is not how you would describe the food or ambience in this crowded eating house, and you may have to stand and wait for your booked table to become free. But service can be friendly and helpful, especially for those who show interest in real Chinese food. Skip appetisers and such non-Cantonese stalwarts as deep-fried shredded beef, or crispy duck. Splendid examples of the gutsy flavours and textures of Cantonese urban peasant cooking are listed on the long main menu as chef's specialities. House special bean curd is one, stir-fried prawn cake with seasonal vegetables is another. From the chef's special recommended menu, steamed egg with dried scallop and king prawn, or your choice of green vegetable in oyster sauce, is typical. The window-displayed barbecued pork, duck and more exotic meats are other contenders for the title of signature dishes, and hotpots include braised chicken with yam and coconut sauce, or another house special of seaweed, sea cucumber, fish maw and Chinese mushroom. House wines are £9.

CHEF: Mr Tong PROPRIETOR: Four Seasons (Queensway) Ltd OPEN: all week 12 to 11.15 (10.45 Sun) MEALS: alc (main courses £5.50 to £9). Set L and D £12.50 to £17 SERVICE: 12.5% CARDS: Amex, Delta, MasterCard, Switch, Visa DETAILS: 70 seats. Private parties: 80 main room. Vegetarian meals. Music. Air-conditioned ⊖ Bayswater, Queensway

French House Dining Room

map 15

49 Dean Street, W1D 5BG
TEL: (020) 7437 2477 FAX: (020) 7287 9109

COOKING **3**
BRITISH
£33–£55

The French House Dining Room sits above a pub where French Resistance members met during the war. The food offered in this fairly crowded, simply decorated room is more old British than French, although there might be a terrine of foie gras or quail and aïoli on the daily-changing menu. More traditional fare crops up in the form of beetroot soup, a pickled pigeon starter with red cabbage and watercress, and main courses such as shoulder of lamb with sprouting broccoli and a tang of anchovy. The emphasis is on direct and honest flavours. Fish broth, beef onglet with chicory and mustard, with chocolate St-Emilion to finish, left one diner well satisfied. Others have enjoyed treacle tart, and pear crumble, and skilfully made ice creams include one of Turkish coffee. The wine list is firmly Gallic (a single New Zealand Chardonnay is jostled on all sides by good French growers), and house vin de table is £11.25.

CHEF: Margot Henderson PROPRIETORS: Melanie Arnold and Margot Henderson OPEN: Mon to Sat 12 to 3.15, 6 to 11.15 CLOSED: Christmas, bank hols MEALS: alc (main courses £8.50 to £16) SERVICE: not inc CARDS: Amex, Delta, Diners, MasterCard, Switch, Visa DETAILS: 30 seats. Private parties: 30 main room. Vegetarian meals. No music ⊖ Piccadilly Circus

Fung Shing

map 15

15 Lisle Street, WC2H 7BE
TEL: (020) 7437 1539 FAX: (020) 7734 0284
WEB SITE: www.fungshing.com

COOKING **4**
CHINESE
£31–£75

Fung Shing has an appealingly classical dining room at the back, with chandeliers, yellow walls and round tables that suit group dining; couples tend to find themselves in the more ordinary front room. The restaurant made its reputation with innovative twists to Cantonese cooking, and the long menu still seeks to please both savants and novices: starters range from sesame prawn toast to braised shark's fin in a basket, and main courses from beef with cashew nuts to braised eel with roasted belly pork in hotpot.

Although standards can be variable, the food at its best has delivered, for example, a 'handsomely sliced, fresh and tasty' seafood-stuffed whole squid. Look to the chef's specials for most interest, whether intensely flavoured dishes (minced pork with salted fish), luxury food (fresh carp 'in superior sauce'), or subtle textural pairings (steamed fish maw and mashed prawn with crabmeat sauce). While desserts are unremarkable, service is warm and helpful, and the wine list covers most eventualities and includes a short fine wine selection. House wine is £13.50.

CHEF: Fook-On Chung PROPRIETOR: Forum Restaurant Ltd OPEN: all week, noon to 11.15 (9 on 23 Dec) CLOSED: 24 to 26 Dec MEALS: alc (main courses £7.50 to £16). Set L £17 (2 courses), Set D from £32 (for 2 people) to £80 (for 5 people) SERVICE: 10%, card slips closed CARDS: Amex, Diners, MasterCard, Switch, Visa DETAILS: 120 seats. Private parties: 50 main room, 26 and 50 private rooms. Vegetarian meals. Music. Air-conditioned ⊖ Leicester Square

Gate £

NEW ENTRY **map 13**

72 Belsize Lane, NW3 5BJ
TEL: (020) 7435 7733 FAX: (020) 7435 3311
EMAIL: belsize@gateveg.co.uk
WEB SITE: www.gateveg.co.uk

COOKING **2**
VEGETARIAN
£23–£42

This new up-market vegetarian restaurant, a sister to the original in Hammersmith (see London Round-ups), is set in leafy Belsize Village and makes a welcome addition to the neighbourhood. An inventive menu takes in lots of Japanese influences, as well as Mediterranean, Thai and Middle Eastern touches, so no one can accuse it of being boring. There are no nut rissoles here; instead expect a few vegan options, and dishes such as crunchily intense courgette flowers filled with feta cheese, butternut squash, red onions and herbs, deep-fried and served with tomato and chilli sauce.

Main courses might turn up teriyaki aubergine (with sauté rice noodles, roasted shiitake mushrooms, pak choi and chilli salsa), or a Japanese platter consisting of 'sushi' and 'sashimi', with silken tofu standing in for the raw fish, and served with miso soup, wasabi and pink ginger. Desserts are equally inventive. Ingredients are of a high quality, although some dishes can be hit or miss and there is a tendency to over-salt. Service is uniformly helpful and friendly. The wine list has a decent range and is fairly priced from £9.75. Wines that are vegetarian or certified organic are asterisked.

CHEF: Sol Goodall PROPRIETORS: Adrian and Michael Daniel OPEN: all week L 12 to 3, Mon to Sat D 6 to 11 CLOSED: bank hols MEALS: alc (main courses £7.50 to £11). Set L £10 (2 courses) SERVICE: not inc CARDS: Amex, Delta, MasterCard, Switch, Visa DETAILS: 60 seats. 4 seats outside. Private parties: 20 main room, 20 private room. Vegetarian meals. Children's helpings. No smoking in dining room. Wheelchair access (not WC). No music. Air-conditioned ⊖ Belsize Park, Swiss Cottage

Gaudí

map 13

63 Clerkenwell Road, EC1M 5PT
TEL: (020) 7608 3220 FAX: (020) 7250 1057
EMAIL: gaudi@turnmills.co.uk
WEB SITE: www.turnmills.co.uk/gaudi.html

COOKING **3**
MODERN SPANISH
£45–£61

Pungent smells from an open kitchen complement the vivid, energetic decoration of elaborately moulded plaster, twisted wrought iron and extravagantly coloured and patterned tiles. Visual appeal is also an important component of the food, perhaps a spider crab soufflé (more like a mousse) encased in a thin layer of courgette and dressed to the nines with vegetables all around. The menu's elaborate wording is perhaps necessary, given what's in some dishes: layers of omelette, for example, interleaved with a vegetable mix, covered in bright yellow saffron béchamel, dressed with pine nuts, sultanas and tomatoes, with more vegetables round the perimeter.

Ideas can be both interesting and successful, as in a winter vegetable ragoût (in June) in a tasty, salty gravy spiked with tiny dice of ham and slices of octopus, topped by a scoop of soft Idiazabal cheese; or in a scoop of creamy goats' cheese ice cream on a tuile biscuit, with balls of soft chocolate resembling dumplings and doughnuts, surrounded by an orange and honey dressing. As to service, 'if you like wine and water topped up every few seconds, this is the place'. Wines from £11.50, as proudly Spanish as the rest, make up a short regional list that offers half a dozen by the glass, plus a choice of sherries.

CHEF: Nacho Martinez PROPRIETOR: John Newman OPEN: Mon to Fri L 12 to 2.30, Mon to Sat D 7 to 10.30 CLOSED: Christmas, Easter, bank hols MEALS: alc (main courses £16 to £17.50). Set L £15 (2 courses) SERVICE: 12.5% (optional) CARDS: Amex, Delta, Diners, MasterCard, Switch, Visa DETAILS: 70 seats. Private parties: 45 main room. Vegetarian meals. Children's helpings. No children under 4. No smoking in 1 dining room. Wheelchair access (not WC). Occasional music. Air-conditioned ⊖ Farringdon

Le Gavroche 🍷 map 15

43 Upper Brook Street, W1K 7QR COOKING **7**
TEL: (020) 7408 0881 and 7499 1826 FRENCH
FAX: (020) 7491 4387 and 7409 0939 £43–£149

The impressively preserved basement dining room, heavy with green and red décor, awards, citations and framed photographs of the Roux brothers with various dignitaries, remains resolutely in a time warp of its own making. It flies the flag for a traditional style of French cooking in which old favourites such as soufflé suissesse, caneton Gavroche and omelette Rothschild sit edgily alongside slightly more contemporary red mullet with cockle risotto, or lamb with couscous. It recalls an era when mousses were light and properly made, when sauces were named after people, when domes were lifted, when the slicing of lamb, the cutting of pigeons and the pouring of sauces were done with speed and expertise at table, and when service was impeccably smooth and co-ordinated, as it has been under Silvano Giraldin for as long as anybody can remember.

It seems to have a sense of humour too: why else would it combine two culinary Gallic icons to make a 'stunning' dish comprising two tiny pots of green sauce flavoured with herbs and garlic: plump, whole, lightly textured snails in one, tiny de-boned frogs' legs in the other. Despite a few inconsistencies now and again, materials are exceptionally fine and deftly handled, even if the main items sometimes overshadow their accompaniments: crisp-skinned sea bass timed to the second, with mundane tiger prawns and pasta in a five-spice sauce, or rack of milk-fed lamb for two, carved in front of you of course, tasting delicate yet distinctive with a natural sweetness, served with a mint-flavoured béarnaise, creamy potatoes and ordinary vegetables.

Desserts – tarte Tatin for two, perhaps, or vanilla mousse with a crunchy peanut filling and caramelised bananas – divide reporters: unworthy of the rest of the cooking for one, 'always a cut above the rest' for another. A roll call of the finest producers and vintages of Bordeaux, Burgundy and Champagne still forms the core of the thick-paged wine list. And very good they are too, for expense-account or deep-pocketed wine lovers. Others can take solace in the regional French listing, which mixes Fitou, at £16.50, with Côtes de Duras, at £19; or try one of the hundred-odd halves or house wine starting at £20.

CHEF: Michel Roux PROPRIETOR: Le Gavroche Ltd OPEN: Mon to Fri 12 to 2, 7 to 11 CLOSED: 21 Dec to 7 Jan, bank hols MEALS: alc (main courses £27 to £37). Set L £38.50 (inc wine), Set D £78 SERVICE: 12.5% (optional), card slips closed CARDS: Amex, Delta, Diners, MasterCard, Switch, Visa DETAILS: 60 seats. Private parties: 80 main room, 20 private room. Vegetarian meals. Jacket and tie. No cigars/pipes in dining room. Occasional music. Air-conditioned ⊖ Marble Arch

The text of entries is based on unsolicited reports sent in by readers, backed up by inspections conducted anonymously. The factual details under the text are from questionnaires the Guide sends to all restaurants that feature in the book.

The Guide always appreciates hearing about changes of chef or owner.

Gay Hussar

map 15

2 Greek Street, W1V 6NB
TEL: (020) 7437 0973 FAX: (020) 7437 4631
EMAIL: gayhussar@gayhussar.fsnet.co.uk

COOKING **1**
HUNGARIAN
£30–£54

Recent changes are mostly for the better, writes a regular visitor. Staff are 'professional and keen to please', which adds to the pleasure of partaking of 'enthusiastic portions of top-notch fare'. This may start with splendid, traditional chilled wild cherry soup, and continue with crisp roast duck with Hungarian potatoes and apple sauce. Coffee has been deemed excellent, though pancakes – perhaps stuffed with veal goulash and served with creamed spinach – have been thought a touch on the heavy side (no great changes there then). The lunch menu is shorter, but takes in many old favourites, such as veal goulash with thimble egg dumplings, and smoked goose breast with scholet or smoked baked beans. Wines now number 40; 14 are Hungarian table wines, reasonably priced from £10.50, and there are four sorts of Tokaji too.

CHEF: Laslo Holecz PROPRIETOR: Restaurant Partnership plc OPEN: Mon to Sat 12.15 to 2.30, 5.30 to 10.45 CLOSED: bank and public hols MEALS: alc D (main courses £12 to £17). Set L £15.50 (2 courses) to £18.50 SERVICE: 12.5% (optional), card slips closed CARDS: Amex, Delta, Diners, MasterCard, Switch, Visa DETAILS: 70 seats. Private parties: 40 main room, 12 and 25 private rooms. Vegetarian meals. Children's helpings. No pipes in dining room. Wheelchair access (not WC). No music. Air-conditioned ⊖ Tottenham Court Road (£5)

ginger

NEW ENTRY **map 13**

115 Westbourne Grove, W2 4UP
TEL: (020) 7908 1990 FAX: (020) 7908 1991
WEB SITE: www.gingerrestaurant.co.uk

COOKING **3**
BANGLADESHI
£24–£59

This place shows that modern design can work brilliantly. The name, with fashionable lower-case initial, is discreetly inset in the pavement below the window and in the attractive, grey polished-concrete tabletops. Walls, decorated with framed lengths of richly embroidered sari silk, are brilliant turquoise, as are the comfortably upholstered chairs, and tables are elegantly dressed with white cloth napkins and crockery.

Proudly Bangladeshi, the cooking provides a novel style and different flavours for lovers of 'Indian' food. Twelve starters on the short à la carte menu include lamb patties incorporating chopped fresh herbs to please eye and palate, and tandoori-roasted bekti, a flaky white fish in a richly flavoured yellow crust. Jhol is a type of Bengali curry thinner than the North Indian style, and macher kofta jhol, with fish dumplings, has a delicate chilli spiciness, 'not throat-grabbing – a gentle love-bite'. Also commended are luchi (a light, puffy fried bread), goat curry, and sim (Bangladeshi green beans). The short wine list starts at £12. Service is added, but credit-card slips are still left open.

CHEF: Albert Gomes PROPRIETORS: Ollie Rahman, Allen Hussain and Abdul Quadir OPEN: all week 12 to 4, 6 to 11 CLOSED: 25 and 26 Dec MEALS: alc (main courses £7.50 to £12.50). Set L £10 to £15 (all 2 courses) SERVICE: 12.5% (optional) CARDS: Amex, Delta, MasterCard, Switch, Visa DETAILS: 95 seats. Private parties: 40 main room. Vegetarian meals. Children's helpings. No smoking in 1 dining room. Music. Air-conditioned ⊖ Notting Hill Gate (£5)

Golden Dragon

map 15

28–29 Gerrard Street, W1V 7LP
TEL: (020) 7734 2763 FAX: (020) 7734 1073

COOKING **2**
CHINESE
£26–£53

At lunchtime animated crowds, predominantly Chinese, fill the traditionally decorated room, with its barbecue 'stall' of glossy chickens and ducks. Special dim sum, on a table card in Chinese, were (partly) explained to our inspector by a 'friendly and efficient waiter'. Special seafood egg and tofu dumplings 'looked, and tasted, like savoury miniature crème caramels' topped by chopped prawns and gelatinous sauce. Crisp, deep-fried seafood rolls (a chef's speciality from the main dim sum list) contain scallop, prawn and crab meat in a sweet citrussy sauce. Other successes have included pork and prawn siu mai, and sweet egg tarts. Note your order if you want to check the bill. Our cooking mark is for dim sum only, since reports on meals from the main menu are mixed. House wines are £8.50.

CHEF: Y.C. Man PROPRIETOR: Mr Lam OPEN: all week noon to 11.30 (midnight Fri and Sat, 11 Sun) CLOSED: 25 Dec MEALS: alc (main courses £6.30). Set D £12 (2 courses) to £22.50 (all min 2 or more) SERVICE: 10% CARDS: Amex, Delta, Diners, MasterCard, Switch, Visa DETAILS: 250 seats. Private parties: 330 main room, 10 and 40 private rooms. Vegetarian meals. Music. Air-conditioned ⊖ Leicester Square, Piccadilly Circus

Gordon Ramsay

map 14

68–69 Royal Hospital Road, SW3 4HP
TEL: (020) 7352 4441 FAX: (020) 7352 3334
WEB SITE: www.gordonramsay.com

COOKING **9**
FRENCH
£65–£131

Plenty of table space, elegant place settings, and a lot of glass (in mirrors, partitions and sculptures) add up to a sumptuous yet understated dining room. Some consider this the gold standard by which to judge other restaurants, although Gordon Ramsay's involvement in new ventures (in Glasgow with Amaryllis, see entry; Claridge's, scheduled to open soon after the Guide is published; and abroad) inevitably prompts some to question how long the original will retain its sparkle. Is the normally show-stopping seared foie gras quite as sizzlingly *à point* as before? Is the wonderfully fresh and vivid tartare of scallops slightly more acidulated than previously? These may be small points, but at this level (and at these prices) every item tends to be scrutinised down to the last detail. Other dishes, such as the braised pork belly starter (accompanied by langoustines and haricots blancs), and Aberdeen Angus fillet (served with a slice of stuffed pig's trotter and truffle sauce), continue to show the kitchen at its reassuringly down-to-earth best.

One thing that often happens to restaurants at the top of the tree is that they cease to innovate. The very dynamism that put them there in the first place can be replaced by don't-rock-the-boat caution. This does not appear to be the case with Gordon Ramsay. Changes may not be dramatic, and some dishes are carried forward from one menu to the next – scallops with a truffle-scented cauliflower purée and beignets, or poached and then grilled Bresse pigeon with Savoy cabbage – while others are refreshed from time to time, so that regulars have something (apart from sheer quality) to come back for, and first timers can be sure of tasting the kitchen's latest enthusiasm: a warm salad of caramelised calves' sweetbreads, perhaps, or braised fillet of line-caught turbot on a lettuce fondue with a light vanilla stock sauce.

Presentation seems to have been given a more prominent role, with dishes arriving as carefully assembled ingredients on a plate, over which a waiter, with due ceremony, dribbles a sauce from a silver gravy boat. But what matters most is that the food is characterised by vivid flavours, which start with the appetiser (perhaps truffle-oiled pumpkin soup), and might progress through an 'awesome' tortellini of lobster and langoustines (with a little ball of vegetable-stuffed cabbage and a fennel sauce), to roast Challandais duck and its memorable endive tart, ending with 'the most fabulous' orange tarte Tatin. Some reports suggest that desserts could do with a bit more magic, but one thing that nobody questions is that maître d' Jean-Claude Breton's irrepressible charm offensive is still going full tilt.

Wine service continues to be praised, but the exclusive-feeling list, in which star labels are made conspicuous by their sky-high price tags, means there is little to be found under £25 – house red and white are £20 and £18 – though a Côtes du Rhône villages is a good tip, coming in at £17.

CHEF/PROPRIETOR: Gordon Ramsay OPEN: Mon to Fri 12 to 2.30, 6.45 to 11 MEALS: Set L £35, Set D £65 to £80 SERVICE: not inc CARDS: Amex, Delta, Diners, MasterCard, Switch, Visa DETAILS: 45 seats. Private parties: 45 main room. No cigars in dining room. Wheelchair access (not WC). No music. Air-conditioned ⊖ Sloane Square

Gourmet Garden £ map 12

59 Watford Way, Hendon, NW4 3AX COOKING **1**
TEL: (020) 8202 9639 CHINESE/MALAYSIAN/SINGAPOREAN
FAX: (020) 8203 5229 £11–£49

This functionally furnished restaurant offers 150 dishes from Singapore and Chinese Malaysia plus regional Chinese specialities. There are interesting things in the main menu, more in the 'Malaysian and Singaporean corner', but most exciting are the 50 'chef's recommendations'. An inspector enjoyed a starter of Teochew Ngoh Hiang, deep-fried bean curd skin stuffed with five-spiced minced pork. Main dishes have exhibited exact flavours in crispy sole fillets with a fine belachan shrimp paste, and a rustic vein in braised pigs' trotters with ginger and vinegar. Char kway teoh, flat rice noodles with prawns and squid, was 'a good rendition of a classic hawker dish'. 'No wimpish cooking here, but robust, in yer face, home/peasant food.' House wine is £7.80, but Tiger or Tsing Tao beers are a better bet.

CHEF: Kia Lian Tan PROPRIETORS: Annie and Kia Lian Tan OPEN: Wed to Mon 12 to 2.15 (2.45 Sun), 6 to 11.15 (10.45 Sun) CLOSED: 25 to 26 Dec, 2 weeks end July to mid-Aug MEALS: alc (main courses £4 to £17). Set L (Mon, Wed to Fri) £5.50 (2 courses) to £9.80 (min 2), Set D £11.80 to £15.80 SERVICE: 10%, not inc CARDS: Amex, Delta, Diners, MasterCard, Switch, Visa DETAILS: 70 seats. Private parties: 70 main room. Vegetarian meals. Children's helpings. Music. Air-conditioned ⊖ Hendon Central

Granita

map 13

127 Upper Street, N1 1QP
TEL: (020) 7226 3222 FAX: (020) 7226 4833

COOKING **3**
MODERN EUROPEAN
£25–£47

Tables are set close together, lighting is low, and the place is usually busy and noisy. A simple to-the-point menu attracts a wide range of customers, offering in staccato form such winning ideas as a soup of squash, beans and spring greens, and crusty yet tender deep-fried, breadcrumbed squid with bulgur wheat. Main dishes are more Italianate, and chargrilling is a favoured technique (applied on one day's menu to tuna, chump of lamb and Greek bream). The vegetarian option might be 'flavoursome and harmonious' home-made tagliatelle with spinach, mushrooms, tomato, lentils and Parmesan. Desserts take in crème brulée, ice creams (surprisingly, no granita) and a tasty, creamy yoghurt cake with almonds and honey. Service at inspection was less than professional, and the time limit on tables means that diners on occasion can be pushed to finish. A short world-wide list of wines is fairly priced (nearly all below £20), starting at £10.95 for house red and white.

CHEF: Ahmed Kharshoum PROPRIETORS: Vikki Leffman and Ahmed Kharshoum OPEN: Wed to Sun L 12.30 to 2.30 (3 Sun), Tue to Sun D 6.30 to 10.30 (10 Sun) CLOSED: 10 days Christmas, 1 week Easter, 2 weeks Aug MEALS: alc D (main courses £11 to £15). Set L £13.50 (2 courses) to £15.50 SERVICE: not inc, 12.5% for parties of 6 or more CARDS: MasterCard, Switch, Visa DETAILS: 75 seats. Private parties: 75 main room. Vegetarian meals. Children's helpings. No cigars/pipes in dining room. Wheelchair access (not WC). No music. Air-conditioned ⊖ Angel, Highbury & Islington

Great Eastern Dining Room

map 13

54–56 Great Eastern Street, EC2A 3QR
TEL: (020) 7613 4545 FAX: (020) 7613 4137

COOKING **3**
MODERN ITALIAN
£29 – £44

Considering its setting in the heart of trendy Hoxton, the Great Eastern's starkly modern style will come as no surprise. In the bar, a young and fashionable crowd congregate for cocktails and snacks of slices of pizza, grilled chicken and Caesar salad, Italian sausages, and ricotta pancakes with beetroot and pancetta. The small dining area cranks up the elegance several notches with quality white linen and subdued lighting, but the food is similarly straightforward, modern and Italian: 'carpaccio' of wild sea trout with watercress, green pepper berries and lime is antipasto for the twenty-first century, though pasta dishes such as spaghetti vongole strike a more traditional note. Main courses range from herb polenta with roast tomatoes, Tuscan beans, rocket and kalamata tapénade, to lavender honey-roast duck with fennel, blood orange and lambs' lettuce. Desserts typically include rhubarb and mascarpone pannacotta, or biscotti with vin santo. About half the wines on the short, global list weigh in under £20, starting with a pair of Italians at £10; eight house wines are available in two sizes of glass.

CHEF: Steve Pooley PROPRIETOR: Will Ricker OPEN: Mon to Sat L 12.15 to 3, Mon to Fri D 6.30 to 11 CLOSED: 21 Dec to 2 Jan; bank hols L MEALS: alc (main courses £8.50 to £10). Bar menu available Mon to Fri SERVICE: 12.5% (optional), card slips closed CARDS: Amex, Delta, Diners, MasterCard, Switch, Visa DETAILS: 65 seats. Private parties: 12 main room. Vegetarian meals. Wheelchair access (not WC). No music ⊖ Old Street

▲ Great Eastern Hotel, Aurora map 13

Liverpool Street, EC2M 7QN COOKING **5**
TEL: (020) 7618 7000 FAX: (020) 7618 7001 MODERN EUROPEAN
WEB SITE: www.great-eastern-hotel.co.uk £55–£80

The reinvented Great Eastern Hotel now hosts a plethora of eateries, including the Terminus all-day bar/grill (see London Round-ups), Miyabi (a sushi and noodle bar) and the Fishmarket (serving crustaceans, shellfish and seafood platters). The centrepiece, though, is Aurora, whose large dining room – dominated by a stained glass-dome – is done out in Conranesque fashion to reflect former glories of the railway age. The courteous welcome and 'outstanding' service by smartly attired staff simply add to the feeling of opulence.

Ambitious menus bring contemporary influences to bear on a fundamentally classical style of cooking. This can produce some elaborate constructions – tian of confit duck with truffle jelly and purple mustard salad, say, or terrine of ham hock with red onions, smoked eel and home-made piccalilli – although there are simpler yet equally appealing ideas, including a 'dreamy' cream of cabbage soup laced with black truffles.

Main courses tend to keep their feet on the ground, offering côte de boeuf with pommes parisienne, wild mushroom fricassée and red wine sauce, or perhaps a bouillabaisse of rock fish with saffron potatoes and semi-dried tomatoes. Desserts draw praise for a 'finest ever' crisp lemon tart with caraway ice cream; there might also be an 'exotic caprice soufflé' with seasonal fruits and strawberry hibiscus sorbet, or orange tian with wild orange marmalade and vanilla ice cream. Wine service is attentive, but hefty mark-ups rather undermine value; prices start at £14.50 and quickly escalate.

CHEF: Robert Stirrup PROPRIETOR: Conran Holdings/Wyndham International OPEN: Mon to Fri 12 to 2.30, 6.45 to 10.45 CLOSED: 21 Dec to 2 Jan, bank hols MEALS: alc (main courses £19.50 to £23) SERVICE: 12.5%, card slips closed CARDS: Amex, Delta, Diners, MasterCard, Switch, Visa DETAILS: 180 seats. Private parties: 180 main room. Vegetarian meals. No smoking in 1 dining room. Wheelchair access (also WC). No music. Air-conditioned ACCOMMODATION: 267 rooms, all with bath/shower. TV. Phone. Room only £210 to £270. Rooms for disabled. Baby facilities ⊖ Liverpool Street

Prices quoted in the Guide are based on information supplied by restaurateurs. The prices quoted at the top of each entry represent a range, from the lowest meal price to the highest; the latter is inflated by 20 per cent to take account of likely price rises during the year of the Guide.

Greenhouse

map 15

27A Hays Mews, W1X 7RJ
TEL: (020) 7499 3331 FAX: (020) 7499 5368
EMAIL: reservations@greenhouserestaurant.co.uk
WEB SITE: www.greenhouserestaurant.co.uk

COOKING **5**
GLOBAL
£33–£75

As the Guide went to press, Greenhouse was about to close for a summer refit; and since David Collins was due to carry out the job you can bet it will involve more than just a fresh coat of paint. It remains to be seen whether or not there will be any changes to the menu format, but it is to be hoped that the set price lunch survives: considering the central location, this has afforded some relief from the high prices that are common in this part of town.

What is unlikely to change is Paul Merrett's ability to coax bold flavours from his ingredients, even down to the 'real vegetables' that accompany main courses. This is not done simply by throwing exotic spices into the pot, but by deploying fine materials and treating them to intelligent juxtapositions: romesco sauce for pan fried John Dory in a mussel broth, or roast stuffed saddle of rabbit with celeriac foam and broad beans. Ideas occasionally take an unexpected turn – perhaps in a casserole of chicken liver, snails and pork confit with red onion jelly and garlic butter ravioli – but there is plenty of traditional stuff to balance it: smoked haddock fish cakes with egg and parsley sauce, or deep-fried brioche doughnuts with blackberry jam. A wine list was not available as the Guide went to press, but house wines are stated to be £13.50.

CHEF: Paul Merrett PROPRIETOR: The Capital Group OPEN: Sun to Fri L 12 to 3, all week D 6 to 11 CLOSED: 25 and 26 Dec, bank hols MEALS: alc exc Sun (main courses £16.50 to £22). Set L Mon to Fri £17.50 (2 courses) to £21 (Sun L price not available as Guide went to press) SERVICE: 12.5% (optional) CARDS: Amex, Delta, Diners, MasterCard, Switch, Visa DETAILS: 70 seats. Vegetarian meals. No pipes in dining room. Wheelchair access (not WC). No music. Air-conditioned ⊖ Green Park

Green Olive

map 13

5 Warwick Place, W9 2PX
TEL: (020) 7289 2469 FAX: (020) 7289 2463

COOKING **2**
ITALIAN
£24–£48

This grown-up and comparatively sophisticated daughter of the Red Pepper (see entry) shares its outstandingly friendly service, and outdoes the parent in brighter décor and better accoutred tables with white cloths and fine glass. No supplements disturb the serenity of set-price menus, or their consumers, and the format is traditional Italian, with antipasti, primi piatti of pasta, risotto or soup, followed by meat or fish main courses. First-class ingredients are cooked in a light style that occasionally lacks the homespun virtues of generous portions and vigorous flavours. Beef tartare with soft-boiled quails' eggs made a fine start for one visitor, who continued with sciafatielli (a tagliatelle-like pasta with seafood and courgettes), and then roast fillet of monkfish with an excellent pumpkin sauce. On the all-Italian list house wines are £12, others are well-chosen but priced more typically of Venice than Little Venice.

CHEF: Maurizio Morelli PROPRIETOR: Red Pepper Group OPEN: Sun to Fri L 12 to 2.15, all week D 7 to 10.15 (10 Sun and bank hols) CLOSED: Christmas, 1 Jan MEALS: Set L £9.50 (2 courses) to £12.50, Set D £23 (2 courses) to £26.50 SERVICE: 12.5% (optional), card slips closed CARDS: Amex, Delta, MasterCard, Switch, Visa DETAILS: 60 seats. Private parties: 35 main room, 20, 35 private rooms. Vegetarian meals. No cigars/pipes in dining room. Music. Air-conditioned ⊖ Warwick Avenue

Haandi

NEW ENTRY **map 14**

136 Brompton Road, SW3 1HY — COOKING **4**
TEL: (020) 7823 7373 FAX: (020) 7823 9696 — INDIAN
WEB SITE: www.haandi-restaurants.com — £22–£66

When the owners of leading Indian restaurants in Nairobi and Kampala planned a London sibling, it was expected to offer Punjabi-Gujarati food with African ingredients, like cassava and tilapia fish, as similar restaurants in Southall or Tooting have done. Being opposite Harrods, it was also assumed that it would be smart and expensive with smooth service. Not so in either case! Service is pleasant but unsophisticated, and the most attractive feature of the bright, spacious basement is the corner kitchen with its huge glazed window. The food – far from expensive for the location – is described as North Indian frontier style, majoring on tandoori dishes.

Curries are generously served in haandis, wide-bellied, narrow-necked pots. The rather confusing menu starts with cold appetisers including lassi, in a novel and delicate ginger- and cumin-flavoured version. Other high points include machli mahasagar (subtly marinated, tandoori-grilled flaky white fish) and Kashmiri kabarga (tandoori lamb cutlets, crisp outside, succulent inside). Gosht-ki-haandi, described as a spicy curry, is not really hot but lightly tomatoed and spiked with cumin, coconut and chillies. Most enjoyable of all at an inspection meal was dum aloo Kandhari: cylinders of potato with a dried fruit stuffing in a sauce with sun-dried apricots. In an otherwise fully priced short list, house wines are £9.95.

CHEFS: Alam Singh and Ratan Singh PROPRIETOR: Haandi Restaurants Ltd OPEN: all week 12 to 3, 6 to 11 (11.30 Fr and Sat) MEALS: alc (main courses £4 to £13). Set D £15 to £25. Bar menu also available SERVICE: not inc CARDS: Amex, Diners, MasterCard, Switch, Visa DETAILS: 80 seats. Private parties: 80 main room, 12 private room. Music. Air-conditioned ⊖ Knightsbridge (£5)

Hakkasan

NEW ENTRY **map 15**

8 Hanway Place, W1P 9DH — COOKING **3**
TEL: (020) 7927 7000 FAX: (020) 7907 1889 — CHINESE
EMAIL: mail@hakkasan.com — £39–£93

Buried deep in a basement (formerly a car park), in a small alley off a back street joining Oxford Street with Tottenham Court Road, Hakkasan is a restaurant of two halves: lunch and dinner. Its décor is a world away from the minimalism that Alan Yau applied to the Wagamama chain he founded (see entry, London); indeed, the only minimal thing about it is the lighting. Operating as a bar and lounge as well as a restaurant, it has a lengthy cocktail list, waitresses dressed in cheong-sams, and an open-plan kitchen.

Lunchtime dim sum appears to be the success story. Although a bit short on pork and offal, it nevertheless offers near uniform excellence in dishes that combine freshness and delicacy to an impressive degree: recommendations include steamed prawn dumplings, char siu cheung fun, fried mooli bean curd roll, shark's fin and seafood dumpling consommé, and steamed sticky rice with wind-dried pork and salted duck's egg yolk. Sweet items are equally noteworthy: for example, an almond bean curd mousse with caramelised mandarin. Dinner sees a hike in price and a dip in quality. Pu-er tea is a supreme example of its kind, and house wines start at £15.50 (£4 a glass).

CHEF: Tong Chee Hwee PROPRIETOR: Alan Yau OPEN: all week 12 to 3 (4.30 Sat and Sun), 6 to 12 (11 Sun) MEALS: alc (main courses £8.50 to £28) SERVICE: 12.5% (optional), card slips closed CARDS: Amex, Delta, MasterCard, Switch, Visa DETAILS: 180 seats. Private parties: 225 main room. No children after 7pm. No cigars in dining room. Music. Air-conditioned

Holly

map 12

38 Holly Grove, SE15 5DF
TEL/FAX: (020) 7277 2928

COOKING **3**
FRENCH/DUTCH
£25–£38

Norbert van Hest's offbeat restaurant, in a corner site near a railway bridge where downtown trains rumble past and traffic swishes round the one-way system, is 'good news for Peckham', in the view of a south Londoner. Consisting of a couple of interconnected rooms with a tiny courtyard at the back, it opens for dinner only, offering a choice of three dishes at each stage of a three-course menu. The format might embrace monkfish medallions with parsnip and leek purée, followed by duck leg confit with honey and fig compote or, for those who prefer their fish and meat the other way round, pigeon breast with blackberries and mushrooms, and then red bream on spätzli with roasted courgettes and beurre blanc. The third option in each case is always vegetarian. Finish with a bavarois of lemon and elderflower served with clementine sauce. The modest wine list is on much the same scale as the rest of the operation, opening with Vin de Pays de l'Hérault in red and white for £10.50.

CHEF/PROPRIETOR: Norbert van Hest OPEN: Tue to Sat D only 6 to 11 CLOSED: Christmas, August MEALS: alc (main courses £8.75 to £12.75) SERVICE: not inc CARDS: Amex, MasterCard, Switch, Visa DETAILS: 35 seats. 12 seats outside. Private parties: 12 main room. Vegetarian meals. Music

House

map 14

3 Milner St, SW3 2QA
TEL: (020) 7584 3002 FAX: (020) 7581 2848

COOKING **5**
MODERN EUROPEAN
£31–£49

The homely feel is the first striking thing (for London) about this Searcy-Corrigan operation in a quiet residential street in Chelsea 'village': for one visitor the candlepower, dark green antique chairs, starched white linen and '1900 house' ambience recalled his great-grandmother's home. If the setting is the antithesis of modernity, the menu is reassuringly on the ball, offering smoked quail with corn cake and verjuice butter, 'spot-on' cured foie gras with wet walnuts and apple balsamic, and fillet of hake with clams and chorizo. Many of the sensible-sounding dishes have a pleasingly solid feel: beef rump skirt with oxtail sauce, or roast belly of Gloucester Old Spot with scallops and pancetta. The latter's surf and turf combination also appeared successfully in a starter of pork- and pepper-stuffed squid with saffron rice and chorizo cream.

Here is a chef with a sound understanding of how flavours work together, who doesn't add anything to a dish without good reason, and whose strength is 'unflashy food delivered with much skill'. Although desserts are not a highlight, a delicately saffron-flavoured poached pear, served alongside a creamy crème caramel and an almond biscuit, has been commended. Service has varied from attentive to unobservant, and a short, tidy wine selection starts at £13.50 for house Vin de Pays d'Oc, soon hopping over the £20 barrier.

CHEF: Graham Garrett PROPRIETOR: Searcy-Corrigan Restaurants OPEN: Mon to Fri L 12 to 2.30, Mon to Sat D 6 to 11 MEALS: Set L £14.50 (2 courses) to £18, Set D £22 (2 courses) to £27 SERVICE: 12.5% (optional), card slips closed CARDS: Amex, Delta, Diners, MasterCard, Switch, Visa DETAILS: 60 seats. Private parties: 6 to 24 private rooms. Vegetarian meals. Children's helpings. No cigars/pipes in dining room. Occasional music ⊖ Sloane Square

Ibla

map 15

89 Marylebone High Street, W1M 3DE — COOKING **4**
TEL: (020) 7224 3799 FAX: (020) 7486 1370 — ITALIAN
EMAIL: ibla@ibla.co.uk — £30–£62

This shop-front restaurant is simple and rather stylish. It consists of two dining rooms, the front one painted green, the back one a dramatic ox-blood red, with wooden floorboards throughout. The look is casual and informal, the welcome warm. A short Italian menu doesn't follow any particular school: be prepared to find rather unusual combinations, as in a starter of pan-fried scallops and rhubarb in a green tea jelly, or a main course of risotto with gremolata and paprika frogs' legs in port sauce.

Fish figures large, as does feather-light pasta in umpteen sauces, depending on the season. In addition to desserts such as a flavour-packed lavender mousse in a caramel case with white peppercorn sauce, there is a selection of Italian cheeses from an annotated list. France and Italy dominate the wine list, which has a number of interesting bottles and good producers, though mark-ups are high. Nine excellent-quality sherries are offered by the £4 glass. Bottles start at £14 for white, £16 for red.

CHEF: Stefano Frigerio PROPRIETOR: Luciano Pellicano OPEN: Mon to Fri L 12 to 2.30, Mon to Sat D 7 to 10.30 MEALS: Set L £15 (2 courses) to £18, Set D £30 to £35 SERVICE: not inc CARDS: Amex, Delta, Diners, MasterCard, Switch, Visa DETAILS: 45 seats. Private parties: 25 main room, 25 private room. Vegetarian meals. Children's helpings. Wheelchair access (not WC). No music. Air-conditioned ⊖ Baker Street, Bond Street

Report forms are at the back of the book; write a letter if you prefer; or email us at goodfoodguide@which.net

Incognico

map 15

117 Shaftesbury Avenue, WC2H 8AD
TEL: (020) 7836 8866 FAX: (020) 7240 9525

COOKING 5
FRENCH
£24–£72

The offspring of cheznico (see entry) is smart, discreet, conservative, even 'austere', with nothing much to distract attention from its cream walls and abundant dark wood. Its food tends to be in the same rich and reassuringly soothing vein as the Park Lane parent (indeed, some items such as terrines, bread, and ice creams come directly from there). It has the great merit of simplicity, evident in an open ravioli of goats' cheese with basil oil and roast peppers and tomatoes, and in lightly pan-fried John Dory fillets in a thyme-scented olive oil dressing.

The kitchen doesn't stint on good ingredients, which may go some way towards explaining the prices, and the mostly classic dishes are generally well rehearsed and delivered: tender, high-quality veal with rosemary jus, exactly grilled Dover sole with tartare sauce, or well-timed salmon with plum sauce and spinach. One thing that Nico Ladenis's chefs can do well is risotto, and the 'exemplary' Parmesan version here is of 'perfect creaminess' with a long finish. Vegetables and garnishes are charged extra, which seems an odd arrangement since some dishes seem to need them, some don't.

Output can be variable, not least among desserts, although chocolate mousse, and apple tart with thin flaky pastry have been recommended. But the biggest and most consistent niggles concern service: generally French and plentiful, but hardly hospitable or co-ordinated, and sometimes involving long waits. The set-price lunch (two choices per course; also available pre-theatre) is considered extremely good value, and 14 wines on the concise global list, arranged in price order, are served by the glass. House red starts at £13, white at £12.50.

CHEFS: Richard Hugill and Tim Johnson PROPRIETORS: Nico and Dinah-Jane Ladenis OPEN: Mon to Sat 12 to 3, 5.30 to 12 CLOSED: 10 days Christmas, 4 days Easter, bank hols MEALS: alc (main courses £10.50 to £17). Set L and D 5.30 to 7 £12.50 SERVICE: 12.5% (optional), card slips closed CARDS: Amex, Delta, Diners, MasterCard, Switch, Visa DETAILS: 85 seats. Private parties: 10 main room. No pipes in dining room. Wheelchair access (not WC). Music. Air-conditioned ⊖ Leicester Square, Tottenham Court Road

▲ Inter-Continental, Le Soufflé 🍷

map 14

1 Hamilton Place, W1J 7QY
TEL: (020) 7318 8577 FAX: (020) 7491 0926
EMAIL: london@interconti.com
WEB SITE: www.interconti.com

COOKING 4
MODERN EUROPEAN
£43–£95

The plush, heavily patterned turquoise-and-gold carpet, plain white ceiling, white piano and promised 'dinner and dance' on Friday and Saturday nights, may make this a blast from an unknown past for younger diners. This is hotel dining à l'ancienne, (complete with excellent, mainly French service), although it was scheduled to get a face-lift as the Guide went to press.

Although Peter Kromberg has been at Le Soufflé for 25 years, the menu hasn't been preserved in aspic. One innovation is a three-course organic menu at dinner, along with a selection of organic and biodynamic wines. Small symbols on the main menu denote 'healthy heart' and vegetarian items. A starter of skilfully cooked red mullet and crab has turned up in a watercress sauce, while a main course of lasagne of lobster has come with roast pepper sauce with basil oil. Among desserts, soufflés live up to expectation, for example a chocolate and Grand Marnier version with chocolate sauce. A high falutin' French-dominated wine list (starting at £19.50 and disappearing into the stratosphere) acknowledges rather than embraces the New World, offering every opportunity for indulgence (fancy a 1918 Ch Latour?). A Sommelier's Selection helps to focus attention, and there is a page of wines by the glass.

CHEF: Peter Kromberg PROPRIETOR: Bass Hotels & Resorts OPEN: Tue to Fri and Sun L 12.30 to 3, Tue to Sat D 7 to 10.30 (11.15 Sat) CLOSED: 2 weeks after Christmas, bank hols; open for D only in Aug MEALS: alc D (main courses £15 to £28.50). Set L £21.50 (2 courses) to £33.50, Set L Sun £32, Set D £40 to £47 SERVICE: not inc CARDS: Amex, Delta, Diners, MasterCard, Switch, Visa DETAILS: 80 seats. Vegetarian meals. Children's helpings. Music. Air-conditioned ACCOMMODATION: 458 rooms, all with bath/shower. TV. Phone. Room only £305 to £440 (prices exc VAT). Rooms for disabled ⊖ Hyde Park Corner (£5)

Isola 🍷 — map 14

145 Knightsbridge, SW1X 7PA — COOKING **4**

TEL: (020) 7838 1044 FAX: (020) 7838 1099 — ITALIAN

£41–£77

The dramatic volume and 'chic utilitarian' style, reminiscent of 1950s airport architecture, combine to give Isola an imposing presence. As the Guide went to press Oliver Peyton changed the layout, creating a single restaurant on the ground floor and a cocktail and wine bar on the first. The style of Bruno Loubet's cooking is unchanged, with the restaurant continuing to mix straight Italian dishes (buffalo mozzarella with roast peppers and pesto) with more contemporary European ideas such as terrine of foie gras with salmon and aubergine confit. Cooking was rather hit and miss at inspection, but successes have included decent pasta, roast suckling pig with a top-notch gravy, and a generous piece of roast venison served with a rich macaroni gratin and sweet-sour crunchy beetroot. Outstanding among desserts is a pleasingly French rendition of a light but intense dark chocolate tartlet with a coffee ice cream.

Two pages of by-the-glass Italians from all corners of the country are a microcosm of the full wine list, which stretches from the heat-infused styles of Calabria to more reserved wines from the cooler hills of Veneto, with an extended stay in Tuscany (check out the Super-Tuscans), all starting at £19.50. For the explorer there are 'tasters' of five 750-centilitre glasses in a themed grouping from £13.50. House Italians start at £18.

CHEF: Bruno Loubet PROPRIETOR: Oliver Peyton OPEN: all week 12 to 3 (3.30 Sat and Sun), 6 to 11 (9.30 Sun) CLOSED: 1 Jan MEALS: alc (main courses £11.50 to £25) SERVICE: 12.5% (optional), card slips closed CARDS: Amex, Delta, Diners, MasterCard, Switch, Visa DETAILS: 140 seats. Private parties: 110 main room. Wheelchair access (also WC). Music. Air-conditioned ⊖ Knightsbridge (£5)

🍾 denotes an outstanding wine cellar; 🍷 denotes a good wine list, worth travelling for.

Istanbul Iskembecisi £

map 12

9 Stoke Newington Road, N16 8BH
TEL: (020) 7254 7291
WEB SITE: www.londraturk.com/istanbuliskembecisi

COOKING **2**
TURKISH
£16–£29

This cheerful café with upholstered chairs and white table-cloths is open from midday to dawn every day of the year. Its welcome extends to 'kids and babies of all ages', and, although lacking wheelchair access, it does have Braille menus. Mezes include the usual Middle Eastern dishes plus yogurtlu kizartma (fried ratatouille with yoghurt and garlic); Arnavut cigeri, Albanian-style liver, can be a starter or main course. The 'eponym dish', iskembe, is a broth of finely chopped tripe (bland – until you add salt, pepper, vinegar and lemon juice to taste); dil paça is a variant using lamb's tongue. Main dishes (for those with room) are kebabs and grills of chicken or lamb, plus some stews. Then, perhaps, try one of the exciting desserts or pastries. The short wine list, including five from Turkey, and French house selections, starts at £7.95.

CHEFS/PROPRIETORS: Ahmet Poyraz and Ali Demir OPEN: all week noon to 5am MEALS: alc (main courses £6 to £10) SERVICE: not inc, 10% for parties of 10 or more CARDS: none DETAILS: 80 seats. Private parties: 90 main room. Vegetarian meals. Children's helpings. Music. Air-conditioned ⊖ Highbury & Islington (£5)

Itsu

map 14

118 Draycott Avenue, SW3 3AE
TEL: (020) 7590 2400/7590 2401
FAX: (020) 7590 2403
WEB SITE: www.itsu.co.uk

COOKING **3**
JAPANESE
£21–£40

Not quite as authentically Japanese as Gilbert and Sullivan's *Mikado*, this, and its new sister in Soho (see below), offer much innocent pleasure for lovers of Asian food. The furthest departure from classic sushi are hot dishes, such as stuffed prawns grilled on skewers and served in an appetising red broth, its sweetness balanced by the sharpness of lemon grass. Other hot things include chicken in coconut sauce, and chicken teriyaki. Conventional cold snacks take in sushi, fingers and rolls, beef carpaccio, and sashimi. Salmon (smoked or fresh organic) dominates the menu, with seared, tartare and sashimi (either new-style or plain) among the choices. Desserts might include a softly set crème brûlée. To drink, there is saké, hot or cold, interesting fruit drinks, and a very few wines from £11.50.

CHEF: Clive Fretwell PROPRIETORS: Clive Schlee and Julian Metcalfe OPEN: all week noon to 11 CLOSED: 24 Dec to 2 Jan MEALS: alc (main courses £2.50 to £3.75) SERVICE: not inc CARDS: Amex, MasterCard, Switch, Visa DETAILS: 70 seats. Private parties: 50 main room. No smoking in dining room. Wheelchair access (not WC). Music. Air-conditioned ⊖ South Kensington

indicates that there has been a change of chef since last year's Guide, and the Editor has judged that the change is of sufficient interest to merit the reader's attention.

Itsu (Soho) £

NEW ENTRY map 15

103 Wardour Street, W1V 3TD
TEL: (020) 7479 4794 FAX: (020) 7479 4795
WEB SITE: www.itsu.co.uk

COOKING 2
JAPANESE
£18–£36

White mosaic walls, stainless steel, wood and Perspex: this is a twenty-first century successor to the restaurant concept. It is more relaxing than many conveyor-belt places, with comfortable low chairs replacing stools by the counter, and benches for foursomes. Modern chopsticks, joined at the top, make miniature tongs. Prices are lower than at the Kensington sister branch (see entry above) for the same snacks, based partly on sushi, partly on warm, fusion-Japanese tapas. Recommended choices include a 'fresh, clean-tasting' crayfish and coriander roll, 'well engineered' beef carpaccio with an added kick of wasabi in the citrus dip, and new-style salmon sashimi with subtly combined seasonings of sesame, chives and ginger. Beer, cold or hot saké, green tea and a few wines from £10.50 are offered on 'help-yourself' basis.

CHEF: Angela Baird PROPRIETORS: Clive Schlee and Julian Metcalfe OPEN: all week 12.30 to 11 (midnight Fri and Sat) CLOSED: 24 Dec to 2 Jan MEALS: alc (sushi £1.50 to £3.45). Set L 4 to 7.30 £9.95 SERVICE: not inc CARDS: Amex, MasterCard, Switch, Visa DETAILS: 70 seats. Private parties: 70 main room. Vegetarian meals. No smoking in dining room. Wheelchair access (also WC). Music. Air-conditioned ⊖ Piccadilly Circus

Ivy

map 15

1–5 West Street, WC2H 9NQ
TEL: (020) 7836 4751 FAX: (020) 7240 9333
EMAIL: reservations@the-ivy.co.uk

COOKING 5
MODERN BRITISH
£28–£89

Converging streets squeeze the Ivy into an odd shape, and wood panelling and stained glass windows give it a churchy feel, an impression soon dispelled by the noise (so you have to shout, so it gets noisier). The problem is getting a table: easy for stars of stage and screen, but lesser mortals must book in April for lunch in August (the experience of our inspector). There are some very British items – potted shrimps, fish and chips, Eton Mess – while international dishes run to hamburger, corned beef hash, bang bang chicken and baked Alaska. If this sounds school-dinnerish, there is grown-up stuff too, including seasonal Wye elvers, steamed razor clams, and asparagus with poached duck egg. And, even if the printed menu tends to lag behind the seasons, there's something for most customers, from lobster and chips to curried chicken masala.

Fish is well rendered – witness a substantial chargrilled halibut steak, and moist and tasty cod with parsley sauce – and a fine sauté foie gras sits on caramelised apples in a sticky-sweet, raisin-strewn sauce, but flavours can sometimes be fugitive. Desserts (such as rhubarb and apple pie with crisp, sugary pastry and a tart cinnamon flavoured filling) come with a mega-dollop of clotted cream. Friendly, attentive staff ensure time limits are adhered to, and wines, from £11.25, span a fair range of styles and prices.

CHEFS: Alan Bird and Tim Hughes PROPRIETOR: Belgo Group Plc OPEN: all week 12 to 3 (3.30 Sun), 5.30 to 12 CLOSED: 25 and 26 Dec, 1 Jan, Aug bank hol MEALS: alc (main courses £10 to £36.50). Set L Sat and Sun £16.50. Cover £1.50 SERVICE: not inc CARDS: Amex, Delta, Diners,

MasterCard, Switch, Visa DETAILS: 100 seats. Private parties: 6 main room, 60 private room. Vegetarian meals. Wheelchair access (not WC). No music. Air-conditioned ⊖ Leicester Square

Iznik

map 13

19 Highbury Park, N5 1QJ
TEL: (020) 7704 8099 FAX: (020) 7354 5697

COOKING **2**
TURKISH
£20–£30

'Warm, attentive service makes it feel as if you are being welcomed into the owner's home.' And a very beautiful wooden-floored home it is, crammed with antiquities such as carved wooden doors and arches, and hanging lamps. At night it is lit by romantic candles in blue glass holders, and suitably haunting Turkish music wails gently in the background. The unchanging menu offers a range of meze, including spinach with yoghurt, garlic and butter; mildly spiced meatballs; and filo pastry böreks filled with feta cheese or minced lamb and herbs. Main dishes include grills such as shish kebab of marinated lamb, or chicken breasts marinated in milk and cream. Other dishes range from moussaka, via baked lamb knuckle, to kofta meatballs with green peppers, potatoes and tomato sauce. Half a dozen vegetarian dishes are variously based on chickpeas, or courgette and feta cheese, or fresh spinach (though meat eaters may get the better deal portion-wise). Desserts are sweet Ottoman pastries or seasonal fruit-based specialities. The short, low-priced wine list starts with Turkish house wines at £8.95.

CHEFS: Adem Oner and B. Pehlivan PROPRIETORS: Adem and Pirlanta Oner OPEN: all week 10 to 4, 6 to 11 CLOSED: 25 Dec MEALS: alc (main courses L £5.50 to £7, D £7 to £9.50) SERVICE: L not inc, D 10% CARDS: Delta, MasterCard, Switch, Visa DETAILS: 78 seats. Private parties: 78 main room. Vegetarian meals. Wheelchair access (not WC). Music ⊖ Highbury and Islington

John Burton-Race at the Landmark 🍷

map 13

222 Marylebone Road, NW1 6JQ
TEL: (020) 7723 7800 FAX: (020) 7723 4700
EMAIL: jbrthelandmark@btconnect.com
WEB SITE: www.landmarklondon.co.uk

COOKING **7**
FRENCH
£47–£123

The hotel was built in the heyday of the railways, in an opulent style to celebrate the age of travel, and the sheer drama and scale of the glassed-in open courtyard contrasts with the big, square, joyless dining room, whose cornices, chandeliers, and carved elephants holding an enormous potted plant cannot escape their institutional feel. John Burton-Race's food, presented in a variety of set-price options (the one at £70 offers greatest choice), takes luxury materials in its stride, from a ballottine of foie gras with spiced cherry jelly, via ravioli of langoustine tails and truffle-scented potato, to a circle of thinly sliced marinated raw scallops with a warm sauce vierge and black olive dressing.

The kitchen has produced some stunning dishes, among which seafood stands out particularly. A creamy, velvety, sweet and delicate crab soup is ladled from an enormous silver tureen over an expertly made cannelloni of springy crab mousse spiked with coriander and ginger; and for simple excellence it is hard to beat a whole baby sea bass roasted in a salt crust, the moist fish undressed and filleted at table. Poultry is also well handled – for example, a roast guinea fowl with a 'smooth as satin' onion cream – although the cooking seems to have lost some of its precision and polish, and lacks the energy and excitement of which John Burton-Race is so obviously capable.

Like everything else, desserts yield variable results, although an assiette framboise has impressed for its well-made soufflé, light and flaky mille-feuille, exceptional sorbet, and chocolate-wrapped mousse, and French cheeses are kept in prime condition. Service at its best is personable, professional and friendly. Wine service is equally on the ball, and mark-ups encourage the sampling of more exclusive bottles, which, as is expected in such a setting, are plentiful. Check the seasonal selection for a variety of characterful drinking under £50 and for by-the-glass offerings. House red and white come in at £18.

CHEFS: John Burton-Race and Martin Burge PROPRIETOR: John Burton-Race OPEN: Mon to Fri L 12 to 2.15, Mon to Sat D 7 to 10.15 MEALS: Set L £23 (2 courses) to £160 (2 people), Set D £48 to £160 (2 people) SERVICE: not inc CARDS: Amex, Delta, Diners, MasterCard, Switch, Visa DETAILS: 85 seats. Private parties: 150 main room, 28 to 200 private rooms. Vegetarian meals. Children's helpings. No cigars in dining room. Wheelchair access (not WC). No music. Air-conditioned ⊖ Marylebone

J. Sheekey

map 15

28–32 St Martin's Court, WC2N 4AL
TEL: (020) 7240 2565 FAX: (020) 7240 8114

COOKING **5**
BRITISH SEAFOOD
£26–£93

In an alley just off Charing Cross Road, the restaurant looks as if it has been there for a century; in fact, it was founded in 1890. With frosted-glass windows and framed photographs of famous stage stars, this series of small, dark-panelled rooms has a theatrical air. It's a no-nonsense place with unfussy wooden chairs and small tables with simple table settings. Rigorously sourced and well-prepared fish is the big story here, although the menu promises that meat dishes (unspecified) are available. This is one of the few places to find River Wye elvers on the specials list (in season), and jellied eels on the permanent menu.

First-course tiger prawns with tomato and coriander sauce are well timed, and chargrilled razor clams come with young broad beans and chorizo. Fish pie is stuffed with salmon and a mustardy, creamy sauce under mashed potato, and plainly grilled Dover sole with béarnaise is perfectly handled. Retro comfort food sums up desserts such as creamed rice pudding, and spotted dick. The weekend set-lunch menu is good value, but with vegetables an extra charge on the carte, the final bill can be surprisingly high. Service is smiling and self-assured, and the eclectic wine list is somewhat pricy, although a number of bottles are also sold by the 50-centilitre pot. House red, from France, is £13.50, white, from Italy, £11.25.

CHEFS: Tim Hughes and Elliot Ketley PROPRIETOR: Belgo Group plc OPEN: all week 12 to 3 (3.30 Sun), 5.30 to 12 CLOSED: bank hols MEALS: alc (main courses £10 to £29.50). Set L Sat and Sun £10.75 (2 courses) to £14.50. Cover £1.50 SERVICE: not inc CARDS: Amex, Delta, Diners, MasterCard, Switch, Visa DETAILS: 105 seats. Vegetarian meals. Children's helpings. No cigars/pipes in dining room. Wheelchair access (not WC). No music. Air-conditioned ⊖ Leicester Square

K10 £ map 13

20 Copthall Avenue, EC2R 7DN
TEL: (020) 7562 8510 FAX: (020) 7562 8515 COOKING **2**
EMAIL: copthall@k10.net JAPANESE
WEB SITE: www.k10.net £18–£31

The focal point of K10 is a conveyor belt carrying colour-coded plates; this Japanese self-service system, kaiten, is what gives the place its punning name. Seating is mainly stools at the counter, but there are also a few tables set at right angles, making it easier for groups of four to converse. The bare white décor, enlivened by coloured lighting, has a modern square mile ambience. On the plates, colour coded to denote prices, come classical nigiri, rolled maki sushi, sashimi and modern Japanese notions such as smoked salmon nigiri, inside-out salmon and avocado rolls, or seared tuna with sesame seeds. More substantial are traditional prawn tempura or teriyaki chicken, or fusion-style crispy duck salad with sesame and honey sauce, and the remarkable green tea noodles with asparagus. Notable afterthoughts include fruit-filled spring rolls. Drink unlimited mineral water for £1, tea, wine from £12.50, beer or saké.

CHEFS: Mr Nacer and Miguel Choy PROPRIETOR: K10 Ltd OPEN: Mon to Fri 11.30 to 3, 5 to 10 CLOSED: Christmas and New Year, bank hols MEALS: alc (main courses £1 to £3.50) SERVICE: not inc, card slips closed CARDS: Amex, Delta, Diners, MasterCard, Switch, Visa DETAILS: 65 seats. Private parties: 100 main room. Vegetarian meals. No smoking in dining room. Wheelchair access (also WC). Music. Air-conditioned ⊖ Moorgate, Liverpool Street

Kastoori £ map 12

188 Upper Tooting Road, SW17 7EJ COOKING **2**
TEL: (020) 8767 7027 GUJARATI
£20–£36

The brightness of Kastoori's white, blue and yellow décor is reflected in its clear and distinct spicing. The all-vegetarian menu lists about 60 options, not all available every day. They are predominantly Gujarati and Ugandan Indian, plus a few South Indian dishes, such as dosa pancakes and sambar (lentil and vegetable soup-sauce). Particular successes have included a sev puri starter, an onion bhajia 'a touch above cliché', and home-made chutneys (especially the pungently spicy coriander, garlic and green chilli version) accompanying poppadoms. Potato curry (in tomato and onion sauce), mutter paneer (cottage cheese and peas), and mung bean curry have been good, while a chana curry (chickpeas and potato in a dark spicy sauce) has excelled. Breads take in non-greasy parathas and very fresh chapatis. Home-made shrikand – a dessert of curd cheese flavoured with nutmeg, cardamom, saffron and sugar, topped with pistachios – is well balanced and very smooth. A well-chosen, modestly priced wine list starts with French house wines at £7.75.

CHEF: Manoj Thanki PROPRIETOR: Dinesh Thanki OPEN: Wed to Sun L 12.30 to 2.30, all week D 6 to 10.30 CLOSED: 25 and 26 Dec, 1 week mid-Jan MEALS: alc (main courses £4 to £6) SERVICE: not inc, card slips closed CARDS: MasterCard, Visa DETAILS: 82 seats. Private parties: 20 main room. Vegetarian meals. Children's helpings. Wheelchair access (not WC). Music. Air-conditioned ⊖ Tooting Broadway

Kensington Place 🍷 map 13

201 Kensington Church Street, W8 7LX
TEL: (020) 7727 3184 FAX: (020) 7229 2025
EMAIL: kpr@place-restaurants.com

COOKING **6**
MODERN BRITISH
£29–£72

In 2002 Rowley Leigh will clock up 15 years at what was, in its day, a pioneering restaurant. But instead of slipping slowly into oblivion, as many old restaurants do, this one still breathes vitality, still has something worth saying. Perhaps the best testament to this is the noise that hits you as you enter, amplified by floor-to-ceiling windows on to the street, and hard surfaces everywhere else. But if conversation is difficult, the menu is reassuring. In a world where so many restaurants try to mix exotic ingredients and follow the latest fads, it is comforting to find one with an enduringly common-sense approach.

One of the great things about the cooking is its unabashed simplicity: how many other restaurants would have the nerve to offer a herb omelette, or morels on a thick slice of brioche toast? And how much more straightforward could the food be than smoked haddock topped with a poached egg and cheese sauce? Yet ingredients are first-class and execution hard to fault, not least when it comes to seafood: the now-classic combination of fresh, carefully timed scallops surrounding a velvety pea purée, with a well-judged mint vinaigrette; and full-flavoured grilled tuna, smeared with a rich tomato ragoût and served with courgettes and lightly cooked spinach.

Although the menu lists many old favourites, it also comes up with seasonal items, from gulls' eggs to game birds. Among desserts, baked apricots filled with a moist almond frangipane-style sponge have won approval. New and exciting styles sit alongside more tried and tested ones on the wine list, making for great diversity and interest. A choice from around the world is to be had under £20, including Spanish and French house wines starting at £13.50, though most bottles are above £25.

CHEF: Rowley Leigh PROPRIETOR: Moving Image Restaurants OPEN: all week 12 to 3 (3.30 Sat and Sun), 6.30 to 11.45 (10.15 Sun) CLOSED: 3 days Christmas MEALS: alc (main courses £12.50 to £18.50). Set L Mon to Sat £16, Set L Sun £18.50 SERVICE: 12.5% (optional), card slips closed CARDS: Amex, Diners, MasterCard, Switch, Visa DETAILS: 145 seats. Private parties: 120 main room, 45 private room. Vegetarian meals. Children's helpings. Wheelchair access (also WC). No music. Air-conditioned ⊖ Notting Hill Gate

Kiku map 15

17 Half Moon Street, W1J 7BE
TEL: (020) 7499 4208 FAX: (020) 7409 3259

COOKING **3**
JAPANESE
£30–£77

Just inside the entrance, steps lead to a spacious traditional sushi bar seating 15 at the counter and 20 at tables. There is an elegant austerity about the interior, with its slate floor, wooden-panelled walls and plain tables and chairs. Set dinners of eight to eleven courses might include tempura, grilled fish, or sunomono (fish in a delicate vinegar dressing). 'Casserole' hardly does justice to the delicacy of nimono: fish, chicken or pork with vegetables in broth. Main courses can be sukiyaki; its poached version, shabu-shabu; or the unusual ishiyaki, beef or seafood grilled on a hot stone. The seasonal à la carte includes such enticing starters as grilled aubergine with soy sauce, or salmon roe on grated mooli. Set lunches, with grilled fish or tempura as the main dish, are reasonably priced. Service is friendly, children are welcome, and Mrs Taoka helpfully advises newcomers, as well as efficiently overseeing the service. Well-chosen, fairly priced Corney & Barrow wines from £11.50 provide serious competition to fine saké.

CHEFS: Y. Hattori, H. Yamauchi and Y. Hikichi PROPRIETORS: Hisashi and Mariko Taoka OPEN: Mon to Sat 12 to 2.30, 6 to 10.15 MEALS: alc (main courses £10 to £50). Set L £10 to £21, Set D £34 to £51 SERVICE: 12.5%, card slips closed CARDS: Amex, Delta, Diners, MasterCard, Switch, Visa DETAILS: 96 seats. Private parties: 50 main room, 10 private room. Wheelchair access (also WC). Music. Air-conditioned ⊖ Green Park (£5)

Kulu Kulu Sushi £ — map 15

76 Brewer Street, W1F 9TX — COOKING 2
TEL: (020) 7734 7316 FAX: (020) 7734 6507 — JAPANESE
£19–£28

Décor is virtually non-existent in this small, basic kaiten with sushi and a few other items passing on a conveyor belt. Prices are appropriately modest, with a good choice of £1.20 plates, and others at £1.80, £2.40 and £3. Only two achieve top price: prawn tempura hand roll, and sea urchin, that great Mediterranean, as well as Japanese, delicacy. Those occupying stools here (for no longer than 45 minutes) are evenly divided between locals and Japanese; the latter are happy to find crab sticks in the California rolls. Salmon sashimi is £1.80, mixed sashimi is £10. Tempura, aubergine in soya bean paste, and deep-fried bean curd are much like formal restaurant small dishes. Drink beer, saké, free tea, or house wine at £12 (N.B. 'pram wine' is not for infants: it is Japanese plum wine, a fine sweetie for adults).

CHEF/PROPRIETOR: Mr Toyama OPEN: Mon to Sat 12 to 2.15, 5 to 10 CLOSED: Christmas, bank hols MEALS: alc (sushi £1.20 to £3) SERVICE: not inc CARDS: Delta, MasterCard, Switch, Visa DETAILS: 30 seats. No smoking in dining room. Music. Air-conditioned ⊖ Piccadilly Circus

Langan's Brasserie — map 15

Stratton Street, W1J 8LB — COOKING 1
TEL: (020) 7491 8822 FAX: (020) 7493 8309 — ANGLO-FRENCH
WEB SITE: www.langansrestaurants.co.uk — £35–£60

With its old-fashioned décor, studiously formal waiting staff and long menu of Anglo-French dishes, this is a venue from another era, and proud of it. It's still a fave rave for admiring habitués, and the place does get very busy. The menu includes the likes of Parma ham with melon, or seafood salad for starters, while main courses might take in steak haché with a fried egg and onion rings, or roast fillet of sea bass on a warm potato salad with chive sauce. Desserts are pure, unadulterated comfort food: chocolate mousse cake, treacle tart with custard, and rice pudding among them. Service is swift and attentive, and everything proceeds at a lively pace. The wine list isn't as extensive as the menu, but there's no denying its value for money. Diners can drink quite well for under £20.

CHEF: Ken Whitehead PROPRIETOR: Richard Shepherd OPEN: Mon to Fri 12.15 to 11.45, Sat 7 to 12 CLOSED: bank hols MEALS: alc (main courses £11 to £15). Cover £1.50 SERVICE: 12.5% (optional) CARDS: Amex, Delta, Diners, MasterCard, Switch, Visa DETAILS: 220 seats. Vegetarian meals. Music. Air-conditioned ⊖ Green Park

Lansdowne

map 13

90 Gloucester Avenue, NW1 8HX
TEL: (020) 7483 0409

COOKING **2**
MODERN BRITISH
£24–£50

The restaurant upstairs at The Lansdowne is a peaceful contrast to the busy, noisy pub below. Decorated in terracotta and charcoal, it feels as though it could be in Madrid or Rome. The menu, too, has an Iberian feel to it, although the cooking can be rather uneven. There are starters such as mellow, succulent quail escabèche with watercress and almond dressing, or esquiaxada (Basque salt cod) with tomatoes, peppers and olives. For main courses, grilled paprika sausages may come with escalivada, or roast duck with figs and bacon. Desserts are fairly simple, like cherry and almond tart with crème fraîche, or chocolate mousse. Service is pleasant, but the short wine list (omitting the names of most producers) is uninspired. There are a few halves and wines by the glass, and bottle prices start at £11.50.

CHEFS: Amanda Pritchett and James Knight PROPRIETOR: Amanda Pritchett OPEN: Sun L 1 to 3, Tue to Sat D 7 to 10.30 MEALS: alc (main courses £8.50 to £14.50). Set L Sun £15, Set D £19.50 SERVICE: 12.5%, card slips closed CARDS: MasterCard, Switch, Visa DETAILS: 70 seats. Private parties: 70 main room. Vegetarian meals. Music ⊖ Chalk Farm

Launceston Place 🍷

map 14

1A Launceston Place, W8 5RL
TEL: (020) 7937 6912 FAX: (020) 7938 2412

COOKING **3**
MODERN BRITISH
£31–£65

Little changes at Launceston Place. The setting and ambience remain delightfully old-fashioned; 'inside the country-house-style dining room, you could imagine you were in an upmarket restaurant beside the cathedral close of an English country town.' The décor is a tasteful miscellany of still-life prints, paintings and mirrors on panelled walls, while service by appropriately turned-out staff is brisk, efficient and professional, though nobody would complain if they lightened up a bit. The menu meanwhile takes a modern British line, with forays into some exotic flavours, making imaginative use of fresh ingredients.

Among some nine choices at each level, a fine starter of seared scallops is complemented by its hot and spicy lentil purée, while roast turbot with curried mussel cream, or veal cutlet with bean purée and morels, might vie for mains selection. Finish with more familiar desserts: perhaps two brûlées (apple and vanilla), or steamed blueberry sponge and custard. The wine list, helpfully arranged by style, shows few bottles under £20 (a Bourgogne Aligoté at £15 and an Argentinian Cabernet at £14.50 among them), though it has eight by the glass and house French from £14.

CHEF: Phillip Reed PROPRIETOR: Christopher Bodker OPEN: Sun to Fri L 12.30 to 2.30 (3 Sun), Mon to Sat D 7 to 11.30 CLOSED: Christmas, Easter, bank hols MEALS: alc (main courses £15 to £17.50). Set L Mon to Fri £15.50 (2 courses) to £18.50, Set L Sun £22.50, Set D 7 to 8 £15.50 (2 courses) to £18.50 SERVICE: not inc CARDS: Amex, Delta, Diners, MasterCard, Switch, Visa DETAILS: 80 seats. Private parties: 85 main room, 14 and 30 private rooms. Vegetarian meals. No pipes in dining room. No music. Air-conditioned ⊖ Gloucester Road

Lindsay House 🍷 map 15

21 Romilly Street, W1V 5TG COOKING **7**
TEL: (020) 7439 0450 FAX: (020) 7437 7349 MODERN BRITISH
£40–£100

Richard Corrigan's down to earth style is evident immediately, from the plank floor and square-topped tables to the 'cheap and cheerful' tableware of this ground floor dining room. His food is in the same vein. It is 'a very offally sort of place', delighting in sautéed veal kidneys with North African spices and couscous, and a piece of yielding, seared veal tongue, accompanied by spinach, wild mushrooms and deep-fried foie gras gnocchi.

The cooking is bold and full of character, taking a commendably individual note, and arousing the senses. Sinuous strands of sweet, smoky, fragrant eel, for example, are coiled into a serpent and interspersed with dandelion and beet leaves, the whole scattered with quartered discs of chorizo, and set about with dollops of mellow green olive tapenade; a dish whose marriage of flavours took in sweet, smoky, fatty, bitter, salt and fruity.

Often gutsy, sometimes challenging, this food is not cautious or safe, and never boring. A saddle of rabbit, for example, comes with sweetbreads, black pudding and crusty, creamy polenta, surrounded by dollops of a thick emulsion tasting of sage and rosemary. The price of excitement is an occasional wobble in standards, overlaid with a rather cavalier approach to seasoning, and yet when everything works dishes can be first class, as in a starter of sprue asparagus with morels, girolles, and three fat, firm, juicy, deeply flavoured langoustines, all in an intense shellfish veloute.

Desserts may be quieter, but can still produce a frison, as in a buttery shortbread base with a compote of lightly cooked, tart rhubarb and thin slices of mango, given a spicy lift from grated cloves. Service is typically friendly, and a knowledgeable maitre d' helps things along. Wines from South West France and Corsica match the boldness of the cuisine, but, surprisingly for this category, rarely come in under £20. The same is true of the remaining global wines, which include novel as well as classic examples. A 'Fine Wine Reserve' offers legendary French and Italian bottles in some great vintages, with predictably three-figure prices.

CHEF: Richard Corrigan PROPRIETOR: Corrigan Restaurants Ltd OPEN: Mon to Fri L 12.15 to 2.15, Mon to Sat D 6 to 11 CLOSED: 25 Dec to 2 Jan, Easter, 2 weeks Aug, bank hols MEALS: alc (main courses £15 to £24). Set L £23, Set D £44 to £65 SERVICE: 12.5% (optional), card slips closed CARDS: Amex, Delta, Diners, MasterCard, Switch, Visa DETAILS: 50 seats. Private parties: 8 to 36 private rooms. Vegetarian meals. No cigars/pipes in dining room. No music. Air-conditioned ⊖ Leicester Square, Picadilly Circus

Little Georgia £

map 12

2 Broadway Market, E8 4QJ
TEL: (020) 7249 9070

COOKING **1**
GEORGIAN/RUSSIAN
£21–£37

On a corner site in southern Hackney, right by the Grand Union Canal, this former pub is a friendly, informal venue decorated with traditional Georgian artefacts and pictures reflecting life in the former Soviet state. Its very existence represents a refreshing triumph of substance over style at a time when the opposite is usually the case. For this is not cooking that seeks out trendy exotic ingredients, nor does it attempt to dazzle with artistic presentation. Georgian cuisine, according to the owners, is 'robust and very tasty comfort food – a heady mix of flavours from herbs and spices', and reporters tend to agree. The platter of Georgian 'meze' is a good introduction to the cuisine – the cheese-filled bread is a highlight – while main courses take in rich, spicy lamb stew with aubergines and potato, and whole poussin with tangy walnut sauce. The mainly French wine list also includes a few Georgian wines that go well with the food. Prices start at £10.

CHEF: Elena Gambashidze PROPRIETOR: Antony Jones OPEN: Sun L 1 to 3, Tue to Sat D 6.30 to 10 (10.30 Fri and Sat) MEALS: alc (main courses £7 to £12) SERVICE: not inc CARDS: Delta, MasterCard, Switch, Visa DETAILS: 45 seats. 12 seats outside. Private parties: 50 main room. Vegetarian meals. Children's helpings. Wheelchair access (not WC). Music. Air-conditioned ⊖ Bethnal Green

Livebait

map 13

43 The Cut, SE1 8LF
TEL: (020) 7928 7211 FAX: (020) 7928 2279
WEB SITE: www.santeonline.co.uk

NEW CHEF
SEAFOOD
£26–£70

There are now clones in Covent Garden (21 Wellington Street, tel (020) 7836 7161), Notting Hill (175 Westbourne Grove, tel (020) 7727 4321), Wandsworth (2 North Side, tel (020) 7326 8580); and now Manchester (see main entry). Each branch copies the cafeteria-style décor of this, the original, with black and white tiled walls and booth seating, and a convivial atmosphere generally prevails. Richard Gilberd was appointed too late for us to receive any feedback, but the cooking style is typically both varied and interesting, taking in bowls of shellfish, seafood platters, and fish and chips, as well as smoked haddock sausage with kumera mash, or perhaps pink bream with red Thai paste. A decent list of white wines includes plenty by the glass; prices start at £12.50.

CHEF: Richard Gilberd PROPRIETOR: Groupe Chez Gérard OPEN: Mon to Sat 12 to 3, 5.30 to 11.30 MEALS: alc (main courses £13 to £28). Set L and D 5.30 to 7 and 10 to 11.30 £12.50 (2 courses) to £15.50 SERVICE: 12.5%, card slips closed CARDS: Amex, Delta, MasterCard, Switch, Visa DETAILS: 102 seats. Private parties: 35 main room. Vegetarian meals. No smoking in 1 dining room. Music. Air-conditioned ⊖ Waterloo

Net prices *in the details at the end of an entry indicates that the prices given on a menu and on a bill are inclusive of VAT and service charge, and that this practice is clearly stated on menu and bill.*

Livebait's Café Fish

map 15

36–40 Rupert Street, W1V 7FR
TEL: (020) 7287 8989 FAX: (020) 7287 8400

COOKING **2**
SEAFOOD
£27–£72

Café Fish catches the West End crowds with its trade-mark haul of fresh fish, lively menus, upbeat professional service and informal, bustling atmosphere. Covering two floors, it goes in for open-plan kitchens, fishy prints on the walls, wooden floors and small, tightly packed tables. Those who prefer their seafood straight can select from the menu's lavish platters of rock oysters, prawns or perhaps bowls of cockles or whelks. But the kitchen also works with innovative combinations: deep-fried tempura squid with an oriental dipping sauce to start, followed perhaps by fiery blackened Cajun-spiced marlin with wild rocket, pico de gallo and sour cream. Desserts lean towards fruity concoctions of perhaps mango parfait with raspberry sorbet and mango tortilla. The short, fish-friendly wine list is arranged by style (mostly white). Most are under £20, house French is £11.25 and there are bags by the glass.

CHEF: Martin Manning PROPRIETOR: Groupe Chez Gérard OPEN: Mon to Sat 12 to 11, Sun 2 to 9 CLOSED: 24 to 26 Dec MEALS: alc (main courses £11 to £26). Set L £7.50 (1 course) to £15.50, Set D 7 to 10.30 £18.50. Cover £1.50 SERVICE: 12.5% (optional), card slips closed CARDS: Amex, Delta, Diners, MasterCard, Switch, Visa DETAILS: 200 seats. Children's helpings. No smoking in 1 dining room. Wheelchair access (also WC). Music. Air-conditioned ⊖ Piccadilly Circus, Leicester Square (£5)

Lobster Pot

map 13

3 Kennington Lane, SE11 4RG
TEL: (020) 7582 5556

COOKING **3**
FRENCH SEAFOOD
£23–£61

The nautical blue frontage – at which you are welcomed by a life-size, two-dimensional version of Hervé Régent and then regaled with taped sea shanties – announces that this is a fish restaurant to its gills. Waiters in striped jerseys, including from time to time the chef-patron himself, serve up marine cuisine of a freshness and facility not much found in this part of south London. Star billing must go to the platter of fruits de mer, a generous serving of crab, oysters, prawns, winkles and so forth, with a half-lobster as an optional add-on. A couple who took the eight-course *menu surprise* singled out the crab with green mayonnaise, and lobster mousse with morels for particular praise, and they remarked that everything they ate was 'obsessively fresh and intensely flavoured'. Cajun-spiced monkfish and tuna sauced with tomato, garlic, ginger, chilli and coriander are among more unexpected offerings. Finish with tarte Tatin or a sorbet soused in vodka. The short French wine list does a quick sprint from Muscadet sur lie at £14.50 to Corton-Charlemagne at £81.

CHEF: Hervé Régent PROPRIETORS: Hervé and Nathalie Régent OPEN: Tue to Sat 12 to 2, 7 to 10.45 CLOSED: 24 Dec to first week in Jan MEALS: alc (main courses £14.50 to £18.50). Set L £10 (2 courses) to £39.50, Set D £19.50 to £39.50 SERVICE: 12.5% (optional), card slips closed CARDS: Amex, Delta, Diners, MasterCard, Switch, Visa DETAILS: 30 seats. Private parties: 30 main room, 16 and 30 private rooms. Children's helpings. No cigars/pipes in dining room. Wheelchair access (not WC). Music. Air-conditioned ⊖ Kennington (£5)

Lola's 🍷 map 13

The Mall Building, 359 Upper Street, N1 0PD
TEL: (020) 7359 1932 FAX: (020) 7359 2209

COOKING 2
MODERN EUROPEAN
£32–£48

A bright first-floor dining room in the rather forbidding-looking Mall Building at the epicentre of happening Islington, Lola's uses billowing drapes, Grecian-style columns and sculptures to achieve a neoclassical effect. Spanish, French and Italian are the principal tongues of the menus, with appropriate ingredients conscientiously sourced. Sharp and stimulating flavours characterise dishes such as Spanish-style beef with piquillo peppers, goats' cheese and caper berries, as well as main courses of seared scallops with mash, melted onions and gremolata, or Welsh Black beef ribeye with chips and Caesar salad. A poached pear for dessert is all the rage nowadays, and it turns up here with its own sorbet and chocolate sauce, or there might be an oatmeal and raisin brûlée with honeyed apples. 'Lola's Flights' offer the chance to explore the list and compare wines in themed groupings, which change regularly. The list itself is packed with wines from off the beaten track that are ripe for discovery, with prices reasonable enough to facilitate doing so. Prices open at £10.50.

CHEF: Gary Lee PROPRIETORS: Carol George and Morfudd Richards OPEN: all week 12 to 2.30 (3 Sat, 3.30 Sun), 6 (7 Sun) to 11 (10 Sun) CLOSED: some bank hols MEALS: alc exc Sun D (main courses £11 to £15). Set L Mon to Fri £10 (2 courses), Set D Mon to Sat 6 to 7 £10 (2 courses), Set D Sun £12.50 (2 courses). Cover £1. Bar menu available SERVICE: not inc, 12.5% for parties of 5 or more CARDS: Amex, Delta, Diners, MasterCard, Switch, Visa DETAILS: 80 seats. Vegetarian meals. Music. Air-conditioned ⊖ Angel (£5)

Lomo map 14

222 Fulham Road, SW10 9NB
TEL/FAX: (020) 7349 8848
EMAIL: lomomail@btinternet.co.uk
WEB SITE: www.lomo.co.uk

COOKING 2
SPANISH
£32–£52

It throbs like a popular tapas bar in Seville, but this modern Chelsea bar serves not tapas but 'raciones': similar food in portions about twice the size. Simple ones include tortilla, salt cod brandade, and grilled wild mushrooms. More elaborate are sizzling beef with mushrooms, and chorizo cooked in red wine with peppers. Plates of charcuterie naturally include lomo (sliced cured loin of pork), and paella appears at weekends; there are daily blackboard specials too. The food, there to support the drinks, is eaten at little high pedestal tables, at the bar, or at a few conventional tables. There are as many cocktails as wines, but the latter, many Spanish, range from £10.50 to £38.75 for Priorato, and there is also a list of fine sherries.

CHEF: Andrew Nabrezki PROPRIETOR: Julian Ritcher OPEN: Sat and Sun L from noon, all week D 5 to 11.30 (11 Sun) MEALS: alc (main dishes £3.50 to £15). Cover £1.50 SERVICE: not inc CARDS: Amex, Delta, MasterCard, Switch, Visa DETAILS: 60 seats. Vegetarian meals. Wheelchair access (also women's WC). Music. Air-conditioned ⊖ Earls Court, South Kensington (£5)

Lou Pescadou

map 13

241 Old Brompton Road, SW5 9HP
TEL: (020) 7370 1057 FAX: (020) 7244 7545

COOKING **2**
SEAFOOD
£21–£60

The name, Provençal for 'The Fisherman', indicates what to expect at this dark-blue-fronted restaurant in a parade of shops near Earl's Court Exhibition Centre. The downstairs Rugby Bar contains a collection of old photographs and shirts, and nautical blue and white are appropriate in the ground-floor dining area. Here you see the kind of readily comprehensible seafood menu that age has not withered. Marinière de coquillages is a chunky soup: various species of shellfish in a hearty broth enriched with tomato and basil. A main-course assiette of grilled fish has included a scallop, a huge king prawn, sea bass, swordfish and mullet, lubricated with a ribbon of beurre blanc. If you must avoid fish, try a salad of Crottin de Chavignol with shredded apple and carrot, then escalope de veau Vallée d'Auge (in a cream and alcohol sauce). Side orders of impeccable chips are worth signing up for. Desserts are more humdrum: apple tart and chocolate mousse, but also a top-notch oeufs à la neige. Friendly French staff and a traditional French wine list complete the picture. House Provence is £10.80.

CHEF: Laurent David PROPRIETORS: Daniel Chobert and Laurent David OPEN: all week 12 to 3, 7 (6.30 Sat and Sun) to 12 CLOSED: 23 Dec to 4 Jan MEALS: alc (main courses £7.50 to £14). Set L £9.90, Set D Sat and Sun £13.50. Cover £1.50 SERVICE: 15% (optional), card slips closed CARDS: Amex, Delta, Diners, MasterCard, Switch, Visa DETAILS: 60 seats. 20 seats outside. Private parties: 45 main room. Vegetarian meals. Children's helpings. Wheelchair access (not WC). No music. Air-conditioned ⊖ Earl's Court (£5)

Lundum's

map 14

119 Old Brompton Road, SW7 3RN
TEL: (020) 7373 7774 FAX: (020) 7373 4472

COOKING **3**
DANISH
£24–£55

For three years South Kensington has been the place to go if you hanker for Danish cuisine. In a stylish dining room with good linen, floral table decorations and large, gleaming mirrors, you may lunch on traditional open sandwiches, fish or sausage platters and akvavit; dinner pursues a more contemporary style that seems equally successful. Salmon starters are well reported, whether a classic trio of tartare, gravad lax and smoked, or salt-cured salmon with its own caviar, horseradish cream and cucumber brunoise. A butter sauce and cranberries partner plaice, while meat eaters might favour pork fillet with Danish sweet potatoes and shallots in a sauce of prunes and armagnac. If you started on akvavit or Carlsberg brewed in Denmark, it may seem apposite to finish with a plate of Danish cheeses; desserts such as wild berry soup, or pear compote (spiced with star anise, cinnamon and vanilla), are alternatives. There is no Danish wine, so the list majors on France, opening with house Chardonnay and Merlot from the pays d'Oc at £12.25.

CHEFS: Franck Dietrich, Tanja Jensen and Kay Lundum PROPRIETORS: the Lundum family OPEN: all week L 12 to 3 (4 Sun), Mon to Sat D 6 to 10 CLOSED: Christmas, 1 Jan, 2 weeks end Aug MEALS: alc exc Sun (main courses L £6.50 to £15, D £10.50 to £16). Set L Mon to Sat

£12.50 (2 courses) to £15.50, Sun brunch £15.50 (buffet), Set D £17.25 (2 courses) to £21.50 SERVICE: 12.5% (optional), card slips closed CARDS: Amex, Delta, Diners, MasterCard, Switch, Visa DETAILS: 40 seats. 15 seats outside. Children's helpings. No cigars in dining room. Wheelchair access (not WC). Music. Air-conditioned ⊖ Gloucester Road

Maison Novelli

map 13

29 Clerkenwell Green, EC1R 0DU
TEL: (020) 7251 6606 FAX: (020) 7490 1083

COOKING **4**
MODERN EUROPEAN
£39–£78

Lavender-blue walls, tall windows and lots of mirrors help to lighten this large corner plot on two floors (one split-level) in Clerkenwell. While some dishes reflect the owner's French background – a duck rillettes and gizzard terrine with white beans and garlic dressing, perhaps – there is enough in the way of chorizo oil, mozzarella, salsas and the like to confirm a broader interest: like spicy couscous timbale, topped with a yoghurt dressing and served with halves of baby aubergine with which one meal began.

The food is gutsy, and portions can be large: a strongly flavoured starter of wild mushrooms wrapped in a poppy seed pancake for one May visitor, and a main course of accurately timed beef fillet, wrapped in Beaufort cheese, on a bed of mushroom risotto. While the kitchen can turn out some fine dishes – simply cooked bream on Mediterranean vegetables, or a salmon fishcake (properly crisp outside, moist within) topped with a fried quail's egg – execution can be disappointing: 'Is Jean-Christophe really cooking here?' wondered a reporter with fond memories of the old days.

Meals might end with a citrus fruit tart, a chocolate plate, or an intensely flavoured passion fruit parfait on a light raspberry coulis. Young French staff maintain an informal tone, and a lively wine list excels in the middle range; prices start at £14.95 but soon hop over the £20 barrier.

CHEF/PROPRIETOR: Jean-Christophe Novelli OPEN: Mon to Fri L 12 to 3, Mon to Sat D 6 to 11 MEALS: alc (main courses £14.50 to £24) SERVICE: 12.5% (optional), card slips closed CARDS: Amex, Delta, Diners, MasterCard, Switch, Visa DETAILS: 120 seats. 20 seats outside. Private parties: 70 main room, 30 to 72 private rooms. Vegetarian meals. No children under 5. No cigars/pipes in dining room. Music. Air-conditioned ⊖ Farringdon

Mandarin Kitchen

map 13

14–16 Queensway, W2 3RX
TEL: (020) 7727 9012 FAX: (020) 7727 9468

COOKING **1**
CHINESE
£23–£76

This large eating hall is frantically busy in the evenings, a tribute to the beautifully cooked dishes, especially seafood, that its kitchen is renowned for. But there can be disappointments too, sometimes about the absence of flavours expected from the menu descriptions (possibly related to an inspector's comment – not the only one – that 'what we ate was what not always what we had ordered'). Also, brusque service at the tightly packed tables does not always contribute to enjoyment of the expensive lobster and crab specialities or the eel, monkfish, pomfret and unpriced sea bass and Dover sole. Carnivores are not neglected; a wide choice takes in shredded pork with preserved pickles and bean shoots, veal chop in four different ways, and chicken dishes from sweet and sour to whole Emperor chicken with ginger and spring onion. House wines are £10.50.

CHEF: K.W. Man PROPRIETOR: Steven Cheung OPEN: all week noon to 11.30 CLOSED: 25 to 27 Dec MEALS: alc (main courses £6 to £30). Set L and D £10.90 (2 courses) to £20 SERVICE: not inc CARDS: Amex, Delta, Diners, MasterCard, Switch, Visa DETAILS: 120 seats. Private parties: 120 main room. Vegetarian meals. Wheelchair access (not WC). Music. Air-conditioned ⊖ Queensway

▲ Mandarin Oriental Hyde Park, Foliage 🍷 map 14

66 Knightsbridge, SW1X 7LA — COOKING **7**
TEL: (020) 7201 3723 FAX: (020) 7201 3619 — MODERN EUROPEAN
WEB SITE: www.mandarinoriental.com — £41–£80

Beyond the bar, where exotic drinks are served in equally exotic glasses, is a smart, agreeable, beige-coloured dining room with high ceilings, tall glass partitions enclosing white silk leaves, comfortable seating and stylish tableware. 'Foley-arge', as the large numbers of cheerful and professional staff pronounce it, is a friendly, welcoming place, where dishes are quite complex, and luxury materials abound. Foie gras might be prepared three ways to start – as a creamy pâté, sauté, and marinated in port – and served with a leek salad, and one visitor found a starter of lobster and caviar with crab vinaigrette to be a 'beautiful, restrained creation'.

Fish is the source of much enjoyment, and although there is a lot going on, dishes always appear balanced and unified: as in the case of accurately timed red mullet fillets with a langoustine beignet on a disc of smoked aubergine, and fresh-tasting roast sea bass fillet on a celeriac purée, with lobster tortellini and a raisin and caper vinaigrette. Equally successful meats have included 'the finest partridge I have ever eaten' for one January visitor, and another's large lobe of creamy but well-roasted calves' sweetbreads, accompanied by a pasta envelope containing chopped ceps, as well as slices of baked Jerusalem artichoke and braised cos lettuce.

Top-notch desserts provided a dazzling highlight for a couple who ate baked coconut soufflé with passion fruit sorbet, and white chocolate mille-feuille with blood orange jelly. Portion sizes are just right, taking into account the chef's hugely enjoyable 'extras', and although dinner has escalated in price quite a bit since last year, the set lunch, with only two or three choices per course, remains particularly good value. Drawbacks include being asked for credit card details when booking. A smart selection of French, Italian and New World wines constitutes the bulk of the list, which offers only three bottles below £20, two of them house red and white; look to Italy (particularly outside the mainstream) for interest, and to France for half bottles.

CHEF: Hywel Jones PROPRIETOR: Manderin Oriental Hyde Park OPEN: Mon to Fri L 12 to 2.30, Mon to Sat D 7 to 10.30 MEALS: Set L £24, Set D £42.50 to £55 SERVICE: 12.5% CARDS: Amex, Delta, Diners, MasterCard, Switch, Visa DETAILS: 46 seats. Private parties: 20 to 400 private rooms. Wheelchair access (also WC). No music. Air-conditioned ACCOMMODATION: 200 rooms, all with bath/shower. TV. Phone. Room only £295 to £2,000. Rooms for disabled. Baby facilities (*The Which? Hotel Guide*) ⊖ Knightsbridge

Mantanah

map 12

2 Orton Buildings, Portland Road, SE25 4UD — COOKING **4**
TEL: (020) 8771 1148 — THAI
WEB SITE: www.mantanah.co.uk — £25–£48

Mantanah's blue façade stands out in a grey part of south-east London, just as its fine cuisine stands out against the general level of Thai, or pseudo-Thai, cooking in the West. Chef-patron Tym Srisawatt's inventiveness shows this year in five new 'signature' dishes, which she says are their own favourites. Two are stir-fries (one of meat in tamarind curry sauce, another of vermicelli with pork, vegetables, sesame and egg); 'touch of Tym' is sweet-and-sour, slightly hot roast duck in tamarind and palm sugar sauce; supaporn, a Laotian steamed chicken curry with bamboo shoot, is wrapped in banana leaves. Vegetarian versions of these supplement the generous choice of vegetarian set meals and à la carte dishes. Chilli-hot Thai salads include yum lanna, based on banana blossom and shredded chicken in coconut sauce. Thai beer is the best-selling drink, but a short wine list runs from £8.50 for house wines to £17 for Pouilly-Fumé, while 'bins end' at £11.50 offers a lucky dip from the cellar.

CHEF: Mrs Tym Srisawatt PROPRIETOR: Mantanah Ltd OPEN: Tue to Sun D only 6.30 to 11 CLOSED: 25 and 26 Dec, 1 Jan, 2 weeks Aug MEALS: alc D (main courses £5 to £8.50). Set D £15 to £22 (min 2 to 4) SERVICE: not inc, card slips closed CARDS: Amex, Delta, MasterCard, Switch, Visa DETAILS: 40 seats. Private parties: 40 main room. Vegetarian meals. Children's helpings. No cigars/pipes in dining room. Wheelchair access (not WC). Music. Air-conditioned (£5)

Masala Zone £

NEW ENTRY **map 15**

9 Marshall Street, W1F 7ER — COOKING **1**
TEL: (020) 7287 9966 FAX: (020) 7287 8555 — INDIAN
WEB SITE: www.realindianfood.com — £18–£28

The latest in Namita Panjabi's stable, which includes Chutney Mary (see entry), is a brisk, lively restaurant offering Indian street snacks, thalis, lunchtime sandwiches and meal-in-one rice plates and curried noodles. Khaki-coloured walls are enlivened by painted designs from Indian tribal artists. Most diners sit at benches, listen to house music and watch proceedings in the open-to-view kitchen, from which dishes arrive in no particular order. An inspection meal included an enjoyable snack of aloo tikki chat (potato patty with a sambal, coriander-laced yoghurt and chickpeas), while a small portion of butter chicken boasted fresh spicing, a pleasing lack of oiliness, and plenty of boiled rice. A thali featured prawn curry, dhal, sag aloo, rice, and pumpkin curry flavoured with lemon grass. Vegetarian food is prepared in a separate kitchen, staffed by Brahmins. The concise wine list starts at £9.75.

CHEF: H.S. Bhatty PROPRIETORS: Ranjit Mathrani and Namita Panjabi OPEN: all week 12 to 3, 5.30 to 11.30 (6 to 10.30 Sun) MEALS: alc (main courses £3 to £6.50). Set L and D (2 courses) £7.50 to £9 SERVICE: 10% (optional), card slips closed CARDS: Diners, MasterCard, Switch, Visa DETAILS: 160 seats. Private parties: 50 main room. Vegetarian meals. Children's helpings. No smoking in dining room. Music. Air-conditioned ⊖ Oxford Circus

Mash 🍷 map 15

19–21 Great Portland Street, W1W 8GB | COOKING **3**
TEL: (020) 7637 5555 FAX: (020) 7637 7333 | MODERN BRITISH
EMAIL: mashoxfordcircus@gruppo.co.uk | £26–£53

Though the Manchester original is now defunct, the London outlet of Oliver Peyton's Mash concept is still going strong. Vast stainless steel vats spanning two floors behind a glass screen produce the beers that are served along with a long list of cocktails to a noisy young crowd in the downstairs bar. Upstairs, meanwhile, in the slightly more sedate dining room, Maddalena Bonino continues to produce a varied, modern menu that starts in Britain but brings in influences from across Europe and the Far East.

The wood-fired oven turns out excellent ciabatta-style bread and various pizzas with non-traditional toppings, such as duck with cucumber and herbs, as well as being used to roast other items: salmon, for example, which comes with marinated fennel, and mizuna with a parsley and almond dressing. Grilling is another favoured method, applied to mackerel fillets served with roasted peppers and pickled lemon gremolata dressing, or to quails accompanied by wilted tatsoi, fragrant rice, red onions and a sweet chilli and peanut dressing. 'Ultra-casual' waiting staff have led one visitor to describe the 12.5 per cent levied for service as 'impertinent'. Effort has been made to source a good spread of modern wine styles, and prices tend to reflect this, starting at £13 for 'Mash Series' house French. Twelve wines are available by the glass from £4.50.

CHEF: Maddalena Bonino PROPRIETOR: Oliver Peyton OPEN: Mon to Sat 12 to 3 (4 Sat), 6 to 11 MEALS: alc (main courses £9 to £15). Set L and D £25. Set L Mon to Fri 11.30 to 4 £10. Set D Mon to Sat 6 to 7.30 £12 (2 courses) to £15. Bar menu available SERVICE: 12.5%, card slips closed CARDS: Amex, Delta, Diners, MasterCard, Switch, Visa DETAILS: 165 seats. Private parties: 165 main room, 28 private room. Vegetarian meals. Wheelchair access (also WC). Music. Air-conditioned ⊖ Oxford Circus

Mela £ map 15

152–156 Shaftesbury Avenue, WC2H 8HL | COOKING **2**
TEL: (020) 7836 8635 FAX: (020) 7379 0527 | INDIAN
WEB SITE: www.melarestaurant.co.uk | £14–£46

Bright colours, Indian artefacts, lively music and rapidly changing, colourful customers make this ideal for a pre- or post-theatre (or instead-of-theatre) meal. The kitchen, in full view behind glass produces a short menu of dishes from the tandoor and the tawa (a concave hotplate). There are some traditional curries, also interesting vegetarian options from tarka dal to paneer pasandida (cottage cheese cake stuffed with garlic-flavoured spinach). But Mela really stands out for its lunchtime Paratha Pavilion. You choose the bread base – perhaps paratha, naan, or roti – and the flour it is made from (maize, sorghum, whole wheat, among others); there are even South Indian dosa and uttapam pancakes. Then select a curry to complete a snack lunch costing from £1.95 to £4.95; the one supplement is prawns or shrimps at £5 extra. The short, well-varied wine list starts with house selections from £10.90.

CHEF: Kuldeep Singh PROPRIETORS: Kuldeep Singh, Ashraf Rahman and D. Mody OPEN: all week 12 to 2.45, 5.30 to 11.30 (10.30 Sun and bank hols) MEALS: alc (main courses £5 to £12.50). Set L £4.95 (1 course) to £34.95 (min 2), Set D £24.95 to £34.95 (all min 2). Snack L menu also available SERVICE: not inc, card slips closed CARDS: Amex, Delta, Diners, MasterCard, Switch, Visa DETAILS: 130 seats. 12 seats outside. Private parties: 45 main room, 45 private room. Vegetarian meals. Children's helpings. No smoking in 1 dining room. Wheelchair access (not WC). Music. Air-conditioned ⊖ Leicester Square (£5)

Mem Saheb on Thames £ map 15

65-67 Amsterdam Road, E14 3UU
TEL/FAX: (020) 7538 3008 COOKING **1**
EMAIL: table@memsaheb.co.uk INDIAN
WEB SITE: www.memsaheb.co.uk £23–£39

This light and airy modern restaurant in the revitalised docklands is modern also in its approach to Indian cookery, with regional dishes including several from Bangladesh and Goa. Chicken anarash is cooked with pineapple in a mild coconut and almond sauce; tok gosht is lamb with tamarind sauce; reicado is a whole marinated trout cooked in the tandoor, then stuffed with prawns. But tradition – in the shape of the classic British curry repertoire – is respected. Listed as 'old favourites' are korma, bhuna, Madras, dansak, dopiaza, even chicken tikka masala. Combination dishes include, as well as such expected meat duets as rogon and dansak, a vegetarian pairing of potato alongside spinach and cheese, or the marine king prawn bhuna with masala fish. House wines, 'French Dry White' or 'French Dry Red', are £7.95.

CHEFS: Anwar Hussain and Faisal Rashid PROPRIETORS: Mridul Kanti Das, Rabiul Hoque and Iuliana Kadir OPEN: Mon to Fri L 12 to 2.30, all week D 6 to 11.30 CLOSED: 25 to 26 Dec MEALS: alc (main courses £6 to £10). Cover £1 SERVICE: not inc CARDS: Amex, Delta, Diners, MasterCard, Switch, Visa DETAILS: 90 seats. 16 seats outside. Private parties: 90 main room, 40 private room. Car park. Vegetarian meals. Children's helpings. No smoking in 1 dining room. Wheelchair access (not WC). Music ⊖ Crossharbour (DLR) (£5)

Metrogusto Battersea map 12

153 Battersea Park Road, SW8 4BX COOKING **4**
TEL: (020) 7720 0204 FAX: (020) 7720 0888 MODERN ITALIAN
£29–£47

Sitting on a corner in Battersea Park Road, the tastefully decorated Metrogusto is 'elegant, modern and unfussy'. High ceilings, white walls, striking contemporary paintings and square-topped, dark-wood tables set the scene for its modern Italian food. A nod to English cooking shows in a chargrilled veal chop with beetroot chips and mash, while starters take in more typical pasta corta with aubergine, tomato and buffalo mozzarella, or perhaps tagliolini neri with crispy red mullet. Though meat is more in evidence – witness crispy duck and red onion tart teamed with Chinese greens – fish might include pan-fried cod fillet and black olive tapénade with broccoli. Finish with 'a treat' of pear and almond tart with pecorino ice cream, or an appealing lemon tart (like a crème brûlée in a pastry case) with raspberry sorbet. There is good espresso and Italian bread, and attentive and polite service leaves reporters feeling 'well looked after'. The solid and tempting Italian wine list impresses for both class and range; six house wines are £12.50 (3.25 a glass), but prices soon hop over £20.

CHEF: Mr Raffaele PROPRIETOR: Ambro and Susi Ianeselli OPEN: Mon to Sat 12 to 2.30 (3 Fri, Sun), 6.30 to 10.45 (10.45 Fri, Sun) MEALS: alc (main courses £9.50 to £14.50) SERVICE: 10% (optional), card slips closed CARDS: Delta, MasterCard, Switch, Visa DETAILS: 48 seats. Vegetarian meals. Music

Metrogusto Islington

NEW ENTRY map 13

13 Theberton Street, N1 0QY
TEL/FAX: (020) 7226 9400

COOKING **4**
MODERN ITALIAN
£29–£46

But for the tables, this new sibling of the Metrogusto in Battersea (see above) might be an art gallery. Artworks and objets trouvés of every size and style adorn its white walls, while pale woodwork, tiled floors, dark wood tables and high-backed leather chairs complete the comfortable-but-modern look. There are two dining areas, one on the ground floor, another down near the kitchen. Warm Italian bread and a dish of olive oil arrive while you peruse the menu. The impressive cooking shows bags of skill in what appear to be quite simple dishes; it doesn't aim to be outlandish, but there is an obvious commitment to flavour. Pasta is silky, golden and perfectly timed, as in ravioli packed full of chunky guinea fowl, served with a wild mushroom ragoût. Lemon sole may come deep-fried and topped with sesame seeds. For afters, choose a plate of Italian cheeses, or perhaps delizia Piedmontese (a cross between chocolate mousse and chocolate soufflé) with caramel sauce and amaretti. Service is impressively professional. An all-Italian wine list embraces some very go-ahead producers, but there is not much under £30 (bar the dozen house wines from £12.50).

CHEF: Davide di Croce PROPRIETORS: Susi and Ambro Ianeselli OPEN: Tue to Sun 12 to 2.30 (3 Sat and Sun), 6.30 to 10.30 (11 Sat, 10 Sun) CLOSED: bank hols, 23 Dec to 3 Jan, New Year; Easter MEALS: alc D (main courses £9.50 to £14.50). Set L £18.50 (2 courses) to £22.50 SERVICE: 10% (optional), card slips closed CARDS: Delta, MasterCard, Switch, Visa DETAILS: 50 seats. Private parties: 24 main room. Vegetarian meals. Children's helpings. No children under 1 after 10pm. No smoking in 1 dining room. Wheelchair access (not WC). Music. Air-conditioned ⊖ Angel, Highbury & Islington

Mezzo

map 15

100 Wardour Street, W1F 0TN
TEL: (020) 7314 4000 FAX: (020) 7314 4040
WEB SITE: www.mezzo.co.uk

COOKING **3**
MODERN EUROPEAN
£27–£88

What started, back in 1995, as a basement restaurant with a grand entrance has become a collection of bars, eating and entertainment areas on two levels under one roof. Mezzo Café majors on snacks with a Middle Eastern theme, Mezzonine serves Thai-style dishes, DJs do their stuff in the bar, and the recently refurbished Mezzo, with vividly coloured screens, a stage and dance floor, has a nightly programme of live music. Chefs perform behind glass, breaking down any last conceptual boundary between food and theatre, and they read from a largely European script. Seafood remains in the spotlight – oysters, crab and lobster simply served – supported by dishes, or rather lists of ingredients, such as trout pâté, beetroot jam, sour dough, or pan-fried foie gras, grilled pineapple, brioche. Otherwise, main dishes might take in goats' cheese mille-feuille with field mushrooms and two tapénades; or loin of lamb with wilted spinach, garlic cream and roast artichoke; Desserts, meanwhile, offer passion fruit crème caramel, or pecan pie with a whiskey glaze. A savvy list of wines offers around 20 by the glass, starting with Vin de Pays d'Oc at £13.50 (£3.50 a glass).

CHEF: David Laris PROPRIETOR: Conran Restaurants OPEN: Wed to Fri and Sun L 12 to 3 (3.30 Sun), all week D 6 to 12 (3am Fri and Sat, 11 Sun) CLOSED: 25 Dec, 1 Jan MEALS: alc (main courses £12.50 to £31). Set L £12.50 (2 courses) to £15.50, Set D 6 to 7 £12.50 (2 courses) to £15.50. Cover £5 after 10pm SERVICE: 12.5% (optional), card slips closed CARDS: Amex, Delta, Diners, MasterCard, Switch, Visa DETAILS: 350 seats. Private parties: 350 main room, 44 private room. Vegetarian meals. Wheelchair access (also WC). Music. Air-conditioned ⊖ Piccadilly Circus (£5)

Mirabelle 🍷 map 15

56 Curzon Street, W1Y 8DL COOKING **6**
TEL: (020) 7499 4636 FAX: (020) 7499 5449 FRENCH
WEB SITE: www.whitestarline.org.uk £34–£86

Halfway between a brasserie and a posh restaurant, Mirabelle captures the spirit of the times, serving generally unfussy and well-prepared food in an eye-catching environment. Once past the bare lobby and through the bar, a spangly ball revolving overhead (shades of ballroom dancing) heralds the smart dining room. Arrive early to contemplate the trompe l'oeil wall paintings and glimpse the small outdoor terrace, or fetch up later to catch the dynamism and buzz. The appeal is not hard to find: a practised kitchen delivers a succession of classic dishes, many with a French background, and delivers them 'big time'. The straightforwardness of the cooking is a confidence booster, as the repertoire runs from flavourful, creamy mussel soup, via calf's liver lyonnaise, to grilled lobster with béarnaise.

Another element at work is the comfort factor (this is Mayfair), which produces omelette Arnold Bennett, foie gras in a couple of guises (a terrine with Sauternes jelly, a parfait with truffle jelly), and rich braises of beef or pork cheek, followed by lemon tart, or raspberry soufflé. Regular customers know what to expect, but even so the close-together tables, noise level, and lack of smoking restrictions get up reporters' noses; and given that results on the plate appear to be variable, it is no surprise that some consider it good value, some the reverse. Service is generally sharp, and staff are friendly, but watch out for time limits on tables. Printed on the extra-large menu, the wine list is filled with fashionable names old and new, and prices reflect this. A dazzling array of Château d'Yquem vintages dating back to 1847 is a showy addition, with attention-grabbing prices (up to £30,000 a bottle). Scouring the list will produce a number of bottles under £25 however, some in the concise sommelier's selection; these are also available by the glass from £3.60.

CHEF: Martin Caws PROPRIETORS: Marco Pierre White and Jimmy Lahoud OPEN: all week 12 to 2.30, 6 to 11.30 (10.30 Sun) MEALS: alc (main courses £14.50 to £28.50). Set L £16.50 (2 courses) to £19.95 SERVICE: 12.5% (optional), card slips closed CARDS: Amex, Delta, Diners,

MasterCard, Switch, Visa DETAILS: 110 seats. 40 seats outside. Private parties: 125 main room, 33 and 48 private rooms. No cigars/pipes in dining room. No music. Air-conditioned ⊖ Green Park

Mr Kong £

map 15

21 Lisle Street, WC2H 7BA
TEL: (020) 7437 7341 FAX: (020) 7437 7923

COOKING 3
CHINESE
£23–£54

In the functional, narrow dining room the plain décor detracts neither from the food, nor from the relaxed yet brisk service. Many Chinese customers, and sinophile Westerners, order authentic Cantonese dishes from the 30 items on the chef's special list. In an inspector's hotpot of braised pork belly with yam, the cooking juices 'nicely suffused' the yam slices. Also approved from the long conventional menu were 'fresh, plump, nicely timed' steamed scallops, and prawn and coriander spring rolls. Successful main dishes have included prawns with cashew nuts; and stir-fried pak choi in 'sea of spicy sauce'. There is also a 'today chef's special' menu, some of its dishes unchanged from the 1999 version. It is probably safe to assume that deep fried crispy Mongolian lamb with lettuce leaf wrap retains its appeal, but we wonder if the same will be said in 2004 of fried cuttlefish cake with angled loofah and black fungus. The wine list is basic, with house wines £7.50, but tea is recommended.

CHEF/PROPRIETOR: Mr K. Kong OPEN: all week 12 to 2.45 MEALS: alc (main courses £6 to £15). Set £9.30 (min 2) to £22 (min 4) SERVICE: not inc CARDS: Amex, Delta, Diners, MasterCard, Switch, Visa DETAILS: 100 seats. Private parties: 30 main room, 20 private room. Vegetarian meals. Wheelchair access (not WC). Music. Air-conditioned ⊖ Leicester Square

Mon Plaisir

map 15

21 Monmouth Street, WC2H 9DD
TEL: (020) 7836 7243 FAX: (020) 7240 4774
EMAIL: eatafrog@mail.com
WEB SITE: www.mon-plaisir.co.uk

COOKING 2
FRENCH
£21 – £59

Few places in the West End feel as though they could have been transplanted directly from France, but Mon Plaisir, plumb in the heart of theatreland, still has gastronomic maps of the mother country on the walls. The menu itself has branched out a bit, though. Monkfish pizza with tomato and basil fondue, grilled aubergine and a dressing of aged balsamic hardly sounds traditional, but there are still rock oysters with shallot vinegar, and pork knuckle with carmalised apple and boulangère potatoes. Finish with orange and vanilla crème brûlée or chocolate fondant with praline ice cream, and perhaps vintage armagnac or calvados. A handful of wines from the New World brings up the rear of a shortish and otherwise French list; house wines are £10.50.

CHEF: Richard Sawyer PROPRIETOR: Alain Lhermitte OPEN: Mon to Fri L 12 to 2.15, Mon to Sat D 5.45 to 11.15 CLOSED: Christmas, New Year, bank hols MEALS: alc (main courses L £9.50 to £17, D £15 to £17). Set L £15.95, Set D before 8 £11.95 (2 courses inc wine) to £14.95 (inc wine), Set D £23.50 (min 2 inc wine) SERVICE: 12.5% (optional) for à la carte meals, service included for set meals, card slips closed CARDS: Amex, Delta, Diners, MasterCard, Switch, Visa DETAILS: 100 seats. Private parties: 12 main room. Music. Air-conditioned ⊖ Covent Garden, Leicester Square

▲ Montcalm Hotel, Crescent map 15

34–40 Great Cumberland Place, W1H 7TW COOKING **4**
TEL: (020) 7402 4288 FAX: (020) 7724 9180 MODERN BRITISH
EMAIL: montcalm@montcalm.co.uk £30–£52

The Montcalm is a charming hotel with an elegant Georgian façade in a quiet crescent not far from the bustle of Marble Arch and Oxford Street. Swags, pelmets, drapes, brocade settees, and bucolic murals of a gently English nature contribute to its calm, sophisticated feel. All reports bar one stress the value (meals include a half-bottle of house wine): 'one of the best-kept secrets for exceptionally good value in London' is a typical assessment.

Many cuisines contribute to the repertoire, which ranges from lobster bisque with lobster ravioli, to roast sea bass with a sesame prawn crust, served with pot stick dumplings and stir-fried vegetables. Dishes and their components are diligently prepared, as in a robust portion of full-flavoured, succulent braised lamb shank, with an unctuous haricot bean stew. Desserts appear to be a highlight, judging by a tall white chocolate case enclosing tiramisù, served with a Galliano-flavoured ice cream and a profusion of summer fruits, and by a beguiling assiette of chocolate desserts too numerous and intricate to describe. Service is prompt, willing, friendly and attentive. A compact and appealing wine list is made even more appetising by the large number available by the 125-millilitre glass.

CHEF: Stephen Whitney PROPRIETOR: The Montcalm Nikko Hotel OPEN: Mon to Fri L 12.30 to 2.30, all week D 6.30 to 10.30 MEALS: Set L and D £20 (2 courses) to £25 (inc wine). Bar menu available all week. Supper menu available Sun SERVICE: not inc, card slips closed CARDS: Amex, Delta, Diners, MasterCard, Switch, Visa DETAILS: 60 seats. Private parties: 80 main room, 20 to 80 private rooms. Vegetarian meals. Children's helpings. No smoking in 1 dining room. Wheelchair access (also WC). Music. Air-conditioned ACCOMMODATION: 120 rooms, all with bath/shower. TV. Phone. Room only £230 to £250. Rooms for disabled. Baby facilities ⊖ Marble Arch (£5)

Monte's NEW ENTRY map 14

164 Sloane Street, SW1X 9QB COOKING **3**
TEL: (020) 7245 0896 FAX: (020) 7235 3456 MODERN ITALIAN/MEDITERRANEAN
WEB SITE: www.montes.co.uk £40–£74

It is not difficult to be cynical about Monte's. Young lad is plucked from anonymity, wows the nation's mums and daughters with his cheeky, matey *Naked Chef* appearances, then opens a posh West End restaurant and waits for the fans and money to roll in. But it is not quite like that. In the first place Jamie Oliver is a 'consultant', not the chef, and in the second he could hardly have lent his name to a less likely venue. Despite the trade mark scooter parked outside, this is a formal, masculine, clubby setup, done in regulation dark brown and taupe, that looks like a cross between a directors' dining room and a first-class airline lounge: 'not Jamie at all'.

His influence, however, may be more apparent on the contemporary Anglo-Mediterranean menu, which takes its sourcing seriously. A herb-laden frittata uses free-range eggs (from the unusual Old Cotswold Legbar breed), 'handmade' pasta takes in linguine (with sardines), and panzotti of ricotta (with lemon and basil). 'Excellent ingredients, well executed, but not cheap' is a fair summing-up of the package, and the advice is to go for a couple of courses off the carte rather than the set-price lunch. One visitor came away well satisfied by a fresh, well-timed sea bass with a tapénade crust. If desserts are disappointing, the wine list certainly isn't. It fizzes and crackles with splendid up-to-the-minute wines from ace producers, put together in thought-provoking sections, with Italy a strong suit. But with only a few wines under £20 (and even that price disappears as soon as you slap on the service charge) and high mark-ups elsewhere, it is simply too expensive for normal budgets.

CHEFS: Jamie Oliver and Ben O'Donoghue PROPRIETOR: Desert Express Ltd OPEN: Mon to Sat L only 12 to 2.30 (D members only) MEALS: alc (main courses £17 to £23). Set L £19.50 (2 courses) to £23 SERVICE: 12.5% (optional), card slips closed CARDS: Amex, Delta, Diners, MasterCard, Switch, Visa DETAILS: 80 seats. Private parties: 80 main room, 16 private room. Vegetarian meals. Wheelchair access (also WC). Music. Air-conditioned ⊖ Knightsbridge

Moro

map 13

34–36 Exmouth Market, EC1R 4QE
TEL: (020) 7833 8336 FAX: (020) 7833 9338

COOKING **5**
SPANISH/NORTH AFRICAN
£29–£47

When Moro opened in 1997, Clerkenwell was still an up-and-coming district. Today, both have well and truly arrived. The large, simply decorated, 'vibrant, enjoyable watering hole' features comfortable banquette seating, a long zinc bar and an open-to-view kitchen with a wood-fired oven; and it can get noisy. A Spanish/Moorish theme to the menu allows Mediterranean herbs and North African spices to pep up a daily-changing list of tapas and more substantial dishes. Pink, lightly charred calf's liver with crispbread, cumin and yoghurt made a 'terrific start' to one meal, while warm broad beans with sorrel, feta and dill also exhibit 'fine ingredients with good balance of flavours'.

For main courses, chargrilled lamb might be teamed with beetroot purée, tahini, braised beetroot leaves and wheatberries ('exciting flavours from seemingly ordinary ingredients'), while wood-roasted skate could be accompanied by sherry vinegar sauce, garlic and spring greens braised with capers. Well-kept Spanish cheeses, and desserts including 'super' ice creams (praise for both the rosewater and the cardamom) round things off. Service, from a young team dressed in cool black, is friendly, helpful and generally (if not always) timely. The small, well-considered wine list, entirely southern European in content, includes a varied choice of sherries. House wines are £10 (white) and £10.25 (red).

CHEFS: Sam and Samantha Clark PROPRIETORS: Mark Sainsbury, and Samuel and Samantha Clark OPEN: Mon to Fri L 12.30 to 2.30, Mon to Sat D 7 to 10.30. Bar tapas served 12.30 to 10.30 MEALS: alc (main courses £11.50 to £14.50) SERVICE: not inc, 12.5% for parties of 7 or more CARDS: Amex, Delta, Diners, MasterCard, Switch, Visa DETAILS: 85 seats. 15 seats outside. Private parties: 80 main room, 14 private room. Vegetarian meals. Wheelchair access (also WC). No music. Air-conditioned ⊖ Farringdon

Moshi Moshi Sushi

maps 12 and 13

24 Upper Level, Liverpool Street Station, EC2M 7QH
TEL/FAX: (020) 7247 3227
7-8 Limeburner Lane, EC4M 7HY
TEL: (020) 7248 1808 FAX: (020) 7248 1807
Level 2, Cabot Place East, Canary Wharf, E14 4QT
TEL: (020) 7512 9911 FAX: (020) 7512 9201
EMAIL: anya@moshimoshi.co.uk
WEB SITE: www.moshimoshi.co.uk

COOKING **2**
JAPANESE
£12–£26

Moshi Moshi Sushi, the first restaurant in the UK to feature a 'kaiten' conveyor belt, is widely regarded as still the best. It also remains 'amazing value' for the quality of sushi on offer, with plate prices starting at £1.20. Décor is slightly different at each branch – the one high above Liverpool Street's platforms has views of trains coming and going – but the formula is identical at all four outlets (the fourth is in Brighton; see Round-up entry). Sit at the counter and grab the colour-coded plates of sushi as they pass; a picture chart aids identification and serves as a menu, so if you don't see what you like on the conveyor belt you can ask one of the chefs to prepare it for you. The range of raw fish is wide, including toro tuna, horse mackerel, octopus, grey mullet and sea urchin roe, and as well as nigiri, maki and sashimi there are plates of 'Japanese tapas'. The drinks list includes various sakés, Japanese beer and a handful of wines from £8.80. Details below are based on the Liverpool Street branch; Enrico Venzon is executive chef for all three branches.

CHEF: Enrico Venzon PROPRIETOR: Caroline Bennett OPEN: Mon to Fri 11.30 to 9 MEALS: alc (plate prices £1.20 to £3.50). Set L and D £6.70 to £11.50. Cover 50p SERVICE: none, card slips closed CARDS: Delta, Diners, MasterCard, Switch, Visa DETAILS: 70 seats. Private parties: 100 main room. Vegetarian meals. No smoking in dining room. Wheelchair access (not WC). Music. Air-conditioned ⊖ Liverpool Street

National Gallery, Crivelli's Garden

map 15

Trafalgar Square, WC2N 5DN
TEL: (020) 7747 2869

COOKING **4**
FRENCH/MEDITERRANEAN
£28–£47

Set above the lobby of the National Gallery's Sainsbury Wing, this is just the place to sit in peace watching the comings and goings in Trafalgar Square. Cooking is simple, and the Italian menu is short, with brief selections of salads, antipasti, pastas and main courses. In addition, there are a dozen pizzas, as at other restaurants in the Red Pepper Group (Red Pepper, White Onion, Green Olive – see London entries); these might include toppings of mozzarella, egg, asparagus and Parmesan, or perhaps tomato, mozzarella, spinach and Gorgonzola.

A zingy, thick courgette soup with squid may start a meal off, followed by a fillet of well judged veal with mozzarella, accompanied by a frisée, cherry tomato and black olive salad. Well-executed desserts – such as lime semifreddo with strawberries, or meringue with apricot sorbet and redcurrant coulis – feature good flavour combinations. Service has been judged friendly but inexpert and can be slow; booking can be difficult. Although there are bottles from throughout the wine-making world on the shortish list, the Italian selections are perhaps the most interesting. Prices start at £9.95 for Puglian red and white.

CHEF: Paolo Zanca PROPRIETOR: Red Pepper Group Ltd OPEN: all week L 11.30 to 3, Wed D 5.30 to 7.45 MEALS: alc (main courses £12 to £13.50) SERVICE: 12.5% (optional), card slips closed CARDS: Amex, Delta, MasterCard, Switch, Visa DETAILS: 130 seats. Private parties: 30 main room. Vegetarian meals. No smoking in dining room. Wheelchair access (also WC). No music. Air-conditioned ⊖ Charing Cross

National Portrait Gallery, Portrait map 15

Orange Street, WC2H 0HE
TEL: (020) 7312 2490 FAX: (020) 7925 0244
EMAIL: portrait.restaurant@talk21.com

COOKING **3**
MODERN BRITISH
£33–£59

High up on the roof, the National Portrait Gallery's restaurant is a long, narrow space with picture windows along its full length, so there is every chance of getting a table with a view: of the back of Nelson on his column above Trafalgar Square, and beyond to Big Ben and the London Eye. With acoustically unfriendly hard surfaces all round, it is unsurprising that most reporters complain about the high noise level. Service, though friendly and willing, has also caused dissatisfaction, with delays and mixed-up orders a common theme in correspondence.

The food makes a better impression. Menus have a predominantly British feel but encompass pan-European influences, starting with marinated herrings with beetroot and warm potato salad, and poached egg and asparagus wrapped in bacon with hollandaise. Roast rabbit has made a successful main course, with complementary flavours coming from Parma ham, black olives, mint and sun-dried tomatoes. Other options might be as familiar as plaice with chips and tartare sauce, or as original as guinea fowl and ginger sausages with braised lentils and onion gravy. At dessert stage the kitchen likes to experiment with new twists on old themes – tapioca brûlée, for example. The wine list is succinct but full of choice for smart drinking, principally from the French regions. Prices are kept moderate, with house reds and whites starting off at £12.50 and around 20 wines by the glass from £3.20.

CHEF: Seamus Riordan PROPRIETOR: Searcy Tansley and Co Ltd OPEN: all week L 11.45 to 2.45, Thur and Fri D 5 to 8.30 MEALS: alc (main courses £11.50 to £16.50) SERVICE: 12.5% (optional), card slips closed CARDS: Amex, Delta, Diners, MasterCard, Switch, Visa DETAILS: 100 seats. Private parties: 120 main room. Vegetarian meals. Children's helpings. No smoking in dining room. Wheelchair access (also WC). No music. Air-conditioned ⊖ Leicester Square

Neal Street Restaurant map 15

26 Neal Street, WC2H 9PS
TEL: (020) 7836 8368 FAX: (020) 7240 3964
EMAIL: gisellebd@nealstreet.co.uk

COOKING **2**
ITALIAN
£37–£75

A bright interior with light colours, mirrored walls, imaginative pictures and sardine-packed tables is the setting for Antonio Carluccio's original restaurant (he now has three cafés to his name as well, all in London W1). Mushrooms feature prominently whatever the season – in a soup, a fry-up, a salad, and a main course such as medallions of pink lamb with morels – while luxuries include shavings of truffle on threads of 'divine' tagliolini. Other pasta options might include venison ravioli with a game sauce, or a daily special, perhaps with mussels and clams.

Sauces can be quite strident (a sweet saba one to accompany first-rate foie gras, for example), and the cooking can be rather routine, but well-rendered desserts have included mandarin pannacotta, and a passion fruit and Campari sorbet. The absence of an inexpensive set lunch seems odd, although perhaps not to the many expense-account customers. Service is generally efficient and accommodating, wines are almost entirely Italian and not cheap, though there are some wines under £25 and several by the glass from £3.50

CHEF: Flavio Giacoletto PROPRIETOR: Antonio Carluccio OPEN: Mon to Sat 12 to 2.30, 6 to 11 CLOSED: 25 Dec to 2 Jan MEALS: alc (main courses £10.50 to £19.50) SERVICE: 12.5% (optional), card slips closed CARDS: Amex, Delta, Diners, MasterCard, Switch, Visa DETAILS: 65 seats. Private parties: 65 main room, 24 private room. Vegetarian meals. No music. Air-conditioned ⊖ Covent Garden

Neat Restaurant

NEW ENTRY **map 13**

Second Floor, Oxo Tower Wharf,
Barge House Street, SE1 9PH
TEL/FAX: (020) 7928 5533 — COOKING **5**
EMAIL: eat@neatrestaurant.co.uk — FRENCH
WEB SITE: www.neatrestaurant.co.uk — £44–£88

Housed a few floors down from Oxo Tower (see entry), the grey and purple dining room's view of the river is equally intriguing, if a little less romantic at such close quarters. Readers may remember Richard Neat from his days at Pied-à-Terre in Charlotte Street (see entry), before he disappeared to Cannes to become one of the few Englishmen to achieve culinary distinction on French soil. His return was heralded by hundreds of laudatory column inches in the gastro-press, and great things were expected. His canvas is a straightforwardly presented menu with around seven items per course at dinner (two items per course at lunch), in which some unusual flavour combinations surface: roast scallops with black pudding, scrambled egg and caramelised apple, for instance, or rillettes of red mullet with prune purée and almond cream.

At its best the cooking has displayed some precise technique – in the timing of seared turbot fillet, 'still smoking' as it arrived, accompanied by fine pasta interleaved with tiny shelled shrimps – although early reports indicated some dramatic swings in quality. Highly rated desserts include chocolate fondant with a 'sensational' coconut sorbet, and a disc of rhubarb mousse topped with syrupy rhubarb batons and a light and crispy sesame tuile. If the food has neither the consistency nor the intensity of Neat's earlier days, this may not be unconnected with the fact that he appears to divide his time between London and Cannes. Service from formally dressed staff varies from 'attentive' to 'inefficient' to 'arrogant', and meals are sometimes well paced, sometimes slow. The wine list is a good one, with a fine French section well supported by Italy and Spain, although mark-ups are off-putting. Neat Brasserie, on the same floor, deals in some innovative dishes such as garlic soup with rabbit offal, and red mullet Wellington; desserts are from a trolley.

CHEF: Richard Neat OPEN: Mon to Fri L 12 to 2, Mon to Sat D 7 to 10 CLOSED: 25 Dec MEALS: Set L £29, Set D £49 SERVICE: 12.5% (optional), card slips closed CARDS: Amex, Delta, MasterCard, Switch, Visa DETAILS: 120 seats. Private parties: 120 main room, 150 private room. No smoking in 1 dining room. Wheelchair access (also WC). Music. Air-conditioned ⊖ Waterloo, Southwark

New Tayyabs £ map 12

83 Fieldgate, E1 1JU COOKING **2**
TEL: (020) 7247 9543/8521 FAX: (020) 7247 9543 PAKISTANI
WEB SITE: www.tayyabs.co.uk £11–£34

This simple restaurant opens when Tayyabs, its even more basic daytime sister next door, closes at 5pm. In a pleasant, basically furnished room it provides simple meals of Pakistani Punjabi food comprising tandoori dishes and karahi bowls of curry. Tikkas are listed only as starters, but an assortment of chicken, lamb and fish with naan or roti bread, and perhaps a karahi of dhal, okra or chickpeas, can be more than satisfying. Main-course karahi dishes include, in addition, quails, large or small prawns, and varied combinations of meat and vegetables. There are also daily specials, usually two, except on Fridays (one: meat biryani) and Saturdays (four). The restaurant is closed for the month of Ramadan, and no alcohol is sold at any time, but you may bring your own, and no corkage is charged.

CHEF/PROPRIETOR: M. Tayyab OPEN: all week D only, 5 to 11.30 CLOSED: 1 month during Ramadan MEALS: alc (main courses £3 to £8) SERVICE: not inc CARDS: none DETAILS: 70 seats. 8 seats outside. Vegetarian meals. Music ⊖ Whitechapel, Aldgate East

Nicole's map 15

158 New Bond Street, W1Y 9PA COOKING **4**
TEL: (020) 7499 8408 FAX: (020) 7409 0381 MODERN EUROPEAN
£44–£72

Nicole's caters for well-heeled shoppers in Ms Farhi's trendy clothing emporium, serving breakfasts and afternoon teas as well as a bar menu and a full restaurant carte. But this is not your average in-store canteen: décor is suitably stylish, featuring lots of bare wood, mirrors and large vases of lilies. Seasonally changing menus offer modern European cooking with Californian influences, with the emphasis on wholesome ingredients and simple presentation, avoiding unnecessary flourish. Grilling is a favoured treatment, applied to tuna, served with roasted globe artichokes, braised chickpeas and aïoli, and to rump of lamb, accompanied by roasted squash and a pomegranate and mint relish. These might be preceded by warm wild mushrooms on toasted onion bread, or Roquefort, chicory and pear salad, and followed by rhubarb and custard meringue tartlet. As with the tailoring, quality materials are handled with great assurance to produce food that is 'good in every detail', though prices reflect the Mayfair location, not least on the short wine list, which opens at

£12.50 but soon escalates beyond the £20 horizon, although nearly 20 wines are offered in two sizes of glass.

CHEF: Annie Wayte PROPRIETOR: Stephen Marks OPEN: Mon to Sat L 12 to 3.30, Mon to Fri D 6.30 to 10.45 CLOSED: bank hols MEALS: alc (main courses £16.50 to £20). Cover £1. Bar menu available L SERVICE: 15% (optional), card slips closed CARDS: Amex, Delta, Diners, MasterCard, Switch, Visa DETAILS: 90 seats. Private parties: 80 main room. Vegetarian meals. No-smoking area. Music. Air-conditioned ⊖ Green Park, Bond Street

Noble Rot

map 15

3–5 Mill Street, W1R 9TF
TEL: (020) 7629 8877 FAX: (020) 7629 8878
EMAIL: noblerot@noblerot.com
WEB SITE: www.noblerot.com

COOKING **5**
MODERN EUROPEAN
£46–£101

The surroundings may be incongruous, and the entrance may not be obvious, but the restaurant is pretty clear where it's coming from. Sweet wines, understandably a strength, partner certain things such as foie gras extremely well, so there is no shortage of it: simply seared with potato cake and rhubarb; a foie gras and smoked eel terrine served with apple jelly; and even a dessert terrine combining foie gras and chocolate. Not all the sweet wines on the list are made from botrytis-affected grapes, which is a blessing because these are notoriously expensive: there are Sauternes in three figures, a Tokaji in four (for 50 centilitres), and other gems from the Loire, Alsace, Germany and elsewhere, about half of them available by the glass.

Those on a tighter budget will find a few relatively affordable alternatives such as Essensia, Elysium, Banyuls and Vin Santo, and those who crave something other than foie gras will find plenty to amuse: from caramelised sweetbreads with verjuice and chive beurre blanc, to seared scallops with truffle mash; from roast turbot with lobster raviolo, to a whole truffled baby chicken with morels and Gewürztraminer sauce. Luxuries obviously abound, but the kitchen seems equally happy serving a dish of roast rabbit and black pudding with mushy peas, and rhubarb and apple crumble with custard. The rest of the wine list constitutes a fine collection but assumes that, outside the house selection, nobody is seriously expecting change from £20.

CHEF: Matthew Owsley-Brown PROPRIETOR: Soren Jessen OPEN: Mon to Fri L 12 to 3, Mon to Sat D 6.30 to 10.30 CLOSED: bank hols MEALS: alc (main courses £13 to £28). Light L menu available SERVICE: 12.5% (optional), card slips closed CARDS: Amex, Delta, Diners, MasterCard, Switch, Visa DETAILS: 60 seats. 20 seats outside. Private parties: 70 main room. Children's helpings. Wheelchair access (also women's WC). Music. Air-conditioned ⊖ Oxford Circus

Occasional music *in the details at the end of an entry means live or recorded music is played in the dining room only rarely or for special events.* No music *means it is never played.*

The Guide's longest-serving restaurants are listed near the front of the book.

New main entries and restaurant closures are listed near the front of the book.

Nobu

map 15

19 Old Park Lane, W1Y 4LB
TEL: (020) 7447 4747 FAX: (020) 7447 4749

COOKING **6**
JAPANESE/SOUTH AMERICAN
£32–£110

After five years, Nobu's cult status remains undiminished. It occupies a long, hard-surfaced, thoroughly contemporary room overlooking Park Lane and Hyde Park, with a small non-bookable sushi bar and a mid-Atlantic feel. Although the booking system and reception can be condescending, once you get to a table the smart staff can't do enough to be charming, helpful and informative. The menu is not easy to come to terms with, offering scores of items in different sections, so the easy option is to put yourself in the hands of the staff, who will painstakingly answer questions about any dish, and eventually work out an appropriate meal that reflects your likes and dislikes.

Impeccable raw materials, seductive presentation and sensitive handling keep reporters coming back for more. What powers the food and gives it vitality is the supreme freshness of fish and shellfish, combined with first-rate cutting and slicing skills, and the fine detail of flavour or texture that can turn a good dish into an exciting one. Among these are yellowtail sashimi with jalapeño, voted 'the best Japanese dish in London' by one who eats around, sushi with either toro tuna or salmon toppings, and a large fillet of miso-marinated black cod, flaking at the touch of a chopstick.

Cooked dishes in the set-price multi-course Omakase menu are less impressive than the raw ones, the highlight at inspection being a pair of plump and dazzlingly fresh sea snails with a sweet-sharp salsa cruda. Desserts get in on the fusion act too, one of the best being a bento box of chocolate cake with an oozing centre, served with a blob of gently bitter green tea ice cream. Not all visitors, it has to be said, are equally happy with results, suggesting a degree of variation that a single cooking mark is unable to reflect. Wines (grouped by style) are tolerably priced for the location, starting at £14.50, but as an alternative consider the varied, well-described saké list. A sister restaurant, Ubon, is located at Canary Wharf (see entry).

CHEF: Mark Edwards PROPRIETORS: Nobuyuki Matsuhisa, Robert De Niro and Drew Nieporent OPEN: Mon to Fri L 12 to 2.15, all week D 6 to 11 (9.45 Sun) CLOSED: most bank hols MEALS: alc (main courses £5 to £27.50). Set L £25 to £50, Set D £70 SERVICE: 15% (optional), card slips closed CARDS: Amex, Delta, Diners, MasterCard, Switch, Visa DETAILS: 150 seats. Private parties: 10 main room, 40 private room. Vegetarian meals. No smoking in 1 dining room. No cigars in dining room. Wheelchair access (also WC). Music. Air-conditioned ⊖ Hyde Park Corner

Noura

NEW ENTRY map 13

16 Hobart Place, SW1W 0HH
TEL: (020) 7235 9444 FAX: (020) 7235 9244

COOKING **4**
LEBANESE
£24–£59

Acres of space, mirrors, green leather banquettes and pistachio walls make this Lebanese restaurant different from most Middle Eastern competitors in London: it is sleek, minimal and functional. Service – from all-male, French-accented and flirtatious waiters – is almost theatrical, with black-clad figures swooping and swerving with precision and panache. As for food, there's a long list of cold and hot mezzes (over 20 of each), and abundant vegetarian dishes (all indicated on the menu). Hummus is spiked with plenty of garlic, lemon juice and smoky, dark tahini. Aubergines, tomatoes and chickpeas are served in numerous flavoursome ways, while batrakh (thinly sliced grey mullet roe) is fried with caramelised, thinly sliced fried garlic.

For meat-eaters, there are mezze of bastorma (thinly sliced smoked beef) and kafta nayeh (lamb tartare with parsley and onion) and a selection of minced, skewered, marinated and grilled meats for main courses. Portions are large, and, despite the variety of salad vegetables, the food can be seem quite dense; some dishes can also be slightly cautious, and so rather lacking in punch. Lebanese coffee is thick and spicy. Lebanon and France (particularly Champagne) dominate the short, rather expensive wine list, whose prices start at £18.

CHEF: Tony Esber PROPRIETOR: Nader Bou Antoun OPEN: all week 11.30am to 11.45pm MEALS: alc (main courses £10 to £18). Set L 11.30 to 6 £12.50, Set D £18.50 to £28.50 (all min 2) SERVICE: not inc CARDS: Amex, Delta, Diners, MasterCard, Switch, Visa DETAILS: 110 seats. Private parties: 125 main room. Vegetarian meals. Wheelchair access (also WC). Music. Air-conditioned ⊖ Victoria

No. 6 George Street NEW ENTRY map 15

6 George Street, W1H 5RA COOKING **2**
TEL: (020) 7935 1910 FAX: (020) 7935 6036 MODERN BRITISH
£26–£46

Beyond the breads, hams, cheeses and vegetables on display in this restaurant-delicatessen off Marylebone High Street is an uncluttered, rustic dining room with scrubbed pine tables. Straightforward lunches are mainly light and salady but with fish (roast sea bass) and meat (chicken club sandwich) for variety. A simple herb omelette, unusual these days, typifies unassuming cooking done with honesty and care. Freshness is palpable: much material comes from Milan market, some from English farms.

Leaves – typically an adventurous and interesting mix – underpin many dishes: supporting pieces of caramelised butternut squash balanced by a sharp goats' cheese and crispy bits of ham, or under chunks of skinless red pepper and croûtons thickly smeared with smoked haddock brandade. Dressings are good too. More substantial are spaghetti with meatballs (finely ground lamb) in fresh-tasting tomato sauce, and an accurately timed and well-balanced rocket and prosciutto risotto. Finally, try chocolate and hazelnut torte sliced from a cake on the counter, served with good vanilla ice cream. Service by a 'wonder woman' is friendly and impressively efficient, though cooking to order can mean slow meals at busy times. Twenty well-chosen wines run from £12.50 to £26.50.

CHEF/PROPRIETOR: Emma Miller OPEN: Mon to Fri L only 12 to 3 CLOSED: 2 weeks Christmas, 2 weeks Aug MEALS: alc (main courses £8 to £14) SERVICE: not inc CARDS: Delta, MasterCard, Switch, Visa DETAILS: 30 seats. Private parties: 40 main room. Vegetarian meals. No smoking in dining room. No music. Air-conditioned ⊖ Bond Street

Although the cuisine style noted at the top of entries has in most cases been suggested to the Guide by the restaurants, some have been edited for brevity or appropriateness.

Oak Room Marco Pierre White

map 15

21 Piccadilly, W1V 0BH
TEL: (020) 7437 0202 FAX: (020) 7851 3141

COOKING 6
FRENCH
£38–£97

The large scale, limed oak, big chandeliers and huge flower displays have combined to make this one of London's grander, more imposing dining rooms. With banquettes down the side, and more expansive tables in the centre, it caters equally for intimate twos and small groups of businessmen. In its time, when Marco himself cooked here, it delivered some of the finest cooking in London, and the kitchen has done sterling service under the direction of Robert Reid.

The repertoire continues to deliver well-rehearsed dishes in which prime ingredients, and smooth, caressing textures produce seductive results. If the supply of luxuries were cut off, the kitchen might not actually grind to a halt, but it would have to find substitutes for its foie gras terrine with Sauternes jelly, its lobster salad, and its ballottine of salmon with caviar. The classical French background also delivers humbler items such as oeuf mollet à la meurette, elixir of tomato and melon with herbs, and braised pig's trotter in the style of Pierre Koffmann. If Bresse pigeon with foie gras is one of the 'must have' main courses, then pyramid of passion fruit and nougat glace is perhaps the dessert equivalent, although there is competition from a gratinée of Alpine strawberries with lime sabayon. There are two wine lists, a 'fine wine' version of great names and vintages, and a 'sommelier selection' supposedly chosen for quality and value, although it assumes you wouldn't dream of paying less than £20 for anything.

CHEF: Robert Reid PROPRIETOR: Marco Pierre White OPEN: Mon to Fri L 12 to 2.45, Mon to Sat D 6.45 to 11.15 CLOSED: 24 Dec to 4 Jan, May bank hols MEALS: alc (main courses £14 to £26). Set L £20 to £27.50, Set D £45 SERVICE: 12.5% (optional), card slips closed CARDS: Amex, Delta, Diners, MasterCard, Switch, Visa DETAILS: 65 seats. Private parties: 100 main room. Children's helpings. Wheelchair access (also WC). No music. Air-conditioned ⊖ Piccadilly Circus

Odette's

map 13

130 Regent's Park Road, NW1 8XL
TEL: (020) 7586 5486 FAX: (020) 7586 0508
EMAIL: rboulert@aol.com

COOKING 4
MODERN BRITISH
£23–£59

Of all the varied eateries in Primrose Hill village, Odette's is the jewel in the crown. The area has gone from sleepy backwater to bustling hangout of media celebs in recent years, and Simone Green's restaurant has followed the vicissitudes, all the time remaining 'exactly what you want from a neighbourhood restaurant'. Downstairs is an informal wine bar, while the ground floor is an engaging mix of conservatory, a many-mirrored half-landing, and a front area where windows open on to the street in warm weather.

The cooking is contemporary without being too avant-garde. Although it can just about pull off a dish of seared tuna with first-rate tempura-battered tiger prawns, black peppercorn ice cream and duck crackling, its more usual style is exemplified by roast Cornish lobster with sauté asparagus and an expertly made lobster coral foam, and by Norfolk squab pigeon with a huge piece of seared foie gras, peas and truffled mash. 'Potted Horlicks custard' turns out to be a droll take on crème caramel with an accompaniment of glazed banana. Service can, at times, be slow.

The stylistic headings and food-matching recommendations that introduce each section are useful guides to this astutely selected wine list. A 'Cellarman's Choice' selection towards the front offers a handy cross-section, and highlights the diversity and originality on offer. Bottles under £25 are plentiful, with house wines starting at £11.95.

CHEF: Simon Bradley PROPRIETOR: Simone Green OPEN: Sun to Fri L 12.30 to 2.30, Mon to Sat D 7 to 11 CLOSED: 10 days Christmas, Good Fri, Easter Mon, bank hol Mons MEALS: alc (main courses £10.50 to £17.50). Set L £12.50 SERVICE: not inc CARDS: Amex, Delta, Diners, MasterCard, Switch, Visa DETAILS: 68 seats. 6 seats outside. Private parties: 30 main room, 10 and 30 private rooms. Vegetarian meals. No cigars/pipes in dining room. Wheelchair access (not WC). No music ⊖ Chalk Farm

Old Delhi

map 13

48 Kendal Street, W2 2BP
TEL: (020) 7723 3335 FAX: (020) 7258 0181
WEB SITE: www.old-delhi.com.uk

COOKING **1**
INDIAN/IRANIAN
£36–£79

Comfortable, stylish, relaxed and smart, with a decorative theme featuring the crown of Persia, Old Delhi is unusual in that it combines elements of both Indian and Iranian cooking. The latter, less well known in this country, adds a sense of adventure, with classics of its repertoire among the specialities: fesenjune is roast sliced duck with a walnut and pomegranate sauce, while gaimeh is a mix of lamb, aubergine, yellow peas and spices. Elsewhere there are many familiar items from vegetable samosa to lamb and chicken curries, by way of tandoori dishes. As an alternative to the usual sticky sweets, try the cassis ice cream. Poppadums come with standard relishes, service borders on the military, with uniformed staff delivering dishes at the double, and a short list of mostly French wines offers a few reasonable options around £20 to £25.

CHEFS: Mr Betia and Mr Hussain PROPRIETOR: Oldelms Ltd OPEN: all week 12.30 (1 Sat and Sun) to 3.30 (4 Sat and Sun), 6.30 (7 Sat and Sun) to 11 CLOSED: 24 Dec to 2 Jan MEALS: alc (main courses £9 to £26). Cover £2 SERVICE: 15% CARDS: Amex, Delta, Diners, MasterCard, Switch, Visa DETAILS: 55 seats. Private parties: 55 main room. Vegetarian meals. No children after 8. Wheelchair access (not WC). Music. Air-conditioned ⊖ Marble Arch (£5)

Olivo

map 13

21 Eccleston Street, SW1V 2DL
TEL: (020) 7730 2505 FAX: (020) 7824 8190

COOKING **2**
ITALIAN/SARDINIAN
£30–£49

This small, ever-busy Italian restaurant with strong Sardinian credentials is popular with Belgravia locals. Bright yellow-and-blue-painted roughcast walls and small tightly packed tables, wooden floors and chairs afford a rustic, informal air of 'village simplicity'. Service is brisk and efficient, the atmosphere bustling and the cooking straightforward, with chargrilling a favoured method for main courses. Flat spaghetti with green beans, potatoes and pesto, or deep-fried squid with rocket and balsamic, might be followed by well-timed chargrilled calf's liver or beef escalope with marinated tomatoes. To finish, there may be lemon and mascarpone tart. It's also worth checking out the house specialities, among them linguine with crab, spaghetti with red mullet roe, or sea bass baked with Vernaccia and olives. Good espresso, and a short all-Italian wine list with a special Sardinian selection (plus house wine at £13.50), complete the picture.

CHEFS: Marco Melis and Andrea Orru PROPRIETORS: Mauro Sanna and Jean-Louis Journade OPEN: Mon to Fri L 12 to 2.30, all week D 7 to 11 CLOSED: Christmas, bank hols MEALS: alc D (main courses £12.50 to £13.50). Set L £15 (2 courses) to £17. Cover £1.50 SERVICE: not inc CARDS: Amex, Delta, MasterCard, Switch, Visa DETAILS: 42 seats. No cigars/pipes in dining room. No music. Air-conditioned ⊖ Victoria

1 Lombard Street 🍷 map 13

1 Lombard Street, EC3V 9AA
TEL: (020) 7929 6611 FAX: (020) 7929 6622 COOKING **4**
EMAIL: tg@1lombardstreet.com MODERN EUROPEAN
WEB SITE: www.1lombardstreet.com £47–£92

This former bank, its high ceilings topped with a cupola (beneath which sits the circular bar, jumping on Friday nights) is popular for City lunches. Food in the brasserie is rather cheaper than in the restaurant, and there is a wide choice of seafood (including – this being the City – caviar). The restaurant's à la carte menu has some trendy ingredients, such as the black radish, and ginger and lime vinaigrette, that accompany a carpaccio of tuna with Oriental spices and toasted sesame seeds.

Starters tend to be smallish (three langoustines on a tiny quenelle of leek purée) and main courses are happily not quite as intricate as they sound, producing a generous piece of roast turbot on an intense mushroomy ragoût, and beef fillet accompanied by a disc of foie gras and a concentrated red wine reduction. Carbohydrate appears not to feature. Desserts range from lime tart to ginger crème brûlée. Unless you're on an expense account, the set lunch and dinner menus (restaurant only) are simpler and better value. The wine list is big on champagne (24 choices) and has ten well-chosen house wines by bottle or glass (from £14/£3.50), plus regional depth (including some adventurous New World bottles), star names (not always the obvious ones) and a few bins under £20.

CHEF: Herbert Berger PROPRIETOR: Soren Jessen OPEN: Mon to Fri 12 to 3, 6 to 10 CLOSED: 24 Dec to 1 Jan, Easter, bank hols MEALS: alc (main courses £27.50 to £29.50). Set L £32 (2 courses) to £38, Set D £28 (2 courses) to £32. Brasserie menu available SERVICE: 12.5% (optional), card slips closed CARDS: Amex, Delta, Diners, MasterCard, Switch, Visa DETAILS: 40 seats (Brasserie 150). Private parties: 40 main room (Brasserie 200), 40 private room. Vegetarian meals. Wheelchair access (also WC). Air-conditioned ⊖ Bank

The cuisine styles noted at the tops of entries are only an approximation, often suggested to us by the restaurants themselves. Please read the entry itself to find out more about the cooking style.

London Round-ups listing additional restaurants that may be worth a visit can be found after the main London section.

192

map 13

192 Kensington Park Road, W11 2ES
TEL: (020) 7229 0482 FAX: (020) 7229 3300

COOKING **1**
MODERN BRITISH
£25–£55

The enduringly fashionable 192 continues to draw well-heeled crowds, and if the lurid red tables (with no cloths) epitomise the rather dated 1990s décor, then the vibrant, in-place atmosphere still appeals. The menu dances to a modern beat and gives a trendy nod to the Mediterranean, the style reflected in starters of Serrano ham, artichoke and roasted peppers, or truffled pecorino with potato and bean salad. Roast endive, caramelised baby onions and Pernod jus provide the accompaniments for pan-fried cod, while smoked duck risotto is teamed with broad beans and mozzarella. Finish with grapefruit and strawberry sorbets, summer pudding, or cheesecake. Service is well natured and friendly enough, while the globetrotting, well-chosen wine list features some 28 by the glass and a reasonable choice under £20. House wines are £10.50.

CHEF: Mark Parris PROPRIETOR: Capital Venture PLC OPEN: all week 12.30 to 3 (3.30 Sat and Sun), 6.30 to 11.30 (7 to 11 Sun) CLOSED: Aug bank hol MEALS: alc (main courses £8.50 to £15.50). Set L £10 (2 courses) SERVICE: 12.5% (optional), card slips closed CARDS: Amex, Delta, Diners, MasterCard, Switch, Visa DETAILS: 96 seats. 16 seats outside. Private parties: 8 main room. Vegetarian meals. No-smoking area. Wheelchair access (not WC). Music. Air-conditioned ⊖ Ladbroke Grove, Notting Hill Gate

▲ One-O-One

map 14

Williams Street, SW1X 7RN
TEL: (020) 7290 7101 FAX: (020) 7235 8231
EMAIL: oneoone@luxurycollection.com

COOKING **5**
SEAFOOD
£43–£103

Sitting right on the Knightsbridge pavement, 101 is a spacious, civilised aquamarine-coloured room with rag-rolled walls, veneered wooden pillars, striking flower displays, and a 14-foot sculpture of a fish testifying to the kitchen's main business. Inspiration may owe much to Pascal Proyart's native Brittany, but he has moved way beyond the boatloads of shellfish that keep the tourist trade going. Not only are luxury materials much in evidence, but there is a resolutely modern and sometimes innovative approach to the food.

Dishes sometimes involve several components, but don't lose sight of the big picture, as in a skilfully prepared parsley risotto partly wrapped in a thin Parmesan egg pancake, garnished with slivers of truffle and pieces of king crab, all sitting on a bed of thinly sliced tomato, set about with a light, frothy, truffley sauce. Other ideas can be plainer – a piece of turbot roasted on the bone, with thick-cut chips (Pont Neuf potatoes) and a tomato-flavoured béarnaise (sauce choron) – and there are meat options too, including caramelised Barbary duck with spring onion mash and a gently oriental orange and ginger sauce.

Desserts, at least in summer, explore the fruity end of the spectrum, in a simple, light collation of berries with a sorbet and champagne sabayon, or an equally refreshing 'ravioli' made from thin pineapple slices encasing a layer of raspberries, topped with a lemon grass sorbet. If the carte seems aggressively priced, the set lunch, with more straightforward cooking, can be considered a relative bargain. The chatty restaurant manager, Andrew Morgan, is 'worth a chunk of the bill', although wines can easily grab a big share of it too: if you want change from £20, best to drink a half-bottle or a couple of glasses.

CHEF: Pascal Proyart PROPRIETOR: Starwood Hotels and Resorts OPEN: all week 12 to 2.15, 7 to 10.15 MEALS: alc (main courses £18 to £25). Set L £19.50 (2 courses) to £25, Set D £58 to £78 (inc wine) SERVICE: not inc, card slips closed CARDS: Amex, Delta, Diners, MasterCard, Visa DETAILS: 76 seats. Private parties: 100 main room. Children's helpings. No smoking in 1 dining room. Wheelchair access (not WC). Occasional music. Air-conditioned ACCOMMODATION: 289 rooms, all with bath/shower. TV. Phone. Room only £259 to £2,500. Rooms for disabled. Baby facilities ⊖ Knightsbridge (£5)

L'Oranger

map 15

5 St James's Street, SW1A 1EF — COOKING **6**
TEL: (020) 7839 3374 FAX: (020) 7839 4330 — FRENCH/MEDITERRANEAN
£44–£107

There is an ocean-liner feel to the long, thin dining room of this St James's stalwart, although a skylight and clever lighting effectively soften the edges. A set dinner menu (£39.50 for three courses, excluding supplements) constitutes a relatively stable core of dishes, while a more fluid short list of changing specialities offers a roll-call of expensive ingredients such as caviar, lobster, crevettes, langoustines, beef with foie gras, and milk-fed lamb. The main menu is uncompromisingly French and every bit as formal as the largely Francophone staff.

It is an appealing style, ranging from a starter of pork belly (cooked pot-au-feu-fashion), crowned with shavings of black truffle and served with mash, to a main course of roast turbot, surrounded by a ring of baby shrimps and topped with a frothy shrimp sauce. The cooking is generally well-timed, although consistency can suffer when the kitchen is busy, and a tendency to over-season has been noted. The cheeseboard is well tended, and desserts – such as pear tarte Tatin, and lemon thyme crème caramel – are generally in the classic style rather than ground-breakingly original; some seem to be more successful than others. The wine list, a massive tome, lists 587 wines, most from the classic areas of France, with a number of bottles from Italy, the US and Australia, plus token offerings from New Zealand, Argentina and elsewhere. House wines are £25, and mark-ups are generally aggressive.

CHEF: Kamel Benamar PROPRIETOR: A To Z Group OPEN: Mon to Fri L 12 to 2.30, Mon to Sat D 6.30 to 11 CLOSED: Christmas, bank hols MEALS: Set L £20 (2 courses) to £24.50, Set D £35 (2 courses) to £50 SERVICE: 12.5% (optional), card slips closed CARDS: Amex, Delta, Diners, MasterCard, Switch, Visa DETAILS: 55 seats. 10 seats outside. Private parties: 65 main room, 22 private room. No children under 11. No cigars/pipes in dining room. Wheelchair access (not WC). No music. Air-conditioned ⊖ Green Park

---

The nearest Underground station is indicated at the end of London entries.

Card slips closed *in the details at the end of an entry indicates that the total on the slips of credit cards is closed when handed over for signature.*

Orient Restaurant

map 15

157–160 Piccadilly, W1J 9EB
TEL: (020) 7499 6888 FAX: (020) 7659 9300
EMAIL: monicabrown@chinahouse.co.uk
WEB SITE: www.chinahouse.co.uk

COOKING **4**
CHINESE
£32–£70

Next to the Ritz Hotel, the Orient is the first-floor luxury restaurant in the China House complex, which also incorporates a simpler restaurant, two bars and a shop. Admire Piccadilly through the windows, or the modern art inside: cut-outs of Chairman Mao and minimal landscapes. As we went to press, menu improvements were planned, but the style will remain the same: mainly classical Chinese dishes plus a few foreign invaders. One that will stay is Imperial Nam King duck, a Peking duck variation that may appeal to westerners – and perhaps some Chinese – who dislike the traditional version's layer of creamy fat between skin and meat (here it is removed, and the skin replaced). In another upgrade of a popular (some might say hackneyed) dish, crispy 'seaweed' is replaced by crisp whole-leaf spinach with caramelised cashews. Desserts are western with a few oriental ingredients: such as say, sticky tamarind pudding with caramel ice cream, or spiced ginger cheesecake. Côtes du Rhône, white and red, at £18 and £19, are the only wines below £20; the other forty are French and New World classics.

CHEF: Chris Kwan PROPRIETORS: Eddie Wat and Saeb Eigner OPEN: Mon to Fri L 12 to 2.30, Mon to Sat D 6 to 11 CLOSED: bank hols MEALS: alc (main courses £8 to £16). Set L £15 (2 courses) to £17.50, Set D £30 to £60. Clipper Bar menu also available SERVICE: 12.5% (optional) CARDS: Amex, MasterCard, Switch, Visa DETAILS: 120 seats. Private parties: 140 main room, 16 private room. Vegetarian meals. Children's helpings. No music. Air-conditioned ⊖ Green Park

Original Tagines

map 15

7A Dorset Street, W1H 3FE
TEL/FAX: (020) 7935 1545

COOKING **2**
MOROCCAN
£21–£44

New ownership has left the menu virtually unaltered although the name has changed (last year it was called Tajine). The décor too has been improved: attractive ceramic plates replace travel posters on the walls, and table tops are now colourful mosaic. Service is friendly and efficient even at busy times, and the bill laudably says 'gratuities are to be awarded for good service only'. The menu of classic Moroccan dishes takes in such starters as kidneys with mustard sauce, fried or stewed aubergines, and separate salads of red peppers, lentils, tabbouleh and broad beans. The bread is highly commended. B'stilla (chicken or seafood pie) can be a starter, middle or main course, but it would be a pity to miss the eponymous tagines, with their 'divinely harmonious flavours' of meat, vegetables, fruit and spices. Couscous and grills are the other main dishes. Moroccan pastries don't match the main dishes' excellence, but mint tea, traditionally poured from high above the tables, is an ideal way to finish. Moroccan house wines are £11.25, but Guerrouanne rosé (the real rosé, not the gris) is worth an extra £2.

The Good Food Guide 2002
voucher scheme

Valid at participating restaurants, as listed in *The Good Food Guide 2002*, until 30 September 2002

See terms and conditions overleaf

The Good Food Guide 2002
voucher scheme

Valid at participating restaurants, as listed in *The Good Food Guide 2002*, until 30 September 2002

See terms and conditions overleaf

The Good Food Guide 2002
voucher scheme

Valid at participating restaurants, as listed in *The Good Food Guide 2002*, until 30 September 2002

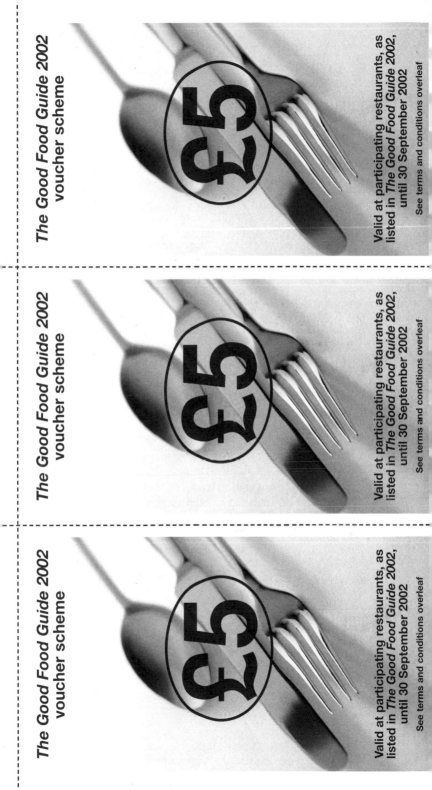

See terms and conditions overleaf

comfortingly soft, producing highly rated pan-fried sweetbreads with flavourful ceps, and pink corn-fed French pigeon, as tender as can be, served with garlic confit and wild mushrooms.

Vegetarians are well treated, given a velouté of new season's garlic with poached quails' eggs, and potato gnocchi with tomato, basil and olive sauce, but then meat eaters don't go hungry either. An assiette of suckling pig ('too much to list; ask your waiter', says the menu) consists of 'a hotchpotch of pig parts', according to one visitor: a slice of belly, piece of shoulder, couple of tiny ribs, and something unidentifiable, all served with cabbage and a disc of black pudding. Desserts may not be quite up to the standard of the rest, although apple and calvados soufflé is 'hard to fault'. Service, which starts with an automated booking system, consists of greeters, waiters, section heads, and various other ranks and echelons, and is 'very skilled'. The wine list is packed with gems, from house vin de pays at £13.50 to the stars of Bordeaux, Italy and California. A succinct range by the glass in lively styles starts at £3.50.

CHEF: Simon Arkless PROPRIETOR: Dickson Poon OPEN: Sun to Fri L 12 to 2.45, all week D 6.30 to 11.15 CLOSED: 25 and 26 Dec MEALS: alc (main courses £11 to £26). Set L £27.50, Set D £60 to £95 (inc wine) SERVICE: 12.5%, card slips closed CARDS: Amex, Delta, Diners, MasterCard, Switch, Visa DETAILS: 130 seats. 75 seats outside. Vegetarian meals. Wheelchair access (also WC). No music. Air-conditioned ⊖ Blackfriars

Ozer

map 15

5 Langham Place, W1B 3DG
TEL: (020) 7323 0505 FAX: (020) 7323 0111 — COOKING **5**
EMAIL: res@ozer.co.uk — MODERN OTTOMAN
WEB SITE: www.ozer.co.uk — £20–£64

In the shadow of the BBC building at Langham Place the interior of this svelte restaurant has more of the swish hotel than the kasbah about it, with its blood-red walls, gleaming marble-tiled floor and concentric copper light fittings. The cooking has certainly caught London's mood, to judge by our postbag. Readers who dined on marinated olives, excellent bread and a spicy dip, followed by fine and varied meze with a bottle of Turkish red, emerged a happy trio. Some feel that the spicing of fish dishes, whether sea bream or monkfish, is a little too heavy to allow the main ingredient to shine, but grills impress, and the aromatic accompaniments – smoky aubergine purée as a bed for gently stewed lamb, or a blend of walnuts, garlic and olive oil to go with fried squid marinated in milk and vodka – are arresting. The full meze deal is particularly good value, embracing imam bayaldi, börek, fried halloumi cheese, tabbouleh, falafel and much more. Baklava with rose-scented ice cream seems a good way to finish, the filo pastry flaky, the filling intensely sweet, and the ice cream as exotically perfumed as can be. Wines are led by France, but include eastern Mediterranean and New World offerings; house Turkish wines are £12.50, French £14.

CHEF/PROPRIETOR: Huseyin Ozer OPEN: all week, noon to midnight MEALS: alc (main courses £7 to £17.50). Set L 12 to 6 £6.95 (2 courses). Set L and D £9.95. Bar menu also available SERVICE: 12.5%, card slips closed CARDS: Amex, Delta, Diners, MasterCard, Switch, Visa DETAILS: 100 seats. 20 seats outside. Vegetarian meals. Children's helpings. Wheelchair access (also WC). No music. Air-conditioned ⊖ Oxford Circus (£5)

Palais du Jardin

map 15

136 Long Acre, WC2E 9AD
TEL: (020) 7379 5353 FAX: (020) 7379 1846
EMAIL: lepalaisdujardin@hotmail.com

COOKING **2**
FRENCH
£30–£61

On hot days Covent Garden is crowded with tables and drinkers spilling out of bars. The Palais is in the thick of all this, and even those staying indoors may find some jostling involved. The mood, though, can be infectious, and the cooking sets out to catch it. Smoked salmon on bubble and squeak with a horseradishy sauce tickled one reader's tastebuds, breast of duck with pak choi and caramelised pineapple making a similarly lively main course. The name is French, so the menu is in French with subtitles, although the food is more outward-looking: tuna tempura with pickled cabbage, cannelloni filled with spinach, pine nuts and feta, and potato-crusted cod with hummus prove it. Service copes professionally amid the bustle. French varietals at £12 open a list that soon overruns £20.

CHEF: Sam Brown PROPRIETOR: Le Palais du Jardin Ltd OPEN: all week 12 to 3.30, 5.30 to 12 MEALS: alc (main courses £8 to £18.50) SERVICE: 12.5% (optional), card slips closed CARDS: Amex, Delta, Diners, MasterCard, Switch, Visa DETAILS: 350 seats. 12 seats outside. Private parties: 100 main room. Vegetarian meals. Wheelchair access (not WC). Music. Air-conditioned ⊖ Covent Garden, Leicester Square

Parade

map 12

18–19 The Mall, W5 2PJ
TEL: (020) 8810 0202 FAX: (020) 8810 0303

COOKING **5**
MODERN EUROPEAN
£24–£52

The Parade's glass frontage makes a rather discreet, clinical statement; inside there's a bar, dark grey carpeting, black leather chairs and a long white rectangular room hung with lots of art works, jazzy and colourful Bruce McCleans and a couple of Elizabeth Frinks among them. Such a smart, cosmopolitan space effectively complements a contemporary style of food already established at sister suburban restaurants, Phoenix and Sonny's (see entries, London).

In the capable hands of Rob Jones (who has worked with Philip Howard at The Square; see entry), the carte runs to some eight options per course: Gruyère and goats' cheese soufflé with mixed leaves and walnuts to start, or seared scallops with black pudding and parsley sauce. Fish is well represented among mains, with perhaps a fillet of turbot (accompanied by fennel risotto, purple sprouting broccoli and Parmesan oil), finding a place alongside a British stalwart of calf's liver with mashed potato, bacon and sage and onion gravy. Finish with sticky toffee pudding, dates and pecans, or lemon grass crème brûlée. Service is friendly and professional, while the short, globe-trotting wine list starts with house at £10.50 and offers a dozen by the glass.

CHEF: Robert Jones PROPRIETORS: Rebecca Mascarenhas and James Harris OPEN: all week L 12.30 to 2.30 (3 Sun), Mon to Sat D 7 to 11 CLOSED: 25 to 26 Dec, bank hols MEALS: alc (main courses £9.50 to £15). Set L £12 (2 courses) to £15. Set L Sun £18.50. Bar menu also available SERVICE: 12.5% (optional), card slips closed CARDS: Amex, Delta, MasterCard, Switch, Visa

DETAILS: 100 seats. Private parties: 14 main room, 40 private room. Vegetarian meals. Children's helpings. No cigars/pipes in dining room. Wheelchair access (also WC). No music. Air-conditioned ⊖ Ealing Broadway

Parsee

NEW ENTRY **map 12**

34 Highgate Hill, N19 5NL
TEL: (020) 7272 9091 FAX: (020) 7687 1139

COOKING **3**
PARSEE
£28–£51

Cyrus Todiwala of Café Spice Namaste (see entries, London) is a Bombay Parsee, and always includes his community's dishes on his menus. In this, Europe's only Parsee restaurant, the fare is almost entirely from this tradition ('almost', because it includes pork vindaloo, a Goanese dish popular in Bombay). In the 'signature dish', dhansak (one of eight mains on the à la carte menu), accurately cooked lamb is ideally complemented by its sparse thick sauce, rice, and a meat ball, which is a customary extra.

Four charcoal grills can be either starters or main dishes; haraan na kavab, made with minced venison, is a richly flavoured version of sheekh kebab. Vegetarian starters, tarkari ni bhajia (crisp, dry and light fritters), and papeta nu saak (sautéed spiced potatoes finished with a drop of lime juice) are 'a delight'. Tempting desserts include rose-petal kulfi, while the short, well-chosen wine list has house wine at £11.90. Service by efficient and charming waiters shows care for customers, and pride in both the cuisine and culture they represent.

CHEF: Cyrus Todiwala PROPRIETOR: The Parsee Ltd OPEN: Sun L 12 to 3, Tues to Sat D 6 to 10.45 CLOSED: 25 to 26 Dec; 1 Jan MEALS: alc (main courses £8 to £14). Set L and D £22 (2 courses) to £25 SERVICE: 10% (optional), card slips closed CARDS: Amex, Delta, MasterCard, Switch, Visa DETAILS: 48 seats. Vegetarian meals. No smoking in 1 dining room. Music. Air-conditioned ⊖ Archway

Passion

NEW ENTRY **map 13**

119 Shirland Road, W9 2EW
TEL: (020) 7289 5667 FAX: (020) 7266 1431

COOKING **2**
MODERN BRITISH
£18–£47

The under-decorated walls of this small, relaxed neighbourhood restaurant may make it look unprepossessing, but Craig Thomas's confident cooking is imaginative, and pays fine attention to detail. He runs a simple but bright-sounding carte with six choices per course, taking in sautéed tiger prawn (with plantain fritters, paw-paw salad and black bean dressing), and lime-crusted tuna (with pickled saffron shallots and deep-fried ginger). Mains have brought impeccable roast rump of lamb with aubergine caviar, white bean purée and red pepper tart, and an enjoyable vegetarian dish of roast artichoke with basil risotto, courgette flower and yellow pepper broth. Desserts at inspection impressed less. Chairs and banquettes can feel cramped, but service is professional, and the wine list – brief, wide-ranging, if not wildly exciting – begins at £10.75 in south-west France.

CHEF: Craig Thomas PROPRIETORS: Eshan Goonesekera and Azam Mahammad OPEN: all week 12 to 2.45, 6.30 to 10.45 MEALS: alc (main courses £12 to £16). Set L £12.50 (2 courses) SERVICE: not inc CARDS: Amex, Delta, Diners, MasterCard, Switch, Visa DETAILS: 46 seats. Private parties: 46 main room. Vegetarian meals. Children's helpings. Wheelchair access (not WC). Music ⊖ Maida Vale (£5)

Passione

map 15

10 Charlotte Street, W1P 1HE
TEL: (020) 7636 2833 FAX: (020) 7636 2889
WEB SITE: www.passione.co.uk

COOKING **4**
MODERN ITALIAN
£33–£60

'More restaurants on Charlotte Street than people' observed one who ultimately plumped for the terracotta-coloured elegance of Passione. Light wood chairs and a dark wood floor create a clean, convivial ambience, and the contemporary Italian cooking echoes this feeling. Air-dried tuna with artichoke salad, truffle-sauced tagliatelle, rabbit with rosemary and sauté potatoes, and orange-flavoured pannacotta with mixed berries suit a fashionable youngish clientele down to the ground. Monkfish is baked with Parmesan and sage, while veal escalope is given a distinctly old-school Parma ham and fontina coating. Others have enjoyed agnolini pasta stuffed with minced venison ('moist and moreish'), the good breads, the house ice cream of wild strawberries and limoncello, and the 'splendidly responsive and caring' service. The wine list, which dips into still largely under-appreciated corners of Italy, starts from £11 for selections from Abruzzo and Puglia.

CHEF: Gennaro Contaldo PROPRIETORS: Liz Przybylski, Gennaro Contaldo and Gennaro D'Urso OPEN: Mon to Fri 12.30 to 2.15, Mon to Sat 7 to 10.15 CLOSED: 1 week Christmas and New Year, bank hols MEALS: alc (main courses £9.50 to £18) SERVICE: 10% (optional), card slips closed CARDS: Amex, Delta, Diners, MasterCard, Switch, Visa DETAILS: 40 seats. 8 seats outside. Private parties: 44 main room, 12 private room. Vegetarian meals. Children's helpings. Wheelchair access (not WC). No music ⊖ Goodge Street

Pétrus

map 14

33 St James's Street, SW1A 1HD
TEL: (020) 7930 4272
WEB SITE: www.petrus-restaurant.com

LONDON GFG 2002 COMMENDED

COOKING **7**
FRENCH
£43–£96

Quiet, discreet, with a seriously French air, Pétrus makes its mark with a distinctive brand of refined, modern, disciplined cooking. Large still-life paintings dominate the spacious dining room, there is ample elbowroom, and creature comforts are well catered for. The food is complex without being fussy, classically based without being old-fashioned, and delivered with consummate ease by a British chef: pan-fried sweetbreads with pickled vegetables, or a fricassee of frogs' legs and ceps with foie gras among starters, for example. Fine ingredients and a sense of balance have produced topnotch pasta – ravioli of lobster with sauté langoustines and celeriac purée – and an appealing tian of crab with caviar, gazpacho coulis and first-rate toasted focaccia.

Fish tend to be prime species – turbot, brill, John Dory and the like – pigeons are from Bresse, and even when the larder occasionally turns to a humble item such as pork belly, it is served with wild mushrooms and truffled pomme mousseline. The cooking is characterised by refinement and precision, even in a dish that apparently 'had no right to work': palpably fresh roast sea bass paired with vanilla foam, dark chocolate, sweetly nutty asparagus and a sharp lemon confit. Cheeses are kept in good fettle, and successful desserts have included a tripartite arrangement on the passion fruit theme, and a handsome-looking raspberry soufflé with chocolate macaroons and chocolate sauce.

Staff deliver tottering towers of food with varying degrees of confidence, and although generally pleasant enough – they 'treated me as if they had been waiting all their lives to meet me' – niggles have surfaced about credit card details being required for a booking, and long waits on arrival with nowhere to sit. Value is not what it once was – price rises do not seem to be pegged to the rate of inflation – and with just a few token bottles from outside France, hardly anything below £30, and a wine at £12,300 (for the 1947, one of 25 or so vintages of Ch. Pétrus), the list is clearly not aiming at real people, although the sommeliers are both friendly and professional.

CHEF: Marcus Wareing PROPRIETORS: Marcus Wareing and Gordon Ramsay OPEN: Mon to Fri L 12 to 2.30, Mon to Sat D 6.45 to 11 CLOSED: Christmas, bank hols MEALS: Set L £26, Set D £50 to £60 SERVICE: not inc CARDS: Amex, Delta, Diners, MasterCard, Switch, Visa DETAILS: 52 seats. Children's helpings. No children under 5. No cigars/pipes in dining room. No music. Air-conditioned ⊖ Green Park

Phoenix

map 12

162–164 Lower Richmond Road, SW15 1LY
TEL: (020) 8780 3131 FAX: (020) 8780 1114

COOKING **3**
MODERN BRITISH
£24–£55

There's a cool, clean, contemporary feel here, with bare wooden floors, white walls and ceilings, large windows, modern paintings, and the same easy-going relaxed feel as at Phoenix's sister restaurants, Sonny's (see entries, London and Nottingham) and Parade (see entry, London). A patio at the front (where tables can be set outside in good weather) is shielded from the road by large plants in enormous metal containers.

The menu sticks close to Europe for inspiration – grilled tiger prawns with crudités and aïoli, or foie gras and chicken liver parfait with toasted brioche – although some dishes, such as a spinach soup with spiced lentils and raita, carry hints of the East. Main courses may feature hot/cold combos, as in a dish of fillet of mackerel (hot) with a salad of rocket, bacon, new potatoes and horseradish, or a perfectly cooked fillet steak with chips and a salad of parsley, Parmesan, tomatoes and olives. Puddings run to a highly rated passion fruit tart, and dark chocolate cake with mint chocolate chip ice cream. Service is generally willing, if a bit short on experience. Wines, arranged by price, take in some commendable modern-style producers from around the Old and New Worlds. Around a dozen are sold by the glass, and house vins de pays are £10.50.

CHEF: Sue Lewis PROPRIETORS: Rebecca Mascarenhas and James Harris OPEN: all week 12.30 to 2.30 (3 Sun), 7 to 11 (11.30 Fri and Sat, 10 Sun) CLOSED: 25 and 26 Dec, bank hol Mons MEALS: alc (main courses £10.50 to £14.50). Set L Mon to Fri and Set D Sun to Thur 7 to 7.45 £12 (2 courses) to £15, Set L Sat £12 (1 course), Set L Sun £18.50 SERVICE: 12.5% (optional), card slips closed CARDS: Amex, Delta, Diners, MasterCard, Switch, Visa DETAILS: 100 seats. 40

seats outside. Private parties: 100 main room. Vegetarian meals. Children's helpings. No smoking in 1 dining room. Wheelchair access (also WC). Music. Air-conditioned ⊖ Putney Bridge (£5)

Pied-à-Terre 🍷 map 15

34 Charlotte Street, W1T 2NH
TEL: (020) 7636 1178 FAX: (020) 7916 1171
EMAIL: p-a-t@dircon.co.uk
WEB SITE: www.pied.a.terre.co.uk

COOKING **8**
FRENCH
£41–£101

Now less austere, sporting floral sprays and candles, the dining room retains a pleasing element of absurdity, the current showpiece being a giant surrealist landscape. If the idea is to focus attention on the food, that's sensible. Shane Osborn's cooking is deliberately complex, full of daring and invention, and succeeds most of the time. Its style, and accomplishment, are typified by a small lobe of barely poached and then seared foie gras on a bed of light pasta in a pea-sprinkled, Sauternes-flavoured consommé: a classic French partnership turned into a subtle modern dish that involves the exact execution of different techniques, yet which hangs together as a whole.

The best dishes involve both creativity and expert handling, exploiting contrasting flavours and textures to the full: like a ceviche of dazzlingly fresh sweet-tasting scallop discs, set around a mound of chopped scallop tartare and avocado topped with filo pastry leaves, the whole enlivened by its lime marinade. Although not all dishes are in the stratospheric league, other successes have included roast pigeon breast with a bewildering array of accompaniments, from a small sausage of leg meat to roast garlic and an intense, gamey, lentil-flecked sauce. Equally elaborate desserts take in a beguiling combination of sticky rice pudding enclosed in slices of mango, sitting on a frothy coconut-infused cream; and a raspberry sablé with two huge dollops of powerfully fruity raspberry granita topped with fromage blanc. Details such as appetiser, pre-dessert and generous-to-a-fault petits fours all receive due attention. Perceptions of service, overseen by David Moore, range from 'obtrusive' to 'unobtrusive', but it is generally professional, correct and plentiful.

Wines pay homage to France with some fine whites and reds, both traditional and modern. Other regions may seem mere tokens in comparison, yet top estates are invaribly represented. Prices are indubitably high, but the odd bottle under £20 can be found (like a £15.50 food-friendly white Rioja); house wines start at £18 (£5 a glass).

CHEF: Shane Osborn PROPRIETOR: David Moore OPEN: Mon to Fri L 12.15 to 2.30, Mon to Sat D 7 to 11 MEALS: alc L (main courses £12 to £30). Set L £19.50 (2 courses) to £23, Set D £39.50 (2 courses) to £50 SERVICE: 12.5% (optional), card slips closed CARDS: Amex, Delta, Diners, MasterCard, Switch, Visa DETAILS: 36 seats. Private parties: 8 main room, 14 private room. Wheelchair access (not WC). Occasional music. Air-conditioned ⊖ Goodge Street

All entries in the Guide are re-researched and rewritten every year, not least because restaurant standards fluctuate. Don't rely on an out-of-date Guide.

Le Pont de la Tour 🍷 map 13

The Butlers Wharf Building,
36E Shad Thames, SE1 2YE
TEL: (020) 7403 8403 FAX: (020) 7403 0267
WEB SITE: www.conran.com

COOKING **4**
FRENCH/MEDITERRANEAN
£42–£90

Beyond the bar and grill (seafood a speciality, pianist every evening and Sunday lunchtime) is a calmer dining room, and a terrace whose views of Tower Bridge make visits particularly pleasurable. The kitchen recognises the benefits of simplicity and the appeal of familiar ideas, offering a generous carte that deals in langoustines mayonnaise, steamed asparagus with a poached egg and chive butter, and grilled chateaubriand with béarnaise. It is all designed to comfort and reassure, helped along by expensive ingredients – half a lobster with a fennel and lemon salad, or pressed terrine of foie gras with red onion chutney – and a generally sound grasp of classical French techniques.

Similar contentment is to be found among desserts of baked lemon cheese tart, or hot chocolate fondant. Prices are considered higher than they should be, and although service can be charming and responsive it appears to lack direction, yet still charges 12.5 per cent. 'Other drinks' (including cocktails and a good selection of brandies and whiskies) outnumber table wines on the list, although the latter still provide interest and balance among regions. Prices are fair, France coming up with the good value for a change, particularly in the form of house red and white at £12.95.

CHEF: Tim Powell PROPRIETOR: Conran Restaurants Ltd OPEN: Sun to Fri L 12 to 2.45, all week D 6 to 11.15 (10.45 Sun) CLOSED: 25 Dec MEALS: alc D and Sun L (main courses £10.50 to £27). Set L Mon to Fri £28.50 SERVICE: 12.5% (optional), card slips closed CARDS: Amex, Delta, Diners, MasterCard, Switch, Visa DETAILS: 105 seats. 66 seats outside. Private parties: 20 private room. Vegetarian meals. Children's helpings. Wheelchair access (also WC) ⊖ Tower Hill, London Bridge

Popeseye map 12

108 Blythe Road, W14 0HD
TEL: (020) 7610 4578

COOKING **2**
STEAK AND CHIPS
£23–£60

Ruby-red and rare (or otherwise exactly as you order) is the fare at this single-minded steakhouse. There are no starters, and the menu offers six-, eight-, twelve- and twenty-ounce Aberdeen Angus fillet, sirloin or rump (called popeseye in Scotland) hung for at least two weeks. Chips are included, as are béarnaise sauce, ketchup and mustards, and the only extra is salad. To follow, there are farmhouse cheeses and a couple of puddings. The steaks are cooked at a small bar at the back of the room, which is simply decorated with white walls and brightly coloured pictures. On the tables are white paper covers and simple settings that include properly sharp serrated knives. House wines are £11.50. There are two whites, and the rest of the serious list consists of properly mature (some very mature) French classics and other European and New World reds, mostly over £20 and rising to £75. Another branch can be found at 277 Upper Richmond Road, SW15 (tel: (020) 8788 7733).

CHEF/PROPRIETOR: Ian Hutchison OPEN: Mon to Sat D only 6.45 to 10.30 (11 Fri and Sat) CLOSED: Aug MEALS: alc (main courses £9.50 to £30) SERVICE: 12.5% (optional) CARDS: none DETAILS: 34 seats. Wheelchair access (not WC). No music ⊖ Olympia (£5)

Porte des Indes

map 13

32 Bryanston Street, W1H 7EG
TEL: (020) 7224 0055 FAX: (020) 7224 1144
EMAIL: pilondon@aol.com
WEB SITE: www.la-porte-des-indes.com

COOKING **2**
INDIAN
£34–£68

This mammoth gateway to India is in a side street near Marble Arch. A wall of water alongside the staircase forms the high point of the spectacular décor, and colourful fabrics, pictures, artefacts and flowers remind one that this is a sibling of the Blue Elephant (see entry, also London). Peanut shells on the floor of the Jungle Bar do not signify scruffiness but symbolise Indian hospitality. The set Menu Maison and Royal Vegetarian Menu offer a variety of dishes, mostly familiar (even if some hide behind new names); between starters and main dishes you can choose either lentil soup or tamarind sorbet. The carte is also sprinkled with dishes from the creole cuisine of 'les Indes françaises'. Service could do with sharpening up, and the eclectic wine list starts at £11 with another dozen under £20.

CHEF: Mehernosh Mody PROPRIETOR: Blue Elephant International Plc OPEN: Sun to Fri L 12 to 2.30 (3 Sun), all week D 7 to 11.30 (6 to 10.30 Sun) CLOSED: 25 and 26 Dec, 1 Jan MEALS: alc (main courses £9.50 to £21). Set L and D £35 to £40 (both inc wine). Lunch buffet £16.75, Sun brunch £17.50. Cover £1.50 SERVICE: not inc CARDS: Amex, Delta, Diners, MasterCard, Switch, Visa DETAILS: 300 seats. Vegetarian meals. Children's helpings. Wheelchair access (not WC). Music. Air-conditioned ⊖ Marble Arch

Le Potiron Sauvage

NEW ENTRY map 12

755 Fulham Road, SW6 5UU
TEL: (020) 7371 0755 FAX: (020) 7371 0695

COOKING **3**
MODERN FRENCH
£25–£66

When previous owners Alan and Georgina Thompson left this address for the Cotswolds (see The Royalist, Stow-on-the-Wold), Mark McCann, previously in contract catering, moved into this attractive street-corner restaurant. He changed the name from 755, but kept the smart blue and yellow colour scheme, and set his cap at modern French cooking. Among his headline-grabbing ideas is an open lasagne of eel confit, baby leeks and chestnuts, with a truffle and oyster velouté, although the very thing that attracts attention can also give the food a slightly fuzzy focus, as it plays with several ideas at once: sea bass with a choucroute of celery and a solferino of vegetables, or roast cod with foie gras and frogs' legs, and so on.

While not all visitors have been impressed, some are very keen indeed, enjoying for example a dish of grilled, saffron-marinated red mullet fillets with a ceviche of vegetables, accompanied by pink grapefruit segments and orange sorbet. Desserts display more than a touch of artistry, in the shape of a highly successful trompe l'oeuil cappuccino consisting of a cup of coffee mousse with a frothy chocolate-dusted top, cubes of dark and white chocolate, and a spoon-shaped biscuit. Around three dozen very drinkable wines are divided into Old (mostly France) and New Worlds, starting with Vin de Pays d'Oc varietal house wnes at £15.

CHEF: Mark McCann PROPRIETORS: Linda and Mark McCann OPEN: Sun L 12 to 2.30, Tue to Sat D 6 to 10.30 MEALS: Set L Sun £20, Set D Tue to Sat £24 (2 courses) to £30 SERVICE: 12.5% (optional), card slips closed CARDS: Amex, Delta, MasterCard, Switch, Visa DETAILS: 52 seats. Private parties: 25 main room, 25 private room. Vegetarian meals. Children's helpings. Wheelchair access (not WC). Music. Air-conditioned ⊖ Parsons Green (£5)

Putney Bridge Restaurant

map 12

Embankment, SW15 1LB
TEL: (020) 8780 1811 FAX: (020) 8780 1211
EMAIL: demetre@globalnet.co.uk
WEB SITE: www.putneybridgerestaurant.com

COOKING **6**
MODERN FRENCH
£38–£104

One thing all reporters agree on: this is a terrific spot beside the river. Sited opposite the start of the Boat Race, its glass and steel structure gives it a 'glitzy Manhattan feel', appealing whether you are inside looking out or outside looking in. And no one could accuse Anthony Demetre of not trying: dishes pile on invention and excitement. Examples include a lightly smoked pork flan with a warm salad of frogs' legs; turbot cooked in a salt crust with hay, mussels and sumac; and a brochette of scallops, chorizo and snails, served with lentils and a smear of scallop coral and carrot purée.

The kitchen can achieve an exceptional level of execution – the acme was represented at inspection by a well-timed dish of line-caught sea bass on boulangère potatoes with asparagus and leeks – but this is not always sustained. Perhaps the attempt to dazzle with daring flavour combinations is a shade too ambitious. Desserts, too, are high-octane: a warm Valrhona chocolate moelleux (aka fondant) with a soft turron (nougat) ice cream, or a fine mango mousse, decorated with shards of chocolate and sitting on a coconut sponge, accompanied by caramelised pineapple.

Cheeses are extensive and generally good, incidentals from appetisers to bread and pre-dessert are first class, and service is friendly enough, if not always as expert as it might be. Wine prices win the restaurant no friends, though: a shame, given the excellence of both the selection and the sommelier. House Argentinian is £15 (£5 a glass).

CHEF: Anthony Demetre PROPRIETOR: Gerald Davidson OPEN: Tue to Sun L 12 (12.30 Sun) to 2.30 (3 Sun), Tue to Thur D 7 to 10.30, Fri and Sat D 6.30 to 10.30 CLOSED: Christmas, New Year, bank hols MEALS: Set L Tue to Sat £22.50, Set L Sun £25.50, Set D £45 to £69.50 SERVICE: 12.5% (optional), card slips closed CARDS: Amex, Delta, Diners, MasterCard, Switch, Visa DETAILS: 90 seats. Private parties: 30 main room. Vegetarian meals. Children's helpings. No children under 10 (exc Sun). No pipes in dining room; no cigars before 10pm. Wheelchair access (also WC). No music. Air-conditioned ⊖ Putney Bridge (£5)

The text of entries is based on unsolicited reports sent in by readers, backed up by inspections conducted anonymously. The factual details under the text are from questionnaires the Guide sends to all restaurants that feature in the book.

Quaglino's

NEW ENTRY **map 15**

16 Bury Street, SW1Y 6AL
TEL: (020) 7930 6767 FAX: (020) 7839 2866
EMAIL: florences@conran-restaurants.co.uk
WEB SITE: www.quaglinos.co.uk

COOKING **2**
MODERN EUROPEAN
£27–£80

Missing from the main entries of last year's Guide's due to an awkwardly timed chef change, Quaglino's returns, its impressively symmetrical dining room sporting serried ranks of tables, big pillars and bright clean colours. But the shellfish counter at the end is not just decorative, filled as it is with molluscs and crustacea to service the plateau de fruits de mer, or plates of crabs, lobsters or langoustines simply served with mayonnaise. The range of brasserie items extends from fish and chips with sauce tartare to chateaubriand with béarnaise, via more modish sardine bruschetta, or a tasty, smooth-textured smoked haddock brandade with roasted piquillo pepper.

The kitchen adeptly handles everything from basics (including crisp buttery pastry for a mushroom tartlet) to neatly grilled calf's liver with thin slices of pancetta, and plump, crisp-skinned guinea fowl breast and confit leg, served with lemony spinach. Finish, perhaps, with a rich-tasting, silky-textured chocolate pudding. Professional service from mature staff is on the ball, and the wine list features a few bottles under £20 amid top names from France, California and the Antipodes. House Domaines Virginie red and white are £13.50 (£3.75 a glass).

CHEF: Julian O'Neill PROPRIETOR: Conran Restaurants Ltd OPEN: all week 12 to 3, 5.30 to 12 (1 Fri and Sat, 11 Sun) CLOSED: 25 Dec MEALS: alc (main courses £10 to £24). Set L and D till 6.30 £12.50 (2 courses) to £15. Bar menu also available SERVICE: 12.5% (optional), card slips closed CARDS: Amex, Delta, Diners, MasterCard, Switch, Visa DETAILS: 267 seats. Private parties: 300 main room, 40 private room. Vegetarian meals. Children's helpings. Wheelchair access (not WC). Music. Air-conditioned ⊖ Green Park

Quality Chop House

map 13

94 Farringdon Road, EC1R 3EA
TEL: (020) 7837 5093 FAX: (020) 7833 8748

COOKING **3**
BRITISH
£27–£68

At first glance, the bright white lights, dark wooden bench seating and black-and-white tiled floor may strike some as a bit institutional, but they set off the honest-to-goodness, simple cooking of a self-styled 'progressive working-class caterer'. 'Working-class' might apply to jellied eels, grilled kippers and poached egg, or steak-and-kidney pie, but the 'progressive' side of things seems to be taking centre-stage now: asparagus with pecorino, lobster and rocket salad, confit of duck, and tuna steak with 'salsa rossa' if you please (not ketchup). Wide choice, impeccably fresh ingredients and careful preparation keep the place popular, as do the unrepentantly rich puddings such as rhubarb crumble. Most of the white wines are under £20, most of the reds not, and if you are upwardly mobile, there's Méo-Camuzet's 1994 Clos Vougeot for £70; house French is £11.

CHEF/PROPRIETOR: Charles Fontaine OPEN: Sun to Fri 12 to 3 (4 Sun), all week 6.30 (7 Sun) to 11.30 CLOSED: 23 Dec to 3 Jan MEALS: alc (main courses £6.75 to £22) SERVICE: not inc CARDS: Delta, MasterCard, Switch, Visa DETAILS: 65 seats. Private parties: 10 main room. Children's helpings. No-smoking area. No music. Air-conditioned ⊖ Farringdon

Quo Vadis

map 15

26–29 Dean Street, W1V 6LL
TEL: (020) 7437 9585 FAX: (020) 7734 7595
WEB SITE: www.whitestarline.org.uk

COOKING 3
ITALIAN/MEDITERRANEAN
£32–£84

Stained- and etched-glass windows give Quo Vadis an air of serious theatricality, while its starched white napery and rust leather banquettes make it all feel padded and comfortable. Service is informed and professional, although changes are afoot in the kitchen, as both menu and wine list were scheduled for a makeover as the Guide went to press: the new approach will be more Mediterranean, but not exclusively Italian. Fish has figured prominently under Curtis Stone, taking in some imaginative renditions – such as confit of salmon saltimbocca (wrapped in Parma ham) with aubergine caviar – although the sea-salt smack of freshness was absent in a couple of dishes at inspection. Accurate timing, however, has made a success of rare roast pigeon breast with thyme and fondant potatoes, and sensitive handling has characterised sweet roast rump of lamb with salty clams and earthy, parsleyed roasting juices. Desserts of cardinal-red gelée of fruits, or a simple lemon tart, round out the meal. Anchored in France, the wine list garners good names from across the world; prices start at £16.50, but the choice under £25 is limited.

CHEF: Curtis Stone PROPRIETORS: Marco Pierre White and Jimmy Lahoud OPEN: Mon to Fri L 12 to 2.30, Mon to Sat D 5.30 to 11.45 MEALS: alc (main courses £10.50 to £24). Set L £14.95 (2 courses) to £17.95. Pre-theatre set D 5.30 to 6.45 £14.95 (2 courses) to £17.95 SERVICE: 12.5% (optional), card slips closed CARDS: Amex, Delta, Diners, MasterCard, Switch, Visa DETAILS: 90 seats. Private parties: 12 main room, 12 to 80 private rooms. Vegetarian meals. Children's helpings. No pipes in dining room. Wheelchair access (not WC). No music. Air-conditioned ⊖ Tottenham Court Road, Leicester Square

Radha Krishna Bhavan £

map 12

86 Tooting High Street, SW17 0RN
TEL: (020) 8682 0969
EMAIL: tharidas@aol.com
WEB SITE: www.mcdosa.com

COOKING 3
SOUTH INDIAN
£17–£37

Kerala is 'one of ten paradises found on earth', write the owners of this colourfully decorated eating house whose photographs depicting the state's coast and luxuriant vegetation go some way to justifying the claim. Unhurried, friendly waiters guide newcomers through the long menu. Curry-house dishes – biryanis, vindaloos, Madras curries and the like – are included, but it's the South Indian specialities of Kerala and Cochin that draw attention.

'Ever Popular Specialities' are mainly vegetarian classics such as adai (pancake), uthappam ('pizza') as well as vadai and iddly, which are various fried or steamed 'doughnuts'. Deservedly popular are dosai – rice and lentil flour pancakes – rolled and usually stuffed with potatoes, served with chutneys and vegetable sauces. 'Exotic Cochin Specialities' include chicken, lamb, prawn and fish 'fries'; and chilly chicken is not unique in being pretty hot. Long lists of vegetables, curried or dry, include tempting rarities of beetroot, green banana, and beans with coconut. There are all the usual, and some unusual, breads and rice. House wines are £8, but beer or excellent lassi is a better bet.

CHEFS: Mr Salam and Mr Azaraf PROPRIETORS: T. Haridas and family OPEN: all week 12 to 3, 6 to 11 (12 Fri and Sat) CLOSED: 25 and 26 Dec MEALS: alc (main courses £2 to £8). Set L Sun £5.95 to £7.95 SERVICE: 10%, card slips closed CARDS: Amex, Diners, MasterCard, Switch, Visa DETAILS: 50 seats. Private parties: 60 main room. Vegetarian meals. Children's helpings. Music. Air-conditioned ⊖ Tooting Broadway (£5)

Rani £ — map 12

7 Long Lane, N3 2PR

TEL/FAX: (020) 8349 4386 — COOKING **1**

EMAIL: ranivegetarian@aol.com — GUJARATI VEGETARIAN

WEB SITE: www.rani.uk.com — £20–£34

The Kathiawadi region of Gujarat provides inspiration for Rani's all-vegetarian menu. Popadoms with chutneys (mango is especially recommended) get meals off to a racing start. Then there are pooris, soups, and hot starters such as kachori, a deep-fried pastry with lentil and sultana filling served with tamarind sauce. Main courses include slow-cooked Gujarati sak dishes (banana methi in rich tomato gravy, for instance), thalis, masala dosa, and weekly specials such as tindoora (ivy gourd) with potato in yoghurt. Perhaps finish with a 'very fine' hot carrot halva. One visitor found the food and the friendly (if inexperienced) staff ample compensation for the worn crockery. Two wines (red or white at £9.70) grace the drinks list, but beer, spirits and herbal teas are alternatives.

CHEF: Sheilia Pattni PROPRIETORS: Jyotindra and Sheilia Pattni OPEN: Sun L 12.15 to 2.30, all week D 6 to 10 CLOSED: 25 Dec MEALS: alc (main courses £6 to £10). Set L and D £12.45 (2 courses, min 2) SERVICE: 10% (optional), card slips closed CARDS: Amex, Delta, MasterCard, Switch, Visa DETAILS: 70 seats. Private parties: 50 main room. Vegetarian meals. Children's helpings. No smoking in dining room. Wheelchair access (not WC). Music ⊖ Finchley Central (£5)

Ransome's Dock Restaurant — map 12

35–37 Parkgate Road, SW11 4NP

TEL: (020) 7223 1611 FAX: (020) 7924 2614 — COOKING **5**

EMAIL: chef@ransomesdock.co.uk — MODERN EUROPEAN

WEB SITE: www.ransomesdock.co.uk — £31–£65

Despite its out-on-a-limb location in a cul-de-sac leading to a tiny river dock, Martin Lam's restaurant has an appreciably broad catchment area. A stylish set packs in – and a certain amount of packing in is definitely the feeling – to a basically appointed room with a tiled floor, bare tables, and windows that open on to the quay. Its principal focus is contemporary cosmopolitan cooking, built on a foundation of well-sourced supplies, from Shorthorn beef to Oxford Down lamb (pink saddle perhaps, with broad bean purée and minted hollandaise), from Scottish scallops to Norfolk smoked eel, the last briefly grilled and served with charred potatoes and horseradish cream.

A general lightness is evident, in a 'fresh and verdant' pea and mint soup, and in a fillet of roast turbot on baby fennel shoots with a creamy sauce, as well as in desserts such as an exemplary prune and armagnac soufflé, browned to resemble the penny buns of yore. Pannacotta is well made too, and European cheeses are scrupulously maintained. Although a few minor quibbles have been registered, long-standing, mature staff handle service professionally. As well as providing some sound classics, the wine list offers ample opportunity for exploration outside the mainstream. Digestifs are a strong point, and dessert wines from around the world can be bought by the glass or half-, two-third or, of course, the full bottle; but do not expect the smaller sizes to be cheap, as pedigree is outstanding. House wines start at £13.50.

CHEFS/PROPRIETORS: Martin and Vanessa Lam OPEN: all week L 12 to 5 (3.30 Sun), Mon to Sat D 6 to 11 CLOSED: Christmas, Aug bank hol MEALS: alc (main courses £9.50 to £18.50). Set L £13.50 SERVICE: 12.5% (optional), card slips closed CARDS: Amex, Delta, Diners, MasterCard, Switch, Visa DETAILS: 55 seats. 20 seats outside. Private parties: 16 main room. Car park. Vegetarian meals. Children's helpings. No pipes in dining room. Wheelchair access (also WC). Music. Air-conditioned ⊖ Sloane Square

Rasa/Rasa W1 £ — maps 12 and 15

55 Stoke Newington Church Street, N16 OAR
TEL: (020) 7249 0344
6 Dering Street, W1R 9AB
TEL: (020) 7629 1346 FAX: (020) 7491 9540
WEB SITE: www.rasarestaurants.com

COOKING **2**
INDIAN VEGETARIAN
£24–£44

The multi-coloured façade and South Indian décor of the two Rasa restaurants stand out in Stoke Newington, and just off Oxford Street. Their menus are almost identical except in price, where the differences are considerable (see details below). Among starters are steamed or crisply fried lentil or vegetable patties. One of these, rasa idli, is, according to the menu, topped with the chef's vegetable massager: probably a masala, not a gadget for beating aubergines. Dosa, thin giant pancakes served rolled with a spicy sauce, may be plain or stuffed with potatoes and other vegetables. Vegetables themselves may be curried, stir-fried, roasted or dry-fried. Typical desserts from Kerala include a version of rice pudding, and kesari, a Brahmin recipe of semolina, mango, cashews and raisins. Service at Dering Street could be friendlier. House wines in both branches are £9.50, though the rest are, again, higher priced in Oxford Street.

CHEF: Rajan Karattil (Rasa), Sivaparasad Mahade Van Nair (Rasa W1) PROPRIETOR: Das Sreedharan OPEN: Rasa Sat and Sun 12 to 2.45, all week D 6 to 10.45; Rasa W1 Mon to Sat 12 to 2.45, 6 to 10.45 CLOSED: 24 Dec to 1 Jan MEALS: Rasa alc (main courses £3.50 to £5); Set L and D £15. Rasa W1 alc (main courses £6 to £13), Set L and D £22.50 SERVICE: 12.5% (optional), card slips closed CARDS: Amex, Delta, Diners (not at Rasa), MasterCard, Switch, Visa DETAILS: 45 seats (Rasa) 80 seats (Rasa W1). Private parties: 45 main room (Rasa W1). Vegetarian meals. No smoking in dining rooms. Music. Air-conditioned ⊖ Oxford Circus (Rasa W1)

Rasa Samudra

NEW ENTRY map 15

5 Charlotte Street, W1P 1HD
TEL: (020) 7637 0222 FAX: (020) 7637 0224
WEB SITE: www.rasarestaurants.com

COOKING 4
INDIAN SEAFOOD/VEGETARIAN
£35–£58

The Rasa group's flagship is decorated in the same vibrant colours as its sisters (see entries above), including the amazing pink frontage. Subtler touches inside include coloured muslin hung from ceilings as lampshades, a different colour in each room of the rambling ground floor, and a first-floor room with turquoise seats against pink walls. Service is friendly and quite sophisticated but the easiest way to order unpronounceable dishes is to tick your choices on a take-away menu.

This Rasa is not just vegetarian, but also spotlights the fish cooking of Kerala. The extraordinary collection of poppadums constituting 'pre-meal snacks' and an accompanying portion of chutneys, including fish and prawn varieties, make a substantial starter for two. Other tempting first courses include crisply fried king fish; tuna and cassava cutlets; and samudra rasam (a thick, rice-based soup with prawns, squid, mussels and crab with lively spicing). Masala dosa pancakes and vegetable curries support the fish main dishes, most of which can be loosely described as curries. A global collection of 50 wines starts with Trebbiano and Merlot at £10.50.

CHEF: Ajit Kumar PROPRIETOR: Das Sreedharan OPEN: Mon to Sat L 12 to 2.30, all week D 6 to 10.30 CLOSED: 25 Dec MEALS: alc (main courses £6 to £13) SERVICE: 12.5% (optional), card slips closed CARDS: Amex, Delta, Diners, MasterCard, Switch, Visa DETAILS: 120 seats. Private parties: 80 main room, 15 to 60 private rooms. Vegetarian meals. No smoking in 1 dining room. No music. Air-conditioned ⊖ Tottenham Court Road, Goodge Street

Rasa Travancore

NEW ENTRY map 12

56 Stoke Newington Church Street, N16 0NB
TEL: (020) 7249 1340
WEB SITE: www.rasarestaurants.com

COOKING 1
INDIAN
£23–£37

A small group known for vegetarian food, and more recently fish, has ventured into meat-eaters' territory. Opposite the original Rasa, this little sister flaunts the group's colourful façade and interior. It also shares the tasty, substantial mixed poppadom and pickle pre-meal snacks, and some South Indian starters. The rest of the menu is based on the Syrian Christian tradition of Kerala, some dishes being credited to individual families. Starters include Travancore kozhukkatta (steamed balls of rice flour stuffed with spiced lamb), and among mains are duck fry, various dishes associated with Christmas and Easter (including lamb and chicken stews, with a difference), and green curries of chicken, lamb and fish. Other seafood dishes are shared with Rasa Samudra in Charlotte Street (see entry above). The short wine list starts at £9.50.

CHEF: Mr Panchalya PROPRIETOR: Das Sreedharan OPEN: all week D only 6 to 10.45 (11.30 Fri and Sat) CLOSED: 24 to 31 Dec MEALS: alc (main courses £5 to £7.50). Set D £20 SERVICE: 12.5%, card slips closed CARDS: Delta, MasterCard, Switch, Visa DETAILS: 45 seats. Private parties: 20 main room. Vegetarian meals. No smoking in dining room. No music. Air-conditioned

The Real Greek

map 13

15 Hoxton Market, N1 6HG
TEL: (020) 7739 8212 FAX: (020) 7739 4910
WEB SITE: www.therealgreek.co.uk

COOKING **4**
GREEK
£33–£52

Vivid blue outside, this converted pub is more of an essay in brown inside, its unadorned walls, bare floorboards, simply laid tables, and heart-on-sleeve open-to-view kitchen lending it a 'purposefully informal' air. Menus aim to reflect both regional and seasonal aspects of Greek cooking, and change every ten weeks or so, although the sometimes inventive treatments suggest that the kitchen owes as big a debt to London as to Greece. Much of the interest centres around mezedes, groups of items arranged into intriguing combinations: for example a plate of slightly sour cabbage, densely meaty sausage, pan-fried lamb's tongue, and tsatsiki, or one of home-salted cod fillet in batter, skordalia-potato and garlic aïoli, beetroot in vinegar, and cured sardines. In addition there are small and main-sized dishes: of scallops accompanied by courgettes stuffed with minced lamb perhaps, or a hotpot of kid with a green dandelion and leek fricassee. Ask the staff to explain how big the portions are, and what the highlights are. Dairy and fruit combinations dominate desserts, from rizogalo with satsuma jelly, to yogurt served with stuffed figs and thyme honey. Wines are about as interesting as Greek wines get, and grouped according to broad suitability for the food; eight are available by the glass, and house Kretikos (from Crete) is £12.50.

CHEF: Theodore Kyriakou PROPRIETORS: Paloma Campbell and Theodore Kyriakou OPEN: Mon to Sat 12 to 3, 5.30 to 10.30 CLOSED: 2 weeks Christmas and New Year; bank hols exc Good Fri MEALS: alc (main courses £15 to £17). Set L and D 5.30 to 7 £14.50 (2 courses) SERVICE: not inc, 12.5% for parties of 7 or more CARDS: Delta, MasterCard, Switch, Visa DETAILS: 65 seats. Private parties: 10 main room, 8 private room. Vegetarian meals. No cigars/pipes in dining room. Wheelchair access (not WC). No music Old Street

Redmond's

map 12

170 Upper Richmond Road West, SW14 8AW
TEL: (020) 8878 1922 FAX: (020) 8878 1133

COOKING **5**
MODERN BRITISH
£24–£47

Redmond's is a popular and reliable neighbourhood restaurant. The décor is slickly modern, light and airy, brightened by strong colours and bold modernist paintings. The cooking is often bold too, based on fresh, seasonal, high-quality ingredients and well-thought-out combinations. France and the Mediterranean are among the sources of inspiration, with occasional flashes of Japanese or Middle Eastern flavours. Fish dishes seem particularly well-handled, as in a dish of accurately rare-grilled tuna with linguine, griddled aubergine and coriander salsa, and another of sweet, firm, flavourful chargrilled scallops with spinach, ginger, parsley and garlic sauce.

Satisfaction also comes in the shape of a robust, richly textured celeriac and cep soup with a dressing of truffle cream, and a risotto of roast courgettes and roast tomatoes with Parmesan that proved the 'ultimate comfort food' for one visitor. Desserts can be as zippy as a piquant lemon tart, or as savoury as a selection of British and Irish cheeses from Neal's Yard, served in good condition.

The wine list, organised by price (from 13.50), combines modern French classics with the best of the New World. There is a very good selection of half-bottles, too.

CHEF: Redmond Hayward PROPRIETORS: Redmond and Pippa Hayward OPEN: Sun to Fri L 12 to 2 (2.30 Sun), Mon to Sat D 7 to 10.30 CLOSED: 4 days Christmas, 1st week Jan MEALS: Set L £10 (2 courses) to £21, Set D £23 (2 courses) to £27 SERVICE: not inc, 10% (optional) for parties of 6 or more CARDS: Amex, Delta, MasterCard, Switch, Visa DETAILS: 54 seats. Private parties: 54 main room. Vegetarian meals. Children's helpings. No cigars/pipes in dining room. Wheelchair access (not WC). No music. Air-conditioned

Red Pepper

map 13

8 Formosa Street, W9 1EE
TEL: (020) 7266 2708 FAX: (020) 7266 5522

COOKING **4**
ITALIAN
£30–£48

The liveliness suggested by the name is born out: the fount and origin of the Red Pepper Group is small and overcrowded, with heavy music beating all the time. There may be time limits on tables but, no matter, the kitchen works as fast as the helpful, friendly waiters. The menu lists a few starters, such as quails' egg salad, fried cheese-stuffed courgette flowers, or tuna in a filo parcel. Fifteen pizze permutate tomato, cheeses, anchovies, capers, olives, ham, mushrooms and more. One, the Calabrese, omits tomato altogether, making its impact with spicy Abruzzi salami and moist, tasty black olives. Among blackboard mains might be calf's liver: succulent thick slices with a marmalade of the subtle pickled Italian white onions, a world away from the hoary old British acid-balls of the same name. Adventurous pasta might include wild boar ravioli; linguine with swordfish, aubergine and sun-dried tomatoes; and saffron and sweetbread risotto. Desserts include the signature tiramisù served on a crisp pastry tulip. Some 30 wines, all Italian, start from £9.90.

CHEF: Walter Benenati PROPRIETOR: Red Pepper Group OPEN: Sat and Sun L 12.30 to 2.30 (3.30 Sun), all week D 6.30 to 10.45 (10.30 Sun) MEALS: alc (main courses £6 to £13) SERVICE: 12.5% (optional), card slips closed CARDS: Delta, MasterCard, Switch, Visa DETAILS: 60 seats. 12 seats outside. Private parties: 25 main room. Vegetarian meals. Children's helpings. No cigars/pipes in dining room. Music. Air-conditioned ⊖ Warwick Avenue

Rhodes in the Square

map 13

Dolphin Square, Chichester Street, SW1V 3LX
TEL: (020) 7798 6767 FAX: (020) 7798 5685
EMAIL: rhodesinthesquare@sodexho-uk.com

COOKING **6**
MODERN BRITISH
£34–£71

A flag flies outside the glass entrance, to help distinguish it from the surrounding apartment block, while the smart interior 'oozes taste and class'. This feels like a place that will take care of you. Against a background of dark blue carpet, cream walls, linen cloths and napkins comes a menu that indulges our taste for grown-up British nursery food, dealing as it does in smoked haddock soup, lobster omelette thermidor, and a steamed mushroom and onion suet pudding flavoured with marjoram.

The accomplished style offers foie gras – combined into a faggot with pigeon, and served on a potato cake with mustard cabbage – alongside humbler but equally comforting materials such as a rabbit version of Irish stew, or rillettes of braised oxtail accompanied by horseradish cream. Carefully managed textures contribute to the cosseting: in the shape of a deep-fried poached egg ('very clever') that comes on a well-dressed salad with crisp Bayonne ham, and in succulent, pink, grilled calf's liver on a bed of gently pickled red onions, served with a small copper saucepan of finely puréed potato.

Puddings aim to be equally soothing, taking in Rhodes's classic version of bread-and-butter, glazed lemon tart, and a warm chocolate mousse with bitter chocolate sorbet. A compact yet agreeably varied wine list (with plenty of headroom for those who want to splash out) starts with ten representative sommelier's suggestions available by the bottle or glass from £16.50 (£3.90).

CHEFS: Gary Rhodes and Michael James PROPRIETOR: Sodexho OPEN: Tue to Fri L 12 to 2.30, Tue to Sat D 7 to 10 CLOSED: 26 Dec, 1 and 2 Jan MEALS: Set L £17.80 (2 courses) to £19.80, Set D £30.50 (2 courses) to £36.50 SERVICE: 12.5% (optional) CARDS: Amex, Delta, Diners, MasterCard, Switch, Visa DETAILS: 70 seats. Private parties: 100 main room. Vegetarian meals. Children's helpings. No cigars in dining room. Music. Air-conditioned ⊖ Pimlico

Riso

map 12

76 South Parade, Chiswick, W4 5LF — COOKING **3**
TEL/FAX: (020) 8742 2121 — ITALIAN
WEB SITE: www.risorestaurant.co.uk — £30 – £41

Hospitality, warm even by Italian standards, extends to children – who are especially welcomed on Sundays, with high chairs for the shortest – and the cheerful ambience survives table time limits on busy Friday and Saturday evenings. The food, apparently, never fails to please either, offering set menus ranging from one course to four: perhaps including starters such as grilled polenta with pecorino and marinated aubergine, or marinated anchovies with rocket and fresh tomatoes.

Main-course pasta dishes range from penne with salmon and vodka sauce, to home-made mascarpone gnocchi with asparagus sauce. Ten pizze take in one with mozzarella, tomato, chicken and onions, and a vegetarian calzone. Blackboard daily specials one evening offered pan-fried plaice with pepperonata and saffron new potatoes; and corn-fed chicken wrapped in Parma ham on sauté fennel. Finish in traditional Italian mould with pannacotta and a mixed berry sauce. House wines at £11.50 start an all-Italian list with 20 bottles under £20 and a few that are more expensive. Except for Frascati, it ventures no further south than Tuscany.

CHEF: Sandro Medda PROPRIETORS: Mauro Santoliquido, Maurizio Rimerici and Sandro Medda OPEN: Sun L 12 to 12.30, Tue to Sun D 7 to 10.30 CLOSED: Christmas, Easter MEALS: Set L and D £8.50 (1 course) to £24.50 SERVICE: 12.5%, card slips closed CARDS: Delta, MasterCard, Switch, Visa DETAILS: 66 seats. Private parties: 55 main room. Vegetarian meals. No-smoking area. Music ⊖ Chiswick Park

The Guide's top-rated restaurants are listed near the front of the book.

▲ Ritz

map 15

150 Piccadilly, W1J 9BR
TEL: (020) 7493 8181 FAX: (020) 7493 2687
EMAIL: enquire@theritzlondon.com
WEB SITE: www.theritzlondon.com

COOKING **4**
FRENCH/ENGLISH
£51–£190

The dining room of this landmark hotel is elegant, spacious and ornate; its painted ceiling may not be quite the Sistine Chapel, but it is not a bad secular overhead from which to hang the chandeliers, just as its marble-effect walls provide a fitting backdrop to some imposing gilded statues. Despite all this, it is more relaxed than people may imagine, always providing that high prices don't make you feel jittery. Three-course lunches and four-course dinners are supplemented by an extensive carte that will hold few surprises for those used to luxury eating. Soups take in lobster bisque, and artichoke velouté with truffle cream; foie gras comes with Périgueux sauce; and there is a small section devoted to oysters, smoked salmon and caviar.

As well as simple grills of Dover sole or calf's liver, there is first-rate roast beef, and perhaps guinea fowl with creamed morels, while puddings involve a bit of showmanship, as Grand Marnier soufflé or crêpes suzette are flambéed at table. Chocolate is another favourite theme, while fruity desserts run to a terrine of seasonal berries with passion fruit coulis. To dip into the wine list requires a serious budget, although a few under £30 are worth trying, like the house claret or Chablis, both £22, or lively examples from the south of France.

CHEF: Giles Thompson PROPRIETOR: Ellerman Investments OPEN: all week 12 to 2.30, 6 to 11 MEALS: alc (main courses £28 to £68). Set L £35, Set D £44 to £59 SERVICE: not inc, card slips closed CARDS: Amex, Delta, Diners, MasterCard, Switch, Visa DETAILS: 120 seats. 24 seats outside. Private parties: 20 main room, 20 to 50 private rooms. Vegetarian meals. Children's helpings. Jacket and tie. Wheelchair access (also WC). Music. Air-conditioned ACCOMMODATION: 133 rooms, all with bath/shower. TV. Phone. Room only £357 to £1,587. Rooms for disabled. Baby facilities ⊖ Green Park

Riva

map 12

169 Church Road, SW13 9HR
TEL/FAX: (020) 8748 0434

COOKING **4**
NORTH ITALIAN
£34–£60

Andrea Riva can usually be seen drifting from table to table, overseeing the antithesis of contemporary London-Italian eating. There is not much show or glamour, just a long, narrow dining room with mirrors and cloth-covered tables, where doors are flung open on summer evenings to emphasise the Continental feel. In genuine Italian style, however, the food is simple, modestly inventive and based on fine materials. The cured ham – in a starter with figs, smoked sturgeon, apples and horseradish – is highly esteemed culatello; one reporter's moist, lightly grilled squid with chopped herbs and garlic was about as good as this cephalopod gets.

Northern dishes predominate – expect gnocchi, risotto and osso buco, for instance – but there are also other delicacies, such as bottarga (cured grey mullet roe) shaved over spaghetti with mussels and clams. Alcohol features in desserts, from sbrisolona (maize and almond crumble soaked in Vin Santo) to grappa-stewed prune and blueberry pancakes. There are nine dessert wines by the glass, as well as an all-Italian list, short but varied and well-chosen (with more unlisted bottles behind the scenes), starting with house Merlot and Pinot Bianco at £11.50.

CHEF: Francesco Zanchetta PROPRIETOR: Andrea Riva OPEN: Sun to Fri 12 to 2.30, all week 7 to 11 (9.30 Sun) CLOSED: 25 Dec, Easter, bank hols, last 2 weeks Aug MEALS: alc (main courses £10 to £17) SERVICE: 10%, card slips closed CARDS: Amex, MasterCard, Switch, Visa DETAILS: 45 seats. 8 seats outside. Private parties: 40 main room. Vegetarian meals. Children's helpings. No cigars/pipes in dining room. Wheelchair access (not WC). No music. Air-conditioned ⊖ Hammersmith

River Café 🍷 map 12

Thames Wharf Studios, Rainville Road, W6 9HA
TEL: (020) 7386 4200 FAX: (020) 7386 4201 COOKING **6**
EMAIL: info@rivercafe.co.uk ITALIAN
WEB SITE: www.rivercafe.co.uk £53–£76

This is a large, high ceilinged, rectangular room with big windows that open on to a terrace. Tubular chairs compound the feel of '80s modernism, a large clock face ticks on the wall, and a carpet absorbs some of the noise from the mass of tables. Although most of the action takes place out of view, the cooking's openness is evident from the wood-burning oven and the long counter behind which all the prepping is done. The food combines simplicity – no ceremonials, no appetisers – and robust, honest flavours 'that I just wanted to keep on eating'. It is fuelled by organic meats, wild salmon, and a seasonal profusion of leaves, vegetables and herbs, from artichoke, sea kale and asparagus to rocket, basil and marjoram.

The oven earns its keep, turning out half a dozen moist and fresh sardine fillets, their skin just blistering, next to a pile of oil-dressed rocket leaves, with a scattering of toasted pine nuts and a kick of lemon; and pink, flavourful, crisp-skinned Bresse pigeon marinated in amarone and thyme, accompanied simply by Swiss chard and Castelluccio lentils. The lack of unnecessary adornment is appreciated, for example by one who enjoyed chargrilled leg of lamb with a mix of artichokes, peas and broad beans (appropriate for May) in a 'meaty tapénade' of chopped olives and prosciutto, with meat juices and olive oil to moisten the lot. Among desserts, chocolate nemesis remains both an abiding curiosity and an accomplished cross between a mousse and a cake, just gooey enough in the middle.

Casually dressed staff are young, friendly and on the ball, and prices are high: 'you pay for great buying, careful handling and, well, they can get away with it,' reckoned one visitor. Wine isn't cheap either. The 11-strong 'glass selection' offers the best value, for both glass and bottle prices; house wines, Merlot from Veneto and Sicilian white, are £10.50. Beyond that, a range encompassing both the classic and the thoroughly modern explores vinous variety from all corners of Italy.

CHEFS: Rose Gray, Ruth Rogers and Theo Randall PROPRIETORS: Rose Gray and Ruth Rogers OPEN: all week L 12.30 to 3, Mon to Sat D 7 to 9.30 CLOSED: Christmas, New Year, Good Fri, Easter Mon, bank hols MEALS: alc (main courses £24 to £28) SERVICE: 12.5% (optional), card slips closed CARDS: Amex, Delta, Diners, MasterCard, Switch, Visa DETAILS: 100 seats. 40 seats outside. Car park. Children's helpings. No cigars/pipes in dining room. Wheelchair access (also WC). No music ⊖ Hammersmith

Rosmarino

map 13

1 Blenheim Terrace, NW8 0EH
TEL: (020) 7328 5014 FAX: (020) 7625 2639

COOKING **3**
MODERN ITALIAN
£35–£60

In a stately Edwardian terrace this restaurant is pleasingly light and expansive (especially in summer, when the main room opens onto a spacious terrace). The elegance extends to heavily clothed tables (each with an orchid), though they are small and closely set. Set dinner (good value, even with several £3 supplements) is in Italian style, with five risotto and pasta dishes separating starters and main courses: pasta with roast quail and pea sauce has been a well-executed and unusual combination. Successful starter salads have included one of dressed sardines, and one of octopus with new potatoes, green beans and a mustard sauce.

Simply cooked fish main dishes, and rack of lamb with artichokes, have been enjoyed, and sorbets have been outstanding among desserts. Service is friendly but unco-ordinated, with daily specials offered late, and wine kept out of reach so refills have to be requested. An Italian wine list reaches beyond classic Chiantis from Antinori and Fattoria le Corti to sun-baked southern styles from Puglia and Sicily with their unique native-grape combinations. Prices move upwards swiftly from £12.50 for house red and white, but there is some choice under £20.

CHEF: Stefano Stella PROPRIETOR: A To Z Restaurants Ltd OPEN: all week 12 to 2.30 (3 Sun), 7 to 10.30 (10 Sun) MEALS: alc L (main courses £9 to £14). Set Sat and Sun L and all week D £22.50 (2 courses) to £30 SERVICE: 12.5% (optional), card slips closed CARDS: Amex, Delta, MasterCard, Switch, Visa DETAILS: 45 seats. 25 seats outside. Private parties: 48 main room. Vegetarian meals. No cigars/pipes in dining room. Music. Air-conditioned ⊖ St John's Wood (£5)

Roussillon

map 14

16 St Barnabas Street, SW1W 8PB
TEL: (020) 7730 5550 FAX: (020) 7824 8617
EMAIL: tanna@roussillon.co.uk
WEB SITE: www.roussillon.co.uk

COOKING **4**
MODERN FRENCH
£31–£69

Roussillon's innovative kitchen delivers out-of-the-ordinary flavours, emphasising quality seasonal ingredients from ecologically sound sources. The cooking is ambitious, and, if occasional combinations are near misses, there is no lack of talent; 'classic reduced meat and fish stocks' show just how French it is. On offer is a weekly-changing set lunch, a brace of tasting menus, and a carte divided into 'classics', 'garden', 'sea' and 'land'. In spring one might try 'a clever blend' of purple artichoke, green pea and cos lettuce cooked in a pot, then a fine combination of caramelised red mullet on its skin with pink raw radishes, pea shoots and crustacean jus. Donald Russell's organic Angus beef may be served with thick French fries.

Finish with a satisfying and rather British steamed ginger pudding with treacle sauce, or chocolate soufflé. Service is polite and professional, and the stylish, sophisticated French country-house setting complements the food, its yellow walls carrying pictures of garden mazes and herbs. A heavyweight wine list concentrates on France (with understandable emphasis on Rousillon and neighbouring Languedoc) but also assembles a serious bunch of other European and world wines. Finding anything under £25 is hard, but a strong range by the glass (from £3) numbs the pain.

CHEF: Alexis Gauthier PROPRIETORS: James and Andrew Palmer and Alexis Gauthier OPEN: Mon to Fri L 12 to 2.30, Mon to Sat D 6.30 to 11 CLOSED: Christmas, Easter, bank hols MEALS: Set L £15 (2 courses) to £18, Set D £29 (2 courses) to £42 SERVICE: 12.5% (optional), card slips closed CARDS: Amex, Delta, MasterCard, Switch, Visa DETAILS: 80 seats. Private parties: 65 main room, 20 and 34 private rooms. Vegetarian meals. Wheelchair access. Occasional music. Air-conditioned ⊖ Sloane Square

Royal China

maps 13 and 15

40 Baker Street, W1V 7AJ
TEL: (020) 7487 4688 FAX: (020) 7935 7893
13 Queensway, W2 4QJ
TEL: (020) 7221 2535 FAX: (020) 7792 5752
68 Queen's Grove, NW8 6ER
TEL: (020) 7586 4280 FAX: (020) 7722 2681
WEB SITE: www.royalgourmet.co.uk

COOKING **4**
CHINESE
£20–£85

The décor takes in lacquered panelled walls and mirrors, black ceilings, and decently spaced tables with good cloths. Uniformed staff are efficient and usually helpful. All this is common to the three branches, as is most of the menu and the skilled cooking of first-class ingredients. Authenticity can be found in dishes such as preserved dried seafood hotpot, pan-fried egg plant with minced shrimp in black bean sauce, and pan-fried minced pork with salted egg. Among recommended dishes are golden fried scallops with cucumber (where the sliced mollusc is bread-crumbed and deep-fried between cucumber slices), and stewed belly pork with vegetables in a clay pot. Dim sum receive the accolade of long queues at weekends (there is no booking), and reports have highlighted fresh, tasty fried Vietnamese spring rolls, and soft-shell crabs 'not frozen, but crunchy, moist and full of flavour'. Wines start at £13 and rise rapidly in price. A fourth branch opened as the Guide went to press (30 West Ferry Circus, E14, tel (020) 7719 0888).

CHEF: David Pang (Baker Street), Mr Man (Queensway), Mr Nan (Queen's Grove) PROPRIETOR: Royal China Restaurant Group OPEN: all week 12 to 11 (11.30 Fri and Sat, 10 Sun) MEALS: alc (main courses £6 to £20). Set L £8 to £10, Set D £25 to £32 (min 2) SERVICE: 12.5% CARDS: Amex, Delta, MasterCard, Switch, Visa DETAILS: 120 seats (Baker Street), 240 seats (Queensway), 100 seats (Queen's Grove). Private parties: 80 main room, 15 private room (Baker Street), 240 main room, 22 private rooms (Queensway), 90 main room (Queen's Grove). Vegetarian meals. No music. Air-conditioned ⊖ Baker Street, Queensway, St John's Wood

Use the lists towards the front of the book to find suitable restaurants for special occasions.

RSJ 🍷 map 13

13A Coin Street, SE1 8YQ
TEL: (020) 7928 4554 FAX: (020) 7401 2455 COOKING **3**
EMAIL: sally.webber@rsj.uk.com MODERN FRENCH
WEB SITE: www.rsj.uk.com £28–£58

Convenient for the National Theatre, Festival Hall and other South Bank attractions, RSJ adjusts its opening hours accordingly; friendly service makes it a pleasure to eat before or after performances without feeling rushed. The vaulted basement may be more crowded than the comparatively soothing main dining room, but the kitchen 'consistently delivers the goods' in both. Choose between a decently priced set menu, with three options per course, and a carte, with half a dozen.

Even contemporary dishes favour tried and tested combinations, such as scallops with black pudding, or seared tuna on roast Mediterranean vegetables, while main courses have included 'a good fillet steak cooked as requested', and roast chicken with potato fondant and stick vegetables. Bread-and-butter pudding in crème anglaise has also been 'well-prepared, tasty and handsomely presented'. Ever the exponent of wines from the Loire, Nigel Wilkinson crams his list full of prime examples of its reds, whites, and especially sweets. Despite token offerings from other corners of France and the world, it would be a pity not to explore these wide-ranging styles; as if extra encouragement is needed, many (including the house Saumurs at £12.50) are under £20.

CHEFS: Ian Stabler and Kevin Broome PROPRIETOR: Nigel Wilkinson OPEN: Mon to Fri L 12 to 2, Mon to Sat D 5.30 to 11 CLOSED: 24 to 27 Dec MEALS: alc (main courses £14 to £18). Set L and D £15.95 (2 courses) to £16.95 SERVICE: 12.5% (optional), card slips closed CARDS: Amex, Delta, Diners, MasterCard, Switch, Visa DETAILS: 100 seats. 10 seats outside. Private parties: 8 main room, 24 and 30 private rooms. Vegetarian meals. No cigars/pipes in dining room. No music. Air-conditioned ⊖ Waterloo

Rules map 15

35 Maiden Lane, WC2E 7LB
TEL: (020) 7836 5314 FAX: (020) 7497 1081 COOKING **3**
EMAIL: info@rules.co.uk BRITISH
WEB SITE: www.rules.co.uk £33–£66

On this site for over 200 years, London's oldest restaurant is understandably a champion of traditional, even classic, British cooking. It flies the flag for Morecambe Bay potted shrimps with crab butter, and lots of feathered and furred game (reared in Teesdale) from roast grouse and ptarmigan, to rabbit casserole and haunch of fallow deer. Despite that, much of the menu consists of modern interpretations. Cornish crab has come dressed with coriander, avocado, tomato and fennel; and roast and confit Gressingham duck has a Bramley apple and five-spice chutney and red cabbage.

Cooking does not hit the button all the time, but praiseworthy starters have included Stilton and walnut tart with spiced pear and apple chutney, and smoked haddock with poached quails' eggs and hollandaise. Décor revels in the past, which is part of its appeal, not least to overseas visitors. Service is generally friendly but can be stretched (literally, over small, jam-packed tables). French house red and white come accommodatingly by the glass, 50cl jug, bottle (£13.95) and magnum, but very little else is under £20.

CHEF: David Chambers PROPRIETOR: John Mayhew OPEN: all week noon to 11.30 (10.30 Sun) CLOSED: 3 to 4 days over Christmas MEALS: alc (main courses £17 to £22.50). Set L and D £19.95 (2 courses, Mon to Fri 3 to 5 and after 10) SERVICE: not inc CARDS: Amex, Delta, Diners, MasterCard, Switch, Visa DETAILS: 130 seats. Private parties: 12 to 24 private rooms. No smoking in dining room. No music. Air-conditioned ⊖ Covent Garden (£5)

Sabras

map 12

263 High Road, Willesden Green, NW10 2RX
TEL/FAX: (020) 8459 0340

COOKING **4**
INDIAN VEGETARIAN
£26–£45

With its improved, but still simple décor, the Desai family restaurant continues to evolve, the new, or revived, dishes on its menu celebrating the vegetarian cuisines of many Indian regions. Sev puris please with their 'wonderful contrasts of flavours and textures', the little pastry balls 'crunchy outside with a tangy liquid centre', garnished with coconut, coriander and lemon juice. Also recommended are panch kuti dal, five varieties of lentil cooked with garlic and herbs; sakkariya, 'tender slices of slow-cooked sweet potato lightly coated with spices'; and mutter paneer, a classic dish of 'non-chewy' home-made cottage cheese cubes fried with 'good-quality' petits pois.

Other novelties include palak-makai-paneer, combining pink-stem spinach, steamed sweet corn and paneer in a mild sauce; and banana-methi gota, mashed unripe banana fried with gram flour and fenugreek. House wines from £10 on the short list compete with beers including Goanese Ambari. Fruit juices take in predictable passion and orange, but also apple and carrot, while varied lassis include salt and cumin, sugar and ground pistachio, and natural honey.

CHEF: Nalinee Desai PROPRIETOR: Hemant Desai OPEN: Tue to Sun D only 6.30 to 10.30 MEALS: alc (main courses £5 to £7.50). Cover 60p SERVICE: 12.5%, card slips closed CARDS: Amex, Delta, Diners, MasterCard, Switch, Visa DETAILS: 32 seats. Private parties: 20 main room. Vegetarian meals. No cigars in dining room. Wheelchair access (not WC). Music ⊖ Dollis Hill (£5)

St John

map 13

26 St John Street, EC1M 4AY
TEL: (020) 7251 0848 FAX: (020) 7251 4090
EMAIL: reservations@stjohnrestaurant.co.uk
WEB SITE: www.stjohnrestaurant.co.uk

COOKING **5**
BRITISH
£30–£59

The spacious, bare-brick interior of this former smokehouse near Smithfield Market is painted pure white, its dining room bright, airy and bare, with no plants or pictures to distract, just refectory-style wooden chairs, paper tablecloths over linen, and an open-to-view kitchen. Nor is Fergus Henderson a man to waste words. His menu is one of the tersest around, listing just 'terrine' or 'lemon sole' or 'devilled kidneys', all of which suits the equally unadorned style of cooking. Where he is generous is where it matters, supplying flavour 'by the bucket load', and although it may not please all comers, this is a beacon for real British food.

'Crayfish' turns out to be as simple as it sounds: fresh, moist, plentiful, and served with a little seaweed. Timing is a forte, making textures a joy, for example in the crisp batter and squidgy texture of deep-fried calves' brains, accompanied by a 'dazzling' parsley salsa. Given the restaurant's pig logo, pork should perhaps be a speciality; the ability to source top-quality material is crucial, producing a satisfyingly robust, deeply flavoured, 'stonkingly good' braised belly of Middle White, served with broad beans and a 'fabulous gravy'. To finish, light, moist Eccles cake comes with a creamy Lancashire cheese, and prune suet pudding is meant for two or three to share. Bread is first-rate, informal staff are knowledgeable, professional and agreeable, wine glasses are a joke, and a one-page, largely French wine list offers a generous number by the glass. Vin de Pays d'Oc varietals are £11.50 (£2.35 a glass).

CHEF: Fergus Henderson PROPRIETORS: Trevor Gulliver and Fergus Henderson OPEN: Mon to Fri L 12 to 3, Mon to Sat D 6 to 11 CLOSED: Christmas and New Year, Easter MEALS: alc (main courses £10 to £15) SERVICE: not inc CARDS: Amex, Delta, Diners, MasterCard, Switch, Visa DETAILS: 100 seats. Private parties: 150 main room, 18 private room. Vegetarian meals. No music. Air-conditioned ⊖ Farringdon

Salisbury Tavern

map 12

21 Sherbrooke Road, SW6 7HX
TEL: (020) 7381 4005 FAX: (020) 7381 1002

NEW CHEF
MODERN BRITISH
£29–£48

The Salisbury is a 'wonderful if noisy' modern pub-restaurant, under the same ownership as Admiral Codrington (see entry) and run along similar lines. It combines a lively bar and stylish dining room in one large open space that takes up the whole of the ground floor, including a glass-roofed conservatory extension. The arrival of Michael O'Connor came to our attention too late for us to assess his cooking, but you can expect a blend of traditional favourites with modern classics: starters of Caesar salad with soft-poached egg and roasted prosciutto, or crispy fried squid with warm potato and shallot salad, alongside main courses of smoked haddock fillet, or grilled ribeye steak with béarnaise. Nearly everything on the list of two dozen wines is available by the glass; prices start at £11 for a white Bordeaux and a self-styled 'good ordinary claret'. Reports please.

CHEF: Michael O'Connor PROPRIETOR: Longshot Estates Ltd OPEN: all week 12 to 2.30 (3 Sat, 3.30 Sun), 7 to 10.30 CLOSED: 24 and 26 Dec MEALS: alc (main courses £8 to £13). Cover 50p at D. Bar menu available SERVICE: 12.5% (optional), card slips closed CARDS: Amex, Delta, MasterCard, Switch, Visa DETAILS: 70 seats. Private parties: 20 main room. Vegetarian meals. Wheelchair access (also WC). Music. Air-conditioned ⊖ Fulham Broadway

£ *means that it is possible to have a three-course meal, including coffee, half a bottle of house wine and service for £25 or less per person, at any time the restaurant is open, i.e. at dinner as well as lunch. It may be possible to spend considerably more than this, but by choosing carefully you should find £25 or less achievable.*

Salloos

map 14

62–64 Kinnerton Street, SW1X 8ER
TEL: (020) 7235 4444 FAX: (020) 7259 5703

COOKING **3**
PAKISTANI
£27–£63

Barely a stone's throw from Hyde Park Corner, down a back street of mewsy Victorian terraces, Salloos seems to attract plenty of custom from international business visitors, tourists and gravely wealthy local inhabitants. White geometric-patterned grilles over the windows give an Islamic feel to the first-floor dining room, chandeliers and well-spaced tables lend a touch of opulence, and primitive-style paintings add colour. The menu may hold few surprises for the average frequenter of a curry house, but the kitchen's strength lies in a light touch and expert spicing: a skewer of minced lamb sausages is a prime example.

Main courses include familiar Punjabi-style dishes such as chicken karahi ('small chunks of juicy breast'), plus a few more esoteric recipes such as haleem akbari, where shredded lamb is simmered with lentils and spices into a homogeneous stew. Salloos' reputation has been soundly based on tandoori cooking, although the scorching heat of the oven seems to have been tamed in recent times. For dessert, try creamy, nutty kulfi ices, or 'warm, appetising' halwa gajar carrot cake, both of which are less sugary than the south Asian norm. Staff, polite and discreet, are well used to guiding novices through the cuisine. House wine, from Corney & Barrow, is £12.50.

CHEF: Abdul Aziz PROPRIETOR: Muhammad Salahuddin OPEN: Mon to Sat 12 to 2.30, 7 to 11.15 MEALS: alc (main courses £11 to £14). Set L £16. Cover £1.50 SERVICE: 12.5% (optional), card slips closed CARDS: Amex, Delta, Diners, MasterCard, Switch, Visa DETAILS: 60 seats. Private parties: 60 main room. Vegetarian meals. No children under 8 at D. No cigars/pipes in dining room. No music. Air-conditioned ⊖ Hyde Park Corner, Knightsbridge

Salt House

map 13

63 Abbey Road, NW8 0AE
TEL: (020) 7328 6626 FAX: (020) 7625 9168

COOKING **1**
MODERN EUROPEAN
£21–£33

Salt House occupies a delightful corner position on Abbey Road where diners can chose to eat in the spacious dining room, or outside at teak tables complete with dark blue square parasols. The restaurant's grey walls are enlivened by stained-glass windows, and a large abstract in shades of orange creates interest, colour and atmosphere. The straightforward, no-nonsense food displays a Mediterranean slant in starters of grilled halloumi, chorizo and herb salad, or 'crisp, hot and light' deep-fried squid with black bean dressing. Plain sounding but equally convincing main courses take in pan-fried skate wing with black butter and 'huge' capers, and roast tomato tarte Tatin with crispy pastry, red onions and pecorino. To finish, an inspector recommends a tart gooseberry crumble served with vanilla ice cream. The short wine list comes almost exclusively under £20, and offers a large selection by the glass (from £2.40). French house starts at £9.75.

CHEF: James Thompson PROPRIETORS: Adam and Katie Robinson OPEN: all week 12.30 to 3 (4 Sat and Sun), 6.30 (7 Sat and Sun) to 10.30 (10 Sun) CLOSED: 25 Dec, 1 Jan MEALS: alc (main courses L £5.50 to £12, D £7 to £12). Set L Mon to Fri £8.95 (2 courses) to £11.95 SERVICE: 12.5% (optional), card slips closed CARDS: Amex, Delta, MasterCard, Switch, Visa DETAILS: 40 seats. 80 seats outside. Private parties: 27 private room. Vegetarian meals. No cigars/pipes in dining room. Wheelchair access (not WC). No music. Air-conditioned ⊖ St Johns Wood

Salusbury

map 13

50–52 Salusbury Road, NW6 6NN
TEL/FAX: (020) 7328 3286
WEB SITE: www.thesalusbury.com

COOKING **3**
MODERN ITALIAN
£23–£46

The dining room is a natural outgrowth of the pub, so expect a degree of hue-and-cry in the evenings. Plain white walls and lots of stained wood give a distantly Japanese air, and entertainingly outlandish floral arrangements incorporate spiky cacti. A fortnightly-changing menu offers 'cooking with a sense of place', according to the owners, the place generally being somewhere in Italy.

A soup of borlotti beans, rice and mussels, or a starter of seafood linguine with tomato and chilli, is typical of the hearty style favoured. Most pasta dishes may be taken as either first or main courses, and other options might run to tuna cooked rare and served with agrodolce onions, or grilled chicken paillard with rocket. Italian desserts include the classic cantucci with Tuscan vin santo, but an amaretto, ricotta and almond pudding, or a soft lemon sorbet anointed with grappa, may be just as hard to resist. Oddly, the wine list doesn't major in Italy but offers a fair global spread at mostly acceptable prices, starting with southern French vins de pays at £9.75.

CHEF: Enrico Sartor PROPRIETORS: Nicholas Mash and Robert Claassen OPEN: Tue to Sun L 12.30 to 3.30, all week D 7 to 10.30 CLOSED: 25 and 26 Dec, 1 Jan MEALS: alc (main courses £9 to £15). Set L Sun £12 (2 courses) to £15. Mon to Fri L £5 (1 course) SERVICE: not inc, 12.5% for parties of 7 or more in restaurant CARDS: Delta, MasterCard, Switch, Visa DETAILS: 50 seats. 24 seats outside. Private parties: 10 main room. Vegetarian meals. Children's helpings. No children after 8.30pm. No cigars/pipes in dining room. Wheelchair access (not WC). No music ⊖ Queens Park

Sarkhel's £✱

map 12

199 Replingham Road, Southfields, SW18 5LY
TEL: (020) 8870 1483 FAX: (020) 8874 6603

COOKING **2**
INDIAN
£21–£48

This charming restaurant, run by a former Bombay Brasserie chef and his wife, produces regional Indian cuisine using fresh ingredients and spicing. The à la carte ranges widely – Koondapuri chicken, for example, is described as a hot, home-style curry 'learned from a friend's mum in a tiny village in Mangalore' – and covers curry and tandoori dishes from Kashmir to Cape Cormorin. A one-platter express lunch at £5 offers vegetarian options and three chicken curries. In the three-course lunch or early-evening menu, five starters include a Bombay speciality of spiced batter-fried fish, and five mains take in achar gosht (lamb cooked in a sealed pot) and Allepey fish, a light and hot South Indian curry. Of

40 wines (mainly French, a few New World, four Indian), just two cost over £20; house selections are £10.90.

CHEF: Udit Sarkhel PROPRIETORS: Veronica and Udit Sarkhel OPEN: Fri to Sun L 12 to 2.30, Tue to Sun D 6 to 10.30 (11 Fri and Sat) CLOSED: 25 and 26 Dec MEALS: alc (main courses £6.50 to £9). Set L £5 (1 course, not Sun) and £9.95, Set D before 8 £10 (2 courses) to £12 SERVICE: not inc CARDS: Amex, Delta, MasterCard, Switch, Visa DETAILS: 90 seats. Private parties: 100 main room. Vegetarian meals. Children's helpings. No smoking in 1 dining room. Wheelchair access (also women's WC). Music. Air-conditioned ⊖ Southfields (£5)

Sartoria 🍷 map 15

20 Savile Row, W1X 1AE
TEL: (020) 7534 7000 FAX: (020) 7534 7070

COOKING **2**
ITALIAN
£36–£76

Well, what other theme could a Savile Row restaurant have? The dining room is recognisably from the Terence Conran pattern book – dark marble floor, white walls and black ash furniture – and the tailoring motif shows in such whimsies as ashtrays resembling tape measures. Cooking is classical Italian and tends to keep things simple. Antipasti take in prosciutto with figs, and grilled sea trout with broad beans. Pasta dishes may be as straightforward as linguine with chilli and garlic, while main courses are only slightly more complex: steamed halibut with Swiss chard, oregano and lemon among fish options; rabbit with porcini, potatoes, parsley and garlic typical of meat offerings. To finish, there are Italian formaggi, or dolci such as baked peaches and amaretti with zabaglione. The wine list provides a great opportunity to explore the byways of Italy's highly varied wine regions, and taste classy names next to more humble yet flavour-packed new styles. Very little bar house Chardonnay and Merlot from Veneto at £14 is offered under £20, however, as Saville Row prices apply.

CHEF: Piero Boi PROPRIETOR: Conran Restaurants Ltd OPEN: Mon to Sat L 12 to 3, all week D 6.30 to 11.30 CLOSED: 25 and 1 Jan, bank hols MEALS: alc (main courses £15 to £19). Set L and D 6.30 to 8 £18.50 (2 courses) to £22.50, Set D 6.30 to 8 £19.50 (2 courses) to £23.50 SERVICE: 12.5%, card slips closed CARDS: Amex, Delta, Diners, MasterCard, Switch, Visa DETAILS: 120 seats. Private parties: 120 main room, 16 private room. Vegetarian meals. Wheelchair access (also WC). Music. Air-conditioned ⊖ Oxford Circus

Searcy's map 13

Level 2, Barbican Centre, Silk Street, EC2Y 8DS
TEL: (020) 7588 3008 FAX: (020) 7382 7246
EMAIL: searcys@barbican.org.uk
WEB SITE: www.barbican.org.uk

COOKING **4**
MODERN BRITISH
£36–£80

The annual merry-go-round of chefs has turned once again at Searcy's, Chris McGowan's arrival coinciding with a 'relaunch' of the restaurant: the bar area has been refurbished, though the rest of the dining room remains unchanged, snaking along one side of the Barbican centre with views over the pond and gardens. Like Richard Corrigan before him, McGowan demonstrates a passion for earthy flavour combinations – often involving offal – on his modern British menus: braised pig's trotter stuffed with black pudding and served in a pool of red wine sauce with a generous heap of mash is typical of the style, impressing for its rich 'basso profundo' flavours.

Among starters might be a 'smooth, well-flavoured' ballottine of foie gras on celeriac rémoulade, or or tea-snoked salmon with Chinese cabbage. Attractive presentation is apparent in a dessert such as a flavoursome praline parfait served as three cylinders, each wrapped in chocolate, next to a pool of crème anglaise. The list of around 50 wines has its centre of gravity firmly in France and choice below £20 is somewhat limited; house Cuvée George Blanc red and white are £15.40.

CHEF: Chris McGowan PROPRIETOR: Searcy's OPEN: Sun to Fri L 12 to 3, all week D 5 to 10.30 (7.30 Sun) CLOSED: phone to check during Christmas period and Aug MEALS: alc (main courses £16.50 to £24.50). Set L and D £19.50 (2 courses) to £22.50 SERVICE: 12.5%, card slips closed CARDS: Amex, Delta, Diners, MasterCard, Switch, Visa DETAILS: 100 seats. Vegetarian meals. Wheelchair access (not WC). Occasional music ⊖ Barbican, Moorgate

Singapore Garden

map 13

83–83A Fairfax Road, NW6 4DY
TEL: (020) 7328 5314 FAX: (020) 7624 0656

COOKING **2**
SINGAPOREAN
£18–£59

The décor of the Lims' family restaurant has unobtrusive lighting, Japanese screens, orchids and pictures of old Singapore. Tables are well spaced and covered with two linen cloths, one being removed after the main course. Relaxed, helpful service makes it easy to choose from the many conventional Chinese dishes, but more tempting are such Singaporean and Malaysian specialities as mild rendang beef curry, and noodles: fried, braised, or in soups such as Hokkien hay mee, or laksa. Squid, bean sprouts, spinach, aubergine or okra are all cooked with fiery balachan (dried shrimp paste). Other Chinese exotica include claypot prawns and scallops, and Teochew braised pig's trotters, while Assam fish curry with okra, and Thai green chicken curry are welcome finds. A respectable, if fully priced, list of 50 wines starts with house selections from £11.50.

CHEF: Mrs Siam Kiang Lim PROPRIETOR: Singapore Garden Restaurant Ltd OPEN: all week 12 to 2.45, 6 to 10.45 (11.15 Fri and Sat) CLOSED: 1 week Christmas MEALS: alc (main courses £5 to £14.90). Set L £7 (2 courses) to £8.50, Set D £17.50 to £30 SERVICE: 12.5% (optional), card slips closed CARDS: Amex, Delta, Diners, MasterCard, Switch, Visa DETAILS: 100 seats. 10 seats outside. Private parties: 60 main room, 60 private room. Vegetarian meals. No cigars in dining room. Music. Air-conditioned ⊖ Swiss Cottage

All details are as accurate as possible at the time of going to press, but chefs and owners often change, and it is wise to check by telephone before making a special journey. Many readers have been disappointed when set-price bargain meals are no longer available. Ask when booking.

Smiths of Smithfield, Top Floor 🍷

NEW ENTRY map 13

67–77 Charterhouse Street, EC1M 6HJ
TEL: (020) 7236 6666 FAX: (020) 7236 5666
EMAIL: eat@smithsofsmithfield.co.uk
WEB SITE: www.smithsofsmithfield.co.uk

COOKING **4**
MODERN BRITISH
£44–£83

Opposite Smithfield Market, Smith's is a multi-level gastrodome. Pass the doorman, various lively bars and a dining room to reach the Top Floor restaurant. This has fine views over the City skyline, glass doors on two sides, leather chairs, white linen, an oak floor and an understated, upmarket atmosphere. The menu has a strong British focus, plus odd detours to the Mediterranean and beyond (perhaps seared tuna with a Szechuan pepper crust and black bean dressing to start), and stresses organic/additive-free ingredients, rare-breed meats and line-caught fish. Its Fine Meats section notes breed, source and hanging time (Chesterton Farm Longhorn fillet, hung 22 days), and the meat is then treated to commendably simple grilling or pan-frying, with the option of béarnaise sauce, red wine butter or creamed horseradish to accompany.

And there's plenty besides beef: rack of parsley-crusted Oxford Down lamb with dauphinoise, perhaps, or line-caught cod with spinach, salsify and rosemary. Finish with pavlova plus passion fruit sauce, or chocolate fondant and strawberry sorbet. 'Service makes it a pleasure being here, and the cellar deserves applause.' The well-balanced list offers classics from Burgundy and Bordeaux, but also includes good southern hemisphere estates and interesting Spanish items such as Castell de Remei's Gotim Bru. There is plenty by the glass from £4, and vins de pays start prices off at £14.50.

CHEFS: Ashely Shergold and Tony Moyse PROPRIETOR: John Torode OPEN: Sun to Fri L 12 to 3, all week D 7 to 11 MEALS: alc (main courses £14.50 to £25). Brunch and Sun L menus also available SERVICE: 12.5% (optional), card slips closed CARDS: Amex, Delta, Diners, MasterCard, Switch, Visa DETAILS: 70 seats. 30 seats outside. Private parties: 70 main room, 30 private room. Vegetarian meals. Children's helpings. Wheelchair access (also WC). No music. Air-conditioned

Snows on the Green

map 12

166 Shepherd's Bush Road, W6 7PB
TEL: (020) 7603 2142 FAX: (020) 7602 7553

COOKING **2**
MODERN BRITISH/MEDITERRANEAN
£26–£52

The bright interior has a touch of Van Gogh (southern France, anyway) in the boldly coloured chairs and walls and the bare boards of the floor. A short corridor connects the separate front and rear dining areas, and the approach of staff is both convivial and proficient. Sebastian Snow has been here a decade now, and still offers a confident, market-oriented menu mobilising the best of seasonal produce. That could mean a salad of artichokes, French beans, rocket, Parmesan and toasted almonds, or parsnip and sherry soup with hazelnut pesto to start, followed by duck à la ficelle with cotechino sausage, spring vegetables and bone marrow. Chargrilled swordfish has come with chickpea salad and aubergine caviar. If it all sounds breathlessly trendy, note that a traditional roast is also now offered at Sunday lunchtime. Desserts range from butterscotch tart with fresh raspberries, or blood orange and champagne jelly, to a textbook tarte Tatin with caramel ice cream. A modern wine list offers reasonable choice below £20, starting with a Cabernet-Merlot Vin de Pays de l'Aude at £10.95.

CHEF/PROPRIETOR: Sebastian Snow OPEN: Sun to Fri L 12 to 3, Mon to Sat D 6 to 11 CLOSED: 24 to 28 Dec, bank hol Mons MEALS: alc (main courses £10 to £15). Set L £13.50 (2 courses) to £16.50 SERVICE: not inc CARDS: Amex, Delta, Diners, MasterCard, Switch, Visa DETAILS: 80 seats. 12 seats outside. Private parties: 80 main room, 14 and 20 private rooms. Vegetarian meals. Children's helpings. No-smoking area. Wheelchair access (not WC). Music. Air-conditioned ⊖ Hammersmith

Soho Spice

map 15

124/126 Wardour Street, W1F 0TY
TEL: (020) 7434 0808 FAX: (020) 7434 0799
EMAIL: info@sohospice.co.uk
WEB SITE: www.sohospice.co.uk

COOKING **1**
INDIAN
£26–£65

There's an upbeat feel here, due to the décor (walls variously turquoise, orange and blue), young clientele, Indian pop music and the prime location. A carte of North Indian classics is supplemented by monthly set meals (changed every six weeks) highlighting a regional cuisine; the latter are often the most interesting. At inspection, mahi lasooni tikka, a starter of juicy tandoori salmon, was well-paired with 'refreshing' coriander chutney. Shatkora mangsho (from a Bangladeshi set meal) featured the merest hint of tangy shatkora (wild lemon) with 'tender' lamb in a tomato-based sauce and came, like all main courses, with rice, dhal, naan and a vegetable dish (a 'dull' mix of sweetcorn, cabbage and peas). Waiters can seem bored. Drinks include a fair choice of globally sourced wine (from £12.95) and bottled beer.

CHEF: Mr Suresh and Mr Matto PROPRIETOR: Amin Ali OPEN: all week noon to 1am (3am Fri and Sat) CLOSED: 25 Dec MEALS: alc (main courses £11 to £17). Set L Mon to Fri £7.50 (2 courses), Set D £16.95. Pre-theatre D Mon to Sat 5 to 7 £7.50 (2 courses) SERVICE: not inc CARDS: Amex, Delta, Diners, MasterCard, Switch, Visa DETAILS: 200 seats. Private parties: 100 main room, 50 private room. Vegetarian meals. Wheelchair access (also WC). Music. Air-conditioned ⊖ Tottenham Court Road, Oxford Circus

Sonny's

map 12

94 Church Road, SW13 0DQ
TEL: (020) 8748 0393 FAX: (020) 8748 2698

COOKING **3**
MODERN EUROPEAN
£27–£55

Situated in a row of shops, Sonny's large front windows with their cool, green-painted frames look directly on to the street. Next door is a food shop, which sells Poilaîne bread and other morsels. A glass-topped bar has a few high stools for perching, and the dining areas are hung with colourful paintings, the main room decked out in duck egg blue and featuring a back wall made up of glass bricks and a modern fireplace. It all creates a feeling of 'subtle sophistication'.

Sonny's serves up dishes that combine light and delicate flavours – no heavy sauces in sight – as in a starter of asparagus and new potato salad with poached egg, hollandaise sauce and truffle oil. Main courses can be more complex. Fish, for example, is served in a number of innovative ways: a thick chunk of steamed fillet of halibut is accompanied by a pea and mint pancake with tomato and lemon dressing; and fresh sea bass fillet comes on confit potatoes with asparagus, samphire, black olives and watercress. Under-seasoning detracts from some dishes, however, and desserts have not always hit the high notes of what's gone before. Service is swift and friendly, and the short wine list features some good modern producers at generally fair mark-ups. House wines are £10.50.

CHEF: Leigh Diggins PROPRIETORS: Rebecca Mascarenhas and James Harris OPEN: all week L 12.30 to 2.30 (3 Sun), Mon to Sat D 7.30 to 11 CLOSED: bank hols MEALS: alc (main courses £10.50 to £15). Set L £13 (2 courses) to £16. Set L Sun £18.50, Café menu available Mon to Sat 12 to 4 SERVICE: 12.5% (optional), card slips closed CARDS: Amex, Delta, Diners, MasterCard, Switch, Visa DETAILS: 100 seats. Private parties: 20 private room. Vegetarian meals. Children's helpings. No cigars/pipes in dining room. No music. Air-conditioned ⊖ Hammersmith (£5)

Spiga

map 15

84–86 Wardour Street, W1V 3LF
TEL: (020) 7734 3444 FAX: (020) 7734 3332

COOKING **3**
ITALIAN
£33–£46

The trendy and smart exterior of this large modern-day Italian draws the London film and club crowds. Its take on Italian cuisine is refined and, some feel, 'far superior to its ambience', which on a Saturday night can range from vibrant to deafening. Beige walls are hung with '50s panels in irregular shapes and colours, and a curved bar, glaring lights and quarry-tiled floor make for an interior that is bright and minimalistic. The printed menu rolls out familiar pizza/pasta combinations, and mozzarella, rocket and Parmesan accompaniments, but nevertheless delivers.

Start with goats' cheese ravioli with an 'understated and rich' pistachio sauce, or head straight for the pizzas from a wood-fired oven; Siciliana perhaps, topped with mozzarella, sun-dried peppers, courgettes, capers, mushrooms, anchovies and black olives. Desserts have proved 'outstanding', not least the cliché tiramisù, while fresh strawberries with a peach sorbet and prosecco has been praised too. Service is polite and efficient, and the succinct Italian wine list (on the reverse of the menu) offers four by the glass and half-bottle, and house wine from £12. A new branch, Spiga Chelsea, is at 312–314 King's Road, SW3; tel (020) 7351 0101.

CHEF: Nick-Melmoth Coombs PROPRIETOR: A To Z Restaurants Ltd OPEN: all week 12 to 3, 6 to 12 (Sun to Tues 11) CLOSED: Christmas, 31 Dec MEALS: alc (main courses £7 to £14.50) SERVICE: 12.5% (optional), card slips closed CARDS: Amex, Delta, Diners, MasterCard, Switch, Visa DETAILS: 120 seats. Private parties: 22 main room. Vegetarian meals. No smoking in 1 dining room. Wheelchair access (also WC). Music. Air-conditioned ⊖ Piccadilly Circus, Leicester Square

London Round-ups listing additional restaurants that may be worth a visit can be found after the main London section.

Spread Eagle

map 12

1–2 Stockwell Street, SE10 9JN
TEL: (020) 8853 2333 FAX: (020) 8305 0447
EMAIL: goodfood@spreadeagle.org
WEB SITE: www.spreadeagle.org

COOKING **2**
FRENCH
£26–£55

Today we might call this seventeenth-century coaching inn a gastro-pub: although it became a restaurant in the 1960s it still retains a pubby ambience, with a warm welcome from friendly, gossiping staff. The table d'hôte changes frequently, and might include mussel and pumpkin soup, navarin of lamb, and spiced pear tart with caramel sauce. The more complicated à la carte dishes are titled in French (or Franglais: 'civet de légumes en Yorkshire'). Most are modern takes on traditional dishes; reporters mention 'a generous portion' of accurately cooked magret de canard à l'orange with shiitake mushrooms and a pleasingly sharp sauce; and a 'light, unpretentious' starter of feuilleté of warm asparagus with lemon-grass sauce. Le caprice du patron, on the menu for 20 years, is sweet pickled herring with rye bread, light curry mayonnaise and soft-boiled egg, plus a gloriously un-Gallic slug of schnapps. The mostly French wine list starts with house selections at £10.50.

CHEF: Bernard Brique PROPRIETOR: Richard Moy OPEN: all week L 12.30 to 3 (3.30 Sun), Mon to Sat D 6.30 to 10.30 CLOSED: 25 to 28 Dec MEALS: alc (main courses £12.50 to £17.50). Set L and D (D Mon to Thur) £13.50 (2 courses) to £16.75 SERVICE: 12.5% (optional), card slips closed CARDS: Amex, Delta, Diners, MasterCard, Switch, Visa DETAILS: 85 seats. 20 seats outside. Private parties: 45 main room, 30 and 45 private rooms. Vegetarian meals. Children's helpings. Occasional music. Air-conditioned ⊖ Cutty Sark (DLR) (£5)

Square

map 15

6–10 Bruton Street, W1X 7AG
TEL: (020) 7495 7100 FAX: (020) 7495 7150

COOKING **8**
MODERN FRENCH
£42–£113

A relaxed, noisy atmosphere testifies to the Square's enjoyment rating; there is no sense of worshipping at a shrine, just a businesslike feel derived from its polished wooden floor, walls hung with abstract modern art, and fresh flowers on well-spaced tables. Philip Howard refers to his style of cooking as progressive modern French, based on seasonal produce from the UK or neighbouring temperate countries: so expect Italy to feature as well, but not Thailand. Choice on the carte is generous, running from an intense and refreshing jelly of duck, scattered with diced root vegetables and a warm vinaigrette, to a salad of young organic vegetables served with truffle cream and a breadcrumbed deep-fried duck's egg with a runny yolk.

Fish is generally a highlight, taking in a moist, fresh-tasting cushion of turbot partnered by sweet-salty langoustines, its champagne beurre blanc combining richness and acidity; and carefully roasted halibut with a crisp and salty skin, served with a sweet pea purée and a small copper pan of vegetables. Frothy sauces feature: in starters of fresh crab lasagne with shellfish cappuccino, and fat roast scallops with a whisked-up velouté of haricot beans and truffle. Only one dish, during an entire year of reports, seems to have been inedible, and that was an inspector's papillote of sea bass, the cost of which was refunded. It was followed, however, by 'probably the best cheesecake I have ever eaten', made from Brillat-Savarin and surrounded by blueberries.

Although cheeses are not always at their best (a shame, given the price supplement), the well-risen prune and armagnac soufflé continues to draw praise: the waiter inserts a large prune and a scoop of armagnac ice cream at table. French service is professional, charming and efficient, and although there can be long waits, staff are individually on the ball: 'the sommelier poured every glass of wine himself – this with a full restaurant.' Going almost over the top in its champagne selection, the wine list offers many rare vintages to please the most extravagant celebrator. Leading on, it covers France in great detail, but also makes room for classic and new styles from the rest of Europe and further afield. French and Italian house wines are £18.50.

CHEF: Philip Howard PROPRIETORS: Philip Howard and Nigel Platts-Martin OPEN: Mon to Fri L 12 to 2.45, all week D 6.30 to 10.45 (10 Sun) CLOSED: 25 and 26 Dec, 1 Jan, L bank hols MEALS: Set L £20 (2 courses) to £65, Set D £50 to £65 SERVICE: 12.5% (optional), card slips closed CARDS: Amex, Delta, Diners, MasterCard, Switch, Visa DETAILS: 70 seats. Private parties: 100 main room, 18 private room. No cigars/pipes in dining room. Wheelchair access (also WC). No music. Air-conditioned ⊖ Green Park

Sri Siam Soho

map 15

16 Old Compton Street, W1D 4TL
TEL: (020) 7434 3544 FAX: (020) 7287 1311

COOKING **2**
THAI
£25–£59

This large, buzzing restaurant is simply decorated, with motifs of tropical vegetation painted on its pastel-coloured walls, and tableware is plain white or blue-and-white. The menu, credited to Ken Hom, offers satisfying set meals with several choices of main course; some are designed for a minimum of two, so that larger parties can also enjoy some variety. Although the à la carte has been shortened just a little, its range is still wide, with stir-fries, grills, mild to hot curries, spicy soups, an even more spicy Thai salad, and seafood prepared with various Thai sauces and garnishes. Interest on the list of 40 wines (organised by style) can be found under £20 – a McLaren Vale Riesling from d'Arenberg for £19, or a Primitivo from Puglia at £14, for example – though a few pounds more will offer something a little classier or in more limited production. House wines are from £10.95.

CHEF: Phuvanai (Nico) Thongsumrit PROPRIETOR: Noble House Leisure Ltd OPEN: Mon to Sat L 12 to 3, all week D 6 to 11.15 MEALS: alc (main courses £7.50 to £141). Set D £14.95 to £24.95 (some min 2). Lunch box menu also available SERVICE: 12.5% (optional), card slips closed CARDS: Amex, Delta, Diners, MasterCard, Switch, Visa DETAILS: 145 seats. Private parties: 20 main room, 30 private room. Vegetarian meals. No music. Air-conditioned ⊖ Leicester Square, Tottenham court road (£5)

'As the head waiter showed us to our table, [my friend] remarked that if she'd known what it was like "I'd've fetched me tiara".' (On eating in Manchester)

Stepping Stone

NEW ENTRY map 12

123 Queenstown Road, SW8 3RH
TEL: (020) 7622 0555 FAX: (020) 7622 4230
EMAIL: thesteppingstone@aol.com

COOKING 4
MODERN BRITISH
£27–£48

Looking modern and sharp from outside, and large and airy inside, this Battersea restaurant goes in for solid blocks of colour, its walls a mix of acid yellow, shocking pink, mauve and pale green. It's a no-frills operation concentrating on well-cooked food based on high-quality ingredients, where service is calm, pleasant and efficient. The short menu is decidedly modern British, with France and the Mediterranean being the main influences: sauté squid, for example, is served with chorizo, black olives, fennel and tomato.

Not all dishes aim for such vibrant effect – a starter of crisp mushroom tart comes filled with wild mushrooms in a light cream sauce, topped with rocket leaves – but flavour combinations are well judged: calf's liver with bacon and parsley mash for example, and haunch of wild Cairngorms venison with beetroot and peppercorn sauce. A chocaholic's dream of chocolate pudding with chocolate ice cream might turn up alongside something fruity like summer pudding, or apple tart with ricotta ice cream. The wine list, arranged by style, requests customers to 'please be adventurous'. Its wares are fairly priced, starting at £10.75, and there are certainly enough unusual and well-chosen bottles to grab the attention of oenophiles.

CHEF: Michael Bird PROPRIETORS: Gary and Emer Levy OPEN: Sun to Fri L 12 to 2.30, Mon to Sat D 7 to 11 CLOSED: 5 days Christmas, Sun L July and Aug, bank hols MEALS: alc (main courses £9 to £15). Set L Mon to Fri £12.50 (2 courses), Set L Sun £18.50 SERVICE: 12.5% (optional), card slips closed CARDS: Delta, MasterCard, Switch, Visa DETAILS: 65 seats. Private parties: 65 main room. Vegetarian meals. Children's helpings. No smoking in 1 dining room. Wheelchair access (not WC). No music. Air-conditioned ⊖ Sloane Square, Clapham Common (£5)

Sugar Club

map 15

21 Warwick Street, W1R 5RB
TEL: (020) 7437 7776 FAX: (020) 7437 7778
WEB SITE: www.thesugarclub.co.uk

COOKING 5
FUSION
£40–£73

Behind a discreetly expensive exterior in one of the less colourful parts of Soho, smokers unfortunately get the ground floor with its big picture window, while non-smokers are poured into the noisy, windowless basement where comfort does not seem to be of prime concern. The pace of culinary action is fast and furious, though, sometimes to the point of bafflement. 'It's as if you're expected to pass some sort of foodie Mastermind before you order your dinner,' reckoned one who ordered salmon sashimi with chipotle chilli salsa, coriander, mujjol and lemon-yuzu dressing, finding her tiny translucent wafers of salmon dotted with fish eggs (mujjol) and dressed with a thin citric juice (yuzu).

As it happens, some of the now classic dishes, and some of the simplest, turn out to be the best, among them grilled scallops with sweet chilli sauce and crème fraîche. Happily, confident technique ensures that even when flavour combinations don't quite hit the mark, results are still impressive. Pausing only briefly to look up pandan syrup and feijoa sorbet in the encyclopedia, you may then wish to give full attention to desserts, which offer the prospect of maple syrup bavarois with poached tamarillo, or date and pecan pudding with poached quince, mirin-toffee sauce and galangal cream. Staff are well briefed on the menu, and a sharp, varietally organised wine list is kind to those with more than £20 to spend, although house Vin de Pays d'Oc is £12.50.

CHEF: David Selex PROPRIETORS: Ashley Sumner and Vivienne Hayman OPEN: all week 12 to 2.45, 6 to 10.45 (10.30 Sun) CLOSED: 25 and 26 Dec, 1 Jan MEALS: alc (main courses £14 to £20) SERVICE: 12.5% (optional), card slips closed CARDS: Amex, Delta, Diners, MasterCard, Switch, Visa DETAILS: 140 seats. Private parties: 55 main room. Vegetarian meals. No smoking in 1 dining room. No cigars/pipes throughout. Wheelchair access (not WC). No music. Air-conditioned ⊖ Oxford Circus, Piccadilly Circus

Sushi-Say

map 12

33B Walm Lane, NW2 5SH
TEL: (020) 8459 2971 and 7512
FAX: (020) 8907 3229

COOKING **3**
JAPANESE
£17–£75

Recently refurbished, this is now a restaurant rather than an eating house. The cluttered knick-knacks and overcrowded small tables have gone, though the six-seater, semi-private tatami room at the back remains. Katsuhari Shimizu has made new decorations, at first sight like wood-cut prints, cut from the green plastic sheets used to decorate plates of sushi. Mrs Shimizu has been studying wine, and the result is a short, fairly priced, mainly French list with house wines at £9.80. Service under her supervision is friendly and willing, if occasionally a trifle disjointed. Most of the fare is traditional, especially the daily specials which may include Japanese fish rarely seen here: such as hairtail, and the lightly salted dried filefish with the texture of Bombay duck that was approved by a Japanese visitor. Set lunches are good value, and ten set dinner menus help those daunted by the long à la carte covering most of the Japanese repertoire except sukiyaki. Among home-made ice creams, sesame and wasabi flavours exemplify Mr Shimizu's innovative approach.

CHEF: Katsuharu Shimizu PROPRIETORS: Katsuharu and Yuko Shimizu OPEN: Sat and Sun L 12 to 2.30, Tue to Sun D 6.30 to 10.30 CLOSED: 25 and 26 Dec, 1 Jan, 1 week Aug MEALS: alc (main courses £6 to £19). Set L £6.90 (2 courses) to £12.40, Set D £17.70 to £27.90 SERVICE: not inc CARDS: Amex, Delta, MasterCard, Switch, Visa DETAILS: 36 seats. Private parties: 20 main room. Vegetarian meals. No-smoking area. Wheelchair access (also WC). No music. Air-conditioned ⊖ Willesden Green

'One of us had used the spoon laid for dessert to eat the excellent sauce with the rump. Although the matire d' type chap had taken away the plates, he'd not noticed this. So when it came to dessert, he had to be asked for a spoon. With a double-take worthy of John Cleese noticing a rat racing across the dining room, his jaw dropped and he uttered, complete with Fawlty intonation, ''Well there was one there before,'' and just stood looking at us in amazement. ''Yes, there was,'' [my wife] replied, ''but there's not now'' . . . . He then asked where it had gone and looked under the table cloth.' (On eating in Derbyshire)

Tabla

NEW ENTRY map 12

The Dockmaster's House, West India Dock Gate,
Hertsmere Road, E14 8JJ
TEL: (020) 7345 0345 FAX: (020) 7363 1013 COOKING **2**
EMAIL: info@tablarestaurant.com INDIAN
WEB SITE: www.tablarestaurant.com £28–£56

Tabla was originally called the Dockmaster's House, a fitting tribute to the splendid Georgian mansion housing it close by Canary Wharf. Décor and lighting do not quite live up to that, although the large garden is fine for pre-curry drinks. Albert Ray, once of the Ivy and St John (see entries), is manager; and co-owner is Iqbal Wahhab, whose flagship is now the Cinnamon Club (see entry). Their seasonally changing menu is a short carte of classic Indian cooking incorporating regional specialities of Kashmir, Rajasthan and Gujerat as well as tandoori dishes. Starter portions are small, main dishes generous. Daily specials one evening were Rajasthani beef in red chilli paste, not as hot as it sounds, and peas in a spiced yoghurt sauce. Desserts include cracked pepper, cinnamon and cardamom ice creams. Thirty wines from £12 include some interesting bottles.

CHEF: Yogesh Battia PROPRIETORS: Albert Ray and Iqbal Wahhab OPEN: Sun to Fri L 12 to 3, all week D 6 to 11 CLOSED: 25 and 26 Dec, 1 Jan MEALS: alc (main courses £8 to £16). Set L £10 (1 course). Bar menu available SERVICE: not inc, 10% for parties of 7 or more CARDS: Amex, Delta, Diners, MasterCard, Switch, Visa DETAILS: 100 seats. 80 seats outside. Private parties: 120 main room, 20 to 50 private rooms. Car park. Vegetarian meals. Children's helpings. No smoking in 1 dining room. Wheelchair access (also WC). No music (£5)

Tamarind

map 15

20 Queen Street, W1J 5PR
TEL: (020) 7629 3561 FAX: (020) 7499 5034 COOKING **3**
EMAIL: tamarind.restaurant@virgin.net MODERN INDIAN
WEB SITE: www.tamarindrestaurant.com £27–£70

A polished wooden floor, golden pillars and a huge urn containing a striking flower arrangement give an attractive modern oriental feel to the large, octagonal room. Much of Atul Kochhar's 'classy, impeccably prepared' food is from the familiar north-west Indian repertoire, so the regularly changing menu usually contains classics such as rogan josh, and tandoori dishes like garlicky sheekh kebabs (served surrounded by 'dabs and puddles of yoghurt sauces and oils'). Inspired departures from this norm have included jalpari chaat, a starter salad of king prawns and queen scallops in a yoghurt dressing with grapes and julienne vegetables, and a much-praised curry of prawns in tomato sauce with coriander and fenugreek. Tradition is tweaked in such starters as grilled peppers, onion and pineapple in vinegar and palm sugar dressing; and in main courses such as fish curry with coconut and lemon balm, or seasonal game dishes. To finish, a sorbet of mixed fruits 'powerfully redolent of passion fruit and mango' has been admired. Service is slick, if occasionally over-insistent, and there is a two-hour limit on tables. House wines – from a list encompassing New World and Old – start at £14.50.

CHEF: Atul Kochhar PROPRIETOR: Indian Cuisine Ltd OPEN: Sun to Fri L 12 to 2.45, all week D 6 to 11.30 CLOSED: 25 and 26 Dec MEALS: alc (main courses £10.50 to £18). Set L £12.50 (2 courses) to £32.50, Set D £30.50 to £45 SERVICE: 12.5% (optional), card slips closed CARDS: Amex, Delta, Diners, MasterCard, Switch, Visa DETAILS: 90 seats. Private parties: 94 main room. Vegetarian meals. Jacket and tie. No smoking in 1 dining room. No children under 7. Music. Air-conditioned ⊖ Green Park (£5)

La Tante Claire 🍷 map 14

Wilton Place, SW1X 7RL COOKING **8**
TEL: (020) 7823 2003 FAX: (020) 7823 2001 FRENCH
EMAIL: office@latanteclaire.demon.co.uk £41–£124

Although it may lack the distinction and character it used to have in Chelsea (reporters still hanker after the old regime), Tante Claire's present generous space is classily designed in green and purple, and feels comfortable, relaxed and civilised. Menus are written in French with no English translation, although kitchen staff are quite capable of writing in English, usually on dessert plates: 'Happy Anniversary' to one couple, and 'Please eat a little of this' to one lady who had declined dessert.

The high French style visits many luxurious ingredients in its quest for the best: foie gras might be roasted with root vegetables, truffle cooked in a pithiviers with truffle sauce, and scallops partnered with langoustines, crab, caviar and oysters. Prime cuts of meat and fish constitute another strand, perhaps poached turbot, roast leg of Pyrenean lamb with ceps, or Aberdeen Angus beef Rossini. But Pierre Koffmann has never been one to neglect the earthier end of the spectrum, and aficionados are pleased to see the pig's trotter still in place (stuffed with calves' sweetbread and morels), and a starter of snails, either in a salad, or accompanied by girolles and a cep duxelles.

Assemblies are thoughtful – for one reporter a salad of sweet scallops and rare pigeon breast in a sticky but well-balanced stock reduction – timings are careful, and dishes have an inherent simplicity and coherence which gives them a timeless feel: mallard, for example, lightly cooked and jointed, served with a hollowed-out turnip stuffed with liver and minced flesh. The two set-price lunch menus (three courses each) offer no choice, but dishes can be exchanged between them; among those enjoyed have been a light, warm terrine of turbot and red mullet with beurre blanc, chocolate tart with a scoop of vanilla ice cream, and omelette norvégienne (a small baked Alaska) with a lemon sauce.

'Very expensive but worth it' is a typical summing up (at least water comes free of charge), and reporters have received impeccably friendly and efficient service from a multitude of staff. Modest budgets beware though: much sifting through top-class, top-price wines is needed to reveal anything under £25 on the wine list. 'World Wines' that have been carefully chosen for using native grape varieties provide novelty and often the best value, although French country wines, like the house Syrah from the Drôme at £17, do as well. Taking the recommended wine with lunch (starting at £7.50 a glass) can cut the finger work and cost.

CHEF/PROPRIETOR: Pierre Koffmann OPEN: Mon to Fri L 12 to 2, Mon to Sat D 7 to 11 CLOSED: Christmas, Easter MEALS: alc (main courses £27 to £40). Set L £28 SERVICE: 12.5%, card slips closed CARDS: Amex, Delta, Diners, MasterCard, Switch, Visa DETAILS: 80 seats. Private parties: 80 main room, 14 and 16 private rooms. No cigars/pipes in dining room. Wheelchair access (also WC). No music. Air-conditioned ⊖ Hyde Park Corner

Tas £ — map 13

33 The Cut, SE1 8LF — COOKING **2**
TEL: (020) 7928 1444 FAX: (020) 7633 9686 — TURKISH
£19–£40

The Cut, an unprepossessing main road, is enlivened by this buzzing open-plan brasserie. The menu lists a multitude of Turkish mezze, hot and cold, as well as kebabs, and meat or vegetarian casseroles. There are artichokes, aubergines, lentils, chickpeas and yoghurt in many combinations. A reporter particularly enjoyed kabak-pirasa salad: raw baby leeks and lots of herbs, topped with grilled courgettes. Fish plays a big role; mussels and squid fried in a very light batter make a starter, while mains include steamed cod, halibut, sardines with vine leaves, salmon, sea bass, even Dover sole. Sutlac rice pudding with rosewater and lemon zest sounds exciting. Modestly priced wines include Turkish house bottles at £9.90.

A new branch at 72 Borough High Street, SE1 (tel: (020) 7403 8557) has an identical menu, and Tas Café, also on Borough High Street, offers mezze, sandwiches, and other light snacks.

CHEF/PROPRIETOR: Onder Sahan OPEN: all week, noon to 11.30 (10.30 Sun) MEALS: alc (main courses £4.65 to £14.50). Set L and D £6.95 (2 courses) to £18.50 SERVICE: 10% CARDS: Amex, Delta, MasterCard, Switch, Visa DETAILS: 130 seats. 4 seats outside. Private parties: 60 main room, 50 private room. Vegetarian meals. No cigars/pipes in dining room. Wheelchair access (also WC). Music. Air-conditioned ⊖ Southwark, Waterloo

Tate Gallery Restaurant 🍷 — map 13

Millbank, SW1P 4RG
TEL: (020) 7887 8825 FAX: (020) 7887 8902 — COOKING **3**
EMAIL: taterestaurant@tate.org.uk — MODERN BRITISH
WEB SITE: www.tate.org.uk/britain/information — £32–£60

Rex Whistler's mural 'Expedition in Pursuit of Rare Meats' runs round this popular, agreeable, if somewhat noisy, luncheon room. Black leather banquettes, armchairs and napkins contrast with white tablecloths and crockery, and black-clad staff cope well with numbers. Richard Zuber's one-page menu has a light, contemporary edge, offering a carte and a two-choice set menu drawn from it, and the straightforward style is typified by warm goats' cheese and onion tart with rocket, or seared scallops with spinach and fried basil.

Chargrilling is an effective technique, applied to a thick, fresh, meaty chunk of swordfish fillet (served with lemon, peppers, ginger and a parsley 'salad'), and to filet mignon, which comes in familiar guise with béarnaise and hand-cut chips. Presentation is a strong point, though seasoning could be improved. Among tempting desserts might be double chocolate mousse, or apple tarte

Tatin with caramel ice cream. A classic wine list concentrates on France's traditional regions as well as on serious names from newer areas; aptly, Western Australia's Leeuwin Estate 'Art Series' figures among New World bottles. Prices may look daunting, but there is choice under £20 (house wines are £15), and the range of half-bottles will keep afternoons productive and costs down.

CHEF: Richard Zuber PROPRIETOR: Tate Catering Ltd OPEN: all week L only 12 to 3 (4 Sun) CLOSED: 24 to 26 Dec MEALS: alc L (main courses £10 to £17). Set L £16.75 (2 courses) to £19.50 SERVICE: not inc, card slips closed CARDS: Amex, Delta, Diners, MasterCard, Switch, Visa DETAILS: 90 seats. Private parties: 40 main room. Children's helpings. Wheelchair access (also WC). No music. Air-conditioned ⊖ Pimlico

Teatro

map 15

93–107 Shaftesbury Avenue, W1V 8BT
TEL: (020) 7494 3040 FAX: (020) 7494 3050
EMAIL: info@teatrolondon.co.uk

COOKING 3
MODERN EUROPEAN
£26–£69

The low-key entrance and long walk to the dining room make entering Teatro feel a bit like using the stage door; although the elegant dining room itself is hardly theatrical, its off-white walls are given welcome splashes of colour by contemporary artworks. The cooking under John Newton is still influenced mainly by Italy and France, with hints of traditional British.

Fish and seafood dominate starters: a warm smoked mackerel salad with horseradish has impressed for its lightly smoked, sushi-like fish. Main courses cover imaginative modern dishes, such as peppered tuna steak with sauce bois boudran and aubergine chips, and more traditional offerings like a succulent pork chop with a smooth-textured black pudding and wedges of fried apple. Vanilla cheesecake with poached pear and roast hazelnuts has been a successful dessert. Helpful service is from formally dressed Frenchmen. Wines span a wide range of styles and nationalities, a good number available by the glass; prices tend to be on the high side but start at a reasonable £13.50.

CHEF: John Newton PROPRIETORS: Lee Chapman and Leslie Ash OPEN: Mon to Fri 12 to 3, Mon to Sat 5.30 to 11.45 CLOSED: 1 week Christmas, bank hol Mons MEALS: alc (main courses £12.50 to £17). Set L 12 to 2 and D 5.30 to 7.30 £11.50 (2 courses) to £14. Cover £1.50 SERVICE: 12.5% (optional), card slips closed CARDS: Amex, Delta, Diners, MasterCard, Switch, Visa DETAILS: 100 seats. Private parties: 100 main room. Vegetarian meals. Wheelchair access (also WC). Occasional music. Air-conditioned ⊖ Leicester Square

Teca

map 15

54 Brooks Mews, W1Y 2NY
TEL: (020) 7495 4774 FAX: (020) 7491 3545

COOKING 4
MODERN ITALIAN
£38–£76

This corner-site restaurant flaunts its modernity with stainless steel, smoked glass, polished wood floors and sleek banquettes. The menu, too, is modern; praiseworthy raw materials are turned into carpaccios and risottos, and there may be stuffed courgette flowers and bottarga, while other dishes, such as marinated tuna with crispy vegetables and soy and ginger sauce, look further afield.

Helpings are generous, but Marco Torri's style 'is light enough to leave one feeling comfortable rather than stuffed'. Fish looms large – perhaps a 'fresh, sweet, lightly cooked' sea bream fillet with red pepper sauce – and vegetarian options are more than mere gestures, while meats might take in roast rabbit with aubergine, courgette and tomato. Desserts can surprise: a dish of Gorgonzola semifreddo with fruit salad triumphantly confounded doubters with its surprisingly delicate flavour. Wines – all Italian, arranged by region – aren't cheap (no great choice under £20, though prices start at £15), but producers are top-notch, and there are plenty of unusual Italian varietals to investigate. Thirteen wines are served by the glass.

CHEF: Marco Torri PROPRIETOR: A To Z Restaurants Ltd OPEN: Mon to Fri L 12 to 2.30, Mon to Sat D 7 to 10.30 CLOSED: Christmas, Easter, bank hols MEALS: Set L £19.50 (2 courses) to £24.50, Set D £25 (2 courses) to £48.50 SERVICE: 12.5% (optional), card slips closed CARDS: Amex, Delta, MasterCard, Switch, Visa DETAILS: 60 seats. Private parties: 60 main room. Vegetarian meals. Wheelchair access (also women's WC). Music ⊖ Bond Street

Tentazioni **map 13**

2 Mill Street, SE1 2BD
TEL/FAX: (020) 7237 1100 — COOKING **4**
EMAIL: tentazioni@aol.com — MODERN ITALIAN
WEB SITE: www.tentazionirestaurant.co.uk — £30–£60

Partially hidden behind the Design Museum, Tentazioni is a short walk from the lively goings-on of Butlers Wharf. With its narrow arched frontage and folding patio doors, this Italian restaurant could almost pass for a French café. Redecorating was being planned as the Guide went to press, and walls are likely to change from cream to something 'warmer', though the well-spaced good-sized tables elegantly set with heavy white damask cloths are likely to remain.

The menu is written in Italian with English translations, delivering at dinner a five-course tasting menu as well as à la carte. The cooking is upmarket, stylish and imaginative, based on seasonal ingredients with some clever pairing of flavours: for example in an attractively presented tartare of sea bass with baby broad beans, cucumber and tomato, and in a rather intriguing lasagne of courgette, kidneys and quail, the vanilla-flavoured pasta complementing the other ingredients extraordinarily well. Main courses might include beef fillet with foie gras and port sauce, or salmon bocconcini served with fennel and sauté potato with basil sauce.

For afters, a cheese selection vies for attention with classic cassata and more adventurous ricotta cheese with a green tomato compote. Service is charmingly smooth. Wines are all Italian (apart from champagne) and, although not cheap, do include some agreeable modern-style bottles from forward-looking producers. A fine reds section lists some of Italy's best-known names (three vintages of Sassicaia among them, yours for £155 to £200), but house wines are a friendlier £12.50.

CHEF: Riccardo Giocomini PROPRIETORS: Christian di Pierro and Maurrio Rimerici OPEN: Tue to Fri L 12 to 2.30, Mon to Sat D 6.45 to 10.45 CLOSED: Christmas week, last week Aug MEALS: alc (main courses £12 to £18). Set L £15 (2 courses) to £19, Set D £36 SERVICE: 12.5%

(optional), card slips closed CARDS: Amex, Delta, Diners, MasterCard, Switch, Visa DETAILS: 50 seats. Private parties: 40 main room, 25 private room. Vegetarian meals. Children's helpings. Music ⊖ London Bridge (£5)

Terrace map 13

33C Holland Street, W8 4LX COOKING **3**
TEL: (020) 7937 3224 FAX: (020) 7937 3323 MODERN BRITISH
£28–£64

Down a quiet Kensington side-street, this place profits from a fairly secluded location to offer a terrace worthy of the name, unassailed by traffic fumes. Behind a little hedge dotted with fairy lights and under a protective awning, one eats in tranquillity, while tables are rather crammed indoors to maximise the use of space. Here a convivial local bunch dines on asparagus in season, seared foie gras, wild mushroom risotto, or steaks with roast field mushrooms, horseradish butter and red wine sauce.

Not all ideas are familiar, though: irreproachably fresh scallops might come with an intriguingly piquant orange and thyme sauce, while roast rump of lamb is well-matched with hummus and minted yoghurt. Slight overcooking of red meats can be a problem: specify clearly what you want. 'Light but richly satisfying' chocolate mousse, topped with brandy cream, gains intensity from a gingery syrup, while the pannacotta is properly wobbly and vanilla-laden. 'Exceedingly welcoming' service makes you feel like a valued guest. Restrained mark-ups distinguish a well-chosen French-based list opening with Languedoc house wines from £11.50.

CHEF: Martin Moore PROPRIETOR: Steven Loveridge OPEN: all week 12 to 2.30 (12.30 to 3 Sun), 7 (5.45 summer) to 10.30. Sun D in summer only CLOSED: 24 Dec to 4 Jan MEALS: alc (main courses £11 to £20). Set L £14.50 (2 courses) to £17.50 SERVICE: 12.5% (optional), card slips closed CARDS: Amex, Delta, Diners, MasterCard, Switch, Visa DETAILS: 27 seats. 14 seats outside. Private parties: 27 main room. Vegetarian meals. No music. Air-conditioned ⊖ High Street Kensington (£5)

Thai Garden £ map 12

249 Globe Road, E2 0JD COOKING **1**
TEL: (020) 8981 5748 THAI SEAFOOD AND VEGETARIAN
EMAIL: thaigarden@hotmail.com £25–£35

Minimalist décor with flashes of colour is the style of this basic, compact and usually crowded eating house. What distinguishes it from other Thai restaurants is what isn't on the menu. A most welcome omission is MSG, unnecessary because well-spiced and judiciously herbed natural ingredients provide plenty of flavour. Another big omission is meat, on a menu of about 40 each of vegetarian and seafood dishes. Among recent additions is the cheerfully named morning glory, a.k.a. water spinach or Cantonese ung choy, prepared with garlic, chilli and black-bean sauce. Tofu, Thai aubergines, water chestnuts and various mushrooms are among other vegetables on a long list. Equally varied seafoods include scallops, king prawns, mussels, crab claws, fish balls, pomfret and tilapia. House wines are £7.50.

CHEF: Mrs N. Duff PROPRIETORS: Suthinee and Jack Hufton OPEN: Mon to Fri L 12 to 2.45, Mon to Sat D 6 to 10.45 CLOSED: bank hols MEALS: alc (main courses £4.50 to £7.50). Set L £7.50 (2 courses), Set D £16 to £20 SERVICE: 10%, card slips closed CARDS: Delta, MasterCard, Switch, Visa DETAILS: 32 seats. Private parties: 14 main room, 12 private room . Vegetarian meals. No smoking in 1 dining room. Wheelchair access (not WC). Music ⊖ Bethnal Green (£5)

La Trompette 🍷

LONDON NEWCOMER OF THE YEAR

NEW ENTRY map 12

5–7 Devonshire Road, W4 2EU
TEL: (020) 8747 1836 FAX: (020) 8995 8097

COOKING **7**
FRENCH
£33–£63

Cool, modern, comfortable, with a wood-block floor, a less-than-exciting brown colour scheme, and a slightly formal feel induced by white linen tablecloths and napkins, La Trompette comes with sound credentials: it is under the same ownership as Chez Bruce and Glasshouse, and related to the Square (see entries, London and Kew). Like its siblings, it adopts a straightforward approach, mercifully free of manic experimental flavour combinations or flashy effects, and the predominantly French dishes span a range from ultra-traditional (or retro if you prefer) to contemporary, taking in tomato and goats' cheese tart with pesto, halibut with a shellfish ragoût and horseradish mousseline, and chocolate profiteroles.

The kitchen exhibits confidence and assurance, whether making a good fist of a rustic, smoky cassoulet, or producing a creamy mash worthy of the best to serve with fresh, accurately timed pan-fried cod. There is no hiding behind rich ingredients; rather there is real skill in making a few carrots taste like carrots, or in getting the best out of fennel: shredded, to accompany generous fillets of highest-quality, rare grilled tuna, served cold with a spoonful of guacamole. Likewise, deep-fried sole is encased in a light batter, and served with a pool of well-balanced, creamy-textured tartare sauce, an item that has become so devalued it can be something of a shock to find what it tastes like when properly made.

Among desserts, apricot and vanilla yoghurt with sugary beignets is as good as at the Square, and crisp apple tart comes in classic style with light, delicate pastry, served with a scoop of smooth, creamy caramel ice cream and a drizzle of caramel sauce. Bread is first-class too. Service is relaxed and friendly, and knows its way around the extensive cheeseboard; the pace is just right, and wines are carefully topped up. Wines by the glass (including sherries and a fine selection of dessert wines, as well as Cloudy Bay Pinot Noir) are a feature of an inviting list which otherwise concentrates on classic regions of France, and offers a fair showing in Italy. Care has been taken to source the less obvious (such as Primo Estate Amarone from South Australia). Prices start at £14.50.

CHEF: Ollie Couillaud PROPRIETORS: Nigel Platts-Martin and Bruce Poole OPEN: all week L 12 to 2.30 (12.30 to 3 Sun), Mon to Sat D 6.30 to 10.30 MEALS: Set L £15 (1 course) to £19.50, Set D £15 (1 course) to £25 SERVICE: 12.5%, card slips closed CARDS: Amex, Delta, MasterCard, Switch, Visa DETAILS: 70 seats. 20 seats outside. Private parties: 70 main room. Children's helpings. Wheelchair access (also WC). No music. Air-conditioned ⊖ Turnham Green

Turner's

map 14

87/89 Walton Street, SW3 2HP
TEL: (020) 7584 6711 FAX: (020) 7584 4441
EMAIL: turnerrest@aol.com

COOKING 4
MODERN EUROPEAN
£31–£76

A dark blue and gold colour scheme, comfortably upholstered chairs, and assorted framed mirrors and pictures make this a calm and pleasant setting. Despite television commitments, Brian Turner is still to be seen a few days a week at the restaurant he set up in 1986. The menu he presides over is not cutting-edge, sticking instead to familiar ideas such as a creamy shellfish soup, artichoke heart stuffed with smoked haddock, and calf's sweetbreads with spinach and Madeira sauce.

Cooking is 'demonstrably skilful', producing well-timed meats, and saucing is a strength: beef fillet comes with a rustic shallot sauce, duck breast and confit leg with a mustard and dry sherry version. Desserts range from a straightforward and enjoyable summer pudding with clotted cream, to a pain perdu made with cinnamon-flavoured genoise and served with honey ice cream. The set-price lunch is considered one of the best bargains in London. Service is generally speedy and attentive, while the all-French wine list is brief and conservative. A selection of ten house wines starts at £16 (all available by the glass at £4.50), although the main list is considerably more pricey.

CHEFS: Brian Turner and Jonjon Lucas PROPRIETOR: Brian Turner OPEN: Mon to Fri L 12.30 to 2.30, Mon to Sat D 7.30 to 11 MEALS: alc (main courses £22.50 to £25.50). Set L £15 (2 courses) to £17.50, Set D £26.50 (2 courses) to £32.50 SERVICE: not inc CARDS: Amex, Delta, Diners, MasterCard, Switch, Visa DETAILS: 52 seats. Private parties: 52 main room. Vegetarian meals. Children's helpings. Music. Air-conditioned ⊖ South Kensington

Two Brothers £

map 12

297–303 Regents Park Road, N3 1DP
TEL: (020) 8346 0469 FAX: (020) 8343 1978

COOKING 2
FISH 'N' CHIPS
£20–£49

Little changes at this popular Finchley fish restaurant; but once you have perfected the art of fish and chips, why change the formula? Cod, haddock, plaice, skate and sole – according to availability – are cooked in exemplary batter or matzo meal and served with lashings of chips and lashings of home-made tartare sauce, plus traditional side orders of mushy peas and gherkins. Starters include old favourites like prawn cocktail, jellied eels or fish soup, and main-course alternatives are Arbroath smokies, salmon fishcakes or sauté sardines (you could have steak or fried chicken, but that would be missing the point). The smart, somewhat old-fashioned dining room is decorated with nautical prints, and the perfunctory wine list opens with 'our very own house wine' at £9.80.

CHEFS/PROPRIETORS: Leon and Tony Manzi OPEN: Tue to Sat 12 to 2.15, 5.30 to 10.15 CLOSED: Christmas, last 2 weeks of Aug, bank hols (exc Good Fri), Tue after bank hols MEALS: alc (main courses £7 to £14) SERVICE: not inc, card slips closed CARDS: Amex, Delta, MasterCard, Switch, Visa DETAILS: 90 seats. Children's helpings. No cigars/pipes in dining room. Music. Air-conditioned ⊖ Finchley Central

Ubon

NEW ENTRY map 12

34 West Ferry Circus, Canary Wharf, E14 8RR
TEL: (020) 7719 7800

COOKING 4
JAPANESE
£41–£110

On the fourth (top) floor of an oddly shaped building close to the river, Ubon is spacious, with lots of daylight and fine 180-degree views. Its big windows and lights are hung with strings of coloured glass beads, and although its sister restaurant Nobu (see entry) wins in the glamour stakes (and its food has a slight edge too) Docklands and nearby City folk seem to have taken it to their hearts. After being greeted with synchronised cries of welcome in Japanese, one way to deal with the long menu is to choose a dish from each section.

Ingredients are beyond reproach, and at its best the food can be innovative and accomplished, with a great variety of tastes and textures: salmon skin roll, for example, or the fresh, lively flavours of lobster pieces and crunchy asparagus in a fiery yet not overpowering wasabi sauce. Not all dishes are special – new-style and more elaborate offerings tend to take a back seat – the best ones at inspection being traditional sushi made with first-class rice (try the fatty tuna and freshwater eel), feather-light rock shrimp tempura, and silken tenderloin teriyaki served with a benchmark miso soup.

As with anything Japanese, presentation is of the highest order: as in a refreshing, mousse-like egg custard (chawan mushi) flavoured with black cherry. Service has been charming but inexperienced, and prices can be 'staggering', not least on the 70-strong wine list, broadly arranged by style: only two come in under £20, but there are half a dozen by the glass.

CHEF: Youssef Kelil PROPRIETORS: Nobuyuki Matsuhisa and B.S. Ong OPEN: Mon to Fri L 12 to 2.30, Mon to Sat D 6 to 10.30 MEALS: alc (main courses £10 to £27). Set L £25 to £40, Set D £70 SERVICE: 12.5% (optional) CARDS: Amex, Delta, Diners, MasterCard, Switch, Visa DETAILS: 120 seats. Private parties: 120 main room. Car park. Vegetarian meals. No-smoking area. No cigars/pipes in dining room. Wheelchair access (also WC). Music. Air-conditioned

Utah

map 12

18 High Street, SW19 5DX
TEL: (020) 8944 1909 FAX: (020) 8944 1890
EMAIL: mail@utahfood.co.uk
WEB SITE: www.utahfood.co.uk

COOKING 4
CONTEMPORARY AMERICAN
£23–£54

The huge plate-glass windows of this chic venue on Wimbledon High Street let passers-by see inside, where décor – in lime green, dark green and claret, offset with frosted glass – is elegant and understated. As the name suggests, the modern cooking has a North American slant. A starter of smoked duck Caesar salad has a whiff of the barbecue about it, and pleasingly textured cod and crayfish cakes are served with coriander and lime. Main courses include an imposing-sounding Creole-style 'voodoo stew', and a grilled Iowa ribeye steak.

A weekend brunch menu features American-style buttermilk pancakes, 'hand-spanked sirloin burger', and a 'whatever omelette', while two-course set lunches during the week are a very reasonable £11.95. Cooking is generally well executed, though is sometimes uneven; desserts can prove less than exemplary.

There is no denying the quality of the wine list, which is organised by style (light, medium or full) and fairly equally divided between Old World and New, the former including some refreshingly go-ahead names. Prices start at £12, and the by-the-glass selection (from £3) is commendably adventurous.

CHEF: Iain Wilkie PROPRIETOR: Hartford Group plc OPEN: Mon to Fri L 12 to 2.30 (brunch 11 to 4 Sat and Sun and bank hols), all week D 6.30 to 10.30 MEALS: alc (main courses £7 to £16). Set L £11.95 (2 courses), Set D 6.30 to 7.30 £12.95 SERVICE: 12.5% (optional), card slips closed CARDS: Amex, Delta, MasterCard, Switch, Visa DETAILS: 80 seats. 30 seats outside. Private parties: 50 main room. Vegetarian meals. Children's helpings. Wheelchair access (also WC). Music. Air-conditioned ⊖ Wimbledon (£5)

The Vale £ **NEW ENTRY** map 13

99 Chippenham Road, W9 2AB
TEL: (020) 7266 0990 FAX: (020) 7286 7224

COOKING **1**
MODERN EUROPEAN
£21–£46

This smart neighbourhood restaurant, with its deep, bright colours, has 'a pleasant informal atmosphere without any pretension', says one reporter. The brief, daily-changing menu lists some lighter dishes, such as salads and sandwiches, as well as a keenly priced set meals and an à la carte. Expect modern European dishes like perfectly executed chargrilled squid with Thai vegetables, chilli, ginger and sesame. Main courses are often Mediterranean-oriented – with ratatouille, tapénade and roasted fennel likely to make an appearance – and one reporter felt a passion fruit jelly with fresh orange slices was 'sublime'. Cooking is competent, although seasoning can be uneven. Service is good and energetic. The wine list starts at £10.50 and has a decent selection of interesting New World bottles, as well as some from go-ahead producers in France and Italy.

CHEF: Robin Tarver PROPRIETORS: Francesca Melman and Robin Tarver OPEN: Tue to Fri L 12.30 to 2, Mon to Sat D 6.30 to 11, Sun brunch 11 to 5 CLOSED: 25 to 31 Dec MEALS: alc (main courses £7 to £14). Set L £9.50 (2 courses) to £12, Set D £12 (2 courses) to £15. Sun brunch menu also available SERVICE: 12.5% (optional), card slips closed CARDS: Delta, Diners, MasterCard, Switch, Visa DETAILS: 70 seats. Private parties: 38 main room, 14 to 32 private rooms. Vegetarian meals. Children's helpings. No smoking in 1 dining room. Wheelchair access (not WC). Occasional music ⊖ Maida Vale

Villandry map 15

170 Great Portland Street, W1W 5QB
TEL: (020) 7631 3131 FAX: (020) 7631 3030

COOKING **3**
MODERN EUROPEAN
£29–£53

It would be a waste to visit here without also browsing in the well-stocked deli, with its breads, vegetables, cured meats, chocolates and much besides. And the café-bar is worth keeping in mind for snacks: plates of charcuterie and cheese, plus a few simple dishes such as onion tarte Tatin, or grilled swordfish niçoise. Food in the main high-ceilinged dining room is hardly more elaborate, and the relatively generous assortment of starters makes it a good candidate for light meals of leek and potato soup with truffle oil, grilled sardines with chickpea and anchovy salad, or poached belly pork with pak choi and hot mustard.

Even main courses keep a spring in their step, offering leek and Gruyère tart, pan-fried brill, and braised chicken with artichoke, courgettes and asparagus. The combination of sound materials, modest ambition and accurate cooking is compelling. Moist chocolate cake is a regular, but there may also be seasonal items such as rice pudding with rhubarb compote, or fruit crumble with custard. A short list of agreeably priced wines adds to the appeal, starting with house Languedoc at £11.

CHEF: Steven Evenett-Watts PROPRIETORS: Jeremy Sinclair and Martha Greene OPEN: all week L 12 to 3, Mon to Sat D 6 to 10.30 CLOSED: 25 and 26 Dec, 1 Jan MEALS: alc (main courses £10 to £16). Bar menu available SERVICE: 12.5% (optional), card slips closed CARDS: Amex, Delta, Diners, MasterCard, Switch, Visa DETAILS: 100 seats. 25 seats outside. Private parties: 100 main room. Vegetarian meals. No smoking in dining room. Wheelchair access (not WC). No music. Air-conditioned ⊖ Great Portland Street

Wagamama £ — map 15

4A Streatham Street, WC1A 1JB
TEL: (020) 7323 9223 — COOKING **1**
EMAIL: mail@wagamama.com — JAPANESE-STYLE
WEB SITE: www.wagamama.com — £14–£27

Wagamama calls itself a 'new style noodle bar', loosely modelled on the ramen shops that have been popular in Japan for 200 years. The philosophy is informal, hearty and healthy eating: bookings are not taken – simply turn up and join the queues (waiting time is rarely more than a few minutes), then take your place at one of the long canteen-style benches. Huge bowls of ramen noodles in broth with various meaty, fishy or vegetarian toppings (perhaps chilli beef, chargrilled salmon or mixed vegetables) are the mainstay; there are also rice dishes and teppan-fried noodles (with egg, chicken, shrimps, peppers, bean sprouts and spring onions, for example). Side orders include various gyoza dumplings and 'raw salads', but the size of portions usually means starters and desserts are redundant. Alcohol is served (wine prices start at £9.75) but to really take part in the Wagamama experience try one of the 'raw juices'. Franchises are cropping up like shiitakes all over London (now six branches), and there are outlets in Dublin, Amsterdam, Manchester and Nottingham.

CHEF: Mon Khadraoui PROPRIETOR: Wagamama Ltd OPEN: Mon to Sat 12 to 11, Sun 12.30 to 10 MEALS: alc (main courses £5 to £10) SERVICE: not inc CARDS: Amex, Delta, Diners, MasterCard, Switch, Visa DETAILS: 104 seats. Vegetarian meals. No smoking in dining room. No music ⊖ Tottenham Court Road

Wapping Food — NEW ENTRY — map 12

Wapping Hydraulic Power Station,
Wapping Wall, E1W 3ST — COOKING **3**
TEL: (020) 7680 2080 FAX: (020) 7680 2081 — MODERN BRITISH
EMAIL: wappingfood@wapping-wpt.com — £33–£53

Wapping Food reverses the recent trend to open a restaurant in an art gallery by placing an art gallery inside a restaurant. The art in question is contemporary: video installations are set on the hulks of machinery that remain as relics of the former power station, and dinner customers may be treated to performance art in the stairwell at one end of the room. This is dinner theatre for the twenty-first century, yet even without the art it can lay claim to being one of London's more atmospheric venues: on a light summer evening the cavernously high ceiling and full-length windows create the feeling of dining outdoors.

And the food is no mere afterthought: a short, imaginative menu provides plenty to divert attention, starting with razor clam ceviche with diced avocado and lime on a bed of rocket, or black pudding with ruby chard, poached egg and mustard. Despite the surroundings it concentrates on sensible mainstream ideas such as stuffed roast pigeon with turnips, foie gras and Madeira, and crisp, golden-crusted pan-fried brill with earthy Jersey Royals and creamed dill-flavoured leeks. Successful desserts have included bitter chocolate torte 'with a texture somewhere between a brownie and a soufflé', accompanied by a scoop of coffee ice cream. Service is friendly and laid back but efficient. The compact wine list is a treasure trove of Australian varietals, including less widely seen Grenache and Marsanne, and South Australia's upwardly mobile Riesling. Much is priced at £25 and under, with house Ryecroft Flametree red and white starting at £12.50.

CHEF: Justin Aubrey PROPRIETOR: Women's Playhouse Trust OPEN: all week L 12 (10 Sat and Sun for brunch) to 2.30 (4 Sun), Mon to Sat D 7 to 11 MEALS: alc (main courses £10.50 to £16). Light L menu available, brunch menu Sat and Sun SERVICE: 10% (optional), card slips closed CARDS: Amex, Delta, Diners, MasterCard, Switch, Visa DETAILS: 100 seats. 50 seats outside. Private parties: 80 main room. Car park. Vegetarian meals. Wheelchair access (also WC). Music (£5)

Waterloo Bar and Kitchen **map 13**

131 Waterloo Road, SE1 8UR
TEL: (020) 7928 5086 FAX: (020) 7928 1880

COOKING **2**
GLOBAL
£25–£47

This informal bar-restaurant behind the Old Vic theatre is considered 'a real prize for the area', providing an attractive environment and well-cooked food at reasonable prices; even the background music is unobtrusive. At least, that is one version of events: others have found it 'noisy, smoky and uncomfortable', and service has been amateurish on occasion. The high-ceilinged space nevertheless has a pleasantly old-fashioned feel, with splashes of colourful abstract art enlvening its cream walls and bare floors.

'The quality of ingredients can't be faulted,' thought one diner, who enjoyed seared fillet of beef with a peanut and rocket salad and a 'sticky, tangy and hot' sweet chilli sauce. The straightforward modern brasserie fare generally comes in for praise: chargrilled strips of calf's liver arrive on a mountain of mash perked up with bits of chorizo and dressed with a balsamic jus. Not only are prices low but portions are also massive: dessert may not be necessary, although ginger crème brûlée and orange chocolate tart make appealing options. Wines start at £10.50 a bottle, £2.70 a glass, for house Cabernet Merlot and Sauvignon Blanc.

CHEF: Bruce Miller PROPRIETOR: Clive Watson OPEN: Mon to Fri L 12 to 2.45, Mon to Sat D 5.30 to 10.30 CLOSED: 22 Dec to 2 Jan, bank hols MEALS: alc (main courses L £5 to £10, D £10 to £14). Set L £10.95 to £12.95 (both 2 courses), Set D £13.95 to £15.95 (both 2 courses) SERVICE:

not inc, 10% for parties of 6 or more CARDS: Amex, Delta, Diners, MasterCard, Switch, Visa DETAILS: 60 seats. 10 seats outside. Private parties: 40 main room. Vegetarian meals. No pipes in dining room. No music ⊖ Waterloo

White Onion

map 13

297 Upper Street, Islington, N1 2TU
TEL/FAX: (020) 7359 3533

COOKING **4**
FRENCH
£35–£45

A big window frontage, one white wall and one in aubergine, with nothing hung upon either, and a plinth with an enormous floral display are all the décor there is. But it is nevertheless 'classy and restful'. High chef turnover lately has seen standards fluctuate, but the core repertoire remains as beguiling as ever. Chilled cream of fresh petit pois with spring shallots and garlic croûtons provides a refreshing start to a hot-weather meal, and pan-fried foie gras with a tartlet of celeriac and nutmeg a rather richer one.

Roast John Dory has made an accurately rendered main course, sharply accented by artichokes, dried tomatoes and thyme; or try rack of lamb with Parmesan butter, ratatouille, olives and basil. To finish, Cavaillon melon and Gariguettes strawberries are spiced up with an orange and coriander reduction and an ice cream containing cracked white pepper, while more traditional desserts might include a thin, warm apple tart with vanilla ice-cream and caramel sauce. Service does its best, although there are reports of serious lapses. France underpins the wine list, but the southern hemisphere bottles have friendlier prices. House wines are a Tempranillo from La Mancha and a Soave at £13.

CHEF: Boris Rabin PROPRIETOR: Red Pepper Group OPEN: Mon to Sat D only 6.30 to 10.30 MEALS: alc (main courses £13.50 to £16.50). Set D £15.50 (2 courses) to £17.50 SERVICE: 12.5% (optional) CARDS: Amex, Delta, MasterCard, Switch, Visa DETAILS: 62 seats. Private parties: 50 main room, 50 private room. No music. Air-conditioned ⊖ Angel, Highbury & Islington

William IV

map 12

786 Harrow Road, NW10 5JX
TEL: (020) 8969 5944 FAX: (020) 8964 9218
WEB SITE: www.william-iv.co.uk

COOKING **2**
MODERN EUROPEAN
£26–£49

Preserving some Victorian features and décor, this large pub's spacious dining room makes for civilised dining and quiet conversation: or you can eat outside in the comfortably heated garden. Though claimed to be influenced by Far Eastern and African cooking, the modern-style cuisine is mainly Mediterranean-accented. Starters might take in an aubergine, roast garlic and rosemary soup; Serrano ham with rocket and Manchego cheese; or grilled tiger prawns with wild garlic leaves and gremolada. Main dishes have included braised lamb shank with blewits and Jerusalem artichokes; ricotta and spinach parcels with oregano and Greek salad; and steak with red onion and tarragon rösti and sauce béarnaise. To finish, there's pear and hazelnut crumble with custard, or lime curd tart. Some 50 wines start at £10.50, with only four just over £20. Listing is not by geography but by style: 'soft and juicy' reds, for instance, or 'light and crisp' whites.

CHEF: Rufus Deakin PROPRIETORS: Carlos Horrillo, Patrick Morcas and Nick Daniel OPEN: all week L 12 to 3 (4 Sat and Sun), all week D 6 (7 Sat and Sun) to 10.30 (10 Sun, 11 Thur and Fri) CLOSED: 25 Dec, 1 Jan MEALS: alc (main courses £7 to £13). Set L £7.50 (1 course, inc glass of wine or beer). SERVICE: not inc, 10% (optional) for parties of 5 or more CARDS: Amex, Delta, Diners, MasterCard, Switch, Visa DETAILS: 80 seats. 60 seats outside. Private parties: 40 main room. Vegetarian meals. No cigars/pipes in dining room. Music. Air-conditioned ⊖ Kensal Green (£5)

Wiltons

map 15

55 Jermyn Street, SW1Y 6LX
TEL: (020) 7629 9955 FAX: (020) 7495 6233
EMAIL: wiltons@wiltons.co.uk
WEB SITE: www.wiltons.co.uk

COOKING **2**
TRADITIONAL ENGLISH
£33–£100

It is coming to something when such a staunchly conservative outfit as this makes a few changes. Refurbishment – more light, new banquettes – has been matched by new additions to the menu: just when everybody else thought they had seen the last of sun-dried tomatoes, here they pop up in a risotto. But nothing of significance appears to have been dropped to make room for it, so there is still dressed crab, pâté de foie gras Strasbourg, potted shrimps, and grills galore, from Dover sole to lamb cutlets and kidneys, all with their 'classic and correct' accompaniments. 'A memorable experience, but at an outrageous cost,' summed up one reporter, who dined on the best native oysters he had ever eaten. Game is another preoccupation: roast partridge for a January visitor, grouse with its minced liver on toast for a September one. Savouries provide a welcome alternative to desserts (fresh fruit salad, sherry trifle), while claret and burgundy dominate the wine list at predictable prices. House French red and white are £17.50.

CHEF: Ross Hayden PROPRIETORS: the Hambro family OPEN: Sun to Fri 12 to 2.30, 6 to 10.30 (10 Sun) CLOSED: Christmas and New Year MEALS: alc (main courses £8 to £29). Set L Sun £19.75. Cover £1.50 SERVICE: not inc CARDS: Amex, Diners, MasterCard, Visa DETAILS: 90 seats. Private parties: 16 main room, 18 private room. Jacket and tie. No pipes in dining room. Wheelchair access (not WC). No music. Air-conditioned ⊖ Green Park

Yatra

NEW ENTRY **map 15**

34 Dover Street, W1S 4NG
TEL: (020) 7493 0200 FAX: (020) 7493 4228
EMAIL: yatra@lineone.net
WEB SITE: www.yatra.co.uk

COOKING **3**
INDIAN
£29–£70

The modern colours – white ceiling, dark yellow and red walls – are moderated by subdued spot lighting, and some of the low tables, made of black stone, have pale brown strips of tablecloth. Contemporary Indian background music provides a counterpoint to the downstairs Bar Bollywood disco, and black-uniformed waiters are capable and attentive. The two sides of the menu are headed respectively 'traditional' and 'contemporary'. Salad appears in both, either as a complete dish or as a garnish for grilled minced chicken wrapped around a crab claw, with a sweet chilli sauce acting as an effective foil. Traditional methi chicken breast has been pleasingly flavoured with fenugreek, in a rich dark sauce tasting of ginger and coriander. A contemporary vegetarian main course (godamber) is a wrap of Indian cheese cooked with cumin and bell pepper, in thin whole wheat bread. Home-made ice creams include mango, cardamom and kaffir lime. The minimum charge for food is £19.50 but an entirely European three-course lunch or pre-theatre menu is £17.50. House wines at £14 are French, others are listed by style.

CHEF: Anurag Gautam PROPRIETOR: Cafe Bollywood (UK) Ltd OPEN: Mon to Fri L 12 to 3, Mon to Sat D 6 to 11.30 CLOSED: 25 Dec, bank hols MEALS: alc (main courses £12.50 to £19.5). Set L £14.50 (2 courses) to £17.50, pre-theatre set D 6 to 7.30 £14.50 (2 courses) to £17.50 SERVICE: 12.5% (optional) CARDS: Amex, Delta, MasterCard, Switch, Visa DETAILS: 80 seats. 6 seats outside. Private parties: 135 main room, 40 private room. Vegetarian meals. No smoking in 1 dining room. Wheelchair access (also WC). Music. Air-conditioned ⊖ Green Park

Zafferano

map 14

15 Lowndes Street, SW1X 9EY
TEL: (020) 7235 5800 FAX: (020) 7235 1971

COOKING **6**
ITALIAN
£35–£77

Despite Giorgio Locatelli's departure, Zafferano still flies the flag for fine Italian food. Surroundings are as modest as ever – a couple of dining areas decorated in shades of ochre, orange and terracotta – and the carte falls into four sections in classic Italian style. Varied salads (of baby artichoke, of grilled cuttlefish, or of peas and broad beans with pecorino) are prominent among first courses. For those following the format, the pasta that comes next produces flashes of 'real brilliance'. Its texture is exemplary: in 'osso buco' ravioli for example, and in tortellini in brodo, although sauces and broths may not have quite the expected depth of flavour.

Chargrilling is favoured for main courses – applied to swordfish (well partnered by rocket), and to rolled pork stuffed with herbs – while pan-frying has produced prawns with sweet chilli and borlotti beans, for example, and calf's liver with balsamic vinegar. Desserts can be as traditional as tiramisù, as refreshing as macerated peaches with iced almond milk, or as straightforward as pink grapefruit with basil sorbet. Good bread comes with olive oil for dipping, and front-of-house staff manage arrivals and departures like a 'strict school mistress', speedily but with calm efficiency. The staunchly Italian list starts from £12.50 but soon leaps the £20 barrier. Quality is consistently high, though, with some very fine bottles from Tuscany and Piedmont in particular.

CHEF: Andy Needham PROPRIETOR: A To Z Restaurants Ltd OPEN: all week 12 to 2.30, 7 to 11 CLOSED: Christmas, Easter MEALS: Set L £19.50 (2 courses) to £23.50, Set D £29.50 (2 courses) to £39.50 SERVICE: 12.5% (optional) CARDS: Amex, Delta, Diners, MasterCard, Switch, Visa DETAILS: 55 seats. Vegetarian meals. No cigars/pipes in dining room. Music. Air-conditioned ⊖ Knightsbridge

Zaika

map 13

1 Kensington High Street, W8 5NP — COOKING **5**
TEL: (020) 7795 6533 FAX: (020) 937 8854 — MODERN INDIAN
WEB SITE: www.zaika-restaurant.co.uk — £31–£77

Since last year Vineet Bhatia has moved on from his Fulham Road site and split himself in two. Bar Zaika Bazaar (see entry) is the more informal outlet, while Zaika proper has shifted to Kensington, its transposed statues and artefacts combining with silks and coloured lighting to produce a rather chic and upmarket feel. Acting as both a catalyst and a pioneer, Bhatia has produced a sophisticated and updated version of Indian food, vitalised by its subtle yet assertive spicing. The menu's 'old faithfuls' are justly acclaimed – tandoori smoked salmon tikka is 'dazzling', as are the pickles – while less familiar dishes garner similar praise: soft-shell crab, tandoori pheasant on black lentil dhal, or a pastry-topped biryani with prawns and butterfish. Even purists fail to protest at the cross-cultural approach, won over by the sheer success of signature dishes such as Indian-style risotto.

No matter how recognisable the names, results are like no other Indian restaurant's: from chicken tikka to fresh-tasting, accurately timed king prawns in a deep dish of coconut masala sauce with lime leaves and cardamom seeds. Puffy naans are good, the rice is fragrant, and vegetables are properly handled, from cauliflower bhajia to a sweet-sour salad with chunks of spiced, baked potato lightly bound with yoghurt and served with a tamarind chutney. Set meals are considered good value, and staff are efficient and quite formal, although service is 'never the high point'. An enterprising roll call of grape varieties and styles gives the wine list its oomph, although bottles under £20 are in the minority.

CHEF: Vineet Bhatia PROPRIETOR: Cuisine Collection OPEN: Sun to Fri L 12 to 2.30 (2.45 Sun), all week D 6.30 to 10.45 (10 Sun) CLOSED: Christmas, some bank hols MEALS: alc (main courses £10 to £21.50). Set L £12.95 (2 courses) to £33.50, Set D £33.50. Cover £1.50 SERVICE: 12.5% (optional), card slips closed CARDS: Amex, Delta, MasterCard, Switch, Visa DETAILS: 70 seats. Private parties: 70 main room, 14 private room. Vegetarian meals. No cigars in dining room. Wheelchair access (not WC). No music. Air-conditioned ⊖ South Kensington

London Round-ups

With so many venues vying for attention, finding a place to eat out in London that offers the right blend of food, location, style and price to suit the occasion can often be very much down to potluck. This section aims to make choosing easier by providing details of a broad range of restaurants, bistros, cafés, hotel dining rooms, and so on, that are deserving of attention, though they do not merit a full entry. There are also one or two rising stars, well worth keeping an eye on, and in some cases establishments have been included here rather than in the main entries because of significant late changes or a lack of positive feedback. Reports on these places are particularly welcome. Brief details of opening times are given in each entry where available.

a.k.a WC1
18 West Central Street map 15
(020) 7836 0110
This is more like the bar of a club, which it actually is, than a formal restaurant, with exposed heating ducts, bright lights, pounding music and a giant screen showing sporting activities. The previous chef has left, so we await reports of his successor, whose menus have included Caesar salad followed by pasta dishes, steaks, or maybe Cajun marinated swordfish. There's a bar menu too. France and Spain get a good look-in on the short wine list, which also offers a dozen champagnes – but cocktails are the big thing, with names as stimulating as their ingredients. Open D only Wed to Fri.

Asakusa NW1
265 Eversholt Street map 13
(020) 7388 8399
Under wall posters offering special dishes, incomprehensible except to the many Japanese customers, you sit close enough to neighbouring tables to steal their food with your chopsticks. But you won't need to, for portions are generous and prices low. A large part of the Japanese repertoire is robustly prepared without undue attention to presentation, and little bamboo skewers of various parts of chicken are accurately cooked. Choosing set meals makes ordering easier. Open Mon to Sat D only.

Aurora W1
49 Lexington Street map 15
(020) 7494 0514
Relaxed and intimate Soho place with a walled garden at the back for al fresco eating and a globetrotting culinary outlook. A salad of lamb, lentils and chickpeas comes with beetroot and mint; chilled poached salmon gets an Asian tweak with sweet-and-sour cucumber, jasmine rice and wasabi mayonnaise; while lemon chicken is served on sweetcorn mash with roast tomato chutney and mizuna. Open Mon to Sat L and D.

L'Aventure NW8
3 Blenheim Terrace map 11
(020) 7624 6232
In this traditional French-style restaurant with a large verdant patio, the menu du jour is £28.50 at dinner, but £18.50 for lunch with coffee included. A reporter's soupe de petits pois à la Muscade, and tarte de légumes à la tapénade was followed by carré d'agneau à l'ail sous chemise and magret de canard au miel et fruits rotis. Both duck and lamb have been called 'first quality': each has been tender and cooked exactly as ordered. Wines are good if fully priced, while service is attentive and French too. Open Mon to Fri L and Mon to Sat D.

Balzac Bistro W12
4 Wood Lane map 12
(020) 8743 6787
Long-serving favourite at the Shepherds Bush end of Wood Lane. Classic French bistro cooking is the kitchen's stock in trade, and dishes offer fair value for money. Starters might include tian of smoked chicken and avocado with basil mayonnaise, while main courses span anything from herb-crusted rack of lamb with ratatouille risotto to grilled sea bass with 'white butter sauce' and saffron potatoes. There's strawberry tart to finish; wines are mostly French. Closed Sat L and all day Sun.

Belgo Centraal/Noord/Zuid
50 Earlham Street (Centraal) WC2
(020) 7813 2233
72 Chalk Farm Road (Noord) NW1
(020) 7267 0718
124 Ladbroke Grove (Zuid) W10
(020) 8982 8400 maps 13/15
The Belgo brand is as strong as some of the beers, and most people probably know by now to expect mussels and chips. There is much more on the menu, of course, from duck breast with fondant potato and cassis beer jus, to steamed sea bream with crab and ginger, although the mussels and the range of beers are undoubtedly the main strength. All three restaurants are noisy, casual and 'good fun', with the Chalk Farm original still looking 'contemporary' after nearly ten years. Open all week.

Bellamys Dining Room SE11
332 Kennington Lane map 13
(020) 7582 9569
Modern décor, relaxed rather than modish, and friendly service back up a short, similarly modern but not modish menu. The full flavours of ballottine of duck confit, and terrine of pork with roasted glazed figs, was a happy contrast to the subtlety of an asparagus, pea, mint and lemon risotto. Double Gloucester cheese and spring onion omelette was cooked as ordered and accompanied by a small salad with tiny new potatoes and sliced radish on the leaves. Open Mon to Fri L and D.

Beotys WC2
79 St Martin's Lane map 15
(020) 7836 8768/8548
Venerable West End institution that continues to flourish, regardless of fashions and trends. What it offers is broad-spectrum Continental cooking, with an obvious affection for things traditionally Greek: stuffed vine leaves, moussaka, chicken afelia and so on. It is also happy to make seasonal detours for, say, partridge in the autumn. Reporters continue to eat their way through whitebait and veal Holstein, or avocado with prawns followed by plaice, and confirm that the restaurant is 'first-class'. Closed Sun.

Bertorelli's WC2
44A Floral Street map 15
(020) 7836 3969
Handy venue for culture vultures attending the nearby Royal Opera House. Blue tiling and huge mirrors define the mood, and the full menu skips through traditional and modern classics, with fish and pasta showing up particularly well. The cover charge pays for bread, olives, gherkins and olive oil. Light meals are available in the café downstairs. Fifty staunchly Italian wines. A branch is at 19–23 Charlotte Street, W1, tel (020) 7636 4174. Closed Sun.

Boisdale SW1
15 Eccleston Street map 13
(020) 7730 6922
With a fixed-price menu headed '1745', there's no doubting where this restaurant's true allegiances lie. 'Excellent' Scottish produce from the country's top producers runs to MacSween's haggis, Aberdeen Angus beef, wild Highland venison and Hebridean lobster, not to mention four kinds of Scottish smoked salmon (including the hot-smoked version from Lochcarnan). The whole Boisdale package includes an atrium, bar, cigars and after-dinner jazz in a leather-armchair setting that is Belgravia club to a tee. Some have

commented on the high prices. Closed Sat L and all day Sun.

Books for Cooks W11
4 Blenheim Crescent map 13
(020) 7221 1992
Books are the main business here, but you can try the morning's work from their test kitchen. Vegetarian dishes predominate, although chicken appears occasionally, and a typical day's output might be sweet corn and spring onion tarts with polenta crust; green leaf salad with shaved fennel; chicken cooked with bay, garlic and white wine; and creamy potato gratin. All come with Books for Cooks focaccia. Lunch starts at noon so arrive early; closed Sunday.

Brady's SW18
513 Old York Road map 12
(020) 8877 9599
You can break away from the standard 'chippy' menu by starting with half a pint of prawns, cod's roe pâté, or anchovies and sweet herring. Then you could go on to grilled sea bass, skate, John Dory, brill, plaice, black or red bream, or sole – Devon or lemon. Nonetheless fried cod or haddock still takes centre stage and to follow there is apple crumble, treacle tart or steamed treacle pudding. Wines run from £7.95 to £13.45 and two London beers are supplemented by Czech Budvar. Open Mon to Sat D only.

Bush W12
45A Goldhawk Road map 12
(020) 8746 2111
Once inside the portals of this west London newcomer (look for the black-jacketed doorman outside to find it), a huge, warehouse-sized space awaits. An open kitchen, where a multitude of chefs can be seen beavering away, has produced unpretentious though moderately inventive food. A starter of pissaladière with ceps is generously sized, spread with pesto and cooked in a wood-fired oven, followed by confit of duck with spinach and sauté potatoes, or simple but perfectly cooked roast salmon with asparagus and artichokes. Finish with pannacotta served on plum compote. The chef changed just as we went to press, so reports please. Open all week.

Le Cadre N8
10 Priory Road map 12
(020) 8348 0606
Unchanging provincial bistro close to Alexandra Palace that has been run for many years by David Misselbrook. Art nouveau pictures and posters line the walls, and chef Yannick Chuat remains true to his French roots. Red mullet and orange soup, or crotin of goats' cheese en croûte, might precede halibut steak poached in champagne with dill, smoked salmon and asparagus, or roast breast of duck with green peppercorn and Armagnac sauce. Fixed-price seasonal menus cast their net wider for chargrilled tuna with plum tomato and herb relish, or bread-and-butter pudding. Closed Sat L and all day Sun.

Café du Marche EC1
22 Charterhouse Square map 13
(020) 7608 1609
As patriotically French as the Marseillaise, this bistro down an alleyway off Charterhouse Square continues to deal in dishes with a strong Gallic accent. Starters are things like soupe de poisson, and asparagus with hollandaise sauce. Main courses are equally familiar: ballottine of chicken with tarragon, grilled king prawns with aïoli, vegetable gâteau with tomato salad bolstered by fish from the market, and a plat du jour. France gets top billing on the short wine list. Open Mon to Fri L and Mon to Sat D.

Café Portugal SW8
6A Victoria House map 13
(020) 7587 1962
Lively establishment on the edge of an 'enclave of Portugal' full of bars and shops. Seafood shows up strongly on the restaurant menu: not only the ubiquitous salt cod (done three ways), but wreck fish, black scabbard fish, and octopus. Meaty alternatives might be pork with clams and

sauté potatoes, and rabbit in red wine sauce. 'High-quality' tapas in the bar include 'one of the best patatas bravas in London', according to a reporter. Friendly, informative service. Inexpensive Portuguese wines start at £8.50. Open all week.

Carluccio's Caffe W1
8 Market Place map 15
(020) 7636 2228
Espresso machines hiss, there's plenty of purposeful bustle, and smoking seems 'almost compulsory' in Carluccio's Continental café-cum-deli. Bread combos are 'artfully arranged in loaf tins'; otherwise the menu is mostly snacks such as focaccia, calzone and crostini, based on top-class ingredients. A few more substantial dishes also surface in the shape of rich mushroom soup with 'knockout aromas', risottos, and grilled swordfish with a salad of green beans. Ristretto (a short espresso) is the genuine article, and some quaffable Italian wines appear on the short list. There are branches at Fenwick's department store in New Bond Street and St Christophers Place. Open all week.

Chapel NW1
48 Chapel Street map 13
(020) 7402 9220
The world-embracing menu of this pub/restaurant is typified by a single starter of marinated fillet beef carpaccio with wasabi and tequila; an alternative might be baby squid stuffed with chicken, shrimp, cashews and chilli. Then you could go on to confit tuna niçoise with quails' eggs and beetroot chips, or roast guinea fowl with butternut squash purée, wilted ruby chard and port and passion fruit juice. To finish there is Kahlua pot au chocolat, or to return to (relatively) familiar territory, banoffi pie. Open all week.

Chapter Two SE3
43–45 Montpelier Vale map 12
(020) 8333 2666
Overlooking the green outside Blackheath village, the décor is all modern colour schemes, although 'Rothko has a lot to answer for', observed one keen-eyed correspondent. In similar vein, the kitchen delivers contemporary-sounding dishes: duck liver and foie gras parfait with truffle mayonnaise; pan-fried sea bass on niçoise potatoes with a cherry tomato and clam dressing; cinnamon poached pears with fromage frais, raspberries and puff pastry. Regulars confirm that service still has its shortcomings. Open all week.

Che SW1
23 St James's Street map 14
(020) 7747 9380
Will cigar-smoking readers of the Guide please send more reports on this deluxe bar/restaurant in the heart of St. James's? Visiting this former bank might require an overdraft, particularly if you choose lobster and green beans salad with caviar mayonnaise, to precede fillet steak béarnaise with zucchini fritte, and a dessert such as chocolate fondant soufflé with malted ice cream. The separate vegetarian menu tempts with summer vegetables, tomato jelly and spiced mayonnaise, or ravioli of asparagus with truffle oil. Closed Sat L and Sun.

Cheng-du NW1
9 Parkway map 13
(020) 7485 8058
Soft background jazz, and gentle, caring service add to the pleasing ambience of this attractively decorated restaurant. The food too is Westernised, so flavours are delicate, occasionally bland, but careful cooking and presentation of fine ingredients compensate. The menu, short by Chinatown standards, takes in such interlopers as vegetarian tempura and 'sizzle grilled sesame steak with teriyaki sauce'. Classic Chinese dishes include various fish, grilled or steamed in three ways, including a colourful version with red dates, black fungi and golden lilies. Short, interesting wine list with house selections £9.80. Open all week.

Chuen Cheng Ku W1
17 Wardour Street map 15
(020) 7734 3281
A totem pole marks the spot where this Chinatown old campaigner on three floors plies its trade. In cavernous spaces, trolleys float around dispensing excellent dim sum: one waiter is assigned to your table to keep an eye on progress. Prawn cheung fun and won ton soup noodles topped with roast duck have been endorsed. The full menu cruises around the Cantonese repertoire, although set meals are vigorously promoted. Open all week, dim sum served 11 to 5.30pm.

Como Lario SW1
22 Holbein Place map 14
(020) 7730 2954
Always packed, and often frenetic, Como Lario must be doing something right. The menu springs pleasant surprises with starters of baby squid sautéed with peas and polenta, warm rolls of Parma ham with smoked mozzarella, or marinated raw tuna with broad beans and spring onions. Cannelloni are stuffed with spider crab and scampi, ravioli are filled with ricotta cheese, and spinach with a walnut sauce. That leaves no space for main dishes (never mind desserts), which is how many feel after antipasti and pasta. Closed Sun.

Corney & Barrow WC2
116 St Martin's Lane map 15
(020) 7655 9800
In this handsome stone-built converted bank, the ground floor wine bar is for serious drinking and light eating, the quieter room upstairs is the brasserie. Modern, tasteful abstract paintings ensure that its décor is not too minimalist for relaxed appreciation of a short carte that offers starters such as roasted goats' cheese salad, or pasta with tiger prawns, and main courses ranging from pan-fried salmon to beef fillet tagliata. Wines are suggested for every dish, and interestingly described fine bottles include a 'Super Tuscan' from Spain. Closed Sat L.

Daphne NW1
83 Bayham Street map 13
(020) 7267 7322
A pleasing, unpretentious family-run venue with a dedication to Greek-Cypriot cooking. The printed menu runs the gamut from hummus to baklava, but it pays to consider the specialities of the day. Garidakia (Mediterranean prawns, feta cheese and aubergines in filo pastry), revithia (chickpeas with spinach and tomatoes), and kalamarakia yemista (whole squid stuffed with its tentacles, spinach and rice, cooked in red wine) are some new arrivals. Quaffable Greek-Cypriot wines top the list. Closed Sun.

Daquise SW7
20 Thurloe Street map 14
(020) 7589 6117
This famous Polish venue continues to run and run. The house special, crispy potato pancakes with sour cream and apple sauce, is bolstered by authentic dishes like kaszanka (black buckwheat sausage) with mash, bigos (hunter's stew), and golabki (stuffed cabbage). From further afield come Russian zrazy (minced pork and veal roll), Bavarian marinated pork knuckle, and trout with almonds. Beetroot is used three ways in soup, and shows up among the side orders. Work your way through the Polish vodkas listed, otherwise drink beer or tea. Open all week.

Diwana Bhel Poori NW1
121 Drummond Street map 13
(020) 7387 5556
The most consistent address for vegetarian food in Drummond Street's 'Little India', across the road from Euston Station. The décor may seem like a '70s wholefood café (wooden benches and tables with jugs of water), but the kitchen delivers the goods. The eponymous bhel poori remains a star turn, and dosas (stuffed rice pancakes) receive praise. Specials of the day have also been approved (kofta balls with rice, raita and salad, for example), and buffet lunches are cheap and cheerful. Unlicensed, but lassi is some of the best in town. Open all week.

Ebury Wine Bar SW1
139 Ebury Street map 13
(020) 7730 5447
A new chef, previously Josh Hampton's sous-chef, started in summer 2001 and plans to continue in a similar vein as his mentor in this lively, pioneering wine bar/ restaurant. The trompe l'oeil library décor of the back-room restaurant will continue to induce smiles – or groans – at its punning, and the well-chosen wine list will surely remain a major feature. Reports please. Open all week.

Efes Kebab House W1
80 Great Titchfield Street map 15
(020) 7636 1953
Efficient service, and the warmth of this long-running Turkish restaurant – and its nearby sister at 175 Great Portland Street, W1; tel: (020) 7436 0600 – draw old and new customers. A reporter's meze started with cold dips, including prawn cocktail, and continued with hot, such as feta cheese pastry and 'delicious' liver with onions. The main course, 'a feast in itself', was doner kebab, kidney, chicken, beef, lamb and salad with French dressing. Fruit salad is famously presented in a scooped-out pineapple and garnished with indoor fireworks. Closed Sun.

Esarn Kheaw W12
314 Uxbridge Road map 12
(020) 8743 8930
The cooking at this pleasant pavilion among the Shepherd's Bush shops had been a tad too hot for most European palates. Now the spicy style of north-eastern Thailand has been discreetly adapted to local tastes; the chilli still kicks, but doesn't dominate, Esarn Kheaw sausages, king prawn tom yum soup, or green curries with their two varieties of aubergine. More subtle still are son-in-law eggs, hard-boiled, and finished in a tangy sweet-sour sauce. Service remains friendly and relaxed even when it has problems coping with the level of business. Open Mon to Fri L and all week D.

Fish Central EC1
151 King's Square map 13
(020) 7253 4970
This is a fish and chip shop, and a lot more, starting with the choice of batter or matzo meal on your fried fish. Then there are wing or middle-cut grilled skate; smoked haddock and wild mushroom parcel; a fisherman's platter for two; and roast cod with rosemary and Mediterranean vegetables. Even carnivores are not neglected: they can choose steak; lambs' liver and bacon; stuffed chicken breast; or hand-made pork and leek sausages. House wines on the short list are £7.90. Closed Sun.

Frederick's N1
Camden Passage map 13
(020) 7359 2888
An old-stager on the Islington scene, but with a modern outlook. Chef Andrew Jeffs has headed the kitchen since 1995 and continues to produce contemporary dishes with a European accent. Typically, you might find gratin of asparagus, morels and crayfish; cured lamb shank with minted peas and roast onion; and baked halibut with basil mash and spicy ratatouille. There's pineapple Alaska or tarte Tatin to finish. Set lunches and pre-theatre menus are affordable deals. Eat in the Garden Room with its vaulted glass roof, or outside under parasols when the weather allows. Closed Sun.

Gate W6
5 Queen Caroline Street map 12
(020) 8748 6932
This 'striking, high-ceilinged' restaurant, once an artist's studio, has championed the vegetarian cause with great success since 1989. The cooking bristles with interesting ideas: potato gnocchi lightened with pumpkin purée, aubergine schnitzel layered with tomato and gruyère ('a slight overload on the senses'), and Thai lemon tart show the style. Sushi and salads flesh out the menu. Friendly, enthusiastic staff, reasonably priced

wines. Closed Sat L and all day Sun. A new branch has now opened in Belsize Lane, NW3 (see London, main entry).

Gilbeys W5
77 The Grove map 12
(020) 8840 7568
Directly imported, mainly French wines, at very reasonable prices win the day here. This member of the Gilbey mini-chain is in a quiet street close to Ealing Common, with a conservatory and floodlit garden. Fixed-price lunches offer the best value, with the likes of mussels in Chinese rice wine, and warm chicken Caesar salad. The carte takes in brasserie-style dishes such as Parmesan-crusted sardines with roasted asparagus; brochette of pork with basil creamed potatoes; and banana Tatin with caramel ice cream. There are branches in Eton and Amersham (see entry, England Round-ups). Closed Sun D and all day Mon.

Golborne House W10
Golborne Road map 13
(020) 8960 6260
On a corner, and adjacent to the railway line, Golborne House has risen from the ashes of a local boozer to provide a modern interpretation of the urban pub. Stripped wooden floors and tables help create a casual-yet-stylish setting, and the large, high-ceilinged space works as somewhere both to eat and to drink. The drinks list extends to some decent wines by the glass and bottle, with cocktails joining the more traditional real ale and lagers. The menu takes a global approach: white onion soup with Parmesan crostini, alongside Thai rare beef salad as starters, and main courses of ribeye steak with big chips and beetroot confit, or egg fettuccini with walnut and rocket pesto. Open all week.

Le Gothique SW18
Royal Victoria Patriotic map 12
Building, Fitzhugh Grove
(020) 8870 6567
Extraordinary Gothic edifice that has done duty as orphanage, hospital and later the wartime home of MI5 and MI6. French cooking is the order of the day, with dishes including moules marinière, magret of duck with orange and Cointreau sauce, navarin of lamb, and tarte Tatin. The extensive grounds are ideal for al fresco dining. Wines are fairly priced. It's off the beaten track, so check directions when booking. Closed Sat and Sun.

Great Eastern Hotel, Terminus EC2
map 13
Liverpool Street
(020) 7618 5000
This light, airy, loud bar/restaurant/bistro is much appreciated by uninhibited revellers before their rail journeys. 'The smiley faces and sheer energy of the serving team' also delighted an inspector, whose roast sea bass with grilled Mediterranean vegetables and Genèvoise oil was competently executed. That dish is typical of a menu which also pays respect to the station's early days with escalope of pork Holstein. It ventures further in such desserts as raspberry lilikoi mille-feuille, but returns to home ground with baked chocolate fondant, and summer pudding. Open all week, breakfast 7 to 11, and Sun brunch 11 to 4.

Great Nepalese NW1
48 Eversholt Street map 13
(020) 7388 6737
A refreshing bolt-hole for Euston commuters, just across the road from the station. A frosted-glass frontage with the restaurant logo hides a pleasant dining room run with great courtesy by Gopal Manandar's sons. Bypass the dhansaks and biryanis (although these are fine) and focus on the Nepalese specialities, which make the place 'just that little bit different': bhutuwa chicken is regularly mentioned, likewise toriko sag (spinach). Also note masco bara (black lentil pancakes), the duck specialities, aloo bodi tama (potatoes, bamboo shoots and beans), and green coriander 'achar'. There is 'delicious' mango lassi, or drink beer. Open all week.

Greek Valley NW8
130 Boundary Road map 13
(020) 7624 3217
This family-run neighbourhood taverna, just off Abbey Road, deals in a repertoire of mostly familiar Greek-Cypriot stalwarts. A good showing of hot and cold meze, backed up by kleftiko, souvlaki and beef stifado, as well as a handful of fish dishes including grilled whole sea bass with chips, lead the way. Vegetarians might opt for louvia me lahana (black-eyed beans with greens and rice). Sarma (stuffed cabbage) keeps out the winter chill, and Easter specialities are served in season. Plenty of quaffable Greek wines are priced from £9. Open Mon to Sat D only.

Havelock Tavern W14
57 Masbro Road map 12
(020) 7603 5374
Brook Green gastro-pub with an informal bar area with tables dotted around. Starters that have impressed include goujons of haddock and salmon with 'excellent' home-made onion chutney, and celery and celeriac soup. More substantial dishes might range from Goan-style sweet-and-sour pork to roast duck breast with braised Puy lentils, Savoy cabbage, orange and red wine gravy. There's warm apple and treacle tart, or chocolate fudge brownie, to finish. Decent wines are listed on a blackboard. Open all week.

ICA Café SW1
12 Carlton House Terrace map 15
(020) 7930 8619
The Institute of Contemporary Arts is ahead of the times, not just of them, and it has a café that takes inspiration from around the globe. Vietnamese-style salad and 'classic' chop suey are bar-eats alongside salt beef sandwich with potato salad, and Jamaican-style jerk chicken. New York-style street food embraces stacked lox deluxe (vodka cured gravadlax with sauerkraut), and the Italian lunchtime menu might feature rare organic beef with rosemary and balsamic vinegar. Service has been friendly and caring. Open all week.

Ichi-Riki SW1
17 Strutton Ground map 13
(020) 7233 1701
Japanese and locals fill this bright little pine-furnished basement for light sushi or something more substantial. Side dishes cum starters include grilled eel with soy-based sauce, spinach with a sesame-seed sauce, gyoza pork dumplings, and takoyaki (wheat balls with octopus, bonito flakes and brown sauce). À la carte sushi take in ama-ebi (sweet water shrimps), and red snapper, as well as the expected tuna and salmon. Set meals with miso soup start from £9 for cooked sushi. Closed Sat and Sun.

Inaho W2
4 Hereford Road map 13
(020) 7221 0754
Although Japanese customers are now fewer, this little eating house fills its 20 seats with locals who appreciate the typically relaxed style, with dishes arriving in random order. Choose from the short menu, or specials on little wooden table-boards. Successful dishes from the usual repertoire have included fried fishcake, mixed tempura, assorted sushi nigiri, and white miso soup with silky tofu. Specials worthy of the name are salmon kasuzuke (grilled with a Japanese equivalent of marc), yellowtail sushi, and 'sensationally crisp' grilled salmon skin with ponzu (lemon) sauce.

L'Incontro SW1
87 Pimlico Road map 14
(020) 7730 3663/6327
Escapees from the neighbouring antique shops can mull over potential purchases at this smart Italian restaurant. Specialities, many of Venetian origin, include fresh crab salad, bean and pasta soup, truffled salami with poached egg and baby spinach, and king prawns with water melon and mustard sauce. The set lunch menu (three courses for £19.50) might include tagliolini with shrimps, roast

rabbit with black olives, and chocolate cake or tiramisù. Closed Sat and Sun L.

Joe Allen WC2
13 Exeter Street map15
(020) 7836 0651
Habitués of Broadway and Shaftesbury Avenue are equally at home in this lively basement where the food matches either milieu. Two-course lunches and pre-theatre meals starting at £13 might offer smoked salmon vichyssoise, or spicy chicken wings with blue cheese dip, followed by merguez sausages with roast potatoes and green beans, or calf's liver ragoût with wild mushrooms. Hamburgers don't appear in the menu because 'everyone knows about them', but eggs Benedict and steak sandwiches are there. To finish consider pecan pie, or cheesecake. Open all week.

Kandoo W2
458 Edgware Road map 13
(020) 7724 2428
'Great little place, authentic-style Persian food' is one verdict on this distinctive restaurant in a rather unsalubrious setting. A splendid mosaic-glazed oven (kandoo) stands in the window, colourful paintings line the walls. It is run by ultra-keen and friendly staff. The menu comprises a range of skilfully flavoured and distinctive meze starters, assorted grills of lamb and chicken, plus a daily special: Tuesday is zereshk polo (sweet-and-sour forest berries with Persian saffron served with rice and chicken). Bread and rice are both outstanding. Unlicensed, but BYO or drink doogh (a thin yoghurt beverage). Open all week.

Konditor and Cook SE1
Young Vic Theatre map 13
(020) 7620 2700
Hand-made cakes and puddings from the company's two 'bespoke bakeries' are the highlights at this modest theatre restaurant. Breakfast (from 8.30 to 11.30am weekdays) promises smoked salmon with scrambled eggs; free-range Ayrshire bacon with maple syrup; and strawberry salad. From noon to 8pm there are more substantial offerings, such as kedgeree, penne with pancetta and Dolcelatte, and guinea fowl with tabbouleh. Closed Sun. For those wanting purchases, the bakeries (both in SE1) are at 22 Cornwall Road and 10 Stoney Street; a third outlet was due to open near Chancery Lane as we went to press. Closed Sun.

Lahore Kebab House E1
2 Umberston Street map 13
(020) 7488 2551
It may not be one of the smartest restaurants in the Guide, but it is surely one of the least expensive: two can share a meal for less than £20. The short menu offers vegetable samosas, tikkas, sheekh kebab, and grilled lamb chops as starters. Karahis (curries in metal bowls) include chicken, meat, prawns, fish, and birds not that common in E1 – quails. Biryanis are £5 but of course you don't need extra rice. No alcohol is sold but BYO is acceptable, even encouraged (corkscrews are provided). Open all week.

Lavender
171 Lavender Hill SW11
(020) 7978 5242
24 Clapham Road SW9
(020) 7793 0770 map 12
These two lively bistro-bars have their different, daily-changing menus on blackboards, where intriguing twists distinguish dishes from standard versions. Soup might be roast fennel, mushroom and tarragon; seared chilli squid comes with guacamole; and fried black pudding is accompanied by thyme potato rösti, caper-dressed leaves and mustard dressing. For vegetarians there might be pasta with roast celeriac and a cashew-nut pesto dressing. Originality extends to desserts such as warm strawberries with green peppercorn sauce and ice cream. The short list of wines starts at £8.95. Open all week L and D, brunch 10.30 to 4 Sat and Sun.

Lemonia NW1
89 Regents Park Road map 13
(020) 7586 7454
'Simple and untrendy with dedicated and friendly service,' writes a reporter on this modestly priced Greek-Cypriot restaurant. The ultra-cheap set lunch might offer cannellini beans and aubergines with feta cheese in salsa, then a main course of perhaps either silver gilthead bream, or meat-stuffed courgettes, with watermelon to finish. Daily specials might include grilled scallops, sea bass, or calf's liver and lagos stifado (hare in red wine). All the standard meze and main dishes are available too. Closed Sat L and Sun D.

Light House Restaurant SW19
75–77 Ridgway map 12
(020) 8944 6338
Ultra-modern décor makes this an attractive if noisy place where locals appreciate cooking which could be described as Italian-fusion. Ox tongue comes with walnuts, piccalilli and guindillas as a starter, and a main-course risotto nero includes lemon grass, scallops, squid, clams and mussels. Desserts can also be well fused, though less exotic steamed marmalade pudding has also been highly commended. The midday £12.50 menu for two courses is simpler, although one day's dishes included grilled mackerel with another rarity, tomato ketchup. We have been informed that the chef is leaving in late 2001, so reports please. Open all week.

LMNT E8
316 Queensbridge Road map 13
(020) 7249 6727
Converted street corner boozer in Dalston that has been given lavish interior treatment: it is now awash with artefacts, friezes and urns mostly inspired by Egyptian and ancient Greek mythology – although one reporter thought it a 'cross between a grotto and a galleon'. There are tables everywhere. Early indications are that the kitchen can deliver: handpicked crab on diced avocado with an intense gazpacho was a fine start to one meal. Even better was stuffed loin of rabbit with artichokes and broad beans: an intricate construction that also involved ravioli on a tower of black pudding. To finish, chocolate fondant with passion fruit sorbet was 'faultless'. Open all week.

Mandalay W2
444 Edgware Road map 13
(020) 7258 3696
A tiny Burmese café that tries hard in an unpromising Edgware Road location. Family owners and staff are as courteous, gracious and helpful as can be. Dishes have authentic names, but the menu is really a straightforward run through starters, salads and variations on curries, rice and noodles. Start with shrimp and lime soup, or one of the unusual fritters, then move on to pickle-style lamb, chicken with tamarind, or king prawns with spicy tomatoes. Finish with tapioca, or coconut agar-agar jelly. Closed Sun and public holidays.

Manzi's WC2
1–2 Leicester Street map 15
(020) 7734 0224
In business since 1928 and still going strong, the Manzi family's old stager is now something of a London landmark. It's not only handy for the shows and the high life (Leicester Square is round the corner), but 17 bedrooms above the restaurant are just the ticket for an affordable West End sleepover. The menu is fish cookery from days gone by (devilled whitebait, scampi provençale, scallops mornay), but simple dishes can work well: plump grilled sardines still receive applause and the chips have been 'good' of late. Staff tend to be 'old soldiers' but know their trade. Closed Sun L.

Matsuri SW1
15 Bury Street map 15
(020) 7839 1101
'Matsuri' means 'festivals', and the décor in this basement restaurant is full of celebratory artefacts. It has a swish address next to Quaglino's (see London main

entries), and what it offers is high-art sushi and the theatrical flamboyance of teppanyaki. Both can be mightily impressive. As a back-up you will find benchmark versions of tempura, sashimi and the like. Compared with the full works (kaiseki) in the evening, set lunches seem positively affordable: look for the okonomi pizzas. First-class ingredients, impeccable service. Closed Sun.

Mezzanine SE1
National Theatre map 13
(020) 7452 3600
The 'happy few' here are not King Hal's Agincourt army, but those who booked early enough to get a table with a view of the Thames. 'Pleasant and willing' staff serve with the expedition needed by pre-theatre diners, and the menu is helpful in this respect. Moules and frites, salmon fishcakes, and pasta can be starters or main dishes. There is a 'national dish of the day' and theatre specials, but more typical are herb-crusted lamb rump, creamy mushroom feuilleté, and 'traditional fish and chips with mushy peas'. Open Mon to Sat L and D.

Mirch Masala SW16
1416 London Road map 12
(020) 8679 1828
Queues start forming at 7 o'clock for the food in this casual, lively Indian with an open kitchen at the back. The menu is divided into 'warmers', 'steamers' and 'coolers'. Chicken tikka, and patra (a spicy 'Swiss roll' made from banana leaves) are the real thing. Elsewhere, reporters have enthused about butter chicken, and a 'stunning' version of panir tikka masala with big lumps of cheese. Unlicensed, so BYO or drink lassi. Open all week.

Mitsukoshi SW1
Dorland House map 15
(020) 7930 0317
A traditional dining room and sushi bar are hidden below a smart Japanese department store. Six- or seven-course set menus are £35 to £50 plus 15 per cent service, or choose à la carte grilled fish or meat, steamed or simmered dishes, soup, appetisers, or simple sashimi and sushi. Everything is strictly classical, except California sushi rolls. The bargains in this basement are at lunchtime, when service is included in a £12 set meal that takes in an appetiser, pork cutlet, soup and rice. Closed Sun.

Miyama W1
38 Clarges Street map 15
(020) 7499 2443
A London Japanese restaurant of the old school, where the eponymous and 'very friendly' Mr Miyama has held court since 1982. A firm favourite with the Japanese business crowd, it embraces all aspects of classic cuisine from zensai appetisers to tempura, plus a decent measure of sushi and sashimi. Set menus provide a good introduction to the full range on offer. A mini-menu labelled 'One More Step Forward' offers a selection of 'unusual but healthy minded dishes', including deep-fried soft-shell crab with ponzu, and teppanyaki lobster with beansprouts. Closed L Sat and Sun.

Momo W1
25 Heddon Street map 15
(020) 7434 4040
Mayfair meets Morocco at this boisterous downstairs venue. A new chef arrived in 2001, but the menu seems much as before. Tagines and couscous appear in different guises, alongside monkfish with sauté vegetables and fennel seeds in saffron stock, or chargrilled chicken breast with okra and a red pepper jus. There are savoury pastries filled with wild pigeon or lamb, dried apricots and almonds to start, sweet versions to finish. Next door, at 23 Heddon Street is Mo ('a salad bar, tea room and bazaar'), offering light dishes and exotic 'sandwiches'. Open all week.

MPW Brasserie NW3
Forte Posthouse, Haverstock Hill map 13
(020) 7435 6080
This hotel restaurant has an extensive heated terrace, and a bright if rather bare interior, relieved by abstract paintings.

Rather formal white tablecloths and uniformed staff contrast with brasserie-style cooking that crosses the Channel more often than Eurostar. A 'rich-flavoured, light textured' parfait of foie gras and chicken livers might be followed by venison au poivre, creamed cabbage and pomme fondante. Desserts run to apricot and passion fruit crumble, or a tarte Tatin of apples. House wines at £12.95 head the 30-strong list. Open all week.

New World W1
1 Gerrard Place map 15
(020) 7434 2508
'On cracking form recently,' enthuses a devotee of this cavernous Cantonese 700-seater restaurant. It remains 'the front-runner' for 'trolley' dim sum in Soho Chinatown. Legions of 'eagle-eyed' waitresses tour the tables delivering all manner of delightful morsels, including steamed dumplings, deep-fried dishes, roast meats, big bowls of soup with noodles, duck or barbecued pork, and extras such as aubergines stuffed with minced prawns. There are also sweet buns and custard tarts. 'Consistent standards, unbeatable prices, huge entertainment value'. Open all week.

Orsino W11
119 Portland Road map 12
(020) 7221 3299
There are no ingredients here that would puzzle Italians, but there are some intriguing combinations. A starter salad brings together wild rocket, dandelion, cucumber, orange, broad beans, spring onion and pine nuts. Pizza and pasta are traditional, but there are also main dishes of baked wild salmon with new potatoes and lime leaves, and breaded veal escalopes with broad bean salad. The early, and late, three-course set dinner at £16.50 might start with chicken, vegetable and tarragon soup which might be just like what mama used to make. Open all week L and D.

Patio W12
5 Goldhawk Road map 12
(020) 8743 5194
'Polish vodka on the house' (with your meal, of course) is the clarion call at Ewa Michalik's friendly, old-fashioned venue. Reviews line the walls, samovars sit on sideboards, and the fixed-price menu promises bigos ('hunter stew'), pirogi (home-made dumplings), and golobki, as well as Polish takes on duck, pork and calf's liver. Added to this might be home-made hare pâté, rabbit in horseradish sauce, and halibut with dill. Desserts could feature Polish cheesecake or Cracovia gâteau with walnuts. Open Mon to Fri L and all week D.

Philpotts Mezzaluna NW2
424 Finchley Road map 13
(020) 7794 0455
David Philpott moved across Finchley Road in 2000 after his previous restaurant Quincy's changed hands. His fixed-price menus now have a strong Italian accent: risotto of porcini, ravioli filled with Ricotta, tomato and basil, and so on. For something more substantial try lamb shank in Barolo with crushed potatoes, veal chop with rosemary and artichokes, or John Dory with basil purée. Sweets follow the same theme: date budino with Mascarpone, iced torrone tutti frutti, or pannacotta with raspberries. The wine list is dominated by well-chosen bottles from Italy and Portugal. Closed all Mon and Sat L.

Pizza Metro SW11
64 Battersea Rise map 12
(020) 7228 3812
There are few tables for couples, but plenty set ready to cram in large parties at this noisy and lively place where food comes on communal trays. Thin, classic pizzas come in 25-centimetre portions but come in party sizes too. Spaghetti misto mare pleased an inspector with a 'brilliantly evocative' sauce of roasted cherry tomatoes and seafood, while antipasti at £4.95 per person might include accurately roasted aubergines and

courgettes. Open Sat and Sun L and Tue to Sun D.

Pizzeria Castello SE1
20 Walworth Road map 13
(020) 7703 2556
Eleven basic pizzas with 25 optional extra ingredients might be enough for most people, but there are specials too, such as pizza del pescatore with clams, prawns, baby octopus, cuttlefish, mussels and king prawns. Pasta is nearly as varied, and house specials add even more choice: halibut steak in butter, lemon and wild fennel seeds with spinach, for example. Salsa dancing with a live band adds to the buzz every Monday evening. An all-Italian list of more than 20 fairly priced wines starts with house selections at £8.60. Closed Sat L and all day Sun.

The Poet EC3
20 Creechurch Lane map 13
(020) 7623 3999
Despite the name, this is more of a sports café with TV screens. It is not particularly cheap, although it is cheerful. The short menu offers starters of home-cured herrings with beetroot and horseradish; leek risotto with poached egg, Parma ham and truffle oil; and seared scallops with a spicy Thai salad. To follow, consider tandoori monkfish with tomato and coriander salad, or T-bone steak with all the trimmings. Chunky chips come with a choice of three sauces; the wine list includes 20 by the glass, all under £5. Closed Sat and Sun.

Pomegranates SW1
94 Grosvenor Road map 13
(020) 7828 6560
Since 1974 Patrick Gwynn-Jones has ploughed a distinctive, eclectic furrow, plundering the globe for inspiration. In the clubby basement dining room you can try anything from Turkish bureks with Sudanese pepper sauce, via Cantonese roast duck, to seared tuna with ginger salsa. Meanwhile, boiled salt beef and carrots, Aberdeen Angus steaks, and beef Wellington will keep the traditionalists happy. To finish, how about the wacky-sounding bourbon and green Tabasco ice cream? Closed Sat L and all day Sun.

Poons WC2
27 Lisle Street map 15
(020) 7437 4549
In this long-running simple Chinatown eating house, plate meals such as mixed barbecue meat on rice, or mixed seafood chow mein noodles, are popular. One step up are comforting hotpots, rice with spare ribs in black bean sauce, or the signature dish, wind-dried meat. Better still, choose, with advice from Shirley Poon, a modestly priced banquet. Start perhaps with Peking dumplings, continue with fried prawns and scallops in a crisp noodle basket, and mu shu rou (fine chopped mixed meat and vegetables eaten in lettuce leaves). Open all week.

Poons W2
Unit 205 Whiteleys, map 13
151 Queensway
(020) 7792 2884
Part of the Poons empire (see entry above), this mirrored dining room is tacked on to the Whiteleys shopping centre. The menu quickly homes in on its Cantonese roots, although it's less esoteric than some. Lunchtime dim sum might run to asparagus wrapped in mashed prawns, or Thai-style marinated cold chicken's feet. Elsewhere there is everything from steamed Dover sole with tangerine peel, via casseroled spare ribs with preserved plums, to bean curd with minced beef and preserved cabbage. Open all week exc Sun D.

Prospect Grill WC2
4–6 Garrick Street map 15
(020) 7379 0412
A successful blend of modern décor with formal clubbiness under low lighting, the Prospect Grill fuses the twenty-first century with the mid-twentieth. While prawn cocktail and French onion soup are old-style, grilled asparagus with Parmesan and balsamic dressing is current; and just as chargrilled steak is then, seared tuna burger, or swordfish steak with salsa, is

now. Good bread and 'wonderfully crisp' chips in a side bowl are, we hope, eternal. Baked egg custard with cinnamon ice cream provides a note of true fusion to end on. Forty wines start at £11.50. Closed Sun.

Ragam W1
57 Cleveland Street map 15
(020) 7636 9098
In this cheerful and bright little eating house South Indian vegetarian specialities – dosa pancakes, vadai lentil cakes and uthappam pizza – are one aspect of the menu; curry house dupiazas, kurmas, dansaks, and biryanis are the other. Separately listed are 'exotic specialities' such as chilli chicken, green mutton curry, and nadan fish curry, while for hurried lunchtime customers there are plate meals such as keema peas or lamb curry, served with pilau rice and chapati, at £4.95. Open all week.

Randall & Aubin W1
16 Brewer Street map 15
(020) 7287 4447
Order anything from a hot chicken baguette with chips to caviar with blinis at this atmospheric champagne and oyster bar sympathetically converted from a Soho butcher's shop. The décor is all original tiles, marble and stone; fresh seafood displays fill the window, and an 'antique' rotisserie delivers spit-roasts. Japanese fishcakes; sausage and mash; and fillets of sea bass with herb dressing are typical; otherwise there are mighty platefuls of fruits de mer. A new chef arrived in 2001, so more reports please.

Rebato's SW8
169 South Lambeth Road map 12
(020) 7735 6388
Not as locally fashionable as it used to be, but still a place 'to be cherished'. The tapas bar is 'authentic, dark and nearly always full'. Here you can nibble on fresh anchovies, albondigas (meatballs), baby squid and white asparagus from Navarra. At the back – and 'into the light' – is the dining room, where the menu is an Anglo-Spanish mix that includes plenty of 'beautiful-quality' fish. Grilled halibut with lemon butter, zarzuela (seafood stew), and cutlets of Welsh lamb with garlic mayo have been praised. Crème brûlée is the sweet to choose. 'Service is professional, and jolly with it.' Drink Torres house wines. Closed Sat L and all day Sun.

Saga W1
43–44 South Molton Street map 15
(020) 7408 2236
Sukiyaki and shabu-shabu cooked at your table are specialities here, though there are also modestly priced soup noodles and set lunches from £8.50 that will suit Bond Street shoppers. Climbers of the gastronomic heights can ascend to sushi or sashimi of yellow tail, sea urchin, turbot fins, and greatly prized fatty tuna. Wappa dishes are rice with toppings, steamed in cedar wood, and the extensive list of sakés also includes one served warm in a square wooden box with salt on one corner. Closed Sun L.

Selasih W1
114 Seymour Place map 13
(020) 7724 4454
Home-style Malaysian cooking in modest premises off Marylebone Road, delivering 'express' one-plate lunches at bargain-basement prices such as rice with chicken and stir-fried veg and egg; the lunch buffet is good value, too. Otherwise the menu features most of the classic staples of the cuisine, including gado-gado, longtong (coconut soup with rice cakes, chicken and vermicelli), beef rendang, and grilled whole mackerel in a banana leaf – along with a contingent of rice and noodle dishes. Also note the side orders of aubergine sambal, beansprouts with salted fish, and so on. Closed Sun L.

So.Uk SW4
165 Clapham High Street map 12
(020) 7622 4004
This off-shoot of Teatro (see main entry, London) is a drinking den with food, bringing theatreland brio to Clapham.

Pronounce it 'souk' if you prefer, for the reasonably priced fare served at low brass tables fuses North African and oriental with classical French intruders. Starters range from traditional meze dips to sashimi, and from Moroccan kofta to crispy ricotta cannelloni, while main dishes might include chicken in tagine or in green coconut curry, or fillet of bream en papillote with fennel and red onions. Wine and other drinks can bring the bill up to Clapham's highlands. Open all week D and Sat and Sun L.

Sofra WC2
36 Tavistock Street map 15
(020) 7240 3773
This bright modern café gives off a healthy buzz, part of which no doubt comes from the approving murmurs of those partaking of its 'healthy meal'. This comprises 11 mezes, including tabbouleh, hummus and falafel, as well as less familiar cerkez tavugu (chopped chicken breast with milk, breadcrumbs and walnuts), and guvechs (lamb and chicken casseroles). The full menu runs to 90 items, and the unexpected includes melon with feta cheese, warm hummus with lamb and pine kernels, and 'Albanian liver of the Ottoman period'. Pasta dishes, grills and fish provide an extended choice. Other branches are at 18 Shepherd Market (tel (020) 7493 3320) and 1 St Christopher Place (tel (020) 7224 4080), both in W1. Open all week.

Sotheby's, The Café W1
34–35 New Bond Street map 15
(020) 7293 5077
Classy café attached to the equally classy New Bond Street auction house, and good for light lunches between the shops. Try warm English asparagus with poached egg and black truffle dressing, or penne with grilled Mediterranean vegetables, pesto and Parmesan crisp, or that famous transatlantic import, the lobster club sandwich. Round things off with fig and pear sorbet, espresso and chocolate truffles. Pedigree wines – including Sotheby's champagne – are served by the glass. Breakfast and afternoon tea available. Open Mon to Fri.

Soviet Canteen SW10
430 King's Road map 13
(020) 7795 1556
Polished stainless-steel tables, wooden chairs and posters set the tone in this basement devoted to Russian cooking, and the kitchen is well stocked with rye bread, smoked sturgeon, beetroot and caviar. Zakuski is a selection of mixed hors d'oeuvres served with a shot of chilled vodka, while pork jablokny consists of pan-fried fillets with spiced cabbage, creamed swede and apple sauce. Steak stroganoff with onion marmalade served with crisp 'chipski' is a typical main course. Round things off with rhubarb and strawberry kissel (fruit soup). Over 50 vodkas, plus beers and cocktails. Expect warm, welcoming service. Open Mon to Sat D only.

La Spighetta W1
43 Blandford Street map 15
(020) 7486 7340
A light healthy meal in this airy basement was enjoyed by a reporter who chose smoked swordfish and raw fennel salad followed by rare chargrilled tuna with rocket and tomato. But centre stage is shared by pasta – ranging from simple versions with Bolognese sauce or pesto to tagliolini with crab or lobster – and by exactly cooked pizzas from the wood-fired oven. Porcetto has peppers and roast pork, and the four seasons version includes savour-boosting shiitake mushrooms along with the ham, artichokes and olives. Open Mon to Fri L and Mon to Sat D. Closed Sun in Aug.

Stafford Hotel SW1
16–18 St James's Place map 15
(020) 7493 0111
Top-notch hotel behind St James's with a dining room that oozes grandeur thanks to gilded columns and crystal chandeliers. There's a traditional feel to East Anglian lobster with minted new potatoes and Dover sole meunière, although Chris

Oakes also keeps pace with the trends. Cornish lamb cutlets are served on a ragoût of wild mushrooms, roasted peppers and parsley with 'banana potatoes' and truffle essence, while a burgundy wine risotto is jazzed up with artichoke hearts, pumpkin seeds and Parmesan. Similarly, desserts range from junket with marinated strawberries to iced Marsala zabaglione with a baked stuffed peach. Closed Sat L.

Star of India SW5
154 Old Brompton Road map 14
(020) 7377 2901
Owner Reza Mohammed presides like a supernova over this long-established restaurant with its glorious painted Roman décor, and its home-from-home feeling for many Kensington residents. The menu's Star specialities include interesting vegetarian dishes such as morels and mushrooms stuffed with potatoes and paneer, first fried then simmered in a rich saffron and coriander sauce. Four set menus from £25 offer wide-ranging dishes with two or three starters and four to seven mains as well as rice, breads, lychee kulfi and coffee. Open all week L and D.

Tate Modern SE1
Bankside map 13
(020) 7401 5020
A café, but a 'very superior' one on the seventh floor of the Tate Modern Gallery, with spectacular views over the Thames towards St Paul's. You need to arrive early and be prepared to queue: they no longer take bookings. Come for breakfast, afternoon tea, or perhaps a lunch of hock of ham on Colcannon mash with a decent bottle of wine. Other options might range from Greek salad and quiche Lorraine to salt-crusted cod with haricot beans and chorizo, or penne with spinach and creamed Gorgonzola. To finish, choose between Westcome Cheddar, home-made chutney and walnut bread; or apple and blackberry crumble. Open 10 to 5.30 Sun to Thur, 6 to 9.30 Fri and Sat.

Tbilisi N7
91 Holloway Road map 13
(020) 7607 2536
Georgian is different, no doubt of that. Here it means the style of food and hospitality of the country in the Caucasus south of Russia. Starters for two people are £6.95; five combinations each contain three items. Beetroot purée with walnuts and herbs comes with cheese bread, and spinach purée with walnuts, the latter a speciality of the country. Excellent borscht includes versions with beetroot, gherkin or smoked sausage. Among main dishes are chicken in walnut sauce, lamb baked with aubergine, and pork and beef, brought together in spicy sausages. Open all week D only.

Thai Bistro W4
99 Chiswick High Road map 12
(020) 8995 5774
Very reliable local haunt in media-rich Chiswick with communal bench seating and 'odd lighting'. Food is a cut above the Thai norm, thanks to authentic ingredients and skilful cooking. Tom yum goong has a 'pleasing complexity of flavour', and pad Thai noodles have 'excellent texture', while vegetables are stir-fried with care, and red curries are good versions. Service is friendly and efficient. Closed Tue and Thur L.

3 Monkeys SE24
136–140 Herne Hill map 12
(020) 7738 5500
Those familiar with modern Indian restaurants will find this lively one different, with understated, but not austere, décor, and dishes as original as chilled shrimp and yoghurt soup, or scallops sautéed with grapes. Follow with prawn toran, with onion, mung dhal and coconut accompanied by roasted semolina and a side dish of diced spinach fritters tossed with date and tamarind chutney. Cardamom cream custard could complete an adventurous meal. The new chef started in spring 2001 so more reports please. The long, interesting wine list is

fairly priced. Open Mon to Sun D, and Sun L.

Tokyo Diner WC2
2 Newport Place map 15
(020) 7287 8777
The formula is simple and successful: no bookings for parties under six, no cheques (although credit cards are OK) and no tipping. And, if you are conversant with Japanese, there are also newspapers to read as you sit on cushioned stools at small tables. What you get is a Soho version of Tokyo street food: sushi and sashimi, plus bento lunch boxes, udon and soba noodles, mildly spiced curries and donburi (one-plate rice dishes). Tea is free, otherwise drink saké, beer or plum wine. Open all week D and Mon to Fri L.

Truc Vert W1
42 North Audley Street map 15
(020) 7491 9988
Jean-Charles Carrarini – the owner of the original Villandry Dining Room in Marylebone High Street – has re-surfaced at this corner site in the vicinity of Grosvenor Square. The formula is virtually unchanged: an easy-going café/ restaurant (named after J.C.'s favourite beach near Bordeaux) almost exclusively done out in wood, with a deli selling charcuterie, cheeses and so on. Everyone rates the salad of queen scallops, and there have been votes for 'sublime' artichoke and courgette risotto, and for vegetable soup with chestnuts. Puddings such as chocolate mousse cake, and raspberry Pavlova are 'too good to ignore'. Closed Sun D.

Vama–The Indian Room SW10
438 Kings Road map 14
(020) 7351 4118
The menu, as sophisticated as the restaurant's Chelsea setting and décor, is drawn from the north-west frontier, Punjab and Rajasthan. Many dishes – not just tandooris – are finished in the clay oven. There are enticing vegetarian ideas such as tori bharwa (roast zucchini stuffed with potatoes), sukhi pilli dal (dry yellow lentils with onion and garlic masala), or phalli aloo (fresh green beans and new potatoes). Another unusual starter is kebabs of smoked lamb with papaya. Blackboard specials always include game in season. Wines are mostly over £20, though start at £12.95. Open all week.

Vasco & Piero's Pavilion W1
15 Poland Street map 15
(020) 7437 8774
This long-serving Italian, family-run veteran continues to please. Best value is on the fixed-price light lunch and supper options, but more intriguing possibilities show up among the full menus. Carpaccio of pink roast lamb with raddichio and Pecorino, or sauté squid on cannellini beans are promising ways to start, while centrepieces might include home-made tagliolini with king prawns, or fillet of pork Milanese with tomato and red onion salad. Open Mon to Sat D and Mon to Fri L.

Village Bistro N6
38 Highgate High Street map 12
(020) 8340 5165
A modest north London bistro serving generous helpings of mostly familiar, modern-sounding dishes. Tuna spring rolls with ginger, coriander and soy dressing is a typical starter, while main dishes could encompass anything from fillet of sea bass with saffron mash, courgette ribbons and smoked salmon butter sauce to confit of duck with chorizo on warm potato salad with honey vinaigrette. There's hot hazelnut soufflé to finish. Closed Sun.

Vrisaki N22
73 Myddleton Road map 15
(020) 8889 8760
Andreas Antoniou has run this no-nonsense Greek-Cypriot kebab house in a north London precinct since 1981. No surprises on a menu that offers a full meze for two along with shish and doner kebabs, chargrilled veal chop, and a fistful of grilled fish, including sea bass and grey

bream. Tahini, tzatsiki and taramosalata to start, a trolley load of sweets to finish.

Wiz W11
123A Clarendon Road map 13
(020) 7229 1500
'Eating the Wiz way' involves considering a list of world tapas that takes in mini chorizo with hot potatoes; potato pakora with two chutneys; peppery potato skins; and Caesar salad. This outpost of celebrity chef Antony Worral Thompson's empire also has a full menu divided into 'raw' (Irish rock oysters, carpaccio of Buccleuch beef), 'room temperature' (braised and grilled chicory with seared tuna), and 'warm/hot' (grilled organic chicken with vegetables à la grecque). Brunch is available at weekends. Open Mon to Sat D and Tue to Sun L.

Yoshino W1
3 Piccadilly Place map 15
(020) 7287 6622
Just off Piccadilly, this modern place is a Japanese favourite little known to Westerners. Oden (poached fish or vegetables in broth) are among classic dishes in the most expensive set dinner at £34.80, which like the others has home-made tofu as the first course. Sushi by the new chef are also in that menu (reports would be welcome). Modest lunches are available from £5.80. Try ginger or mint sorbet as an unusual finish, and Japanese wheat or sweet potato vodka as an equally curious drink. Closed Sun.

Zilli W11
210 Kensington Park Road map 13
(020) 7792 1066
This 'noisy' Notting Hill outpost of Aldo Zilli's fashionable Soho destination has turquoise washed walls and scallop-shaped wall lights, making you feel as if 'you are underwater', The cooking and most of the keen, 'competent' staff are Italian. Results on the plate have been promising: a 'very fine' pasta dish of black pappardelle with squid, prawns and a touch of chilli, for example, or sea bass subtly flavoured with ginger and garlic. No fireworks on the dessert menu, but there have been decent renditions of lime cheesecake and tiramisù. Short, Italian wine list. Open all week. A sibling is in Covent Garden (see entry below).

Zilli Fish Too WC2
145 Drury Lane map 15
(020) 7240 0011
Aldo Zilli's latest venture, just round the corner from (not actually on, despite its address) Drury Lane, puts fish centre stage. The frontage is bright blue, while inside it can get noisy and smoky as the evening winds up. The cooking has a strong Italian tilt, although it veers off occasionally for things like sushi. One well-reported meal began with a fine dish of mussels arrabiata: well-timed molluscs with a noticeable kick of chilli. Approved main courses have included wood-roasted sea bass ('on or off the bone') with sweet pepper salsa, and hand-made ravioli of lobster with shellfish sauce. As a finale, try mango and Grand Marnier parfait with raspberry sorbet. Closed Sun.

Zinc Bar & Grill W1
21 Heddon Street map 15
(020) 7255 8899
A 12-metre zinc bar dominates proceedings in this Conran outlet just off Regent Street. Best value is the fixed-price menu (available noon to 7pm), which runs along the lines of sweet potato and lemon-grass soup, salmon fishcakes with tartare sauce, and double chocolate tart. Otherwise the repertoire spans everything from ciabatta sandwiches at lunchtime to slow-roasted belly pork with spring onion mash and salsa verde. Eight wines are served by the glass (including champagne). Closed Sun.

England

ABINGER HAMMER Surrey map 3

Drakes on the Pond

HOME COUNTIES NEWCOMER OF THE YEAR

NEW ENTRY

Dorking Road, Abinger Hammer RH5 6SA
TEL/FAX: (01306) 731174

COOKING **5**
MODERN EUROPEAN
£30–£54

Opened shortly after the last edition of the Guide appeared, this renovated cottage is a pleasantly relaxed place with simple, elegant, modern décor. The owners have made it attractive without throwing money at it (a point often appreciated by readers), using soft, spring-like primrose and lemon tones, diaphanous curtains and white tablecloths, while service combines the quiet efficiency of John Morris and the natural charm of Tracey Honysett.

Steve Drake, who has spent time in some prestigious London kitchens, combines a manageable menu with some unusual ideas, such as marinated potato wrapped in spinach with a cep casserole, and cold jellied terrine of smoked duck and lobster, garnished with savoury carrot slices. Encouragingly, he appears to be obsessive about high-quality materials, especially Devon-sourced fish, whose dazzling freshness and brief cooking have produced gleaming, bouncy, roast John Dory fillets interlaced with pea purée and red wine sauce.

His precise, ungimmicky cooking has yielded pink meats such as Gressingham duck breast with creamed leeks and sarladaise potatoes, and a thin, neatly crimped raviolo 'stuffed to bursting' with fresh, sweet langoustine, served with shredded cabbage trailed through a light beurre blanc sauce. Among desserts, a light and wobbly baked vanilla custard renversée in a pool of dark orange-flavoured chocolate sauce has been dubbed 'the ultimate nursery food'. A balanced wine list does justice to the food, offering a good spread of styles and prices. One French and five southern hemisphere house wines cost around £10 to £15.

CHEF: Steve Drake PROPRIETORS: John Morris and Tracey Honeysett OPEN: Tue to Fri L 12 to 1.30, Tue to Sat 7 to 9.30 CLOSED: Christmas, New Year, 2 weeks Aug MEALS: Set L £16 (2 courses) to £19, Set D £28 (2 courses) to £32.50 SERVICE: not inc CARDS: Amex, MasterCard, Switch, Visa DETAILS: 34 seats. Private parties: 34 main room. Car park. No children under 10. Wheelchair access (not WC). Occasional music. Air-conditioned (£5)

Subscribers to Which? Online can access The Good Food Guide *on www.which.net.*

ADDINGTON Greater London map 3

Planet Spice

NEW ENTRY

88 Selsdon Park Road, Addington CR2 8JT
TEL: (020) 8651 3300 FAX: (020) 8651 4400
EMAIL: eandjrahman@hotmail.com
WEB SITE: www.planet-spice.com

COOKING **3**
INDIAN
£17–£48

Emdad Rahman, owner of Babur Brasserie (see entry, London) now has a second restaurant, which brings the colours (both pastel and primary) of Indian décor and food to Addington. On white linen tablecloths, candles are surrounded by flowers floating in little bowls, while plain white plates show off the tastefully presented food prepared by a number of chefs from India, headed by Dulal Pal. Among the offerings are patra, rarely seen outside Indian homes; this paste of gram flour, pounded chickpeas and spices rolled in avari leaves, is steamed, sliced and finally fried. Dishes from many regions (but particularly Goa) include South Indian chicken Chettinad, notable for its carefully balanced spicing, and 'very fresh, gently marinated' tandoori prawns, while accompaniments take in rich, thick dal, and good breads, chutneys and pickles. Among desserts mango sorbet is 'packed with flavour', and there is a novel chocolate version of kulfi. Vegetarians can choose from the varied à la carte or opt for a thali served on a silver platter.

CHEF: Dulal Pal PROPRIETOR: Planet Spice Ltd OPEN: all week 12.30 to 2.15, 6.30 to 11.15 CLOSED: 25 and 26 Dec MEALS: alc (main courses £7.50 to £12). Set L all week £9.95, Set D Sun to Thur £9.95 (2 courses) SERVICE: 10% (optional), card slips closed CARDS: Amex, Delta, Diners, MasterCard, Switch, Visa DETAILS: 90 seats. Private parties: 50 main room. Car park. Vegetarian meals. Children's helpings. Wheelchair access (also WC). Music. Air-conditioned (£5)

ALDEBURGH Suffolk map 6

Lighthouse 🍷 £

77 High Street, Aldeburgh IP15 5AU
TEL/FAX: (01728) 453377

COOKING **3**
MODERN BRITISH-PLUS
£22–£40

The bistroesque Lighthouse in the heart of town is popular, bustling, down-to-earth, cramped: 'it's almost a victim of its own success'. Wooden chairs, flooring and tightly packed tables set a no-frills, informal tone. Downstairs walls have bright posters, while the no-smoking, air-conditioned first floor is decorated with pictures (all for sale). 'Turnover is so quick, people slide into tables almost before they are vacated,' but it's all part of the atmosphere; staff rush around, but service is pleasant and friendly. Menus change daily to reflect availability and seasonality, with seafood well to the fore: perhaps dressed Cromer crab, or potted Norfolk shrimps to start, followed by Aldeburgh cod, skate wing, Dover sole, or whole sea bass (maybe with red pepper salsa, spinach and lemon oil).

For meat eaters there might be beef stroganoff with basmati rice, or pan-fried fillet steak with shallot gravy, chips and salad. The style is straightforward ('no attempt at anything sophisticated'), with house classics backed up by nightly specials at dinner. Desserts (less successful) have included vanilla crème brûlée, and lemon tart with crème fraîche. The wine list kicks off with a seven-strong house selection, all priced at £10.75 (£2.45 a glass), which range from a white Rueda to an Australian Shiraz-Cabernet. Good value extends to the rest of the list – a Prosecco at £15.25, for example, provides an interesting sparkling alternative to Champagne – with most bottles staying below £20.

CHEFS: Sara Fox and Guy Welsh PROPRIETORS: Sara Fox and Peter Hill OPEN: all week 12 to 2.30, 7 to 10 CLOSED: 2 weeks Jan, 1 week Oct MEALS: alc (main courses £6 to £10.50). Set D £13.75 (2 courses) to £16.50 SERVICE: not inc, card slips closed CARDS: Delta, MasterCard, Switch, Visa DETAILS: 95 seats. 25 seats outside. Private parties: 45 main room, 20, 25 private rooms. Vegetarian meals. No smoking in 1 dining room. Wheelchair access (also WC). No music. Air-conditioned (£5)

Regatta £

171 High Street, Aldeburgh IP15 5AN — COOKING **3**
TEL: (01728) 452011 FAX: (01728) 453324 — SEAFOOD/EUROPEAN
WEB SITE: www.regattaaldeburgh.com — £18–£37

The welcoming cream and blue frontage on the High Street gives way to a cheerfully bright blue and white dining room with a seascape mural on one wall, and flowers and pale blue candles on the tables. Robert Mabey's speciality is fish and seafood, much of it local and some of it smoked in-house: cod roes, prawns, and Aldeburgh sprats, for example. There are a few meaty offerings, ranging from Thai chicken curry to breast of Gressingham duck with lime, and local game appears in season, but reports suggest the best bet is to stick to fish. Among starters might be 'nostalgic prawn cocktail', or Mediterranean fish soup, while daily-changing main courses, listed on a blackboard, run to griddled fillet of mackerel with roast peppers and basil oil, and sea bass with samphire. Regular themed events include a Japanese evening, 'gourmet duck' evening, Orford lobster week, and Irish oyster and stout week. A short list of wines opens with a pair of house French at £9.50 (£2.50 a glass), and prices remain under £20 throughout most of its varied international selection.

CHEF: Robert Mabey PROPRIETORS: Mr and Mrs Robert Mabey OPEN: all week 12 to 2.30, 6 to 10 CLOSED: Mon to Wed and Sun D Nov to Mar MEALS: alc (main courses £8 to £12). Set D 6 to 7 exc Sat £10 SERVICE: not inc CARDS: Amex, Delta, MasterCard, Switch, Visa DETAILS: 95 seats. Private parties: 40 main room. Vegetarian meals. Children's helpings. No-smoking area. Wheelchair access (not WC). Occasional music. Air-conditioned (£5)

ALTRINCHAM Greater Manchester — **map 8**

Juniper

21 The Downs, Altrincham WA14 2QD — COOKING **7**
TEL: (0161) 929 4008 FAX: (0161) 929 4009 — MODERN FRENCH
EMAIL: reservations@juniper-restaurant.co.uk — £33–£70

Major refurbishment since last year has extended the kitchen and given the dining room a new, more luxurious look. Its colour scheme derives from an enormous copy of Uccello's 1456 painting hanging in the room, *The Battle of San Romano*, known to art students everywhere as the first example of linear perspective. A change in ownership has also given Paul Kitching and Kate

O'Brien (she runs front-of-house) a financial stake in the operation, and staff in both kitchen and out front have been increased. At the same time the menu offers greater choice; indeed, the effects of all this liberation are quite marked as the cooking appears ever more innovative, producing such pioneering partnerships as ragoût of scallops with rabbit and coriander, calves' sweetbreads with cucumber and banana, and saddle of hare with white chocolate cream. Is there no combination he won't try?

At their best these can be as 'seriously exciting' as they are unusual, as in a starter of creamy, frothy yeast soup served with a bird's nest of braised leeks containing three spicy olives deep-fried in light batter. Individual items are given minute attention, flavours remain honest despite the complexity, and the whole dish typically hangs together: for example in a starter of sauté scallop parked on top of a small haggis beignet, in turn on a chunk of lightly curried cod, all resting on a rösti-like bed of caramelised onion, and set about with two sauces, one stock-based, the other tasting of melon, decorated with a band of deep-fried herbs. Such incessant creativity may prove a little wearing, as elements of a dish become too numerous to appreciate and enjoy, yet it's hard to beat for culinary thrills: whatever else, you won't be bored.

Desserts tend to be a little calmer, perhaps taking in a tall tulip-shaped strudel pastry, the top edge curled outwards, enclosing a whole, peeled and cored baby pineapple, served with a scoop of butterscotch ice cream. Bread is still first-rate, and service is well managed and informative. An expanded wine list offers some fine and interesting bottles from around the world, although prices are high. Two French and two Italians are served by the glass at £3.25.

CHEF: Paul Kitching PROPRIETORS: P. and D. Keeling, Paul Kitching and Kate O'Brien OPEN: Tue to Fri L 12 to 2.15, Tue to Sat D 7 to 9.30 CLOSED: first week Jan, 2 weeks July to Aug MEALS: alc (main courses £15 to £21). Set L £14 (2 courses) to £18 SERVICE: not inc, card slips closed CARDS: Amex, Delta, MasterCard, Switch, Visa DETAILS: 34 seats. Private parties: 34 main room. No smoking in dining room. Music. Air-conditioned (£5)

ALVECHURCH Worcestershire **map 5**

Mill

Radford Road, Alvechurch B48 7LD
TEL: (0121) 447 7005 FAX: (0121) 447 8001

COOKING **3**
MODERN BRITISH
£27–£41

Although the current trend for reclaimed industrial spaces is for minimalism and functionality, the Mill goes in for a traditional décor, with plenty of chintz, prints on the walls, and colour-co-ordinated crockery and napery. Run with courtesy and unassuming friendliness, it is very English and slightly old-fashioned. But then the McKernons and chef Carl Timms have had plenty of time to figure out what their regular customers like, having been here for close to a decade.

The menu changes monthly and may include a starter of home-made goats' cheese ravioli with a classically made pesto sauce, and a main course breast of duck (from a French breed) with caramelised apples and cinnamon. Desserts are predictably simple: rich chocolate and hazelnut parfait with coffee bean sauce, or fruity bread pudding with rum, for instance. Although flavourings may seem a bit timid to palates used to bolder spicing, regular visitors praise the food's reliability. An extensive list majors on the traditional wines of France and has a good selection of dessert offerings and Ch. Musar vintages. Enthusiasts will find the bin-end section worth a browse. The house selection starts at £9.75.

CHEF: Carl Timms PROPRIETORS: Stefan, Geoffrey and Vivienne McKernon OPEN: Tue to Sat D only 7 to 8.30 (9 Fri, 9.30 Sat) CLOSED: first week Jan, first 2 weeks Aug MEALS: Set D Tue to Fri £17.50 (2 courses) to £19.50, Set D Sat £26.50 SERVICE: not inc CARDS: Amex, Delta, MasterCard, Switch, Visa DETAILS: 26 seats. Private parties: 24 main room. Car park. Vegetarian meals. No children under 8. No smoking in dining room. Music (£5)

AMBLESIDE Cumbria **map 8**

Glass House

Rydal Road, Ambleside LA22 9AN
TEL: (01539) 432137 FAX: (01539) 433384
EMAIL: enquiries@theglasshouserestaurant.co.uk

COOKING **3**
MODERN EUROPEAN
£21–£48

The glass studio and workshop in a fifteenth-century mill, with working weir and millrace, makes an attractive neighbour for the restaurant in the same building. Although its gradual evolution from a café to a full-blown restaurant continues, it still serves sandwiches, salads and home-made pasta dishes until 5pm. And the 'early doors' dinner from 6 to 7.30 offers three simple choices for each of three courses. A la carte lunch and dinner menus present meat eaters with a restricted choice, but there is plenty for vegetarians and fish eaters, and a couple of inspectors who fell into that category enjoyed smoked salmon with avocado and coleslaw; scallops with parsley butter and pancetta; and sea bass fillet with spinach and potato cake in a sea of herb butter. Successful desserts have included a soft, creamy warm raspberry soufflé, and home-made ginger ice cream. House wines are £10.50, and unusual beers include Belgian, Dutch, Australian and local.

CHEF: Stuart Birkett PROPRIETOR: Neil Farrell OPEN: all week 12 to 3, 6 to 10 CLOSED: 23 to 26 Dec MEALS: alc (main courses £8 to £15). Set D 6 to 7.30 Sun to Fri £9.95 (2 courses) to £12.50. Light lunch menu available 11 to 5 most days summer SERVICE: not inc CARDS: Delta, MasterCard, Switch, Visa DETAILS: 100 seats. 30 seats outside. Private parties: 100 main room. Vegetarian meals. Children's helpings. No smoking in dining room. Wheelchair access (not WC). Music (£5)

▲ Rothay Manor

Rothay Bridge, Ambleside LA22 0EH
TEL: (015394) 33605 FAX: (015394) 33607
EMAIL: hotel@rothaymanor.co.uk
WEB SITE: www.rothaymanor.co.uk
off A593 to Coniston, ¼m W of Ambleside

COOKING **3**
MODERN BRITISH
£21–£49

'What a warm welcome,' enthused one visitor, stumbling upon a cheerful coal fire on a chilly March day. Rothay does its best to accommodate everyone, offering light lunches (anything from sandwiches to chicken tikka or venison pie), afternoon teas, a vegetarian menu with half a dozen main courses options, and dinner with a similar choice. Starters run from a straightforward cocktail of orange and melon, by way of foie gras parfait, to caponata spiked with tuna, capers and olives, and despite a little couscous here, and a salsa there, dishes tend to have an old-fashioned reassurance about them. Tender chicken breast comes with a mildly curried cream sauce, and a generous fillet of poached salmon arrives with a prawn sauce. Apple tarte Tatin and pannacotta also come recommended. House wines in an array of styles kick off the list at a great-value £12 each. A page of 'suggested wines', also good value, take in California and France, and the rest of the list is a cross-section of global bins, mostly under £25. Those wanting a changeover through the meal can take half of a full bottle at just over half the full price.

CHEFS: Jane Binns and Colette Nixon PROPRIETORS: Nigel and Stephen Nixon OPEN: all week 12.30 (12.45 Sun) to 2 (1.30 Sun), 7.45 to 9 CLOSED: 3 Jan to 8 Feb MEALS: alc L (main courses £8.50). Set L Mon to Sat £13.50, Set L Sun £17.50, Set D £25 (2 courses) to £31. Light L available SERVICE: not inc CARDS: Amex, Delta, Diners, MasterCard, Switch, Visa DETAILS: 70 seats. Private parties: 35 main room. Car park. Vegetarian meals. Children's helpings. No children under 8 at D. No smoking in dining room. Wheelchair access (also WC). No music. Air-conditioned ACCOMMODATION: 18 rooms, all with bath/shower. TV. Phone. B&B £65 to £140. Rooms for disabled. Baby facilities (*The Which? Hotel Guide*)

APPLETHWAITE Cumbria **map 10**

▲ Underscar Manor

Applethwaite CA12 4PH COOKING **6**
TEL: (017687) 75000 FAX: (017687) 74904 ANGLO-FRENCH
off A66, ½m N of Keswick £39–£71

On a good day the Italianate house at the foot of Skiddaw has splendid views across to Derwentwater and Cat Bells; in poor visibility there is the compensation of red squirrels and guinea fowl on the lawn. Failing that, there is a whole menagerie of stuffed toys within, and although the décor may be a bit fussy (it has 'the air of Christmas for all seasons'), there is no denying the comfort. Robert Thornton's cooking is both skilful and appealing, relying on fine technique to deliver dishes of wide appeal. His take on standards of the repertoire includes a fish pie gâteau with king prawns and parsley sauce, and seared diver-caught scallops given the Indian treatment with a lentil curry sauce.

Concentration on quality never falters, helped by a commitment to sound supplies. Organic materials play their part, not least when it comes to poultry: roast breast and Parma ham-wrapped leg meat of chicken with a lemon sauce, or honey roast breast of duck with a Chinese-style pancake stuffed with crispy vegetables. Fish options – perhaps an updated version of sole Mornay – can be taken as either a first or main course, and desserts have a soothing familiarity about them, from a daily-changing soufflé via trifle, rice pudding and crêpes suzette to warm apple charlotte. The surprise menu has also met with approval. A classically inclined wine list, with France to the fore, finds room for more up-to-the-minute bottles, a Malbec and Chardonnay from Argentina among them. Prices start at £15.

CHEF: Robert Thornton PROPRIETORS: Pauline and Derek Harrison, and Gordon Evans OPEN: all week 12 to 1, 7 to 8.30 (9 Sat) MEALS: alc (main courses £19 to £21). Set L £28, Set D £30 SERVICE: not inc, card slips closed CARDS: Amex, Delta, MasterCard, Switch, Visa DETAILS: 55 seats. Private parties: 35 main room. Car park. Vegetarian meals. No children under 12. Jacket required for men. No smoking in dining room. Occasional music ACCOMMODATION: 11 rooms, all with bath/shower. TV. Phone. D,B&B £180 to £250. No children under 12. Swimming pool (*The Which? Hotel Guide*)

ARNCLIFFE North Yorkshire — map 8

▲ Amerdale House

Arncliffe, Littondale BD23 5QE
TEL: (01756) 770250 FAX: (01756) 770266
WEB SITE: www.amerdalehouse.co.uk

COOKING **4**
MODERN EUROPEAN
£40–£48

One enthusiast describes this well-kept hotel in a remote corner of the Dales as 'the best value anywhere in Yorkshire'. It is a friendly place with relaxing service and a short dinner menu. The food is 'not too complicated', the style 'light and interesting', taking in starters of mushroom tart, grilled Somerset goats' cheese, and a terrine of oranges in a Campari and orange jelly. The no-choice intermediate course ranges from melon with Parma ham to a pan-fried scallop on olive mash with salsa verde, and local produce continues to feature, from Dales lamb reared in Pateley Bridge (served on minted couscous) to flavourful Gloucester Old Spot pork (perhaps roast tenderloin with grain mustard sauce).

Vying for attention with local cheeses such as Coverdale, Swaledale and Blue Wensleydale are desserts of marzipan roast peaches with vanilla ice cream, and soufflé fritters with cinnamon sugar and lemon sauce. Coffee is the only disappointment that one otherwise satisfied customer was able to register. Wines appeal to fans of both and Old and New Worlds, styles are varied, and prices ungreedy. Two house wines – a Chilean Cabernet Sauvignon and a French Chardonnay – are available by the glass.

CHEF: Nigel Crapper PROPRIETORS: Paula and Nigel Crapper OPEN: all week D only 7.30 to 8.30 CLOSED: mid-Nov to mid-Mar MEALS: Set D £30 SERVICE: not inc, card slips closed CARDS: MasterCard, Switch, Visa DETAILS: 24 seats. Car park. No children under 8. No smoking in dining room. No music ACCOMMODATION: 11 rooms, all with bath/shower. TV. Phone. D,B&B £82.50 to £149. Baby facilities (*The Which? Hotel Guide*)

ASENBY North Yorkshire — map 9

▲ Crab & Lobster

Dishforth Road, Asenby YO7 3QL
TEL: (01845) 577286 FAX: (01845) 577109
EMAIL: info@crabandlobster.co.uk
WEB SITE: www.crabandlobster.co.uk
off A168, between A19 and A1

COOKING **2**
FISH/MODERN EUROPEAN
£24–£70

Rooms in the hotel (Crab Manor) are designed to recall exotic locations from around the world, while the old thatched pub that constitutes the restaurant is eccentrically packed with so many items of bric-à-brac that it looks 'like Steptoe & Son's living room'. A similarly magpie approach seems to lie behind the dauntingly long menu: 34 savoury dishes don't automatically inspire confidence, although variety is not in question, given Thai crab soufflé, rabbit terrine, Moroccan-style salmon, monkfish and prawn tagine, and fish and chips with mushy peas. Seafood is indeed a strength, with good reports of smoked haddock risotto, and cod with fennel sauce, while puddings might take in lemon crème puff with Yorkshire rhubarb, or an exotic fruit crumble with caramelised pineapple and coconut custard. Interest (there is a Canadian Pinot Blanc) and fair pricing characterise the 50-strong wine list, which starts with house Duboeuf at £12.95.

CHEFS: David Barnard and Steve Dean PROPRIETORS: David and Jackie Barnard OPEN: all week 12 to 2.30, 6.30 to 10 (12 to 10 Sun) MEALS: alc (main courses £9.50 to £29). Set L £10 (2 courses) to £13.50, Set D Sun to Thur £27.50 SERVICE: not inc CARDS: Amex, MasterCard, Switch, Visa DETAILS: 180 seats. 120 seats outside. Private parties: 100 main room, 12 to 50 private rooms. Car park. Vegetarian meals. No smoking in dining room. Wheelchair access (also WC). Occasional music. Air-conditioned ACCOMMODATION: 12 rooms, all with bath/shower. TV. Phone. B&B £110 to £150. Rooms for disabled (*The Which? Hotel Guide*)

ASHBOURNE Derbyshire — map 8

▲ Callow Hall

Mappleton, Ashbourne DE6 2AA
TEL: (01335) 300900 FAX: (01335) 300512
EMAIL: reservations@callowhall.co.uk
WEB SITE: www.callowhall.co.uk
from Ashbourne market place take A515, at top of hill turn W at crossroads with Bowling Green pub on left, Mappleton Road is first on right after bridge

COOKING **3**
MODERN BRITISH-PLUS
£29–£61

The Spencers run this imposing Victorian stone country-house hotel like clockwork. Dinner orders are taken in the drawing room, where small appetisers may be served, before guests move to intimate dining rooms with well-spaced, beautifully set tables. More exciting than the three-course Sunday lunch is the five-course dinner, which may involve starters of well-trimmed, fresh-tasting, slightly crisp asparagus spears served with an escalope of seared, lightly cooked home-smoked salmon and beurre blanc sauce, or sauté duck livers with cured bacon, spring leaf salad and a good Madeira-flavoured jus. Next comes a fish course or sorbet preceding perhaps breast and confit leg of guinea fowl with roast shallots and green peppercorn sauce, or roast loin of lamb with figs baked in puff pastry and mint jus. Well-judged desserts, such as apple and cinnamon tart with apple and calvados cream, give way to good cafetière coffee. The wine list has a traditional French focus, but offers up interest from elsewhere too, such as Bonny Doon's organic Californian red and white and a collection from star Aussie winemaker Grosset. French and German house wines offer a range of lively drinking, starting at £11.95.

CHEFS: David and Anthony Spencer PROPRIETORS: David, Anthony and Dorothy Spencer OPEN: Sun L 12.30 to 1.30, Mon to Fri D 7.30 to 9 (Sun D residents only) CLOSED: 25 and 26 Dec MEALS: alc D (main courses £16.50 to £20). Set L £20.50, Set D £38 SERVICE: not inc CARDS: Amex, Delta, Diners, MasterCard, Switch, Visa DETAILS: 70 seats. Private parties: 40 main room, 24, 24 private rooms. Car park. Vegetarian meals. Children's helpings. No smoking in dining room. No music ACCOMMODATION: 16 rooms, all with bath/shower. TV. Phone. B&B £85 to £165. Rooms for disabled. Fishing (*The Which? Hotel Guide*) (£5)

ASHBURTON Devon map 1

Agaric

NEW ENTRY

30 North Street, Ashburton TQ13 7QD COOKING **4**
TEL: (01364) 654478 MODERN BRITISH-PLUS
WEB SITE: www.agaricrestaurant.co.uk £32–£48

Chef/proprietor Nick Coiley spent many years as head chef with Joyce Molyneux at the Carved Angel in Dartmouth (see entry). In this new venture his menus are brief, and change frequently in response to well-sourced, fresh ingredients. Simply prepared dishes might take the form of Dartmouth crab and avocado salad, or prawn bisque, but Mediterranean and Oriental touches appear too: in a starter of cuttlefish cooked in coconut milk with lime and chilli, or a main-course of baked cod fillet with a sun-dried tomato, olive and rosemary crust. Simple treatment with herbs and spices does nothing to detract from original flavours.

For dessert, try a light, crisp tart filled with a 'delectable custard' of Seville orange and lemon, or opt for local cheeses such as Devon Blue, Sharpham and Denhay Cheddar. Varied home-made breads include Portuguese cornbread, milk rolls, and herb plait. The uncluttered dining room has terracotta and mustard walls, and tables and chairs of plain pine; paintings and sculptures by local artists add a touch of distinction. Service is unfussy yet professional, and while the short wine list may lack breadth and a sense of adventure, it has some good bottles, starting with French and Italian house wines at £9.95.

CHEF: Nick Coiley PROPRIETORS: Nick Coiley and Sophie Crossley OPEN: Wed to Sun L 12 to 2.30, Wed to Sat D 7 to 9.30 CLOSED: first 2 weeks Oct, first 2 weeks Feb MEALS: alc (main courses £14 to £17). Set L £19.50 (2 courses) to £22.50, Set D £27.50. Light lunches also available SERVICE: not inc, card slips closed CARDS: Delta, MasterCard, Switch, Visa DETAILS: 30 seats. 20 seats outside. Private parties: 30 main room. Vegetarian meals. Children's helpings. No smoking in dining room. Wheelchair access (also WC). No music

ASHFORD Derbyshire map 9

▲ Riverside House

Ashford in the Water, Bakewell DE45 1QF COOKING **4**
TEL: (01629) 814275 FAX: (01629) 812873 CLASSICAL FRENCH-PLUS
EMAIL: riversidehouse@enta.net £33–£64

In a village north-west of Bakewell, this creeper-covered Georgian house sits beside the Wye; two dining rooms, elegantly appointed, enhance the sense of gracious living. John Whelan cooks in unashamedly French style, importing some ingredients directly. A quail from Périgord, roasted in a honey coat, has been served with an earthy salad of French beans and lentils as a starter; another has combined a mousse of delicately smoked chicken with crab and oyster sauce. A classical approach underlies local beef with horseradish potatoes and a truffled Madeira sauce, while an innovative impulse has produced cannelloni of duck and aubergine served with braised chicory, accompanied by a risotto of dried ham and a lemon thyme sauce. The vegetarian option may be a strudel of roast Mediterranean vegetables, and desserts calm the palate with soft spices: cinnamon in the ice cream accompanying plum tarte Tatin, and saffron in the liquor of a poached pear with vanilla and lemon pannacotta. Professional and assured service helps things along, and the French-led wine list includes many good producers; house selections start at £14.50 for Concha y Toro Chileans.

CHEF: John Whelan PROPRIETOR: Penelope Thornton Hotels Ltd OPEN: all week 12 to 2.30, 7 to 9.30 MEALS: Set L £26.95, Set D £39.95 SERVICE: not inc CARDS: Amex, Delta, Diners, MasterCard, Switch, Visa DETAILS: 50 seats. 20 seats outside. Private parties: 32 main room, 14 and 16 private rooms. Car park. Vegetarian meals. No children under 12. No smoking in dining room. No music ACCOMMODATION: 15 rooms, all with bath/shower. TV. Phone. D,B&B £95 to £235. No children under 12. Fishing (£5)

AYLESBURY Buckinghamshire **map 3**

▲ Hartwell House

Oxford Road, Aylesbury HP17 8NL
TEL: (01296) 747444 FAX: (01296) 747450
EMAIL: info@hartwell-house.com COOKING **3**
WEB SITE: www.hartwell-house.com BRITISH
on A418, 2m from Aylesbury towards Oxford £36–£64

Space is not in short supply at Hartwell, given a 90-acre estate containing a lake, pavilions and a ruined church. The sumptuously restored interior (most of the house is eighteenth century) boasts large, formal yet comfortable drawing rooms and a big, airy dining room in the style of Sir John Soane. The kitchen works hard, fashioning smoked chicken and spring onions into a sausage, and filling tortellini with a confit of Jerusalem artichoke, while a generous menu brings plenty of variety: from a starter of scrambled egg and Cornish crab to meaty roast halibut on an unctuous herb risotto, and lamb shank on creamed potato and lentils.

Recommended desserts, meanwhile, have included chocolate fudge tart on thin, crisp pastry with a white chocolate mousse. Helpful staff deliver attentive and well-drilled service in a grand yet friendly manner. Although nearly 30 wines (approaching 15 per cent of the total) are under £20, many more cost over £100, and anywhere that lists Cloudy Bay Sauvignon Blanc at £55 cannot expect to be taken seriously. House red and white are £14.90.

CHEF: Daniel Richardson PROPRIETOR: Historic House Hotels Ltd OPEN: all week 12.30 to 1.45, 7.30 to 9.45 CLOSED: dining room closed to non-residents Christmas and New Year MEALS: Set L Mon to Sat £22 (2 courses) to £31, Set L Sun £31, Set D £46 SERVICE: net prices, card slips closed CARDS: Delta, MasterCard, Switch, Visa DETAILS: 60 seats. Private parties: 60 main room, 18 to 60 private rooms. Car park. Vegetarian meals. No children under 8 in dining room. Jacket and tie at D. No smoking in dining room. Wheelchair access (also WC). Occasional music ACCOMMODATION: 46 rooms, all with bath/shower. TV. Phone. Room only £140 to £345. Rooms for disabled. No children under 8 in accommodation. Swimming pool. Fishing (*The Which? Hotel Guide*)

The Guide office can quickly spot when a restaurateur is encouraging customers to write recommending inclusion. Such reports do not further a restaurant's cause. Please tell us if a restaurateur invites you to write to the Guide.

BAKEWELL Derbyshire map 8

Renaissance

Bath Street, Bakewell DE45 1BX
TEL: (01629) 812687

COOKING 4
FRENCH
£21–£47

This smartly converted barn in the heart of Derbyshire has the feel of a traditional restaurant. Elegantly laid candlelit tables are set against a backdrop of painted stone walls and a pitched, beamed ceiling, and background accordion music is very much in tune with Eric Piedaniel's classical French cooking. He keeps himself busy in the kitchen, offering around half a dozen fairly elaborate choices per course: a fish casserole starter, for example, is given a pastry lattice lid, which in turn is topped with a smoked salmon soufflé. Similarly, lamb fillet is wrapped in a herb crust and served on a potato pancake, and pork fillet is stuffed with black pudding and finished with plum sauce, while for dessert there may be chocolate and caramel gâteau with white chocolate sauce. Fortunately, this tendency for embellishment does not obscure sound cooking, and flavours are to the fore. Occasional supplements can augment the bill, but the midweek set-price menu offers excellent value and no one has a bad word for the quality of service. Perhaps surprisingly, there are almost as many 'rest of the world' wines as French on the reasonably priced list. House selections are £10.99 a bottle.

CHEF: Eric Piedaniel PROPRIETORS: Eric and C. Piedaniel, and D. Béraud OPEN: Tue to Sat and first and second Sun of month L 12 to 1.30 (2 Sun; booking essential at L), Tue to Sat D 7 to 9.30 (10.30 Sat) CLOSED: 25 Dec to second week Jan, first 2 weeks Aug MEALS: Set L and D £21.95, Set L Sun £14.95, Set D Tue to Thur £13.95 SERVICE: not inc CARDS: Delta, MasterCard, Switch, Visa DETAILS: 70 seats. Private parties: 55 main room, 25 private room. Vegetarian meals. Children's helpings. No smoking in dining room. Wheelchair access (women's WC). Music

BARNET Hertfordshire map 3

Mims

63 East Barnet Road, Barnet EN4 8RN
TEL: (020) 8449 2974 FAX: Same

COOKING 6
MEDITERRANEAN
£24–£34

Mims, a true neighbourhood restaurant in an unprepossessing shopping parade in East Barnet, seems to offer its customers an innovation each year. Last time we recorded the appointment of a maitre d'; a couple of reports have noted his absence, and now a no-corkage bring-your-own wine policy has been introduced: a move that will please regular patrons.

Fundamentally, the whole operation rests on Ali Al-Sersy's superbly crafted cooking, which continues to produce inventive and subtle dishes to a high level of consistency. Handwritten menus don't give much away, especially about desserts; the elaborately presented dishes flagged simply as 'lemon sorbet' or 'strawberry cheesecake' surprise and delight when they arrive. Before that, you may have had a poached-egg-topped salad of smoked haddock in a beetroot dressing, or grilled prawns and squid with tomato and garlic; then grilled calf's liver with roast potato, sage and onion, or perhaps pot-roast fillet of lamb with roast vegetables. Courteous and efficient service still seems 'slow to get started'. The short wine list, mostly pitched below £20, opens with Old Bush Vines red and white (French, despite the moniker) at £9.50. Or take your own.

CHEF/PROPRIETOR: A. Al-Sersy OPEN: Tue to Sun; 12.30 to 2.30, 6.30 to 10.30 MEALS: Set L £10.50 (2 courses) to £15, Set D £14 (2 courses) to £18.50. BYO (no corkage) SERVICE: 10% CARDS: MasterCard, Visa DETAILS: 45 seats. Private parties: 60 main room. No children under 8. No cigars/pipes in dining room. Wheelchair access (not WC). Music (£5)

BARNSLEY Gloucestershire **map 2**

▲ Village Pub NEW ENTRY

Barnsley, Cirencester GL7 5EF
TEL: (01285) 740421 FAX: (01285) 740142 COOKING **3**
EMAIL: reservations@thevillagepub.co.uk MODERN BRITISH
WEB SITE: www.thevillagepub.co.uk £26–£41

The Barnsley House gardens of horticultural star Rosemary Verey, open to the public, are opposite the Cotswold-stone inn, so that's two reasons to visit this sleepy hamlet near Cirencester. Inside the pub are oil paintings, a rough-hewn stone fireplace and flagged floors, while a couple of high-chairs suggest that, whatever their age, all are welcome. Dominic Blake cooks ultra-modern pub food, limiting choices to five per course, but scoring some palpable hits. Haddock fritters with aïoli and salad leaves have made a crisp, garlicky treat of a starter, while celeriac rémoulade and walnuts have been successfully paired with roast pigeon breast. Meats appear to be well-timed – as in grilled ribeye with well-made béarnaise sauce – and fish, delivered daily from Cornwall, is treated innovatively: curried sweet potato and cauliflower partnering roast sea bass, for example. Desserts include passable sticky toffee pudding, and an impeccably proper crème caramel. Home-made breads are a bonus, as is the professional and courteous service. A card lists value-led wines (only one above £20) from across the world, including 17 by the glass from £2.80; house Vins de Pays d'Oc are £10.95 apiece.

CHEF: Dominic Blake PROPRIETORS: Tim Haigh and Rupert Pendered OPEN: all week 12 to 2.30 (3 Sat and Sun), 7 to 9.30 (10 Sat and Sun) CLOSED: 25 Dec MEALS: alc (main courses £9.50 to £14) SERVICE: not inc, 12.5% (optional) for parties of 8 or more, card slips closed CARDS: Delta, MasterCard, Switch, Visa DETAILS: 100 seats. 50 seats outside. Private parties: 20 main room. Car park. Vegetarian meals. Children's helpings. No smoking in 1 dining room. No music ACCOMMODATION: 6 rooms, all with bath/shower. TV. B&B £55 to £125 (£5)

'[It was] a striking dining room with towering pillars and enough marble to satisfy a Third World dictator.' (On eating in London)

The Guide's top-rated restaurants are listed near the front of the book.

London Round-ups listing additional restaurants that may be worth a visit can be found after the main London section.

BARNSLEY South Yorkshire map 9

Armstrongs

102 Dodworth Road, Barnsley S70 6HL
TEL/FAX: (01226) 240113
EMAIL: rob@armsrtongs98.freeserve.co.uk
WEB SITE: www.armstrongsrestaurant.co.uk
1½m from Jct 37 of M1 towards Barnsley

COOKING **4**
MODERN EUROPEAN
£25–£50

In this converted Victorian house on the outskirts of Barnsley preprandial drinks are served in the first-floor bar, where a pianist plays on Saturday evenings. Downstairs in the dining room you will find proficient modern cooking priding itself on attention to detail. Taking breads alone, the half-dozen varieties usually offered (all baked in-house) may include red onion, sun-dried tomato, and a black pudding and chorizo version.

Menus centre on appetising combinations. A seared tuna starter comes with carrot strips and chilli rémoulade, while sage butter sauce and onion jam accompany calf's liver. Dishes are slightly lighter at lunchtime than in the evening (though robust appetites are still catered for): beef fillet, seared and served with horseradish mash at lunch, may be roasted with potatoes, wild mushrooms and beer-based gravy for dinner. Chicken en croûte with smoked bacon, spinach and Gruyère makes a superior pasty. Finish with peach parfait or malted chocolate marquise with white chocolate sauce. The two-section wine list – separating bins that rarely exceed £20 from a choice of pricier 'fine wines' – balances French regions with other countries; three £12.50 house wines are also available by the glass.

CHEF: Robert Crookes PROPRIETORS: Robert and Elizabeth Crookes OPEN: Wed to Fri L 12 to 2, Wed to Sat D 7 to 9 (9.30 Sat) CLOSED: 24 Dec, 1 Jan MEALS: Set L £9.95 (2 courses), to £14.45, Set D Wed to Fri £24.95, Set D Sat £29.95 SERVICE: not inc CARDS: MasterCard, Switch, Visa DETAILS: 40 seats. Private parties: 40 main room. Car park. Vegetarian meals. No children. No smoking in dining room. Music

BARWICK Somerset map 2

▲ Little Barwick House

Barwick BA22 9TD
TEL: (01935) 423902 FAX: (01935) 420908
EMAIL: reservations@barwick7.fsnet.co.uk
WEB SITE: www.littlebarwickhouse.co.uk
take first exit off A37 roundabout 1m S of Yeovil; Little Barwick House ¼m on left

COOKING **6**
MODERN ENGLISH
£24–£64

Serenely set in three and a half acres of garden, the house is simply and comfortably furnished, with a strikingly bare Georgian dining room whose wooden floorboards and white tablecloths make it seem 'very quiet and English'. Canapés are served either in the sitting room in front of a log fire or on the terrace, depending on season, and menus offer a generally cosseting style of food exemplified by langoustine ravioli with crayfish sauce, or pink roast squab pigeon with braised lentils. Fish and game are indeed strong suits – grilled

Cornish red mullet on herb couscous, and medallions of roe deer with beetroot purée for one visitor – but variety is evident in a pithiviers of goats' cheese with rocket pesto, and calves' sweetbreads served with a wild mushroom risotto.

First-class materials provide a solid foundation, and a sound technical grasp ensures that these are dealt with confidently. If dishes tend to be more conservative than exciting, at least one can be certain that all the elements will be well rendered. To finish, apricot délice with white peach sorbet comes recommended, or there may be hot passion fruit soufflé, or banana tarte Tatin with star anise ice cream, but bear in mind the West Country cheeses, from Montgomery Cheddar to Dorset Blue Vinney. 'I can't recall better value in the West Country,' summed up one luncher. Grouped into broad styles, the wine list offers variety from around the world, including good New World names at fair prices and mature French vintages. A varied mixture of 30-plus half-bottles opens up choice. House wines are £11.50 and £12.50.

CHEFS: Tim Ford, Max Perrier and Stuart Judge PROPRIETORS: Tim and Emma Ford OPEN: Tue to Sun L 12 to 2, Tue to Sat D 7 to 9 (9.30 Fri and Sat) MEALS: alc L (main courses £12 to £18). Set L Tue to Sat £12.50 (2 courses) to £13.95, Set L Sun £16.95, Set D £21.95 (2 courses) to £27.95 SERVICE: not inc, card slips closed CARDS: Amex, MasterCard, Switch, Visa DETAILS: 40 seats. 12 seats outside. Private parties: 50 main room. Car park. Vegetarian meals. Children's helpings. No smoking in dining room. No music. Air-conditioned ACCOMMODATION: 6 rooms, all with bath/shower. TV. Phone. B&B £55 to £103. Baby facilities (*The Which? Hotel Guide*) (£5)

BASLOW Derbyshire **map 9**

▲ Cavendish Hotel, Gallery Restaurant

NEW ENTRY

Baslow DE45 1SP
TEL: (01246) 582311 FAX: (01246) 582312
EMAIL: info@cavendish-hotel.net
WEB SITE: www.cavendish-hotel.net

COOKING **2**
MODERN CLASSICAL
£35–£56

At this hotel on the Chatsworth estate 'every whim is diligently pandered to', by helpful and friendly staff who could hardly be more charming. Eric Marsh has transformed the Gallery – where open fires, flowers, and ethereally draped windows create an impression of light and space – and, recognising that customers no longer want expensive, complicated food, has abandoned last year's set price format (one course cost £27.75!) for a more informal carte. The unaffected robust cooking caters for hearty appetites, offering duck breast with orange oil mash; rabbit fillet with chorizo oil and a couscous version of tabbouleh; and seared tuna steak with a beetroot and potato salad. Some dishes come in two sizes, emphasising flexible eating, and vegetarian options are plentiful. To finish, steamed treacle sponge is served with orange ice cream, and spiced fig tartlet with Chatsworth honey. Fine paintings adorn both the walls and the short wine list, divided into 'everyday' (mostly under £20) and 'fine' bottles. French house wines are £12.95.

CHEF: Chris Allison PROPRIETOR: Eric Marsh OPEN: all week 12 to 2, 6 to 10 MEALS: alc (main courses £12.50 to £18). Garden Room menu also available SERVICE: not inc CARDS: Amex, Delta, Diners, MasterCard, Switch, Visa DETAILS: 50 seats. Private parties: 50 main room, 10 and 16 private rooms. Car park. Vegetarian meals. Children's helpings. No smoking in dining room. Occasional music ACCOMMODATION: 23 rooms, all with bath/shower. TV. Phone. Room only £95 to £145. Baby facilities. Fishing (*The Which? Hotel Guide*)

▲ Fischer's Baslow Hall

Calver Road, Baslow DE45 1RR — COOKING **8**

TEL: (01246) 583259 FAX: (01246) 583818 — MODERN EUROPEAN

£37–£73

The Edwardian house built of dark stone, reached up a steep, tree-lined drive, has had a bit of a makeover since last year. The oak-panelled hall remains in place for pre-dinner drinks, but more space has been created by turning the former café into a new lounge. In place of the Café Max operation, a less expensive Max's Menu is now available in the main dining room weekdays in the evening, in addition to the regular set-price menu.

Dishes are simply described, some of them exploring variations on a theme. The Best of English Veal combines loin, kidney and liver, and Farmed Dutch Rabbit Served Two Ways consists of a tiny pan-fried saddle and rack, an enormous stuffed and braised shoulder, and some liver and kidney thrown in for good measure, all in a professionally made stock and red wine sauce, with buttery egg noodles and spinach. Where the cooking is simple it is nevertheless sophisticated, and where it is complex it has a point. Fine judgement (and it doesn't come much finer) is brought to bear on a powerfully flavoured saffron, lemon and coriander dressing to accompany plump, nuttily roasted scallops; slices of sauté potato provide a plain backdrop, and accompanying salad leaves are in prime condition (a kitchen garden helps).

Fish dishes vary daily, and game is a strong suit, for example wild Forest of Dean venison, its quality beyond reproach, its flavour and texture all that one could ask, with a bittersweet, cinnamon-infused chocolate sauce: 'a marvel of a dish', confidently delivered. Some desserts take the theme and variation route – an assiette of rhubarb consisting of strudel, sorbet, trifle, crumble and a prune beignet – but contrasts of taste and texture are par for the course, as in a shortcrust pastry tartlet filled with sharp-tasting apricots alternating with mounds of hazelnutty frangipane, accompanied by an intensely flavoured vanilla ice cream and an apricot beignet, its stone replaced by rice pudding.

Meals come with lots of extras in the way of nibbles, appetisers and pre-dessert, too many for some appetites. Staff are formally dressed, and Susan Fischer's experienced and professional approach is much appreciated. Rising regional stars, like A. Mano's Primitivo from Puglia – again the red house wine at £14 – are scattered throughout the classy, adventurously compiled wine list, offering pleasurable drinking at good prices. Helpful notes are on hand to guide the drinker through.

CHEF: Max Fischer PROPRIETORS: Max and Susan Fischer OPEN: Sun to Fri L 12 to 1.30, all week D 7 to 9.30 CLOSED: 25 and 26 Dec MEALS: Set L Mon to Fri £20 (2 courses) to £24, Set L Sun £27, Set D £48 SERVICE: not inc CARDS: Amex, Delta, Diners, MasterCard, Switch, Visa DETAILS: 62 seats. Private parties: 40 main room, 12 and 24 private rooms. Car park. No children in dining room after 7. Jacket and tie. No smoking in dining room. Wheelchair access (not WC). No music ACCOMMODATION: 11 rooms, all with bath/shower. TV. Phone. B&B £100 to £150. Baby facilities (*The Which? Hotel Guide*)

BATH Bath & N.E. Somerset map 2

▲ Bath Priory

Weston Road, Bath BA1 2XT
TEL: (01225) 331922 FAX: (01225) 448276 COOKING **6**
EMAIL: bathprioryhotel@compuserve.com MODERN EUROPEAN
WEB SITE: www.thebathpriory.co.uk £40–£87

In a quiet leafy suburb, with its own large and secluded garden, the comfortably appointed Priory takes a traditional line in décor, from its chandeliers to pictures of a military, sporting and motoring nature. The food, meanwhile, strikes a balance between classical and contemporary; nothing is outlandish or challenging, and much of it is highly refined. Three big, fresh, accurately timed and nutty-tasting seared scallops, for example, are served with a small pool of creamy Jerusalem artichoke velouté, plus a Parmesan crisp with a pleasingly incisive bolt of flavour. One of Robert Clayton's strengths is that he doesn't pile on the extras. He knows when to stop and keeps everything simple: a macho dish of venison, for example, cooked in a piece and then sliced, comes on finely shredded red cabbage, with a couple of figs and a wedge of potato cake imbued with the freshness of lemon thyme.

Timing can be conservative, and materials a little uneven, but combinations are well judged, and saucing is a strong point. Quantities can be generous, as in a large caramelised poached pear, served with tuile biscuits and a scoop of coconut ice cream, but dishes can also be light: at one meal a moulded fruit jelly served with vanilla ice cream. Cheeses are cut from a trolley selection by somebody who knows his way round it, and accompanied by a handsome assortment of fruit, bread and nuts. At these prices, supplements seem a bit unnecessary. Service tends towards the grand hotel style, and wine service could be sharpened up, but everything is done with a smile. Wines are packed with interest, and a budget of £25 should bring plenty of high-quality choice, particularly among whites. Eight house recommendations start the ball rolling, and half-bottles are not neglected.

CHEF: Robert Clayton PROPRIETOR: Andrew Brownsword OPEN: all week 12 to 1.45, 7 to 9.30 (9.45 weekends) MEALS: Set L £17.50 (2 courses) to £25, Set L Sun £29.50, Set D £45 SERVICE: not inc CARDS: Amex, Delta, Diners, MasterCard, Switch, Visa DETAILS: 60 seats. Private parties: 60 main room, 20 private room. Car park. Vegetarian meals. Children's helpings. No smoking in dining room. Wheelchair access (not WC). Occasional music ACCOMMODATION: 28 rooms, all with bath/shower. TV. Phone. D,B&B £170 to £375. Rooms for disabled. Swimming pool (*The Which? Hotel Guide*)

Le Clos

1 Seven Dials, Saw Close, Bath BA1 1EN
TEL: (01225) 444450 FAX: (01225) 404044 COOKING **3**
EMAIL: reservations@leclos.co.uk MODERN FRENCH
WEB SITE: www.leclos.co.uk £23–£57

Formerly the Clos du Roy, Le Clos has had a change of ownership and chef since last year's entry. The interior now sports bright primrose walls, recessed spotlighting, thick green carpets, well-upholstered chairs and white linen. Peter

Quinion's cooking, though, remains essentially French. Le Clos is next door to the Theatre Royal, and the lunch and pre-theatre menu is a particular bargain. From this you might find such modern amalgamations as a starter of crottin de Chavignol with a green bean and olive salad, or an imaginative combination of smoked salmon with beetroot salsa, baby spinach and tomato dressing. Main courses might include soft, juicy fillet of pork with a shallot, black pudding and Puy lentil jus, or full-flavoured, perfectly roasted salmon on tapénade potato purée with sun-dried tomato butter. Desserts such as bitter chocolate parfait with ginger and confit pear are equally well conceived. The carte is more expensive but keeps to the modern French theme, from pan-fried foie gras on celeriac purée, to honey-roasted duck leg confit with a morel jus. The wine list, arranged by style, offers plenty of good, sensibly priced bottles to choose from, as well as a French-dominated 'classic' list and a selection of bin-ends. Prices open with Vins de Pays d'Oc at £9.95.

CHEF: Peter Quinion PROPRIETOR: David John Gerhardt OPEN: all week L 12 to 2.30, Mon to Sat D 6 to 10 MEALS: alc (main courses £10.50 to £17.50). Set L and pre-theatre D £10.95 (2 courses) to £13.95, Set D £17.50 (2 courses) to £19.50 SERVICE: not inc, card slips closed CARDS: Amex, Delta, Diners, MasterCard, Switch, Visa DETAILS: 60 seats. Private parties: 80 main room. Vegetarian meals. Children's helpings. No smoking in 1 dining room. No cigars/ pipes in dining room. Wheelchair access (not WC). Music (£5)

FishWorks Green Street Seafood Café

6 Green Street, Bath BA1 2JY — NEW CHEF
TEL: (01225) 448707 FAX: (01225) 311326 — FISH
WEB SITE: www.fishworks.co.uk — £28–£59

'Café' just about sums up this modest room above a fishmonger's, part of a burgeoning empire with branches in Christchurch and Bristol (see entries). Refurbishment has brought tiled floors and a new terrace, and the modern fish and seafood cookery on which it is founded is now in the hands of Gary Rosser, listed last year at the Glass Boat in Bristol. Whelks receive equal billing with lobster, alongside plenty of other straightforward seafood – oysters, home-smoked salmon, chargrilled prawns – and a wood grill might be applied to whole sea bass with rosemary and sea salt, or squid with thyme and garlic. There are also sandwiches to take away. The frequently changing, good-value wine list understandably concentrates on whites, though there are also several good light reds. House wines are £9.95, and a handful are offered by the glass.

CHEF: Gary Rosser PROPRIETOR: FishWorks plc OPEN: Tue to Sat 12 to 3, 6 to 10 MEALS: alc (main courses £9 to £20) SERVICE: not inc, card slips closed CARDS: Amex, Delta, Diners, MasterCard, Switch, Visa DETAILS: 40 seats. Private parties: 20 main room. Vegetarian meals. Children's helpings. Music (£5)

Net prices *in the details at the end of an entry indicates that the prices given on a menu and on a bill are inclusive of VAT and service charge, and that this practice is clearly stated on menu and bill.*

The Good Food Guide *is a registered trade mark of Which? Ltd.*

▲ Lettonie

35 Kelston Road, Bath BA1 3QH
TEL: (01225) 446676 FAX: (01225) 447541
EMAIL: sian@lettonie.co.uk
WEB SITE: www.lettonie.co.uk
2m out of Bath on A431

COOKING **6**
MODERN EUROPEAN
£43–£102

'With every visit to Lettonie there are more and more photographs of the Blunos family in frames on every available surface: mantelpieces, occasional tables, on the walls. . . .' While family snaps pepper the lounges, with their button-backed black leather sofas and heavy silk brocade curtains, the dining room makes the most of its position overlooking the sloping garden, its walls hung with cheerful paintings of fruit, fish, lobsters and cheese.

Dinner offers six or seven alternatives per course, some recalling the chef's Latvian origins – a fresh and perky bortsch terrine, perhaps, served with underwhelming shredded beef pirogi – while others are cast in more conventional mould: slices of seared scallop, for example, with two purées (sweet parsnip, and tomato and chilli), or two baby lamb chops with a circus tent of shepherd's pie (Martin Blunos doesn't miss a chance to sculpt or build a visual pun). Pasta is a favoured partnering device, appearing in the form of horseradish tortellini to accompany braised pork belly, and as a smoked haddock raviolo paired with a small piece of brill and parsley purée. Among more unusual ideas has been tortellini of kipper with cucumber and tomatoes in a Sauternes cream sauce.

Those who eschew the signature starter of scrambled duck egg with caviar (which now carries a £10 supplement) may still sample the trompe l'oeil 'boiled egg' of vanilla cream and mango that comes as a pre-dessert, followed perhaps by a plate of miniatures on an apricot theme, or rhubarb soufflé with vanilla ice cream. Despite manifest workmanship, flavours and timings at inspection were not as impressive as they have been in the past and, given the price of dinner, reporters expect more of a wow experience than they are getting. Regulars are also aware that some dishes have been in the repertoire a long time, and are seeking new thrills. Wines, though good, are hardly kind on the pocket: even house wines fail to make it under the £20 barrier.

CHEF: Martin Blunos PROPRIETORS: Siân and Martin Blunos OPEN: Tue to Sat 12 to 2, 6.30 to 9.30 (10 Sat) CLOSED: 2 weeks Christmas, 2 weeks Aug MEALS: Set L £25, Set D £47.50 to £65.50 SERVICE: not inc CARDS: Amex, Delta, Diners, MasterCard, Switch, Visa DETAILS: 38 seats. Private parties: 38 main room, 12 private room. Car park. Children's helpings. No smoking in dining room. Occasional music ACCOMMODATION: 4 rooms. TV. Phone. B&B £95 to £150 (*The Which? Hotel Guide*) (£5)

Occasional music *in the details at the end of an entry means live or recorded music is played in the dining room only rarely or for special events.* No music *means it is never played.*

Several sharp operators have tried to extort money from restaurateurs on the promise of an entry in a guidebook that has never appeared. The Good Food Guide *makes no charge for inclusion.*

Moody Goose

7A Kingsmead Square, Bath BA1 2AB
TEL/FAX: (01225) 466688 — COOKING **5**
EMAIL: moody-goose@excite.co.uk — ENGLISH
WEB SITE: www.moody-goose.com — £27–£55

Descend the stairs into a comforting lounge with squashy armchairs and a fire in winter, where amuse gueules and a glass of sherry started off a 'very civilised' evening for one couple. Seasonal materials are a strength; apart from Brixham fish most are sourced locally, the roll call taking in a starter of scallops with parnsip purée and black pudding, followed perhaps by roast rump of honey-crusted lamb with a casserole of flageolet beans. Dishes are never less than interesting and the food relies on careful execution rather than surprises for its impact. Presentation is well crafted, and vertical arrangements are not only the norm, they seem to have a point: there are interesting bits to discover as a starter of crab meat layered with bacon and cabbage is dismantled, likewise in a main course of 'succulently underdone' partridge breast with chicken livers and blueberries sitting on a potato galette.

Desserts are no less appealing. Poached fig clafoutis is paired with a thyme ice cream, and a creamy aniseed parfait on a chocolate base is surrounded by plums and sculpted pear flesh in a red wine reduction. Lunch is considered a bargain, taking in smoked salmon with an oyster fritter, pigeon breast with shiitake mushroom sauce, and almond chocolate tart for one visitor. Service is polite, natural and unstuffy, and wines are intelligently chosen and sensibly priced, starting with eight house wines under £17 (£3.80 a glass).

CHEF: Stephen Shore PROPRIETORS: Stephen and Victoria Shore OPEN: Mon to Sat 12 to 2, 6 to 9.30 (10 Sat) CLOSED: 2 weeks Jan, bank hols (exc Good Friday) MEALS: alc D (main courses £16 to £18). Set L £12 (2 courses) to £16, Set D 6 to 7 £12 (2 courses) to £23 SERVICE: not inc CARDS: Amex, Delta, Diners, MasterCard, Switch, Visa DETAILS: 30 seats. Private parties: 20 main room, 8 and 8 private rooms. Vegetarian menu available with notice. No children under 8. No smoking in dining room. Music

▲ Queensberry Hotel, Olive Tree

Russel Street, Bath BA1 2QF
TEL: (01225) 447928 FAX: (01225) 446065 — COOKING **4**
EMAIL: reservations@batholivetree.com — MODERN BRITISH-PLUS
WEB SITE: www.batholivetree.com — £27–£59

The building is 'very Bath, very Georgian', and rooms are calmly decorated, with a plethora of Middle Eastern rugs to absorb the sound, and contemporary sketches and watercolours on the walls. The menu plays safe enough so as not to offend the large number of overseas visitors the hotel attracts, yet it also finds room for slightly more unusual items to boost local interest: provençale fish soup comes with the usual trimmings, while Aberdeen Angus fillet is served with roast yam and salsa verde. Timings tend to be rather conservative, rendering fish rather dry at inspection, although there is nothing wrong with the ideas: roast sea bass with vanilla risotto, for example, or seafood brochette with coriander-flecked couscous.

Perhaps the kitchen is happier with more leisurely cooking, because slow-roast belly of organic pork is a star dish, the meat silky textured and infused with star anise, topped with a lava-like eruption of bright green, partly mashed peas. Desserts include a few fruit-based items, from a fresh, revivifying gratin of blood oranges and blueberries to more substantial pineapple fritters with ginger ice cream. Service is French and enthusiastic, and well-chosen bottles bring colour, as well as great value, to the wine list. France is refreshingly a provider of many of the bottlings under £15, and a useful section of recommendations offers bins from newly exciting Portuguese and French regions.

CHEFS: Jason Horne and Rachel Milsom PROPRIETORS: Stephen and Penny Ross OPEN: Mon to Sat L 12 to 2, all week D 6.45 to 10 CLOSED: 4 days Christmas MEALS: alc (main courses £12.50 to £19). Set L £13.50 (2 courses) to £15.50, Set D Sun to Fri £26 SERVICE: not inc CARDS: Delta, MasterCard, Switch, Visa DETAILS: 70 seats. Private parties: 50 main room, 25 private room. Vegetarian meals. Children's helpings. No smoking in dining room. Wheelchair access (not WC). Occasional music. Air-conditioned ACCOMMODATION: 29 rooms, all with bath/shower. TV. Phone. B&B £90 to £210. Rooms for disabled. Baby facilities (*The Which? Hotel Guide*)

Richmond Arms £

7 Richmond Place, Lansdown, Bath BA1 5PZ — COOKING **2**
TEL: (01225) 316725 — FUSION
£18–£32

Despite their reputation for food, the Cunninghams strive to maintain the pubbiness of their small hostelry in a Georgian terrace. Drinkers and diners mingle in the informal bar, where clean yellow walls and polished floorboards give the ambience a welcome lightness; weather permitting, the south-facing garden is also popular. A good-value menu offers around six choices per course, the cooking's Far-Eastern ideas often combining with more homely ones: among them Malaysian chicken laksa, home-smoked duck breast salad with hot sweet-and-sour peanut sauce, and braised lamb shank with sun-dried tomato sauce. There may even be pan-fried kangaroo steak with chilli mayonnaise, and, among desserts, blueberry iced terrine with coconut and rum coulis. A small wine selection is listed on blackboards behind the bar; most bottles are under £10, and seven come by the glass from £1.75.

CHEF: Marney Cunningham PROPRIETORS: John and Marney Cunningham OPEN: Tue to Sun L 12 to 2, Tue to Sat D 6 to 8.30 (9 Fri and Sat) CLOSED: 25 Dec to 2 Jan MEALS: alc (main courses L £4 to £5.50, D £7.50 to £10.50) SERVICE: not inc CARDS: none DETAILS: 25 seats. 20 seats outside. Private parties: 20 main room. Vegetarian meals. No children under 14. Occasional music

▲ Royal Crescent, Pimpernel's

16 Royal Crescent, Bath BA1 2LS
TEL: (01225) 823333 FAX: (01225) 339401 — COOKING **5**
EMAIL: reservations@royalcrescent.co.uk — FUSION
WEB SITE: www.royalcrescent.co.uk — £41–£95

Since the hotel is bang in the middle of the Royal Crescent, there is perhaps no need for a sign: not even a tiny nameplate advertises its presence. At the back is a secluded garden, and beyond that the Dower House, where Pimpernel's welcomes with lots of mirrors, large murals of classical pastoral scenes, and piped 'cocktail trio' music. Given the setting, one might expect a traditional country-house style of cooking, but there are no waves of 'extras', and, thanks to a significant Asian input, Steven Blake's food is much more inventive and characterful than the norm.

First-class raw materials and a high level of technical skill are what drive the kitchen, be it in a Japanese-inspired starter of just-seared, highly peppered blue-fin tuna with a tempura of vegetables ('the batter couldn't have been fresher or lighter') and a peanut-flavoured orange miso dressing, or in a more Western dish of honeyed Trelough duck prepared two ways: the breast pink and juicy, the boneless leg turned into confit, its skin parked on top like a giant crisp. Dishes are attractively arranged on elegant plates and ceramics, making the most of their contrasting colours.

Intense flavours continue into desserts of, for example, a cherry soufflé, served with small scoops of vanilla ice cream and two pitted cherries encased in hard spun sugar, both resting in a light, eggy biscuit basket. Although lunch is a set price, supplements can soon bump it up. Vegetarians get their own carte, meals are well paced and staff are plentiful, although service is routine and co-ordination is not a strong point. The wine list majors on prestige bottles at high prices – even house wine is over £20 – but there is a decent choice by the glass.

CHEF: Steven Blake PROPRIETOR: Cliveden Limited OPEN: all week 12.30 to 2, 7 to 10 MEALS: alc D (main courses £18 to £35). Set L £18 (2 courses) to £25 SERVICE: not inc CARDS: Amex, Delta, Diners, MasterCard, Switch, Visa DETAILS: 60 seats. 45 seats outside. Private parties: 40 main room, 10 private room. Car park. Vegetarian meals. Children's helpings. No smoking in dining room. Wheelchair access (not WC). Occasional music. Air-conditioned ACCOMMODATION: 45 rooms, all with bath/shower. Room prices approx £220 and higher. TV. Phone. Rooms for disabled. Baby facilities (*The Which? Hotel Guide*)

BEAMINSTER Dorset **map 2**

▲ Bridge House

3 Prout Bridge, Beaminster DT8 3AY
TEL: (01308) 862200 FAX: (01308) 863700
EMAIL: enquiries@bridge-house.co.uk
WEB SITE: www.bridge-house.co.uk

COOKING **1**
MODERN BRITISH
£23–£45

Old and new blend seamlessly together in this comfortable country hotel, parts of which date from the thirteenth century. More recent additions include the light, wood-panelled dining room, which is of Georgian origin, and those staying the night can enjoy breakfast in the pretty, modern conservatory overlooking the garden. The cooking likewise is a blend of old-fashioned classics, such as grilled lemon sole with lemon and parsley butter, and more modern ideas, like gurnard fillet on a bed of herbed couscous with citrus sauce, teriyaki-style pork tenderloin, or smoked chicken salad with crispy bacon, quails' eggs and sweet chilli dressing. Vegetarians have their own menu, typically featuring mushroom risotto, or vegetable tempura, while desserts might include lemon tart, or crème brûlée. Eleven house wines from around £11 kick off a list that remains fairly priced throughout.

CHEF: Linda Paget PROPRIETOR: Peter Pinkster OPEN: all week 12 to 2, 7 to 9 CLOSED: 27 to 31 Dec MEALS: Set L £10.25 (2 courses) to £14.25, Set D £25.50 (2 courses) to £28.50 SERVICE: not inc, CARDS: Amex, Delta, Diners, MasterCard, Switch, Visa DETAILS: 46 seats. 15 seats outside. Private parties: 46 main room, 20 private room. Car park. Vegetarian meals. Children's helpings. No smoking in dining room. No music ACCOMMODATION: 14 rooms, all with bath/shower. TV. Phone. B&B £50 to £128. Baby facilities (*The Which? Hotel Guide*)

BEESTON Nottinghamshire **map 5**

La Toque

61 Wollaton Road, Beeston, COOKING **3**
Nottingham NG9 2NG FRENCH
TEL: (0115) 922 2268 FAX: (0115) 922 7979 £35–£47

Mattias Karlsson takes a determinedly French approach to both décor and food, choosing to write the menu in two languages when one would quite probably suffice. Perhaps it is meant to reflect the ambition of his cooking: creamy lobster soup arrives under a pastry lid for example, and poached halibut comes with goats'-cheese tortellini and a langoustine sauce. Materials are well selected, prepared and cooked, and the food aims for classical heights: expect to find lamb cutlets wrapped in crépinette, served with château potatoes and confit garlic. As an alternative to a dessert such as roast pineapple with rum butter sauce and pistachio nuts, consider warm Brie de Meaux filled with truffle. Extras include a small starter cup of soup, a pre-dessert sorbet, and petits fours to finish, and service (for which an 'optional' 10 per cent charge has now been added) is prompt, charming, courteous and helpful. Some two dozen varied wines are rated for body or sweetness, and start with house French at £12 (£3 a glass).

CHEF/PROPRIETOR: Mattias Karlsson OPEN: all week L 12 to 2.30, Mon to Sat D 6.45 to 10.30 CLOSED: 26 to 30 Dec and bank holidays MEALS: alc (main courses £13.50 to £15.00) SERVICE: 10% (optional), card slips closed CARDS: Delta, Diners, MasterCard, Switch, Visa DETAILS: 45 seats. Private parties: 30 main room, 20 private room. Small car park. Vegetarian meals. No children under 10. No smoking in 1 dining room. Music (£5)

BIRCH VALE Derbyshire **map 8**

▲ Waltzing Weasel

New Mills Road, Birch Vale SK22 1BT
TEL/FAX: (01663) 743402
EMAIL: w-weasel@zen.co.uk COOKING **2**
WEB SITE: www.w-weasel.co.uk ANGLO-EUROPEAN
on A6015, ½m W of Hayfield £26–£43

Old furniture, log fires and a bar for drinks and snacks give this stone-built country inn the feel of a pub. A small dining room overlooking the hills serves à la carte lunches and set-price dinners with a cheerily European thrust, from pizzas, via pollo al chilindron, to stifado. A daily soup (creamy celeriac for one visitor) may precede duck with cherries or a gamey jugged hare. Vegetarians get more than token recognition, with a tarte provençale or vegetable crêpe, and a board lists the fish of the day and a 'peasant' stew or casserole. Finish with a sweet, gooey treacle tart with custard, or a fine Welsh rarebit. Portions seem large, perhaps because plates are small. A serviceable wine list, mostly under £20, starts with house French at £11.95.

CHEFS: Tracey Young and Barbara Ruff PROPRIETORS: Michael and Linda Atkinson OPEN: all week 12 to 2, 7 to 9 (8.30 Sun) MEALS: alc (main courses £8.50 to £13). Set D £22.50 (2 courses) to £26.50. Bar menu available SERVICE: not inc, card slips closed CARDS: Amex, Delta, MasterCard, Switch, Visa DETAILS: 80 seats. 20 seats outside. Private parties: 35 main room. Car park. Vegetarian meals. No children under 5. Children's helpings. No smoking in dining room. Wheelchair access (not WC). No music. Air-conditioned ACCOMMODATION: 8 rooms, all with bath/shower. TV. Phone. B&B £45 to £105 (*The Which? Hotel Guide*)

BIRKENHEAD Merseyside map 8

Beadles

15 Rose Mount, Oxton, Birkenhead CH43 5SG COOKING **2**
TEL: (0151) 653 9010 MODERN EUROPEAN
£17–£44

This may not be the most fashionable venue on Merseyside – don't expect too much pizazz in the single art-furnished room stretching from entrance to kitchen – but it is the Wirral's best shot at serious eating. The generally southern European tilt takes in lots of garlic and tomatoes, a Basque casserole of rabbit, and a duck gizzard salad, as well as a more universal best end of lamb with mushrooms, and guinea fowl casserole with smoked bacon and red wine sauce. Mellanie Dixon-Peel delivers generally good home cooking, and although it can suffer from a lack of sharpness in execution she has also delivered a light, tasty, roasted red pepper mousse with a white butter sauce at inspection, and a fine individual plum custard tart with a fresh plum coulis. Set menus offer good value, Richard Peel's personal approach is attentive and informative (he spells out all the dishes in detail), and a tiny wine list barely shows its head above the £20 parapet.

CHEF: Mellanie Dixon-Peel PROPRIETORS: Mellanie and Richard Peel OPEN: Tue to Fri L 12 to 2, Tue to Sat D 6.30 (7 Sat) to 9.30 MEALS: alc (main courses L £5 to £8, D £14 to £15.50). Set L Tue to Fri 12 to 2 £6.95 (2 courses), Set D Tue to Fri £12.95 (2 courses) to £14.95 SERVICE: not inc, 10% for parties of 8 or more CARDS: Delta, MasterCard, Switch, Visa DETAILS: 32 seats. Private parties: 35 main room. Vegetarian meals. Children's helpings. No children under 7. Wheelchair access (not WC). Music (£5)

BIRMINGHAM West Midlands map 5

Bank

4 Brindleyplace, B1 2JB
TEL: (0121) 633 4466 FAX: (0121) 633 4465 COOKING **3**
EMAIL: birmres@bankrestaurants.com MODERN EUROPEAN
WEB SITE: www.bankrestaurants.com £21–£65

Bank is every inch a modern urban brasserie, from the near-anonymity of its dark glass frontage to the Mao-style suits worn by keen-to-please front-of-house staff. Pictures on the backs of menus and wine list may evoke various bygone eras, but what's on the front is pure turn-of-the-century (this one). After starters of salt cod fritters with lemon mayonnaise, or seared Thai tuna, come pasta and risotto options, crustacea, vegetarian choices, and then fish such as chargrilled marlin with ratatouille, and meats like duck leg confit with red cabbage and salsa verde. Monkfish wrapped in bacon on mashed potato is appreciated, as is ribeye steak and chips. Desserts encompass banoffi pie with lime sorbet, and baked cheesecake with blueberry compote. The wine list, arranged by colour and style (with some pricier 'Bank Cellar' bottles at the end), ranges from Guigal's 1994 Côte-Rôtie La Turque for £235 (only one bottle available) to house vins de pays (Chardonnay and Merlot) at £10.90, or £2.75 a glass.

CHEF: David Colcombe PROPRIETOR: Bank Restaurant Group Plc OPEN: Mon to Sat L 12 (11 Sat) to 3, Mon to Sat D 5.30 to 11 (11.30 Fri and Sat), Sun 11 to 9.30 MEALS: alc (main courses £8.50 to £17). Set L and D 5.30 to 7 and 10 to 11 £9.95 (2 courses) to £12.50. Bar menu, Sat and Sun brunch available SERVICE: 10% (optional), card slips closed CARDS: Amex, Delta, Diners, MasterCard, Switch, Visa DETAILS: 140 seats. 50 seats outside. Private parties: 100 main room, 100 private rooms. Vegetarian meals. Children's helpings. No-smoking area. Wheelchair access (also WC). Occasional music. Air-conditioned (£5)

▲ Birmingham Marriot, Sir Edward Elgar

12 Hagley Road, Five Ways, Birmingham B16 8SJ
TEL: (0121) 452 1144 FAX: (0121) 452 7012 — COOKING **5**
EMAIL: reservations@birmingham.whitbread.com — FRENCH/MEDITERRANEAN
WEB SITE: www.marriotthotels.com/bhxbh — £31–£66

This swanky hotel, by a busy road junction, used to be known as the Swallow, but despite the name change it is business as usual in the sumptuous restaurant. The décor is indulgently comfortable – chinoiserie fabric wall-coverings, vast oil paintings, plush French-style seating and well-spaced, accommodating tables – staff are numerous and well drilled, and a piano-player entertains diners with easy-listening favourites. In this setting it comes as no surprise to find an abundance of luxury ingredients, with prices to match, though ladies will be spared blushes due to the quaint practice of giving them an unpriced version of the menu.

Ian Mansfield's accomplished cooking is based on classic French technique but shows more modern sensibilities, encompassing lively variations on timeworn themes, and up-to-the-minute turns: on the one hand, roast Brecon venison on red cabbage with orange and bitter chocolate sauce; on the other, ravioli of goats' cheese poached in chicken bouillon with leeks, prunes and marjoram. Desserts, along similar lines, range from warm bread-and-butter pudding with vanilla sauce to a gratin of rhubarb and strawberries with ginger and saffron ice cream. A few extra bottles have been introduced at the lower end of the scale on the wine list, but on the whole prices remain unforgiving to those on a tight budget. House wines come in at £13.50.

CHEF: Ian Mansfield PROPRIETOR: Whitbread Hotel Co OPEN: Sun L 12.30 to 2.30, Tue to Sun D 7 to 10 MEALS: alc D (main courses £16 to £22). Set L £21.50, Set D £32.50 to £36.50 SERVICE: not inc CARDS: Amex, Delta, Diners, MasterCard, Switch, Visa DETAILS: 70 seats. Private parties: 20 main room, 5 to 20 private rooms. Car park. Vegetarian meals. Children's helpings. No smoking in 1 dining room. Wheelchair access (also WC). Music. Air-conditioned ACCOMMODATION: 98 rooms, all with bath/shower. TV. Phone. Room only £99 to £195. Rooms for disabled. Baby facilities. Swimming pool (*The Which? Hotel Guide*) (£5)

Chung Ying £

16–18 Wrottesley Street, Birmingham B5 4RT — COOKING **1**
TEL: (0121) 622 5669 FAX: (0121) 666 7051 — CHINESE
WEB SITE: www.chungying.co.uk — £25–£62

For 20 years this restaurant has plied its trade a stone's throw from the Hippodrome Theatre. The décor is described by the management as 'homely' and the cooking as 'traditional Cantonese – this is how the people of Hong Kong eat'. A huge à la carte offers over 300 dishes; many are predictable, but close perusal reveals a few unexpected items such as steamed fish ball dumplings, and pork and prawn noodle rolls, both among the dim sum. Main dishes include deep-fried stuffed duck, with or without crab meat sauce, and ox tripe is a favoured ingredient. Casseroles run to stewed goose web with mushrooms (anyone who has been kicked by a goose knows there's plenty of meat in those feet). Desserts include various fritters and ice creams, and house wines are £11, with most of the rest well below £20.

CHEF: T. C. Tsang PROPRIETOR: Siu Chung Wong OPEN: all week noon to midnight (10.30 Sun) CLOSED: 25 Dec MEALS: alc (main courses £6 to £15). Set L and D from £28 for 2 people, to £108 for 6 people SERVICE: not inc, card slips closed CARDS: Amex, Delta, Diners, MasterCard, Switch, Visa DETAILS: 250 seats. Private parties: 120 main room. Vegetarian meals. Wheelchair access (not WC). Music. Air-conditioned

▲ Hotel du Vin & Bistro 🍷

NEW ENTRY

Church Street, Birmingham B3 2NR
TEL: (0121) 236 0559 — COOKING **3**
EMAIL: reservations@birmingham.hotelduvin.com — MODERN EUROPEAN
WEB SITE: www.hotelduvin.com — £38–£54

The largest and latest in this townhouse chain (see Bristol, Tunbridge Wells and Winchester entries) is a stylish and individual conversion of a former Victorian eye hospital. The charming and informal bistro has handsome sash windows, polished floorboards and small wooden tables and chairs; its ochre walls sport wine prints and memorabilia, and empty bottles adorn every windowsill. Results from the interest-laden, daily-changing menu can be variable, but a terrine of tuna escabèche with saffron vinaigrette is a well-reported starter; or try seared scallops with pickled ginger and crispy pancetta. Meat dishes might include marinated rump of lamb with couscous and sauce ravigote, or a (less successful) braised rabbit leg and wild mushroom fricassee.

Desserts run from crème brûlée to a highly praised cherry clafoutis with cherry coulis. French sticks come with breadboard and knife, and service by a young European team is polite and enthusiastic. In common with other branches, wine plays an important part in proceedings, and the list sweeps knowledgeably through fine French domaines, revels in California and Australia, and even gives Austria an airing. Listings are unordered within countries, which makes it time-consuming to explore, and prices don't give anything away, but the quality is undisputed. House wines start at £11.50.

CHEF: Eddie Grey PROPRIETOR: Hotel du Vin Ltd OPEN: all week 12 to 2, 6 to 10 MEALS: alc (not Sun L; main courses £10.50 to £15). Set L Sun £22.50 SERVICE: not inc CARDS: Amex, Delta, Diners, MasterCard, Switch, Visa DETAILS: 95 seats. Private parties: 18 to 80 private rooms. Vegetarian meals. Children's helpings. No cigars/pipes in dining room. Wheelchair access(also WC). No music ACCOMMODATION: 66 rooms, all with bath/shower. TV. Room only £110 to £395. Rooms for disabled. Baby facilities (book in advance) (*The Which? Hotel Guide*)

Le Petit Blanc

9 Brindley Place, Birmingham B1 2HS — COOKING **4**
TEL: (0121) 633 7333 FAX: (0121) 633 7444 — MODERN FRENCH
WEB SITE: www.petit-blanc.com — £24–£52

A modern restaurant with big windows and well-spaced tables, Petit Blanc appears to satisfy on several levels, combining a pleasant ambience with well-executed food, cheerful, friendly service and good value in a way that charms most reporters. While following the principles, and producing dishes, common to all branches (see entries in Cheltenham, Manchester and Oxford), it is Walter Blakemore's generally consistent delivery that keeps it afloat. He deals in dishes with an indisputably French background, such as fish soup with rouille, as well as a range of others designed with broader appeal: tomato and feta salad, black pudding with apple and celeriac purée, and deep-fried crab cake. Quality materials are noted, flavours and saucing complimented, and staples such as confit duck with red cabbage and mash well rendered.

There are plenty of options for those in need of a snack or a quick meal, and a special menu for under-11s, while the main menu balances lighter dishes of scrambled egg and smoked salmon, or ricotta and spinach ravioli, against more substantial braised shank of lamb, or grilled Scottish ribeye with frites and béarnaise. Lemon tart with raspberry ice cream has won praise, and the choice might also include tiramisù and a classic tarte Tatin. Wines are designed to suit the circumstances: a short list (around half of them under £20) arranged by grape variety, starting with southern French house red and white at £11.

CHEF: Walter Blakemore PROPRIETOR: Raymond Blanc OPEN: all week 11.30 to 3, 6 to 11 CLOSED: 25 Dec MEALS: alc (main courses £8.50 to £16). Set L and D 5.30 to 7 £12.50 (2 courses) to £15 SERVICE: not inc, 10% for parties of 8 or more CARDS: Amex, Delta, Diners, MasterCard, Switch, Visa DETAILS: 154 seats. 40 seats outside. Private parties: 200 main room, 26 private room. Vegetarian meals. Children's helpings. No smoking in 1 dining room. Wheelchair access (also WC). Music. Air-conditioned (£5)

La Toque d'Or

NEW ENTRY

27 Warstone Lane, Hockley,
Birmingham B18 6JQ — COOKING **3**
TEL/FAX: (0121) 233 3655 — FRENCH
WEB SITE: www.latoquedor.co.uk — £26–£61

Readers may remember Didier Philipot from his five years at nearby Brockencote Hall at Chaddesley Corbett. Shortly after the last edition of the Guide appeared he took over the premises formerly inhabited by Restaurant Gilmore, intending to oversee a more informal setup. That could hardly be easier, given the grandeur of Brockencote and this relaxed, brick-walled dining room, complete with metal girders, in the city's jewellery quarter. Despite the modest surroundings, Didier Philipot is not afraid to be ambitious and inventive, turning out a courgette flower filled with chicken and chive mousse, accompanied by lamb sweetbreads, and a dish of seared tuna served with a creamy 'marmalade' of grey mullet spiked with pine nuts. A blackboard lists a few additional seasonal or luxurious dishes at a supplement.

The kitchen is fired by genuine effort, and individual components are well rendered, even if combinations do not always achieve the desired cohesion. Among successes have been tender, flavourful roast leg of lamb, served with diced provençale vegetables, a fine pistachio soufflé with strong-tasting cocoa ice cream, and an innovative mille-feuille filled with lemon cream, accompanied by a jasmine tea and basil granita. French service tries hard to make everything enjoyable, and two French house wines, at £12.50, open the short wine list.

CHEF: Didier Philipot PROPRIETOR: SSPG Consulting Ltd OPEN: Tue to Fri L 12.30 to 2, Tue to Sat D 7 to 9.30 CLOSED: 10 days Christmas to New Year, 1 week Easter, first 2 weeks Aug MEALS: Set L £12.50 (2 courses) to £15.50, Set D £23.50 SERVICE: not inc CARDS: Amex, Delta, MasterCard, Switch, Visa DETAILS: 32 seats. Private parties: 40 main room. Vegetarian meals. Children's helpings. Wheelchair access (also WC). Music. Air-conditioned

BISHOP'S WALTHAM Hampshire map 2

Peppers

NEW ENTRY

The Square, Bishop's Waltham SO32 1AR
TEL: (01489) 891515 FAX: (01489) 891577

COOKING **4**
MODERN EUROPEAN
£24–£50

This new entrant has occupied a corner site in the town's main square since autumn 2000. The Ruthven-Stuarts (he was previously chef at the Old House in nearby Wickham, see entry) have created an unstuffy feel, with style, simplicity and comfort as the watchwords. The ground floor contains a dining room and handsome bar with wide wooden stairs leading to the main dining room, which has glossy white woodwork and two fireplaces. The menu is a mix of old favourites (twice-cooked cheese soufflé, provençale fish soup with aïoli) and up-to-the-minute dishes, attractively prepared and plated.

Meals might start with a fine crispy duck confit with bacon and lentil salad dressed with soy, honey and ginger, or a tartlet of caramelised onion with melted goats' cheese. Main courses of mahogany-varnished coq au vin, or a more daring fricassée of mixed fish with a coriander sauce and couscous have been appreciated, along with suitably rich desserts and strong coffee. Service is 'friendly, efficient and knowledgeable.' The brief but imaginative wine list is very sensibly priced, starting at £10.75 (white) or £11.50 (red), and includes a 'cellar selection' for those wanting to splash out.

CHEF: Nicholas Ruthven-Stuart PROPRIETORS: Nicholas and Christina Ruthven-Stuart OPEN: Tue to Sat 12 to 2.15, 7 to 9.45 CLOSED: first 2 weeks Jan, last week Aug MEALS: alc (main courses £9 to £16). Set L £10 (2 courses) to £15 SERVICE: not inc, card slips closed CARDS: Delta, MasterCard, Switch, Visa DETAILS: 55 seats. Private parties: 30 main room, 16 private room. Vegetarian meals. Children's helpings. No smoking in 1 dining room. Wheelchair access (also WC). Occasional music

BLACKPOOL Lancashire map 8

September Brasserie

15–17 Queen Street, Blackpool FY1 1NL
TEL: (01253) 623282 FAX: (01253) 299455

COOKING 3
MODERN BRITISH
£23–£45

It is fair to say that Blackpool would not be the first stop-off on any gastronome's itinerary, but here, within sight of the candyfloss and novelty rock on the Golden Mile, Michael Golowicz offers inventive contemporary cooking in a down-to-earth setting. Short, daily-changing, fixed-price menus are where the value lies, and dishes sound intriguing. Lemon sole fillets are stuffed with salmon and sorrel, while a blue version of Lancashire cheese is made into a terrine to be served with baby spinach and plum tomatoes. Main courses might run to loin of Australian wild boar with creamed mushrooms and buckwheat, or, in lighter mode, halibut garnished with tapénade and sweet-and-sour leeks. There may even be a rendition of cassoulet made, properly enough, with duck and Toulouse sausage. Finish with sticky toffee pudding, white chocolate bavarois, or lemon tart. Service combines efficiency and good cheer. A clearly presented wine list offers value and flavour from all over the vinous globe, with prices starting at £14.75.

CHEF/PROPRIETOR: Michael Golowicz OPEN: Tue to Sat 12 to 2, 7 to 9.30 (pre- and post-theatre D by arrangement) CLOSED: 2 weeks summer, 2 weeks winter MEALS: alc (main courses L £6 to £10, D £11 to £14.50). Set D £16.95 (2 courses) to £19.95 SERVICE: not inc, 10% for parties of 6 or more CARDS: Amex, Delta, Diners, MasterCard, Switch, Visa DETAILS: 40 seats. Private parties: 35 main room. Vegetarian meals. Children's helpings. Music (£5)

BLAKENEY Norfolk map 6

▲ White Horse Hotel

4 High Street, Blakeney NR25 7AL
TEL: (01263) 740574 FAX: (01263) 741303
off A149 between Cley and Morston

COOKING 2
GLOBAL FUSION
£27–£43

The restaurant at the White Horse is, appropriately enough, in the former stables, which overlook a walled garden and the old courtyard. Chris Hyde runs a kitchen proud to use local supply lines: all the shellfish and much of the fish come from fishermen along the coast, game is from local estates and so is asparagus in season. Expect these raw materials to turn up in the form of a warm terrine of scallops with leeks, grilled halibut with rocket and chard salad, or loin of venison on braised red cabbage with a red wine sauce. Finish things off in creamy style with buttermilk pudding on plum compote, or iced caramel and orange parfait. A traditionally French-led wine list does some justice to the New World too, the generally modest prices starting at £10.95.

CHEF: Chris Hyde PROPRIETORS: Daniel Rees and Sue Catt OPEN: Tue to Sat and bank hol Sun D only 7 to 9 CLOSED: 7 to 21 Jan MEALS: alc (main courses £9 to £15). Bar menu available SERVICE: not inc CARDS: Amex, Delta, MasterCard, Switch, Visa DETAILS: 100 seats. 60 seats outside. Private parties: 40 main room. Car park. Vegetarian meals. Children's helpings. No smoking in dining room. Wheelchair access (not WC). Occasional music ACCOMMODATION: 10 rooms, all with bath/shower. TV. Phone. B&B £30 to £90. Baby facilities

BOLTON ABBEY North Yorkshire map 9

▲ Devonshire Arms, Burlington Restaurant

Bolton Abbey BD23 6AJ
TEL: (01756) 710441 FAX: (01756) 710564
EMAIL: sales@thedevonshirearms.co.uk
WEB SITE: www.thedevonshirearms.co.uk
at junction of A59 and B6160, 5m NW of Ilkley

COOKING **6**
MODERN BRITISH
£30–£69

The Bolton estate (in Devonshire hands for 250 years) occupies one of the most attractive spots in the Dales, and the Burlington restaurant, part of a large, luxurious country-house hotel, is smartly set in traditional style, with a small conservatory extension. Although Steve Williams can be a bold chef, serving roast hare with pear boulangère and a chocolate and Armagnac sauce, for example, he offers more traditional options too: three fat scallops (nutty outside, soft within) on potato blini with a well-dressed salad of frisée and smoked bacon.

Given the prices, some luxuries might be expected: a trio of foie gras, followed perhaps by pan-fried quail, its crisp legs arranged on celeriac fondant, the stock-based sauce scattered with wild mushrooms and truffle shavings. Flavours are well judged, dishes balanced, and timing and seasoning spot on, as in a tender, pink, herb-crusted chump of lamb on a bed of spinach and sweet garlic purée in a rosemary-infused stock reduction garnished with sweetbreads. Desserts steer clear of the icky-sticky country-house norm, but may include an indulgent iced prune and armagnac parfait formed into a tower, standing on a syrup-soaked disc of cake, served with prune compote and first-class amaretti biscuits.

A brasserie and functions – from wedding receptions to 'murder weekends' (not related, one hopes) – can strain both kitchen and service at busy times, although welcoming staff generally relate well to guests. Wines aim high – with stars from France, Italy and beyond, like the interesting mature range from Western Australia's Mosswood – but, barring some relief in Italy and the southern hemisphere, there is little for modest spenders. House Spanish is £15.

CHEF: Steve Williams PROPRIETOR: The Duke and Duchess Of Devonshire OPEN: Sun L 12 to 2.30, all week D 7 to 10 MEALS: Set L Sun £19.95, Set D £45 SERVICE: not inc, card slips closed CARDS: Amex, Delta, Diners, MasterCard, Switch, Visa DETAILS: 70 seats. Private parties: 90 main room, 10 to 30 private rooms. Car park. Vegetarian meals. Children's helpings. No smoking in dining room. Wheelchair access (not WC). No music ACCOMMODATION: 41 rooms, all with bath/shower. TV. Phone. D,B&B £125 to £325. Rooms for disabled. Swimming pool. Fishing (*The Which? Hotel Guide*)

BOROUGHBRIDGE North Yorkshire map 9

Dining Room

NEW ENTRY

20 St James Square, Boroughbridge YO51 9AR
TEL/FAX: (01423) 326426
EMAIL: lisaastley@virgin.net

COOKING **4**
MODERN BRITISH
£23–£47

This new establishment, overlooking St James Square in the centre of the town, has a relaxing, contemporary feel. Upstairs is a huge lounge with dark wooden floors, bookcases, sofas and a welcoming fire; downstairs the dining room itself is elegant and restrained, with well-spaced tables, white napkins and sparkling glassware. Lisa Astley ably looks after front-of-house ('she really cares about giving diners the best experience she can'), while husband Chris mans the stoves; some readers may remember him from his days at Swinside Lodge in Keswick.

The menu is suitably contemporary, with starters such as warm salad of black pudding with onion marmalade and pancetta, and main courses of Gressingham duck, crisp outside, tender within, complemented by damson chutney, or a well-hung, tender chargrilled fillet of beef with port and truffle sauce. Portions are generous, but desserts are worth saving room for: rich iced blackcurrant parfait in its own coulis has received the thumbs-up, or perhaps choose warm prune and Armagnac frangipane tart with crème Chantilly. The annotated wine list starts with a lively New World house selection from £11.50. Thereafter French classics mix with the new wave at reasonable prices, and groupings of finer wines offer the likes of Corton Charlemagne or Eileen Hardy Shiraz from Australia.

CHEF: Christopher Astley PROPRIETORS: Christopher and Lisa Astley OPEN: Tue to Sun L 12 to 2 (2.30 Sun), Tue to Sat D 6.30 to 9.30 MEALS: alc (main courses £7 to £16). Set L Tue to Sat £10.50 (2 courses), Set L Sun £12.95, Set D £19.95 (2 courses) to £25 SERVICE: not inc, card slips closed CARDS: Delta, MasterCard, Switch, Visa DETAILS: 26 seats. Private parties: 32 main room. Vegetarian meals. Children's helpings. No smoking in dining room. Wheelchair access (not WC). Music (£5)

BOSTON SPA West Yorkshire **map 9**

Spice Box

152 High Street, Boston Spa LS23 6BW — COOKING **4**
TEL: (01937) 842558 FAX: (01937) 849955 — MODERN BRITISH-PLUS
WEB SITE: www.spiceboxrestaurant.co.uk — £25–£39

In bucolic, A1-bypassed Boston Spa there was once a chemist's shop. The small, neat drawers that held emetics and aperients still line the walls and, together with candlelit table settings, create an intimate-feel. The place seems hugely popular, so booking is advised. Karl Mainey has worked in Europe and Australia, absorbing pan-Asian seasonings and judiciously inventive fish cookery in particular. Red bream is steamed en papillote with lemon, tarragon and sweet wine, salmon slow-cooked with star anise and served with asparagus and a red-wine risotto, or there is a bouillabaisse-style medley of fish cooked with tomatoes and thyme.

Meats show the same imagination, whether slow-roasted lamb confit stuffed with oranges, apricots and sweet potato, or pork fillet sauced with brandy, mascarpone and green peppercorns. Starters stay relatively simple – crab tian, say, or duck terrine with walnut toast – and puddings include old English favourites: brandy-snap filled with lemon posset, or sticky ginger cake with toffee sauce. Cheeses are noteworthy too. Interesting wines, many from the New World, range from France to Patagonia and from £10.50 up to around £40. Another branch has opened in Harrogate.

CHEF: Karl Mainey PROPRIETORS: Karl and Amanda Mainey OPEN: Tue to Sat L 12 to 2, Mon to Sat D 6.45 to 10 CLOSED: 26 Dec to 2 Jan MEALS: alc (main courses £9 to £13.50). Set L £7.95 (2 courses). Set L and D £16.95 SERVICE: not inc CARDS: Amex, Delta, MasterCard, Switch, Visa DETAILS: 57 seats. Private parties: 57 main room. Vegetarian meals. Children's helpings. No smoking in dining room. Wheelchair access (not WC). No music

BOUGHTON LEES Kent **map 3**

▲ Eastwell Manor

Eastwell Park, Boughton Lees TN25 4HR
TEL: (01233) 213000 FAX: (01233) 635530
EMAIL: eastwell@btinternet.com
WEB SITE: www.eastwellmanor.co.uk
on A251, 3m N of Ashford

COOKING **3**
ANGLO-FRENCH
£27–£85

A long drive and immaculate grounds set up expectations that the stone floors, dark wood panelling, tapestries and log fires confirm: here is a seriously ancient and well-cared-for building of character. Aidan McCormack's materials tend towards the luxury end of the scale, evident in the choice of fish, for example: turbot, Dover sole and sea bass. His menus combine relatively simple and classic ideas – such as cannon of lamb with confit garlic and rosemary jus, or a thick and truffley risotto brimful of different types of wild fungus – with more enterprising ones, such as seared scallops with chorizo tortellini, or braised suckling pig with Chinese five-spice and honey.

The kitchen is a busy one, turning out terrines of creamy-textured chicken and mango, or one combining oxtail, foie gras and cabbage, as well as an artfully constructed dessert of milk chocolate mousse with mango sorbet, sitting on a chocolate chequerboard with alternating squares of chocolate and mango sauce. Attentive staff still lift domes as they present main courses. Classy French wines dominate the list (choice elsewhere is uneven), which opens with a handful of less expensive house recommendations, from £13, and wines by the glass, from £4.

CHEF: Aidan McCormack PROPRIETORS: Turrloo and Jackie Parrett OPEN: all week 12 to 2.30 (3.30 Sun), 7 to 10 MEALS: alc (main courses £15 to £25.50). Set L Mon to Sat £10 (2 courses) to £15, Set L Sun £24.50, Set D £32 to £55. Bar menu available 10am to 10pm SERVICE: not inc, card slips closed CARDS: Amex, Delta, Diners, MasterCard, Switch, Visa DETAILS: 70 seats. 30 seats outside. Private parties: 140 main room, 12 to 140 private rooms. Car park. Vegetarian meals. Children's helpings. No smoking in dining room. Wheelchair access (also WC). Music ACCOMMODATION: 62 rooms, all with bath/shower. TV. Phone. B&B £170 to £355. Rooms for disabled. Baby facilities. Swimming pool (*The Which? Hotel Guide*) (£5)

'The French waiter looked very unlikely, and broke three things in the restaurant to our knowledge. We even heard a crash outside, but everything was so cheap it didn't matter.' (On eating in London)

To find a restaurant in a particular area use the maps at the centre of the book.

Dining rooms where music, either live or recorded, is never played are signalled by No music *in the details at the end of an entry.*

BOWNESS-ON-WINDERMERE Cumbria map 8

▲ Linthwaite House

Crook Road, Bowness-on-Windermere LA23 3JA
TEL: (015394) 88600 FAX: (015394) 88601
EMAIL: admin@linthwaite.com
WEB SITE: www.linthwaite.com
off B5284, ¾m S of Bowness, near Windermere golf club

COOKING **5**
MODERN BRITISH
£29–£61

Overlooking Lake Windermere, Linthwaite combines a colonial air (old travelling trunks serve as tables for aperitifs on the verandah and in the lounge) with a hint of luxury: a single orchid graces each table in its comfortable dining room. The kitchen's pride in native produce – Lakeland beef, Cumbrian lamb and venison, locally smoked salmon, and a largely British cheese selection – continues under new chef Andy Nicholson, who arrived from the Devonshire Arms, Bolton Abbey (see entry) in spring 2001. His menus adopt the modish telegraphese style, so expect 'rabbit terrine, mixed leaves, tarragon dressing', followed perhaps by 'turbot, creamed leeks, spinach, girolle mushrooms, chive sauce'.

A fine sense of timing, and careful consideration for ingredients, has turned up such items as smoked haddock risotto with a poached egg and whisked-up fish stock, and sauté corn-fed chicken breast on charred potato and skinned broad beans in a rich Madeira sauce. Lightness of touch is brought to bear in desserts of passion fruit mousse with pineapple sorbet, and even in a traditional steamed ginger pudding served with a well judged rhubarb compote. Service from waitresses 'kitted out like pupils of St Trinian's' is pleasant and attentive. The stylistically arranged wine list is stuffed with good growers, but prices rise steeply from their £15 starting point.

CHEF: Andy Nicholson PROPRIETOR: Mike Bevans OPEN: Sun L 12.30 to 1.30, all week D 7.15 to 8.45 MEALS: Set L Sun £15.95, Set D £39. Bar menu available Mon to Sat L SERVICE: not inc, card slips closed CARDS: Amex, Delta, MasterCard, Switch, Visa DETAILS: 60 seats. Private parties: 45 main room, 16 to 45 private rooms. Car park. Vegetarian meals. Children's helpings. No children under 7. No smoking in dining room. Wheelchair access (also WC). Music ACCOMMODATION: 26 rooms all with bath/shower. TV. Phone. D,B&B £89 to £225. Rooms for disabled. Baby facilities. Fishing (*The Which? Hotel Guide*) (£5)

Porthole Eating House

3 Ash Street,
Bowness-on-Windermere LA23 3EB
TEL: (015394) 42793 FAX: (015394) 88675
EMAIL: gianni.berton@which.net
WEB SITE: www.porthole.fsworld.co.uk

COOKING **4**
ANGLO-ITALIAN
£22–£57

For 30 years the Bertons have recreated Tuscany in a seventeenth-century cottage on a busy, pedestrianised street in Bowness. Its intimate feel comes from white stone walls, low and vivid red ceilings, and cheerful, friendly waiters. Menus, based on time-honoured Italian cuisine, also include English staples and the odd oriental-style dish. The good-value set lunch might involve a 'generous, piquant plateful' of crostini Tuscan style – capers and gherkins enhancing the minced veal and beef – followed by beef and horseradish sausages (made in-house) with garlic mash and red wine gravy, a dish that 'raised bangers and mash to a higher level'. Dinner on the other hand might begin with red onion tart and continue with fillet of John Dory in a mild Thai curry sauce. Tried and tested desserts like tiramisù will have fans of rich, creamy sweets humming along to the taped Italian opera.

While some restaurants are dropping German wines from their lists, here they are offered by the page; more recent enthusiasms, such as New Zealand and Oregon reds, are represented; and look out for Vega Sicilia, wines from the Jura, and a Cockburn '08 port. Many prices rise skyward, but a characterful range is offered under £20, and house Italians are £12.

CHEF: Andrew Fairchild PROPRIETORS: Gianni and Judith Berton OPEN: Mon, Wed to Fri and Sun L 12 to 2.30, Wed to Mon D 6.30 to 10.30 CLOSED: 22 Dec to 14 Feb MEALS: alc (main courses L £7.50 to £10, D £11 to £16). Set L £12.50 SERVICE: not inc, card slips closed CARDS: Amex, Delta, Diners, MasterCard, Switch, Visa DETAILS: 40 seats. 30 seats outside. Private parties: 40 main room, 70 private room. Vegetarian meals. Children's helpings. Wheelchair access (also WC). Music

BRADFORD West Yorkshire map 8

Akbar's £ **NEW ENTRY**

1276 Leeds Road, Thornbury, Bradford BD3 8LF COOKING **2**
TEL: (01274) 773311 INDIAN
WEB SITE: www.akbars.co.uk £19–£38

The exterior of these adjoining houses in a stone terrace gives no hint of the wildly colourful interior, with mock fountain, tented ceiling in one room and 'flaming-brazier-effect' wall lights. Waiters, some with headsets for telephone bookings, provide 'affable, accommodating and efficient service'. The traditional North Indian fare has no modernist pretensions, except for serving naan suspended from metal frames that are left on the table. Vegetarian samosas are 'crisp and un-greasy', or choose from starters such as chicken-liver tikka, and fish pakoras. Main dishes include baltis, while others brought to table in iron pots include rishan lal (good lamb in rich tomato and pepper sauce) and karai gosht: also lamb, but drier, its 'fierce hotness tempered by lemon'. Several specialities combine different meats, such as makai ka sewata: lamb and chicken with lemon segments. For dessert there are traditional Indian sweets and ice creams. House wines are £6.95, or drink lassi.

CHEF: Tailb Hussain PROPRIETOR: Shabir Hussain OPEN: all week, D only 5 (4 Sun) to 12 (12.30 Fri and Sat) MEALS: alc (main courses £4.50 to £8). Set D £9.95 to £19.95 (all min 6) SERVICE: not inc CARDS: none DETAILS: 240 seats. Private parties: 180 main room, 50 private room. Car park. Vegetarian meals. No smoking in dining room. Music, Wheelchair access.

'Though they made much of their sojourn in France, and [the chef's] training there, for all the effect on the food on the plate he might as well have trained in Outer Mongolia.'
(On eating in the Midlands)

BRAITHWAITE Cumbria map 10

▲ Ivy House

Ivy House Hotel, Braithwaite CA12 5SY
TEL: (01768) 778338 FAX: (01768) 778113
EMAIL: stay@ivy-house.co.uk
WEB SITE: www.ivy-house.co.uk
just off B5292 Keswick to Braithwaite road

COOKING **2**
MODERN ENGLISH
£31–£41

This small hotel is 'a thoroughly pleasant place with very friendly proprietors'. Wendy Shill's ever-evolving cooking style has produced a starter of crispy Chinese-style duck legs as one hit on the four-course dinner menu, but this might also include homely black pudding with wholegrain mustard sauce and smoked bacon, or even moules marinière. It's the same with main courses: from haunch of venison with a juniper sauce and smoked bacon mash, via Moroccan-style tagine of lamb with couscous, to medallions of monkfish on a mild curry sauce. Finish perhaps with rhubarb and ginger pavlova. 'Not everything works,' mused one reporter, 'but intentions are good, and, more importantly, ingredients are well sourced.' Organised by style and helpfully annotated, this year's wine list proclaims new offerings such as the renowned Pesquera from Ribera del Duero. Eight 'house' vins de pays are £11.95 (£2 a glass).

CHEFS: Wendy Shill and Kati Hoffman PROPRIETORS: Nick and Wendy Shill OPEN: all week D only 7 to 7.30 CLOSED: Jan MEALS: Set D £21.95 SERVICE: not inc CARDS: Amex, Delta, Diners, MasterCard, Switch, Visa DETAILS: 30 seats. Private parties: 12 main room. Car park. Vegetarian meals. Children's helpings. No children under 6. No smoking in dining room. Music ACCOMMODATION: 12 rooms, all with bath/shower. TV. D,B&B £49.95 to £119.90. Rooms for disabled. Baby facilities

BRAMPTON Cambridgeshire map 6

▲ Grange Hotel

NEW ENTRY

115 High Street, Brampton PE28 4RA
TEL: (01480) 459516 FAX: (01480) 459391
EMAIL: enquiries@grangehotelbrampton.com
WEB SITE: www.grangehotelbrampton.com

COOKING **2**
MODERN EUROPEAN
£25–£48

Refurbishment of this red brick house (which dates back to 1773) was ongoing as the Guide went to press, the aim being to offer a 'restaurant with rooms'. Nick Steiger has worked at the Old Bridge in nearby Huntingdon and at the Pheasant at Keyston (see entries), both part of the Huntsbridge group, and brings with him a broad-minded approach to food. Staples of the European repertoire (Mediterranean fish soup, spinach risotto, deep-fried halibut with tartare sauce) share the billing with more unusual items such as a starter of smoked tomato with prawns, avocado and red chilli jam, but the style is generally straightforward. A tower of crunchy asparagus, for example, comes with Parma ham, endive, and a good vinaigrette, while well-timed sea bass has been paired with samphire in a butter sauce. Finish perhaps with pancakes, Eton Mess in a long-stemmed wine glass, or the well-kept all-British cheeseboard from Jeroboam's. Wines offer excellent choice under £20, including a New Zealand Riesling at £15.50 and a cru Bourgeois for £15. An Italian duo starts the wide-ranging selection of house styles at £9.25, and 14 wines are available by the glass.

CHEF: Nick Steiger PROPRIETOR: Steiger Partnership OPEN: all week L 12 to 2 (2.30 Sun), Mon to Sat D 7 to 10 CLOSED: first week Jan MEALS: alc (main courses £6.50 to £16.50). Bar menu available SERVICE: not inc CARDS: Amex, MasterCard, Switch, Visa DETAILS: 40 seats. 12 seats outside. Private parties: 40 main room, 18 private room. Car park. Vegetarian meals. Children's helpings. No smoking in dining room. Occasional music ACCOMMODATION: 8 rooms 7 with bath/shower. TV. Phone. B&B £45 to £75. Baby facilities (£5)

BRAMPTON Cumbria **map 10**

▲ Farlam Hall

Brampton CA8 2NG
TEL: (016977) 46234 FAX: (016977) 46683
EMAIL: farlamhall@dial.pipex.com
WEB SITE: www.farlamhall.co.uk
on A689, 2½m SE of Brampton (not at Farlam village)

COOKING **3**
ENGLISH COUNTRY HOUSE
£43–£52

Delightfully set in a peaceful spot not far from Hadrian's Wall, the largely Victorian house has been turned into a welcoming, comfortable, family-run country-house hotel with the 'hospitality of a bygone era' from considerate and attentive staff. Barry Quinion's cooking combines elements of both classic and homely styles, taking in calf's liver with bacon and mash, and Gressingham duck breast with braised red cabbage. It is comforting to know that not every chef feels the need to be cutting edge, and that there is good reason why some old favourites stand the test of time, although the repertoire also finds room for simply grilled sea bass with herbs and olive oil, served as a starter with Mediterranean vegetables. Materials are sound, their handling effective, and choice is sensibly limited to three options per course (more at pudding stage). Cheeses are kept in good condition, followed perhaps by a light vanilla crème brûlée, chocolate terrine, or glazed lemon tart. A roving list of wines at fair prices starts with four southern hemisphere house wines at £13.75.

CHEF: Barry Quinion PROPRIETORS: the Quinion and Stevenson families OPEN: all week D only 8 to 8.30 MEALS: Set D £32.50 SERVICE: not inc, card slips closed CARDS: MasterCard, Switch, Visa DETAILS: 45 seats. Private parties: 45 main room, 24 private room. Car park. No children under 5. Wheelchair access (not WC). No music ACCOMMODATION: 12 rooms, all with bath/shower. TV. Phone. D,B&B £125 to £260. No children under 5 (*The Which? Hotel Guide*)

BRAY Berkshire **map 3**

Fat Duck

High Street, Bray SL6 2AQ
TEL: (01628) 580333 FAX: (01628) 776188

COOKING **8**
MODERN EUROPEAN
£43–£99

Although hardly sumptuous or opulent, the newly preened duck is no longer as rustic or spartan as it was. Refurbishment, with red-brown leather sofas, fibre-optic lighting, white walls and contemporary art has given it a more modern, elegant, cheerful and metropolitan feel; and at long last it has an indoor toilet. It is still relaxed, and Britain's most innovative chef continues to tease, delight and provoke with his strikingly individual approach to food. If you want a name for it, Heston Blumenthal suggests 'molecular gastronomy', and if you want to enjoy it, leave your preconceptions at the door.

Meals (now at a set price) require curiosity and concentration to get the best out of them, since not only is each deliberately small dish complex in itself, but there are so many of them. This is cerebral cooking, designed as much to make you stop and think as to fill you up. In the first place the palate's 'attention span' is responsible for the decision to serve lots of small courses, a format that seems to serve other gastronomic cultures well. And the extra dishes are not just random 'gifts from the chef', but serve a purpose which requires explanation.

Rather than cooking lean meats such as saddle of lamb to a higher temperature than required, then allowing it to cool and relax, Blumenthal prefers not to let it exceed the serving temperature during cooking; this yields pink but not bloody meat, and is a slower process. Hence by making the main course the fifth to be served he builds enough time into the schedule. While a tiny minority of reporters fail to see what all the fuss is about, all recognise the amount of hard work and technical wizardry involved, and most are bowled over by results.

Flavour combinations are challenging, and many have come a long way from their starting point: he does crazy things to familiar materials, and some appear to work better than others. Consider mustard ice cream with a gazpacho of red cabbage juice (extracted by centrifuge) poured over sweet garlic cream covered in coffee flavoured jelly; caviar paired with white chocolate; or the carefully designed palate cleanser of green tea and lime foam that starts a meal (with a dash of vodka to disperse any fat on the tongue).

The assortment of foams, froths, and distillations are not just fashionable gestures either; Blumenthal uses jellies and creams to recreate comforting childhood pleasures, and sometimes to trick our palates about sweetness and acidity. He turns the classic English breakfast on its head for dessert – in a smoked bacon and egg ice cream, partnered by pain perdu, tomato jam and cep velouté – and serves up a 'very bold, very clever' dark chocolate fondant with avocado risotto, coconut sorbet and sweetcorn purée.

'Never leave without trying the petits fours' advised one visitor, which include chocolates that perhaps should carry a health warning since they are infused with tobacco. Apart from occasionally slow service (especially at lunchtime), the largely French-speaking staff remain professional and helpful, although more than one reporter has been put off by the insistence on credit card details when booking, and smoking can interfere with the business of unravelling the food's intricate smells and flavours. Highlights of the wine list – a deep-pocketed traditionalist's playground – include row upon row of fine Alsatian Rieslings and a virtual wine tour of the Rhône Valley. One of the greatest attractions, however, is the opportunity to order any wine by the glass, except for the oldest and rarest. Full bottles are not cheap, however, with house wines kicking off at £17.

CHEF/PROPRIETOR: Heston Blumenthal OPEN: Tue to Sun L 12 to 2 (2.30 Sat, 3 Sun), Tue to Sat D 7 to 9.30 (10 Fri and Sat) CLOSED: 2 weeks Christmas MEALS: Set L £25.75, Set D £55 SERVICE: 12.5% (optional), card slips closed CARDS: Amex, Delta, Diners, MasterCard, Switch, Visa DETAILS: 48 seats. 20 seats outside. Private parties: 52 main room. Children's helpings. No cigars/pipes in dining room. Music

▲ Waterside Inn

Ferry Road, Bray SL6 2AT
TEL: (01628) 620691 FAX: (01628) 784710
EMAIL: reservations@waterside-inn.co.uk
WEB SITE: www.waterside-inn.co.uk

COOKING **9**
FRENCH
£48–£166

Helped by mirrors and artful lighting, this is reckoned to be one of the country's most appealing dining rooms, especially in summer when it is open to the river and drinks can be taken on the terrace under a weeping willow. Cuisine doesn't come much more haute than this, and much of it is 'simply outstanding'. Materials, techniques, flavours and textures come together to produce a seamlessly enjoyable meal.

The satisfaction of finding a poached egg in the middle of a perfectly textured smoked haddock and dill soufflé is hard to beat, as is the simple delight of finding first-rate ingredients expertly handled: in fillets of accurately poached John Dory for example, sitting on a bed of Parmesan risotto surrounded by queen scallops, all resting on a cream-based nage containing morels. The wonder is that it can all seem so effortless, which is a sign of true art. And dishes are impeccably balanced, another testament to the kitchen's culinary intelligence: Bresse pigeon breasts, for example, on a rustic bed of potato and shredded cabbage laced with quail meat, the rich, deep, full-flavoured sauce spiked refreshingly with lime, the ensemble admirably accompanied by a 'superb salad of the freshest leaves'.

Desserts, according to one who gets around, are probably the best in the country; indeed, it is quite possible that 'the pastry chef here is a genius'. A plate of chocolate desserts has included a velvety ice cream encased in a meringue shell, a fondant with a white chocolate filling, a smooth white chocolate mousse, and a white chocolate crème brûlée, all surrounding (just for contrast) a pastry shell with finely chopped apple and strawberry sauce. A light Grand Marnier soufflé, wrapped in two delicate crêpes, has also impressed.

Coffee and petits fours get top marks, the menu exceptionnel has gone down well, as has the 'back-to-my-roots' version, and breakfast is well reported, although prices are of course high (ladies wouldn't know this, since their menus are unpriced). Cosseting French service is friendly, helpful and able to replace a dropped napkin almost before it reaches the floor. The wine list is also French, but the restaurant has not seen fit to furnish the Guide with a copy.

CHEFS: Michel Roux and Alain Roux PROPRIETOR: Michel Roux OPEN: Wed to Sun and Tue D June to Aug 12 to 2 (2.30 Sat and Sun), 7 to 10 CLOSED: 26 Dec to 31 Jan MEALS: alc (main courses £32.50 to £49.50). Set L Wed to Fri £33.50 to £74, Set L Sat and Sun £49.50 to £74, Set D £74 SERVICE: 12.5% (optional), card slips closed CARDS: Amex, Delta, Diners, MasterCard, Switch, Visa DETAILS: 75 seats. Private parties: 80 main room, 8 private room. Car park. Vegetarian meals. Children's helpings. No children under 12. No cigars/pipes in dining room. Occasional music ACCOMMODATION: 9 rooms, all with bath/shower. TV. Phone. B&B £160 to £290. No children under 12

Report forms are at the back of the book; write a letter if you prefer; or email us at goodfoodguide@which.net

BRIGHTON & HOVE East Sussex map 3

Black Chapati

12 Circus Parade, New England Road, Brighton BN1 4GW
TEL: (01273) 699011

COOKING **4**
GLOBAL
£31–£49

Just off Preston Circus, with a bike shop and pizzeria for neighbours, Black Chapati brightens up an otherwise uninspiring neighbourhood. Not that it has had money thrown at it – indeed, the black and yellow theme seems to confirm a shoestring approach to décor – but the short and lively repertoire crackles with entertaining ideas, from Sri Lankan lamb patties to a dish of roast cod with a salad of dried shrimp and fresh lime. Despite an occasional excursion elsewhere – such as roast rack of lamb with couscous – the thrust of the cooking is South East Asian, taking in pan-fried scallops with glass noodles, grilled five-spice duck breast, and 'excellent' braised belly pork with steamed rice and pak choi. Long practice in the small kitchen has honed dishes to a fine edge, and the pace doesn't falter among the more European-style desserts, such as cardamom crème brûlée, or dark chocolate and orange cake. The thumbnail wine list incorporates a good range of grape varieties, and most bottles are under £20, starting with house vins de pays at £10.50.

CHEFS/PROPRIETORS: Stephen Funnell and Lauren Alker OPEN: Tue to Sat D only 7 (6.30 Sat) to 10 MEALS: alc (main courses £12 to £15.50) SERVICE: 10%, card slips closed CARDS: Amex, Delta, MasterCard, Switch, Visa DETAILS: 32 seats. Private parties: 8 main room. Vegetarian meals. No children after 9pm. Wheelchair access (not WC). Music

C

NEW ENTRY

17 Atlingworth Street, Brighton BN2 1PL
TEL: (01273) 645755 FAX: (01273) 621304
WEB SITE: www.crestaurant.co.uk

COOKING **3**
MODERN EUROPEAN
£31–£50

Blink and you'll miss it! C (after chef/proprietor Cass Titcombe) is the restaurant of (but under separate ownership from) the burgundy-painted Blanch House Hotel, hidden in a terrace off the seafront in Kemptown. Ring to get in, dive into the bar for a drink, then head through to a high-minimalist white dining-room. Despite a paucity of windows, the effect is warm and pleasing, although the laid-back feeling can also affect service.

A daily-changing menu zips along, offering roast morcilla with pickled rhubarb, and tamarind-glazed venison with roast parsnips and curly kale. Output is variable, but among things that have come off well are scallop ravioli with a subliminal smear of smoked anchovy butter, and roast lamb served with cumin and chilli lamb meatballs, chickpeas and super-pungent wild garlic pesto. Desserts are not to be missed, judging by a dark chocolate and beetroot cake (concealing a nugget of rich white chocolate) its sweetness complemented by a blob of sour crème fraîche; a trifle of blood orange, rhubarb and walnuts under a slick of white chocolate sauce exorcised one visitor's memories of packet jelly and powdered custard forever. A decent wine list concisely covers Old and New Worlds; house vins de pays are £11.50.

CHEF: Cass Titcombe PROPRIETORS: Cass Titcombe and Anthea McNeill OPEN: Thu to Sun L 12 to 3, Tue to Sun D 7 to 10.45 CLOSED: 25 and 26 Dec MEALS: Set L £15 (2 courses) to £20, Set D £25 (2 courses) to £30 SERVICE: 10% (optional), card slips closed CARDS: Delta, MasterCard, Switch, Visa DETAILS: 32 seats. Private parties: 8 main room. Vegetarian meals. No cigars/pipes in dining room. Music (£5)

La Fourchette

101 Western Road, Brighton BN1 2AA
TEL/FAX: (01273) 722556

COOKING **4**
FRENCH
£19–£38

Western Road's numbering might have been designed to confuse enemy aliens (it originated when Brighton and Hove – whose boundary once bisected it – were separate entities). Find Waitrose, then look beyond the traffic lights and across the road for this pint-sized but classy French restaurant. Tables may feel a little close together, but the décor is bright and pleasing, and the menu even more so.

A confident way with novel but coherent combinations brings on dishes such as quail ravioli with spinach mousse and mustard sauce, and main courses of knuckle of lamb with crushed potatoes and a spicy masala sauce, or the day's fresh fish (chalked on a board). Timing is sound, textures delight (in a melting confit of duck Parmentier for example) and tarte fine aux abricots shows that it can all look good too. Or you could have 'Triomphe': coffee sponge layered with coffee buttercream and chocolate ganache. Service seems to have improved and is now 'friendly, prompt and excellent'. Almost all the concise wine list's (not exclusively French) bottles are under £20.

CHEF/PROPRIETOR: Pascal Madjoudj OPEN: Tue to Sat L 12 to 2.30 (3 Sat), Mon to Sat D 7 to 10 (10.30 Sat) CLOSED: 2 weeks Jan, 2 weeks Aug MEALS: Set L £7.50 to £10, Set D £18 to £22 SERVICE: 10%, card slips closed CARDS: Amex, Delta, Diners, MasterCard, Switch, Visa DETAILS: 40 seats. Private parties: 40 main room. Vegetarian meals. Music (£5)

Gingerman

21A Norfolk Square, Brighton BN1 2PD
TEL/FAX: (01273) 326688

COOKING **4**
MODERN EUROPEAN
£22–£46

Despite the address, the entrance is in a street off the south edge of Norfolk Square. Gingerman looks like a typical small tea shop, until you see the menu. Ben McKellar has contributed to Brighton & Hove's culinary renaissance with up-to-the-minute but unpretentious cooking that shows clear understanding of flavours and textures.

Lunch offers two choices at each stage, perhaps centring on roast cod with a smoked bacon dressing, or pot-roast pork belly with buttery mash and sun-dried tomatoes. At dinner (six choices per course) highlights have included a gently smoked haddock soup with cumin and chives, fillet of bream on a bed of textbook imam bayaldi, and roast venison accompanied by braised Savoy cabbage, potato gratin and an invigorating, sticky sweet sauce. Sophisticated desserts cosset with feather-light strawberry soufflé embracing a scoop of vanilla ice cream, or perhaps hot chocolate fondant with mandarin sorbet. 'The atmosphere is relaxed and jolly,' says one report, which also bemoans the problem of cigarette smoke in a fairly confined space. A succinct wine list offers a good range of low- to mid-priced bins, striking a balance between countries and styles, starting with French house wines at £9.95.

CHEF: Ben McKellar PROPRIETORS: Ben McKellar and Pamela Abbott OPEN: Tue to Sat 12.30 to 2, 7.30 to 10 CLOSED: 2 weeks summer, 2 weeks winter MEALS: Set L £9.95 (1 course) to £14.95, Set D £21 (2 courses) to £23.50 SERVICE: not inc, 10% for parties of 8 or more CARDS: Amex, Delta, Diners, MasterCard, Switch, Visa DETAILS: 32 seats. Private parties: 32 main room. Children's helpings. Music

New Whytes

33 Western Street, Brighton BN1 2PG — COOKING **3**
TEL: (01273) 776618 FAX: (01444) 410822 — MODERN EUROPEAN
WEB SITE: www.whytesrestaurant.com — £31–£44

This cottagey, white-fronted restaurant just off the seafront is deceptively spacious inside. Tables at ground-floor level may feel a little shoehorned in, but there are more seats in a basement room, and the whole place operates with smooth and amiable efficiency. The approach is of the old school: amuse-bouches and fine mid-meal sorbets make you feel looked after, the better to appreciate new boy Jordan Webb's accomplished cooking. Among starters, a well-crafted raviolo filled with rabbit and foie gras on a bed of stewed leeks is a textural and gustatory triumph, and a fillet of red mullet on celeriac rémoulade with good olive oil is pretty impressive too.

Main courses tend to be rich and substantial, using caramelised pork fillet or rack of lamb amid a welter of vegetables on aromatic stock reductions (orange and vanilla in the case of the pork), and there is always a vegetarian option such as wild mushroom pie with a sauce of peas. Intensely flavoured sorbets are a reasonably good bet at dessert stage, although the liquidised melon they are sauced with doesn't add a great deal, but chocolate mousse on a ginger-biscuit base with blueberry coulis fires on all cylinders. The rather jumbled wine list is worth rummaging for the odd bargain it throws up, even if producer information may be missing and vintages inaccurate. House wines are £9.95.

CHEF: Jordan Webb PROPRIETOR: John Anthony OPEN: Tue to Sat D 7 to 9.30 (earlier/later by arrangement) CLOSED: 26 Dec to 1 Jan, first weekdays of New Year MEALS: alc (main courses £12.50 to £14). Set D £25 (by prior arrangement only) SERVICE: not inc, card slips closed CARDS: Amex, Delta, MasterCard, Switch, Visa DETAILS: 40 seats. Private parties: 26 main room, 20 private room. Vegetarian meals. Music (£5)

One Paston Place

1 Paston Place, Brighton BN2 1HA — COOKING **6**
TEL: (01273) 606933 FAX: (01273) 675686 — MODERN EUROPEAN
£29–£63

'Nothing better in Brighton,' confirmed one visitor to this unchanging venue, where bare floorboards, a pastel-coloured mural and trimly dressed tables create an atmosphere of relaxed calm. It offers a highly refined style of cooking, using top-quality ingredients, in which the more traditional ideas are probably the safer options: smoked cod soufflé perhaps, or a fresh and flavoursome warm salad of langoustine, scallop and monkfish with curry-spiced pineapple chutney. Innovation may not be Mark Emmerson's first priority, but he is a more than capable chef, deploying sound technique, accurate timing and seasoning to produce, for example, first-rate deep-fried spring rolls of minced brown crab meat and salt cod to accompany rolled fillets of Dover sole.

Clean, clear flavours are a trademark, evident in a pastry case sitting on a piece of gingery eggy bread ('pain d'épice perdu' for the record), piled with bitter endive and topped with foie gras slices, the whole arrangement teamed with mandarin segments in a sticky veal reduction. Professional stock-based saucing contributes to the 'rich and satisfying' feel, notable also in the discreetly caramelly version accompanying a firm, thick piece of rare-cooked Scottish beef. Classical foundations underpin desserts too: as in a toffeeish, iced parfait of chicory, pecan and maple syrup, encased in a crisp tuile on a light sponge base. If the carte seems expensive, try the set lunch. France dominates the wine list, which includes a serviceable 30 by the half-bottle. Four house wines, all French, start at £14.

CHEF: Mark Emmerson PROPRIETORS: Mark and Nicole Emmerson OPEN: Tue to Sat 12.30 to 1.45, 7.30 to 9.45 CLOSED: first 2 weeks Jan, first 2 weeks Aug MEALS: alc (main courses £20 to £22). Set L £16.50 (2 courses) to £19 SERVICE: net prices, card slips closed CARDS: Amex, Delta, Diners, MasterCard, Switch, Visa DETAILS: 45 seats. Private parties: 10 main room. No cigars/pipes in dining room. Wheelchair access (not WC). Music. Air-conditioned

Terre à Terre

71 East Street, Brighton BN1 1HQ — COOKING **4**
TEL: (01273) 729051 FAX: (01273) 327561 — MODERN GLOBAL VEGETARIAN
£26–£46

Co-owner Amanda Powley says Terre à Terre was 'born out of a passion to create "knock your socks off" food' without using meat. This is done by avoiding the beans-and-lentils cliché; instead, a sound understanding of flavours and top quality organic and biodynamic ingredients are combined in a fearlessly inventive and vibrant cooking style of global scope. A typically diverse menu may feature scrumpy Camembert soufflé accompanied by sage fritters and apple snaps; a version of laksa made with sweet potatoes and topped with spiced aubergine and plantains; and 'arepas mojo', a Latin American-style dish of stacked corn cakes with chipotle and tamarillo salsa and a lime and oregano sauce. Röstis are a speciality, served with a variety of toppings. As the Guide went to press, the restaurant was due to close briefly for refurbishment, expanding the dining room and adding an outdoor area. The wine list, totally organic and vegetarian, includes several biodynamic and vegan wines, plus organic beers and spirits; wine prices start at £11.50 a bottle (£3.65 a glass).

CHEFS: Lawrence Glass and Paul Morgan PROPRIETORS: Philip Taylor and Amanda Powley OPEN: Tue to Sun L 12 to 6, all week D 6 to 10.30 (open bank hols) CLOSED: Christmas MEALS: alc (main courses L £9 to £10.50. D £10.50 to 11.50) SERVICE: not inc, 10% for parties of 6 or more CARDS: Amex, Delta, Diners, MasterCard, Switch, Visa DETAILS: 80 seats. Private parties: 30 main room. Vegetarian meals. Children's helpings. Wheelchair access (also WC). Music. Air-conditioned

BRIMFIELD Herefordshire map 5

▲ Roebuck Inn

Brimfield SY8 4NE
TEL: (01584) 711230 FAX: (01584) 711654
EMAIL: dave@roebuckinn.demon.co.uk
WEB SITE: www.roebuckinn.demon.co.uk
just off A49 Leominster to Ludlow road, 4m W of Tenbury Wells

COOKING **3**
MODERN BRITISH
£24–£52

Visitors generally start in the welcoming bar of this village pub, where they order over a drink and then move to the bright, comfortable, conservatory-style dining room. A generous menu offers a number of dishes in either first- or main-course sizes – wild mushroom risotto, perhaps, or crab filo parcels – and the range extends from an old-fashioned steak and mushroom suet pudding to chicken breast with a tasty pearl barley, leek and smoked bacon risotto. Specials, listed on a board, tend towards fish and game: perhaps a commendable starter of scallops with pea and mint sauce, followed by Cornish lobster with orange and coriander butter, or fillet of wild venison with damson purée. Fish pie, made from dill-flavoured salmon, cod and prawns topped with leek mash and glazed with cheese, is 'rightfully famous'. British cheeses (all made with vegetarian rennet) provide a viable alternative to desserts of apple and pear charlotte, or banana mousse in a brittle caramel box with mango sauce. Service is prompt, polite and well informed, and the globally sourced wine list, arranged by style, is full of interest. Prices only occasionally creep above £20, starting at £9.95.

CHEFS: Jonathan Waters and David Willson-Lloyd PROPRIETORS: David and Susan Willson-Lloyd OPEN: all week 12 to 2.15, 6.30 to 9.30 CLOSED: 25 Dec MEALS: alc (main courses £8 to £20) SERVICE: not inc, card slips closed CARDS: Delta, MasterCard, Switch, Visa DETAILS: 80 seats. 12 seats outside. Private parties: 50 main room, 14 private room. Car park. Vegetarian meals. Children's helpings. No smoking in dining room. Wheelchair access (not WC). No music ACCOMMODATION: 3 rooms, all with bath/shower. TV. Phone. B&B £45 to £70. Baby facilities (*The Which? Hotel Guide*) (£5)

BRISTOL Bristol map 2

Bell's Diner

1–3 York Road, Montpelier, Bristol BS6 5QB
TEL: (0117) 924 0357 FAX: (0117) 924 4280
EMAIL: info@bellsdiner.co.uk
WEB SITE: www.bellsdiner.co.uk
take Picton Street off Cheltenham Road (A38) – runs into York Road

COOKING **5**
MODERN BRITISH
£25–£49

This discreet corner restaurant does not immediately grab the attention of passers-by but is considered a gem by those in the know. Inside there are three dining areas with an old-fashioned feel thanks to dark green-painted panelling, an ancient fireplace, rustic furniture and cobalt-blue glass lampshades. Tables are packed in fairly close together, prompting one visitor to comment: 'no need for sardines on the menu.' Christopher Wicks, a devotee of wild foods, has employed a picker to search the area for local delicacies such as wild garlic, pignuts and St George mushrooms, which are brought together with other carefully sourced ingredients and subjected to a broadly modern and British style of cooking.

The repertoire covers a wide range, extending from roast herbed chicken breast with baby leeks, truffle mash and thyme, to a version of laksa containing spiced pumpkin and butter beans. Fish is a strong point – shellfish bisque has impressed for strength of flavour and well-made accompanying rouille – while the star turn of an inspection meal was crisp-crusted roast turbot served with a thyme-flavoured tomato sauce containing pieces of artichoke and potato, plus a tempura-style deep-fried courgette flower stuffed with ricotta. Successes at dessert stage have included rhubarb soufflé with stem ginger ice cream, and a trio of chocolate sorbet, mousse-like ganache and warm chocolate pudding with a dark liquid centre. Ten house wines from £10 a bottle, £2.25 a glass, open a fairly short but well-chosen list.

CHEFS: Christopher Wicks and Jin Ren Huang PROPRIETOR: Christopher Wicks OPEN: Tue to Fri L 12 to 2.30, Mon to Sat D 7 to 10.30 CLOSED: 24 to 30 Dec MEALS: alc (main courses £8.50 to £15.50) SERVICE: not inc, 10% for parties of 8 or more CARDS: Amex, Delta, MasterCard, Switch, Visa DETAILS: 60 seats. Private parties: 30 main room. Vegetarian meals. Children's helpings. No smoking in dining room. Music (£5)

Deason's

NEW ENTRY

43 Whiteladies Road, Bristol BS8 2LS
TEL: (0117) 973 6230 FAX: (0117) 923 7394
EMAIL: deasons.restaurant@virgin.net
WEB SITE: www.deasons.co.uk

COOKING **3**
MODERN BRITISH
£21–£52

A deal of thought seems to have gone into this house conversion, its polished wooden floors, whirling ceiling fans, fresh flowers and well-spaced tables translating well into an attractive, stylish modern restaurant. Jason Deason's quest for 'originality of flavours' takes him on a journey through herring with scallops and basil, to meat and fish partnerships such as sea bass with chorizo, and roast salmon with oysters and smoked bacon. But he seems equally happy to provide more mainstream dishes such as pink and tasty loin of lamb (generously endowed with plum tomatoes, cannellini beans and grilled field mushrooms stuffed with garlic butter), and crisp-skinned duck breast with couscous, olives and a watercress salad. For dessert, warm pineapple with spiced genoese, natural yoghurt and organic honey also offers 'a fine contrast of flavours that work well together'. Front-of-house (run by Jodie Deason) is calm and professionally assured, and the wine list offers a handful of bottles from each major country, a decent showing of halves, and seven house wines from £10.75 (£2.75 a glass)

CHEF: Jason Deason PROPRIETORS: Jason and Jodie Deason OPEN: all week L 12 to 2.30 (3 Sun), Mon to Sat D 6.30 to 10 (10.30 Fri and Sat) CLOSED: 25 and 26 Dec, 1 Jan MEALS: alc (not Sun L; main courses £13 to £20). Set L £8.50 (2 courses) to £11.50, Set L Sun £9 (2 courses) to £12, Set D £15.50 (2 courses) to £19.50 SERVICE: 10% (optional), card slips closed CARDS: Amex, Delta, Diners, MasterCard, Switch, Visa DETAILS: 80 seats. 20 seats outside. Private parties: 40 main room, 12 private room. Vegetarian meals. Children's helpings. No smoking in dining room. Music. Air-conditioned (£5)

FishWorks Seafood Café

NEW ENTRY

128 Whiteladies Road, Clifton, Bristol BS8 2RS
TEL: (0117) 974 4433 FAX: (0117) 974 4933
WEB SITE: www.fishworks.co.uk

COOKING **4**
FISH
£30–£73

The eyes of passers-by are drawn by the spider crabs, glistening and twitching lobsters and iridescent mackerel on display in fridges in the picture windows of the Bristol branch of Mitchell Tonks's attempt at piscine domination of the Southwest (see FishWorks Green Street Seafood Café, Bath, and FishWorks, Christchurch). It repeats the formula of the Bath original, but if anything has more of a buzz, at times heaving with people enjoying prime-quality fish and seafood and making plenty of noise about it.

The success of the venture lies partly in the exemplary freshness of materials (helped by possession of a fishing boat, operating out of Newlyn), and partly in the policy of serving it simply steamed, fried, grilled or even raw, usually accompanied by a simple sauce, often herb- and butter-based. Choose your fish or seafood from the display and watch it being prepared and cooked in the open-plan kitchen (it reminded one visitor of holidays in Greece and Turkey). But there are plenty of bright ideas on the menu, from roasted razor clams with butter, garlic, lemon and parsley, to kingfish ('like a cross between tuna and mackerel') with rosemary and anchovy butter. 'Amiable and competent' waiting staff cope well even on the busiest nights. A short, good-value list of predominantly white wines completes the picture. Prices start at £8.95.

CHEF: Matthew Prouse PROPRIETOR: FishWorks plc OPEN: Tue to Sat 11 to 11, Sun 11 to 3 MEALS: alc (main courses £9 to £20) SERVICE: not inc CARDS: Amex, Delta, MasterCard, Switch, Visa DETAILS: 50 seats. 6 seats outside. Private parties: 50 main room, 14 and 36 private rooms. Vegetarian meals. Children's helpings. No smoking in 1 dining room. Wheelchair access (not WC). Music (£5)

Harveys

12 Denmark Street, Bristol BS1 5DQ
TEL: (0117) 927 5034 FAX: (0117) 927 5003
EMAIL: wendy.tullett@adswev.com
WEB SITE: www.j-harvey.co.uk

COOKING **5**
MODERN EUROPEAN
£50–£70

A stained-glass window in Bristol blue, and hugely vaulted ceilings, gave the dining room the aura of a cathedral for one visitor; wine may have been worshipped in these former cellars for centuries, but in place of hushed and prayerful silence there is now an air of bonhomie. The menu will put a smile on most faces, not least for the provenance of its wares, including organic Glenarm salmon, Scottish scallops, Cornish sea bass, and duck foie gras from Périgord. There is no shortage of luxury items, but these are intelligently handled, and while there is a strong classical foundation to the cooking – corn-fed Anjou pigeon is served with a sherry vinegar jus – it is not without invention: roast monkfish, for example, has come with braised cabbage, bacon and girolles, in a jus of crab and guinea fowl.

'Geometry', the prizewinning pud, may be slightly 'oversold' on the menu, but there is no question of any slackening of the pace at dessert stage, given such enticements as a hot poêlé of apples and plums served with a black truffle ice cream. Bread is offered throughout the meal, water is topped up as required, and service generally achieves the right degree of attentiveness. Interesting bins at sensible prices characterise the wine list, with most major regions represented, although a remarkable 'wine library' of mature vintages inevitably sees prices soar. Around 20 wines by the glass and 25 half-bottles widen choice, and the Harvey sherry connection is responsible for a dozen by the glass from £2.50. Prices open at £13.

CHEF: Daniel Galmiche PROPRIETOR: John Harvey and Sons OPEN: Mon to Fri L 12 to 2, Mon to Sat D 7 to 10 CLOSED: Christmas, New Year, third week Feb, first 2 weeks Aug, bank hols MEALS: alc (main courses £21 to £23). Set L £6 (1 course) to £22.50 SERVICE: net prices CARDS: Amex, Delta, Diners, MasterCard, Switch, Visa DETAILS: 60 seats. Private parties: 110 main room. Car park at D. Vegetarian meals. No smoking in dining room. Music. Air-conditioned

▲ Hotel du Vin & Bistro

The Sugar House, Narrow Lewins Mead,
Bristol BS1 2NU
TEL: (0117) 925 5577 FAX: (0117) 925 1199
EMAIL: info@bristol.hotelduvin.com
WEB SITE: www.hotelduvin.com

COOKING **3**
MODERN EUROPEAN
£31–£51

The Bristol arm of this small, quirky hotel chain (see entries in Birmingham, Tunbridge Wells and Winchester) is to be found in an eighteenth-century building, once a sugar refinery and later a clay pipe factory. In its present incarnation it is an oenophile's paradise, with vinous prints and empty wine bottles decorating the dimly lit Bistro that is reached by crossing a courtyard. Straightforward bistro cooking takes in ham hock terrine with Puy lentils and chutney, Caesar salad, and tuna niçoise among starters, and main courses such as a fresh and skilfully timed piece of John Dory with Jerusalem artichokes and ruby chard, or chargrilled ribeye of Aberdeen Angus with chips and an accomplished béarnaise. The cheese selection shows imagination, extending perhaps to Brique de Brébis and Olde Stowey, while the tally of favourite puddings encompasses tiramisù, caramelised lemon tart, and an admirably wobbly pannacotta with fresh raspberries. The sommelier deserves a special mention for his 'knowledge, enthusiasm and helpfulness'. The wine list has its fair share of serious French classics (some commanding three figures), but is underpinned by a well-priced selection of less-often-seen styles such as a Madiran from south-west France at £12.50 and a Rueda Verdejo from Spain for £14. Both major and minor regions are treated in some depth, with bins listed by country, and there is plenty of variety in the half-bottle section. House wines start at £11.50.

CHEF: Robert Carr PROPRIETOR: Hotel Du Vin Ltd OPEN: all week 12 to 2, 6 to 9.45 MEALS: alc (exc Sun L; main courses £10.50 to £14.50). Set L Mon to Fri £15 (2 courses; whole table must order). Set L Sun £22.50 SERVICE: not inc, card slips closed CARDS: Amex, Delta, Diners, MasterCard, Switch, Visa DETAILS: 85 seats. Private parties: 9 main room, 12 to 72 private rooms. Car park. Vegetarian meals. Children's helpings. No cigars/pipes in dining room. Wheelchair access (also WC). No music. Air-conditioned ACCOMMODATION: 40 rooms, all with bath/shower. TV. Phone. Room only £109 to £225. Rooms for disabled. Baby facilities (*The Which? Hotel Guide*)

Markwicks

43 Corn Street, Bristol BS1 1HT
TEL/FAX: (0117) 926 2658

COOKING **5**
MODERN BRITISH
£30–£57

The Markwicks have been at this address for a dozen years, cooking for a loyal following of supporters. 'It hasn't really changed since I first went there ten years ago,' claimed one visitor, noting the grape motif ceiling lights in this former bank vault, the professionalism of Judy Markwick, and a repertoire largely composed of classics: from a 'beautifully judged' morel risotto, via braised leg of hare, to the rich, thick and 'canonically correct' fish soup served in massive individual tureens with all the usual accompaniments.

Carefully sourced supplies include much from the West Country, plus organic Glenarm salmon from Ireland, and vegetables (charged extra) from their own market garden, enabling them to choose the type, variety, size and picking time: a city location is no longer a bar to this kind of self-sufficiency. Sensitive handling has produced pink pigeon breast 'heavy with juice', and 'memorably tender' rump of lamb cut in big chunks, while desserts have yielded a baked prune and armagnac rice pudding, and a chocolate trio consisting of mousse, warm tart and chilled pancake. A selection of 14 house wines in a range of styles, chosen to offer both value and character, starts at £12. Then comes a broad range of good-value wines, including Albariños from Spain and a Sicilian red, leading to a collection of reasonably priced bin-ends of mature vintages from well-respected estates.

CHEF: Stephen Markwick PROPRIETORS: Stephen and Judy Markwick OPEN: Mon to Fri L 12 to 2, Mon to Sat D 7 to 10 CLOSED: 1 week Christmas to New Year, 1 week Easter, last 2 weeks Aug, bank hols MEALS: alc (main courses £15.50 to £18). Set D £27.50. Light L available SERVICE: not inc, card slips closed CARDS: Amex, Delta, Diners, MasterCard, Switch, Visa DETAILS: 45 seats. Private parties: 8 main room, 6 and 16 private rooms. Vegetarian meals. Children's helpings. No music

Quartier Vert

85 Whiteladies Road, Bristol BS8 2NT
TEL: (0117) 973 4482 FAX: (0117) 974 3913
WEB SITE: www.quartiervert.co.uk

COOKING **4**
MEDITERRANEAN
£25–£52

This laid-back neighbourhood local, which champions organic produce, has al-fresco dining out-front, a busy modern bar for drinks and tapas (called 'little dishes') inside, a more formal dining room out back, and even a bakery. White walls and ceiling and wood floors give a bright minimalist feel. Barny Haughton's repertoire, drawing inspiration from provincial Europe with Spanish overtones, shows clear, clean flavours, as well as deftness and lightness. Menus change daily: blackboard tapas take in calamares fritos, hummus and marinated anchovies, while the carte contains such regulars as provençale fish soup, and seared scallops, perhaps with pancetta and pea-and-mint purée.

Mains that have pleased include accurately timed monkfish, a mussel and saffron broth with spinach and Jersey Royals, and 'well-balanced' saddle of rabbit with tagliatelle, baby leeks, broad beans, cherry tomato confit and truffle oil. Try pannacotta with strawberries and a berry coulis to finish. Service is competent, unflappable and friendly, though reporters have found unrestricted smoking a problem. The wine list suits the menu, with its distinct continental edge, but also covers the New World. Five organic wines feature in the 17-strong international house selection that is sold by bottle, carafe or glass from £2.25, £8.50 and £10.95 respectively.

CHEF/PROPRIETOR: Barny Haughton OPEN: all week 12 to 3, 6 to 10.30. (Light snacks 3 to 6) MEALS: alc (main courses £10.50 to £18). Set L £12.95 (2 courses) to £15.95. Tapas ('Little Dishes') menu also available SERVICE: not inc CARDS: Amex, Delta, MasterCard, Switch, Visa DETAILS: 78 seats. 34 seats outside. Private parties: 80 main room, 20 private room. Vegetarian meals. Wheelchair access (not WC). Music

riverstation

The Grove, Bristol BS1 4RB — COOKING **3**
TEL: (0117) 914 4434 FAX: (0117) 934 9990 — MODERN BRITISH-PLUS
WEB SITE: www.riverstation.co.uk — £22–£48

This friendly and unpretentious place is reckoned to be one of the city's 'noisier, hipper, slicker' foodie haunts. On the ground floor is a cheerful deli and an inexpensive café serving snacks all day, while upstairs is the big, loud, restaurant proper, with a serious-looking bar; those who opt for a no-smoking table in the L-shaped dining room get the bonus of a river view.

A longish menu tries to please all in a very contemporary way; the grafting of Mediterranean and Asian styles on to British roots allows for plenty of vegetarian and fish options as well as meat and offal dishes. Results range from an ultra-simple starter of sauté oyster mushrooms with parsley, lemon and garlic on sourdough bruschetta, to protein-rich main courses of crisp-skinned, pink-fleshed roast Hereford duck breast (with braised endive, celeriac gratin and a rich veal jus), to a fricassee of lambs' sweetbreads and neck fillet (with broad beans, baby onions and mint). Service might be improved, but ten house wines from £10.50 a bottle, £2.75 a glass, open a well-chosen and reasonably priced list.

CHEFS: Peter Taylor and Simon Green PROPRIETORS: Peter Taylor, Shirley-Anne Bell, John Payne and Mark Hall OPEN: all week 12 (10.30 Sat) to 2.30 (3 Sun), 6 to 10.30 (11 Fri and Sat, 9 Sun) MEALS: alc (main courses £9 to £16). Set L Mon to Fri £11.50 (2 courses) to £13.75, Set L Sun £12.75 (2 courses) to £15, Set D 6 to 7.15 £7 (1 course with wine) SERVICE: not inc, 10% for parties of 8 or more CARDS: Delta, Diners, MasterCard, Switch, Visa DETAILS: 120 seats. 24 seats outside. Private parties: 120 main room. Vegetarian meals. Children's helpings. No-smoking area. No music

The 2003 Guide will be published before Christmas 2002. Reports on meals are most welcome at any time of the year, but are particularly valuable in the spring (no later than June). Send them to The Good Food Guide, *FREEPOST, 2 Marylebone Road, London NW1 4DF. Or email your report to goodfoodguide@which.net*

Prices quoted in the Guide are based on information supplied by restaurateurs. The prices quoted at the top of each entry represent a range, from the lowest meal price to the highest; the latter is inflated by 20 per cent to take account of likely price rises during the year of the Guide.

Severnshed

The Grove, Harbourside, Bristol BS1 4RB
TEL: (0117) 925 1212 FAX: (0117) 925 1214
EMAIL: info@severnshed.co.uk
WEB SITE: www.severnshed.co.uk

NEW CHEF
MODERN ORGANIC
£19–£43

With new owners and a facelift, as well as a new chef, Severnshed has taken a different direction, its aim now being to concentrate on local organic produce. The menu has more of a European caste than before – taking in pan-fried sardines on spinach, and butternut tart with goats' cheese and asparagus – although it also offers 'Pile Bay', a dish from the chef's home town in Barbados, made from marinated tuna, cod, salmon, mussels, tiger prawn and squid, served with stir-fried vegetables. Banoffi pie provides a very English way to finish. A new wine list was also under construction as the Guide went to press. Reports please.

CHEF: Kerryn Carter PROPRIETOR: Organic Ventures Ltd OPEN: all week 12.30 to 3.30, 6 to 11.30; café 12 to 12 MEALS: alc (main courses £10 to £14.50). Set L £8.95 (2 courses) to £10.95 SERVICE: not inc, 10% for parties of 6 or more CARDS: Amex, Delta, MasterCard, Switch, Visa DETAILS: 200 seats. 100 seats outside. Private parties: 200 main room. Car park. Vegetarian meals. Children's helpings. No smoking in dining room. Wheelchair access (not WC). Music. Air-conditioned (£5)

BRITWELL SALOME Oxfordshire **map 2**

The Goose

Britwell Salome OX9 5LG
TEL: (01491) 612304 FAX: (01491) 614822
on B4009, just outside Watlington, 5 min from M40 junction 6

COOKING **4**
ENGLISH
£19–£56

An ordinary-looking pub with wooden tables and chairs, The Goose confounds expectations with its striking colours and seriously artistic ambitions: pictures for sale cover every available inch of wall space, and there's even a catalogue to accompany them. Menus, both à la carte and set price, are kept sensibly short, with just three options per course, and although a fondness for macho red meat main courses can seem slightly odd in today's climate, lovers of poultry and game will be pleased to find something of interest: from partridge with bubble and squeak to breast of Gressingham duck with flageolet beans.

Starters are attractively varied, offering a choice perhaps between cream of lentil and truffle soup, cheese soufflé, and ragoût of clams, while mains make a virtue of simplicity, taking in roast rack of lamb with purple-sprouting broccoli, or sea bass with spinach and tomato sauce. Desserts rarely venture beyond familiar territory, embracing pannacotta, chocolate brownie, and lemon cheesecake. Reports variously suggest that sauces, portions and wine glasses might be more generous, although the short, sensibly compiled wine list is charitable enough with choice under £20, starting with house French and Italian at £11.50.

CHEF/PROPRIETOR: Chris Barber and Michael North OPEN: Tue to Sun L 12 to 2, Tue to Sat D 7 to 9 CLOSED: 25 Dec MEALS: alc L Tue to Sat (main courses £13 to £20). Set L Tue to Sat £10, Set D and Sun L £21 (2 courses) to £26. Light L menu available Tue to Sat SERVICE: not inc, 10% for parties of 8 or more CARDS: Delta, MasterCard, Switch, Visa DETAILS: 42 seats. 20 seats outside. Private parties: 32 main room. Car park. Children's helpings. No smoking in dining room. Music (£5)

BROADHEMBURY Devon map 2

Drewe Arms

Broadhembury EX14 3NF
TEL: (01404) 841267 FAX: (01404) 841765
off A373, between Cullompton and Honiton

COOKING **3**
SEAFOOD
£29–£59

Positioned at the more upmarket end of the pub/restaurant scale, this fifteenth-century custard-hued inn stands next to the church at the centre of a quaint village of thatched cottages. Its somewhat idiosyncratic décor shows artistic sensibilities, and the predominantly fish-themed prints covering the walls illustrate the kitchen's passion. Indeed, the menu is almost exclusively piscine, with only a couple of token meat offerings and nothing for vegetarians. The main set-price three-course menu is accompanied by a list of daily specials, both dealing principally in straightforward and appealing treatments ranging from old favourites to modern classics. It is all described rather tersely, and when the food arrives it usually turns out to be as simple as described: 'scallops – seared – rouille', 'sea bass – pesto', 'fillet of brill – rémoulade sauce' and 'sea bream – orange and chilli'. There is also a list of sandwiches for those after a snack. House wines from £11.50 are the starting point of a short list, which stays mostly under £20 and includes a page of half-bottles.

CHEFS: Andrew and Nigel Burge PROPRIETORS: Nigel, Kerstin and Andrew Burge OPEN: all week L 12 to 2 (1.30 Sun), Mon to Sat D 7 to 9.30 CLOSED: Christmas, 31 Dec MEALS: alc (main courses £10 to £23.75). Set L and D £27. Bar menu available SERVICE: not inc CARDS: Delta, MasterCard, Switch, Visa DETAILS: 40 seats. 40 seats outside. Private parties: 24 main room. Car park. Children's helpings. No smoking in dining room. Wheelchair access (also WC). No music

BROADWAY Worcestershire map 5

▲ Dormy House

Willersey Hill, Broadway WR12 7LF
TEL: (01386) 852711 FAX: (01386) 858636
EMAIL: reservations@dormyhouse.co.uk
WEB SITE: www.dormyhouse.co.uk
just off A44, 1m NW of Broadway

COOKING **5**
MODERN EUROPEAN-PLUS
£30–£65

This is just the sort of place that visitors hope to find in the Cotswolds: a seventeenth-century farmhouse conversion set grandly above the Vale of Evesham with expansive views, mellow stone walls and oak beams, and yet with every last word in twenty-first-century comfort. There are conference facilities, and 'leisure facilities' for those who enjoy working out in a gym, as well as a tapestried conservatory dining room where Alan Cutler's busy dinner menus seem to require a small army to put together: there is no overlap between the 30-plus dishes on the combined table d'hôte, à la carte and 'gourmet' menus.

While there is a perfectly sound classical foundation to the cooking – in the shape of pork fillet with glazed apple, or corn-fed chicken breast with braised cabbage and smoked bacon – the food is not without a bit of spice: a mango and coriander relish accompanies monkfish terrine, and grilled tiger prawns and scampi come with saffron rice on a cardamom sauce. These surroundings also demand a little cosseting, and the kitchen obliges with smoked haddock risotto accompanied by a poached egg and hollandaise, and a hot banana and pecan tart served with honey ice cream. Fair prices characterise the wine list, which takes a serious trawl through France with back-up from the rest of Europe and the New World. A few favourites are picked out, and a ten-strong, mainly French house selection comes in under £20.

CHEF: Alan Cutler PROPRIETOR: Jorgen Philip-Sorensen OPEN: Sun L 12.30 to 2, all week D 7 to 9.30 (9 Sun) CLOSED: 24 to 26 Dec MEALS: alc (main courses £16.50 to £23). Set L £19.95, Set D £32.50 to £37.50. Bar menu available SERVICE: not inc CARDS: Amex, Delta, Diners, MasterCard, Switch, Visa DETAILS: 80 seats. Private parties: 40 main room, 8 and 14 private rooms. Car park. Vegetarian meals. No children under 6 at D. No smoking in 1 dining room. Occasional music. Air-conditioned ACCOMMODATION: 48 rooms, all with bath/shower. TV. Phone. B&B £75 to £179. Rooms for disabled. Baby facilities (*The Which? Hotel Guide*)

BROCKENHURST Hampshire **map 2**

Simply Poussin

The Courtyard, Brookley Road,
Brockenhurst SO42 7RB
TEL: (01590) 623063 FAX: (01590) 623144
EMAIL: sales@simplypoussin.co.uk
WEB SITE: www.simplypoussin.co.uk

COOKING **3**
MODERN BRITISH
£25–£53

As the name indicates, this is the less formal sibling of the original Poussin, now at Lyndhurst (see entry). In the centre of town its sign above an archway identifies The Courtyard, where you will find a small, cream-painted restaurant decorated with Ronald Searle wine cartoons. Karl Wiggins cooks a brasserie-style menu taking in smoked salmon rolls with avocado salsa, asparagus in puff pastry with spinach and beurre blanc, and main courses such as herb-crusted fillet of cod, and steak au poivre. Roast saddle of lamb at inspection was a good piece of meat, accurately cooked and served on a highly accomplished stock reduction sauce. Opinions of the hot passion fruit soufflé differ, but an inventive dessert partnering toasted pineapple with coconut ice-cream, gingered rice and caramel has been applauded. Service is efficient enough, though it could do with a bit of cheering up. The wine list on the back of the menu darts between hemispheres to pick up interesting bottles, some available by the glass; house Sauvignon and Gamay, from Touraine, are £9.95.

CHEF: Karl Wiggins PROPRIETOR: Le Poussin Ltd OPEN: Tue to Sat 12 to 2, 7 to 10 CLOSED: 25 and 26 Dec, 1 Jan MEALS: alc D (main courses £10 to £17). Set L £10 (2 courses) SERVICE: 10% (optional) at D, not inc at L, card slips closed CARDS: Amex, Delta, MasterCard, Switch, Visa DETAILS: 30 seats. 6 seats outside. Private parties: 30 main room. Car park. No smoking. Music

BROMSGROVE Worcestershire map 5

▲ Grafton Manor

Grafton Lane, Bromsgrove B61 7HA
TEL: (01527) 579007 FAX: (01527) 575221
EMAIL: steven@grafman.u-net.com
WEB SITE: www.graftonmanorhotel.co.uk
off B4091, 1½m SW of Bromsgrove

COOKING **4**
MODERN INDIAN/EUROPEAN
£31–£53

Although only parts of the original Elizabethan manor remain – the rest was destroyed by fire in the early eighteenth century – the red-brick and sandstone house standing in 25 acres of grounds still charms with its moulded plaster ceilings, stone carvings and family coat of arms. The kitchen is unusual in that it injects a few Indian ideas into its country-house style: less a consequence of its proximity to Birmingham than a result of Simon Morris's fascination with, and trips to, the subcontinent.

In among the goats' cheese tart, pink-roast breast of duck, and salmon with avocado purée might be Bombay prawns and chutney, or marinated chicken with aloo palak mash. The common denominator is a lively sense of flavours, whatever their origin, taking in rainbow trout with aubergine salsa and horseradish sauce, as well as a stem ginger and Kahlua icebox cake served with a chocolate sorbet. Some reliable bottles, intelligent sourcing and reasonable pricing combine to make the wine list interesting and user-friendly. House Vins de Pays d'Oc are £9.80.

CHEFS: Simon Morris and William Henderson PROPRIETORS: the Morris family OPEN: Sun to Fri L 12 to 1.30, all week D 7 to 9.30 MEALS: Set L £20.50, Set D £27.85 to £32.75 SERVICE: not inc, card slips closed CARDS: Amex, Delta, Diners, MasterCard, Switch, Visa DETAILS: 60 seats. Private parties: 60 main room, 60 private room. Car park. Vegetarian meals. Children's helpings. No smoking in dining room. Wheelchair access (not WC). No music ACCOMMODATION: 9 rooms, all with bath/shower. TV. Phone. B&B £85 to £150. Rooms for disabled (*The Which? Hotel Guide*)

BRUTON Somerset map 2

Truffles

95 High Street, Bruton BA10 0AR
TEL/FAX: (01749) 812255
EMAIL: trufflesbruton@tinyworld.co.uk

COOKING **5**
MODERN BRITISH
£24–£43

The Botterills' smart restaurant is located in a stone-built house in a peaceful Somerset village. Crisp white napery and dark blue upholstered chairs lend a sense of comfort to the compact interior, but don't expect traditional English heritage cooking. The owners have been to Australia since the last Guide appeared, drawing inspiration from the latest in Pacific Rim fusion cooking while they were there. Among results are a Thai-style, lemon grass-scented broth with king prawns and shiitake mushrooms, and a main course of fillets of grey mullet stuffed with crab mousse and dressed in soy and ginger. Other successful combinations have included bradan rost (roasted hot-smoked salmon) with celeriac and apple salad, and duck confit on mustard mash sauced with shallots and Madeira. Well-conceived vegetarian dishes, meanwhile, take in baked, stuffed aubergine topped with mozzarella and served with a tomato and thyme sauce. Nor does invention flag at dessert stage, which might feature iced white chocolate and date parfait with lemon sauce, or coconut and rum mousse with gingered bananas, alongside the house gâteau (layers of sponge, chocolate mousse and meringue). Seven house wines from £11.95, plenty of half-bottles, and careful choices in the southern hemisphere distinguish the wine list.

CHEF: Martin Bottrill PROPRIETORS: Denise and Martin Bottrill OPEN: Tue to Sat D only 7 to 10 (weekday L by arrangement; open for Mothering/Easter Sun L) CLOSED: 2 weeks Feb MEALS: Set D £13.95 (2 courses, Tue to Thur) to £24.50 SERVICE: not inc, card slips closed CARDS: Delta, MasterCard, Switch, Visa DETAILS: 30 seats. Private parties: 20 main room, 10 and 20 private rooms. Vegetarian meals. No children under 8. Wheelchair access (not WC). No music. Air-conditioned (£5)

BUCKLAND Gloucestershire **map 5**

▲ Buckland Manor

Buckland WR12 7LY
TEL: (01386) 852626 FAX: (01386) 853557
EMAIL: enquire@bucklandmanor.com
WEB SITE: www.bucklandmanor.com
off B4632, 2m SW of Broadway

COOKING **5**
MODERN BRITISH
£37–£86

Built of warm Cotswold stone, next door to a thirteenth-century church, the house looks like every American visitor's dream of what olde Englande was like. Inside it is all tapestries, friezes, oil paintings, log fires, rugs, hangings, and heavy fabrics and cushions, plus a small army of attentive, observant and knowledgeable staff who make it their job to see that 'you get to feel fairly special'. The menu's rather precious language – a pillow of smoked salmon, herb froth, and sea scallops (what other kind are we to expect?) – is echoed in a fastidious approach that takes in an array of extras from 'fabulous' appetisers through an old-fashioned mid-meal sorbet to accomplished petits fours: 'the kitchen staff must be as numerous as the waiting staff.'

This industry pervades the food – mushroom consommé comes with tortellini filled with smoked quail, for instance – which combines well-sourced materials with a generous helping of luxuries: scallop and truffle are baked in brioche, and served on a scallop and cabbage rosette to start, and foie gras tortellini accompany fillet of Angus beef. The sense of pampering derived from comforting textures extends to desserts of Grand Marnier soufflé with orange flower ice cream, and banana tarte Tatin with chocolate brownie ice cream. The formally bound wine list is bulging with goodies, its pages lined with the pick of estates from Bordeaux, California, Australia and elsewhere but, to prove it has something for everyone, bottles under £25 have been expanded to around 50. These include many of the long list of house wines, starting at £16.50.

CHEF: Kenneth Wilson PROPRIETORS: Roy and Daphne Vaughan OPEN: all week 12.30 to 1.45, 7.30 to 9 MEALS: alc (main courses £24.50 to £27.50). Set L Mon to Sat £28.50, Set L Sun £24.50. Light L menu available SERVICE: not inc CARDS: Amex, Delta, Diners, MasterCard, Switch, Visa DETAILS: 36 seats. 30 seats outside. Private parties: 36 main room. Car park. No children under 12. Jacket and tie. No smoking in dining room. No music ACCOMMODATION: 13 rooms, all with bath/shower. TV. Phone. B&B £200 to £345. No children under 12. Swimming pool (*The Which? Hotel Guide*)

BUCKLAND Oxfordshire map 2

▲ Lamb at Buckland

Lamb Lane, Buckland SN7 8QN
TEL: (01367) 870484 FAX: (01367) 870675

COOKING **2**
BRITISH
£25–£57

The ovine-decorated bar has the same menu but is smaller than the more stylish no-smoking dining room of this stone-built Cotswold pub. Paul Barnard, more chef/patron than mine host, uses fine ingredients cooked simply and accurately and continues to please reporters. The menu extends to globe artichoke with seafood bourride, a morel and pecorino risotto, and orange and cardamom tart, but traditional dishes evoke most praise. A 'perfect Sunday lunch' of soft herring roes, then 'wonderful roast beef with roast parsnips and succulent red cabbage' finished with a generous slice from a large treacle pudding with vanilla-flecked custard. Other combinations of traditional and exotic include Peruvian style pot-roasted pork, and roast saddle of lamb with couscous. Six house wines start from £10.25, and 50 more bottles are intelligently chosen from France and the New World.

CHEF: Paul Barnard PROPRIETORS: Paul and Peta Barnard OPEN: all week 12 to 2 (2.45 Sun), 6.30 to 9.30 CLOSED: 25 and 26 Dec MEALS: alc (main courses £7.50 to £21). Set L Sun £20.95 SERVICE: not inc, card slips closed CARDS: Amex, Delta, MasterCard, Switch, Visa DETAILS: 118 seats. 60 seats outside. Private parties: 70 main room, 18 private room. Car park. Vegetarian meals. Children's helpings. No smoking in dining room. Wheelchair access (not WC). Music ACCOMMODATION: 4 rooms, all with bath/shower. TV. Phone. B&B £42.50 to £59.50 (£5)

BUCKLERS HARD Hampshire map 2

▲ Master Builder's House Hotel, Riverside Restaurant

NEW ENTRY

Bucklers Hard SO42 7XB
TEL: (01590) 616253 FAX: (01590) 616297
EMAIL: res@themasterbuilders.co.uk
WEB SITE: www.themasterbuilders.co.uk

COOKING **3**
MODERN EUROPEAN
£31–£53

Wooden sailing ships used to be built at Bucklers Hard, where the Master Builder used to live – in one of a group of red-brick houses – on Lord Montagu's estate on the Beaulieu estuary. It is a serene setting, with impressive views, a light and airy dining room with lots of wood, beige-grey colours, and paintings by John Illsley: of Dire Straits fame, and owner of the George Hotel (see entry, Yarmouth) and East End Arms (see entry, East End). The lack of pretension is appreciated, and although the appetiser crisps and peanuts and the offer to grind pepper over everything are rather at odds with the location and potential, the food is thankfully not too ambitious, taking in monkfish medallions with herb butter sauce, and braised venison with wild mushrooms, red cabbage and onion sauce. Fine raw materials are behind the success of tagliatelle with tiny flavourful mussels and strips of salmon, and the organic vegetables that need to be ordered separately. Individual flavours and components are generally well rendered, although they may not always do a lot for each other when they meet on the plate, and desserts are not a highlight. Eleven varied house wines at £12.50 make a promising start to a global list arranged in price bands.

CHEF: Denis Rhoden PROPRIETORS: Jeremy Willcock and John Illsley OPEN: all week 12 to 3, 7 to 10 MEALS: alc (main courses £12.50 to £17.50). Set L £16.95 (2 courses) to £19.95, Set D £29.50 SERVICE: not inc, card slips closed CARDS: Amex, Delta, MasterCard, Switch, Visa DETAILS: 60 seats. 26 seats outside. Private parties: 80 main room, 40 private room. Car park. Vegetarian meals. Children's helpings. No cigars in dining room. Wheelchair access (also WC). Occasional music. Air-conditioned ACCOMMODATION: 25 rooms, all with bath/shower. TV. Phone. B&B £115 to £245

BURFORD Oxfordshire **map 5**

▲ Jonathan's at the Angel

NEW ENTRY

14 Witney Street, Burford OX18 4SN
TEL: (01993) 822714 FAX: (01993) 822069
EMAIL: jo@theangel-uk.com
WEB SITE: www.theangel-uk.com

COOKING **5**
MODERN EUROPEAN/BRASSERIE
£29–£51

This newcomer opened too late to get into last year's Guide. Jonathan Lewis – previously chef at Wesley House, Winchcombe (see entry) – and his wife have moved to this pretty sixteenth-century coaching inn, which they describe as a brasserie with rooms, though it has the feel of a French auberge. Woodblock flooring, dark ceiling beams, pale walls and scrubbed wooden tables add to the impression; the menu is chalked up on a board, and the place has a happy atmosphere, enhanced by unobtrusive, efficient service.

A short, keenly priced menu is wide-ranging, delivering starters such as spicy fried kofta with flat bread, salad leaves and yoghurt, before more traditional offerings of tender roast chump of lamb with beans and a spring onion and pea mash, or decently sized sirloin of beef topped with a spicy crust of crushed pepper and herbs. Desserts may include simple dishes such as summer pudding with coulis and clotted cream, or moist, flavoursome tiramisù. Among home-made breads (charged at £1.30 and worth it) may be a soft, textured cob served warm. Although the short wine list may lack range, prices (from £12.75) are reasonable and eight table wines are available by the glass.

CHEF: Jonathan Lewis PROPRIETORS: Jonathan and Josephine Lewis OPEN: Thur to Sun L 12 to 2, Tue to Sat D 7 to 9.30 (later closing Sat eve and Sun L) MEALS: alc (main courses £9 to £15). (Set L and D by arrangement) SERVICE: not inc, 10% for parties of 10 or over, card slips closed CARDS: Delta, MasterCard, Switch, Visa DETAILS: 34 seats. 20 seats outside. Private parties: 18 main room. Vegetarian meals. Children's helpings. No children under 9. No smoking in dining room. Music ACCOMMODATION: 3 rooms, all with bath/shower. TV. Phone. Room only £65 to £95 (£5)

The 2003 Guide will be published before Christmas 2002. Reports on meals are most welcome at any time of the year, but are particularly valuable in the spring (no later than June). Send them to The Good Food Guide, *FREEPOST, 2 Marylebone Road, London NW1 4DF. Or email your report to goodfoodguide@which.net*

See inside the front cover for an explanation of the symbols used at the tops of entries.

BURNHAM MARKET Norfolk map 6

Fishes'

Market Place, Burnham Market PE31 8HE
TEL: (01328) 738588 FAX: (01328) 730534

COOKING **3**
SEAFOOD
£21–£48

Gillian Cape has put Fishes' on the market, but says she is in no hurry to sell. While retirement hovers as a tantalising prospect in the middle distance, she remains as fully committed as ever to the bright, homely restaurant she has been running for nearly 30 years. Best get in while you still can, then, for some simple and appealing fish cookery based on fresh local supplies. It takes in the likes of deeply flavoured crab soup, mussels baked with garlic, and main courses such as grilled sea bass with lemon and dill, or a duo of poached salmon and halibut with hollandaise. Skate wings come in their traditional dress of capers and black butter, while the shellfish plate is a generous assemblage of crab, shrimps, prawns, crevettes, mussels and oysters. Finish with plum cheesecake, perhaps, or the signature 'pile-it-high' rhubarb meringue pie. The handwritten wine list majors on whites, of course, with house Dordognes at £9.

CHEFS: Gillian Cape and Sarah Leech PROPRIETOR: Gillian Cape OPEN: Tue to Sun L 12 to 2, Tue to Sat D 6.45 to 9 (later for bookings) CLOSED: 24 to 27 Dec, 3 weeks Jan MEALS: alc (main courses L £7.50 to £9, D £8.25 to £14.50). Set L weekdays £13.50, Set L weekends £15.50 SERVICE: not inc, card slips closed CARDS: Amex, Delta, Diners, MasterCard, Switch, Visa DETAILS: 40 seats. Private parties: 14 main room. Children's helpings. No children under 5 after 8.30. No smoking in dining room. No music (£5)

▲ Hoste Arms £

The Green, Burnham Market PE31 8HD
TEL: (01328) 738777 FAX: (01328) 730103
WEB SITE: www.hostearms.co.uk
on B1155, 5m W of Wells

COOKING **3**
MODERN EUROPEAN/PACIFIC RIM
£24–£48

More smart modern country hotel than old-fashioned inn, this substantial buttercup-yellow seventeenth-century building on the village green none the less maintains an informal atmosphere. Locals mingle with tourists in the bar, and there are also three dining areas plus a patio garden where food is served in summer. One menu is offered throughout, the lunch version featuring a selection of sandwiches. The cooking style takes in a broad range of contemporary influences from around the world, but at the heart of it is some fine native produce, much of it local, including oysters from Burnham Creek and fish landed at nearby Cromer.

Starters typically range from salmon and chilli fishcake with sweet and salt spinach and tsatsiki, to confit of duck on pancetta and chorizo salad, while main courses encompass whole grilled sole with lemon cockle butter, spicy Szechuan chicken, and pot-roast lamb shank with a rosemary jus. Wines also cover a wide range of styles and nationalities, with prices starting a touch under £10 for full-fruited southern French and reaching into three-figure sums for mature claret. A short version of the list makes choosing easier and features 12 wines available in two sizes of glass.

CHEF: Andrew McPherson PROPRIETOR: Paul Whittome OPEN: all week 12 to 2, 7 to 9 MEALS: alc (main courses £8 to £15.50) SERVICE: not inc CARDS: Delta, MasterCard, Switch, Visa DETAILS: 140 seats. 80 seats outside. Private parties: 80 main room. Car park. Vegetarian meals. Children's helpings. No smoking in 1 dining room. Wheelchair access (also WC). No music. Air-conditioned ACCOMMODATION: 28 rooms, all with bath/shower. TV. Phone. B&B £66 to £126. Rooms for disabled (*The Which? Hotel Guide*)

BURNSALL North Yorkshire map 8

▲ Devonshire Fell

Burnsall BD23 6BT
TEL: (01756) 729000 FAX: (01756) 729009
EMAIL: sales@thedevonshirearms.co.uk
WEB SITE: www.devonshirefell.co.uk

COOKING **3**
MODERN BRITISH
£23–£50

This brightly decorated hotel and restaurant is set into the side of a fell above the village of Burnsall, with a fabulous view down to the village and over the Dale. It is under the same ownership – and as the Guide went to press was temporarily under the same executive chef – as Devonshire Arms (see entry, Bolton Abbey). The menu is concise to the point of terseness, which reflects the food's underlying simplicity, especially at lunchtime, when a twice-baked cheese soufflé with tomato coulis might be on offer. Dinner brings a four-way choice at each stage, perhaps taking in roast chump of lamb with pea purée and lamb jus, or roast chicken with thyme crushed potatoes and firm green beans, served with a dark, sticky red wine reduction.

The range also takes in a starter of beef carpaccio with balsamic vinegar and beurre blanc, and pan-fried scallops with truffle oil and champagne velouté, although vegetarians options are few. Well-presented desserts run to strawberry clafoutis with rhubarb compote, and iced chocolate soufflé. Service has been described as efficient but cool. The short wine list, laid out in no particular order, has a few decent choices under £20, with house wines £9.95.

CHEF: Steve Williams PROPRIETORS: The Duke and Duchess of Devonshire OPEN: all week 11.30 to 2.30, 6.30 to 10 MEALS: alc (main courses £8.50 to £17). Set L Sun £15.95 SERVICE: not inc CARDS: Amex, Delta, Diners, MasterCard, Switch, Visa DETAILS: 26 seats. 40 seats outside. Private parties: 70 main room, 70 private room. Car park. Children's helpings. No smoking in dining room. Wheelchair access (also WC). Music ACCOMMODATION: 12 rooms, all with bath/shower. TV. Phone. B&B £70 to £140 (*The Which? Hotel Guide*)

BURPHAM West Sussex map 3

▲ Burpham Country House

NEW ENTRY

Burpham BN18 9RJ
TEL: (01903) 882160 FAX: (01903) 884627

COOKING **2**
ANGLO-FRENCH/SWISS
£35–£42

Don't be put off by the dead-end sign. Narrow lanes lead to this peaceful village hidden in the Downs, where the 'Gothicky, cottagey' eighteenth-century former shooting lodge proves to be 'the epitome of an English country-house hotel', complete with chintzy lounge, conservatory and pleasantly appointed dining room. The food is characterised by sound cooking of good ingredients, from simple starters of smoked trout timbale with asparagus, or a tian of new potatoes with crab and smoked salmon, to a main course such as pink-cooked loin of lamb on ratatouille.

Marianne Walker is Swiss, so a few native items appear, notably spätzli (combined with smoked chicken), butterleberli (strips of calf's liver with onions, sage, garlic and wine jus), and Apfelstrudel, although the owners – who do most of the service – may well retire during the currency of this edition. Wines make a commendable effort to stay affordable, starting with house French red and white at £11.

CHEF: Stephen Piggott PROPRIETORS: George and Marianne Walker OPEN: Tue to Sat D only 7.30 to 8.45 MEALS: Set D £21 (2 courses) to £25 SERVICE: not inc, card slips closed CARDS: Amex, Delta, MasterCard, Switch, Visa DETAILS: 35 seats. Private parties: 40 main room, 20 private room. Car park. Vegetarian meals. No children under 12. No smoking in dining room. Occasional music ACCOMMODATION: 10 rooms, all with bath/shower. TV. Phone. B&B £42.50 to £110. No children under 12 (£5)

BURRINGTON Devon map 1

▲ Northcote Manor

Burrington EX37 9LZ
TEL: (01769) 560501 FAX: (01769) 560770
EMAIL: rest@northcotemanor.co.uk
WEB SITE: www.northcotemanor.co.uk
on A377 between Umberleigh and Crediton, 4m NW of Chulmleigh

COOKING **3**
MODERN BRITISH
£35–£62

A sense of 'well-being and cosseting' pervades this stone-built, wisteria-clad eighteenth-century house in the wilds of Devon, helped by pretty views, mullioned windows, a big oak door, and accomplished service. The menu adds its own pampering note, in the form of smoked salmon and caviar blini, and a creamy, generously endowed crab risotto served with a pool of lemony hollandaise. It relies on more than just luxury materials for effect, however, combining skill and judgement in, for example, a white onion velouté infused with rosemary (that contrived to be 'pungent yet delicate' at the same time) and in crisp-skinned, pink breast of duck in a dark brown cassis-based gravy. Potato accompaniments have included light and fluffy creamed ones, and a version of sarladaise made with onion and bacon; extra vegetables are available on request. Desserts tend towards the rich end of the spectrum, offering perhaps a crisp, puff pastry case of bananas cooked in butterscotch, served with coconut ice cream, and a smooth lightly set pannacotta with a compote of summer fruits. Owner David Boddy understandably promotes his native New Zealand wines (mostly whites), but doesn't stint on good bottles from elsewhere, starting with French and Chilean house wines at £12.95.

CHEF: Chris Dawson PROPRIETOR: David Boddy OPEN: all week 12 to 1.30, 7 to 9.30 MEALS: Set L £18 (2 courses) to £25, Set D £32.50 SERVICE: not inc, card slips closed CARDS: Amex, Delta, Diners, MasterCard, Switch, Visa DETAILS: 40 seats. Private parties: 50 main room, 24 private room. Car park. Vegetarian meals. Children's helpings. No children under 12. No smoking in dining room. Occasional music ACCOMMODATION: 11 rooms, all with bath/shower. TV. Phone. B&B £123.75 to £250 (*The Which? Hotel Guide*) (£5)

BURTON ON THE WOLDS Leicestershire **map 5**

Langs

Horse Leys Farm, 147 Melton Road,
Burton on the Wolds LE12 5TQ
TEL/FAX: (01509) 880980
EMAIL: langsrestaurant@amserve.net
WEB SITE: www.langsrestaurant.com

COOKING **3**
MODERN EUROPEAN
£26–£45

The dining room of this low, brick farmhouse on the B676 is decorated with wicker chairs and oft-seen prints, and the cooking strikes a familiar note too, in the form of wild mushroom risotto or breast of guinea fowl with asparagus. The occasional bold leap, however, results in smoked haddock broth with Bloody Mary syrup. The food is well cooked and presented, although for the most part doesn't pretend to excitement or fireworks: 'pretty basic' was one reporter's view of the house salad with smoked bacon and croûtons, and smoked salmon is smoked salmon. Nevertheless, meals have 'the right shape', in the sense that main courses provide something of a peak: perhaps a hearty dish of venison with red wine sauce, or ribeye steak in a well-flavoured jus with a galette of winter vegetables. A sound array of puddings might include gooey Eaton (sic) Mess, or a not-too-sweet bread-and-butter pudding, while a mainly French list starts with house wine at £12.50.

CHEF: Gordon Lang PROPRIETORS: Gordon Lang and Paul Simms OPEN: Tue to Fri and Sun L 12.15 to 2 (2.30 Sun), all week D 7.15 to 9.45 (10 Sat) CLOSED: 25 Dec, bank hols MEALS: alc D (main courses £10 to £15). Set L £12.95 (2 courses) to £15 SERVICE: not inc, card slips closed CARDS: Delta, MasterCard, Switch, Visa DETAILS: 48 seats. 8 seats outside. Private parties: 56 main room, 12 private room. Car park. Vegetarian meals. No smoking in dining room. Wheelchair access (also WC). Occasional music

BURY ST EDMUNDS Suffolk **map 6**

Maison Bleue

30/31 Churchgate Street,
Bury St Edmunds IP33 1RG
TEL: (01284) 760623 FAX: (01284) 761611
WEB SITE: www.maisonbleue.co.uk

COOKING **2**
FRENCH
£24–£48

This is the kind of 'fishy place' one might find across the Channel, and reporters would not object if it cloned itself in every market town hereabouts. Perch at the long bar for a quick lunch, or book a table at the front, and expect an appropriately Gallic welcome. Materials come both fresh and smoked, grilled and poached, ranging from humble sardines to swankier Dover sole, and taking in plates of shellfish (including langoustines and plump Colchester oysters), via smoked haddock and coriander fish cakes, to grilled black bream on ratatouille. Skate wing, just easing off the bone as it should, is served with capers and black butter. For meat eaters there might be slow-cooked shank of lamb in a red wine sauce. Puddings are ordinary, set meals are considered good value, and a reasonably priced list starts with French house wines at £9.95.

CHEF: Pascal Canevet PROPRIETOR: Régis Crépy OPEN: Tue to Sat 12 to 2.30, 7 to 9.30 (10 Fri and Sat) CLOSED: Jan MEALS: alc (main courses £9 to £16.50). Set L £9.95 (2 courses) to £14.95, Set D £19.95 SERVICE: not inc CARDS: Amex, Delta, MasterCard, Switch, Visa DETAILS: 65 seats. Private parties: 35 main room, 14 and 35 private rooms. Children's helpings. No smoking in dining room. Wheelchair access (not WC). Music

BUSHEY Hertfordshire map 3

St James

30 High Street, Bushey WD2 3DN
TEL: (020) 8950 2480 FAX: (020) 8950 4107

COOKING **2**
MODERN BRITISH
£28–£56

Opposite the parish church, this well-designed, modern restaurant (a welcome find outside London) displays its signature halo on menus and plates. But the vibes are bistroesque, not ecclesiastical; tables are formally dressed, and black-clad young staff are efficient and friendly. Vegetarian dishes (couscous with mozzarella and rocket pesto, say, or a filo parcel of Brie, leeks and roast pepper with a tomato and mango chutney) come as either starters or mains.

Fish predominates marginally over meat, but either can be plain or fancy: grilled sardines with bacon and avocado salad, or confit of duck with oriental vegetable terrine, to start. Then Dover sole meunière, or beef medallions with potato fondant, onion Soubise, asparagus and a port jus. Puds tends to be simple (perhaps jam sponge and custard, or fresh fruit with mango sorbet), and wines from France, Italy (a strong suit) and the New World start at £11.95.

CHEF: Simon Trussel PROPRIETORS: Simon Trussel and Alfonso la Cava OPEN: Mon to Sat 12 to 2.15, 6.30 to 9.45 CLOSED: 25 Dec, bank hols MEALS: alc (main courses £11 to £15). Set L Mon to Fri £13.95 (2 courses), Set D Mon to Fri £14.50 (2 courses) to £18.95 SERVICE: 10%, card slips closed CARDS: Amex, Delta, MasterCard, Switch, Visa DETAILS: 86 seats. Private parties: 65 main room, 45 private room. Vegetarian meals. No smoking in dining room. Wheelchair access (also men's WC). Music. Air-conditioned

CAMBRIDGE Cambridgeshire map 6

Midsummer House

Midsummer Common, Cambridge CB4 1HA
TEL: (01223) 369299 FAX: (01223) 302672
EMAIL: reservations@midsummerhouse.co.uk
WEB SITE: www.midsummerhouse.co.uk

COOKING **5**
FRENCH/MEDITERRANEAN
£35–£81

Midsummer House is on Midsummer Common, by the banks of the River Cam. As the name suggests, the conservatory dining room is indeed a salubrious spot to take a midsummer lunch, but it is equally beguiling in the evening, when the trees outside are garlanded with lights. Daniel Clifford's cooking rises fully to the grandeur of the setting, appreciably follows the seasons (the Mediterranean ones as well as our own), and is full of the scents of herbs from the restaurant's own kitchen garden: perhaps basil oil with a mille-feuille of red mullet, or a parsley jus with tortellini of snails and roast frogs' legs.

Technique is decidedly French, with the accent on gentle combinations and textures – fillet of pork with caramelised apples and sauté black pudding –

although dishes can be extremely busy. Just to take one example, a roast fillet of line-caught sea bass has come with noodles, ratatouille, tempura of anchovy, olive purée and a rosemary butter sauce. First courses tend to pile on the luxury materials, with white truffle oil being added to ravioli of quail with a cabbage purée, and a white truffle purée serving to aromatise seared scallops.

Ices and sorbets ease the passage of desserts: perhaps an orange sorbet with chocolate marquise. Service is generally prompt, and there is nothing wrong with the fine, extensive wine list that lower prices couldn't fix. A £20 budget won't exactly leave you spoiled for choice, unless you stick with the house selections, which open with a Côtes de Duras Sauvignon Blanc at £15.95.

CHEF: Daniel Clifford PROPRIETOR: Midsummer House Ltd OPEN: Tue to Sat 12 to 2, 7 to 10 CLOSED: 26 Dec to 9 Jan, 17 to 24 Apr, 21 Aug to 5 Sep MEALS: Set L £15 (2 courses) to £20, Set D £42 SERVICE: not inc, 10% for parties of 7 or more CARDS: Amex, Delta, MasterCard, Switch, Visa DETAILS: 50 seats. Private parties: 50 main room, 20 private room. No smoking in 1 dining room. Wheelchair access (not WC). No music (£5)

22 Chesterton Road 🍷

22 Chesterton Road, Cambridge CB4 3AX
TEL: (01223) 351880 FAX: (01223) 323814 — COOKING **4**
EMAIL: davidcarter@restaurant22.co.uk — MODERN EUROPEAN
WEB SITE: www.restaurant22.co.uk — £35–£50

What one reviewer calls 'a safe choice for a smart dinner in Cambridge', 22 Chesterton Road is a green-shuttered, terraced Victorian house a short stroll from the city centre. Green and salmon-pink décor adds to the period feel, and the small, formal and intimate dining room makes a neat impression with its white linen tablecloths and candles, while smartly turned-out staff deliver 'professional but friendly service'. A monthly-changing set-price dinner (four choices per course) offers an extra no-choice fish course at a £6 supplement – perhaps seafood risotto with Parmesan crisps – and if the food sometimes lacks the 'wow' factor, at least it is reliable. Simple, attractively presented dishes have included a warm ricotta and spinach tart with tomato butter to start, and a well-executed paupiette of salmon with roast fennel and lemon-scented potatoes.

Desserts have a comfortable feel, perhaps warm chocolate and stem ginger fondant with vanilla ice cream, or a knickerbocker-glory-style rhubarb fool with honey cream, toasted oats and sponge biscuits. In its efforts to please both traditionalists and those who prefer 'up-front' flavours, the wine list gathers together a number of fruity styles from the New World and elsewhere (look out for New Tuscans and Australians), to balance the more reserved French offerings. Four house wines start at £10.25 (£3 a glass).

CHEFS: Ian Reinhardt and Martin Cullum PROPRIETOR: David Carter OPEN: Tue to Sat D 7 to 9.45 CLOSED: 1 week Christmas to New Year MEALS: Set D £24.50 SERVICE: not inc CARDS: Amex, Delta, Diners, MasterCard, Switch, Visa DETAILS: 38 seats. Private parties: 26 main room, 12 private room. Vegetarian meals. No children under 10. Occasional music. Air-conditioned

All entries in the Guide are re-researched and rewritten every year, not least because restaurant standards fluctuate. Don't rely on an out-of-date Guide.

CAMPSEA ASHE Suffolk **map 6**

▲ Old Rectory

Campsea Ashe IP13 0PU — COOKING **2**
TEL/FAX: (01728) 746524 — ANGLO-FRENCH
on B1078, 1½m E of A12 — £29–£35

A couple visiting on a snowy night in January appreciated the 'delightful country-house ambience' that greeted them; and the fact that many guests appear to be regulars makes for a friendly dinner party atmosphere. 'Chef proprietor and bottle washer' Stewart Bassett makes commendable efforts to source all his materials from within 20 miles, a task made slightly easier by the fact that he eschews fashionable ingredients such as lemon grass and sticks to a traditional Anglo-French style of cooking that evolves by degrees. The format is a fixed-price menu of three courses, perhaps turning up red mullet with peppers, a main course of Norfolk venison with well-prepared vegetables and sauté potatoes, and chocolate-coated wafer baskets filled with mascarpone cheese to finish. France dominates the wine list, though there are a couple of pages representing other countries. House wines are £9.50.

CHEF/PROPRIETOR: Stewart Bassett OPEN: Mon to Sat D only 7.30 to 8.45 CLOSED: 1 week Christmas, 3 weeks Mar, 1 week Oct MEALS: Set D £19.50 SERVICE: not inc CARDS: Amex, Diners, MasterCard, Switch, Visa DETAILS: 50 seats. Private parties: 36 main room, 20 and 36 private rooms. Car park. Vegetarian meals. Children's helpings. No smoking in dining room. No music ACCOMMODATION: 7 rooms, all with bath/shower. B&B £45 to £78 (*The Which? Hotel Guide*)

CARLISLE Cumbria **map 10**

Magenta's

18 Fisher Street, Carlisle CA3 8RH — COOKING **4**
TEL/FAX: (01228) 546363 — MODERN ENGLISH/MEDITERRANEAN
£30–£45

'What a find in a city not known for its culinary highlights,' begins one report. The Taylor brothers started something by opening their vibrantly coloured cellar restaurant here three years ago. Daring is discernible in much that they do: attested by one reporter's starter of jelly-like stuffed pig's trotter with celeriac. Terrines (perhaps of foie gras, ham hock and leek) have suitably biting vinaigrettes, and a tomato balsamic dressing adds piquancy to tuna. More than one reader commends the ribeye of beef with braised oxtail and shallots, but it is perhaps desserts that are particularly cherished. Blueberry tart with cream cheese sorbet is the simple option, while those feeling more expansive might try the assiette of five tiny but intensely flavoured items, or a plate of chocolate variations incorporating fondant, roast hazelnut negus, milk chocolate mousse and white chocolate ice cream. Local cheeses from Crofton Farm are worth investigating too, and enthusiastic, knowledgeable staff serve with cheer. A well-priced wine list, opening at £12.95 for Chilean house wines, suits the cooking's vivid flavours.

CHEFS: Paul and Chris Taylor PROPRIETORS: Alison Watkin and Paul and Chris Taylor OPEN: Tue to Sat D 7 to 9.30 CLOSED: first week Jan MEALS: alc (main courses £13 to £14). Set D £19 SERVICE: not inc CARDS: Delta, MasterCard, Switch, Visa DETAILS: 32 seats. Private parties: 14 main room. Children's helpings. No smoking in dining room (£5)

Number 10

NEW ENTRY

10 Eden Mount, Stanwix, Carlisle CA3 9LY
TEL/FAX: (01228) 524183

COOKING **2**
MODERN BRITISH
£27–£44

Set in a Victorian townhouse at the end of a parade of shops just north of the city centre, Number 10 has been brought to the attention of the Guide after being in business for ten years. It is a small-scale operation run in a relaxed manner by husband and wife team Geoff and Isabel Ferguson: he cooks, she runs front-of-house. The seasonally changing menu blends a predominantly British style with wider European influences, and makes good use of local ingredients. An inspector experienced mixed results but found success in starters of a crisp filo pastry 'moneybag' containing light-textured melting goats' cheese, and an assemblage of warm smoked salmon bound in a potent garlic mayonnaise and set atop a crisp croûton. Fish appears to be a strong suit: among main courses to impress have been a firm, succulent piece of chargrilled marlin on buttered noodles, set off by a 'fab' salsa verde that added a 'galvanising burst of flavour'; and Parmesan-crusted grilled lemon sole accompanied by more of the garlic mayo in a Peter Rabbit eggcup. Well-made desserts have included strawberry shortcake with kirsch, and caramelised marmalade tart with lemon sorbet. Prices on the short wine list start at £9.95 for a pair of house Australians.

CHEF: G.S Ferguson PROPRIETORS: Mr and Mrs G.S Ferguson OPEN: Tue to Sat D only 7 to 9.30 CLOSED: Feb, last week Oct MEALS: alc (main courses £10 to £16.50) SERVICE: not inc, card slips closed CARDS: Amex, Delta, MasterCard, Switch, Visa DETAILS: 24 seats. Private parties: 24 main room. Vegetarian meals. Children's helpings. Wheelchair access (not WC). Music

CARTERWAY HEADS Northumberland map 10

▲ Manor House Inn £

Carterway Heads, Shotley Bridge DH8 9LX
TEL/FAX: (01207) 255268
on A68, 3m W of Consett

COOKING **1**
MODERN BRITISH
£20–£42

A reporter stopping off en route from Scotland to Suffolk was pleasantly surprised to find this small family-run pub/restaurant to be 'quite a delight'. Among its virtues are fine views over the Derwent Valley (weather allowing), as well as friendly service and great value. The same blackboard menu serves both bar and dining room, and choice is as varied as the menu is long, starters taking in anything from locally smoked kippers to pasta with courgettes, aubergines and blue cheese. Main courses run from fillet of beef with claret and juniper to escalope of veal with blood orange and whisky, and puddings might include fig and almond cake with a Baileys and butterscotch sauce. As this is a pub, you will find a decent range of real ales alongside the list of around 50 wines, which include a pair of house French at £8.95 and keep for the most part under £20.

CHEF: Peter Tiplady PROPRIETORS: Chris and Moira Brown OPEN: all week 12 to 2.30, 7 to 9.30 (9 Sun) CLOSED: D 25 Dec MEALS: alc (main courses £6 to £16) SERVICE: not inc, card slips closed CARDS: Amex, Delta, MasterCard, Switch, Visa DETAILS: 58 seats. 30 seats outside. Private parties: 50 main room. Car park. Vegetarian meals. Children's helpings. No smoking in 1 dining room. No music ACCOMMODATION: 4 rooms, all with bath/shower. TV. B&B £33 to £65 (£5)

CARTMEL Cumbria **map 8**

▲ Aynsome Manor

Cartmel LA11 6HH
TEL: (015395) 36653 FAX: (015395) 36016
EMAIL: info@aynsomemanorhotel.co.uk
WEB SITE: www.aynsomemanorhotel.co.uk
off A590, ½m N of village

COOKING **3**
ENGLISH COUNTRY HOUSE
£22–£39

Sitting between fells and sea, and with a commanding view of the Norman priory, Aynsome Manor seems to have developed a new sense of purpose since Nicholas Stopford arrived to head up the kitchen in the summer of 2000. More obvious emphasis on local produce is one result: Cumberland sausage goes into a starter portion of toad-in-the-hole with a red wine sauce, while roast leg of Cumbrian salt-marsh lamb comes with caramelised red onions and a minted reduction of port for a main.

The style remains essentially simple at lunchtime, with an obligatory soup making an appearance after the first course, followed perhaps by seared fresh-tasting fillet of red snapper, or chicken breast on celeriac mash with a rich Madeira sauce. Dinner might bring on the likes of venison and pheasant from nearby Holker estate fashioned into a terrine, or fillet of Fleetwood cod on prawn risotto with lemon and basil velouté. Desserts are still served from a trolley, complete with a bowl of whipped cream. The extensive wine list is pretty uneven in quality, but prices are fair throughout. Half a dozen house wines come from Chile, Australia and Italy, all at £11.65 a bottle.

CHEFS: Nicholas Stopford and Julian Wright PROPRIETORS: Tony, Margaret, Christopher and Andrea Varley OPEN: Sun L 12.30 to 1, Mon to Sat D 7 to 8.30 (residents only Sun D) CLOSED: Jan MEALS: Set L £13.75, Set D £18 to £22 SERVICE: not inc, card slips closed CARDS: Amex, Delta, MasterCard, Switch, Visa DETAILS: 30 seats. Private parties: 30 main room. Car park. Vegetarian meals. No children under 5 at D. No smoking in dining room. No music ACCOMMODATION: 12 rooms, all with bath/shower. TV. Phone. D,B&B £57 to £124. Baby facilities (*The Which? Hotel Guide*) (£5)

'[He is] indicative of a chef with a singular inability to bring out the best in (good) raw materials.' (On eating in the Midlands)

£ *means that it is possible to have a three-course meal, including coffee, half a bottle of house wine and service for £25 or less per person, at any time the restaurant is open, i.e. at dinner as well as lunch. It may be possible to spend considerably more than this, but by choosing carefully you should find £25 or less achievable.*

▲ Uplands

Haggs Lane, Cartmel LA11 6HD
TEL: (015395) 36248 FAX: (015395) 36848
EMAIL: uplands@kencomp.net
WEB SITE: www.uplands.uk.com
2½m SW of A590, 1m up road opposite Pig and Whistle

COOKING **4**
BRITISH
£23–£45

'Our old faithful' is how a couple of regular visitors think of Uplands, which Tom and Diana Peter have been running with commendable reliability for 17 years. It is a 'genteel' place, with a bright lounge, a dining room with a view, and a simple menu that reflects something of the region. The local butcher is an award-winner, game is bought from just across the valley (perhaps venison with blackcurrant and juniper sauce), and fish arrives from Fleetwood in the shape of sea bass (baked with ginger and spring onion), or Dover sole (grilled fillets with lemon butter).

Lunch might begin with a straight choice, the first a hallmark soup – such as curried butternut squash and orange, or pea, pear and watercress – which comes thick and hot in a large help-yourself tureen, accompanied by a whole small loaf straight from the oven. The salad alternative can be both busy and substantial, judging by grilled goats' cheese with anchovies in an onion tartlet on a tomato and fig salad. After a main-course choice of either fish or meat, cheese (typically four kinds) makes a viable alternative to desserts of fruit pavlova, or hot apricot and ginger pudding. Dinner turns three courses into four and offers an extra main dish. A 40-strong wine list, fairly priced and well balanced between Old and New Worlds, starts with six house wines at £11.50.

CHEF: Tom Peter PROPRIETORS: Tom and Diana Peter OPEN: Thur to Sun L 12.30 for 1 (1 sitting), Tue to Sun D 7.30 for 8 (1 sitting) MEALS: Set L £15.50, Set D £28.50 SERVICE: not inc, card slips closed CARDS: Amex, MasterCard, Switch, Visa DETAILS: 28 seats. Private parties: 30 main room. Car park. No children under 8. No smoking in dining room. No music ACCOMMODATION: 5 rooms, all with bath/shower. TV. Phone. D,B&B £88 to £156. No children under 8 (*The Which? Hotel Guide*) (£5)

CASTLE COMBE Wiltshire **map 2**

▲ Manor House, Bybrook Restaurant

Castle Combe SN14 7HR
TEL: (01249) 782206 FAX: (01249) 782159
EMAIL: enquiries@manor-house.co.uk
WEB SITE: www.exclusivehotels.co.uk
on B4039, 3m NW of junction with A420

COOKING **4**
ENGLISH
£31–£84

Manicured lawns, a stream, doves and the old manor house add up to a 'dream-like' setting, all a short hop from the M4. A great stone fireplace, and dark oak with the date 1664 carved into it, lend the baronial dining room a certain gravitas, although there are other bars, lounges and dining rooms as well. The full-on country-house approach takes in a mid-meal sorbet, a cornucopia of professionally made bread, and petits fours with coffee, as well as a range of busily garnished but well-judged dishes: seared scallops come with cauliflower purée, a potato 'net' and a vanilla nage for example.

Dishes are carefully put together, combinations are sometimes imaginative, and the food is highly satisfying without resorting to monster portions, producing loin of lamb with tarragon mash and garlic cream, and roast spiced halibut with risotto nero. Desserts tend towards old favourites, from crêpes suzette to a sweet-sour variation on strawberry vacherin. Service has varied from 'friendly' to 'off-hand' but seems on balance to be both amiable and intelligent. The price of dinner rises at the weekend, but weekday lunch is considered a bargain. Prestigious bottles pepper the wine list, and prices are not friendly, although ten house wines come in under £25.

CHEF: Mark Taylor PROPRIETOR: Manor House Hotel (Castle Combe) Ltd OPEN: all week L 12.15 to 2 (12.30 to 1.30 Sun), D 7 to 9 (9.30 Fri and Sat) MEALS: Set L Mon to Sat £12.95 (1 course) to £18.95, Set L Sun £23.50, Set D Sun to Thu £35, Set D Fri and Sat £45 SERVICE: not inc, card slips closed CARDS: Amex, Delta, Diners, MasterCard, Switch, Visa DETAILS: 100 seats. 20 seats outside. Private parties: 100 main room, 12 to 30 private rooms. Car park. Vegetarian meals. Children's helpings. No smoking in dining room. Wheelchair access (not WC). No music ACCOMMODATION: 46 rooms, all with bath/shower. TV. Phone. D,B&B £135 to £430. Rooms for disabled. Baby facilities. Swimming pool. Fishing (*The Which? Hotel Guide*)

CAUNTON Nottinghamshire **map 5**

Caunton Beck

NEW ENTRY

Main Street, Caunton NG23 6AB COOKING **2**
TEL: (01636) 636793 FAX: (01636) 636828 MODERN EUROPEAN/PACIFIC RIM
£20–£48

The Hopes have always taken hospitality seriously, opening long hours every day of the year, and functioning as a centre for eating, meeting and drinking. This converted sixteenth-century cottage opposite the village church is no exception: open plan with washed ochre walls and wooden tables, it has an appropriately informal atmosphere. Andrew Knight was listed as head chef at Brazz (see entry, Taunton) in the 1999 edition of the Guide, and his move from Taunton to Caunton has livened things up a bit.

Breakfasts and sandwiches are among the offerings, but the main menu (available throughout) takes a zestful contemporary approach, coming up with wasabi roasted quail, BLT of foie gras and plum tomatoes, and soft-shell crab with pak choi, although it also finds room for more straightforward things such as ribeye steak with béarnaise. An early inspection visit turned up a few inconsistencies, and some ingredients in search of improvement, although when it comes to real-time cooking (of a panaché of bream, bass, salmon and monk, served with lovage and saffron mash, for example) there is evident skill. Youthful service is eager to please, and a fairly priced pocket-sized wine list starts with house French at £10.50.

CHEFS: Andrew Knight and Paul Vidic PROPRIETORS: Michael, Valerie and Toby Hope, and Paul Vidic OPEN: all week 8 to 11 MEALS: alc (main courses £9 to £17). Set L and D exc Sat D £9 (2 courses) to £12. Breakfast and sandwich menu available SERVICE: none CARDS: Amex, Delta, Diners, MasterCard, Switch, Visa DETAILS: 120 seats. 40 seats outside. Private parties: 55 main room, 30 private room. Car park. Vegetarian meals. Children's helpings. No smoking in dining room. Wheelchair access (also WC). No music (£5)

CHADDESLEY CORBETT Worcestershire map 5

▲ Brockencote Hall

Chaddesley Corbett DY10 4PY
TEL: (01562) 777876 FAX: (01562) 777872
EMAIL: info@brockencotehall.com
WEB SITE: www.brockencotehall.com
on A448, Kidderminster to Bromsgrove road, just outside village

COOKING **4**
FRENCH
£25–£71

Set in 70 acres of parkland, complete with lake, is this impeccably elegant house. Jerôme Barbançon, who took over the kitchen in late 2000, maintains the French classical style set by his predecessor. The prix-fixe spares no effort, to judge from a choice of three main courses, including roast quail stuffed with wild mushrooms, served on bashed potatoes and Parma ham with sparse plops of Cabernet Sauvignon and orange sauce. Combinations on the carte may be more daring: witness a starter partnering caul-bound scallops with parsnip purée, caramelised pear croustillant and a lightly frothy curry sauce.

Frog legs and foie gras look set to become the new signature dish, accompanied in spring by Savoy cabbage, bacon and a velouté of Jerusalem artichoke; more artichokes – baby globes – have appeared in a lasagne alongside a chargrilled fillet of brill. Finish with praiseworthy chocolate and raspberry torte, or a walnut and hazelnut parfait with citrus and poppy-seed tuile. Service, mainly French, is 'professional' and 'friendly and helpful'. The wine list showcases fine French bottles (Bordeaux and Burgundy are notably well represented) with cursory nods elsewhere; seven house wines open at £12.80.

CHEF: Jerôme Barbançon PROPRIETORS: Alison and Joseph Petitjean OPEN: Sun to Fri L 12 to 1.30, all week D 7 to 9.30 MEALS: alc (main courses £13.50 to £22.50). Set L £12 (2 courses) to £15, Set D £27.50 SERVICE: net prices, card slips closed CARDS: Amex, Delta, Diners, MasterCard, Switch, Visa DETAILS: 50 seats. 10 seats outside. Private parties: 48 main room, 12 to 20 private rooms. Car park. Children's helpings. No smoking in dining room. Wheelchair access (also WC). Occasional music ACCOMMODATION: 17 rooms, all with bath/shower. TV. Phone. B&B £88 to £170. Rooms for disabled. Baby facilities (*The Which? Hotel Guide*) (£5)

CHAGFORD Devon map 1

▲ Gidleigh Park

Chagford TQ13 8HH
TEL: (01647) 432367 FAX: (01647) 432574
EMAIL: gidleighpark@gidleigh.co.uk
WEB SITE: www.gidleigh.com
from Chagford Square turn right at Lloyds Bank into Mill Street, take right fork after 150 yards and follow lane for 1½m

COOKING **8**
MODERN EUROPEAN
£47–£94

The black and white building hidden in the woods at the end of a long drive never ceases to appeal, as if in its own world: 'it feels like our best-kept secret, a wonderfully relaxing retreat.' For 25 years Paul and Kay Henderson have set the standard in the southwest, and while the décor may change slightly from year to year, the essentials remain: a log fire in the entrance hall with cats draped around it, oak panelling, big lounges with fine views, two dining rooms with acres of space between tables, and a refreshing lack of stuffiness.

Prices may be 'stellar' but it is a seductive place to spend money if you have it, made more so by the luxury ingredients that feature in so many dishes: a simple but unctuous slab of foie gras with a thin layer of Madeira jelly covering the plate, or veal sweetbreads with truffled potato purée. Smooth and creamy textures also lend the food a sumptuous dimension, as in a pastry case filled with a mushroom and truffle mix, supporting a quail breast and leg, in between which were five soft-poached quails' eggs, around it all a strewing of spring vegetables in a gentle balsamic dressing. This was a dish whose different components were 'unified by their sheer indulgence'.

Fish comes in for special commendation on account of its freshness and sympathetic handling, be it sea bass in 'absolutely prime condition', or turbot partnered with scallops, mushrooms, broad beans and peas (this in early February, incidentally). More seasonal-sounding for the time of year have been roast pheasant with chestnuts and lentils, and pink, gently gamey partridge. Presentation is such that 'it feels shameful destroying these creations', not least when it comes to desserts of hot chocolate soufflé served with a pistachio ice cream hiding inside a thin biscuit parcel, or the orange combination of mousse, tart, sorbet, and rich cream inside a circle of orange peel confit.

Among a formidable array of appetisers, the lemon sole goujons with tartare sauce stand out, and attention to fine detail pervades the strong crusty bread, petits fours, and breakfast. Although there have been disappointments, a combination of Paul Henderson's avuncular presence and Catherine Endacott's cheerful management generally ensures that service is smoothly professional. Buying-trips to Australia and South Africa have expanded those countries' entries on a wine list that already has a strong presence from California as well as a rich selection of classic French offerings. An extremely fair mark-up policy will tempt wine lovers to try even greater names and vintages than usual. Prices start at £17 but – unsurprisingly given the quality on offer – quickly move skywards. Eight wines by the glass range from £6 to £14.

CHEF: Michael Caines PROPRIETORS: Paul and Kay Henderson OPEN: all week 12.30 to 2, 7 to 9 MEALS: Set L £33 to £70, Set D £65 to £70. Light L available SERVICE: net prices, card slips closed CARDS: Delta, MasterCard, Switch, Visa DETAILS: 35 seats. Private parties: 8 main room. Car park. Vegetarian meals. No children under 7. No smoking in dining room. Wheelchair access (not WC). No music ACCOMMODATION: 14 rooms, all with bath/shower. TV. Phone. D,B&B £250 to £480. Baby facilities. Fishing

▲ 22 Mill Street

DEVON GFG 2002 COMMENDED

22 Mill Street, Chagford TQ13 8AW
TEL: (01647) 432244 FAX: (01647) 433101

COOKING **6**
MODERN EUROPEAN
£29–£48

Since the last edition of the Guide the bar-lounge area has been refurbished, the main dining room has been enlarged, and the old golden retriever has been replaced by a younger but equally somnolent model that yawns beside a fire in the entrance lobby. Fancy décor is conspicuous by its absence. The style remains personal, unpretentious, the food 'great value for money', and not just at lunchtime. Duncan Walker's quietly confident cooking knows how to soothe with comforting ideas: a tartlet of poached quails' eggs with spinach and béarnaise, or artichoke heart with mushrooms and a thick coating of glistening hollandaise. These are dishes betraying an easy mastery of classical techniques.

'Big confident flavours, simply presented' is how the cooking strikes reporters, who don't even mind the bossy footnote on the set menu: 'we will not allow any dishes to be substituted, please do not ask.' Risottos are well rendered, whether by themselves, as in a creamy Gorgonzola version, or (made with crab and red pepper) to accompany a fine piece of firm, accurately timed cod in prime condition. Dishes are well balanced and full flavoured, textures capably handled, contrasting, for example, the crisp outside and soft interior of calves' sweetbreads, served on a shredded cabbage surrounded by a pool of burned butter, capers and balsamic.

Among desserts, raspberry soufflé impresses for its lightness and honesty of flavour, the small jug of purée poured in at table adding to its appeal. Meals are supported by good bread, and a sensibly priced and intelligently selected wine list. Prices start at £12.50.

CHEFS: Duncan Walker and Dexter Fuller PROPRIETOR: Duncan Walker OPEN: Wed to Sat L 12.15 to 1.45, Mon to Sat D 7.15 to 9 CLOSED: 25 Dec, 1 Jan, 2 weeks Jan, 1 week May MEALS: Set L £17.50 (2 courses) to £28.50, Set D £25.50 (2 courses) to £32.50 SERVICE: net prices, card slips closed CARDS: MasterCard, Switch, Visa DETAILS: 21 seats. Private parties: 8 main room. No children under 13. No smoking in dining room. No music ACCOMMODATION: 2 rooms, both with bath/shower. TV. B&B £45

CHEESDEN Greater Manchester map 8

Nutters

Edenfield Road, Cheesden,
nr Rochdale OL12 7TY
TEL/FAX: (01706) 650167
on A680 between Norden and Rochdale

COOKING **6**
MODERN BRITISH
£27–£47

Nutters by name, and ... well, certainly somewhat idiosyncratic by nature. The restaurant itself is nothing out of the ordinary, though it is slightly tricky to find, being located in bleak, isolated moorland on the outskirts of Rochdale. Inside, the décor in soft shades of peach is serene and homely, and the welcome is professional. The quirkiness becomes apparent when reading the menu, which is enlivened with colourful descriptions and plenty of eye-catching combinations: monkfish with mango and coriander noodles and a Thai chilli and coconut sauce, for example, and medallions of pork marinated in paprika and pineapple and served with a sweet ginger and spring onion sauce.

Presentation lives up to the billing – one reporter's smoked salmon fillet arrived with pools of different sauces contained within fine onion rings – and flavours are no less impressive: a lightly grilled terrine of goats' cheese, leeks and Parma ham with a ginger ale vinaigrette left its reporter's taste buds tingling, while the sweetness of a piece of brill contrasted effectively with the bitterness of a chicory and orange sauce. Desserts too are 'delightful to look at': chocolate brownie, for example, with a hot, melting centre and a soufflé-like texture. Andrew Nutter is clearly a chef with a sense of fun and adventure, and these virtues are backed up with no small measure of skill, not to mention some fine local produce. Occasional lapses (under-seasoning, soggy pastry) cause some correspondents to moderate their otherwise lavish praise, but most are well satisfied. Burgundy and Bordeaux dominate the wine list, supported by some strong New World contributions, and prices are fair; house Australian is £10.95 a bottle.

CHEF: Andrew Nutter PROPRIETORS: Rodney, Jean and Andrew Nutter OPEN: Wed to Mon L 12 to 2 (4 Sun), D 6.45 (6.30 Sun) to 9.30 (9 Sun) CLOSED: first 2 weeks Aug MEALS: alc (main courses £10 to £17). Set L Sun £19.95, Set D £29.95 SERVICE: not inc, 10% for parties of 10 or more CARDS: Amex, Delta, MasterCard, Switch, Visa DETAILS: 84 seats. Private parties: 40 main room, 40 and 44 private rooms. Car park. Vegetarian meals. Children's helpings. No smoking in dining room. Wheelchair access (also WC). Music

CHELTENHAM Gloucestershire map 5

Le Champignon Sauvage

24–26 Suffolk Road, Cheltenham GL50 2AQ
TEL: (01242) 573449 FAX: (01242) 254365

COOKING 7
FRENCH
£27–£65

It is well worth the ten or fifteen minute stroll from the town centre to this 'sunny Mediterranean' restaurant, where a sumptuous blue and yellow bar-lounge, with a couple of big sofas, gives way to an equally smart and boldly coloured dining room, brightened further by its modern pictures and place settings. At first sight, David Everitt-Mathias's food might sound simple: 'scallops with ham and pickled apple purée', reads the menu, or 'breast of guinea fowl with a light foie gras mousse'. But as soon as first courses arrive, the detailed workmanship that is to be the theme of the meal becomes apparent. His fascination for small-scale items shows, for example, in three tiny torpedoes of the thinnest pasta, enclosing shredded braised beef, sitting on a pile of fine sauerkraut, set about with halved rounds of earthy-tasting beetroot. It may seem like 'the sort of thing you expect a Swiss watchmaker to turn out' but there is a point to it: by the end of a meal you realise that portion sizes have been well judged all along.

Underlying ideas are both sound and appealing. Roast breast of quail, for example, is paired with a minuscule sausage of leg meat, while a dark fillet of lightly cooked Wiltshire pork is partnered by moist black pudding and small balls of cabbage wrapped around minced, steamed pork. The simultaneous sense of unity and contrast that these dishes deliver is only marginally sidelined by the surrounding embroidery, as dishes are scattered, riddled, dotted, sprinkled or drizzled with various extras. Yet there are some relatively simple and classic combinations, for example a fat fillet of ultra-fresh red mullet, timed to the second, on a pile of orange-coloured couscous, given bite by blobs of black olive purée.

The food displays a confidence born of long service (the Everitt-Mathiasses have been here 15 years), and materials and technical skills are both first-class. If some aspects contribute to an old-fashioned impression – sticky, long-reduced sauces, and the same side-plate vegetables served with different main courses – then others are as fresh as can be: for example a wispy, frothy lemon mousse, disintegrating on the tongue like sherbet, served with a scoop of milk sorbet and a sweet-sharp lemon jelly. Either way, this was a dish of great delight that went beyond the sum of its component parts. Cheeses are varied, well kept, and arranged on a plate in order of strength, and service from Helen Everitt-Mathias is 'charm itself'. Traditionalists will be cheered by the wealth of choice on the mainly French list, though the New World gets a look-in too, with a fair number staying well under £20. Interest and value are maintained in the house selection, which features a French Sauvignon Blanc (£11.50) and a full-bodied Côtes du Frontonnais (£13.95).

CHEF: David Everitt-Matthias PROPRIETORS: David and Helen Everitt-Matthias OPEN: Tue to Sat 12.30 to 1.30, 7.30 to 9 MEALS: Set L £16.50 (2 courses) to £19.95, Set D Tue to Fri £19.50 (2 courses) to £46, Tue to Sat £33 (2 courses) to £46 SERVICE: not inc CARDS: Amex, Diners, MasterCard, Switch, Visa DETAILS: 28 seats. Private parties: 24 main room. No smoking before 10 at D. Wheelchair access (not WC). No music (£5)

Lumière

GLOUCESTERSHIRE GFG 2002 COMMENDED

NEW ENTRY

Clarence Parade, Cheltenham GL50 3PA
TEL: (01242) 222200
EMAIL: lumiere@globalnet.co.uk

COOKING **5**
GLOBAL
£40–£55

Regular readers may remember the Chapmans from Le Petit Canard at Maiden Newton, Dorset, last in the Guide in 1999. They have now set up business in a small Regency terrace just off the Promenade, this time with a light, bright, modern, stylish interior with deep chocolate and pale cream colours, leather banquettes, and a few abstract canvases. Geoff Chapman's Pacific Rim style of food may have moved on, but he still puts kangaroo and springbok on the menu, and rustles up a soup of Chinese double chicken egg drop broth with glass noodles, spring onion and crispy shredded duck.

The cooking is underpinned by solid technical skills, positive flavours and workable combinations, as in a properly crisp-skinned confit chicken ('more interesting than most chefs' confit duck') on a sweet onion risotto with spiced watercress oil, or grilled red mullet fillet sitting on steamed mussels scattered with basil and charred red peppers. Good supplies are evident at every turn, as in accurately timed rack of young lamb, served with mash containing chopped scallions and roasted garlic. Desserts at inspection were not quite on a par with the rest, although they look convincing: a tall cylinder of eggy almond biscuit, perhaps, filled with layers of mascarpone, pistachio, and passion fruit purée. Vivacious Lin Chapman runs front-of-house with minimal help. The wine list offers a broad choice of styles (California is a strength), with helpful notes to ease ordering and a back page dedicated to 'classics', not all of them pricy. Indeed there is value throughout, with little over £25, and house wines (frequently changing) are £13.95.

CHEF: Geoff Chapman PROPRIETORS: Lin and Geoff Chapman OPEN: Tue to Sat D 7 to 9 CLOSED: first week Jan MEALS: Set D £28 SERVICE: not inc CARDS: Amex, MasterCard, Switch, Visa DETAILS: 32 seats. Private parties: 36 main room. Vegetarian meals. No children under 8. No smoking. Occasional music. Air-conditioned

---

Although the cuisine style noted at the top of entries has in most cases been suggested to the Guide by the restaurants, some have been edited for brevity or appropriateness.

(£5) *indicates that the restaurant has elected to participate in the* Good Food Guide *voucher scheme. For full details, see page 6.*

Mayflower

32–34 Clarence Street, Cheltenham GL50 3NX
TEL: (01242) 522426 FAX: (01242) 251667

COOKING **2**
CHINESE
£15–£71

This attractive restaurant abandons conventional Chinese scarlet and gold for more restful subdued blues and pinks. It also omits some of the challenging ingredients of metropolitan Chinatown, but there are treasures buried in the extensive à la carte. Garlic and chilli squid, and mussels with black beans lurk among the starters; main dishes include Szechuan seafood hotpot and whole Dover sole in soy sauce; and a whole vegetarian page includes mock duck in five ways. Set banquets start at £21 per head. The £35 special seafood feast's five starters take in crispy fried seaweed with grated dry scallops, and minced king prawn lettuce wrapper, then comes lobster, and sweet-and-sour fish, followed by scallops with cashew nuts, and finally sizzling king prawns served with rice. The 70-strong wine list covers Old World and New; house wines are £10.

CHEFS: C.F. Kong and M.M. Kong PROPRIETORS: the Kong family OPEN: Mon to Sat L 12 to 1.45, all week D 6.15 to 10 (10.30 Fri and Sat) CLOSED: 24 to 27 Dec MEALS: alc (main courses £7.50 to £12). Set L £6.95, Set D £18.50 to £35 SERVICE: not inc CARDS: Amex, Delta, MasterCard, Switch, Visa DETAILS: 120 seats. Private parties: 80 main room, 40 private room. Vegetarian meals. Music. Air-conditioned (£5)

Le Petit Blanc

The Queens Hotel, The Promenade,
Cheltenham GL50 1NN
TEL: (01242) 266800 FAX: (01242) 266801
WEB SITE: www.lepetit-blanc.co.uk

COOKING **4**
MODERN EUROPEAN
£24–£54

The long bar has been refurbished in warm orange and terracotta colours, with a few big armchairs and tables, while the dining room is split in two: a bright, tall-ceilinged affair with big windows and mirrors (which can get clattery and noisy) and a darker red room, feeling more like a nightclub. Metal-topped tables are set with a welcoming bowl of olives, and the menu offers a few special deals (plus a children's menu) as well as a carte in which French regional dishes are picked out in bold type: cherry tomato risotto, and coconut and lime soup must be from the colonies. The food may not have many particularly high or low points, but a steady output is always welcome: the kitchen doesn't try to be cleverer than it needs, nor does it aim to impress with flourishes, but it gets the basics right, which is very satisfying.

Among the well-handled prime materials have been steamed Evesham asparagus with an accurately poached egg and well-rendered hollandaise, crisp-skinned sea bream with a first-rate bouillabaisse sauce, and a tasty, freshly made cherry clafoutis. The lunchtime and early-evening Menu Prix Fixe is judged 'terrific' value: where else would you get a freshly cooked sardine niçoise, a dish of pot-roast pig (including belly, a brain beignet and numerous other bits, plus a big scoop of decent mash), and a well-risen warm caramel soufflé, all for £15? The policy of booking tables for a limited time, even when there is no need, is considered 'daft', although service itself is workmanlike. A varietally arranged wine list includes a fair selection under £20, and a handful by the glass.

CHEF: Tim Cook PROPRIETOR: Raymond Blanc OPEN: all week 12 to 3, 6 to 10.30 CLOSED: 25 Dec MEALS: alc (main courses £8.50 to £16). Set L and D 6 to 7 £12.50 (2 courses) to £15 SERVICE: not inc, 10% for parties of 8 or more CARDS: Amex, Delta, Diners, MasterCard, Switch, Visa DETAILS: 160 seats. 20 seats outside. Private parties: 80 main room, 80 private room. Vegetarian meals. Children's helpings. No smoking in dining room. Wheelchair access (not WC). Music. Air-conditioned (£5)

CHESTER Cheshire **map 7**

▲ Chester Grosvenor Hotel, Arkle

Eastgate, Chester CH1 1LT
TEL: (01244) 324024 FAX: (01244) 313068
EMAIL: marketing@chestergrosvenor.co.uk
WEB SITE: www.chestergrosvenor.co.uk

COOKING **5**
TRADITIONAL EUROPEAN
£41–£92

Despite the slightly austere feel of the dining room, this traditional hotel (under the same ownership since 1865) does a good line in pampering, from a pianist in the reception room, via friendly, attentive and formal service, to all the usual lavish trappings of table furniture, appetisers, mid-meal sorbet and ten different kinds of bread. Given its well-heeled customer base, the food can hardly aim to be cutting edge; rather it soothes with expensive ingredients such as foie gras, turbot, lobster and truffles. A seasonally changing menu might offer hot pork cheek with foie gras and apples, grilled lobster vinaigrette with sweetbread pasta, or a three-piece dish of beef incorporating fillet, braised oxtail pudding, and ox tongue crépinette, while well-executed vegetarian options have included wild mushroom risotto, and pasta sheets with asparagus and herbs in a light butter sauce.

Reporters are divided over the cooking, but an inspection meal found that variation in quality between dishes militated against total success, given the level of ambition. The highlight was a huge slab of fresh, unevenly cooked turbot on the bone, ordinarily presented on a bed of thyme-flavoured caramelised onions (nothing wrong with that, apart from the absence of carbohydrate, but look at the price). Technical wizardry seems to reach its peak when it comes to dessert, for example a chocolate pastry case filled with pistachio ice cream, with a cooked chocolate soufflé on top: 'how this was achieved was a mystery.' Great mature vintages from illustrious estates underpin the wine list, setting the price ceiling beyond the reach of ordinary drinkers. But there is also a choice of well-sourced wines under £20, and a Chilean red starts off the house selection at £12.75.

CHEF: Simon Radley PROPRIETOR: Grosvenor Estate OPEN: Tue to Sun L 12 to 2.30, Tue to Sat D 7 to 9.30 CLOSED: 25 Dec to 23 Jan (exc 31 Dec), third week Aug MEALS: Set L £30 to £48, Set D £40 (2 courses) to £48 SERVICE: not inc, 12.5% for parties of 6 or more CARDS: Amex, Delta, Diners, MasterCard, Switch, Visa DETAILS: 40 seats. Private parties: 22 main room, 60 and 240 private rooms. Vegetarian meals. Children's helpings. No smoking in dining room. Wheelchair access (not WC). Music. Air-conditioned ACCOMMODATION: 85 rooms, all with bath/shower. TV. Phone. Room only £159 to £277. Rooms for disabled. Baby facilities

The Guide's longest-serving restaurants are listed near the front of the book.

Brasserie 10/16 £

NEW ENTRY

Brookdale Place, Chester CH1 3DY
TEL: (01244) 322288 FAX: (01244) 322325
WEB SITE: www.brasserie1016.com

COOKING **4**
MODERN EUROPEAN
£21–£44

This is the second restaurant opened by the Bates/Jones duo, following their successful original establishment in Hawarden (see entry, Wales). The look is light and airy, with stripped-wood flooring and plain painted walls, and the approach to cooking is similar to that taken by its elder sibling: good modern brasserie fare, sound ingredients, and sharply executed dishes.

Strong flavours, some of them Eastern, are generally handled well. Among starters might be grilled mackerel fillets with Thai green sauce, or a light, appetising dish of dressed crab with tomato and mango served with cumin crisps. Even more straightforward dishes are effective, however, judging by accurately roasted monkfish on a bed of garlic mash with lentils and pesto, and a large tasty chicken breast on mushroom risotto. Vegetarian options can be equally appealing, as in a tart of Mediterranean vegetables with rocket and a roasted pepper dressing.

Successful desserts run to a light bread-and-butter pudding with apricot coulis, and fluffily textured toffee cheesecake with banana ice cream. Service is friendly and knowledgeable, although background music can be a bit strident for some ears. Most of the 40 or so wines on the short global list stay under £20, and six house wines range from £9.95 to £13.75.

CHEFS: Mark Jones and Ian Derbyshire PROPRIETORS: Neal Bates and Mark Jones OPEN: all week 12 to 10 MEALS: alc (main courses £7 to £16). Set L and D 12 to 6 £9.95 (2 courses) SERVICE: not inc CARDS: Amex, Delta, MasterCard, Switch, Visa DETAILS: 130 seats. Private parties: 70 main room. Vegetarian meals. Wheelchair access (also WC). Music

CHINNOR Oxfordshire map 2

Sir Charles Napier

Sprigg's Alley, Chinnor OX9 4BX
TEL: (01494) 483011 FAX: (01494) 485311
take B4009 to Chinnor from M40 junction 6, turn right at mini-roundabout and continue up hill for 2m to Sprigg's Alley

COOKING **4**
MODERN ANGLO-FRENCH
£38–£63

Red kites circle above Bledlow Ridge in the Chilterns where, at the end of a long track, this old flint and red-brick inn can startle first-time visitors with its unusual outdoor sculptures and its quirky dining room strewn with pots, statues, and a seemingly orphaned collection of odd chairs. Its informal style, warm welcome and efficient service are well matched by a menu that rejoices in the variety of materials available, from a robust and 'deeply fungoid' mushroom soup, via smoked duck breast and confit of rabbit to a golden-crusted twice-baked soufflé with a rich creamy sauce.

Fish is a strong suit, delivering briskly grilled sea bream, roast halibut, and a starter of three notably fresh scallops, just stiffened and crisped, on a raft of firm, sweet ceps and artichokes. Risottos (butternut squash, for example) also come highly recommended, while desserts run to lemon tart with light pastry and a creamy filling. Long, lazy lunches (on the lawn or terrace in summer) make a fine way to write off an afternoon. A highly informative wine list offers stellar names from a wide range of regions. Such pedigree is matched by high prices, but value can be found in the round-the-world house selection, which starts at £12.95 and stays below £25.

CHEF: José Cau PROPRIETOR: Julie Griffiths OPEN: Tue to Sun L 12 to 2.30 (3.30 Sun), Tue to Sat D 7 to 10 CLOSED: 3 days Christmas MEALS: alc (main courses £13.50 to £18.50). Set L Tue to Fri £14.50 (2 courses), Set D Tue to Fri £15.50 (2 courses). Light L available Tue to Fri SERVICE: 12.5% (optional), card slips closed CARDS: Amex, Delta, Diners, MasterCard, Switch, Visa DETAILS: 70 seats. 70 seats outside. Private parties: 50 main room, 25 and 50 private rooms. Car park. Vegetarian meals. Children's helpings. No children under 7 at D. No smoking in 1 dining room. Wheelchair access (not WC). Occasional music. Air-conditioned

CHIPPING NORTON Oxfordshire **map 5**

Chav Brasserie

7 Horse Fair, Chipping Norton OX7 5AL
TEL: (01608) 645968 FAX: (01608) 646794 COOKING **4**
EMAIL: chavignol@virginbiz.com MODERN EUROPEAN
WEB SITE: www.chavignol.co.uk £26–£47

Chavignol has moved to Shipston on Stour (see entry), leaving its former premises in the capable hands of Paul and Rachael Haywood. Transformation of the end-of-terrace cottage has involved reducing the size of tables but not much else, and its atmosphere is more restful and 'upper-class rural' than flash brasserie. Service comes across as French professionalism at its very best: 'they spread your napkin on your lap – how brasserie is that?'

Ideas range from Thai-spiced prawn samosas with lime pickle, to classic French country dishes such as a meaty, gelatinous pig's head terrine wrapped in Parma ham, served with a first-rate 'salad gribiche'. The relatively casual style of food may be designed to encourage more frequent eating at affordable prices, but it is skilfully handled, as in a well-timed skinless fillet of roast salmon, served on a bed of 'rough-and-ready' mash containing shredded beef and spring onion, with a tarragon-flavoured pool of lentil-strewn meat stock sauce. If there were any doubt about mastery of technical skills, it would be dispelled by desserts such as the 'exemplary' griottine cherry and caramel nougatine glacé. 'Fabulous' bread comes with fine olive oil for dunking, and around 15 of the three dozen sensibly chosen wines are available by the glass.

CHEF: Paul Haywood PROPRIETORS: Chavignol Ltd/Mark Maguire OPEN: Tue to Sat L 11.30 to 2.30, Mon to Sat D 6.30 (7 Mon) to 10 (9.30 Mon) MEALS: alc (main courses £8 to £14.50) SERVICE: not inc CARDS: Amex, Delta, Diners, MasterCard, Switch, Visa DETAILS: 30 seats. Private parties: 25 main room. Vegetarian meals. Children's helpings. No smoking in dining room. No music

The text of entries is based on unsolicited reports sent in by readers, backed up by inspections conducted anonymously. The factual details under the text are from questionnaires the Guide sends to all restaurants that feature in the book.

CHOBHAM Surrey map 3

Quails

1 Bagshot Road, Chobham GU24 8BP
TEL/FAX: (01276) 858491

COOKING **3**
MODERN BRITISH-PLUS
£26–£52

This blue-painted, family-run neighbourhood restaurant in the centre of town draws regulars with its imaginative cooking and friendly, efficient service. Lemon walls are hung with rural scenes, and large windows with swagged curtains, providing a simple backdrop for Christopher Wale's contemporary, monthly-changing menus. These embrace the Continent and Asia with equal conviction, praise being registered for Mediterranean-influenced starters such as buffalo mozzarella with plum tomatoes and basil oil, and plump asparagus with quails' eggs and dolcelatte dressing, while main courses take in sweet chilli crispy duck with bean sprouts, spring onions, plum and ginger, and fillets of sea bass with saffron sauce, a drizzle of wasabi and soba noodles. Desserts by contrast have a homely ring, from hot chocolate pudding with saffron ice cream, to an enjoyable bread-and-butter pudding with chunky marmalade. Excellent vegetables, and good cheeses and breads provide support. The compact wine list is helpfully arranged by style and offers six wines by the glass and by the half-bottle. House French is £10.95.

CHEF: Christopher Wale PROPRIETORS: the Wale family OPEN: Tue to Fri L 12 to 2, Tue to Sat D 7 to 9.30 MEALS: alc (main courses £14 to £17.50). Set L £9.95 (1 course) to £15.95, Set D Tue to Fri £13.95 (2 courses) to £16.95 SERVICE: not inc, 10% for parties of 6 or more CARDS: Amex, Delta, Diners, MasterCard, Switch, Visa DETAILS: 50 seats. Private parties: 50 main room. Car park. Vegetarian meals. Wheelchair access (not WC). Music. Air-conditioned (£5)

CHRISTCHURCH Dorset

FishWorks Seafood Café

NEW ENTRY

10 Church Street, Christchurch BH23 1BW
TEL: (01202) 487000 FAX: (01202) 487001
WEB SITE: www.fishworks.co.uk

COOKING **4**
SEAFOOD
£31–£82

According to one who knows him, owner Mitchell Tonks has a passion for fish that 'borders on the erotic'. His enthusiasm permeates the very fabric of each of his three FishWorks outlets (see FishWorks Green Street Seafood Café, Bath; and FishWorks, Bristol) and seems to infect the lively crowds that regularly fill all three venues. This branch may be 'slicker and classier' than the Bath original, but prices are no higher and it operates to precisely the same principle of 'wrigglingly fresh fish', simply cooked, in a bright, airy and comfortable dining room where wooden fish mobiles add a jokey decorative touch.

The FishWorks concept is at once utterly simple and completely flexible: either choose something from the menu or whatever catches your eye from the display in the shop, prepared according to your instructions and served with a choice of sauces. There is much to commend, from a generous plate of assertively home-smoked salmon, to velvet-textured, wood-roasted squid flecked with toasted garlic and 'imbued with herby flavours'. Treatments may be standard, but are convincingly done, taking in for example an assortment of fish and seafood, briefly deep-fried in a light, crumbly batter, and served with a pungent aïoli; and a 'top-class nursery plateful' of cod with creamy mash and parsley sauce. Wines are mostly white and fairly priced throughout the short selection, starting at £8.95.

CHEF: Abbie Bennett PROPRIETOR: FishWorks plc OPEN: Tue to Sat 11 to 11 MEALS: alc (main courses £9.50 to £28) SERVICE: not inc CARDS: Amex, Delta, MasterCard, Switch, Visa DETAILS: 50 seats. 6 seats outside. Private parties: 30 main room, 14 and 36 private rooms. Vegetarian meals. Children's helpings. No smoking in dining room. Wheelchair access (not WC). Music (£5)

Splinters

12 Church Street, Christchurch BH23 1BW | COOKING **5**
TEL: (01202) 483454 FAX: (01202) 480180 | FRENCH/INTERNATIONAL
WEB SITE: www.splinters.uk.com | £34–£57

Splinters shouldn't be too hard to find: it stands on a cobbled street in the shadow of the eleventh-century priory, the dominant landmark in these parts. Inside, the restaurant is divided into several dining areas of contrasting appearance. One is reminiscent of a 1960s bistro, with varnished pine-clad walls and cosy booth seating; another, called the Blue Room, is done out in a coolly austere and modern style. The eclecticism apparent in the décor is a theme that carries through to Jason Davenport's cooking. Here is a man not afraid of novelty, happy to scour the global larder for inspiration, coming up with attractive-sounding combinations, such as roast celeriac soup with smoked chicken ravioli and white truffle oil, and John Dory with Bombay potato, steamed pak choi and coconut sauce. The rest of the menu blends classic French ideas with more mainstream modern themes to produce a warm salad of wood pigeon with pine nuts and blackcurrant sauce, and fillet steak with seared foie gras, rösti and red wine sauce. Desserts run from glazed lemon tart to cappuccino tiramisù, via banana tart with caramel sauce and coconut sorbet. The wine list is well priced throughout, opening with house French at £12.95 a bottle, or £3.40 a glass.

CHEF: Jason Davenport PROPRIETORS: Timothy Lloyd and Robert Wilson OPEN: Tue to Sat (and Sun D bank hols) 12 to 2, 7 to 10 (10.30 Sat) CLOSED: 26 to 30 Dec MEALS: alc (main courses £10.50). Set D Tue to Fri £24.95, Set D Tue to Sat £27 (2 courses) to £32. Bar L menu available SERVICE: not inc CARDS: Amex, Delta, Diners, MasterCard, Switch, Visa DETAILS: 40 seats. Private parties: 24 main room, 8 and 24 private rooms. Vegetarian meals. Children's helpings. No smoking in dining room. Music (£5)

The Guide office can quickly spot when a restaurateur is encouraging customers to write recommending inclusion. Such reports do not further a restaurant's cause. Please tell us if a restaurateur invites you to write to the Guide.

denotes an outstanding wine cellar; denotes a good wine list, worth travelling for.

CLAYGATE Surrey map 3

Le Petit Pierrot

4 The Parade, Claygate KT10 0NU
TEL: (01372) 465105 FAX: (01372) 467642

COOKING **4**
MODERN FRENCH
£22–£48

Large mirrors, a stripy tented ceiling and a collection of clowny masks enliven this 'slightly cramped but pleasant French bistro' in a prosperous-looking parade of shops near the station. It offers an appealing menu, using fine ingredients ably cooked and attractively presented. While seafood ranges from creamed mussel soup to monkfish larded with bacon in a delicate white fish sauce, poultry options have included a warm salad of braised quail with little heaps of onion confit, and a trio of duck combining well-done breast, crispy leg, and a small cone of duck liver mousse. Snails also get a look in, combined with rabbit in a creamy mustard sauce in a light puff pastry square. The grande assiette of desserts is probably worth its price supplement, delivering white chocolate mousse, sponge pudding, and a pair of sorbets and assorted fruits. Service is 'frightfully efficient', although smiles may be rationed. An all-French wine list reflects traditional priorities, prices are not outrageous, and vin de pays Grenache and Sémillon house wines are £11.25.

CHEFS: Jean-Pierre Brichot and Eric Plantareau PROPRIETORS: Annie and Jean-Pierre Brichot OPEN: Mon to Fri L 12.15 to 2, Mon to Sat D 7.15 to 9.30 CLOSED: 1 week Christmas, bank hols MEALS: Set L £12.25 (2 courses) to £20.75, Set D £24.50 SERVICE: not inc CARDS: Amex, Delta, Diners, MasterCard, Switch, Visa DETAILS: 32 seats. Private parties: 32 main room. No pipes. Wheelchair access (not WC). Music

CLITHEROE Lancashire map 8

Auctioneer

New Market Street, Clitheroe BB7 2JW
TEL: (01200) 427153
WEB SITE: www.auctioneer-clitheroe.co.uk

COOKING **4**
MODERN EUROPEAN
£21–£49

A monthly-changing menu featuring different European countries and regions may not be the first thing to expect on the edge of the Trough of Bowland, but Henk Van Heumen's culinary travels around the Continent bring a welcome element of diversity. Portugal, for example, has yielded spider crab with pasta, chicken in a spicy piri-piri sauce, and leitão: slices of roast loin of young pork with a garlic and herb sauce. Not everything is themed – the carte takes a more standard line – but the unifying factor is confident cooking, working within its capacity and not striving too hard for effect: in a light, smooth, impressively fishy-tasting salmon mousseline, for example, served with a generously endowed shellfish sauce.

Other highlights (these from a Trentino month) have included roast polenta topped with well-timed chicken livers and bacon lardons in red wine sauce, and three thick nuggets of pink and juicy lamb fillet served with notably light basil gnocchi. Simply cooked vegetables accompany main courses, and the lightness of approach is apparent also in desserts such as tiramisù. Service from Frances

Van Heumen and helper is knowledgeable, efficient and pleasantly informal, and wines make a good fist of combining interest, value and variety, starting with ten house wines at £12.

CHEF: Henk Van Heumen PROPRIETORS: Henk and Frances Van Heumen OPEN: Thur to Sun L 12 to 1.30, Wed to Sat D 7 to 9 (9.45 Sat) MEALS: alc (main courses £11 to £19). Set L £9.95 (2 courses) to £11.95, Set D £19.75 SERVICE: not inc CARDS: Amex, Delta, MasterCard, Switch, Visa DETAILS: 48 seats. Private parties: 24 main room, 24 private rooms. No smoking in dining room. Music. Air-conditioned

COCKERMOUTH Cumbria map 10

Quince & Medlar

13 Castlegate, Cockermouth CA13 9EU
TEL: (01900) 823579

COOKING **2**
MODERN EUROPEAN/VEGETARIAN
£28–£38

This small, intimate restaurant is close to the castle in the centre of the attractive Lakeland town of Cockermouth. It is very much a family concern, and Colin and Louisa Le Voi are always present, whether front-of-house or in the kitchen. Though they are vegetarians, they aim to appeal to all comers, showing that non-meat cooking need not always be dull and stodgy. Menus certainly read well, demonstrating plenty of imagination: crisp celeriac tuile cones are filled with wild mushrooms cooked in herbs with roasted pine kernels, while courgettes and Wensleydale are baked together with a tomato and tarragon sauce. 'Solyanka' is a dish of shredded Savoy cabbage layered with sweet potato and flavoured with dill and caraway, topped with cheese and baked. Most of the wines on the short list are also vegetarian or vegan, and some are organic. Prices start at £9.45.

CHEFS/PROPRIETORS: Colin and Louisa Le Voi OPEN: Tue to Sat and occasional Sun by arrangement D only 7 to 9.30 CLOSED: 1 week mid-Nov, 2 weeks mid-Jan MEALS: alc (main courses £11 to £12) SERVICE: not inc, card slips closed CARDS: MasterCard, Switch DETAILS: 26 seats. Private parties: 14 main room. Vegetarian meals. No children under 5. No smoking in dining room. Music

COLCHESTER Essex map 6

Lemon Tree £

NEW ENTRY

48 St Johns Street, Colchester CO2 7AD
TEL/FAX: (01206) 767337
EMAIL: reservations@the-lemon-tree.com
WEB SITE: www.the-lemon-tree.com

COOKING **1**
MODERN BRITISH
£16–£43

A lemon tree outside helps to identify this converted warehouse, recently refurbished by the Minders. It occupies a large, agreeably airy space with stripped-wood floorboards, brick walls painted creamy yellow, and part of the Roman town wall running through it. Value is considered good (check out the set-price lunch), daily blackboard specials supplement the carte, and the style runs from roast halibut with couscous to grilled duck breast with sage, onion and apple sauce.

Output is variable (fish does not appear to be a strength), but the kitchen's confidence has shown in a coarse duck terrine with a big dollop of plum chutney, and in a pink-cooked fillet steak with wild mushrooms and a red wine sauce. Desserts, although busily decorated, are well handled, judging by a 'crunchy and creamy' malt whisky and praline ice cream with shortbread. Service is intelligent and helpful, and a short wine list stays helpfully below £20.

CHEF: Patrik Minder PROPRIETORS: Joanna and Patrik Minder OPEN: Mon to Sat 12 to 5, 5 to 10 MEALS: alc (main courses £7 to £15). Set L Mon to Fri £7.45 (2 courses) to £8.95, Set D Mon to Thur £8.95 (2 courses) to £11.95 SERVICE: not inc CARDS: Amex, Delta, Diners, MasterCard, Switch, Visa DETAILS: 85 seats. 40 seats outside. Private parties: 70 main room, 30 private room. Vegetarian meals. Children's helpings. No smoking in dining room. Wheelchair access (also WC). Occasional music (£5)

COLERNE Wiltshire map 2

▲ Lucknam Park

Colerne SN14 8AZ
TEL: (01225) 742777 FAX: (01225) 743536
EMAIL: reservations@lucknampark.co.uk
WEB SITE: www.lucknampark.co.uk
off A420 at Ford, 6m W of Chippenham

COOKING **6**
MODERN BRITISH
£37–£79

'This is possibly the grandest place I've ever been to,' noted one awed visitor. The library (lined by the sort of books you buy by the yard), chandeliers on ruched taffeta sleeves, and big oil paintings give it a 'theme park' Englishness, but it is rescued from museum status by friendly staff who 'make it all seem like the most natural thing in the world': what could be dauntingly grand and formal turns out to be just plain relaxing. A 'scarily expensive' dinner menu artfully combines both rich and humble ingredients, from a pressing of duck confit and foie gras to braised rabbit, from tortellini of crab with sauté langoustines to butternut squash Tatin. It is also larded with purées, dressings, mousses and trufflings, its textures all designed to calm and soothe.

At the same time, however, flavours are well defined, not least thanks to good supplies. Cornish seafood is a strong suit, taking in sea bass with red wine sauce and ginger beurre blanc, or lobster and leek terrine with an oyster dressing. There are time-consuming procedures involved in busy dishes – oxtail tortellini to accompany beef fillet, a mini-hotpot with best end of lamb – but the focus invariably remains clear. If anything, desserts are even keener to persuade with artistic flourishes: if you don't fancy the 'frozen woodland still life', there is always banana parfait layered between crisp chocolate wafers and served with a bitter chocolate sorbet. A few affordable wines on the high-class list lurk among the preposterously big numbers, but don't waste time looking for bargains. Prices open at £17.50.

CHEF: Robin Zavou PROPRIETOR: Lucknam Park Hotels Ltd OPEN: Sun L 12.30 to 2.30, all week D 7.30 to 9.30 (7 to 10 Fri and Sat) MEALS: Set L £25, Set D £45 SERVICE: not inc, card slips closed CARDS: Amex, Delta, Diners, MasterCard, Switch, Visa DETAILS: 80 seats. Private parties: 64 main room, 12 to 22 private rooms. Car park. Vegetarian meals. No children under 12 at D. Jacket and tie. No smoking in dining room. Wheelchair access (also WC). Occasional music ACCOMMODATION: 41 rooms, all with bath/shower. TV. Phone. Room only £155 to £670. Baby facilities. Swimming pool (*The Which? Hotel Guide*) (£5)

COOKHAM Berkshire map 3

Alfonso's

19–21 Station Hill Parade, Cookham SL6 9BR
TEL: (01628) 525775

COOKING **4**
MEDITERRANEAN
£33–£46

First impressions may not be altogether encouraging, but beyond the frontage in a parade of shops the dining room has a homely feel, and the welcome from Alfonso and Maria Baena is warm and sincere. The well-prepared and reasonably priced Mediterranean cooking attracts a devoted following, and the Baenas' Spanish origins are reflected in weekday tapas, featuring such delights as broad beans with chorizo and black pudding, lambs' kidneys with sherry, and Manchego cheese with quince jelly.

The main menu is broader in scope, crossing European culinary borders at will to take in a gâteau of Cornish crab with crab cream, orange, keta and olive oil; bourguignon-style braised leg of rabbit; and pan-fried duck breast with Dijon mustard sauce and calvados. Desserts, on the other hand, have a distinctly English feel: bramble pudding with sloe gin and Devon clotted cream, for example. Wines – divided into Spanish, French and others – are a well-chosen and good-value selection. Each of a pair of house wines is £10, and four bottles are sold by the glass from £2.50.

CHEFS: Mr and Mrs Manzano PROPRIETORS: Alfonso and Maria Baena OPEN: Mon to Fri L 12.30 to 2, Mon to Sat D 7 to 10 CLOSED: bank hols, 2 weeks summer MEALS: Set L £7.50 (2 courses), Set L and D £19.50 (2 courses) to £23. Tapas menu available Mon to Thur SERVICE: not inc CARDS: Amex, Diners, MasterCard, Visa DETAILS: 34 seats. 12 seats outside. Private parties: 34 main room. Car park. Vegetarian meals. Children's helpings. Wheelchair access (not WC). Occasional music (£5)

CORSCOMBE Dorset map 2

▲ Fox Inn £

Corscombe DT2 0NS
TEL/FAX: (01935) 891330
EMAIL: dine@fox-inn.co.uk
WEB SITE: www.fox-inn.co.uk
off A356, 6m SE of Crewkerne

COOKING **2**
MODERN BRITISH
£23–£44

Set in beautiful, lush countryside, this seventeenth-century thatched cottage adorned with a riot of climbing roses, wisteria and clematis lives up to most people's idea of the model country inn. It won't disappoint inside either, whether you eat in the traditional bar or the dining room, which partly occupies the owners' homely kitchen. A blackboard menu offers about 20 daily specials, mostly fish, alongside a similarly lengthy printed menu. Cooking stays mostly straightforward throughout, but the style varies widely, from West Bay crab with chive mayonnaise to halibut steak with a tapénade crust; from glazed lamb shank with mustard mash to breast of Barbary duck with soy and honey sauce. Puddings are mostly old favourites like treacle tart. A page of half-bottles and another of fine wines enhance a good-value list of two dozen wines. Prices start at £9.95, and five house selections are available by the glass from £1.95.

CHEFS: George Marsh and Dan Clarke PROPRIETOR: Martyn Lee OPEN: all week 12 to 2, 7 to 9 (9.30 Fri and Sat) CLOSED: no food served on 25 Dec MEALS: alc (main courses £8 to £16.50) SERVICE: not inc, card slips closed CARDS: Amex, Delta, MasterCard, Switch, Visa DETAILS: 85 seats. 30 seats outside. Private parties: 40 main room, 20 and 35 private rooms. Car park. Vegetarian meals. Children's helpings. No smoking in 1 dining room. Wheelchair access (not WC). No music ACCOMMODATION: 3 rooms, all with bath/shower. TV. B&B £55 to £80. No children under 12 (*The Which? Hotel Guide*)

CORSE LAWN Gloucestershire **map 2**

▲ Corse Lawn House

Corse Lawn GL19 4LZ
TEL: (01452) 780771 FAX: (01452) 780840
EMAIL: hotel@corselawnhouse.u-net.com
WEB SITE: www.corselawnhousehotel.co.uk
on B4211, 5m SW of Tewkesbury

COOKING **2**
ANGLO-FRENCH
£29–£60

With a pond (formerly a coach wash) at the front, and a dozen acres of land including well-tended lawns, this Queen Anne Grade II listed building provides a peaceful setting: 'it still feels like a family home.' The food has a homely dimension too, taking in starters of salmon and haddock fishcake, and baked goats' cheese with tomato salad, while a generous menu choice covers a wide range of Anglo-French ideas: soup (Mediterranean fish, for example) ladled from a large tureen, ribeye of beef with a rich, thick, heavily reduced sauce, and haunch of venison on crushed swede.

Appetisers are large enough to be starters, vegetables on the carte are charged extra, and desserts might offer coconut mousse, strawberries and cream, or honey and walnut tart. Disappointments have included timing in general, from undercooked asparagus to overcooked meat, the handling of wine, and the cost of afternoon tea, but cheeses and coffee are good. A wide range of Spanish and Italian regional wines brings extra life to a list that is otherwise very strong on French classics, with an array of vintages reaching back to the 1970s. The extensive half-bottle section is full of variety, and ten house reds and whites start at £10.50, some available by the glass from £2.50.

CHEFS: Baba Hine and Andrew Poole PROPRIETORS: the Hine family OPEN: all week 12 to 2, 7 to 9.30 CLOSED: 3 days Christmas MEALS: alc exc Sun D (main courses £15 to £20). Set L £16.50 (2 courses) to £18.50, Set D £27.50. Bistro menu available SERVICE: not inc, card slips closed CARDS: Amex, Diners, MasterCard, Visa DETAILS: 80 seats. 40 seats outside. Private parties: 80 main room, 18 and 34 private rooms. Car park. Vegetarian meals. Children's helpings. No smoking in dining room. Wheelchair access (also WC). No music ACCOMMODATION: 19 rooms, all with bath/shower. TV. Phone. B&B £80 to £125. Rooms for disabled. Baby facilities. Swimming pool

▲ *means accommodation is available.*

CRANBROOK Kent **map 3**

▲ Kennel Holt Hotel

Goudhurst Road, Cranbrook TN17 2PT
TEL: (01580) 712032 FAX: (01580) 715495
EMAIL: hotel@kennelholt.demon.co.uk
WEB SITE: www.kennelholt.co.uk

COOKING **3**
MODERN EUROPEAN
£39–£54

'Very Kent, very pretty' was one visitor's impression of this characterful Elizabethan manor house with its pond and topiaried birds, oak-panelled lounge with a giant hearth and smouldering log fire, and quirky dining room displaying Victorian thespian prints. A set-price menu (the same at lunch and dinner) is the format to which Neil Chalmers brings some fine materials, including local lamb, asparagus and soft fruits, and fish from a single-boat fisherman in Rye.

Menus are hardly meant to set the pulse racing, dealing as they do in steak and kidney pudding with roast root vegetables and mash, or roast pheasant with red wine jus and pappardelle, but the domesticity of the cooking is reassuring. Meals might begin with a carrot, parsnip and cumin soup, or a pastry tartlet of creamed leek and Roquefort, followed by stuffed chicken breast, or calf's liver with dauphinois potatoes and Marsala sauce. Finish, perhaps, with tarte Tatin, or panettone bread-and-butter pudding. With a couple of exceptions, wines are all French, starting with house Bergerac white (£12.50) and Bordeaux red (£13.50).

CHEFS: Neil Chalmers and Audrey Radcliffe PROPRIETORS: Neil and Sally Chalmers OPEN: Tue to Fri and Sun L 12.30 to 1.15, Tue to Sat D 7.30 to 8.45 CLOSED: weekday L Oct to Easter exc for pre-booked parties of 6 or more, 1 week Jan MEALS: Set L and D £27.50 to £32.50 SERVICE: 10% (optional), card slips closed CARDS: Delta, MasterCard, Switch, Visa DETAILS: 25 seats. Private parties: 8 main room, 16 private room. Car park. Vegetarian meals. No children under 10 at D. No smoking in dining room. No music ACCOMMODATION: 10 rooms, all with bath/shower. TV. Phone. B&B £90 to £195. No children under 7 exc babes in arms. Baby facilities

CRAYKE North Yorkshire **map 9**

▲ Durham Ox

NEW ENTRY

Westway, Crayke YO61 4TE
TEL: (01347) 821506 FAX: (01347) 823326
EMAIL: enquiries@the-durham-ox.co.uk
WEB SITE: www.thedurhamox.com

COOKING **3**
MODERN EUROPEAN
£25–£53

The Ox is a 300-year-old inn sitting on the very hill up (and down) which the Grand Old Duke of York once marched his 10,000 men. Views over the Vale of York are an essay in tranquillity, and even though the area may feel like a tourist honey pot, the inn itself is still very much a locals' pub, decorated with antique scales and copper pans and kettles. A separate room used as the restaurant puts on its Sunday best, with tables dressed in white linen. Here, Russell Johnson cooks some superior pub food, constructing terrines of ham hock and parsley, served with pease pudding and a quail's egg, making tartlets of plum tomato and goats' cheese, and offering prime-cut main courses built around loin of lamb, salmon escalope, Gressingham duck breast, and fillet of local beef. Mango and chilli salsa brings a touch of the exotic to the highly praised spicy salmon fishcakes, and beetroot gives a sweet pink blush to the mash that goes with lightly cooked calf's liver. To finish, banana tarte Tatin with cinnamon ice cream gets a vote of confidence, while a fine white chocolate ice appears with coffee-flavoured crème brûlée. 'Pleasant and helpful' service is a relief to come across, as is the imaginative wine list that kicks off with a trio of house wines at £10.50 and includes a flight of five Barolos.

CHEFS: Russell Johnson and Michael Ibbotson PROPRIETOR: Michael Ibbotson OPEN: all week D only 7 to 9.30 CLOSED: 25 Dec MEALS: alc (main courses £8 to £20). Set D midweek £14.95 (2 courses), Set D £19.95. Bar menu available SERVICE: not inc, card slips closed CARDS: Amex, MasterCard, Switch, Visa DETAILS: 55 seats. 30 seats outside. Private parties: 30 main room, 16 private room. Car park. Vegetarian meals. No children in restaurant. No smoking in 1 dining room. Wheelchair access (not WC). Music ACCOMMODATION: 6 rooms, all with bath/shower. TV. Baby facilities (£5)

CROSTHWAITE Cumbria map 8

▲ Punch Bowl Inn

Crosthwaite LA8 8HR
TEL: (015395) 68237 FAX: (015395) 68875
EMAIL: enquiries@punchbowl.fsnet.co.uk
WEB SITE: www.punchbowl.fsnet.co.uk
off A5074, 3m S of Windermere

COOKING **4**
MODERN BRITISH
£19–£41

Having disposed of their second pub, the Dohertys now concentrate their considerable efforts on the Punch Bowl, an attractive country inn, set back from the road, where crackling log fires welcome winter travellers. Steven's homely yet inventive menu offers plenty of choice, and technique is highly polished (as befits one who has worked at the Gavroche). One reader's blini piled with smoked salmon and horseradish cream seemed almost too generous before a 'fair-sized' fillet steak with shallots in a red wine sauce. Terrines, perhaps of pork, ham and black pudding (with a wild mushroom and white truffle oil dressing), show up well, while main courses revolve around prime cuts, such as guinea-fowl breast or fillet of lamb, with a fair amount of chargrilling evident. Maintaining the standard are desserts such as Black Forest brownie with morello cherries and kirsch-laced mascarpone, and a banana parfait 'designed to impress' with poppy-seed tuile and a dusting of cinnamon sugar. The sub-£20 wine list opens with a South African and a Pays d'Oc Grenache-Syrah at £9.

CHEF: Steven Doherty PROPRIETORS: Steven and Marjorie Doherty OPEN: Tue to Sun L 12 to 2, D 6 to 9 CLOSED: 25 and 26 Dec, 1 Jan MEALS: alc (main courses £8.50 to £12; no alc on bank hols). Set L Tue to Fri £8 (2 courses) to £10.95, Set L Sun £11.95 (2 courses) to £13.95, Set D before 7 £13.95 (2 courses) to £15.95 SERVICE: not inc, card slips closed CARDS: MasterCard, Switch, Visa DETAILS: 60 seats. 16 seats outside. Private parties: 40 main room. Car park. Vegetarian meals. Children's helpings. No smoking in dining room. No music ACCOMMODATION: 3 rooms, all with bath/shower. TV. B&B £37.50 to £55 (*The Which? Hotel Guide*)

The Guide relies on feedback from its readers. Especially welcome are reports on new restaurants appearing in the book for the first time. All letters to the Guide are acknowledged.

CUCKFIELD West Sussex map 3

▲ Ockenden Manor NEW ENTRY

Ockenden Lane, Cuckfield RH17 5LD
TEL: (01444) 416111 FAX: (01444) 415549
EMAIL: ockenden@hshotels.co.uk
WEB SITE: www.hshotels.co.uk
off A272, 2m W of Haywards Heath

COOKING **5**
MODERN FRENCH
£33–£83

Set at the end of a short lane running from the centre of Cuckfield village, this charming sixteenth-century manor-house hotel surprises with its open rural character and views over the Weald and South Downs. The sitting room is bright, with swagged curtains and a maze of decorative fabrics, while the dining room's oak panelling and moulded ceiling give it a more formal feel. Four menus, including a two-course vegetarian, a multi-course tasting option, and a set-price Sussex Menu, all declare a high level of ambition: expect to come across deep-fried Roquefort ravioli, a home made boudin blanc, and scallops wrapped in thin smoked salmon, baked, and paired with a finely textured pea sauce.

This ambition is matched by technical skills of a high order, overlaid with a degree of originality and enthusiasm, as the kitchen prepares a 'tube' of stuffed chicken breast (cornfed), accompanied by celeriac purée and a truffle sauce. If the cooking has a fault, it is a striving for rather too much refinement and polish at the expense of character, but at its best it delivers 'clean, unmessed-with flavours', for example placing neat rectangles of duck breast in a transparent sauce around a Sarladaise potato cake, with shallots and pak choi for contrast. 'Sparky ideas carried out with style' is a fair summing up of desserts, which have taken in small cubes of apple bound in a biscuit mix and deep-fried. Service is efficient and professional, and wines combine serious quality with some youthful, easy drinkers. A ten-strong house selection hovers mostly around £16, featuring a Grenache-Merlot blend from the South of France and Chardonnay-Semillon from South Africa.

CHEF: Steve Crane PROPRIETORS: Mr and Mrs Goodman OPEN: all week 12.15 to 2, 7 to 9.15 (9 Sun) MEALS: Set L £12.95 (2 courses) to £18.50, Set D £31 to £55. Cover £6.50 for parties of 8 or more SERVICE: not inc CARDS: Amex, Delta, Diners, MasterCard, Switch, Visa DETAILS: 45 seats. 24 seats outside. Private parties: 75 main room, 14 private room. Car park. Vegetarian meals. Children's helpings. No smoking in dining room. No music ACCOMMODATION: 22 rooms, all with bath/shower. TV. Phone. B&B £99 to £270 (*The Which? Hotel Guide*)

DARGATE Kent map 3

Dove

Plum Pudding Lane, Dargate ME13 9HB
TEL: (01227) 751360

COOKING **3**
FRENCH
£25–£43

The Dove has been at the centre of village life in Dargate since the mid-nineteenth century, when it was a small thatched cottage, and its history, right up to the present day, is depicted in sepia-tint photographs lining the walls. It retains the virtues of an old-fashioned country pub, functioning as a focal point for its community, and looks the part too, with mixed pine furniture, bare floorboards and an open log fire, plus assorted knick-knacks adorning every surface. Food is listed on blackboards: a selection of snacks and light meals at lunchtime, and a longer carte in the evening, with the emphasis on traditional items such as pork rillettes with tomato and apple chutney, and confit duck leg on braised red cabbage.

Fish is put to good use: herrings are grilled and flavoured simply with olive oil and garlic, while sea trout is roasted and dressed with capers, anchovies and tomato, or made into a bouillabaisse with langoustines and red mullet. Among meat dishes might be braised lamb shank or a traditional cassoulet. Desserts take in orange and passion-fruit crème brûlée, or an apple and almond tart. Drinks include well-kept Shepherd Neame beers and a succinct wine list, priced from £11.25.

CHEF: Nigel Morris PROPRIETORS: Nigel and Bridget Morris OPEN: Tue to Sun L 12 to 2, Wed to Sat D 7 to 9 MEALS: alc (main courses £11 to £16.50) SERVICE: not inc, card slips closed CARDS: Delta, MasterCard, Switch, Visa DETAILS: 22 seats. 10 seat outside. Car park. Music

DARTMOUTH Devon map 1

DEVON RESTAURANT OF THE YEAR

Carved Angel

2 South Embankment, Dartmouth TQ6 9BH
TEL: (01803) 832465 FAX: (01803) 835141
EMAIL: enquiries@thecarvedangel.com
WEB SITE: www.thecarvedangel.com

COOKING **6**
MODERN BRITISH-PLUS
£40–£84

The Angel is back on form, taking its easy tempo from the setting. Big windows overlooking boats and ferries on the Dart let in lots of daylight; pale colours and bright paintings add to the luminosity; service is calm and serene; and glimpses of the kitchen indicate that here is a place with nothing to hide. 'All dishes sounded tempting,' admitted one couple, and lunch is by no means a poor relation of dinner. There is interest at every turn, from local crab with cucumber jelly and smoked pepper relish, to loin of beef with ox tongue ravioli. Careful attention to textures adds to the appeal: a goats' cheese and chive mousse, for example, layered between Parmesan crisps and accompanied by dollops of a well-judged pear chutney, or a 'bouncy and voluptuous' steamed scallop parfait, as sensuous as it is technically accomplished, served with a creamy artichoke velouté and a dash of truffle oil.

Above all, the kitchen knows when to stop adding things, which is a talent in itself, and the cooking can be unfussy and straightforward, as in a skinless fillet of eminently fresh and accurately timed halibut (a fish of the day), served with beurre noisette and a liquid lemon pickle. Fine presentation is another feature, but not at the expense of character: desserts have included a bulging and properly fruity plum soufflé served with a jug of juice and a scoop of mirabelle ice cream; and a chocolate tart slightly warm, wobbly, with fine thin pastry, and a mint and pistachio ice cream – that 'will haunt me for ever'. Wines feature a sound range of food-friendly styles from around the world, though bottles under £20 are scant, and house recommendations do not dip much below £17.50.

CHEF: David Jones PROPRIETORS: Paul and Andie Roston, and Peter Gorton OPEN: Tue to Sun L 12.30 to 2.30, Mon to Sat D 7 to 9.30 CLOSED: 3 days Christmas MEALS: alc L (main courses £17.50 to 19.50). Set L £25.50, Set D Mon £25, Set D Tue to Sat £39.50 to £55 SERVICE: not inc

CARDS: Amex, Delta, MasterCard, Switch, Visa DETAILS: 50 seats. Private parties: 35 main room, 12 and 20 private rooms. Vegetarian meals. Children's helpings at L. No children under 10 at D. No smoking in dining room. Music

Carved Angel Café £

7 Foss Street, Dartmouth TQ6 9DW
TEL: (01803) 834842 COOKING **3**
EMAIL: enquiries@thecarvedangel.com GLOBAL
WEB SITE: www.thecarvedangel.com £23–£43

Fosse Street is a pedestrianised lane of eighteenth- and nineteenth-century buildings, one of them this café offshoot of the Carved Angel (see entry above; another café-style Angel has opened in Exeter: see Round-up entry). Large plate-glass windows let you peer in to size it up, and the light, bright, uncluttered look may lure you in for homely cooking that still takes note of modern trends.

Dinner is more ambitious than lunch, perhaps offering lamb cutlets with pearl barley and parsnip crisps, or Thai green vegetable curry with coconut rice. A Far-East-style ball of minced pork with spiced crème fraîche has formed the centrepiece of an arresting salad, while a tender duck leg confit, with properly sticky skin, has arrived on unctuously creamy colcannon. Finish with chocolate shortbread tart, or a fruit sorbet. This being a café in more than just name, one can have breakfast, morning coffee, a snack lunch, a cream tea or toasted teacake in the afternoon, or a proper high tea with smoked salmon sandwiches and scones. Five southern-hemisphere wines and one German are all £13.75 a bottle, or £2.95 for a small glass.

CHEF: Brendan Keeley PROPRIETORS: Paul and Andie Roston, and Peter Gorton OPEN: Mon to Sat L 11 to 3, Thu to Sat 7 to 9 (morning coffee from 10) CLOSED: 3 days Christmas MEALS: alc (main courses £6 to £9.50). Set D £15 SERVICE: not inc CARDS: Amex, Delta, MasterCard, Switch, Visa DETAILS: 30 seats. Private parties: 30 main room. Vegetarian meals. Children's helpings. No smoking in dining room. Wheelchair access (not WC). Music

▲ Gunfield

Castle Road, Dartmouth TQ6 0JN
TEL: (01803) 834571 FAX: (01803) 834772 COOKING **1**
EMAIL: enquiry@gunfield.co.uk GLOBAL
WEB SITE: www.gunfield.co.uk £27–£43

Overlooking the River Dart, and with the option of outdoor eating in fine weather, Gunfield has a lot going for it. Bold prints and flowers lend a welcome freshness, and the modern global menu ranges from Thai crab cakes or fried Halloumi to wild duck terrine, rack of local lamb and spinach, and artichoke-heart cannelloni. Fish is understandably well represented: grilled local sea bass with a red pepper sauce, for example, or monkfish and tiger prawn brochette with a citrus and mint salsa. A note of indulgence shows in desserts like hot banana filo with toffee sauce, and Mexican chocolate caramel with vanilla bean ice cream. Service is friendly and efficient, and some 30 wines stay mostly below £20, starting with five southern-hemisphere house wines at £9.50.

CHEF: Chloë Wreford-Brown PROPRIETORS: Mike and Lucy Swash OPEN: Sun L 12.30 to 2.30, Mon to Sat D 7.30 to 9 MEALS: alc (main courses £10 to £15) SERVICE: not inc CARDS: Amex, Delta, Diners, MasterCard, Switch, Visa DETAILS: 50 seats. 80 seats outside. Private parties: 80 main room. Car park. Vegetarian meals. No children under 5. Music ACCOMMODATION: 10 rooms, all with bath/shower. TV. B&B £45 to £145. Baby facilities. Fishing (*The Which? Hotel Guide*)

DEDHAM Essex — map 6

▲ milsoms — NEW ENTRY

Stratford Road, Dedham C07 6HW
TEL: (01206) 322795 FAX: (01206) 323689

COOKING **1**
BISTRO
£24–£37

Straining to capture the young and fun loving market, this new, stylish venue presents a fresh, clean face, with high ceilings, bare sanded floors and slightly quirky décor. Its casual approach is emphasised by a 'no bookings' policy, and by contemporary international bistro-style food that takes in old standards (fish and chips) alongside the up-to-the minute (Goan fish pasty with fiery sambal and cool raita). The cooking tends to be simple and unfussy, based on fresh, quality ingredients, as in moist and fresh-tasting sea bass with pak choi and shiitake mushrooms. For dessert, Eton mess with banana and passion fruit has been endorsed, and elderflower sorbet comes with a shot of Stolichnaya for an extra £1. Service from charming, friendly young staff is relaxed and informal, and a brief, straightforward, good value wine list stays mostly under £20, with house French at £9.25. Co-proprietor Gerald Milsom also owns Le Talbooth (see entry below) and The Pier at Harwich (see entry, Harwich).

CHEF: Stas Anastasiades PROPRIETORS: Paul and Gerald Milsom OPEN: all week 12 to 2.15, 6 to 9.30 (10 Fri and Sat) MEALS: alc (main courses £7 to £10). Light L menu available 9.30 to 12 and 2.15 to 6 SERVICE: not inc CARDS: Amex, Delta, Diners, MasterCard, Switch, Visa DETAILS: 80 seats. 50 seats outside. Private parties: 8 main room, 14 private room. Car park. Vegetarian meals. Children's helpings. No-smoking area. Wheelchair access (also WC). Music ACCOMMODATION: 14 rooms, all with bath/shower. TV. Phone. Room only £80 to £120. Rooms for disabled (*The Which? Hotel Guide*)

▲ Le Talbooth

Gun Hill, Dedham CO7 6HP
TEL: (01206) 323150 FAX: (01206) 322309
EMAIL: talbooth@talbooth.co.uk
WEB SITE: www.talbooth.com
off A12; 6m N of Colchester or 8m S of Ipswich take turning signed Stratford St Mary

COOKING **4**
MODERN EUROPEAN
£34–£82

This half-timbered Tudor house sits idyllically beside the Stour. Leaded windows overlook the garden and river, candelabra lanterns hang from the dining room's vaulted ceiling, and reproductions of local boy Constable's paintings add gravitas. The fixed-price menu favours British dishes along with more speculative combinations (trout on watercress couscous with curried seafood sauce), and the à la carte piles on the luxury.

Descriptions are meticulous – 'breast of guinea-fowl stuffed with crab mousse, with a confit of the leg, ratatouille of tomatoes and a chicken and tarragon cream sauce' – and dishes excite with both colour and flavour. Amid frisée, rocket and lardons of pork belly, a red slice of beef tomato supports a piece of black pudding, itself surmounted by a vivid yellow soft-poached egg. Raspberry crème Chiboust and apricot coulis add zing to a lemon shortbread dessert, and the tang of rhubarb revitalises a crème brûlée. Umesh Sewnundun's front-of-house team is effortlessly proficient, and the wine list impresses with its range of styles and depth of regional offerings, from South Africa especially. Lovers of fine, mature claret will be as heartened as seekers of cheerful, uncomplicated drinking (starting at £13.50).

CHEFS: Terry Barber and Daniel Clarke PROPRIETORS: Gerald and Paul Milsom OPEN: all week L 12 to 2 (3.30 winter Suns), Mon to Sat D 7 to 9 (9.15 Fri and Sat) MEALS: alc Mon to Sat (main courses £16 to £30). Set L £17.50 (2 courses) to £21, Set D £23 (2 courses) to £28.50 SERVICE: 10%, card slips closed CARDS: Amex, Delta, Diners, MasterCard, Switch, Visa DETAILS: 75 seats. 50 seats outside. Private parties: 80 main room, 34 private room. Car park. Children's helpings. Vegetarian meals. Wheelchair access (also WC). Occasional music ACCOMMODATION: 10 rooms, all with bath/shower. TV. Phone. B&B £120 to £210. Rooms for disabled (*The Which? Hotel Guide*) (£5)

DERBY Derbyshire **map 5**

Darleys

Darley Abbey Mill, Darley Abbey,
Derby DE22 1DZ
TEL: (01332) 364987 FAX: (01332) 541356
WEB SITE: www.darleys.com
of A6, 2m N of city centre

COOKING **4**
MODERN BRITISH
£27–£55

Darley Abbey Mill is every bit as redolent of the nineteenth century as the name suggests, yet the restaurant itself is decorated in an elegantly contemporary style with attractive plain furniture and tableware; it now also features a deck terrace with panoramic river views where aperitifs and coffee are served. Its menu, likewise, takes a modern and largely British route, incorporating French and Italian influences, the scope illustrated by a tian of crab and tomato with potato galette and chive pesto, and by chargrilled kidneys on creamy leeks with a devilled jus.

Main courses, meanwhile, range from roast saddle of lamb with potato and black pudding torte, to a tart of red onion and wild mushrooms with watercress salad and chive mascarpone. Among desserts might be that regional speciality Bakewell tart, or perhaps banana mille-feuille, comprising 'superb' banana sorbet sandwiched in layers of thinly sliced dried banana. Service has varied from 'unprofessional' and 'brusque' to 'on the ball'. The wine list has lost the helpful descriptions of previous years, but still offers an intelligently chosen and fairly priced selection, opening with a page of 12 'personal recommendations' from £14.

CHEFS: Kevin Stone and Gavin Allcock PROPRIETORS: David and Gillian Pinchbeck OPEN: all week L 12 to 2 (2.30 Sat, 3 Sun), Mon to Sat D 6.30 to 10 (10.30 Fri and Sat) CLOSED: bank hols MEALS: alc (main courses £13.50 to £18). Set L £13.50 (2 courses) to £17.50, Set D Mon to Fri £22 SERVICE: 10% (optional), card slips closed CARDS: Amex, Delta, Diners, MasterCard, Switch,

Visa DETAILS: 70 seats. 20 seats outside. Private parties: 70 main room. Car park. Vegetarian meals. Children's helpings. No smoking in dining room. Wheelchair access (not WC). Music. Air-conditioned (£5)

DINTON Buckinghamshire map 3

La Chouette 🍷

Westlington Green, Dinton HP17 8UW — COOKING **3**
TEL/FAX: (01296) 747422 — BELGIAN
off A418, following signs to Westlington and Ford — £21–£62

Operating out of a creeper clad building in a quiet village, the owl is a rare bird, not just on account of its fiercely independent and individual owner (M. Desmette seems to do most things himself) but also because it aims to champion his native Belgian food and drink. Although some of the latter finds its way into the former, for example a sauce made with Duvel beer to accompany brill fillet, the majority of dishes are of more general provenance, for example a salad of smoked Scottish salmon, duck breast with green peppercorn sauce, or leg of lamb with seasonal vegetables. In addition to the carte and a couple of set price menus, M. Desmette will also serve you three courses for £11 at lunch, although he may not divulge the menu in advance. But the house style involves commendably simple presentation: of, for example, beef fillet with béarnaise, or John Dory with beurre blanc. Dessert tends to be a 'surprise!' The wine list is a roll call of the great French regions, and fans of the Rhône and Loire have a wide choice. Five bins from other countries are tacked on; two are English. Prices are not low, but red and white French house wines are both £11.50 a bottle.

CHEF/PROPRIETOR: Frédéric Desmette OPEN: Mon to Fri L 12 to 2, Mon to Sat D 7 to 9 MEALS: alc (main courses £12 to £16). Set L £11 to £36.50, Set D £28.50 to £36.50 SERVICE: 12.5% (optional), card slips closed CARDS: Delta, MasterCard, Visa DETAILS: 35 seats. 12 seats outside. Private parties: 45 main room. Car park. Children's helpings. No cigars/pipes in dining room. Music

DORRINGTON Shropshire map 5

▲ Country Friends

Dorrington SY5 7JD — COOKING **6**
TEL: (01743) 718707 — ANGLO-EUROPEAN
on A49, 5m S of Shrewsbury — £40–£53

'Bourgeois', 'conservative' and 'traditionalist' is how the utilitarian setting appears to strike visitors: with its Chesterfield wall seats in the bar and false wood panelling in the dining room, it is 'the last restaurant to which one would apply the word "flashy"'. Rising above its surroundings, the food combines fine raw materials with a high degree of technical accomplishment and care, and has the confidence to turn out dishes of 'outstanding simplicity' that balance flavours and textures well: for example, a starter of pink calf's liver scattered with shallots and apple slices, in a warm and sharp vinaigrette, or monkfish served with a risotto studded with tiny mussels and oozing a deeply fragrant, concentrated cooking liquor.

Depth of flavour is one of the food's distinguishing marks, notable in a baked breast and braised leg of guinea fowl, served with pearl barley and a wild mushroom sauce, and in a venison steak accompanied by strips of pasta and a stickily reduced dill-flavoured sauce. The menu, like much else, moves at a sedate pace. Vegetables – including the long-standing deep-fried cauliflower – come on a separate serving dish, although they are adapted to main courses: red cabbage with meat and game, for instance, fennel with fish. Queen of puddings is another enduring favourite, served with a tangy gin and lime ice cream, and coffee and rum parfait has impressed for its simple presentation and intense flavours. Service is often by the proprietors themselves, and there is no one to beat the affable Charles Whittaker for 'sincere and intelligent bonhomie'. Half-bottles are prominent on the balanced wine list, prices are down to earth, and four house wines weigh in at £12.75.

CHEF: Charles Whittaker PROPRIETORS: Charles and Pauline Whittaker OPEN: Wed to Sat 12 to 2, 7 to 9 (9.30 Sat) CLOSED: 2 weeks mid-July MEALS: Set L and D £27.50 (2 courses) to £33.90. Light L menu available SERVICE: not inc CARDS: Delta, MasterCard, Switch, Visa DETAILS: 40 seats. Private parties: 40 main room. Car park. Vegetarian meals. No smoking in dining room. Wheelchair access (not WC). No music ACCOMMODATION: 1 room with bath/shower. D,B&B £75 to £130. No children

DRYBROOK Gloucestershire **map 5**

Cider Press

The Cross, Drybrook GL17 9EB
TEL: (01594) 544472 COOKING **3**
EMAIL: cider.press@virgin.net MODERN BRITISH/SEAFOOD
WEB SITE: www.cider-press-restaurant.co.uk £28–£44

Country-style tables add to the comfortable and homely feel of this 'sparklingly clean' former shop, the pictures and cartoons on its brick and plaster walls picking up the apple theme. Take heed of the menu's legend, 'We don't hurry the food or the customer', and expect an informal setup, a warm welcome, and a relaxed pace. The cooking centres around fish, much of it from Cornwall, starting perhaps with battered, deep-fried monkfish (referred to, oddly, as an escabèche), followed by whatever is currently available: maybe salt-baked bream, grilled red mullet, or baked hake flavoured with chorizo, lemon and herbs. When it comes to tearing shellfish apart, they don't just provide a finger bowl but, in the case of lobster at least, a bib and hot towel as well.

A penchant for organic, free-range or naturally reared materials drives the rest of the menu, which might feature a seasonal loin of venison flavoured with juniper and allspice, served with red cabbage and a port and crème fraîche sauce. Cheese is a help-yourself farmhouse selection, passed around the room, and desserts run to apple cake with maple syrup ice cream, and a chocolate, hazelnut and Cointreau tart with Greek yoghurt. A sensibly chosen and fairly price wine list offers a few sherries to start, French cider and perry, and half a dozen house wines under £10.

CHEF: Christopher Stephen Challener PROPRIETOR: Bernadette Elizabeth Fitzpatrick OPEN: Wed to Sat D only 7 to 10.30 (L and other D by arrangement) CLOSED: mid-Jan MEALS: alc (main courses £13.50 to £16.50) SERVICE: not inc, card slips closed CARDS: Delta, MasterCard, Switch, Visa DETAILS: 22 seats. 4 seats outside. Private parties: 26 main room. No smoking in dining room. Wheelchair access (not WC). Occasional music

DURHAM Co Durham map 10

Bistro 21

Aykley Heads House, Aykley Heads,
Durham DH1 5TS
TEL: (0191) 384 4354 FAX: (0191) 384 1149

COOKING **2**
MEDITERRANEAN
£23–£57

The building, a couple of miles from the city centre, looks like an old farmhouse from outside, and feels quite 'cottagey' inside, thanks to stripped floorboards, simple pine chairs, and a collection of terracotta pots, kettles, bottles and wine crates. The broadly European style of food (overseen by Terence Laybourne, as at Newcastle and Ponteland), plays to the gallery with staples from the bistro repertoire, including Cheddar cheese and spinach soufflé, fishcakes with parsley sauce and good chips, and profiteroles with pistachio ice cream and hot chocolate sauce.

A blackboard supplements the options, which can range from simply grilled sea bass, or gambas with lime and coriander butter, to richer and more filling blue cheese fritters with an interesting endive and walnut salad. Desserts aim for the comfort zone with a warm, 'puddingy' chocolate mousse, or banana toffee torte on a crumbly biscuit base. Service can be slow. Three dozen workmanlike wines start with house Duboeuf at £10.50.

CHEF/PROPRIETOR: Terence Laybourne OPEN: Mon to Sat 12 to 2, 7 (6 Sat) to 10.30 CLOSED: 25 and 26 Dec, bank hols MEALS: alc (main courses £9.50 to £18). Set L £12 (2 courses) to £14.50 SERVICE: not inc CARDS: Amex, Delta, Diners, MasterCard, Switch, Visa DETAILS: 55 seats. 20 seats outside. Private parties: 60 main room, 10 to 20 private rooms. Car park. Vegetarian meals. Children's helpings. No smoking in dining room. Music

EASTBOURNE East Sussex map 3

▲ Grand Hotel, Mirabelle

King Edwards Parade, Eastbourne BN21 4EQ
TEL: (01323) 412345 FAX: (01323) 412233
EMAIL: reservations@grandeastbourne.com
WEB SITE: www.grandeastbourne.co.uk

COOKING **6**
MODERN EUROPEAN
£30–£59

On the ground floor of the east wing, reached via the hotel or from a side street, an airy and elegant dining room overlooks the gardens and seafront, its tables large and generously spaced. Set-price menus are the form, with around four choices per course at lunch, seven at dinner, and the contemporary style is appealing. Luxury items abound in the shape of foie gras with apple chutney, or red mullet with oyster tempura and truffled cauliflower purée, yet the food does not rely altogether on these for effect.

Savoury dishes are simply and classically designed around three major components, which gives them both variety and focus, as in a breast of guinea fowl with basil orsotto and black olive sauce, or fillet of beef with pomme purée and celery confit. Fish is a strength too, taking in pan-fried sea bass fillet with chargrilled vegetables and herb couscous, and main courses include a vegetarian option such as gnocchi with a collection of vegetables and a sweet pepper sauce. One couple who eat here nearly every week consider themselves well placed to judge that standards remain consistent despite staff changes.

The generally pampering tone induced by soft textures continues in desserts such as blackberry mousse with a Cox's apple sorbet, and an enterprising iced chocolate and tarragon parfait in a pear soup. It may be argued that a grand hotel should have a wine list to match, in which case this one suits very well; high mark-ups (£21 for a bottle of Mouton-Cadet) take much of the pleasure out of drinking, although there is no service charge to add. Despite its traditional approach, the list finds room for good wines from around the world, some under £20, including house French varietals at £16.50.

CHEFS: Keith Mitchell and Lee Knowles PROPRIETOR: Elite Hotels OPEN: Tue to Sat 12.30 to 2, 7 to 10 CLOSED: 1 to 14 Jan MEALS: Set L £19, Set D £35 SERVICE: net prices, card slips closed CARDS: Amex, Delta, Diners, MasterCard, Switch, Visa DETAILS: 40 seats. Car park. No children under 10. Jacket and tie. No smoking in dining room. Music. Air-conditioned ACCOMMODATION: 152 rooms, all with bath/shower. TV. Phone. B&B £125 to £410. Rooms for disabled. Baby facilities. Swimming pool (*The Which? Hotel Guide*)

EAST CHILTINGTON East Sussex **map 3**

Jolly Sportsman

Chapel Lane, East Chiltington BN7 3BA
TEL/FAX: (01273) 890400
WEB SITE: www.thejollysportsman.com
from B2116 ½m E of Plumpton, turn N (signposted East Chiltington), after 1½m turn left (pub is signposted)

COOKING **1**
MODERN EUROPEAN
£28–£57

This isolated pub, down a leafy lane with views across the Downs from its back garden, repays the map-reading needed. The menu shows ambition, with half a dozen or so choices at each course, supplemented by simpler blackboard offerings and a separate vegetarian menu. Start with Cornish crab with coriander, chilli and shrimps, or try Irish oysters with shallots and red wine vinegar. Roast guinea fowl and butternut squash risotto, or brioche-crumbed hake fillet with beurre blanc, might follow, while comforting desserts may feature a well-reported apricot, walnut, ginger and toffee pudding. Olives and breads are good, service friendly, and the wine list wanders the globe, picking up a fair selection of halves, six by the glass and house wines from £9.85.

CHEF: Richard Willis PROPRIETORS: Bruce and Gwyneth Wass OPEN: Tue to Sun L 12.30 to 2 (3 Sun), Tues to Sat D 7 to 9.30 (10 Sun) CLOSED: 5 days at Christmas MEALS: alc Tue to Sat (main courses £10 to £19.50). Set L £10 (2 courses), Set L Sun £15.85 (2 courses). Bar menu also available SERVICE: 10%, card slips closed CARDS: Delta, MasterCard, Switch, Visa DETAILS: 60 seats. 100 seats outside. Private parties: 40 main room, 18 to 40 private rooms. Car park. Vegetarian meals. Children's helpings. Wheelchair access (not WC). No music

New main entries and restaurant closures are listed near the front of the book.

EAST END Hampshire map 2

East End Arms

Main Road, East End SO41 5SY
TEL/FAX: (01590) 626223
EMAIL: jennie@eastendarms.co.uk
off B3054, 2m E of Lymington; follow signs for Isle of Wight ferry and continue 2m

COOKING **3**
MODERN BRITISH/SEAFOOD
£21–£44

'A comfortable pub serving entirely competent food at very reasonable cost,' was one reporter's verdict on the East End Arms. And though it is first and foremost a pub, aiming to cater for all tastes, food is taken seriously: local suppliers provide most of the raw materials, the menu changes frequently and a wide range of fresh fish dishes is usually available. Lunch options listed on a blackboard typically take in cod masala on fragrant rice, pan-fried loin of pork with chips, and various baguettes. In the evenings the kitchen steps up a gear to offer whiting fillet on a warm gazpacho sauce, roast chicken with a casserole of Mediterranean vegetables, and roast spiced bream with carrot and coconut milk. Desserts include nursery favourites (raspberry jelly), as well as more sophisticated offerings such as butterscotch crêpe. Wine prices start at £11 and remain under £20 throughout the very short list.

CHEFS: Paul Sykes and Stuart Ritcher PROPRIETOR: J.E. Illsley OPEN: Tue to Sun L 12 to 2, Mon to Sat D 7 to 9 CLOSED: 1 Jan; no food served 25 and 26 Dec and Tue following bank hols MEALS: alc (main courses £6 to £15). Set D Mon £10 (2 courses) to £12 SERVICE: not inc, card slips closed CARDS: Delta, MasterCard, Switch, Visa DETAILS: 34 seats. 60 seats outside. Private parties: 25 main room. Car park. Children's helpings L. Wheelchair access (not WC). Music

EAST GRINSTEAD West Sussex map 3

▲ Gravetye Manor

Vowels Lane, East Grinstead RH19 4LJ
TEL: (01342) 810567 FAX: (01342) 810080
EMAIL: info@gravetyemanor.co.uk
WEB SITE: www.gravetyemanor.co.uk
off B2110, 2m SW of East Grinstead

COOKING **6**
TRADITIONAL ENGLISH
£41–£91

Reached along a winding road that runs through woodland, Gravetye offers the pleasing prospect (to those who arrive in daylight) of both formal and 'wild' gardens, and a charming terrace for drinks. Dark wood panelling, beams and log fires that are 'an American tourist's dream' provide the backdrop to food that sees no reason to go out of its way to keep up with trends. If the menu seems expensive, it doesn't stint on raw materials, and it does engage attention: for example, with a piece of flavourful veal shin topped with caramelised fried onion shreds and roast scallops, or three quail breasts and legs accompanied by a nest of soft, breadcrumbed and deep-fried quails' eggs and a chilled 'pannacotta' of celeriac.

Textures and flavours are generally carefully husbanded, as in a ballottine of wild salmon decorated with a rosette of home-smoked salmon, and the highlight of an inspection meal was a fine, gutsy and lingering risotto, as pungently redolent of truffle as could be hoped for, garnished with a curly Parmesan wafer. Seafood successes have included medallions of lobster 'of the non-chewy variety so rarely found in restaurant dining rooms' served with basil crème fraîche, and a seriously good plate of langoustine and lemon sole in tarragon sauce. Not all dishes make the grade, however, and the tally of gripes at that inspection, not least with shy flavours and general lack of finesse, suggest that the kitchen can lose its way occasionally. And desserts appear not to be the strongest suit.

Wines focus on high-priced classics from France, but also make well-chosen forays into other parts of the world, particularly Australia and California. Bottles under £25 are scarce, although a close search will uncover the occasional one under £20. Six house wines, five French, one South African, range from £16 to £22.

CHEF: Mark Raffan PROPRIETORS: Peter Herbert and family OPEN: all week 12.30 to 1.45, 7 to 9.30 (9 Sun) CLOSED: D 25 Dec (open for residents) MEALS: Set L Mon to Sat £27 to £52, Set L Sun £35, Set D £37 to £52 SERVICE: net prices, card slips closed CARDS: MasterCard, Switch, Visa DETAILS: 45 seats. 12 seats outside. Private parties: 8 main room, 8 to 16 private room. Car park. Vegetarian meals. No children under 7 in dining room. No smoking in dining room. Wheelchair access (not WC). No music ACCOMMODATION: 18 rooms, all with bath/shower. TV. Phone. Room only £95 to £320. No children under 7 exc babies. Baby facilities. Fishing (*The Which? Hotel Guide*)

EAST WITTON North Yorkshire **map 8**

▲ Blue Lion

East Witton DL8 4SN
TEL: (01969) 624273 FAX: (01969) 624189
EMAIL: bluelion@breathemail.net
WEB SITE: www.thebluelion.co.uk
on A6108 between Masham and Leyburn

COOKING **3**
MODERN BRITISH
£32–£53

As village pubs go, this one is not short of regulation markers – stone floors, piles of logs beside the fire, plain wooden tables – and confirms its dual role with a lively bar menu that takes in Thai-style crab cake with chilli jam, onion and blue Wensleydale tart, and corned-beef hash with a fried egg. The kitchen is well aware of pub priorities, serving up eight-ounce fillet and sirloin steaks in the dining room, alongside grilled lemon sole with tartare sauce, and rich gamey dishes of venison and wild boar. Vegetarians, meanwhile, are accommodated with pesto risotto, tagliatelle with a cream and cep sauce, and Spanish omelette. Desserts aim for the comfort zone with dark chocolate terrine, and tiramisù, but there may also be a pink grapefruit and orange salad with lemon sorbet. If there is a problem with the food it is that 'far too many people want to eat it', so don't be surprised by busy weekends. Wines are well chosen for the environment: affordable, with plenty of scope for experimentation and characterful drinking. House French red and white come in at £10.50, and champagne starts at only £14.95.

CHEF: John Dalby PROPRIETORS: Paul and Helen Klein OPEN: Sun L 12 to 2.15, all week D 7 to 9.30 CLOSED: no food served on 25 Dec MEALS: alc (main courses £13 to £17). Bar menu available SERVICE: not inc CARDS: Delta, MasterCard, Switch, Visa DETAILS: 70 seats. Private parties: 45 main room, 16 private room. Car park. Vegetarian meals. Children's helpings. No music ACCOMMODATION: 12 rooms, all with bath/shower. TV. Phone. B&B £53.50 to £89. Rooms for disabled. Baby facilities (*The Which? Hotel Guide*)

ELY Cambridgeshire **map 6**

Old Fire Engine House

25 St Mary's Street, Ely CB7 4ER COOKING **1**
TEL: (01353) 662582 FAX: (01353) 668364 TRADITIONAL ENGLISH FARMHOUSE
£27–£43

Built in the eighteenth century (within sight of the cathedral) to house Ely's fire engine, the house is now filled with modern artwork. A country-style dining room with scrubbed wooden furniture overlooks a walled garden, and Terri Kindred cooks 'fashion-resistant' food with 'not a Thai spice in sight'. No one, not even the owners, would describe the cooking as sophisticated, but if the domestic pitch seems unexciting, bear in mind that it does include things like locally smoked eel, egg mayonnaise and jugged hare (none of them common nowadays), and that the food is freshly prepared and simply presented. Among recommendations have been tender, flavourful roast pork with good crackling and a fresh herb stuffing, accompanied by a steaming bowl of mange-tout and cauliflower cheese: 'we purred.' And where else, these days, serves second helpings of main courses? Desserts run to syllabub, apple pie with cream, and rhubarb and almond crumble with cream (yes, there is a lot of cream). An inspector notes that the edge seems to have gone off the cooking recently, but helpful staff deliver efficient and charming service, and wines, mostly French, come with detailed notes and start with around eight by the glass.

CHEF: Terri Kindred PROPRIETORS: Ann Ford and Michael Jarman OPEN: all week L 12.15 to 2, Mon to Sat D 7.15 to 9 CLOSED: 2 weeks from 24 Dec, bank hols MEALS: alc (main courses £13.50 to £15) SERVICE: not inc CARDS: Delta, MasterCard, Switch, Visa DETAILS: 58 seats. 20 seats outside. Private parties: 36 main room, 22 private room. Car park. Vegetarian meals. Children's helpings. No smoking in 1 dining room. No music

EMSWORTH Hampshire **map 2**

Spencers

36/38 North Street, Emsworth PO10 7DG COOKING **3**
TEL/FAX: (01243) 372744 MODERN BRITISH
£19–£42

The same food is served at the same prices throughout: eat either in the upstairs dining room (referred to as the restaurant) or in the more informal ground-floor brasserie. The latter seems more popular with reporters, who come for a varied menu that runs from baked goats' cheese to smoked duck salad, from fish soup to pot roast haunch of rabbit. A separate fish menu indicates the kitchen's enthusiasm: roast monkfish with bacon is among endorsements, but there may also be Dover sole with lime and sea salt, or baked brill with chickpeas, chilli and thyme. Note that vegetables are charged extra. Simple desserts of crème brûlée or hot chocolate gâteau conclude proceedings, service is friendly and capable, and a short roving wine list stays mostly under £20. House French and Australians come in at £10.50 (£2 a glass). A sister restaurant, also called Spencers has opened in Petersfield; tel (01730) 231295.

CHEF: Denis Spencer PROPRIETORS: Denis and Lesley Spencer, and Mike Mulchrone OPEN: Mon to Sat L 12 to 2, D 6 to 10.30 CLOSED: 25 and 26 Dec MEALS: alc (main courses £9 to £13.50). Set L and D before 7pm only £6.95 (2 courses) SERVICE: not inc CARDS: Amex, Delta, Diners, MasterCard, Switch, Visa DETAILS: 76 seats. Private parties: 30 main room, 10 private room. Vegetarian meals. No smoking in 1 dining room. No cigars or pipes. Music. Air-conditioned (£5)

36 on the Quay

47 South Street, Emsworth PO10 7EG — COOKING **6**
TEL: (01243) 375592 FAX: (01243) 375593 — MODERN EUROPEAN
WEB SITE: www.36onthequay.co.uk — £34–£69

Occupying a stocky building down by the quay, 36 creates an 'upper-middle-class' impression thanks to its chintzy floral prints, thick carpets, and yards and yards (sorry, metres and metres) of draped curtains. Ramon Farthing's broadly European food takes in many an interesting combination – seared scallops served with a chicken and duck liver sausage, perhaps – and is also shot through with oriental ingredients and ideas: stir-fried vegetables and curry oil to accompany pan-fried sea bass fillets, for example, or a wigwam of cod tempura ('like bendy fish fingers') on sauté pak choi. His elaborate style, however, is taken about as far as it can go (some might say too far): that last starter also involved a bird's nest of crispy seaweed, minuscule bits of potato salad, tiny dice of purple potato mixed with chopped onion and topped with first-rate peeled langoustines, and streaks of 'oriental dressing'.

Raw materials make a fine contribution, and dishes can be impressive, thanks not least to skilful saucing: a deep-flavoured, well-reduced, stock-based version to accompany roast breast and slowly braised leg of guinea fowl, for example. Pastry-making talent is also evident in an outstanding, miniature, savoury beef and vegetable pie, old-fashioned and buttery, to accompany beef fillet, and in a rich tarte Tatin filled with caramelised apple, partnered by a Granny Smith sorbet. Presentation is given a high priority, with different, enormous patterned plates for everything, and a dedication to building towers. Bread might be improved, piped music can be intrusive, and Karen Farthing's helpers don't match her efficient service, but the wine list offers plenty of enjoyable drinking. Choice, though broad in regional terms, is limited under £25. The house selection, however, starting at £13.50 and staying below £20, is a source of lively and good-value bins, mainly from southern France.

CHEF: Ramon Farthing PROPRIETORS: Ramon and Karen Farthing OPEN: Tue to Fri L 12 to 1.45, Mon to Sat D 7 to 9.45 CLOSED: last week Oct, first 2 weeks Jan MEALS: Set L £16.95 (2 courses) to £20.95, Set D £34.95 to £42.95 SERVICE: not inc CARDS: Amex, Delta, Diners, MasterCard, Switch, Visa DETAILS: 40 seats. Private parties: 35 main room, 10 private room. Small car park. Children's helpings. No smoking in dining room. Wheelchair access (not WC). Occasional music

EPWORTH North Lincolnshire — map 9

Epworth Tap

9–11 Market Place, Epworth DN9 1AB
TEL/FAX: (01427) 873333 — COOKING **3**
WEB SITE: theepworthtap.co.uk — MODERN EUROPEAN
3m S of M180 junction 2 — £30–£43

Previous owners John and Helen Wynne, who ran the Tap for many years as one of the country's best wine bars, have retired, proving a hard act to follow as far as commitment and expertise in both food and wine are concerned. The new owners, however, who have retained the flag floors, church pew seating and wooden tables, were fortunate to secure the services of Christopher Randle-Bissell who cooked previously at Hamilton's in Doncaster. His broadly European approach takes in anything from crab spring roll, via twice-baked dolcelatte cheese soufflé, to a red onion tart with a crisp shortcrust pastry base.

Happily, the cooking is uncomplicated, producing, for example, a plain, simple, crisp-skinned fillet of sea bass with a pesto dressing and mashed potato, and a fine-quality, pink-grilled breast of duck with a honey-infused sauce. Desserts follow the same path, in the shape of a plain strawberry shortbread (in March), and a puff pastry dish of sweet, skinned, stewed plums, the highlight of an inspection meal. A value-oriented wine list offers a varied range of styles, mostly under £25, with house wines £11.50 and £12.50 a bottle. A number of mature fine wines represent good value even at £35-plus.

CHEF: Chris Randle-Bissell PROPRIETORS: Gail Perry and Simon Cliff OPEN: Wed L 12 to 2, Wed to Sat D 7 to 9.30 MEALS: alc Wed and Thur (main courses £12.50 to £14.50). Set D Fri and Sat only £25.50 SERVICE: not inc, card slips closed CARDS: Delta, MasterCard, Switch, Visa DETAILS: 60 seats. Private parties: 30 main room, 25 private room. No smoking in dining room. Music (£5)

ERPINGHAM Norfolk — map 6

▲ Ark

The Street, Erpingham NR11 7QB — COOKING **4**
TEL: (01263) 761535 — ENGLISH COUNTRY COOKING
3m off A140 Cromer road, 4m N of Aylsham — £25–£52

After nearly 20 years, and approaching retirement age, the Kidds are scaling down their family-run operation with fewer opening times, although rooms can still be booked for any day of the week, and residents will still be catered for. A relaxed front-of-house style (Mike Kidd may appear in his gardening clothes, fresh from digging vegetables) sits comfortably with serious intent in the kitchen. A backbone of local suppliers of fish and shellfish, meat and game, is matched by a frankness in the cooking. Asparagus has come with hollandaise, home-marinated salmon with mustard and dill sauce, and crab cakes with a yellow capsicum sauce. This is not messed-about food, just plain and simple fare.

Such a straightforward domestic approach is also evident in, for example, main-course roast meats, which are typically stuffed with something – Trelough duck with a bitter orange marmalade farce, or loin of lamb with an apricot, walnut and watercress stuffing – and in desserts of raspberry trifle, or strawberry and almond meringue. The lively selection of wines is not greedily marked up, although there is plenty of variety: from a southern hemisphere Pinot Noir to a Super-Tuscan. Six house wines are £11.75 (£2.75 a glass).

CHEF: Sheila Kidd PROPRIETORS: Mike and Sheila Kidd OPEN: Sun L 12.30 to 2, Thur to Sat D 7 to 9.30 CLOSED: 25 and 26 Dec, 3 weeks Oct MEALS: Set L £16.50, Set D £22.50 (2 courses) to £29.50 SERVICE: not inc CARDS: none DETAILS: 20 seats. 12 seats outside. Private parties: 24 main room. Car park. Vegetarian meals. Children's helpings. No smoking in dining room. No music ACCOMMODATION: 3 rooms, all with bath/shower. TV. D,B&B £70 to £140. Baby facilities

EXETER Devon **map 1**

Brazz £

10–12 Palace Gate, Exeter EX1 1JA
TEL: (01392) 252525 FAX: (01392) 253045
EMAIL: enquiries@brazz.co.uk

COOKING **3**
BRITISH BRASSERIE
£23–£55

Part of a small chain that started in Taunton (see entry), and with plans for a third addition in the future, Brazz is a contemporary fusion of café, brasserie and restaurant. A long bar, scattered tables, a two-storey aquarium, a clever starlit dome, and a first-floor dining room with a view of the kitchen give it a cosmopolitan feel. A wide range of dishes targets a broad spectrum of customers. Reporters come variously for a bowl of pickled quails' eggs and a glass of wine, a slice of terrine (there are Club sandwich and Mediterranean vegetable and pecorino versions), or battered cod and chips (big potato chunks piled on top of one another like 'chip-henge'). Also endorsed are simple pasta dishes, Caesar salad, pan-fried foie gras with lentil purée, and caramel parfait with prunes. Unashamedly populist stuff, maybe, but it is refreshing to find somewhere that is happy serving straightforward, unpretentious food without ceremony, at reasonable prices and with willing, smiley service. Wines are equally friendly (ten of them are served in four sizes, from large glass upwards); house Vin de Pays du Gers is £9.95.

CHEF: Nick Fisher PROPRIETOR: The English Brasserie Company OPEN: all week noon to 10.30 (11 Fri and Sat), reduced menu from 3 to 6; Tue to Sat breakfast from 10am CLOSED: 25 Dec MEALS: alc (main courses £7 to £16). Set L Sun £9.95. Bar menu available SERVICE: 10% (optional), card slips closed CARDS: Amex, Delta, Diners, MasterCard, Switch, Visa DETAILS: 200 seats. Private parties: 120 main room. Vegetarian meals. Children's helpings. Wheelchair access (also WC). Music. Air-conditioned

▲ Michael Caines at Royal Clarence

Cathedral Yard, Exeter EX1 1HD
TEL: (01392) 310031 FAX: (01392) 310032
EMAIL: tables@michaelcaines.com
WEB SITE: www.michaelcaines.com

COOKING **5**
FRENCH
£28–£60

Looking across the close to the Norman tower of the cathedral, which is floodlit at night, the dining room's white and yellow walls are given a lift by some large colourful canvases, while sharp spotlights shine down on pinstripe upholstery, the whole room smart yet relaxing. France is a major source of inspiration for the kitchen, producing, for example, a terrine of small, tender chunks of ham hock (like jambon persillé), served with lightly crunchy green beans and a zigzag of mustard vinaigrette, and ideas are kept fresh without having to stray too far from the straight and narrow.

Local materials make themselves known now and again – as in a salad of deep-fried River Dart oysters and squid with marinated provençale vegetables – and the food is generally well executed, if a little lacking in passion. A watchful eye in the kitchen has ensured crisp skins: on roast chicken, and on a chunk of brill on the bone served with tagliatelle vegetables. Seasonal input has run to well-hung pheasant (with lentil stuffing and black pudding), and recommended desserts have included vanilla mousse with spiced preserved fruits, and a tarte Tatin 'worthy of France' served with a local cider ice cream. As to value, this is 'not cheap, but worth it'. Service, although generally proficient and pleasant, could do with sharpening up. Wines from around the world are arranged varietally, most costing between £20 and £30, and four house wines at £13 (two Chilean, two French) are served by the large and small glass.

CHEF: Jean-Marc Zanetti PROPRIETOR: Michael Caines OPEN: all week 12 to 2.30, 7 to 10 CLOSED: D 25 Dec (residents only) MEALS: alc exc Sun L (main courses £13 to £19). Set L £14 (2 courses) to £17 SERVICE: not inc, 10% for parties of 10 or more CARDS: Amex, Delta, Diners, MasterCard, Switch, Visa DETAILS: 76 seats. Private parties: 30 and 90 private rooms. Vegetarian meals. Children's helpings. No smoking in dining room. Wheelchair access (also WC). No music. Air-conditioned ACCOMMODATION: 56 rooms, all with bath/shower. TV. Phone. Room only £55 to £155. Baby facilities (£5)

▲ St Olaves Hotel

NEW ENTRY

Mary Arches Street, Exeter EX4 3AZ
TEL: (01392) 217736 FAX: (01392) 413054
EMAIL: info@olaves.co.uk
WEB SITE: www.olaves.co.uk

COOKING **4**
MODERN BRITISH
£28–£62

'Elegant, understated, classic and smart' is how the dining room of this Georgian house appears, with its antique pictures and ornaments, and big plates on linen-covered tables. Not only has it undergone extensive refurbishment recently, but its new chef is shaping up, offering a restrained contemporary menu and some deft cooking. The set menu has just four choices per course, to sharpen the focus – perhaps two meat, one fish and a vegetarian main – and the generally mainstream approach has taken in roast rump of lamb with dauphinoise potato, and well flavoured poached salmon sharing a broth with spinach dumplings.

The cooking concentrates on essentials, yielding a rich and satisfying smoked haddock soup, and a stumpy-shaped but delicately flavoured chicken boudin on morel mash offset by an edgy balsamic jus. There are plenty of iced items at dessert, raspberry sorbet partnering baked mango cream, and a lime version coming with lemon tart. Details are well handled – from an intense appetiser soup to excellent flavoured breads – cheeses are good, and friendly, professional staff know their stuff. A serviceable list of wines from around the world (not all at keen prices, though) starts at £12, with nine by the glass from £3.50.

CHEF: Michael Davis PROPRIETORS: Sebastian and Philippa Hughes OPEN: all week 12 to 2, 7 to 9.30 MEALS: alc (main courses £7.50 to £12). Set L and D £19 to £35 SERVICE: not inc, card slips closed CARDS: Amex, Delta, MasterCard, Switch, Visa DETAILS: 42 seats. 20 seats outside. Private parties: 46 main room, 12 private rooms. Car park. Vegetarian meals. No children under 12. No music ACCOMMODATION: 15 rooms, all with bath/shower. TV. Phone. B&B £85 to £145. Baby facilities (*The Which? Hotel Guide*)

FARNBOROUGH Kent map 3

Chapter One

Farnborough Common, Locksbottom,
Farnborough BR6 8NF
TEL: (01689) 854848 FAX: (01689) 858439
WEB SITE: www.chaptersrestaurants.co.uk

COOKING **4**
MODERN EUROPEAN
£31–£61

Set in the suburbs, but with its heart in Soho, Chapter One offers a mix of cosmopolitan modern European cooking and stylish, comfortable surroundings. The venue is a mock-Tudor building, all bare wooden floors, pale walls with splashes of colour, and elegantly dressed tables. Andrew McLeish's cooking is based mostly on classic flavour combinations, though he has a sense of adventure when it comes to presentation: pan-fried salmon fillet, for example, is served with ravioli of ratatouille and candied aubergine, while feta and wild mushrooms are put in a pithiviers and accompanied by potato truffle mousseline and creamed Savoy cabbage.

Among more straightforwardly traditional dishes to receive praise have been a terrine of ham hock, and kleftiko-style rump of lamb, while an understandably popular stalwart among desserts is the hot chocolate fondant. Informal bar meals are also served, ranging from cod and chips with tartare sauce to Thai coconut and seafood soup with rice. Wines, divided into French and 'rest of the world' sections, cover a wide range; mark-ups have raised a few eyebrows, but prices start at £12 for unspecified Italian red and white, and eight are available by the glass from £3.

CHEF: Andrew McLeish PROPRIETOR: Selective Restaurants Group OPEN: all week 12 to 2.30 (3 Sun), 6.30 to 10.30 (11 Fri and Sat) CLOSED: 1 to 3 Jan MEALS: alc D (main courses £13.50). Set L £16 (2 courses) to £19.50. Bar menu available L Mon to Sat SERVICE: 12.5% (optional), card slips closed CARDS: Amex, Delta, Diners, MasterCard, Switch, Visa DETAILS: 120 seats. Private parties: 120 main room, 55 private room. Car park. Vegetarian meals. Children's helpings. No cigars/pipes in dining room. Wheelchair access (not WC). Music. Air-conditioned (£5)

▲ *means accommodation is available.*

All details are as accurate as possible at the time of going to press, but chefs and owners often change, and it is wise to check by telephone before making a special journey. Many readers have been disappointed when set-price bargain meals are no longer available. Ask when booking.

If a restaurant is new to the Guide this year (did not appear as a main entry in the last edition), NEW ENTRY *appears opposite its name.*

FARNHAM Dorset map 2

▲ Museum Inn

DORSET NEWCOMER OF THE YEAR

NEW ENTRY

Farnham DT11 8DE
TEL: (01725) 516261 FAX: (01725) 516988
EMAIL: themuseuminn@supernet.co.uk
WEB SITE: www.museuminn.co.uk
off A354, 9m NE of Blandford Forum

COOKING **6**
MODERN EUROPEAN
£29–£51

Mark Stephenson and Vicky Elliot refurbished this seventeenth-century country inn with a sense of style, acquired the services of Mark Treasure (who has been listed in previous editions of the Guide at the Feathers in Woodstock and Michael's Nook in Grasmere; see entries) and opened for business in early summer 2001. It is so called because, during the nineteenth century, the building was adapted to offer accommodation and refreshment for those visiting a nearby museum opened by General Pitt-Rivers, sometime ethnologist, anthropologist and archaeologist (the menu sports a commemorative portrait of him).

The present team have started cautiously, majoring on bar food and serving restaurant meals just a few evenings a week to begin with, keeping the food manageable but taking supplies seriously: traditionally reared traceable meats, free-range poultry, and local organic herbs, leaves and vegetables all feature. So too does South Coast fish, perhaps in the form of cod with parsley sauce, or a simple, classic rendition of pink-seared tuna, served on ratatouille vegetables with a scoop of tapénade. Main courses have a penchant for roasts and braises, including a sticky, gelatinous lamb shank with a crisp crust, served with flavourful parsley mash, tasty braised celery and a pool of highly seasoned stock sauce.

Perhaps the most straightforward item on the menu is a selection of sorbets, their sensuous texture, bright strawberry, chocolate and passion fruit flavours and accompanying lemony macaroon biscuit all testament to the kitchen's care with detail and sound grasp of fundamentals. The whole place is relaxed yet ambitious, with knowledgeable and committed service, and a sensibly chosen wine list provides good choice under £20, starting with house French at £9.95.

CHEF: Mark Treasure PROPRIETORS: Mark Stephenson and Vicky Elliot OPEN: Sun L 12 to 3, Wed to Sat D 7 to 9.30 CLOSED: 25 and 31 Dec MEALS: alc (main courses £10.50 to £16.50). Bar menu available all week SERVICE: not inc CARDS: Delta, MasterCard, Switch, Visa DETAILS: 35 seats. 36 seats outside. Private parties: 35 main room. Car park. Vegetarian meals. No children under 5. No smoking before 10pm. Wheelchair access (also WC). No music ACCOMMODATION: 8 rooms, all with bath/shower. TV. Phone. B&B £45 to £120. Rooms for disabled. No children under 5. Swimming pool. Fishing (£5)

Not inc *in the details at the end of an entry indicates that no service charge is made and any tipping is at the discretion of the customer.*

indicates that smoking is either banned altogether or that a separate dining room (not just an area) is maintained for non-smokers.

FAVERSHAM Kent map 3

▲ Read's

Macknade Manor, Canterbury Road,
Faversham ME13 8XE
TEL: (01795) 535344 FAX: (01795) 591200
WEB SITE: www.reads.com
on A2 Canterbury Road, ½m E of Faversham

COOKING **7**
MODERN BRITISH
£31–£64

After 25 years Read's has relocated to a Georgian manor house, which could hardly be more of a contrast to the modest timbered building it previously inhabited at Painter's Forstal. The manicured garden is surrounded by fine mature trees, and a half-acre plot produces vegetables and herbs for the kitchen. A comfortable bar overlooks the gravel drive, flowers and white table linen freshen up the dining room, and the same repertoire and careful, craftsmanlike cooking continue as before: for example, in a small shimmering slice of foie gras terrine, dwarfed by its vast Wedgwood plate, paired with shredded roast duck, crisp green cabbage leaves, and headily combined with a sweet fig preserve.

The use of local materials is also unaffected by the move: from Whitstable oak-smoked haddock presented three ways (chive-flecked soup, deep-fried fishcake, and creamy brandade) to slices of new season's, rosemary-infused Kentish lamb, fanned around the plate between ovals of finely diced Mediterranean vegetables, with a cube of creamy, garlicky dauphinois potato in the centre. Everything is attractively presented, although without any sense of gratuitous flourish or gesture, even when dishes get really busy: a 'giant lump' of well-trimmed beef, seared almost black yet pink and tender within, is crowned with finely shredded celeriac, partnered by a slice of 'boulangère' carrot, parsnip and potato, as well as pancetta-wrapped salsify that has been breadcrumbed and deep-fried, and served with a full-flavoured red wine sauce.

Pastry chef John Thorpe is credited on the dessert menu, and among his offerings are a hot Harvey Wallbanger soufflé, a plate of chocolate confections (including a dark sensual mousse covered in even darker 'icing'), and a rice pudding crème brûlée – 'quite liquid, slightly tepid, creamy with a fine crisp topping' – accompanied by a sherry and sultana ice cream. Service, overseen by Rona Pitchford, is warm, attentive and helpful, and wines are a collection of great names, often in more mature vintages at highly reasonable prices. Kicking off the 250-bin list are ten pages of 'best buys', many, including a serious Tavel rosé and a zesty Australian Riesling, priced at £15.

CHEF: David Pitchford PROPRIETORS: Rona and David Pitchford OPEN: Tue to Sat 12 to 2, 7 to 9.30 MEALS: Set L £18.50 to £38, Set D £36 to £38 SERVICE: not inc, card slips closed CARDS: Amex, Delta, Diners, MasterCard, Switch, Visa DETAILS: 40 seats. 18 seats outside. Private parties: 60 main room, 28 to 36 private rooms. Car park. Vegetarian meals. Children's helpings. No cigars/pipes in dining-room. Wheelchair access (also WC). No music ACCOMMODATION: 6 rooms, all with bath/shower. TV. Phone. B&B £95 to £150 (£5)

NEW CHEF *is shown instead of a cooking mark where a change of chef occurred too late for a new assessment of the cooking.*

FERNHURST Surrey map 3

King's Arms

Midhurst Road, Fernhurst GU27 3HA
TEL: (01428) 652005
on A286, 1m S of Fenhurst on sharp bend

COOKING **1**
MODERN BRITISH
£26–£41

This flower-decked country pub lies on a tight bend that makes access to and from the car park fairly fraught, although the low beams and horse brasses add up to a relaxed setting. A blackboard menu homes in on poached salmon on a bed on spinach, rack of lamb with cranberry sauce, and roast beef with all the trimmings. While meals may start with a scallop and citrus salad dressed in chilli and coriander, or chicken liver pâté with Bramley apple jelly and toasted brioche. 'Fragrant' home-made cinnamon ice cream is a lighter way to finish, if you don't have room for chocolate bread-and-butter pudding with marmalade sauce. Scan the section of bin ends in a list that opens with French house wines at £9.85.

CHEF: Michael Hirst PROPRIETORS: Michael and Annabel Hirst OPEN: all week L 12 to 2.30, Mon to Sat 7 to 9.30 CLOSED: bank hol evenings MEALS: alc (main courses £9.50 to £14.50) SERVICE: not inc CARDS: Delta, MasterCard, Switch, Visa DETAILS: 45 seats. 60 seats outside. Private parties: 24 main room, 12 to 50 private rooms. Car park. Children's helpings. No children under 14 after 7pm. No smoking in 1 dining room. Wheelchair access (not WC). No music. Air-conditioned

FERRENSBY North Yorkshire map 9

▲ General Tarleton

Boroughbridge Road, Ferrensby HG5 0PZ
TEL: (01423) 340284 FAX: (01423) 340288
EMAIL: gti@generaltarleton.co.uk
WEB SITE: www.generaltarleton.co.uk
off A6065, 3m N of Knaresborough

COOKING **5**
MODERN BRITISH
£26–£40

This may look like a pub, but it is effectively a restaurant of two halves, like its sister, the Angel Inn (see entry, Hetton), with separate menus for the bar/brasserie and slightly more formal restaurant. The former, with bare tables and cutlery wrapped in paper napkins, offers anything from a simple lunch of bread and soup – perhaps wild mushroom, or a provençale fish version made with chunks of identifiable fish and a first-rate stock reduction – to Lishman's prize-winning sausages with mash, or chargrilled haunch of venison. The combination of flexibility and professionalism throughout gives it great appeal, and if dishes such as the little moneybags of seafood in pastry are familiar to regulars, then there is ample choice elsewhere: from seared scallop on mushroom risotto, to duck breast with home-made black pudding. Well-sourced materials provide a firm foundation, taking in Dales lamb and local cheeses, and meals might end with a 'truly enormous' portion of sticky toffee pudding with butterscotch sauce and superlative vanilla ice cream. Service, although not always the speediest, ensures that customers 'feel welcome and important from entering to leaving', and the predominantly French wines successfully walk a tightrope between quality and affordability, starting with house Vin de Pays d'Oc at £10.95.

CHEFS: John Joseph Topham and Jason Moore PROPRIETORS: Denis Watkins and John Joseph Topham OPEN: Sun L 12 to 1.45, Mon to Sat D 6 to 9.15 (9.30 Sat) CLOSED: 25 Dec MEALS: Set L Sun £18.50, Set D £25. Bar/brasserie menus available SERVICE: not inc CARDS: Amex, Delta, MasterCard, Switch, Visa DETAILS: 80 seats. 30 seats outside. Private parties: 80 main room. Car park. Vegetarian meals. Children's helpings. No smoking in dining room. Wheelchair access (not WC). No music ACCOMMODATION: 14 rooms, all with bath/shower. TV. Phone. B&B £74.95 to £84.95. Rooms for disabled. Baby facilities (£5)

FOTHERINGHAY Northamptonshire **map 6**

Falcon

NEW ENTRY

Fotheringhay PE8 5HZ
TEL: (01832) 226254
FAX: (01832) 226046
off A605, 4m NE of Oundle

COOKING **2**
MODERN EUROPEAN/MEDITERRANEAN
£28–£51

It is 14 years since the Falcon last appeared as a main entry in the Guide, when the Stewarts, somewhat ahead of their time, used to serve superior pub grub. More recently it has joined the Huntsbridge group, a small chain of four (the others being the Pheasant at Keyston, the Three Horseshoes at Madingley and the Old Bridge at Huntingdon; see entries) run as semi-independent entities by Master of Wine John Hoskins. The common format is a modern menu broad enough in scope to allow grazing, snacking or troughing, available throughout the premises: a bar, a dining room with stripy green walls, and a conservatory overlooking the garden and church.

Mediterranean and Far Eastern ideas lend themselves to this kind of treatment, so expect baked goats' cheese with roast cherry tomatoes and focaccia, alongside a Thai-style chicken, noodle and coconut soup. British favourites also show up – thick slices of calf's liver with olive oil mash, bacon and red wine sauce – and fish has been well handled, judging by moist, flavourful roast monkfish paired with a slice of good black pudding. Among desserts, a wedge of orange-flavoured cake and cream dotted with chocolate chips comes with rocky road ice cream (made with coloured marshmallow and more chocolate chips). Portions are generous. The wine list navigates the world's wine regions, picking up lively, out-of-the-ordinary examples – try the Inzolia grape from Sicily – along with classic European bottlings of good pedigree. For value, choose from the section under £20, or from 14 house wines between £11 and £20. If budgets stretch further, mark-ups on more expensive bins are very reasonable.

CHEFS: Ray Smikle PROPRIETORS: John Hoskins and Ray Smikle OPEN: all week 12 to 2.15, 6.30 to 9.30 MEALS: alc (main courses £9.50 to £16). Set L Mon to Sat £11 (2 courses) SERVICE: not inc CARDS: Amex, Diners, MasterCard, Switch, Visa DETAILS: 55 seats. 35 seats outside. Private parties: 50 main room, 30 private room. Car park. Vegetarian meals. Children's helpings. No smoking in dining room. Wheelchair access (also WC). No music

'The ladies' toilets looked as if a rugby team had hibernated in them and decamped moments earlier.' (On eating in London)

FOULSHAM Norfolk map 6

The Gamp £

Claypit Lane, Foulsham NR20 5RW
TEL: (01362) 684114

COOKING 1
MODERN BRITISH
£20–£42

Foulsham is large by Norfolk standards: there are two or three shops, as well as this friendly, old-fashioned inn-like building. Occupying an eighteenth-century edifice with plenty of beams and bare brick, it serves up large portions of honest, fairly priced food along the lines of pork fillet stuffed with sage and apricots, and chicken Marengo. Among highlights have been leek and lovage soup with properly done croûtons, and crisp-skinned roast Norfolk duckling served with a zesty rhubarb compote. Vegetables are more than generous in quantity (among them mashed carrot and swede, and cauliflower with cheese sauce), and desserts run to gooseberry and mead syllabub, and thick Bramley apple and apricot pancakes with a tangy filling. Most bottles on the good-value roving wine list come in under £20, and three house wines (at £8.25) are also sold by the glass.

CHEFS: Andy Bush and Simon Nobbs PROPRIETORS: Daphne and Andy Bush OPEN: Wed to Sun L 12 to 1.30, Tue to Sat D 7 to 9.30 CLOSED: first 2 weeks Jan MEALS: alc exc Sun L (main courses £9.50 to £18). Set L Sun £12.50, Set D Tue to Fri £12.50 SERVICE: not inc, card slips closed CARDS: MasterCard, Switch, Visa DETAILS: 40 seats. Private parties: 40 main room. Car park. Vegetarian meals. Children's helpings. No smoking in dining room. Wheelchair access (also WC). No music

FRITHSDEN Hertfordshire map 3

Alford Arms £

NEW ENTRY

Frithsden HP1 3DD
TEL: (01442) 864480 FAX: (01442) 876893

COOKING 3
MODERN BRITISH
£24–£43

The Alford Arms proclaims its business as 'country pub and eating', which puts the emphasis in exactly the right place: this is a small, cream-painted, busy and solidly professional gastro-pub in an 'impossibly cute' village. There are no tablecloths or linen napkins, and the menu is classic modern British. In addition to the carte, daily specials are chalked up on a board, and local, free-range and organic ingredients make their way into the kitchen. 'Small plates' might include duck liver with wild mushroom and pistachio parfait, or warm crispy duck leg with sesame salad. Among main courses, look for comfort-inducing dishes such as smoked haddock fishcake with samphire and sorrel sauce, or chargrilled polenta with roast Mediterranean vegetables and crème fraîche. Puddings of warm chocolate brownie, and pecan and almond fudge tart, continue the theme. Staff are 'bright, bubbly and keen', and the wine list is brief but sensibly priced. Almost all bottles are also available by the 175- or 250-ml glass. Prices start at £9.75.

CHEF: Damien Ng PROPRIETORS: David and Becky Salisbury OPEN: all week 12 to 2.30 (3 Sun), 7 to 10 CLOSED: 25 and 26 Dec MEALS: alc (main courses £9 to £12.50) SERVICE: not inc CARDS: Amex, Delta, MasterCard, Switch, Visa DETAILS: 70 seats. 82 seats outside. Private parties: 12 main room. Car park. Vegetarian meals. Children's helpings. Music

FUNTINGTON West Sussex map 3

Hallidays

Watery Lane, Funtington PO18 9LF
TEL: (01243) 575331

COOKING **3**
MODERN BRITISH
£23–£46

Set in a timeworn but well-maintained thirteenth-century thatched cottage, Hallidays is a friendly, family-run business. Proceedings in the beamed dining room are overseen by the attentive Peter Creech, while behind the scenes son-in-law Andrew Stephenson takes care of the food. He keeps an eye on the seasons and prefers to scout his own area for supplies (notably turning up asparagus, soft fruits and fish), although an open-minded interpretation of modern British cooking takes in ideas from further afield. Alongside homely roast cod with saffron mash and tomato relish, and rump of English lamb with minted pea purée, broad-ranging options on the carte typically take in a terrine of salt-pork knuckle, chicken and foie gras, served with beetroot relish, and seared scallops with noodles and chilli jam. Desserts run from straightforward crème brûlée to more complex creations like rhubarb jelly with white chocolate mousse. The wine list is dominated by France, although the rest of the world gets a limited look-in. Prices are within the reach of most pockets, and half a dozen house wines open at £9.75 (£2.75 a glass).

CHEF: Andrew Stephenson PROPRIETORS: Andrew Stephenson and Peter Creech OPEN: Tue to Fri and Sun L 12 to 1.30, Tue to Sat D 7 to 9.30 CLOSED: 2 weeks Mar, 2 weeks Sept MEALS: alc (main courses £13 to £15.50). Set L Tue to Fri £11.50 (2 courses) to £13.50, Set L Sun £15.50 SERVICE: not inc CARDS: Delta, MasterCard, Switch, Visa DETAILS: 30 seats. Private parties: 30 main room. Car park. Children's helpings. No smoking in dining room. No music

GATEFORTH North Yorkshire map 9

YORKSHIRE GFG 2002 COMMENDED

▲ Restaurant Martel

Gateforth Hall, Gateforth YO8 9LJ
TEL: (01757) 228225 FAX: (01757) 228189
follow signs from A63 Monk Fryston petrol station

COOKING **4**
MODERN BRITISH
£31–£79

You would be unlikely to stumble across this small, elegant, secluded Victorian house by accident, but those who know it is there consider it worth the journey. A refreshingly cool, down-to-earth ambience suggests this is not a country house in the traditional style; money has not been poured into lavish décor but concentrated where it matters: in the kitchen. Young Martel Smith's confidence shows in an ambitious menu that combines a grounding in classic French cooking with some of his own ideas, and there is no skimping on quality ingredients. Tian of Cornish crab with apple, mascarpone, caviar and chilled tomato essence is a typically labour-intensive starter. It might be followed by baked turbot with thyme crust, buttered noodles, spinach and a chive velouté; or perhaps by braised pig's trotter stuffed with veal sweetbreads and black pudding, and served with celeriac purée and essence of morels. Desserts are a strength: hot pistachio soufflé with bitter chocolate sauce, for example, or a pyramid of honeyed nougat glacé and lemon sorbet. The wine list, arranged by nationality, covers most areas, though France dominates; prices start at £16

CHEF/PROPRIETOR: Martel Smith OPEN: Tue to Fri and Sun 12 to 2, Tue to Sat 7 to 10 CLOSED: 3 days Christmas, 1 week Jan MEALS: alc (main courses £15 to £22). Set L £17 SERVICE: not inc CARDS: Delta, MasterCard, Switch, Visa DETAILS: 45 seats. Private parties: 55 main room. Car park. Children's helpings. No smoking in 1 dining room. Wheelchair access (also WC). Music ACCOMMODATION: 3 rooms, all with bath/shower. Room only £85

GATESHEAD Tyne & Wear **map 10**

▲ Eslington Villa

8 Station Road, Low Fell, Gateshead NE9 6DR
TEL: (0191) 487 6017 FAX: (0191) 420 0667
EMAIL: admin@eslingtonvilla.fsnet.co.uk
leave A1 (M) at Team Valley Trading Estate, approach Gateshead along Team Valley; at top of Eastern Avenue, turn left into Station Road

COOKING **3**
ANGLO-FRENCH
£23–£49

If Gateshead evokes an impression of urban sprawl and industrialisation, then the oasis of calm provided by this modest-looking but comfortably furnished Edwardian hotel will be all the more welcome. Innovation is not what drives the kitchen; it prefers to deal in such familiar items as asparagus with hollandaise, melon and prawn cocktail, and peppered fillet steak. With one or two exceptions dishes are generally well executed: Caesar salad, Thai fishcakes, and duck confit are among successes, followed by bitter lemon tart or a highly rated chocolate mousse with soured cherries. The carte is more varied and inviting than the table d'hôte menu. Service comes in for praise, piped music doesn't. Ten wines under £20 on the roving, 40-strong list are rightly highlighted for interest (Chilean Chardonnay and Argentinian Malbec/Cabernet are among them), and half a dozen house wines start the bidding at £11.50 to £12.50.

CHEF: Barry Forster PROPRIETORS: Nick and Melanie Tulip OPEN: Sun to Fri L 12 to 2, Mon to Sat D 6.45 to 9.45 MEALS: alc (main courses £10 to £16). Set L Mon to Fri £11.50 (2 courses) to £13.50, Set L Sun £15, Set D Mon to Fri £18.50 SERVICE: not inc CARDS: Amex, Delta, Diners, MasterCard, Switch, Visa DETAILS: 80 seats. 20 seats outside. Private parties: 80 main room, 36 private room. Car park. Vegetarian meals. Children's helpings. No smoking in dining room. Wheelchair access (not WC). Music ACCOMMODATION: 17 rooms, all with bath/shower. TV. Phone. B&B £45 to £69.50. Baby facilities (*The Which? Hotel Guide*)

Prices quoted in the Guide are based on information supplied by restaurateurs. The prices quoted at the top of each entry represent a range, from the lowest meal price to the highest; the latter is inflated by 20 per cent to take account of likely price rises during the year of the Guide.

GILLINGHAM Dorset map 2

▲ Stock Hill House

Stock Hill, Gillingham SP8 5NR
TEL: (01747) 823626 FAX: (01747) 825628
EMAIL: reception@stockhillhouse.co.uk
WEB SITE: www.stockhillhouse.co.uk
off B3081, 1m W of Gillingham

COOKING **5**
MODERN EUROPEAN
£33–£56

The grounds are huge, with giant mature trees, the house Victorian, decorated with draped floral fabrics in rich colours, and stuffed with an idiosyncratic collection of furniture, works of art and craft items. Everything is of a piece, the cooking as meticulous as the service and housekeeping, and the kitchen takes pride in its home-grown vegetables, herbs and fruits. A degree of originality suffuses the cooking, taking in mushroom ravioli in lovage cream to start, or red sea bream fillet on fennel tajine with a cumin and coriander infusion. Indeed ingenuity can sometimes get the upper hand; despite a tendency to minute perfectionism, the bigger-scale dishes seem to work better. This makes incidentals rather fussy and main courses the highlight: for example a whole poached shank of flavourful lamb on crushed potatoes with a caper-infused creamy jus.

Peter Hauser's native Austria surfaces most distinctively among desserts of Viennese cheesecake, or a two-part cone of parfait flavoured with rum and poppy seeds, topped with a marzipan rose and set about with rum-soaked prunes and chocolate. Out front the witty and intelligent Nita Hauser, equally perfectionist, oversees formal yet comfortable service. The wine list is traditional, ambitious and predominantly French. Outside four house wines there is nothing under £20 even from the New World, though much of interest around £25 or £30: try Austria or South Africa.

CHEFS: Peter Hauser and Lorna Connor PROPRIETORS: Peter and Nita Hauser OPEN: Tue to Fri and Sun L 12.30 to 1.45, all week D 7.30 to 8.45 MEALS: Set L from £22 to £25, Set D £35 SERVICE: not inc, card slips closed CARDS: MasterCard, Switch, Visa DETAILS: 30 seats. 12 seats outside. Private parties: 24 main room, 12 private room. Car park. Vegetarian meals. Children's helpings. No children under 7. No smoking in dining room ACCOMMODATION: 8 rooms, all with bath/shower. TV. Phone. D,B&B £110 to £290. No children under 7 (*The Which? Hotel Guide*)

GITTISHAM Devon map 2

▲ Combe House

Gittisham EX14 3AD
TEL: (01404) 540400 FAX: (01404) 46004
EMAIL: stay@thishotel.com
WEB SITE: www.thishotel.com
1½m off A30, 2m W of Honiton

COOKING **3**
MODERN BRITISH
£27–£49

The drive leads to an imposing Elizabethan manor house (more interesting than spectacular) that feels lived in, with a big hall, ancient blackened woodwork, a massive fireplace around which aperitifs can be taken, and a dining room with views across the fields. Sound materials run to fish from day-boats out of Beer and Brixham (including grey mullet with a zingily dressed salad), and ideas take in lambs' sweetbreads with a pea cream sauce, and fillet of Red Devon beef with a horseradish beignet. The cooking shows signs of both ability and acumen, for example in a first-rate fig and tomato jam that accompanies an unctuously rich foie gras terrine, although not everything approaches this standard: risotto-making skills, for example, were in short supply at inspection. West Country cheeses are a feature, desserts have included a fine lemon mousse with mascarpone ice cream, and lunch is considered good value. A serviceable wine list, with a few Australian extras and a separate Chablis supplement, starts with six house wines available by the glass.

CHEF: Philip Leach PROPRIETORS: Ken and Ruth Hunt OPEN: all week 12 to 2, 7 to 9.30 MEALS: Set L £12 (2 courses) to £16, Set D £28.50 SERVICE: not inc, card slips closed CARDS: Amex, Diners, MasterCard, Switch, Visa DETAILS: 50 seats. 20 seats outside. Private parties: 30 main room, 30 and 48 private rooms. Car park. Vegetarian meals. Children's helpings. No smoking in dining room. Wheelchair access (also WC). No music ACCOMMODATION: 15 rooms, all with bath/shower. TV. Phone. B&B £99 to £245. Baby facilities. Fishing (*The Which? Hotel Guide*) (£5)

GOLCAR West Yorkshire **map 8**

▲ Weavers Shed

Knowl Road, Golcar HD7 4AN
TEL: (01484) 654284 FAX: (01484) 650980
EMAIL: info@weavers-shed.demon.co.uk
on B6111, 2m W of Huddersfield via A62

COOKING **5**
MODERN BRITISH
£21–£61

This is a comfortable restaurant-with-rooms in a converted cloth-finishing mill (ring for directions) where Stephen Jackson runs a prolific kitchen garden. Defying the northern climate, its aubergines and chillies, asparagus and herbs bring a touch Mediterranean sunshine to otherwise proudly regional menus. Likewise, in a setting of beams and exposed stone walls, it may be a surprise to find a Moroccan-style risotto – with almonds, coriander, fruit, spices and yoghurt – but there is also chargrilled local beef fillet with 'oven chips' (inverted commas on the menu), saddle of Worsborough red deer with 'gingerbread' sauce, and herbed rack of local lamb with a balsamic and rosemary jus.

Serving Yorkshire pudding with onion gravy as a starter is a tradition hereabouts, enjoyed even by those following it with grilled fillet of cod with wholegrain mustard cream, rather than roast beef. A couple who stayed in February found the festive season prolonged when they met a Christmas pudding parfait made with winter fruits and sprinkled with satsuma-flavoured sugar. Otherwise, you might try sticky toffee pudding accompanied by an ice cream made with dates and Earl Grey tea, or the cheese selection that includes a hunk of cake flavoured with Theakston Old Peculier bitter. Breakfasts are good too. A quartet of French and South American house wines at £12.95 opens a list of ambitious breadth and quality.

CHEFS: Ian McGunnigle, Robert Jones, Cath Sill and Stephen Jackson PROPRIETORS: Stephen and Tracy Jackson OPEN: Tue to Fri L 12 to 2, Tue to Sat D 7 to 10 CLOSED: 25, 26 and 31 Dec, 1 Jan MEALS: alc (main courses £10 to £17.50). Set L £9.95 (2 courses) to £12.95 SERVICE: not inc CARDS: Delta, MasterCard, Switch, Visa DETAILS: 50 seats. Private parties: 38 main room, 30 private room. Car park. No cigars/pipes in dining room. Music ACCOMMODATION: 5 rooms, all with bath/shower. TV. Phone. B&B £45 to £70 (*The Which? Hotel Guide*) (£5)

GORING Oxfordshire map 2

Leatherne Bottel

The Bridleway, Goring RG8 0HS
TEL: (01491) 872667 FAX: (01491) 875308
EMAIL: leathernebottel@aol.com COOKING **4**
WEB SITE: www.leathernebottel.co.uk MODERN EUROPEAN
on B4009 out of Goring, 5m S of Wallingford £29–£60

Annie Bonnet and Julia Storey run one of the more characterful venues in the Guide, working on the principle that customers' enjoyment is their only goal, and by and large they achieve it. It helps that there is 'no nicer place to lunch outdoors in the summer', especially when there is boating activity to watch. Julia Storey takes a broad-minded approach to cooking, and incorporates a few of her own inventions: horseradish ice cream, for example, accompanies lemon-grass-tea-smoked salmon.

Other appealing options might include duck liver and fennel sausage with sauté duck livers, spiced Puy lentils and chilli jam; or perhaps lambs' tongues and sweetbreads pan-fried with crisp belly pork. Food generally meets with reporters' approval, but prices on the carte have drawn some less-than-favourable comments; light lunches and midweek set dinners represent relatively good value. There are few wines under £20, though quality is high throughout the selection, and steps have been taken to make the list more readable; four house wines are £14.50.

CHEF: Julia Storey PROPRIETOR: Croftchase Ltd/Annie Bonnet OPEN: all week L 12.30 to 2 (3.30 Sun), Mon to Sat D 7 to 9 CLOSED: 25 Dec MEALS: alc (main courses £16 to £19.50). Set D Mon to Fri £19.50. Light L available Mon to Fri SERVICE: 10%, card slips closed CARDS: Amex, Delta, MasterCard, Switch, Visa DETAILS: 50 seats. 80 seats outside. Private parties: 36 main room. Car park. No children. Wheelchair access (not WC). Occasional music (£5)

GRANGE IN BORROWDALE Cumbria map 10

▲ Borrowdale Gates Hotel

Grange in Borrowdale CA12 5UQ
TEL: (017687) 77204 FAX: (017687) 77254
EMAIL: hotel@borrowdale-gates.com
WEB SITE: www.borrowdale-gates.com COOKING **4**
off B5289, about 3m S of Keswick, ¼m N of Grange ANGLO-FRENCH £26–£65

Set among craggy hills, about a mile south of Derwent Water, the comfortably appointed hotel is praised for its 'peace and beauty', and also gets accolades for its friendly and attentive, if slightly formal, service. Dinner is the main business (lunches, apart from Sunday, are lighter affairs), when three basic courses are extended with the help of canapés, a mid-meal soup or sorbet, and an optional extra cheese plate. Variety and generous choice characterise the menu, which might start with a Stilton, leek and spinach tartlet, grilled sardines with pesto, or veal sweetbreads with caramelised shallots. One or two items, such as Kyle of Lochalsh scallops with Savoy cabbage and bacon, may carry a supplement.

Materials range from humble haddock to posher turbot, from slowly braised shank of lamb or daube of beef, to game such as partridge 'hung to perfection', while desserts have taken in baked egg custard flan, and a dark chocolate ice cream parfait. Cheeses are given serious attention, among them a selection made near Carlisle from unpasteurised goats' milk, while the wine list has a light air about it, with many bins, especially from southern French regions, chosen for value and easy drinking. Globetrotting takes in the Americas, Antipodes, and parts of Europe, but the Gallic-influenced menu determines the focus. French house wines are £12.75.

CHEF: Michael D. Heathcote PROPRIETORS: Terry and Christine Parkinson OPEN: all week 12.15 to 1.30, 7 to 8.45 CLOSED: Jan MEALS: alc L Mon to Sat (main courses £7.50 to £11.50). Set L Sun £15.50, Set D £32.50 SERVICE: not inc CARDS: Amex, Delta, MasterCard, Switch, Visa DETAILS: 60 seats. 15 seats outside. Private parties: 24 main room. Car park. Vegetarian meals. No children under 7 at D. Children's helpings at L. Jacket and tie preferred. No smoking in dining room. Wheelchair access (also WC). No music ACCOMMODATION: 31 rooms, all with bath/shower. TV. Phone. D,B&B £63.50 to £172.50. Rooms for disabled. Baby facilities (*The Which? Hotel Guide*)

GRASMERE Cumbria map 8

▲ Michaels Nook

Grasmere LA22 9RP
TEL: (015394) 35496 FAX: (015394) 35645
EMAIL: m-nook@woodsworth-grasmere.co.uk
WEB SITE: www.grasmere-hotels.co.uk
turn off A591 N of Grasmere village, behind Swan Hotel

COOKING **6**
ANGLO-FRENCH
£43–£66

'Higgledy-piggledy but in a wonderfully comfortable way' was one view of this antique-strewn Victorian country house on the edge of the village. Cruft's certificates and doggy pictures cover the bar walls, while the more formal and polished dining room has gilded mirrors, a moulded ceiling and flowery curtains. Mr Gifford takes the order, then polite international staff serve (meals can last some time). The set price for four courses isn't exactly insignificant, but good ingredients, fine saucing and attractive presentation are among the strong points.

Meals might start with veal sweetbreads between pastry wafers with a morel jus, or a plate of small, contrasting servings of foie gras and Périgord duckling (served cold and decorated with colourful drizzles). Next come frothy soups in small cups: tangy gazpacho of cucumber and horseradish, or creamy velouté of celery with a poached quail's egg in the middle. 'Brilliant, brilliant, brilliant' was one verdict on three roundels of venison, served with wild mushroom ravioli, butternut purée and a stickily reduced sauce. To finish, an assiette of lemon desserts and a trio of mango desserts have drawn praise.

Some dishes require a multiplicity of operations, indeed the cooking can seem more effortful than the results justify, although the decorative appeal is undoubted: in a starter of light goats' cheese ravioli, for example, accompanied by a seared scallop and two tiny pieces of white asparagus. Mrs Gifford looks after the wines, among them some from less-usual quality regions such as Oregon and Washington State. There is plenty to tempt those on a lavish budget, but prices are kept under control, and there is much choice below £20 (down to a Pays d'Oc Syrah for £9.15, although house wines start at £9.95).

CHEF: Michael Wignall PROPRIETOR: R.S.E Gifford OPEN: all week 12.30 to 1, 7.30 to 8.30 MEALS: Set L £34.50, Set D £45 SERVICE: not inc CARDS: Amex, Delta, Diners, MasterCard, Switch, Visa DETAILS: 50 seats. Private parties: 40 main room, 40 private room. Car park. Vegetarian meals. No children under 7. Jacket and tie. No smoking in dining room. No music ACCOMMODATION: 14 rooms, all with bath/shower. TV. Phone. D,B&B £148 to £280 (*The Which? Hotel Guide*) (£5)

▲ White Moss House

Rydal Water, Grasmere LA22 9SE
TEL: (015394) 35295 FAX: (015394) 35516
EMAIL: sue@whitemoss.com
WEB SITE: www.whitemoss.com
on A591, at N end of Rydal Water

COOKING **6**
TRADITIONAL BRITISH
£38–£46

Once owned by William Wordsworth, this 'splendid small hotel' built of Lakeland stone has an enviable position at the north end of Rydal Water. Regular visitors to the pastel-toned dining room say that the style has changed little in the past 20 years. That is not to say that the cooking is out of touch; the emphasis is on quality ingredients treated simply.

The drill is a five-course menu (no-choice until pudding) that usually kicks off with a highly rated soup: perhaps intensely flavoured baby fennel, apple and asparagus. Next might come an equally fine and skilfully balanced smoked haddock soufflé made with free-range eggs and Westmorland smoked cheese, followed by pink, tender, herb-crusted rack of Mansergh Hall organic lamb, attractively presented in a pool of redcurrant, mint and Merlot sauce. Nor are vegetables an afterthought: all are cooked with care and attention. The dessert repertoire, meanwhile, runs from a simple but first-rate strawberry meringue to an accomplished, lightly steamed 'bread-and-buttery' cabinet pudding with fluffy lemon sauce. British cheeses (Shorrock's Lancashire, or local Allerdale goats', perhaps) are served in prime condition.

The wine list – organised by European country and region, each section concluding with New World alternatives – features a formidable number of clarets, some well-chosen red and white burgundies, and an impressive list of quite exciting New World Chardonnays and Pinot Noirs. There's plenty of interest below £20, including some 'personally selected' aromatic whites and lively reds from £10.95, and around ten wines are available by the glass.

CHEFS: Peter Dixon and Robert Simpson PROPRIETORS: Sue and Peter Dixon OPEN: Mon to Sat D only 8 (1 sitting) CLOSED: Dec and Jan MEALS: Set D £29.50 SERVICE: not inc, card slips closed CARDS: MasterCard, Switch, Visa DETAILS: 18 seats. Private parties: 18 main room. Car park. Children's helpings. No smoking in dining room. Wheelchair access (not WC). No music ACCOMMODATION: 8 rooms, all with bath/shower. TV. Phone. D,B&B £69 to £184. Baby facilities. Fishing (*The Which? Hotel Guide*) (£5)

The Guide is totally independent, accepts no free hospitality, and survives on the number of copies sold each year.

GREAT GONERBY Lincolnshire map 6

Harry's Place

17 High Street, Great Gonerby NG31 8JS
TEL: (01476) 561780
on B1174, 1m N of Grantham

COOKING 7
MODERN FRENCH
£56–£84

This is an unusual setup. A single room of a Georgian house in a village high street is decorated with deep-red walls, a dark green carpet, antique furniture and lots of fresh flowers. Its three generously proportioned pine tables and padded chairs seat just ten people. On top of that, the menu (not cheap) offers an economical two options per course. This is small-scale stuff, whichever way you look at it, but it does give Harry Hallam more than a fighting chance of coming up with carefully composed dishes based on ultra-fresh ingredients, an opportunity which he grasps firmly.

Given the limited choice, menus are constructed so that, whichever option is chosen, a balanced meal should result. In addition, the Hallams keep a record of every day's dishes, and can thus generally offer returnees a different menu. One of the starters is usually a soup – of locally grown celeriac, perhaps, or a rich mushroom and truffle oil version – the other typically a lively seafood number: lobster salad, for example, with a mango and ginger relish, or seared Orkney scallops with a chilli marinade. While such bold spicing can come to dominate a dish, sprinklings of herbs tend to add a welcome vibrancy: basil and coriander in a sauce for monkfish, or tarragon and rosemary to partner loin of Cornish lamb. One thing that keeps the cooking on the boil is the diligent sourcing of materials, many of them seasonal. Harry Hallam uses wild fish only, properly reared lamb and beef, and hand-picked game birds, from Yorkshire grouse to roast Lincolnshire woodcock with bacon and sage.

Desserts combine the timeless (chocolate mousse, or prune and armagnac ice cream) with the seasonal: a pancake of strawberries and raspberries, maybe, or an impressive Bramley apple and calvados soufflé. Service is by the 'charming Mrs Hallam'. Wines on the 15-strong list are carefully chosen (each one a different grape variety or blend), although with only one bottle below £25, and the rest climbing steeply, this is not a place to look for bargains. That said, 'house choice' red and white are £4.50 a glass, and sparkling water 'gushes freely'.

CHEF: Harry Hallam PROPRIETORS: Harry and Caroline Hallam OPEN: Tue to Sat 12.30 to 2, 7 to 9.30 CLOSED: 25 and 26 Dec, bank hols MEALS: alc (main courses £25 to £30) SERVICE: not inc CARDS: Delta, MasterCard, Switch, Visa DETAILS: 10 seats. Private parties: 10 main room. Car park. Children's helpings. No children under 5. No smoking in dining room. Wheelchair access (not WC). No music (£5)

Occasional music *in the details at the end of an entry means live or recorded music is played in the dining room only rarely or for special events.* No music *means it is never played.*

New main entries and restaurant closures are listed near the front of the book.

GREAT MILTON Oxfordshire map 2

▲ Le Manoir aux Quat' Saisons

Church Road, Great Milton OX44 7PD
TEL: (01844) 278881 FAX: (01844) 278847
EMAIL: lemanoir@blanc.co.uk
WEB SITE: www.manoir.co.uk
off A329, 1½m from M40 junction 7

COOKING **9**
MODERN FRENCH
£62–£142

The serene Elizabethan manor house has been sympathetically expanded over the years, extra rooms and a bigger car park making it feel more corporate than intimate. Yet it still charms and excites in equal measure. Delightful grounds include the organic garden (supplying some of the kitchen's herbs and vegetables), officially recognised by the Soil Association. Comfort levels, in the small ornate dining room and larger conservatory, are as high as anywhere,

Seasonally changed menus promise many pleasures: in summer, garden vegetables in a herb jus served with a courgette, its flower filled with truffle mousse, followed by a robust yet subtle braised shoulder and roast loin of flavourful rabbit with a red wine sauce and mustard jus. The food may show less youthful passion now, but lightness (try the intense tomato consommé) still leavens the richness of truffles, lobster, wild mushrooms and creamy sauces, and the cooking is considered and remarkably skilful: for example in a tender breast of finest squab pigeon, simply and accurately roasted, with a cappuccino of white beans, melting foie gras and an expertly rendered Madeira jus.

Quality can vary in at a single meal, but it is important to distinguish 'bland' from 'delicate' (both terms have figured in reports), the latter applying to a translucent, outstandingly fresh, milk-poached turbot steak, with a matchless nage of spring vegetables: a 'roaring success' at inspection. Desserts combine 'real ability and true creativity', witness a supremely fine cocoa mille-feuille with chocolate ganache and a hard-to-better coffee-bean ice cream. And what seemed to one visitor like a red fruit salad with a bit of jelly turned out to be the freshest wild strawberry gelée, sharply contrasted with a rhubarb soup, with a refreshing mint and Sauternes granita: 'brilliant simplicity and outstanding delivery'. Benchmark cheeses are kept in pristine condition, bread is as good as it comes, and waves of appetisers in the lounge and at table are matched by superbly crafted pastries with coffee (although, with a garden that size, camomile tea bags are a bit of a let-down).

Service can be slow, confused and disjointed, particularly at lunch, and requesting credit card details on booking gets up some people's noses. But staff (mostly French) are often smooth and charming and, at their best, manage to balance super-efficiency and relaxed friendliness. Prices (and expectations) are high, but – said one visitor – if you choose to eat at one of the country's most expensive restaurants, for heaven's sake enjoy it. A thick wine list explores the great and good of the wine world, with an understandable focus on France. Good-value bins are inevitably scarce; only careful scanning reveals bottles under £30. Head for the south (Italy or France), where prices start at £16, or try one of four available by the glass from £5.

CHEFS: Raymond Blanc and Gary Jones PROPRIETOR: Raymond Blanc OPEN: all week 12.15 to 2.45, 7.15 to 9.45 MEALS: alc (main courses £32 to £36). Set L £45 to £89, Set D £89 SERVICE: not inc CARDS: Amex, Delta, Diners, MasterCard, Switch, Visa DETAILS: 100 seats. Private parties: 8 main room, 50 private room. Car park. Vegetarian meals. Children's helpings. No smoking in dining room. Wheelchair access (also WC). No music. Air-conditioned ACCOMMODATION: 32 rooms, all with bath/shower. TV. Phone. B&B £245 to £750. Rooms for disabled. Baby facilities *The Which? Hotel Guide*

GREAT MISSENDEN Buckinghamshire map 3

La Petite Auberge

107 High Street, Great Missenden HP16 0BB
TEL: (01494) 865370

COOKING **4**
FRENCH
£36–£50

Considered a 'gem' in the area, the auberge is a narrow 'bijou' restaurant fashioned from two knocked-together rooms. Its unchanging 1930s-style décor, pine dresser and French prints convey a sedate feel, and although the menu doesn't change much either, it certainly gives Hubert Martel the chance to hone his skills. The cooking's oft-praised consistency is helped by the fact that if he is not there, the restaurant simply doesn't open. He deals in traditional ideas, from fish soup with rouille and croûtons, via panaché of sea fish and lobster with sauce armoricaine, to magret of duck with chestnuts.

Indications of the skill can be seen in a brace of large sea bass fillets, on an olive oil-based sauce with diced tomato and basil: 'visibly fresh and timed spot-on' sums up the two most important components of its success. Saucing is another strong point, and dishes are carefully put together, as in a starter of courgette flower filled with chunks of white crabmeat, accompanied by a baby courgette in a light sauce made with the brown meat. Desserts are mainly French classics, such as lemon tart, or nougat glace, and the same could be said of the wines, which are fairly priced throughout the short list, starting at £10.50.

CHEF: Hubert Martel PROPRIETORS: Mr and Mrs H. Martel OPEN: Mon to Sat D only 7.30 to 10 CLOSED: 2 weeks Christmas, 2 weeks Easter MEALS: alc (main courses £15 to £16) SERVICE: not inc CARDS: Delta, Diners, MasterCard, Switch, Visa DETAILS: 30 seats. Private parties: 36 main room. Children's helpings. Wheelchair access (also WC). No music

GREAT YELDHAM Essex map 3

White Hart £

Poole Street, Great Yeldham CO9 4HJ
TEL: (01787) 237250 FAX: (01787) 238044

COOKING **4**
ANGLO-FRENCH-PLUS
£22–50

John Dicken, busy man, lists himself as chef/proprietor here and at the longer-standing Dicken's (see entry, Wethersfield). The White Hart is a substantial 500-year-old timbered inn a little way back from the main road through the village; its ancient flagstones, dark timbers, open fireplaces and leaded windows are obviously cared for but unspoiled by development. The food is essentially Anglo-French, with a few more far-flung touches, which may translate as goats' cheese with spiced figs, red onion and walnuts, or sweet potato and coriander soup to start, followed by well-timed roast cod wrapped in pancetta on split-pea purée with a mint and mustard dressing. A fine grilled steak with mushrooms, herbed mash and onion rings makes a very British alternative to some of the more exotic treatments. Desserts include apricot and almond tart with crème fraîche, and tiramisù with cantuccini biscuits. A stylistically arranged wine list offering great breadth of choice starts with a dozen house wines from vins de pays at £9.95 to Australian Riesling at £18.50, and leads into mature clarets at sensible prices.

CHEF/PROPRIETOR: John Dicken OPEN: all week 12 to 2, 6.30 to 9.30 (7 Sun) CLOSED: possibly open Christmas; phone to check MEALS: alc (main courses £6 to £15.50). SERVICE: not inc CARDS: Amex, Delta, Diners, MasterCard, Switch, Visa DETAILS: 60 seats. 35 seats outside. Private parties: 80 main room, 30 private room. Car park. Vegetarian meals. Children's helpings. No smoking in dining room. Wheelchair access (also WC). No music

GRIMSTON Norfolk map 6

▲ Congham Hall NEW ENTRY

Lynn Road, Grimston PE32 1AH
TEL: (01485) 600250 FAX: (01485) 601191
EMAIL: reception@conghamhallhotel.co.uk
WEB SITE: www.conghamhallhotel.co.uk
off A148 or B1153, 7m E of King's Lynn and at W edge of Grimston

COOKING **4**
MODERN BRITISH/FRENCH
£25–£60

This Georgian manor house in 30-acre grounds retains the aura of a baronet's country pile. In the Orangery Restaurant walls are hung with prints of exotic fruits, and large windows look across a terrace to the lawns. James Parkinson (previously with Gordon Ramsay and John Burton-Race) runs the kitchen on complex French haute-cuisine lines with some modern British twists, but using local ingredients. Evenings offer the choice of a menu gourmand or a three-course set dinner and a high level of skill is much in evidence.

Timings are precise, making a success of seared scallops, paired with deep-fried crunchy balls of crabmeat in a first course salad, and presentation is appealing. The food's richness becomes evident by main course stage, be it a juicily tender roast beef fillet with oxtail macaire (potato pancake), or even pan-fried John Dory fillet with parsley potato and a velouté of pea and foie gras. By contrast, an ethereal passion fruit soufflé with coconut ice cream and red fruit coulis demonstrates the kitchen's light handling, or there are British and Irish cheeses. Service is low-key, unfussy and efficient. The wine list, grouped by style and price, features good producers around the globe from £12. Mark-ups are fair, with plenty of choice below £25.

CHEF: James Parkinson PROPRIETOR: Von Essen Hotels OPEN: all week 12.30 to 1.45, 7 to 9.15 MEALS: alc L (main courses £8 to £11.50). Set L £11.50 (2 courses) to £29.95, Set D £27.50 (2 courses) to £39.95. Bar menu available SERVICE: not inc, card slips closed CARDS: Amex, Delta, Diners, MasterCard, Switch, Visa DETAILS: 60 seats. 30 seats outside. Private parties: 60 main room, 20 private room. Car park. Vegetarian meals. Children's helpings. No children under 7 at D. No smoking in dining room. Wheelchair access (not WC). No music ACCOMMODATION: 14 rooms, all with bath/shower. TV. Phone. B&B £85 to £230. Swimming pool (*The Which? Hotel Guide*) (£5)

HALIFAX West Yorkshire **map 9**

Design House

Dean Clough Mills, Halifax HX3 5AX
TEL: (01422) 383242 FAX: (01422) 322732
EMAIL: enquiries@designhouserestaurant.co.uk
WEB SITE: www.designhouserestaurant.co.uk

COOKING **3**
ITALIAN/MODERN BRITISH
£25–£50

Unlikely as it may sound, Design House, occupying one corner of the vast Dean Clough Mills complex, has a veranda where, on warm sunny evenings, you can enjoy an aperitif. As the name suggests, design is an important element of the mix, so expect lots of etched glass, slate flooring and Philippe Starck seating. The menu, too, is decidedly modern. An Italian theme runs through much of Michael Ricci's cooking, with its use of Pantelleria capers, Gorgonzola picante and prosciutto di Carpegna. Another, Asian, theme shows in a starter of seared scallops with bean shoots, udon noodles with shredded pork belly, soy and ginger.

Whatever the origin, a sense of balance pervades the food, for example in main courses such as chargrilled salmon with peas, broad beans and Little Gem lettuce with a white wine sauce. Desserts may not be as reliable, but post-prandial 'savouries' may cover mozzarella and field mushrooms, or selections of Italian and British farmhouse cheeses, and there is a breakfast menu plus all-day sandwiches and cakes. The wine list (surprisingly, more French/New World than Italian) has some decent bottles, and prices are generally agreeable, with house wines from £10.50.

CHEF: Michael Ricci PROPRIETOR: Christian Rooney OPEN: Mon to Fri L 12 to 2, Mon to Sat D 6 to 10 CLOSED: 25 and 26 Dec, 1 Jan MEALS: alc Mon to Fri L and D, Sat D (main courses £9 to £16). Set L and D Mon to Fri £11.95 (2 courses) to £15.95. All-day and café bar menus also available SERVICE: not inc CARDS: Amex, Delta, Diners, MasterCard, Switch, Visa DETAILS: 80 seats. Private parties: 90 main room. Car park. Vegetarian meals. No smoking in dining room. Wheelchair access (not WC). Music. Air-conditioned

HAMBLETON Rutland **map 6**

▲ Hambleton Hall

Hambleton LE15 8TH
TEL: (01572) 756991 FAX: (01572) 724721
EMAIL: hotel@hambletonhall.com
WEB SITE: www.hambletonhall.com
off A606, 3m SE of Oakham

COOKING **8**
MODERN BRITISH
£30–£113

Manicured lawns, a view of Rutland Water, a flagged terrace for drinks in summer: this is an enviable spot for a venerable country house. Comfort and opulence are its currency, marked out by plush sofas, antique furniture, heavy drapes, starched linen, and lots of attention from the largely French staff who, although professional and as formal as the setting, are also friendly, and provide enthusiastic help with the menu. It offers a wealth of ingredients and preparations, including veal with sweetbread tortellini, turbot with morels, and rabbit with grain mustard sauce, as well as a few luxuries such as caviar and foie gras, and seasonal game in the form of venison, hare and grouse.

Naturally reared beef, pork and lamb come from nearby Northfield Farm, a roast loin of pink, tender lamb providing one of the highlights of an inspection meal, served with an artfully judged tian of Mediterranean vegetables – oily roasted aubergine, thin courgette slices, and tiny dice of peppers – alongside a richly reduced red wine sauce infused with rosemary and garlic. Even plain-sounding dishes (such as roast scallops with creamed endive) pack a punch, and the overriding impression is of fresh, lightly prepared ingredients well partnered with their accompaniments: for example, a honey-roast, crisp-skinned Goosnargh duckling breast, served with a puff pastry pie of lightly fatty, shredded leg meat.

If it proves difficult to choose between desserts – and they are all top notch, from tarte au citron, via hot chocolate soufflé, to a sweetly caramelised apple tart balanced by tart blackberries – the assiette of miniatures can hardly be bettered. Breakfast is a superior affair too, with eggs from Hambleton's own chickens. Wines include some great names in a range of both young and mature vintages, and although wine service has disappointed on a couple of occasions, on the plus side is a helpful compilation of particular favourites from around £15 to £40, representing a fair cross-section of the list. Outside this, value is more difficult to winkle out, but to compensate there are surprises from off the beaten track, including a range of Austrian dessert wines.

CHEF: Aaron Patterson PROPRIETORS: Tim and Stefa Hart OPEN: all week 12 to 1.30, 7 to 9.15 MEALS: alc (main courses £27 to £33). Set L Mon to Fri £16.50 (2 courses) to £21.50, Set L Sun £35 to £50, Set D Mon to Fri £29.50 (2 courses), Set D Sat and Sun £35 SERVICE: net prices, card slips closed CARDS: MasterCard, Switch, Visa DETAILS: 64 seats. Private parties: 64 main room, 14 to 40 private rooms. Car park. Vegetarian meals. No smoking in dining room. Wheelchair access (also WC). No music ACCOMMODATION: 17 rooms, all with bath/shower. TV. Phone. B&B £150 to £600. Rooms for disabled. Swimming pool *The Which? Hotel Guide*

HAMPTON HILL Greater London map 3

Monsieur Max 🍷

133 High Street, Hampton Hill TW12 1NJ
TEL: (020) 8979 5546 FAX: (020) 8979 3747

COOKING **5**
FRENCH
£39–£66

The Gallic feel is both deliberate and convincing: 'our French guests described it as "very French".' This is a bourgeois environment with food to match, although it is not without ambition. Indeed, the lengthy menu with nine or ten starters and a similar number of main courses would put many a larger brigade to the test, especially given the number of operations required to bring each one to table. There are boudins and beignets, pastas and risottos, tartes and pithiviers, and mousses and purées galore, all just to accompany main courses. Skate wing fillet, for example, comes with a herb crust, braised lettuce and pancetta, truffle gnocchi and a thyme beurre blanc, while grilled loin of Anjou rabbit comes as 'two towers with lots of accompaniments', among them a beignet of claret risotto and Epoisses, a boudin noir, potatoes creamed with capers, and a red wine and peppercorn sauce.

Perhaps not surprisingly, although rather against the current tide, the food can be rich and the portions large, so not everybody makes it to dessert. Those who do may find chocolate moelleux with pistachio sorbet, or apricot and mandarin soufflé with mascarpone ice cream. Despite an occasional grumble, supporters generally find the place still on song in terms of food, wine and 'excellent unobtrusive' service. Beaujolais is singled out by reporters as worth a punt (it is among the minority of bottles under £20), although the list is full of treasures for those not averse to some steepish mark-ups.

CHEFS: Max Renzland and Alex Bentley PROPRIETOR: Max Renzland OPEN: Tue to Fri and Sun L 12 to 2 (3 Sun), Tue to Sat D 7 to 9.30 CLOSED: 1 week Christmas, 3 weeks Aug MEALS: Set L Tue to Fri £19.50 (2 courses) to £25, Set L Sun £25, Set D Tue to Thur £27.50 (2 courses) to £35, Set D Fri and Sat £35 SERVICE: 12.5% (optional), card slips closed CARDS: Delta, Diners, MasterCard, Switch, Visa DETAILS: 70 seats. Private parties: 12 main room. Vegetarian meals. No children under 8. No cigars/pipes in dining room. Wheelchair access (not WC). No music. Air-conditioned (£5)

HAROME North Yorkshire map 9

Star Inn

Harome YO62 5JE
TEL: (01439) 770397 FAX: (01439) 771833
off A170, 3m SE of Helmsley

COOKING 5
MODERN BRITISH
£25–£54

Picture a converted fourteenth-century thatched long house, in an English village with a duck pond and cricket pitch, where you can eat outside on summer evenings, and you have the Star Inn. The non-bookable bar is kitted out with 'Mousey Thompson' oak furniture, and the dining room (once a byre) has bare tables and slaty-blue fabrics; both make use of regional and seasonal produce, helped by the kitchen's own herb and vegetable garden, and both benefit from Andrew Pern's lively modern take on British ideas. The roll call of dishes runs impressively from foie gras 'toad-in-the-hole' to grilled queen scallops with avocado fritters, from potted smoked duck with sage butter to roast fillet of smoked eel with horseradish galette. It is possible to dine, as one reporter did, on a simple starter of dressed crab, followed by turbot on truffle mash with wild mushrooms, and caramelised lemon tart, but equally tempting to consider deep-fried kipper croquettes with chunky chips, or steamed venison suet pudding, followed by baked ginger parkin with rhubarb ripple ice cream. Sixty-plus wines are chosen to suit all pockets, starting with house South African at £11.50.

CHEF: Andrew Pern PROPRIETORS: Andrew and Jacquie Pern OPEN: Tue to Sat 11.30 to 2, 6.30 (6 summer) to 9.30 (10 Sat), Sun 12 to 6 CLOSED: 1 week Nov, 25 Dec, 2 weeks Jan, bank hols MEALS: alc (main courses £8 to £17) SERVICE: not inc, card slips closed CARDS: Delta, MasterCard, Switch, Visa DETAILS: 60 seats. 40 seats outside. Private parties: 36 main room, 10 private room. Car park. Vegetarian meals. Children's helpings. No smoking in dining room. Music

The cuisine styles noted at the tops of entries are only an approximation, often suggested to us by the restaurants themselves. Please read the entry itself to find out more about the cooking style.

HARROGATE North Yorkshire **map 8**

Drum and Monkey £

5 Montpellier Gardens, Harrogate HG1 2TF
TEL: (01423) 502650 FAX: (01423) 522469

COOKING **4**
SEAFOOD
£17–£46

One menu, operating in both the ground-floor 'atmospheric' bar and the 'more regal' restaurant above, single-mindedly offers nothing for carnivores, and for vegetarians only a cheese salad or sandwich at lunchtime, with mushrooms in garlic butter, or melon in the evening. The style of fish cookery is traditional Anglo-French, and the one surprise is cream of whiting soup, which the owner calls a 'fishyssoise' of mussels, potato and leek stock with whiting purée. At lunchtime a shorter version of the evening carte contrasts the luxurious simplicities of oysters, smoked salmon, and crab, lobster or prawn cocktails against poached sea trout with asparagus hollandaise, smoked haddock florentine, and seafood pie.

Extra main dishes at dinner might include medallions of scallop, monkfish, sea trout and tuna with béarnaise, or fillet of bream stuffed with cream cheese and dill with a bacon and red onion sauce. Alternatives to whole grilled Dover sole are its fillets, either Mornay, stuffed with spinach mousseline, or an unorthodox bonne femme, with crab stuffing, mushrooms and glazed hollandaise. So successful is the formula that you must arrive very early for lunch in the bar or book for the restaurant. Modestly priced wines, nearly all white, start with house selections at £8.65.

CHEFS: Keith Penny and Selina Leamy PROPRIETOR: William Fuller OPEN: Mon to Sat 12 to 2.30, 6.30 to 10.15 CLOSED: 24 Dec to 2 Jan MEALS: alc (main courses £5.50 to £16.50) SERVICE: not inc CARDS: Delta, MasterCard, Switch, Visa DETAILS: 56 seats. Private parties: 10 main room. Children's helpings. No music

HARROW Greater London **map 3**

Golden Palace

NEW ENTRY

146–150 Station Road, Harrow HA1 2RH
TEL: (020) 8863 2333 and 8424 8899
FAX: (020) 8863 3388

COOKING **3**
CHINESE
£24–£101

The wide white façade and darkened windows stand out among a row of shops, the cheerful décor enhanced by abstract pictures and lots of greenery. Perfume from exotic flower displays wafts across the room, as crowds of customers, many from the local Chinese community, sit at white-clothed tables and set the place buzzing; on Sundays dim sum draw even more Chinese customers. Formally dressed staff are courteous, unobtrusive and friendly. The long main menu is conventional, but encompasses such choice items as real Peking duck correctly served in two courses, and lobster baked in five styles. There are tempting special menus, seasonal, vegetarian and Cantonese; and if some dishes from the menu are occasionally unavailable, extra ones may take their place: flavourful, well balanced lamb and tofu hotpot for one visitor. Among other dishes singled out for special praise are 'succulent' charcoal-grilled quarter-duck, French beans with salt and chilli, and a 'rich and potent' hotpot of sea spice seafood and noodles. Service is included but credit card slips are left open. House wine is £9.50, £2.50 a glass.

CHEF/PROPRIETOR: Mr G. Ho OPEN: all week 12 (11 Sun) to 11.30 (10.30 Sun) CLOSED: 25 Dec MEALS: alc (main courses £5.50 to £35. Set L and D £15 to £22 (min 2). Set D 50 (min 2) SERVICE: 10% CARDS: Amex, Delta, Diners, MasterCard, Switch, Visa DETAILS: 150 seats. Private parties: 80 main room, 40 and 40 private rooms. Vegetarian meals. Wheelchair access (also WC). Music. Air-conditioned

HARWICH Essex **map 6**

▲ The Pier at Harwich 🍷

The Quay, Harwich CO12 3HH
TEL: (01255) 241212 FAX: (01255) 551922
EMAIL: info@pieratharwich.co.uk
WEB SITE: www.pieratharwich.com

COOKING **1**
SEAFOOD/ENGLISH
£29–£65

Harwich's pier is a quayside hotel with two restaurants. Downstairs the Ha'penny Bistro thrives on informality; the first-floor Harbourside restaurant is slightly smarter – blue tablecloths and fresh flowers – but is equally down-to-earth. Modern fish cookery is the focus. The kitchen finds inspiration in whatever is landed each morning, typically coming up with lobster bisque, Thai-style fishcakes, roast sea bass with chargrilled vegetables, and monkfish with scallops in Sancerre broth with saffron noodles. Meat alternatives are more than just token offerings, though – warm duck breast salad, and flash-fried calf's liver with bacon and mash, for example – and to finish there may be bread-and-butter pudding or chocolate and Amaretto pannacotta. The wine list – which caters well for seafood – centres on a classic selection from France, plus a showing from the Antipodes. Value lies with South Africa (sourced directly) and house wines from £11.95

CHEF: Chris Oakley PROPRIETORS: Gerald and Paul Milsom OPEN: all week 12 to 2, 6 to 9.30 MEALS: alc (main courses £8.50 to £25). Set L Mon to Sat £16 (2 courses), Set L Sun £18.50, Set D £20.50 SERVICE: 10%, card slips closed CARDS: Amex, Delta, Diners, MasterCard, Switch, Visa DETAILS: 80 seats. 20 seats outside. Private parties: 90 main room, 40 private room. Car park. Vegetarian meals. Children's helpings. Occasional music ACCOMMODATION: 14 rooms, all with bath/shower. TV. Phone. B&B £62.50 to £150. Baby facilities (*The Which? Hotel Guide*)

HASLEMERE Surrey **map 3**

Flutes 🍷

NEW ENTRY

23–27 Lower Street, Haslemere GU27 2NY
TEL: (01428) 645255 FAX: (01428) 644638
EMAIL: reservations@flutes-restaurant.co.uk

COOKING **4**
MODERN EUROPEAN
£30–£85

Reincarnated in summer 2000, this building (formerly Morels, Fleur de Sel and Little Gem) has been renovated and revitalised. Terracotta predominates among the original dark beams, but cream walls and fresh flowers lighten the tone, and the place is run with highly polished efficiency. Fixed-price menus deal in rich and forceful flavours, including a mille-feuille of quail with shallot purée and a grape and Sauternes sauce, and herb-roasted breast of black-leg chicken with a root vegetable confit and truffle sauce.

The quality of raw materials is unimpeachable, and a sense of balance infuses the cooking, as in a starter of seared scallops with caramelised endive and truffled vinaigrette. Seasoning can be variable – a terrine of rabbit, which generally needs all the help it can get, was found wanting at inspection – but careful spicing has given a gingery kick to the crab risotto accompanying a fillet of John Dory with tarragon cream.

Inventive desserts include rum pannacotta and spiced pineapple, pistachio soufflé with chocolate chip ice cream, and an impeccable lemon-grass crème brûlée with lemon and coconut shortbread. Fine breads, powerful coffee and an amuse-gueule (maybe French onion soup fortified with cognac) also bespeak a serious operation. Traditionalists will rejoice in the depth of choice among clarets and burgundies, and in classy examples from Italy, Australia and California. Modestly priced wines are less well represented, but there is a sprinkling of bins under £25, including house wines from £14.

CHEF: Shane McGlinchey PROPRIETOR: Digo Spice Ltd OPEN: Tue to Sat 12 to 3, 7 to 10 CLOSED: 25 and 26 Dec, 1 Jan, first 3 weeks Feb MEALS: Set L £15 (2 courses) to £18.50, Set D £32.50 SERVICE: 12.5% (optional), card slips closed CARDS: Amex, Delta, MasterCard, Switch, Visa DETAILS: 50 seats. Private parties: 50 main room. Children's helpings. No smoking in dining room. Wheelchair access (not WC). Occasional music. Air-conditioned (£5)

HASTINGS East Sussex map 3

Röser's

64 Eversfield Place, St Leonards,
Hastings TN37 6DB
TEL: (01424) 712218 FAX: (01424) 713763
EMAIL: gerald@rosers.co.uk
WEB SITE: www.rosers.co.uk

MODERN EUROPEAN
£30–£69

As the Guide went to press this restaurant closed.

CHEF: Gerald Röser PROPRIETORS: Gerald and Jenny Röser OPEN: Tue to Fri L 12 to 2, Tue to Sat D 7 to 10 CLOSED: first 2 weeks Jan, second 2 weeks June MEALS: alc (main courses £16 to £27.50). Set L £21.95, Set D Tue to Fri £23.95 SERVICE: net prices, card slips closed CARDS: Amex, Delta, Diners, MasterCard, Switch, Visa DETAILS: 30 seats. Private parties: 30 main room, 30 private room. Vegetarian meals. No cigars/pipes in dining room. Wheelchair access (not WC). No music. Air-conditioned

HAWORTH West Yorkshire **map 8**

▲ Weavers

15 West Lane, Haworth BD22 8DU
TEL: (01535) 643822 FAX: (01535) 644832
WEB SITE: www.weaversmallhotel.co.uk

COOKING **3**
MODERN BRITISH
£25–£46

For more than 20 years, Jane and Colin Rushworth have been catering for locals and visiting Brontë fans alike at their restaurant in a row of former weavers' cottages – hence the name. It functions as bar and restaurant, as well as providing accommodation, and enjoys an informal, slightly quirky atmosphere. Colin Rushworth, a Haworth native, uses only local ingredients where possible to give a strongly regional flavour to his cooking, although a few more sophisticated ideas creep in occasionally: among starters might be shredded duck salad with plum dressing and soy sauce, or smoked haddock soup with bacon and potato. Main courses, meanwhile, might feature stuffed chicken breast glazed with rosemary, honey and lemon, fisherman's pie, or beef fillet served with mushroom and onion relish, chips and garlic mayonnaise. Finish with a selection of regional cheeses, or maybe 'old school' bread-and-butter pudding. Eight house wines from £10.25 open a list that runs to around 100 reasonably priced bottles.

CHEFS/PROPRIETORS: Colin and Jane Rushworth OPEN: Tue to Sat D only 6.30 to 9.15 CLOSED: 10 days Christmas MEALS: alc (main courses £8 to £16.50). Bar D available Tue to Fri SERVICE: not inc, 10% for parties of 6 or more CARDS: Amex, Delta, Diners, MasterCard, Switch, Visa DETAILS: 65 seats. Private parties: 16 main room. Vegetarian meals. Children's helpings. No smoking in dining room. Music. Air-conditioned ACCOMMODATION: 3 rooms, all with bath/shower. TV. Phone. B&B £55 to £80 (*The Which? Hotel Guide*) (£5)

Prices quoted in the Guide are based on information supplied by restaurateurs. The prices quoted at the top of each entry represent a range, from the lowest meal price to the highest; the latter is inflated by 20 per cent to take account of likely price rises during the year of the Guide.

All details are as accurate as possible at the time of going to press, but chefs and owners often change, and it is wise to check by telephone before making a special journey. Many readers have been disappointed when set-price bargain meals are no longer available. Ask when booking.

The Guide office can quickly spot when a restaurateur is encouraging customers to write recommending inclusion. Such reports do not further a restaurant's cause. Please tell us if a restaurateur invites you to write to the Guide.

The 2003 Guide will be published before Christmas 2002. Reports on meals are most welcome at any time of the year, but are particularly valuable in the spring (no later than June). Send them to The Good Food Guide, *FREEPOST, 2 Marylebone Road, London NW1 4DF. Or email your report to goodfoodguide@which.net*

HAYDON BRIDGE Northumberland map 10

General Havelock Inn

9 Ratcliffe Road, Haydon Bridge NE47 6ER
TEL: (01434) 684376 FAX: (01434) 684283
EMAIL: generalhavelock@aol.com
on A69, 8m W of Hexham, 100yds from junction with B6319

COOKING **2**
MODERN EUROPEAN
£24–£36

The General's front half is a traditional roadside hostelry, serving real ales and rustic dishes along the lines of Cumberland sausage with mash, and Italian bean broth with Toulouse sausage. To the rear, overlooking the South Tyne river, is the slightly more formal dining room, where a pink and floral decorative theme softens the effect of bare stone walls. Here a set-price menu is offered, though the style of the cooking remains unfussy, typically featuring smoked haddock and goats' cheese quiche, roast pork fillet on cabbage and smoked bacon, and best end of lamb on spinach and potatoes with a rosemary and garlic jus. Chef/proprietor Gary Thompson makes laudable efforts to use local supplies – meat comes from a farm only three miles away – and this family-run establishment has a friendly atmosphere throughout. A short, functional wine list opens with house selections at £10 a bottle.

CHEF: Gary Thompson PROPRIETORS: Gary and Joanna Thompson OPEN: Tue to Sun L 12 to 2, Tue to Sat D 7 to 9 (closed occasional Tue winter) CLOSED: Occasional Tue in winter MEALS: Set L £14.75, Set D £15.25 (2 courses) to £20. Bar menu available L SERVICE: not inc, card slips closed CARDS: Amex, Delta, Diners, MasterCard, Switch, Visa DETAILS: 40 seats. 16 seats outside. Private parties: 30 main room. Vegetarian meals. Children's helpings. No smoking in dining room. Wheelchair access (also WC). No music (£5)

HAYWARDS HEATH West Sussex map 3

Jeremy's at Borde Hill

Balcombe Road, Haywards Heath RH16 1XP
TEL: (01444) 441102 FAX: (01444) 443936
EMAIL: jeremys.bordehill@btinternet.com
WEB SITE: www.homeofgoodfood.co.uk

COOKING **5**
MODERN EUROPEAN
£31–£50

At the entrance to Borde Hill Gardens, off leafy Balcombe Road a short drive out of town, Jeremy's welcomes with warm yellow and vibrant indigo colours, the walls of its smart, airy dining room covered with artwork. Jeremy Ashpool is a confident and skilful chef, serving up an appetising range of dishes based on impressive materials, from local asparagus, via organic Orkney salmon, to thick slices of slow-roast, free-range pork with glistening crackling, served with root vegetable purée, caramelised apple, and a rich, dark reduction.

A tendency to embellish detracts from, rather than adds to, the success of dishes, as flavours sometimes have to battle for supremacy, but successful and well-balanced combinations have included seared tuna with lentils, and a chunk of moist, flavourful, herb-crusted cod on a bed of leeks, with artistic drizzles of gentle tarragon sauce and chilli emulsion. Indeed, two sauces are not uncommon in a single dish: slices of rolled, skewered, pesto-covered veal might be served with roast fennel, and Marsala and red pepper sauces.

Among desserts, lavender and raspberry brûlée has been outshone by a fine pastry tart displaying an 'exemplary balance' of zestily fresh passion fruit and orange under a caramelised top. The food may not be cheap, but value for money is considered fair. Bread is a strength, service from well-drilled staff is efficient, and a well-chosen slate of wines spans a fair price range, starting with house Italian red and white at £12 and £11 respectively.

CHEFS: Jeremy and Vera Ashpool, and Domenic Stanton PROPRIETORS: Jeremy and Vera Ashpool OPEN: Tue to Sun L 12.30 to 2.30, Tue to Sat D 7.30 to 10 MEALS: alc (main courses £12.50 to £17). Set L Tue to Sat £16.50 (2 courses) to £24, Set L Sun £19.50 (2 courses) to £24, Set D Tue to Fri £16.50 (2 courses) to £20.50 SERVICE: not inc, 10% for parties of 8 or more CARDS: Amex, Delta, Diners, MasterCard, Switch, Visa DETAILS: 55 seats. 150 seats outside. Private parties: 55 main room. Car park. Vegetarian meals. Children's helpings. No smoking in dining room. Wheelchair access (also WC). Music (£5)

HEREFORD Herefordshire map 5

▲ Castle House, La Rive

Castle Street, Hereford HR1 2NW
TEL: (01432) 356321 FAX: (01432) 365909 COOKING **7**
EMAIL: info@castlehse.co.uk ANGLO-FRENCH
WEB SITE: www.castlehse.co.uk £31–£69

It is a tranquil setting for a city centre. The dining room of this welcoming Georgian building, a short walk from the cathedral, gives on to a small terrace, garden and leafy stretch of river (once the moat). But the food's impact has created a lot more noise. The theme running through reports has been one of sheer enthusiasm for Hereford's good fortune. As the Guide went to press, La Rive (see entry notes below), under the same ownership and under the direction of chef Stuart McLeod, closed. The name has re-surfaced at Castle House, but we do not expect significant changes to what appears on the plate.

The style is so unashamedly intricate that it begs the question of purpose – does it really set out to be enjoyable, or is it just a clever pyrotechnic display? – but a high level of technical accomplishment ensures that virtually everything is brought off without a hitch: 'one of the most skilfully made meals I have ever eaten' confessed a senior inspector. Put this in the context of the price, and the reason for enthusiasm is obvious.

Raw materials are unsurpassed: scallops, for example, beautifully seared, sitting on a layer of pak choi, topped by an open pasta case containing white crabmeat in a frothy gingery sauce. The elaborate and involved style runs through everything, from a fragrant, soft-textured poached loin of lamb wrapped in smoked venison, sharing the plate with a faggot of knuckle and celeriac in several forms (fondant, purée, wafer-thin deep-fried rings), to desserts that are set about with spun sugar ringlets and trellises, and tend to be variations on a theme: five each on chocolate, banana, or apricots, generally incorporating a parfait, a tiny hot soufflé, ices and sorbets.

Incidentals – nibbles, appetisers, amuse-gueules, pre-dessert and so on – are as complex as everything else, each served on a different kind of plate, and frankly too numerous to keep track of. Attentive service sets a formal tone, and around 170 wines on the round-the-world list turn up a few bottles under £20

once out of France, and there is a page of halves. Four house wines are either £16 or £19 (£3 or £4.50 the glass).

CHEF: Stuart McLeod PROPRIETOR: Dr A. Heijn OPEN: all week 12.30 to 2, 7 to 10 MEALS: alc D (main courses £17 to £24). Set L £18.95, Set D £29.95 to £42.95 SERVICE: not inc, card slips closed CARDS: Amex, Delta, MasterCard, Switch, Visa DETAILS: 36 seats. 30 seats outside. Private parties: 30 main room. Car park. Vegetarian meals. Children's helpings. Wheelchair access (also WC). No music. Air-conditioned ACCOMMODATION: 15 rooms, all with bath/shower. TV. Phone. B&B £90 to £210. Rooms for disabled. Baby facilities (*The Which? Hotel Guide*) (£5)

La Rive

NEW ENTRY

Left Bank Village, Bridge Street,
Hereford HR4 9DG
TEL: (01432) 349009 FAX: (01432) 349012
EMAIL: dining@leftbank.co.uk
WEB SITE: www.leftbank.co.uk

MODERN EUROPEAN
£32–£67

As the Guide went to press this restaurant was incorporated into Castle House (see entry above).

CHEF: Stuart McLeod PROPRIETORS: Dr and Mrs A. Heijn OPEN: Sun to Fri L 12 to 2, Mon to Sat D 7 to 9.30 MEALS: Set L £14 (2 courses) to £18.95, Set D £29.95 to £42.95 SERVICE: not inc CARDS: Amex, Delta, MasterCard, Switch, Visa DETAILS: 40 seats. 20 seats outside. Private parties: 100 main room, 20 to 100 private rooms. Car park. Jacket and tie. Wheelchair access (also WC). Music. Air-conditioned

'The bread presented to us was not fresh. When we complained that it was stale the waiter explained that the bread was freshly delivered only it came from a poor baker! There was no apology.' (On eating in Manchester)

Net prices *in the details at the end of an entry indicates that the prices given on a menu and on a bill are inclusive of VAT and service charge, and that this practice is clearly stated on menu and bill.*

HERSTMONCEUX East Sussex **map 3**

▲ Sundial

Gardner Street, Herstmonceux BN27 4LA
TEL: (01323) 832217 FAX: (01323) 832909

COOKING **5**
FRENCH-PLUS
£31–£80

Although the seventeenth-century brick cottage has been in the Guide for 33 years, there have been changes since the last edition, as the Bertolis departed and the Rongiers arrived. A feeling of space and comfort pervades the pastoral pictures and chintz, and the food is uncompromisingly French bourgeois in style, taking in red-leg partridge with braised cabbage and ceps, and calves' sweetbreads with morels. Although not all reporters are agreed, the consensus is that cooking has improved under the new regime.

There is evidence of real skill, be it in a straightforward smooth and intensely flavoured mushroom velouté with fines herbes, or a dish of large, lightly cooked scallops on a bed of trompette mushrooms with a scant and properly reduced cream sauce. Indeed, both saucing and timing generally show an experienced hand – in a crisp-skinned fillet of sea bass on an unctuous celeriac purée, for example – and ideas are intelligently considered: a heady dish of boned quail on a bed of foie gras was 'more than the sum of its parts' at inspection, helped by a lively sauce périgourdine.

Desserts are no less accomplished: for example, a delectable sliced pear on puff pastry filled with almond cream, with a dark chocolate sauce, and a brace of pancakes folded over apple purée, with an alcoholic orange-flavoured sauce. Set-price options are considered good value, service is engaging, and a rather top-heavy French-dominated wine list offers half a dozen house wines under £20, little by the glass, but pichets of vins de pays for £7.50.

CHEF: Vincent Rongier PROPRIETORS: Mary and Vincent Rongier OPEN: Tue to Sun L 12 to 2, Tue to Sat D 7 to 9.45 MEALS: alc (main courses £17.50 to £25.50). Set L Tue to Sat £19.50, Set L Sun £23.50, Set D Tue £19.50, Set D Wed to Sat £25.50 to £39.50 SERVICE: 10% CARDS: Amex, Delta, Diners, MasterCard, Switch, Visa DETAILS: 50 seats. 20 seats outside. Private parties: 50 main room, 22 private room. Car park. Children's helpings. Music ACCOMMODATION: 1 room, with bath/shower. TV. B&B £55 to £85 (£5)

HETTON North Yorkshire **map 8**

Angel Inn

Hetton BD23 6LT
TEL: (01756) 730263 FAX: (01756) 730363
EMAIL: info@angelhetton.co.uk
WEB SITE: www.angelhetton.co.uk
off B6265, 5m N of Skipton

COOKING **5**
MODERN BRITISH
£20–£53

Here is evidence that even when good food is served apparently in the middle of nowhere people will still happily travel to eat it. The Angel combines an informal no-bookings brasserie (which serves lunch as well as dinner) with a more comfortable dining room. The carte offers greater choice, but the early-bird menu includes wine, and the commitment to local and regional produce is as strong as ever, taking in loin of Dales lamb with spinach and roast garlic, haunch of Green Farm venison with parsnip and potato mash, and whatever Ilkley butcher David Lishman can come up with: if he cannot sell underrated neck of lamb in his shop, for example, the kitchen might stuff it with foie gras and slowly braise it.

The 'moneybags' starter (seafood in filo pastry with lobster sauce) remains a favourite, even in the face of competition from home-made black pudding with braised lentils, and desserts run to a gooey torte of chocolate, walnut and pecan, and a citrus platter of lemon tart, pink grapefruit jelly and lime ice cream. Extras include good walnut bread, a taster of soup, and petits fours with coffee. Service is both efficient and unobtrusive, and good value is still the keynote of the wine list. Around 20 are offered by the glass, starting at only £1.95, and close to three dozen half-bottles open up choice still further. Serious, and pricey, bins creep into the French and Italian sections, but house wines open at £10.95.

CHEFS: John Topham and Bruce Elsworth PROPRIETORS: Denis and Juliet Watkins, and John Topham OPEN: Sun L 12 to 2, Mon to Sat D 6 to 9 CLOSED: 25 Dec MEALS: alc D Mon to Fri (main courses £9.50 to £16.50). Set L Sun £19.50, Set D 6 to 7 Mon to Fri £16.50, inc wine, Set D Sat £29.50. Bar menu available SERVICE: not inc CARDS: Amex, MasterCard, Switch, Visa DETAILS: 56 seats. 48 seats outside. Private parties: 40 main room. Car park. Children's helpings. No smoking in 1 dining room. Wheelchair access (not WC). No music. Air-conditioned

HINDON Wiltshire **map 2**

▲ Grosvenor Arms

High Street, Hindon SP3 6DJ
TEL: (01747) 820696 FAX: (01747) 820869
1m from A350 between Warminster and Shaftesbury

COOKING **3**
MODERN EUROPEAN
£27–£56

The Grosvenor, at the crossroads in the village, has had new owners since February 2001, but chef Chris Lee remains at the stoves. Both bar and main menus may be taken in the bar, lounge, garden (when fine) or in the long, narrow dining room. Superb breads and a quality appetiser (perhaps a little cup of smoked salmon and red pepper soup) presage sustenance several cuts above traditional pub food. Fillet of sea bass on warmly Mediterranean-flavoured couscous makes a handsome first course, and pineapple Tatin with cinnamon ice cream and vanilla syrup is a satisfying dessert. In between, the range encompasses whole roast pigeon with Savoy cabbage, lentils and foie gras, and baked cod with Toulouse sausage and pasta (for vegetarians, perhaps red onion tart with thyme and feta). Dishes are assembled with a sense of clarity (less so perhaps in the case of duck confit with tomato compote and a sweet blackcurrant sauce). Service may not always keep its eye on the ball, but an imaginative and extensive wine list contains delights for both palate and purse; nine house wines from France, South Africa and Australia start at £10.20.

CHEF: Chris Lee PROPRIETORS: Penny Simpson, Jeff Fergus and Bill Laret OPEN: all week L 12 to 2.30, Mon to Sat D 7 to 9.30 (9.45 Fri and Sat) MEALS: alc (main courses £5 to £16) SERVICE: not inc CARDS: Delta, MasterCard, Switch, Visa DETAILS: 100 seats. 40 seats outside. Private parties: 50 main room. Car park. Vegetarian meals. Children's helpings. No children under 2. No smoking in dining room. Wheelchair access (also WC). No music ACCOMMODATION: 7 rooms, all with bath/shower. TV. B&B £45 to £95. No children under 2 (£5)

HINTON CHARTERHOUSE Bath & N.E. Somerset map 2

▲ Homewood Park

Hinton Charterhouse BA2 7TB
TEL: (01225) 723731 FAX: (01225) 723820
EMAIL: res@homewoodpark.com
WEB SITE: www.homewoodpark.com
off A36, 6m SE of Bath

COOKING **4**
MODERN ENGLISH
£30–£75

Homewood Park creates a favourable impression with its romantic looks and verdant setting, and an appropriately Georgian decorative theme sets the tone inside, where a relaxed atmosphere pervades the series of small rooms. With dinner at £38, expectations are naturally high, but the kitchen has proved that it can deliver. Nigel Godwin's style is surprisingly up to date in this context, offering fashionable pairings such as home-cured salmon with beetroot, and Skye scallops with a lime and shallot dressing. Original creations run to roast Trelough duck accompanied by a confit of the leg and neck with Anna potatoes, lentil mousse and a jasmine-scented jus, and an earthy note is sounded by chump of West Country lamb with a sauté of its sweetbreads and kidneys and a parsley and tomato jus. For dessert, the flaming Sambuca soufflé is 'not to be missed', and there may also be hot chocolate fondant with basil-scented ice cream. Wines are unashamedly biased towards France, though the New World is also represented strongly. Quality is high throughout the range, but prices are unforgiving, with little under £20. House selections are £16.

CHEF: Nigel Godwin PROPRIETOR: Alan Moxon OPEN: all week 12 to 1.30, 7 to 9.30 MEALS: Set L Mon to Sat £16, Set L Sun £22.50, Set D £29 (2 courses) to £45 SERVICE: not inc CARDS: Amex, Delta, Diners, MasterCard, Switch, Visa DETAILS: 80 seats. Private parties: 40 main room, 18 and 22 private rooms. Car park. Vegetarian meals. Children's helpings. No smoking in dining room. Wheelchair access (also men's WC). No music. Air-conditioned ACCOMMODATION: 19 rooms, all with bath/shower. TV. Phone. B&B £109 to £250. Rooms for disabled. Baby facilities. Swimming pool (*The Which? Hotel Guide*)

HOLT Norfolk map 6

Yetman's

37 Norwich Road, Holt NR25 6SA
TEL: (01263) 713320
WEB SITE: www.yetmans.net

COOKING **4**
MODERN BRITISH
£45–£61

Just on the edge of town, with a few paintings hung around its small, attractive dining room, Yetman's is the epitome of a husband-and-wife partnership, where a dinner-only format, apart from Sunday lunch, enables them to take an unhurried and careful approach to cooking and yet vary the menu daily. Their response to the seasons brings a chilled summer soup of Italian cherry tomatoes, chargrilled local asparagus with rocket and Parmesan in May, and local partridge in November, marinated in verjuice and served with frazzled bacon, chestnuts and apple.

Some staples appear throughout the year – among seafood, for example, might be fish soup with rouille, Louisiana crab cakes, or deep-fried sardine fillets – but the appeal is a lively repertoire of common-sense ideas that don't try to be too complicated and which appeal for their directness. Cheeses are British, and puddings range from damson and rose-petal bombe, via the River Café's chocolate nemesis, to rhubarb fool. Easy-going but gracious service is appreciated: 'We don't mind Peter in his rugby shirt and trainers and his wild hair coming along to say "What can I get you guys?"' The owners are keen to share their wines of the moment, which include a good stock of Sauvignon Blancs and an array of 'current favourites' (instead of house wines) which, although not as low-priced as normal house offerings, are sold by the glass. All are chosen to suit the cooking style and start at £16.75.

CHEF: Alison Yetman PROPRIETORS: Alison and Peter Yetman OPEN: Sun L 12.30 to 2, Wed to Sat (Wed to Sun and bank hols in summer) D 7 to 9.30 CLOSED: 25 and 26 Dec, 3 weeks Oct to Nov MEALS: Set L and D £25 (2 courses) to £35 SERVICE: not inc CARDS: Amex, Delta, MasterCard, Switch, Visa DETAILS: 32 seats. Private parties: 20 main room. Vegetarian meals. Children's helpings. No smoking in dining room. No music

HOLT Wiltshire **map 2**

Tollgate Inn

Ham Green, Holt BA14 6PX COOKING **2**
TEL: (01225) 782326 FAX: (01225) 782805 MODERN BRITISH/MEDITERRANEAN
£22–£46

The Tollgate is on the main road through this sleepy village not far from Bath, with the village green to one side and a pleasant view down to the Avon from the end of the car park. For food, head upstairs, where Alexander Venables cooks classic dishes with the splash of the Mediterranean never far away. Tomato and basil soup has pesto swirled into it, chargrilled vegetables are layered with mozzarella and served with a balsamic reduction, and minted couscous is the accompaniment for sauté fillet of salmon. Foie gras terrine is 'a bold, thick chunk, definitively flavoured', and served with orange confit, while a main course of partridge comes with a skilful red wine and stock reduction sauce with mushrooms. Finish with apple crumble served with a jug of calvados sauce, or lemon sponge pudding with a sauce of lemon curd. 'A friendly welcome' adds to the charm. The helpfully annotated wine list makes a genuine effort to keep prices within bounds, kicking off with Yaldara red and white from Australia at £11.25. Accommodation is planned for 2002.

CHEF: Alexander Venables PROPRIETORS: Alison Ward-Baptiste and Alexander Venables OPEN: Tue to Sun L 12 to 2, Tue to Sat D 7 to 9.30 CLOSED: 25 Dec, first week Jan MEALS: alc (main courses L £6 to £11, D £9.50 to £15.50). Set L Tue to Sat £9.95 (2 courses) to £11.95 SERVICE: not inc, card slips closed, 10% for groups of 5 or more CARDS: Delta, MasterCard, Switch, Visa DETAILS: 70 seats. 36 seats outside. Private parties: 38 main room. Car park. Vegetarian meals. No children under 10 exc Sun L. No smoking in dining room. Occasional music

Card slips closed *in the details at the end of an entry indicates that the total on the slips of credit cards is closed when handed over for signature.*

HONLEY West Yorkshire map 8

Mustard and Punch

6 Westgate, Honley HD3 3QW
TEL: (01484) 662066

COOKING 3
MODERN EUROPEAN
£20–£47

More relaxed and friendly than the name suggests, this bistro near Huddersfield is decorated with a flair that eschews the clichés of many modern eating places. Mr Punch's hat motif, from the sign outside, is repeated in metal candle-holders that sit on green-checked tablecloths surrounded by seats that include church chairs (with slots for hymn books), banquettes and bentwood chairs. The limited ground floor and basement space is often fully used. Menus venture beyond modern British convention, with starters such as candied shallot, Brie and pancetta soup; calamari with duck confit; and braised pig's cheeks with Parmesan gnocchi, carrots and pork crackling. The six main dishes might include one of lamb cutlet with kidney served with white bean stew, oven-dried figs and anise jus; or another of sea bass fillet with braised iceberg lettuce, tiger prawn ravioli and cumin sauce. Even Whitby cod comes with asparagus and a pea and clam velouté, and for dessert lavender ice cream accompanies white peach Tatin. The varied list of 37 fairly priced wines (plus a few halves) starts with house selections at £10.50; only four exceed £20, and house champagne squeaks in at £19.95.

CHEF: Chris and Richard Dunn PROPRIETORS: Dorota Pencak and Anna Young OPEN: Tue to Fri L 12 to 2, Tue to Sat D 7 to 10 CLOSED: 25 Dec to 1 Jan MEALS: alc (main courses £9.50 to £16), Set L £6.50 (2 courses), Set D Tue to Thur £15.95 (2 courses inc wine) SERVICE: not inc CARDS: Delta, MasterCard, Switch, Visa DETAILS: 60 seats. Private parties: 60 main room. Car park. Vegetarian meals. No cigars/pipes in dining room. Music

HORNCASTLE Lincolnshire map 9

Magpies

71–75 East Street, Horncastle LN9 6AA
TEL: (01507) 527004 FAX: (01507) 524064
EMAIL: magpies@fsbdial.co.uk

COOKING 2
MODERN BRITISH
£18–£44

Occupying a long, low building in a small attractive market town, Magpies welcomes with a cheery greeting, a small bar and a rather more expansive but very pink dining room. A plainly written menu deals in fresh materials: fillets of roast sea bass with a thick, sweet vanilla sauce, and well-trimmed pink rack of lamb with a light yet well-flavoured tarragon jus. Not all dishes hit the mark, temperatures can be surprising – a slice of quiche-like onion tart served cold as a starter – and flavouring and seasoning at inspection both lacked impact, but the help-yourself vegetables are 'a delight', incorporating gratin dauphinoise, lemony cabbage, sweet carrots and fine beans. One party found that rocket came with all their starters, and spinach with all their main courses. Finish with familiar chocolate marquise, sticky toffee pudding, or a wobbly lemon tart with cinnamon ice cream. A characterful wine list provides plenty of reasonably priced choice from around the world, plus a few star bins. Three house wines are £11, or £3 a large glass.

CHEFS: Matthew and Simon Lee PROPRIETORS: the Lee family OPEN: Sun L 12.30 to 2, Wed to Sat D 7 to 10 CLOSED: 2 weeks Aug MEALS: Set L £11, Set D £22 SERVICE: not inc CARDS: Delta, MasterCard, Switch, Visa DETAILS: 42 seats. Private parties: 42 main room, 8 private room. Children's helpings L. No smoking in dining room. Occasional music

HORNDON ON THE HILL Essex **map 3**

▲ Bell Inn

High Road, Horndon on the Hill SS17 8LD
TEL: (01375) 642463 FAX: (01375) 361611
EMAIL: info@bell-inn.co.uk
WEB SITE: www.bell-inn.co.uk
off M25 at junction 30/31, signposted Thurrock, Lakeside; take A13, then B1007 to Horndon

COOKING **2**
MODERN EUROPEAN
£24–£44

This 500-year-old inn with its white, pebble-dash walls conceals a beamed interior complete with flagstone floor, grandfather clock and a collection of foundry memorabilia. The menu changes daily and offers fine country-pub food in the modern idiom, incorporating perhaps smoked haddock ravioli with peas and piccalilli, or breadcrumbed veal sweetbreads with wild garlic to start, followed by roast cod with tomato and red onion fritters, or chump of lamb with celeriac and mustard. The choice of vegetables might extend to pak choi sautéed with peanuts and chilli. Entitled 'Oh Sugar', the pudding list takes in glazed passion-fruit tart with crème Chantilly, and pistachio ice cream with chocolate cookies. An extensive wine list majors in France, but offers a few good New World bottles for price relief. House Australian is £9.75.

CHEF: Finlay Logan PROPRIETORS: J.S.B. and C.M. Vereker OPEN: all week 12 to 1.45 (2.15 Sun), 6.45 to 9.45 CLOSED: 25 and 26 Dec, bank hol Mons MEALS: alc (main courses £9.50 to £13.50). Set L £13.95 (2 courses) to £15.95. Bar and sandwich menus available L only SERVICE: not inc, card slips closed CARDS: Amex, Delta, MasterCard, Switch, Visa DETAILS: 80 seats. 36 seats outside. Private parties: 12 main room, 26 and 36 private rooms. Car park. Vegetarian meals. Children's helpings. No smoking in dining room. No music ACCOMMODATION: 15 rooms, all with bath/shower. TV. Phone. Room only £40 to £85. Rooms for disabled. Baby facilities (*The Which? Hotel Guide*)

HUDDERSFIELD West Yorkshire **map 9**

Bradley's

84 Fitzwilliam Street, Huddersfield HD1 5BB
TEL: (01484) 516773 FAX: (01484) 538386

COOKING **2**
MEDITERRANEAN/MODERN BRITISH
£15–£46

Value for money is what reporters and inspectors comment on most regularly at this bustling bistro on the segment of Fitzwilliam Street that bridges the ring road then slopes steeply into town. On the carte might be main courses of chargrilled calf's liver with black pudding and smoked bacon, and classic desserts such as prune and armagnac tart, or sticky toffee pudding. Set lunch is 'a bargain', according to a reporter who enjoyed a velvety tomato and basil soup, then firm moist salmon fillet with saffron butter sauce, followed by Bakewell tart with good-quality vanilla ice cream. Service is generally friendly, and owner Andrew Bradley 'seems to be a constant presence'. The wine list is fairly brief but thoughtfully chosen, with most bottles under £20. House selections start at £9.95.

CHEFS: Jonathan Nichols and Eric Paxman PROPRIETORS: Andrew Bradley and Jonathan Nichols OPEN: Mon to Fri L 12 to 2, Mon to Sat D 6 to 10 (10.30 Fri and Sat) CLOSED: bank hols MEALS: alc (main courses £9 to £16). Set L £6.95, Set D exc after 7 Sat £14.95 (inc wine) SERVICE: not inc CARDS: Delta, MasterCard, Switch, Visa DETAILS: 120 seats. Private parties: 60 main room. Car park (D only). Vegetarian meals. No smoking in 1 dining room. Wheelchair access (also WC). Music. Air-conditioned

▲ Lodge Hotel

48 Birkby Lodge Road, Birkby, Huddersfield HD2 2BG
TEL: (01484) 431001 FAX: (01484) 421590

COOKING **2**
MODERN EUROPEAN
£22–£44

The motto engraved on the door of this quiet, ivy-clad, family-run hotel is 'Welcome ever Smiles', which its unpretentious, cheery staff work hard to fulfil. Art nouveau interiors are 'exuberant in an oddly sombre sort of way', featuring busy patterns, rich colours, dark-wood panelling and chandeliers. Seasonal menus utilise organic and locally sourced produce, though execution is rather homespun and presentation somewhat dated. A starter of a warm peanut pastry tart of smoked mackerel, fennel and plum tomatoes with gooseberry sauce might have something of a '1980s dinner party' ring to it, while sturdy main courses could feature roast spring lamb with minted pea purée and a garlic and rosemary jus. Desserts hit a familiar comfort note with spotted dick and custard, or queen of puddings with clotted cream. Breads are good, and a pre-main course of crisp salad leaves with cherry tomatoes and quail's eggs has been appreciated. A 'summary' list takes the drinker around the wine world on one easy page, and brings to light the extent of what is available under £15 (full-fruited southern Italians and Bergeracs from as little as £10.95). Highlights of the well-priced, hefty main list include one of Tasmania's renowned Pinot Noirs, Piper Brook's Ninth Island, at £16.25.

CHEFS: Garry and Kevin Birley, and Richard Hanson PROPRIETORS: Garry and Kevin Birley OPEN: Sun to Fri L 12 to 1.45, Mon to Sat D 7.30 to 9.45 CLOSED: 26 to 28 Dec MEALS: Set L £10.95 (2 courses) to £14.95, Set D £23.95 to £26 SERVICE: not inc, card slips closed CARDS: Amex, Delta, Diners, MasterCard, Switch, Visa DETAILS: 60 seats. 20 seats outside. Private parties: 62 main room, 10 to 25 private rooms. Car park. Vegetarian meals. Children's helpings. No smoking in dining room. Wheelchair access (also WC). Music ACCOMMODATION: 13 rooms, all with bath/shower. TV. Phone. B&B £60 to £100. Baby facilities (*The Which? Hotel Guide*)

indicates that there has been a change of chef since last year's Guide, and the Editor has judged that the change is of sufficient interest to merit the reader's attention.

The Good Food Guide *is a registered trade mark of Which? Ltd.*

Thorpe Grange Manor

Thorpe Lane, Almondbury, Huddersfield HD5 8TA
TEL/FAX: (01484) 425115
EMAIL: enquiries@thorpegrangemanor.com — COOKING **5**
WEB SITE: www.thorpegrangemanor.com — ANGLO-FRENCH
off A629, 2m E of Huddersfield — £22–£59

An impression of space and light pervades this eighteenth-century manor house set in two and a half acres of rolling lawns and mature trees. The high-ceilinged bar is expansive, the wooden-floored dining rooms sport large windows, and tables are well spaced. Although the offer of mid-meal sorbets or granitas marks out the style as rather old-fashioned, there is much to commend on Jason Neilson's menus, which shuttle amiably between the Mediterranean (a tartlet of vegetables and black olives topped with goats' cheese and pesto dressing) and nearer home: beef fillet and braised oxtail on Madeira sauce, or pork loin with whole-grain mustard sauce.

The food mostly keeps its feet on the ground, only occasionally reaching for such things as truffles (white with the leek fondue that comes with roast sea bass, black in the cream sauce to accompany John Dory), although it does generally aim for reassuring loins, fillets and breasts in preference to more challenging cuts. Desserts require quite a bit of workmanship and often get help from the liqueur cabinet – cannelloni of dark chocolate with a coffee mousse on sambuca cream, for instance – while the wine list travels widely and is careful to consider most pockets. Six house wines under £12 start the ball rolling.

CHEF: Jason Neilson PROPRIETORS: Ronald, Gillian, Jason and Ruth Neilson OPEN: Tue to Fri and Sun L 12 to 1.45, Tue to Sat D 6 (7 Fri and Sat) to 9.15 CLOSED: 5 to 14 Jan, 19 May to 4 June MEALS: alc Tue to Sat (main courses £14 to £22). Set L Tue to Fri £12.50 (2 courses) to £14.95, Set L Sun £14.95, Set D Tue to Thur before 7.30 £14.95, Set D £19.95 SERVICE: not inc CARDS: Delta, MasterCard, Switch, Visa DETAILS: 60 seats. 20 seats outside. Private parties: 90 main room, 40 and 50 private rooms. Car park. Vegetarian meals. Children's helpings. No children after 7.30pm. No cigars/pipes in dining room. Wheelchair access (also WC). Music. Air-conditioned (£5)

HUNSTRETE Bath & N.E. Somerset — **map 2**

▲ Hunstrete House

Hunstrete, Pensford BS39 4NS
TEL: (01761) 490490 FAX: (01761) 490732 — COOKING **5**
WEB SITE: www.hunstretehouse.co.uk — MODERN BRITISH/EUROPEAN
off A368, 4m S of Keynsham — £26–£79

Set back off the road, with ponies, deer parks and paddocks, Hunstrete is classic country-house territory. Despite walls of books that try to make it feel lived in, a sense of unreal perfection pervades: 'impossibly high' standards of housekeeping, and the dining room's classical trompe l'oeil pillars contribute to the effect, while Philip Hobson's heavily worked menus aim just as high. Seared foie gras comes with both a red wine jus and a Moscato reduction, and chicken and wild mushrooms are wrapped in a potato parcel and served with cep sauce.

The food at its best benefits from simple presentation, accurate timing and some intelligent flavour combinations: expertly grilled, crisp-skinned red mullet fillet with a saffron-infused chive cream sauce to start, and moist guinea fowl with a deep, rich, powerfully flavoured stock reduction. Not all items are equally successful, which is a pity at these prices, but cheese is taken seriously, making it a tempting alternative to desserts such as praline parfait with butterscotch sauce and caramel ice cream. The wine list focuses on serious French bins, with interest and value coming from the livelier southern selection. Few bottles are under £20, but house wines start at £14.95.

CHEF: Philip Hobson PROPRIETOR: Hunstrete House Ltd OPEN: all week 12 to 2, 7 to 9.30 MEALS: alc (main courses £23.50 to £28.50). Set L £15.95 (2 courses) to £19.95. Light L menu available SERVICE: not inc CARDS: Amex, Delta, Diners, MasterCard, Switch, Visa DETAILS: 50 seats. 12 seats outside. Private parties: 50 main room, 12 and 30 private rooms. Car park. Vegetarian meals. Children's helpings. No smoking in dining room. Wheelchair access (not WC). Music ACCOMMODATION: 22 rooms, all with bath/shower. TV. Phone. D,B&B £115 to £300. Rooms for disabled. Baby facilities. Swimming pool *The Which? Hotel Guide*

HUNTINGDON Cambridgeshire **map 6**

▲ Old Bridge Hotel

1 High Street, Huntingdon PE29 3TQ — COOKING **4**
TEL: (01480) 424300 FAX: (01480) 411017 — MODERN BRITISH
EMAIL: oldbridge@huntsbridge.co.uk — £27–£56

The Huntsbridge Group's approach (common to the Falcon Inn at Fotheringhay, the Pheasant Inn at Keyston and the Three Horseshoes at Madingley; see entries) is to serve modern food in an informal manner, backed up by first-class, good-value wines. That the group does not feel like a chain is due to the enlightened policy of giving chef/owner/managers their head, and Martin and Jayne Lee's accomplished style results in bright and colourful cooking that is both sensible and widely appealing. The same generous but manageable menu operates throughout the ivy-covered building, offering Tuscan ribollita, crab boudin with tarragon sauce, and slow-braised pork with ginger. Goosnargh chicken features (perhaps served with morels), as do some locally produced organic vegetables, and there are salads, sandwiches, snacks and other simple options, from wild boar sausages to fish and chips, perhaps followed by sticky toffee pudding, or lemon tart. In-house activities, from baking to making pasta and black pudding, add to the appeal. Reasonable mark-ups for the more expensive wines on the list, plus around 20 house wines by the glass from £2.60, underpin the owners' aim to encourage adventurous drinking. The well-researched range is usefully grouped under price and style headings.

CHEF: Martin Lee PROPRIETORS: John Hoskins and Martin Lee OPEN: all week 12 to 2.30, 6 to 10 CLOSED: D 25 Dec MEALS: alc (main courses £9 to £18). Set L Mon to Fri £15 (2 courses) to £19 SERVICE: not inc CARDS: Amex, Delta, Diners, MasterCard, Switch, Visa DETAILS: 100 seats. 20 seats outside. Private parties: 100 main room, 30 private room. Car park. Vegetarian meals. Children's helpings. No smoking in dining room. Wheelchair access (not WC). No music ACCOMMODATION: 24 rooms, all with bath/shower. TV. Phone. B&B £80 to £160. Rooms for disabled

Report forms are at the back of the book; write a letter if you prefer; or email us at goodfoodguide@which.net

HURST Berkshire map 2

Castle

Church Hill, Hurst RG10 0SJ
TEL: (0118) 934 0034 FAX: (0118) 934 0334
EMAIL: info@castlerestaurant.co.uk
WEB SITE: www.castlerestaurant.co.uk

COOKING **5**
MODERN EUROPEAN
£38–£69

A section of wattle and daub in one of the rooms is preserved as a reminder of the building's 500-year history – it is about half as old as the church opposite – while bare brick walls, exposed beams, iron wall lamps and thick white candles add to the sense of antiquity. This is determinedly modern cooking from a chef with a strong classical background, and although some ideas seem positively outlandish – rillettes of langoustine and duck with coffee foam – most are variants on more familiar items from the repertoire, such as brill with glazed seaweed and thyme-scented chicken jus, or beef bourguignon with snails and morels. Sometimes it is difficult to tell the courses apart: carrot pannacotta with goats' cheese mousseline is a starter, and bortsch and tarragon trifle with whipped goats' cheese is a dessert.

Prices have risen since last year, and 'minute portions on huge plates' do not endear themselves to all reporters, largely because individual components of a dish are deemed too small to make much of an impact. To finish, a pre-dessert such as crème brûlée with pepper caramel might be followed by roast pineapple with vanilla cream and basil syrup, or bitter chocolate tart with coffee bean rice pudding and milk ice cream. The wine list crams a good variety of styles and a fair range of prices within a 50-strong framework, starting with Cabernet Sauvignon and Sauvignon Blanc house wines at £12.25.

CHEF: Damian Broom PROPRIETORS: Anthony Edwards and Amanda Hill OPEN: Tue to Sun L 12 to 2.30 (3 Sun), Tue to Sat D 7 to 10 CLOSED: 26 Dec MEALS: set L £13.95 (1 courses) to £37.50, Set D £29.50 (2 courses) to £44.50 SERVICE: 10% (optional), card slips closed CARDS: Amex, Delta, Diners, MasterCard, Switch, Visa DETAILS: 70 seats. 100 seats outside. Private parties: 40 main room, 11 to 40 private rooms. Car park. Vegetarian meals. No smoking in 1 dining room. Music

HUXHAM Devon map 1

▲ Barton Cross

Huxham, Stoke Canon EX5 4EJ
TEL: (01392) 841245 FAX: (01392) 841942
on A396 to Tiverton, 4m N of Exeter

COOKING **3**
ANGLO-FRENCH
£30–£42

Three rambling, thatched seventeenth-century cottages set in well-kept gardens make up this small, easy-going hotel whose refurbishment in greens, greys and pinks since the last Guide makes the interior a pleasant setting in which to enjoy the more than capable culinary endeavours of chef Paul Bending. His approach is to take the best of Devon produce, notably fish from Brixham, and add in a few luxury items and ingredients from further afield. Among starters, an asparagus and wild mushroom tart is topped with pan-fried foie gras, and a dish of potted smoked haddock and crab comes with a lemon and herb beurre blanc. Main courses blend classical and modern ideas in dishes such as grilled pesto-coated salmon with spinach, saffron-glazed new potatoes and a tomato butter sauce, or breast of Silverton chicken stuffed with wild mushrooms, red peppers and lemon and served with a ragoût of beans. Desserts range from sticky ginger pudding to mille-feuille of praline parfait. The large majority of wines are French, but choice is good and prices are fair. Nine house selections open at £9.25 a bottle, £2.25 a glass.

CHEF: Paul George Bending PROPRIETOR: Brian Hamilton OPEN: all week D only 6.30 to 9.30 (10.30 Sat and bank hols) MEALS: Set D £16.50 (1 course) to £25 SERVICE: not inc, card slips closed CARDS: Amex, Delta, MasterCard, Switch, Visa DETAILS: 50 seats. 10 seats outside. Private parties: 40 main room. Car park. Vegetarian meals. Children's helpings. No smoking in dining room. Wheelchair access (also WC). Occasional music ACCOMMODATION: 8 rooms, all with bath/shower. TV. Phone. B&B £65.50 to £120. Rooms for disabled. Baby facilities (£5)

ILKLEY West Yorkshire **map 8**

Box Tree

35–37 Church Street, Ilkley LS29 9DR
TEL: (01943) 608484 FAX: (01943) 607186
EMAIL: info@theboxtree.co.uk
WEB SITE: www.theboxtree.co.uk

COOKING **6**
MODERN EUROPEAN
£46–£75

After eight years, Thierry LePrêtre-Granet left the kitchens of what had become Yorkshire's most highly rated restaurant, to be replaced by Toby Hill (last listed in the 1998 Guide at Gordleton Mill, Lymington), an appointment confirming Madame Avis's determination to continue running a first-class operation. The room looks much as it always has, with deep rose-pink and gold décor, 'boudoir' chairs and elegant table settings. Not only does the format remain from the old days – three options at each stage on the two-course set-price menu, and about four on the carte – but some of the dishes too: crab bavarois on a bed of artichoke purée with tomato coulis, for example, and nuttily fried Cornish scallops, given the admirable foil of a lightly curry-spiced fruit chutney.

At its best the cooking demonstrates refined and restrained treatment, even at the hearty and comforting end of the spectrum, as in a main course of oxtail – braised, boned, shredded, and wrapped in caul – served with caramelised parsnips and carrots, a stiff potato purée, and surrounded by the braising juices. If Toby Hill has yet to stamp his own identity on the cooking, at least the timing and balance can be take for granted, for example in a dish of accurately cooked red mullet fillets scattered with coarse sea salt sitting on a moulded bed of couscous, surrounded by fried aubergine and a tasty 'essence' of red pepper. Cheeses are well kept, desserts have included a light, hot soufflé of Agen prunes and armagnac with 'good boozy flavour', and wines feature some of the most exciting new varietals from California and the brightest names from Spain. Other regions are treated with respect, too, and alongside a wealth of choice for those on big budgets, there is plenty under £20. House burgundies are £14 a bottle, £3.50 a glass.

CHEF: Toby Hill PROPRIETOR: The Box Tree Restaurant (Ilkley) Ltd OPEN: Tue to Sun L 12 to 2.30, Tue to Sat D 7 to 9.30 CLOSED: 25 Dec to New Year, last two weeks Jan MEALS: alc (main courses £16 to £20). Set L and D £19.50 (2 courses) SERVICE: not inc, card slips closed CARDS:

Amex, Delta, MasterCard, Switch, Visa DETAILS: 50 seats. Private parties: 16 main room, 10 to 28 private rooms. Vegetarian meals. No smoking in dining room. Wheelchair access (not WC). Occasional music

Farsyde

38A The Back Grove, Ilkley LS29 9EE — COOKING **4**
TEL: (01943) 602030 FAX: (01943) 435334 — MODERN BRITISH
WEB SITE: www.thefarsyde.com — £17–£38

Opposite the main car-park, Farsyde could be easily missed, but for its dramatic night-time spotlighting. Behind floor-to-ceiling windows, a convivial interior has bare-board floor, primrose walls and mixed table and booth seating. Gavin Beedham changes menus six-weekly ('keeps the regulars keen'), and offers an early-bird menu from 6 to 7.30 and fish nights on Wednesdays.

This isn't provincial-backwater cooking, though: viz. starters from the main evening menu like tempura-battered mussels and salmon on a kebab with lychees on stir-fried vegetables, or smoked duck and red cabbage mille-feuille in raspberry dressing. Among mains, rump of lamb has a wild mushroom duxelle, spiced couscous, caramelised apples and port sauce, while vegetarians might pick vine leaves stuffed with a risotto of sun-dried tomatoes, spinach and goats' cheese, served on a carrot rösti with tomato and basil dressing. For all their elaboration, most dishes seem to work well, and, if early courses stretch your palate, end with a simple pannacotta, or apple crumble with custard. The wine list has amusingly helpful notes and keen prices (nearly everything under £25), and basic house French is £7.75 (£2 a glass).

CHEF/PROPRIETOR: Gavin Beedham OPEN: Tue to Sun L 11.30 to 2 (11.30 to 2.30 Sat, 12 to 3.30 Sun), Tue to Sat D 6 to 10) CLOSED: Sun L May to Sept MEALS: alc (main courses L £6.50 to £7.50, D £10 to 14). Set L Tue to Sat £11.95), Set D Tue to Thu 6 to 7.30 £11.95 (2 courses) SERVICE: not inc CARDS: Delta, MasterCard, Switch, Visa DETAILS: 55 seats. Vegetarian meals. No cigars/pipes. Wheelchair access (not WC). Music

IPSWICH Suffolk — **map 6**

Mortimer's on the Quay £

Wherry Quay, Ipswich IP4 1AS — COOKING **1**
TEL/FAX: (01473) 230225 — SEAFOOD
£23–£52

The fact that the menu changes daily at this long-running waterside bistro reflects the availability and seasonality of the fresh fish and shellfish that arrive every morning from Grimsby, Lowestoft and Billingsgate. A new section of the menu caters for vegetarians and meat eaters, but the fruits of the sea remain the driving force, as suggested by the dining room's nautical décor. The cooking aims to make the best of supplies by keeping things fairly simple: typical are steamed skate wing with capers and black butter, and chargrilled tuna steak with tagliatelle and a tomato and basil sauce. A long list of starters takes in everything from fish soup to scallops with vermouth, garlic and cream, while desserts might include baked apple and almond pudding. Wines are mostly white and French, starting at £9.95 a bottle.

CHEFS: Kenneth Ambler, Alison Mott and Reda A. Irain PROPRIETORS: Kenneth and Elizabeth Ambler OPEN: Mon to Fri L 12 to 2, Mon to Sat D 6.30 to 9 (8.30 Mon) CLOSED: 24 Dec to 5 Jan MEALS: alc (main courses £8 to £18) SERVICE: not inc CARDS: Amex, Delta, Diners, MasterCard, Switch, Visa DETAILS: 85 seats. Private parties: 35 main room, 30 private room. Vegetarian meals. Children's helpings. No smoking in 1 dining room. Wheelchair access (not WC). Occasional music (£5)

IXWORTH Suffolk map 6

Theobalds

68 High Street, Ixworth IP31 2HJ — COOKING **4**
TEL/FAX: (01359) 231707 — ANGLO-FRENCH
WEB SITE: www.theobaldsrestaurant.co.uk — £26–£50

It is not hard to believe that the building housing Simon Theobald's long-running restaurant dates from 1650: beams and standing timbers in the dining room testify to the fact. The cooking style, however, is far from antique. Instead, it shows a preference for a broadly contemporary way of doing things, relying on sound technique rather than culinary fireworks to impress: perhaps a twice-baked Cheddar soufflé with a crisp cheese top, or a pistachio-studded terrine of wild game with mango chutney and toasted brioche.

Dishes are presented as simply as they are described on the long, seasonally changing menu, offering main courses of hare wrapped in bacon with a mushroom and Madeira sauce, and grilled fillet of sea bass with lardons, garlic, thyme and spring onion on a white wine sauce. Desserts, meanwhile, run from mainstream poached pears and plums on creamed rice, to a less usual chocolate and walnut mousse with orange crème anglaise. Service has been 'very friendly and professional'. The wine list is defined by value and diversity, and has a substantial section of quality half-bottles. Five house wines start at £11.25 a bottle, £2.25 a glass.

CHEF: Simon Theobald PROPRIETORS: Simon and Geraldine Theobald OPEN: Tue to Fri and Sun L 12.15 to 1.30, Tue to Sat D 7 to 9.15 MEALS: alc D (main courses £12 to £17). Set L Tue to Fri £12.50 (2 courses) to £16.50, Set L Sun £18.95 SERVICE: not inc, card slips closed CARDS: Delta, MasterCard, Switch, Visa DETAILS: 50 seats. Private parties: 50 main room, 20 private room. Vegetarian meals. Children's helpings. No children under 6 at D. No smoking in dining room. Wheelchair access (not WC). No music

JEVINGTON East Sussex map 3

Hungry Monk

Jevington BN26 5QF
TEL/FAX: (01323) 482178 — COOKING **2**
WEB SITE: www.hungrymonk.co.uk — ENGLISH/FRENCH COUNTRY COOKING
off A22 between Polegate and Friston — £37–£60

A blue plaque outside this long, low, flint building signals it as the home of banoffi pie, making it something of a destination, if not a shrine, for pudding pilgrims. Nostalgia seems to permeate the rooms too, with their 'nicely cluttered', flowery and 'olde English' décor, although the strand of country cooking that has kept regulars returning for decades is updated on the seasonal menus. Alongside such traditional items as smoked haddock and salmon kedgeree with a poached egg, or duck with orange sauce (choice of crisp Norfolk or pink Barbary breasts) might be a plate of tapas with a glass of chilled fino, or Moroccan-spiced lamb with butternut squash. Desserts likewise delve into the traditional repertoire, pulling out spotted dick with treacle sauce and custard, but also find room for chocolate and chilli pot, or passion fruit custard tart. Changes in the kitchen seem to have produced a wobble in standards, but wines remain a tempting compilation of styles and prices to suit most tastes and pockets, offering among other things a quintet of English wines, and six house wines under £18.

CHEFS: Gary Fisher and Nick Sharman PROPRIETORS: Sue and Nigel Mackenzie OPEN: Sun L 12 to 2.30, all week D 6.45 to 9.45 MEALS: Set L £25.50, Set D £27 SERVICE: not inc, card slips closed, 12.5% for parties of 8 or more CARDS: Amex, MasterCard, Switch, Visa DETAILS: 40 seats. Private parties: 40 main room, 6 to 16 private rooms. Car park. Vegetarian meals. Children's helpings. No children under 3. No smoking in dining room. Occasional music. Air-conditioned (£5)

KELSALE Suffolk map 6

Harrisons Restaurant

NEW ENTRY

Main Road, Kelsale IP17 2RF
TEL/FAX: (01728) 604444

COOKING **3**
MODERN BRITISH
£21–£41

This attractive thatched cottage, with its small, beamed dining room, formerly appeared in the Guide under a different name and ownership. It returns following the arrival early in 2001 of Peter and Melanie Harrison, keen to make a favourable impression. Peter – previously at the Leaping Hare Café in Stanton (see entry) – is evidently a chef in the ascendant. He produces a short, weekly-changing menu of imaginative modern British cooking that emphasises quality local produce. Fish shows up well – maybe as grilled smoked sprats to start, or a main course of baked cod with grilled courgettes, butter beans and cockles – and lightly spiced aubergine with interesting mixed leaves and a minty yoghurt dressing makes an impressive starter. Main courses may include succulent roast Norfolk Horn lamb in a rich reduced gravy with haricot beans and sprouting broccoli, or a large portion of well-flavoured chicken on grilled ratatouille vegetables. To finish there may be damson muffins with lemon curd, or treacle tart with clotted cream ice cream. Prices on the succinct wine list start at £9.95 and stay mostly under £15.

CHEF: Peter Harrison PROPRIETORS: Peter and Melanie Harrison OPEN: Tue to Sun L 12 to 2.30, Tue to Sat D 7 to 10 CLOSED: 24 Dec to 21 Jan MEALS: alc (main courses £8.50 to £13.50). Set L Tue to Fri £10.50 (2 courses) to £12.50 SERVICE: not inc, card slips closed CARDS: Delta, MasterCard, Switch, Visa DETAILS: 50 seats. 12 seats outside. Private parties: 24 main room, 20 private room. Car park. Vegetarian meals. Children's helpings. No children under 10. No smoking in dining room. Wheelchair access (not WC). No music

'The front-of-house person is rather like a cross between a Barbie doll and a lion tamer.'
(On eating in the Midlands)

KENILWORTH Warwickshire **map 5**

Restaurant Bosquet

97A Warwick Road, Kenilworth CV8 1HP
TEL: (01926) 852463

COOKING 5
FRENCH
£38–£53

It takes an eagle eye to spot Bosquet as you speed along the main road: its narrow façade comprises just the front door and a small window. Jane Lignier hosts the operation with friendliness and assurance amid pin-striped wallpaper evoking a bygone era, and ruched curtains hanging beneath an old-fashioned pelmet. The best of tradition is celebrated where it matters, though, in Bernard Lignier's classical French cooking, despite a few innovative flourishes in the modern manner: a rhubarb and ginger chutney accompanying terrine of duck foie gras, or a curried papaya sauce with glazed squab pigeon as a main.

Otherwise, it's likely to be lobster and asparagus on a thin pastry base with crustacean butter sauce, or herb-crusted saddle of lamb served in its own juices. And remember to ask about the daily fish special. Desserts might include a mille-feuille of raspberries, or roast nectarine in a biscuit cup with pistachio ice cream, and there are fine 'fromages de France' to ponder too. An all-French wine list offers a good range of styles and bins for all budgets, with plenty of choice under £20. Generally reasonable mark-ups make more exclusive names fairly approachable, and house wines start with a £12 Corbières.

CHEF: Bernard Lignier PROPRIETORS: Bernard and Jane Lignier OPEN: Tue to Fri L 12 to 1.15 (booking essential), Tue to Sat D 7 to 9.15 MEALS: alc (main courses £17). Set L £26, Set D Tue to Fri £26 SERVICE: not inc CARDS: Amex, Delta, MasterCard, Switch, Visa DETAILS: 26 seats. Private parties: 32 main room. Wheelchair access (not WC). No music

Simpson's

101–103 Warwick Road, Kenilworth CV8 1HL
TEL: (01926) 864567 FAX: (01926) 864510
EMAIL: info@simpsons-restaurant.co.uk
WEB SITE: www.simpsons-restaurant.co.uk

COOKING 5
MODERN FRENCH
£31–£77

On the main road through Kenilworth, like its near neighbour above, Simpson's has a relaxed and welcoming atmosphere, enhanced by a modern, light interior with well-spaced, smartly dressed tables. The seasonally changing menu (weekly-changing for lunch) is annotated with house specialities and dotted with luxury items. 'Great flavour combinations' and attractive presentation characterise a repertoire that brims with interest: starters of hot and cold foie gras with apple and Sauternes, for example, or seared scallops with black pudding, mushy peas, garlic and parsley cream.

Fish is a strong suit, perhaps featuring red mullet with fennel and artichoke barigoule, or one reporter's brill, which came immaculately adorned with potato scales and was served on a bed of spinach. Presentation again comes to the fore at dessert stage, and recommendable dishes include tarte Tatin of bananas with matching ice cream, and pistachio parfait with cinnamon poached pear. Nibbles, appetisers, petit fours and a six-course tasting menu all add further appeal, as does 'attentive, human, unobtrusive' service. The enterprising wine list crosses

the continents and is arranged by colour in ascending price order; it includes 20 halves plus ten house wines from £12.50 to £18.25.

CHEFS: Andreas Antona and Luke Tipping PROPRIETORS: Andreas and Alison Antona OPEN: Mon to Fri L 12.30 to 2, Mon to Sat D 7 to 10 CLOSED: 25 and 26 Dec, bank hols, last 2 weeks Aug MEALS: alc (main courses £17.50 to £19.50). Set L £15 (2 courses) to £20, Set D £25.75 (2 courses) to £49.95 (for whole table only) SERVICE: not inc, 10% for parties of 6 or more CARDS: Amex, Delta, Diners, MasterCard, Switch, Visa DETAILS: 70 seats. Private parties: 40 main room. Car park. Vegetarian meals. Children's helpings. No smoking in 1 dining room. Air-conditioned

KEW Greater London **map 3**

Glasshouse 🍷

14 Station Parade, Kew TW9 3PZ
TEL: (020) 8940 6777 FAX: (020) 8940 3833

COOKING **5**
MODERN BRITISH
£32–£63

This stylish and friendly two-year-old restaurant, in the same group as Chez Bruce and newcomer La Trompette in London (see entries), continues to thrive in a small leafy corner near Kew Gardens Tube station. For a modern dining room, the dark chestnut floor, brown leather seats and attractive abstract pictures strike a benign note, and Anthony Boyd's cooking takes a similarly benevolent and soothing approach in the shape of oxtail ravioli, or a curried smoked haddock and coriander risotto. If 'butcher's meat' is in the minority, other choices are generous, the range taking in John Dory with spinach and ricotta crespelle, an agreeable dish of calf's liver with split peas, and braised duck leg with Morteau sausage, choucroute and pearl barley.

Trios are not uncommon, for example in scallops served three ways – ceviche-style, seared with a little salad, and as a mini-soup flavoured with langoustine – a principle that works to particularly good effect with the distinct flavours and contrasting textures of home-cured salmon served with salt-cod fishcake and grilled rare tuna. Standards, however, appear not to be consistent. Desserts are not much reported, but might include champagne and moscato trifle, or iced coconut parfait with caramelised banana. Service is pleasant and efficient. An interesting range of dessert wines is listed on the menu to complement puddings, and the main list – an exciting mixture of classy global bins and more moderately priced but characterful bottlings – offers more opportunities to choose by the glass. House wines come in at £13.50.

CHEF: Anthony Boyd PROPRIETOR: Larkbrace Ltd OPEN: all week L 12 to 2.30, Mon to Sat D 7 (6.30 Fri and Sat) to 10.30 CLOSED: Christmas MEALS: Set L £17.50 (2 courses) to £19.50, Set D £23.50 (2 courses) to £25 SERVICE: 12.5% (optional), card slips closed CARDS: Amex, Delta, MasterCard, Switch, Visa DETAILS: 60 seats. Private parties: 70 main room. Children's helpings. No babies at D. No cigars/pipes in dining room. No music. Air-conditionedKew Gardens

Report forms are at the back of the book; write a letter if you prefer; or email us at goodfoodguide@which.net

KEYSTON Cambridgeshire map 6

Pheasant Inn

Loop Road, Keyston PE28 0RE
TEL: (01832) 710241 FAX: (01832) 710340
on B663, 1m S of junction with A14

COOKING **5**
MODERN EUROPEAN/BRITISH
£23–£55

The Pheasant's handy location close to the A14 does not go unappreciated by travellers, who also value the contribution of a thatched roof, log fire, stuffed pheasants and farming paraphernalia. Like other members of the Huntsbridge Group (the Old Bridge Hotel at Huntingdon, the Three Horseshoes at Madingley, and the Falcon at Fotheringhay), this one thrives on a mixture of owner/chef autonomy and a relaxed approach to eating: the same menu is available throughout, and one or two courses are as acceptable as three or four.

Italy provides a fair measure of inspiration on the user-friendly carte – a risotto might combine wild mushrooms with Jerusalem artichoke and truffle cream for example – but there is no shortage of bright yet appealing ideas. Roast skate wing comes with oxtail polenta, while foie gras has been served with a scallop and bacon salad with Vin Santo and orange dressing. Equally vigorous desserts might include a tarte Tatin of pineapple infused with lemon grass, chilli and vanilla, and served with coconut ice cream. Snacks and simpler dishes are also available, and service is efficient and helpful. Variety and value are keys to the well-thought-out wine list, which offers a wide and lively choice under £20. It starts with 16 characterful house wines from £11 a bottle and moves to a 'top-class' selection with moderate mark-ups.

CHEF: Clive Dixon PROPRIETOR: Huntsbridge Ltd OPEN: all week 12 to 2, 6.30 to 10 (7 to 9.30 Sun) CLOSED: D 25 and 26 Dec, D 1 Jan MEALS: alc (main courses £9 to £17.50). Set L Mon to Sat £9.90 (2 courses) to £13.50 SERVICE: not inc CARDS: Amex, Delta, Diners, MasterCard, Switch, Visa DETAILS: 90 seats. 24 seats outside. Private parties: 35 main room. Car park. Vegetarian meals. Children's helpings. No smoking in 1 dining room. No music

KING'S CLIFFE Northamptonshire map 6

King's Cliffe House

31 West Street, King's Cliffe PE8 6XB
TEL: (01780) 470172 FAX: (0870) 1268588
EMAIL: kchr@onetel.net.uk

COOKING **4**
MODERN EUROPEAN
£25–£42

Feeling like a private house – which it is, apart from four nights a week – King's Cliffe is welcoming, pleasant and comfortable. Meals start in the lounge with drinks, good olives (marinated in-house and now bottled for sale) and a look at the weekly-changing menu, which typically offers five choices per course. Working within the limitations of their small scale, the proprietors exploit the region for the best materials they can find, using a butcher with a small abattoir, and buying additive-free meat (Dexter beef and Gloucester Old Spot pork) from local farmers. Seasonal ingredients are to the fore, poultry and eggs are free-range, game is from round about, and some mushrooms are gathered in a nearby wood.

The food is presented straightforwardly, starting maybe with a soup (of watercress, squash and sweet potato for one summer visitor), a twice-baked soufflé suissesse (perhaps Ticklemore goats' cheese and wild garlic), or a plate of assorted charcuterie or fish. Main courses ring the changes, depending on circumstances: steamed weever with a brown shrimp sauce one night, the same fish grilled with basil and Sauternes sauce another. Likewise, loin of local lamb might come with a St George's mushroom sauce, or with a cauliflower purée. British cheeses offer an alternative to caramelised rice pudding with roasted rhubarb, or vanilla pannacotta with apricots and peaches in Amaretto syrup. Service from Andrew Wilshaw has been judged both 'slow' and 'impeccable', and the owners take pride in their wine pricing 'to encourage better drinking', an example of which is Western Australia's Cape Mentelle Semillon-Sauvignon at £16.75. The half-bottle selection is particularlyimpressive, now featuring over 50 examples spanning the globe, and pudding wines, both white and red, are a speciality. Prices start at £9.95.

CHEFS/PROPRIETORS: Emma Jessop and Andrew Wilshaw OPEN: Wed to Sat D only 7 to 9.15 CLOSED: 2 weeks autumn, Christmas, 2 weeks spring MEALS: alc (main courses £11 to £14.50) SERVICE: net prices CARDS: none DETAILS: 20 seats. Private parties: 16 main room. Car park. Vegetarian meals. Children's helpings. No smoking in dining room. No music

KINGTON Herefordshire **map 5**

▲ Penrhos Court

Kington HR5 3LH
TEL: (01544) 230720 FAX: (01544) 230754
EMAIL: martin@penrhos.co.uk
WEB SITE: www.penrhos.co.uk
on A44, ½m E of Kington

COOKING **3**
MEDITERRANEAN
£44–£54

If the location is appealing – not far from Hereford, Ludlow, Hay-on-Wye, and close to good walking country – the setting is captivating: a renovated 700-year-old black and white farmstead with stone flag floors, log fires, a great medieval cruck hall, and a whole Elizabethan wing. What animates the entire operation is a long-standing commitment to healthy organic eating. Vegetarians can indulge themselves with lentils, salads, tofu, polenta and the like, and special diets are willingly catered for, while carnivores may find themselves drawn to an offering of chicken (served perhaps with harissa and rösti) or fish (grilled sea bass with ginger pak choi). Those who like a lot of salt may find themselves at a disadvantage. Doubts have been aired about value for money, but not about baking skills (the bread is first-rate, and sticky toffee pudding is a light and airy version), while the amiable and helpful Martin Griffiths comes in for praise. Most wines on the 50-plus list are organic, and most are under £20.

CHEF: Daphne Lambert PROPRIETORS: Martin Griffiths and Daphne Lambert OPEN: all week D only 7.30 to 9.30 (10 Sat) CLOSED: Jan exc for group bookings MEALS: Set D £32.50. SERVICE: not inc, card slips closed CARDS: Amex, MasterCard, Switch, Visa DETAILS: 80 seats. 200 seats outside. Private parties: 80 main room, 20 to 80 private rooms. Car park. Vegetarian meals. Children's helpings. No smoking in dining room. Wheelchair access (not WC). Occasional music ACCOMMODATION: 19 rooms, all with bath/shower. TV. Phone. B&B £65 to £110. Rooms for disabled. Baby facilities (*The Which? Hotel Guide*) (£5)

KIRKHAM Lancashire **map 8**

Cromwellian

16 Poulton Street, Kirkham PR4 2AB
TEL/FAX: (01772) 685680

COOKING **3**
MODERN BRITISH
£29–£46

Small but perfectly formed, like its seasonally changing menu, the Cromwellian sits in a 300-year-old terrace in the heart of the town. Most of the cooking has a simple domestic feel. Reliable supplies of Morecambe Bay shrimps mean these now have a permanent place among starters (potted in spiced brandy butter for 'a dash of subtle piquancy'); alternatively, French beans might be the focus of a warm salad dressed in herbed vinaigrette with bacon, croûtons and shaved Parmesan. Aberdeen Angus fillet has long been a stalwart, though its port and Stilton sauce can be a little shy, and the featured fish might be salmon, poached in white wine and served with roasted peppers. Puddings such as moist lemon cake or chocolate and hazelnut parfait tend to have fruity garnishes and a slightly indulgent dose of liqueur. The wine list, offering a broad range of well-chosen bottles at restrained prices, includes a fair range of halves; house French is £10.50.

CHEF: Josie Fawcett PROPRIETORS: Peter and Josie Fawcett OPEN: Tue to Sat D only 7 to 9 MEALS: Set D £16 (2 courses) to £19.50 SERVICE: not inc, card slips closed CARDS: Amex, Delta, MasterCard, Switch, Visa DETAILS: 30 seats. Private parties: 10 main room, 10 private room. Vegetarian meals. No music

LANGAR Nottinghamshire **map 5**

▲ Langar Hall

Langar NG13 9HG
TEL: (01949) 860559 FAX: (01949) 861045
EMAIL: langarhall-hotel@ndirect.co.uk
WEB SITE: www.langarhall.com

COOKING **4**
ENGLISH
£20–£70

Although the old house and its grounds remain immutable, regulars may notice a few changes within. Refurbishment after 33 years (including a new bar) aims to bring an end to the 'faded gentility' of the place without compromising its individuality. The English thrust of the food continues however, in the shape of Stilton fritters with Cumberland sauce, grilled Dover sole, and calf's liver with bacon and onions, although supplies now include a few of their own lambs, pigs and hens (for breakfast eggs only). Otherwise, beef, sausages and free-range poultry come from the region, fish from Brixham, and game from Belvoir Castle – perhaps saddle of venison with a peppery port sauce – while desserts take in glazed lemon tart, and hazelnut meringue. A useful house selection (starting at £10.75) precedes the main wine list, where French classics rub shoulders with well-chosen bottles from elsewhere, all at fair prices, with value and interest coming especially from southern France.

CHEFS: Toby Garratt and Chris Ansell PROPRIETOR: Imogen Skirving OPEN: all week 12 to 1.45, 7 to 9.30 (10 Sat) MEALS: alc D (main courses £13.50 to £20). Set L Mon to Sat £10 (2 courses) to £12.50, Set L Sun £22.50, Set D Mon to Thur £17.50, Set D Fri and Sat £30. Bar menu available 3 to 7 SERVICE: 5% (optional), card slips closed CARDS: Amex, Delta, Diners, MasterCard, Switch, Visa DETAILS: 60 seats. 20 seats outside. Private parties: 44 main room, 22 private room. Car park. Vegetarian meals. Children's helpings. No smoking in dining room. Wheelchair access (also WC). Occasional music ACCOMMODATION: 12 rooms, all with bath/shower. TV. Phone. Room only £75 to £185. Fishing (*The Which? Hotel Guide*) (£5)

LANGFORD BUDVILLE Somerset **map 2**

▲ Bindon Country House, Wellesley Restaurant

Langford Budville TA21 0RU
TEL: (01823) 400070 FAX: (01823) 400071
EMAIL: stay@bindon.com
WEB SITE: www.bindon.com
from B3187, 2m N of Wellington turn W for Langdon Budville; beyond village turn R for Wiveliscombe, then R again; after 1m turn right for hotel

COOKING **3**
ENGLISH COUNTRY-HOUSE
£29–£66

The bright, white, bow-fronted façade and ornate gabling rise behind a classical balustrade in the wilds of Somerset to the west of Taunton. In seven acres of gardens – a mixture of formal lawns and straggling woodland – the location is choice indeed. Patrick Roberts cooks a fixed-price country-house menu of some distinction, partnering monkfish roasted on the bone with buttered spinach and port; and chump of lamb with sarladaise potato, aubergine caviar and a rosemary sauce. Beef Wellington is not on the menu (the restaurant is named after the Duke of Wellington, who started life as Arthur Wellesley); instead, fillet steak is more likely to be served with calves' sweetbreads, fondant potato and a red wine reduction.

To finish, pears might go into a Chiboust, served with a separate compote of the fruit and coffee ice cream. Otherwise, try chocolate soufflé with orange sorbet, or a selection of cheeses with apple, celery and grapes. A fine wine list majors on France, with good selections from the Antipodes too, and opens with ten house recommendations from France, Spain and South America, starting at £13.50.

CHEF: Patrick Roberts PROPRIETORS: Lynn and Mark Jaffa OPEN: all week 12 to 1.30, 7 to 9 MEALS: Set L £14.95 (2 courses) to £16.95, Set D £29.95 SERVICE: not inc, card slips closed CARDS: Amex, Delta, Diners, MasterCard, Switch, Visa DETAILS: 50 seats. 50 seats outside. Private parties: 50 main room, 12 and 16 private rooms. Car park. Vegetarian meals. Children's helpings. No smoking in dining room. Occasional music ACCOMMODATION: 12 rooms, all with bath/shower. TV. Phone. B&B £85 to £195. Rooms for disabled. Baby facilities. Swimming pool (*The Which? Hotel Guide*) (£5)

Restaurateurs justifiably resent no-shows. If you quote a credit card number when booking, you may be liable for the restaurant's lost profit margin if you don't turn up. Always phone to cancel.

LANGHO Lancashire map 8

▲ Northcote Manor

Northcote Road, Langho BB6 8BE
TEL: (01254) 240555 FAX: (01254) 246568
EMAIL: admin@northcotemanor.com COOKING **6**
WEB SITE: www.northcotemanor.com MODERN BRITISH
on A59, 8 ½m E of M6 junction 31 £26–£77

Bordered by ancient trees, fields, meadows and a busy road junction, and now in its eighteenth year as a restaurant-with-rooms, Northcote Manor shows no sign of lowering its ambitions or resting on its laurels. Its dedication is appreciated: 'we have been many times over the years and never had a disappointing dish', claims one regular; 'uniformly excellent', adds another. The source of this contentment lies in a menu that integrates local ideas and materials with some up-to-date flourishes and a measure of comfort: a soup of Flookborough shrimps with garlic crisps and rouille, corn-fed Goosnargh chicken breast with prune risotto, mallard with celeriac samosas, or a calf's liver and sweetbread sausage.

The combination of invention and regional pride is evident in the 'unlikely but highly successful' partnership of black pudding and buttered pink trout with a mustard and watercress sauce (something of an institution, given its longevity on the menu), and in dishes with a cheese theme: a soufflé of Mrs Kirkham's Lancashire cheese with pickled beetroot to start, or apple tarte Tatin with Lancashire cheese ice cream. A cheese trolley is now in operation too. The set lunch is considered a bargain, and value can be found among the global wine selection, although quality tends to push prices over the £20 mark. Champagne-lovers have plenty to choose from, and so will those who prefer half-bottles. Five house wines, all Old World, come in at £15.

CHEF: Nigel Haworth PROPRIETORS: Craig Bancroft and Nigel Haworth OPEN: Sun to Mon L 12 to 1.30 (2 Sun), all week D 7 to 9.30 (10 Sat) CLOSED: 25 Dec, 1 Jan, bank hols MEALS: alc (main courses £18.50 to £24.50). Set L £16, Set D £25 to £40 SERVICE: 10% (optional) CARDS: Amex, Delta, MasterCard, Switch, Visa DETAILS: 90 seats. Private parties: 90 main room, 30 private room. Car park. Vegetarian meals. Children's helpings. Jacket and tie. No smoking in dining room. Wheelchair access (not WC). Music ACCOMMODATION: 14 rooms, all with bath/shower. TV. Phone. B&B £100 to £150. Rooms for disabled. Baby facilities (*The Which? Hotel Guide*)

LAVENHAM Suffolk map 6

▲ Angel £

Market Place, Lavenham CO10 9QZ
TEL: (01787) 247388 FAX: (01787) 248344
EMAIL: angellav@aol.com COOKING **1**
WEB SITE: www.lavenham.co.uk/angel MODERN BRITISH
on A1141, 6m NE of Sudbury £20–£36

One of the Guide's more venerable establishments, the Angel was first licensed more than 500 years ago. It certainly looks the part, set among the timbered medieval buildings of this pretty, ancient market town. The menu, by way of contrast, takes a contemporary route, offering above-average pub meals ranging from tuna kebab with Parmesan and basil risotto to an exotic warm salad of smoked prawns, mango and ginger. There is also likely to be roast rib of beef with Yorkshire pudding to suit traditionalists at Sunday lunch, and old-fashioned desserts like steamed syrup sponge pudding. The wine list may be fairly basic but so are prices, and around half a dozen wines are available by the glass. House selections start at £8.95.

CHEF: Mike Pursell PROPRIETORS: Roy and Anne Whitworth, and John and Val Barry OPEN: all week 12 to 2.15, 6.45 to 9.15 CLOSED: 25 and 26 Dec MEALS: alc (main courses £5.50 to £11) SERVICE: not inc, card slips closed CARDS: Amex, Delta, MasterCard, Switch, Visa DETAILS: 100 seats. 60 seats outside. Private parties: 50 main room, 14 private room. Car park. Vegetarian meals. Children's helpings. No smoking in 1 dining room. Occasional music ACCOMMODATION: 8 rooms, all with bath/shower. TV. Phone. B&B £45 to £85. Rooms for disabled. Baby facilities (*The Which? Hotel Guide*)

▲ Great House

Market Place, Lavenham CO10 9QZ
TEL: (01787) 247431 FAX: (01787) 248007 — COOKING **2**
EMAIL: info@greathouse.co.uk — FRENCH
WEB SITE: www.greathouse.co.uk — £22–£58

In its seventeenth year, this handsome restaurant-with-rooms has settled into comfortable familiarity. The fine, beamed and panelled dining room has a large inglenook, a wooden floor, and walls hung with attractive paintings from the local art gallery; in good weather diners can sit outside in a central courtyard. Régis Crépy continues to cook resolutely French food, served quite simply (at lunchtime, starters such as mussels with a heavily garlicked parsley butter). Main courses may include tender calf's liver with tarragon or well-seared marinated sea bass. Desserts run to chocolate mousse with orange sauce, and a creditable crème brûlée, while a groaning trolley brings a decent selection of cheeses from Lille market. The predominantly French wine list has a number of well-chosen bottles from £10.20 and also includes a respectable number of halves.

CHEF: Régis Crépy PROPRIETORS: Régis and Martine Crépy OPEN: Tue to Sun L 12 to 2.30, Tue to Sat D 7 to 9.30 (10 Sat) MEALS: alc Tue to Sat (main courses L £8.50 to £13, D £14 to £19). Set L £9.95 (2 courses) to £15.95, Set L Sun £19.95, Set D Tue to Sat £19.95 SERVICE: not inc CARDS: Amex, Delta, MasterCard, Switch, Visa DETAILS: 45 seats. 30 seats outside. Private parties: 60 main room. Children's helpings. No smoking in dining room. Music ACCOMMODATION: 5 rooms, all with bath/shower. TV. Phone. B&B £55 to £140. Baby facilities (*The Which? Hotel Guide*)

LEDBURY Herefordshire — **map 5**

Malthouse

NEW ENTRY

Church Lane, Ledbury HR8 1DW — COOKING **3**
TEL: (01531) 634443 FAX: (01531) 634664 — GLOBAL
£23–£45

Just off the main street, up a cobbled lane full of ancient black and white timber buildings, is a small courtyard set with wooden tables, and a creeper-covered two-storey brick-built house. It is a small operation, with a ground-floor dining room whose bare wooden tables are a pleasing mismatch. A laminated card is supplemented by a few blackboards with the day's extras (mostly fish, sourced from Cornwall), and if the kitchen has a centre of gravity it is poised somewhere between Europe and South East Asia: expect to find anything from wok-fried bream with a Vietnamese dipping sauce, to chargrilled local beef fillet with a Gorgonzola and basil sauce.

The food is simply presented without frills, for example in a starter of yellow-fin tuna wrapped in nori, covered in thin tempura-style batter, quickly deep-fried (leaving the tuna pink in the centre), and served with pickled ginger and wasabi. Timings are good, and textures are well rendered, producing another enjoyable starter of goats' cheese in filo pastry with a niçoise-style dressing, and a main course of pink breast of Hereford duck with tasty cherries in a stock and wine sauce. Desserts are a highlight, judging by a chocolate tart with a moist squidgy filling, accompanied by a poached apricot, and a light, crisp crème brûlée served with a gently honeyed rhubarb compote. Friendly, smiley staff deliver personable and efficient service, and an intelligently compiled wine list shuns big names in favour of interest and value. French and Chilean house varietals are £9.95.

CHEF: Tracy Lipton PROPRIETORS: James and Tracy Lipton OPEN: Sat L 12 to 2, Tue to Sat D 7 to 9.30; also L first Sun each month 11 to 2 CLOSED: 22 Dec to 2 Jan MEALS: alc (main courses £7 to £15.50) SERVICE: not inc, card slips closed CARDS: Delta, MasterCard, Switch, Visa DETAILS: 40 seats. 20 seats outside. Private parties: 30 main room, 14 private room. Vegetarian meals. No smoking in 1 dining room. Wheelchair access (not WC). Music

LEEDS West Yorkshire **map 8**

Brasserie Forty Four

44 The Calls, Leeds LS2 7EW COOKING **5**
TEL: (0113) 234 3232 FAX: (0113) 234 3332 MODERN EUROPEAN
EMAIL: brasserie44@onetel.net.uk £22–£47

Sepia photographs on painted brick walls, and black and silver furniture, give this long narrow space near the Corn Exchange a rather nostalgic air. As a bonus, it overlooks the canal and, despite the brasserie tag, can seem more like a restaurant. Prices are reasonable (check out the lunchtime and early evening deals) and while plates of imam bayaldi, caramelised onion tart, and smoked mackerel pâté are standard enough, a degree of invention also produces a stew of Bury black pudding (with onions and Yorkshire pudding), followed by potted rabbit pie on creamed Savoy cabbage and bacon with a red wine sauce.

In-house salting has been applied to both beef brisket, served with lentils, and Whitby cod, which comes on an aïoli of potato, niçoise olives and fennel. Vegetarian options might include a pizza topped with a poached or fried egg, and desserts can be on the large side: Elephant's Foot is a giant choux bun filled with cherry and hazelnut cream, and the fondue of Toblerone and amaretto (with biscotti and fresh fruit) is meant to be shared. An up-to-date round-the-world wine list starts at £10.65 and offers lots of choice under £20, including house Australian Chardonnay and Chilean Merlot at £13.95.

CHEF: Jeff Baker PROPRIETOR: Michael Gill OPEN: Mon to Fri L 12 to 2, on to Sat D 6 to 10.30 (11 Fri and Sat) CLOSED: bank hols MEALS: alc (main courses £9.50 to £13.50). Set L and D 6 to 7.15 £9.75 (2 courses) to £12.25 SERVICE: 10% (optional), card slips closed CARDS: Amex,

Delta, Diners, MasterCard, Switch, Visa DETAILS: 110 seats. Private parties: 110 main room, 50 private room. Vegetarian meals. Children's helpings by arrangement. No cigars/pipes in dining room. Wheelchair access (also WC). Music. Air-conditioned

Guellers

YORKSHIRE RESTAURANT OF THE YEAR

NEW ENTRY

3 York Place, Leeds LS1 2DR
TEL: (0113) 245 9922 FAX: (0113) 245 9965

COOKING **6**
FRENCH/MEDITERRANEAN
£27–£69

After months of financial difficulties, Simon Gueller eventually emerged as head chef and manager of the restaurant he set up at the end of 2000, with effective day-to-day control of the food and cooking. His return to the stoves (after leaving Rascasse; see entry below) is as welcome as everything else in this sleek, modern ground-floor dining room in a quiet side street. The aim – to produce contemporary classics with a French Mediterranean bias – is clearly evident from a menu that deals in Bayonne ham with celeriac rémoulade and truffle oil, roast sea bass with aubergine caviar, and an archetypal Mediterranean fish soup with the customary rouille, grated Gruyère and crisp croûtons. What's more, prices are considered a steal.

The food's simple and direct appeal is a product of good raw materials and intelligent handling – for example, in a layered terrine of creamy foie gras and moist confit duck bound by a sparse jelly, served with a scoop of chopped, truffle-oiled pear – and its hallmark is clear flavours. Pot-roast chicken breast, its skin scattered with blanched lemon zest, has come with spring vegetables in a dark jus and with a house speciality: a fondant potato worthy of the name. Desserts are on a par, judging by a smooth and boozy prune and armagnac ice cream, and by a light cylinder of iced parfait studded with hazelnuts, topped by a wafer-thin biscuit and served with an intensely fruity raspberry sorbet. Well-drilled service is capably overseen by friendly, knowledgeable Rena Gueller. There are wines under £20 on the well-sourced list (a short house selection starts at £12.50), but prices rise steeply thereafter.

CHEF: Simon Gueller PROPRIETOR: Foilmark Ltd OPEN: Tue to Sat 12 to 2, 6.30 to 10 (10.30 Fri and Sat) MEALS: Set L £12.50 (2 courses) to £25.50, Set D £19.50 (2 courses) to £25.50 SERVICE: 10% (optional), card slips closed CARDS: Amex, Delta, MasterCard, Switch, Visa DETAILS: 52 seats. Private parties: 52 main room. No cigars/pipes in dining room. Wheelchair access (also WC). Music. Air-conditioned

Fourth Floor

Harvey Nichols, 107–111 Briggate,
Leeds LS1 6AZ
TEL: (0113) 204 8000 FAX: (0113) 204 8080
WEB SITE: www.harveynichols.com

COOKING **4**
MODERN BRITISH
£27–£54

Climb to the top floor, walk through the mini-food hall, and (on a busy lunchtime) queue for a small, square, blue-topped table. A maître d' enquires solicitously how many people, smoking or non, and wafts you through the room, while a waiter brings menus and bread. There is plenty to look at – rooftops, a long bar, kitchen activity, customers of all ages – while choosing from the carte or daily set-price menu (go before 7pm for best value). This is not ambitious or tricksy food, just well conceived, and pitched at a level that the kitchen can handle with ease.

Regional input – fish and shellfish from Whitby, meat from Ilkley, cheeses from the Dales, preserves from Harrogate – is turned into varied modern brasserie fare, taking in homely, unadorned, sticky oxtail with horseradish mash, comforting foie gras, and maybe Cajun-spiced ribeye steak. There is nothing outlandish, and vegetarians do well: falafel comes with roast aubergine and tsatsiki, and a wedge of shortcrust tart contrasts the sweetness of caramelised onion with the sharpness of feta cheese. Finish maybe with chocolate cake and pistachio ice cream; note that, although service is included, the credit card slip has space for more; and drink from a short but sharp and sensibly priced wine list.

CHEF: Richard Allen PROPRIETOR: Harvey Nichols & Co OPEN: all week L 12 to 3 (4 Sat and Sun), Thur to Sat D 5.30 (7 Sat) to 10 CLOSED: 25 and 26 Dec, 1 Jan, Easter Sun MEALS: alc (main courses £10 to £16). Set L £13 (2 courses) to £16, Set D Thur and Fri 5.30 to 7 £10.95 (2 courses) to £18, Set D Thur and Fri 7 to 10 £15 (2 courses) to £18. Bar menu available SERVICE: 10% (optional), card slips closed CARDS: Amex, Delta, Diners, MasterCard, Switch, Visa DETAILS: 80 seats. 16 seats outside. Private parties: 90 main room. Vegetarian meals. Children's helpings. No-smoking area. Wheelchair access (also WC). Music. Air-conditioned

Leodis

Victoria Mill, 4 The Embankment, Sovereign Street, Leeds LS1 4BJ
TEL: (0113) 242 1010 FAX: (0113) 243 0432
WEB SITE: www.leodis.co.uk

COOKING **4**
BRASSERIE/MODERN BRITISH
£27–£52

Black furniture, glass 'bricks' to hide work stations, careful lighting and a view across to the city's waterways help to define the character of this busy brasserie. The large space is divided up to make it feel more user-friendly, and the generous menu's wide appeal is evident in a show of brasserie staples from bacon and poached egg salad, via ham hock and foie gras terrine with piccalilli, to Cumberland sausage and mash. The style is bold, good-quality materials are evident, and it would take a very fussy eater not to find something of interest, given asparagus and oyster mushroom frittata, monkfish tart, steak pudding, and a spring onion and Cheddar soufflé omelette. For best value, try the set-price deal: a short selection of items from the carte, ending perhaps with strawberry parfait, or chocolate marquise. The wine list is full of excitement for the adventurous – there's Mourvèdre from Australia and Muscat from Israel – with the more novel offerings joined by classics from France and California. Ten by the glass and over 20 half-bottles encourage further exploration. Prices are fair, with around 50 under £20 and six house wines at £12.95 each.

CHEF: Steve Kendell PROPRIETORS: Martin Spalding, Steve Kendell and Phil Richardson OPEN: Mon to Fri L 12 to 2, Mon to Sat D 6 to 10 (11 Sat) CLOSED: 26 Dec, L bank hols MEALS: alc (main courses £9.50 to £16). Set L and D (exc after 7.15 Sat) £15.95 SERVICE: 10% (optional), card slips closed CARDS: Amex, Delta, Diners, MasterCard, Switch, Visa DETAILS: 180 seats. 60 seats outside. Private parties: 180 main room. Car park at D. Vegetarian meals. Children's helpings. Wheelchair access (also WC). Music

Pool Court at 42

44 The Calls, Leeds LS2 7EW COOKING **7**
TEL: (0113) 244 4242 FAX: (0113) 234 3332 CLASSIC FRENCH/MODERN BRITISH
EMAIL: poolcourt@onetel.net.uk £33–£78

'What a pleasure to eat in a thoroughly grown-up restaurant that serves confident, classically derived food in a tranquil modern dining room, discussed and delivered by correct but not formal staff.' So ran one endorsement of this intimate and sophisticated restaurant down by the city's watery centre. Despite their timeless foundations, ever-changing menus deliver fresh ideas, from lobster consommé containing a silken raviolo of brown and white crab meat, with a jug of thick pesto on the side, to roast loin of hare on braised red cabbage. Typical of the simple, accomplished and (despite some luxurious ingredients) unshowy food at which Jeff Baker excels is a seductively rich terrine of duck foie gras with a plump Agen prune and a light Sauternes jelly.

Main courses may sound complex, but there is no feeling of over-elaboration: charred fillet of veal with caramelised sweetbreads is served with a red wine and morel risotto, and squab pigeon, jointed into four, is simply roasted to rosy pinkness and served with a strewing of vegetables. Desserts run from revivalist crêpe suzette, via a speciality chocolate plate, to a puff-pastry tarte fine of mango slices with a smooth-sharp passion-fruit ice cream. There is no doubting the kitchen's skills, although under-par dishes can slip through the net. Bread, appetisers and pre-desserts are first-rate, however, and a wide-ranging list winkles out some interesting wines at all price levels. House white is a New Zealand Sauvignon Blanc, red is a Chilean Cabernet Sauvignon.

CHEF: Jeff Baker PROPRIETOR: Michael Gill OPEN: Mon to Fri L 12 to 2, Mon to Sat D 7 to 10 (10.30 Fri and Sat) CLOSED: bank hols MEALS: Set L £14.50 (2 courses) to £50, Set D £25 (2 courses) to £50 SERVICE: 10%, card slips closed CARDS: Amex, Delta, Diners, MasterCard, Switch, Visa DETAILS: 38 seats. 18 seats outside. Private parties: 38 main room. Vegetarian meals. Children's helpings. No children under 3. No smoking in dining room. Wheelchair access (also WC). Music. Air-conditioned

Rascasse

Canal Wharf, Water Lane, Leeds LS11 5PS COOKING **4**
TEL: (0113) 244 6611 FAX: (0113) 244 0736 MODERN ANGLO-FRENCH
WEB SITE: www.rascasse-leeds.co.uk £28–£61

The polished wood floors and plain walls of this warehouse conversion overlooking the canal basin convey the feel of a businesslike brasserie, as does its contemporary menu. Daily supplies of fish from Lancashire, Yorkshire and Devon might run to roast John Dory with tortellini of king prawn, while the richer end of the spectrum is explored in some of the hare dishes that now appear, perhaps roast saddle with a pie of leg meat and foie gras, braised cabbage and a quince sauce.

Although the food may not be ground-breaking, it does run to some enterprising ideas – such as seared foie gras with pastilla, lemon confit and Banyuls syrup – and it is impressively and pleasingly cooked: reporters have praised Bayonne ham with goats' cheese and dressed rocket ('fancy name for ham and cheese salad,' says a no-nonsense northerner), magret of duck, and beef medallions piled with tasty oxtail. Extra vegetables include grilled field mushrooms with garlic butter, and 'hand-cut' chips with fleur de sel and malt vinegar.

Desserts entice all comers, offering rum baba with coconut risotto and a rum and raisin ice cream, or old-fashioned treacle tart. Staff are attentive, service is well-judged, and the French-led wine list offers good choice at moderate prices, many under £15. There are lively alternatives to the standards, and half-bottles and ten by the glass encourage experiment.

CHEF: John Lyons PROPRIETOR: Nigel Jolliffe OPEN: Mon to Fri L 12 to 2, Mon to Sat D 6.30 to 10 CLOSED: 1 week after Christmas, bank hol Mons MEALS: alc (main courses £12.50 to £18.50). Set L Mon to Fri and Set D Mon to Sat till 7.30 £14 (2 courses) to £18 SERVICE: not inc CARDS: Amex, Delta, Diners, MasterCard, Switch, Visa DETAILS: 100 seats. 20 seats outside. Private parties: 60 main room. Car park. Vegetarian meals. Wheelchair access (also WC). No music. Air-conditioned

Salvo's £

115 Otley Road, Headingley, Leeds LS6 3PX
TEL: (0113) 275 5017 FAX: (0113) 278 9452 COOKING **2**
EMAIL: bookings@salvos.co.uk MODERN MEDITERRANEAN/ITALIAN
WEB SITE: www.salvos.co.uk £17–£39

With pale floors, ochre walls and open-plan layout, this Leeds stalwart doesn't show its age. Popularity means it can be noisy, and queues are frequent (no bookings at dinner, so it pays to come early). Pizza and pasta are the lead items, the latter – such as lasagne al forno and ravioli al formaggio – sticking closer to tradition than the pizzas. These might include 'pizza carnevale' (with sausage, meatball, chicken, ham, pepperoni, garlic butter and double cheese), or 'pizza Kiev' (a folded pizza stuffed with chicken, ham, garlic butter and cheese). Otherwise there might be stuffed vegetables, grilled salmon, or escalope of veal, with lemon meringue brûlée to finish. Salvo's offers good value, with welcoming, child-friendly staff; bargain hunters, note the new two-course lunch at £5. An unsurprising wine list starts at £10, and only one of its 24 wines is over £20.

CHEF: Michael Leggiero PROPRIETORS: the Dammone family OPEN: all week 12 to 2, 6 to 10.45 (11 Fri/Sat) MEALS: alc (main courses £6.50 to £13). Set L Mon to Sat £5 (2 courses) SERVICE: not inc CARDS: Amex, Delta, Diners, MasterCard, Switch, Visa DETAILS: 60 seats. Vegetarian meals. Children's helpings. Music. Air-conditioned (£5)

Sous le Nez en Ville

The Basement, Quebec House, Quebec Street, COOKING **4**
Leeds LS1 2HA MODERN EUROPEAN
TEL: (0113) 244 0108 FAX: (0113) 245 0240 £20–£52

The longevity of this bustling basement restaurant-cum-bar – after 11 years it is still a city-centre crowd-puller – testifies to the consistency and quality of its food, service and plentiful choice. It is strictly bistro: no tablecloths, just paper napkins, tiled floors and plain walls with bright framed posters. Service is efficient, pleasant and observant, and there is a good-value early-evening menu.

Andrew Carter's repertoire is cosmopolitan. The main carte is divided between a stand-alone fish menu of a half-dozen starters and mains, and a meatier medley of some ten choices at each level, including vegetarian options. Plundering both menus might result in tempura of king prawns with sweet chilli jam, followed by roast best-end of lamb with Mediterranean-style potatoes and rosemary jus. Desserts again mix familiar and exotic, with pear and caramel tart Tatin, or Moroccan baklava with fresh mint yoghurt and vanilla ice cream.

Wines take in lesser-known examples form Spain, serious Australians (some surprisingly mature vintages), and other rarities such as England's reputedly best sparkler, from Nyetimber in Sussex. 'Personal recommendations' are well worth pondering, then the broad house selection cuts to value, starting at £9.95.

CHEF: Andrew Carter PROPRIETORS: Robert Chamberlain and Andrew Carter OPEN: Mon to Sat 12 to 2, 6 to 10 (11 Fri and Sat) CLOSED: 25 and 26 Dec, bank hol Mon, Good Fri L MEALS: alc (main courses £8 to £14.50). Set L Sat £16.95, Set D 6 to 7.30 £16.95 SERVICE: not inc CARDS: Amex, Delta, MasterCard, Switch, Visa DETAILS: 85 seats. Private parties: 20 private room. Vegetarian meals. Music. Air-conditioned (£5)

LEVERTON Lincolnshire **map 6**

Old Barn

Main Road, Leverton PE22 0AU
TEL: (01205) 870215
EMAIL: bookingatoldbarn.co.uk
WEB SITE: www.oldbarn.co.uk

COOKING **2**
SEAFOOD
£17–£53

This old farmhouse sets an appropriate tone in its warren of low-ceilinged interconnected rooms with a décor of piscatorial prints and tanks of fish set into the walls. Non-fish eaters are catered for with a small selection of steaks and other meat dishes, but fish and seafood are the kitchen's main concern: oysters are from a local supplier and the rest comes from Grimsby or Birmingham. Bold flavour combinations are a primary characteristic of the cooking style, whether you choose something traditional like bouillabaisse or pan-fried trout with bacon and garlic, or a more modern dish such as flash-fried shark with mild curry sauce, or spicy crab cakes with lime, mayonnaise and ginger. The set-price menu attracts one or two supplements (lobster for example) but otherwise represents good value. The wine list is understandably stronger in whites than reds; half a dozen house choices get the ball rolling at £9.45 (£1.90 a glass), and prices remain low throughout.

CHEF: Tony Coates PROPRIETORS: Tony Coates and Elaine Martin OPEN: Tue to Fri and Sun L 12 to 2, Tue to Sun D 6.30 to 9 (booking advisable most sessions; phone to check) MEALS: Set L and D £17.50 (2 courses) to £19.50, Set L Sun £6.95 (2 courses) to £8.25 (2 courses) SERVICE: not inc; 5% surcharge for credit cards CARDS: Diners, MasterCard, Switch, Visa DETAILS: 40 seats. Private parties: 25 main room, 10 private room. Car park. No children under 12. Wheelchair access (not WC). Music

See inside the front cover for an explanation of the symbols used at the tops of entries.

KEY MAP

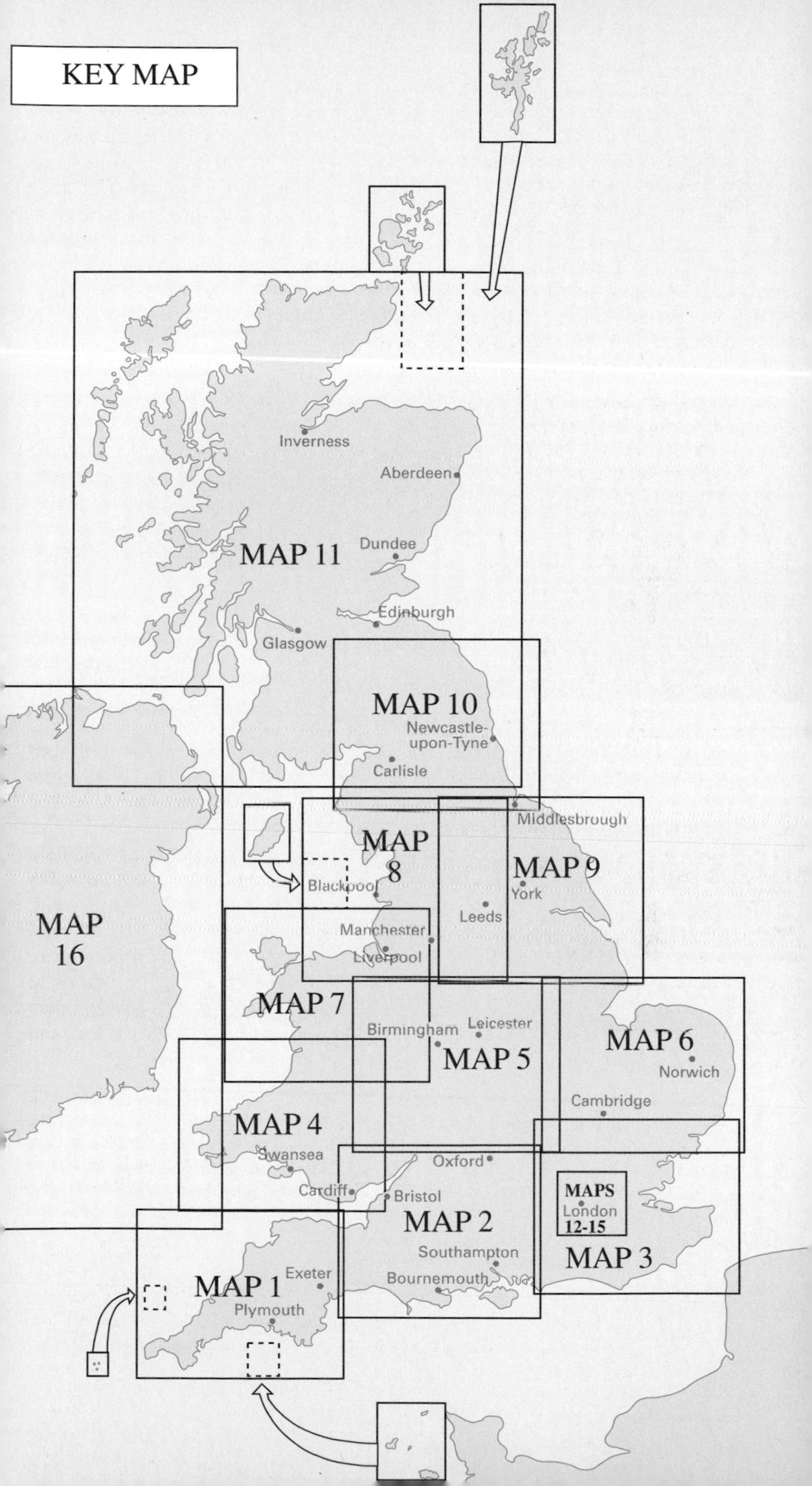

MAP 11
Inverness
Aberdeen
Dundee
Edinburgh
Glasgow
MAP 10
Newcastle-upon-Tyne
Carlisle
Middlesbrough
MAP 8
MAP 9
Blackpool
York
Leeds
Manchester
Liverpool
MAP 16
MAP 7
Birmingham
Leicester
MAP 5
MAP 6
Norwich
Cambridge
MAP 4
Swansea
Oxford
Cardiff
Bristol
MAP 2
MAPS
London
12-15
Southampton
MAP 3
Exeter
Bournemouth
MAP 1
Plymouth

MAP 1

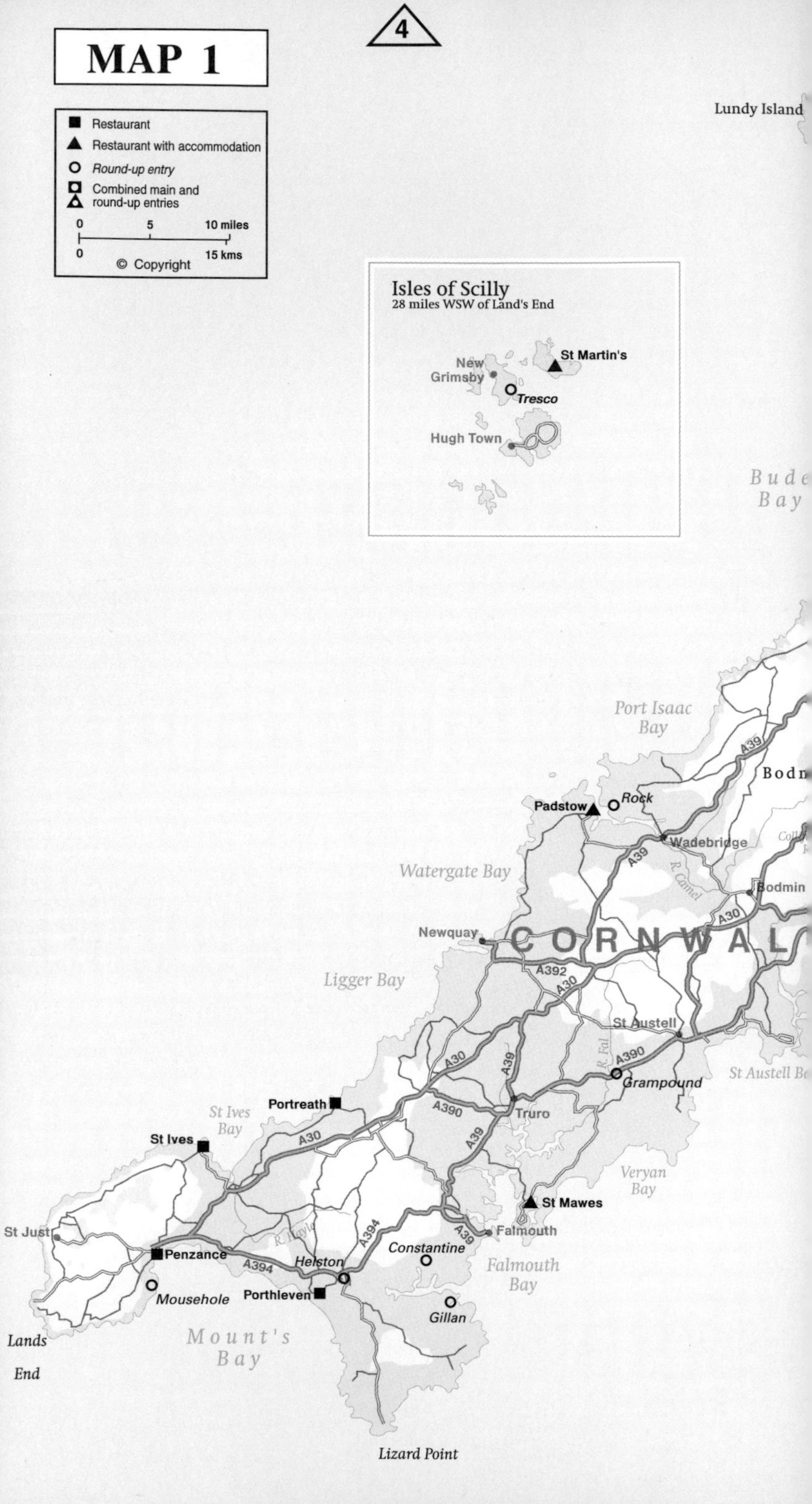
4
Restaurant
Restaurant with accommodation
Round-up entry
Combined main and round-up entries
0 5 10 miles
0 15 kms
© Copyright
Lundy Island
Isles of Scilly
28 miles WSW of Land's End
St Martin's
New Grimsby
Tresco
Hugh Town
Bude Bay
Port Isaac Bay
Bodm
Padstow
Rock
Wadebridge
Watergate Bay
R. Camel
Bodmin
A39
A30
Newquay
CORNWAL
A392
Ligger Bay
St Austell
R. Fal
A390
Grampound
St Austell Ba
Portreath
St Ives Bay
St Ives
Truro
Veryan Bay
St Mawes
St Just
Falmouth
R. Hayle
A394
Constantine
Penzance
Helston
Falmouth Bay
Mousehole
Porthleven
Gillan
Mount's Bay
Lands End
Lizard Point

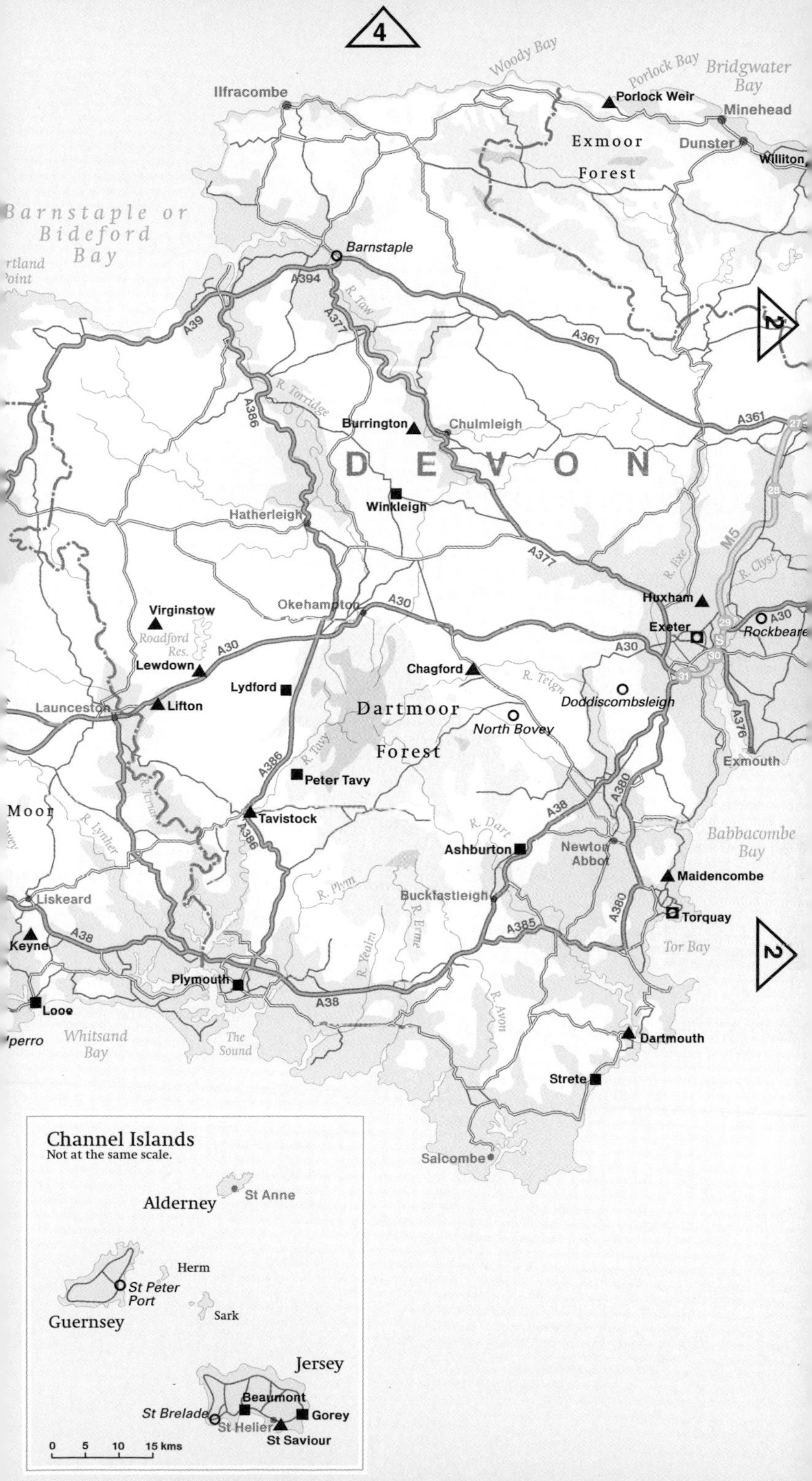

4
Woody Bay
Porlock Bay
Bridgwater Bay
Ilfracombe
Porlock Weir
Minehead
Exmoor Forest
Dunster
Williton
Barnstaple or Bideford Bay
Barnstaple
A394
R. Taw
A377
A39
A361
2
R. Torridge
A386
Burrington
Chulmleigh
A361
DEVON
Winkleigh
Hatherleigh
A377
R. Exe
M5
R. Clyst
Huxham
Okehampton
A30
Virginstow
Roadford Res.
A30
Exeter
A30
Rockbeare
Lewdown
Chagford
R. Teign
Lydford
Doddiscombsleigh
Launceston
Lifton
Dartmoor Forest
North Bovey
A376
R. Tavy
A386
Exmouth
Peter Tavy
A380
Moor
R. Tamar
R. Lynher
Tavistock
A38
R. Dart
A386
Babbacombe Bay
Ashburton
Newton Abbot
Maidencombe
Liskeard
R. Plym
Buckfastleigh
R. Erme
Torquay
Keyne
A38
A385
A380
Tor Bay
2
R. Yealm
Plymouth
R. Avon
Looe
A38
Dartmouth
Whitsand Bay
The Sound
Strete
Salcombe
Channel Islands
Not at the same scale.
Alderney
St Anne
Herm
St Peter Port
Guernsey
Sark
Jersey
Beaumont
St Brelade
Gorey
St Helier
St Saviour
0 5 10 15 kms

4
Crickhowell
Llandewi Skirrid
5
Drybrook
Monmouth
GLOUCESTERSHIRE
BLAENAU GWENT
Merthyr Tydfil
TORFAEN
Clytha
Whitebrook
Pontypool
MONMOUTHSHIRE
Tredunnock
CAERPHILLY
R. Usk
Chepstow
Cotswold
Tetb
Bassaleg
NEWPORT
New Severn Crossing
SOUTH GLOUCESTERSHIRE
Nor
CARDIFF
Cardiff
Portishead
Mouth of the Severn
BRISTOL
Bristol
Castle Combe
Chippen
Colerne
VALE OF GLAMORGAN
N.W. SOMERSET
Bath
Hunstrete
Weston-Super-Mare
Hinton Charterhouse
Holt
BATH & N.E. SOMERSET
Shipham
Mendip Hills
R. Axe
Burnham-on-Sea
Bridgwater Bay
Wells
R. Brue
Shepton Mallet
Warminste
Williton
Glastonbury
Bridgwater
Bruton
R. Parrett
SOMERSET
Gillingham
Taunton
Langford Budville
Stoke-sub-Hamdon
Yeovil
Sturminster Newton
Barwick
Chard
DEVON
1
Evershot
Broadhembury
Corscombe
N. Dorset Downs
Blandf Forum
DORSET
Honiton
Beaminster
Maiden Newton
Gittisham
R. Otter
R. Axe
West Bay
Dorchester
R. Piddle
R. Frome
Lyme Bay
Sidmouth
Weymouth
Weymouth Bay
Babbacombe Bay
Bill of Portland
Restaurant
Restaurant with accommodation
Round-up entry
Combined main and round-up entries
0 5 10 miles
0 15 kms
© Copyright

Cheltenham
Lower Slaughter
Upper Slaughter
5
Woodstock
Burford
Long Crendon
Dinton
Oxford
Thame
Barnsley
Standlake
Tadpole Bridge
Great Milton
Tetsworth
Chinnor
Chiltern Hills
Cirencester
R. Thames
Buckland
Abingdon
Dorchester
Britwell Salome
OXFORDSHIRE
Didcot
Malmesbury
Ardington
Brinkworth
Swindon
Blewbury
Moulsford
3
M4
West Ilsley
Goring
Rotherfield Peppard
Yattendon
Reading
Stockcross
Marsh Benham
Kintbury
Newbury
BERKSHIRE
Rowde
Little Bedwyn
Devizes
WILTSHIRE
Old Burghclere
Salisbury Plain
Odiham
Andover
Whitchurch
A303
HAMPSHIRE
Teffont Evias
Salisbury
Winchester
3
R. Test
Petersfield
Romsey
Bishop's Waltham
Farnham
Chettle
Denmead
Stuckton
R. Avon
Southampton
Wickham
R. Beaulieu
Emsworth
Lyndhurst
Brockenhurst
Bucklers Hard
Merley
New Milton
East End
Portsmouth
Christchurch
The Solent
Seaview
Poole
Milford on Sea
Bournemouth
Poole Bay
Yarmouth
Newport
The Needles
Isle of Wight
Swanage
Ventnor
Aldhem's or Alban's Head
St Catherine's Point

MAP 2

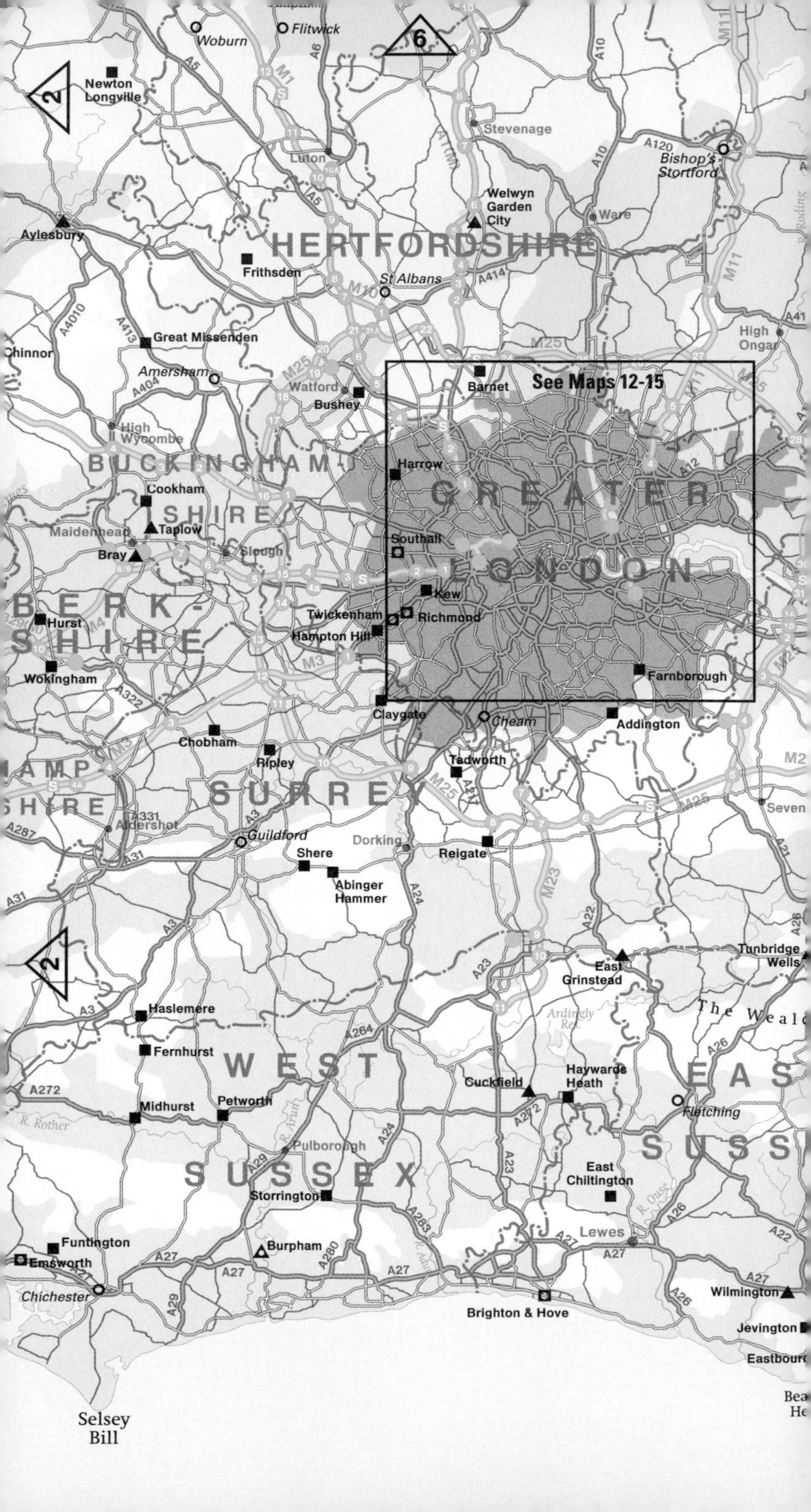

Woburn
Flitwick
6
2
Newton Longville
Luton
Stevenage
Bishop's Stortford
Welwyn Garden City
Ware
Aylesbury
HERTFORDSHIRE
Frithsden
St Albans
High Ongar
Great Missenden
Chinnor
Amersham
Watford
Bushey
Barnet
See Maps 12-15
High Wycombe
BUCKINGHAMSHIRE
Harrow
GREATER LONDON
Cookham
Taplow
Maidenhead
Bray
Slough
Southall
Kew
BERKSHIRE
Hurst
Twickenham
Richmond
Hampton Hill
Wokingham
Farnborough
Claygate
Cheam
Addington
Chobham
Ripley
Tadworth
HAMPSHIRE
SURREY
Sevenoaks
Aldershot
Guildford
Dorking
Reigate
Shere
Abinger Hammer
Tunbridge Wells
2
East Grinstead
The Weald
Ardingly Res.
Haslemere
Fernhurst
WEST
Cuckfield
Haywards Heath
EAST
Fletching
Midhurst
Petworth
R. Rother
R. Arun
Pulborough
SUSSEX
SUSSEX
East Chiltington
Storrington
R. Ouse
Lewes
Funtington
Burpham
Emsworth
R. Adur
Chichester
Wilmington
Brighton & Hove
Jevington
Eastbourne
Selsey Bill

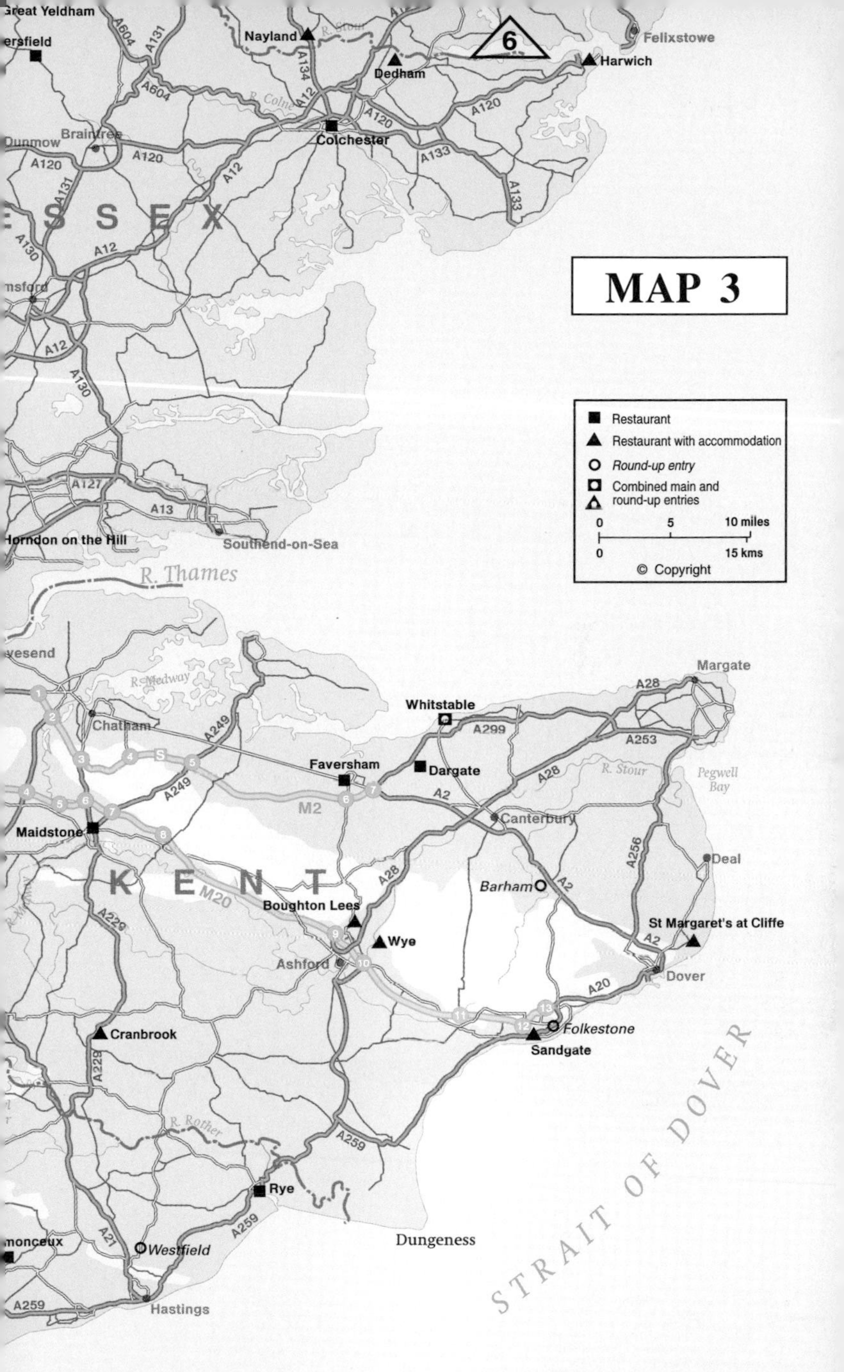

MAP 3
Restaurant
Restaurant with accommodation
Round-up entry
Combined main and round-up entries
0 5 10 miles
0 15 kms
© Copyright
6
Great Yeldham
Nayland
Felixstowe
Dedham
Harwich
Colchester
Braintree
Dunmow
ESSEX
Horndon on the Hill
Southend-on-Sea
R. Thames
R. Medway
Chatham
Maidstone
Whitstable
Faversham
Dargate
Margate
Canterbury
Pegwell Bay
Deal
Barham
St Margaret's at Cliffe
Dover
KENT
Boughton Lees
Wye
Ashford
Folkestone
Sandgate
Cranbrook
R. Rother
Rye
Dungeness
Westfield
Hastings
STRAIT OF DOVER

7

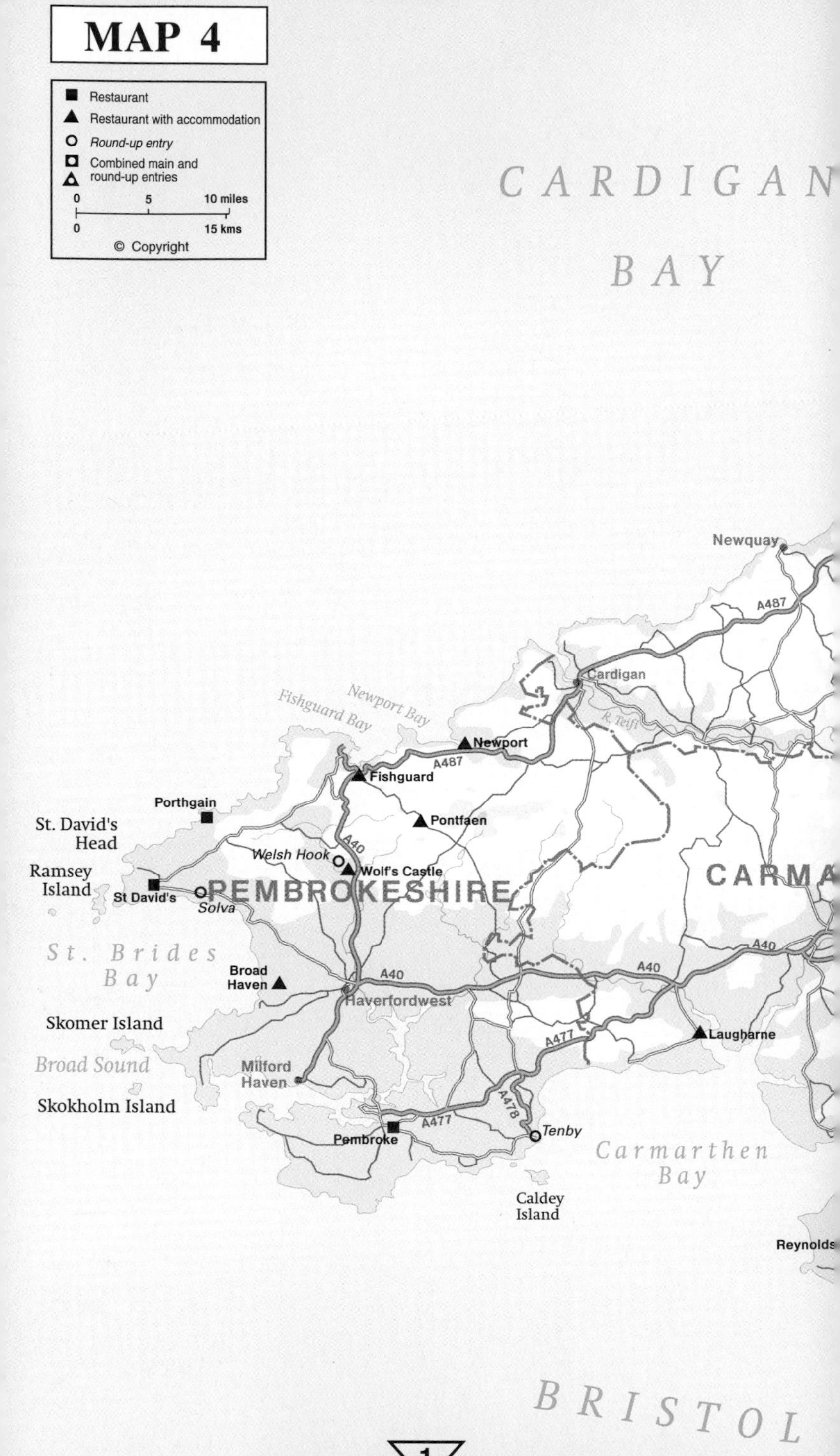
MAP 4
Restaurant
Restaurant with accommodation
Round-up entry
Combined main and round-up entries
0 5 10 miles
0 15 kms
© Copyright
CARDIGAN BAY
Newquay
A487
Cardigan
Newport Bay
Fishguard Bay
R. Teifi
Newport
A487
Fishguard
Porthgain
Pontfaen
St. David's Head
A40
Welsh Hook
Wolf's Castle
Ramsey Island
St David's
Solva
PEMBROKESHIRE
CARMA
A40
A40
St. Brides Bay
Broad Haven
A40
Haverfordwest
Skomer Island
A477
Laugharne
Broad Sound
Milford Haven
A478
Skokholm Island
Pembroke
A477
Tenby
Carmarthen Bay
Caldey Island
Reynolds
BRISTOL

1

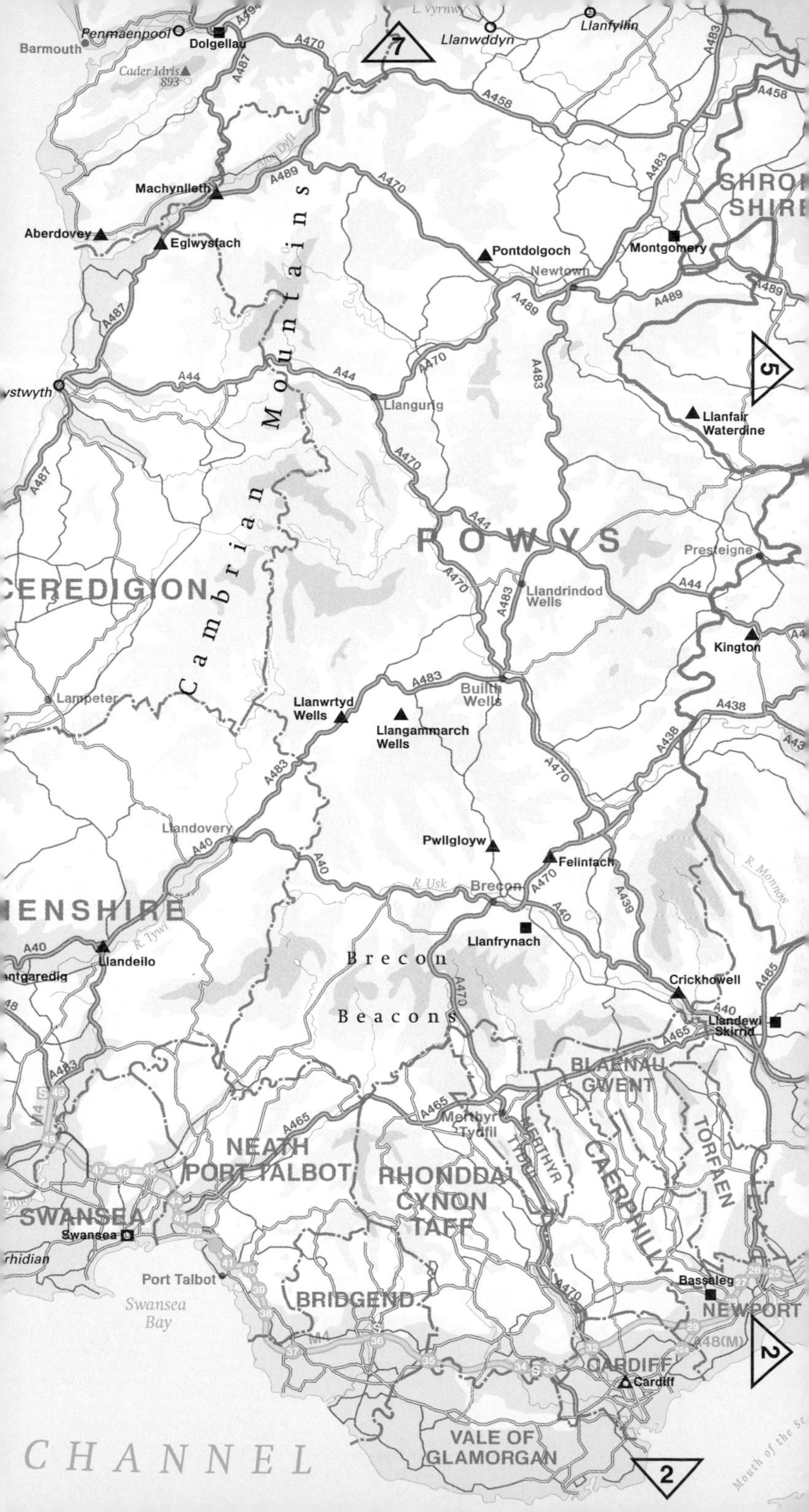

L. Vyrnwy
Penmaenpool
Dolgellau
Barmouth
Cader Idris
893
7
Llanwddyn
Llanfyllin
A470
A487
A458
A483
A489
Afon Dyfi
Machynlleth
Aberdovey
Eglwysfach
Cambrian Mountains
SHROPSHIRE
Montgomery
Pontdolgoch
Newtown
A44
Llangurig
5
Llanfair
Waterdine
POWYS
Presteigne
CEREDIGION
Llandrindod
Wells
Kington
A438
Lampeter
Builth
Wells
Llanwrtyd
Wells
Llangammarch
Wells
Llandovery
A40
Pwllgloyw
Felinfach
R. Monnow
R. Usk
Brecon
A439
HENSHIRE
R. Tywi
Llandeilo
Llanfrynach
Brecon
Beacons
Crickhowell
A465
Llandewi
Skirrid
BLAENAU
GWENT
Merthyr
Tydfil
MERTHYR
TYDFIL
CAERPHILLY
TORFAEN
NEATH
PORT TALBOT
RHONDDA
CYNON
TAFF
SWANSEA
Swansea
Port Talbot
Swansea
Bay
BRIDGEND
M4
Bassaleg
NEWPORT
A48(M)
CARDIFF
Cardiff
2
VALE OF
GLAMORGAN
CHANNEL

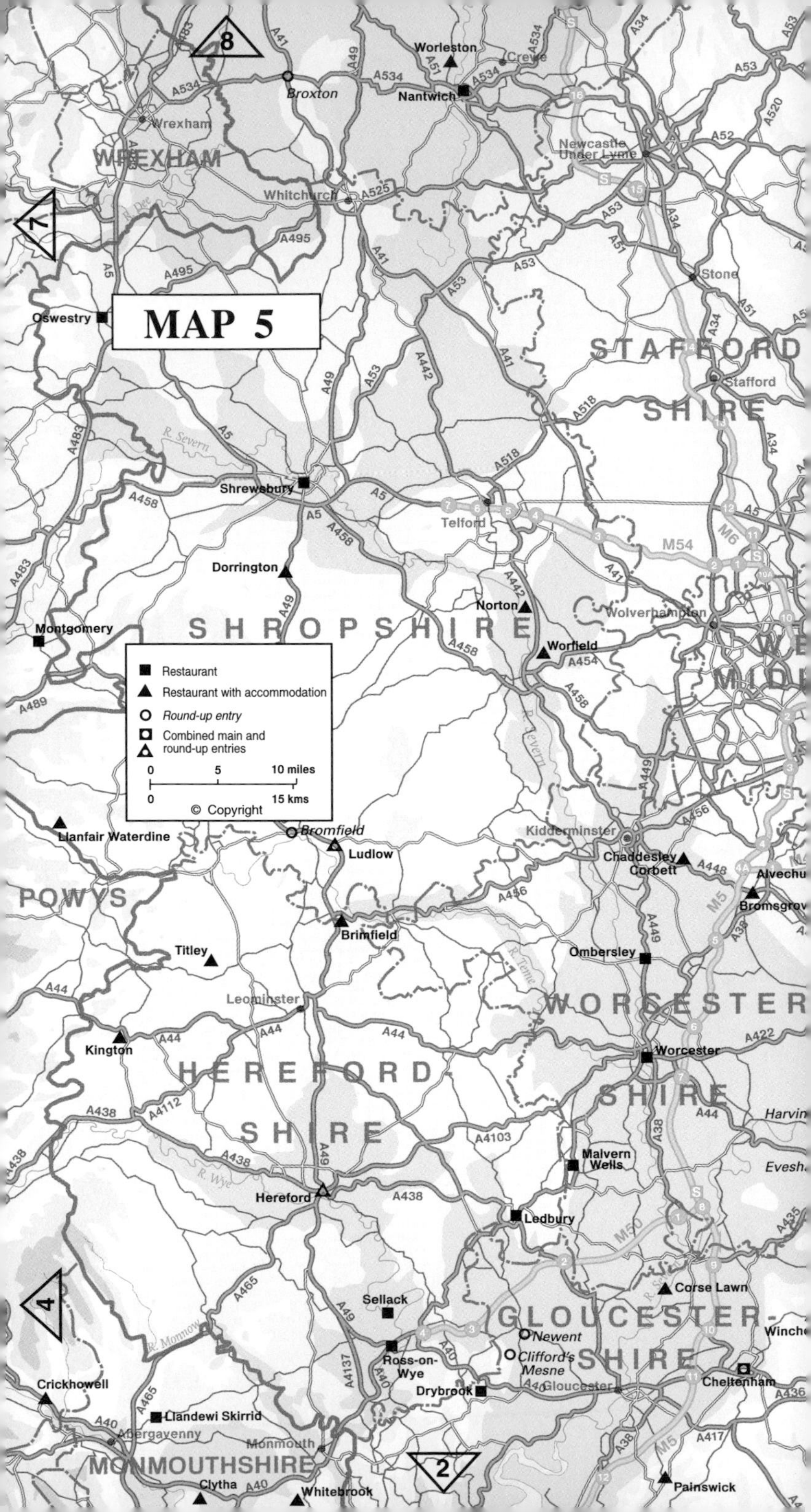

MAP 5
8
7
4
2
Restaurant
Restaurant with accommodation
Round-up entry
Combined main and round-up entries
0 5 10 miles
0 15 kms
© Copyright
Worleston
Crewe
Broxton
Nantwich
Wrexham
WREXHAM
Newcastle Under Lyme
Whitchurch
Stone
Oswestry
STAFFORD SHIRE
Stafford
Shrewsbury
Telford
Dorrington
Norton
Wolverhampton
Montgomery
SHROPSHIRE
Worfield
Llanfair Waterdine
Bromfield
Ludlow
Kidderminster
Chaddesley Corbett
Alvechurch
Bromsgrove
POWYS
Brimfield
Ombersley
Titley
Leominster
WORCESTER SHIRE
Kington
HEREFORD-SHIRE
Worcester
Harvington
Malvern Wells
Evesham
Hereford
Ledbury
Corse Lawn
Sellack
GLOUCESTER-SHIRE
Newent
Winchcombe
Ross-on-Wye
Clifford's Mesne
Cheltenham
Crickhowell
Drybrook
Gloucester
Llandewi Skirrid
Abergavenny
Monmouth
MONMOUTHSHIRE
Clytha
Whitebrook
Painswick
R. Dee
R. Severn
R. Teme
R. Wye
R. Monnow
M54
M6
M5
M50

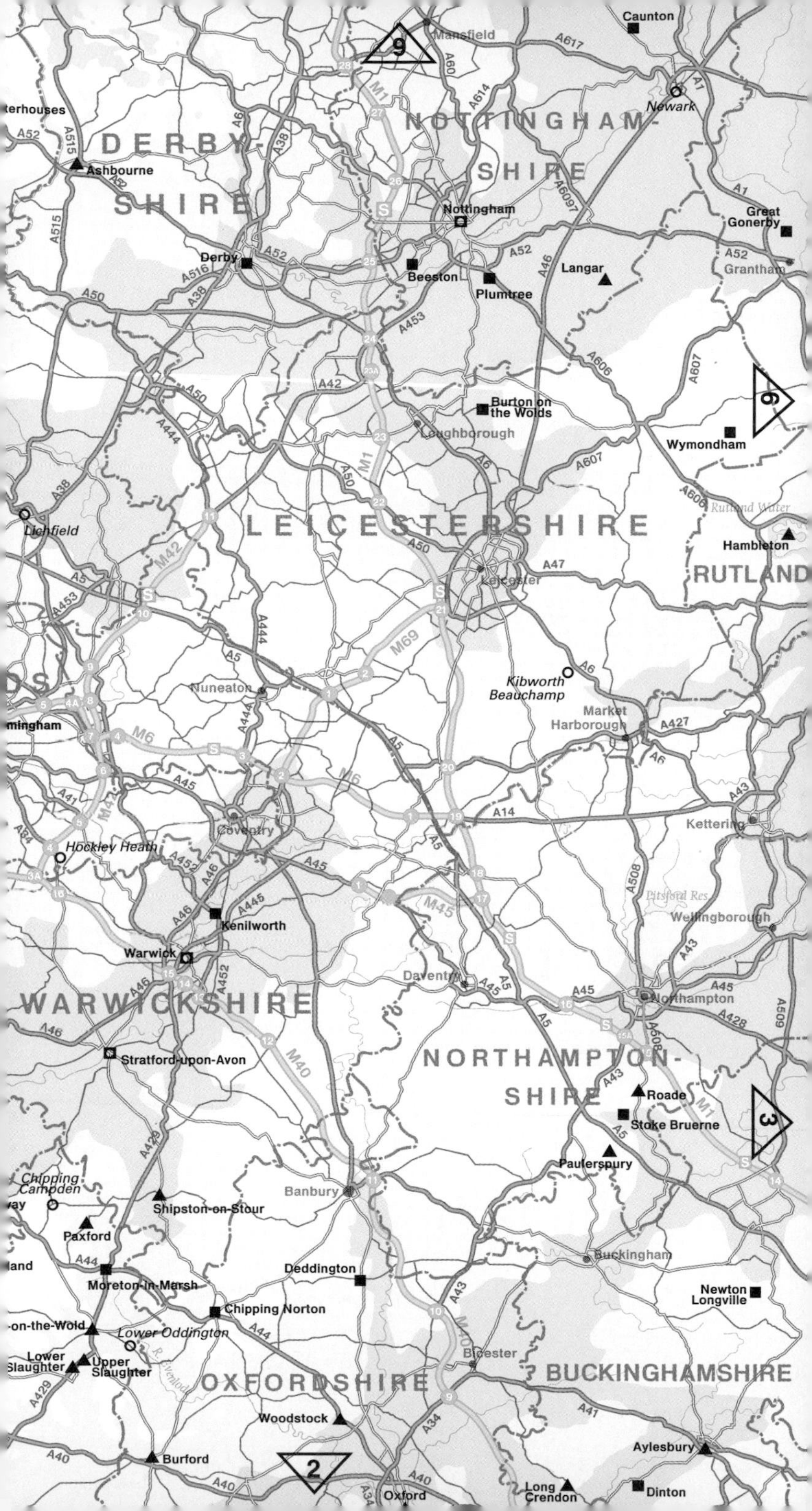

9
Mansfield
Caunton
Newark
NOTTINGHAM-
SHIRE
DERBY-
SHIRE
Ashbourne
Nottingham
Great
Gonerby
Grantham
Derby
Beeston
Plumtree
Langar
Burton on
the Wolds
Loughborough
6
Wymondham
Rutland Water
Hambleton
RUTLAND
Lichfield
LEICESTERSHIRE
Leicester
Kibworth
Beauchamp
Market
Harborough
Nuneaton
Kettering
Coventry
Hockley Heath
Pitsford Res
Wellingborough
Kenilworth
Warwick
Daventry
Northampton
WARWICKSHIRE
Stratford-upon-Avon
NORTHAMPTON-
SHIRE
Roade
Stoke Bruerne
3
Paulerspury
Chipping
Campden
Shipston-on-Stour
Banbury
Paxford
Buckingham
Deddington
Moreton-in-Marsh
Chipping Norton
Newton
Longville
Lower Oddington
R. Evenlode
Lower
Slaughter
Upper
Slaughter
Bicester
OXFORDSHIRE
BUCKINGHAMSHIRE
Woodstock
Aylesbury
Burford
2
Long
Crendon
Dinton
Oxford
M1
M6
M42
M69
M45
M40
A1
A5
A6
A14
A43
A44
A45
A46
A52

LINCOLNSHIRE
Lincoln
Horncastle
9
A158
Burgh le Marsh
Skegness
Steeping R.
A46
A15
A17
R. Witham
A16
A52
Leverton
Boston
The Wash
Great Gonerby
Grantham
A1
5
R. Welland
Gedney Dyke
A151
King's Lynn
Clipsham
A101
A47
A10
A134
RUTLAND
A606
Stamford
Hambleton
Rutland Water
A6003
Wisbech
A1101
A1122
Great Ouse
R. Nene
Peterborough
A43
King's Cliffe
Fotheringhay
A141
A1(M)
Littleport
A6116
A605
A142
Sutton Gault
Ely
Witchford
Kettering
Keyston
A14
A6
CAMBRIDGE-SHIRE
Huntingdon
Brampton
Grafham Water
Wellingborough
A45
A509
R. Cam
Newmarket
Madingley
A428
Cambridge
Milton Ernest
Little Shelford
A11
Bedford
BEDFORDSHIRE
Melbourn
A505
A604
Biggleswade
Houghton Conquest
Saffron Walden
ESSEX
M1
Flitwick
Woburn
A5
M11
Wethersfie
Stevenage
3
Luton
A120
Bishop's Stortford
Lid

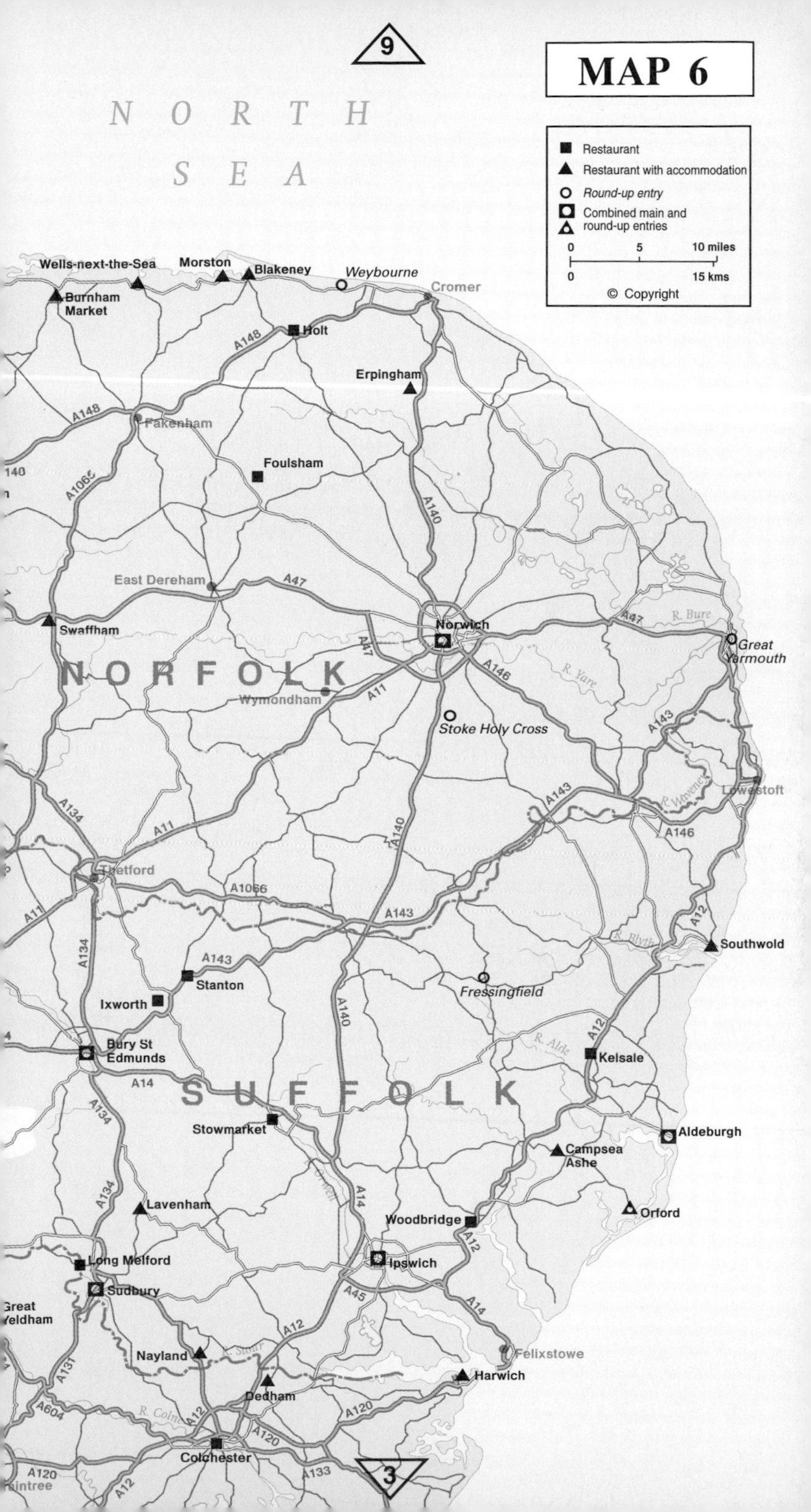

9
MAP 6
NORTH SEA
Restaurant
Restaurant with accommodation
Round-up entry
Combined main and round-up entries
0
5
10 miles
0
15 kms
© Copyright
Wells-next-the-Sea
Morston
Blakeney
Weybourne
Cromer
Burnham Market
Holt
A148
Erpingham
A148
Fakenham
Foulsham
A1067
A140
East Dereham
A47
Swaffham
Norwich
A47
R. Bure
Great Yarmouth
A47
NORFOLK
Wymondham
A11
A146
R. Yare
Stoke Holy Cross
A143
Lowestoft
R. Waveney
A143
A146
A134
A11
A140
Thetford
A1066
A143
A11
A134
A12
R. Blyth
Southwold
A143
Stanton
Ixworth
Fressingfield
A140
R. Alde
A12
Kelsale
Bury St Edmunds
A14
SUFFOLK
A134
Stowmarket
Aldeburgh
Campsea Ashe
R. Orwell
A14
A134
Lavenham
Orford
Woodbridge
A12
Long Melford
Ipswich
Sudbury
A45
A14
Great Yeldham
A12
Nayland
R. Stour
Felixstowe
A131
Harwich
Dedham
A604
R. Colne
A12
A120
A120
Colchester
A120
A133
Braintree
A12
3

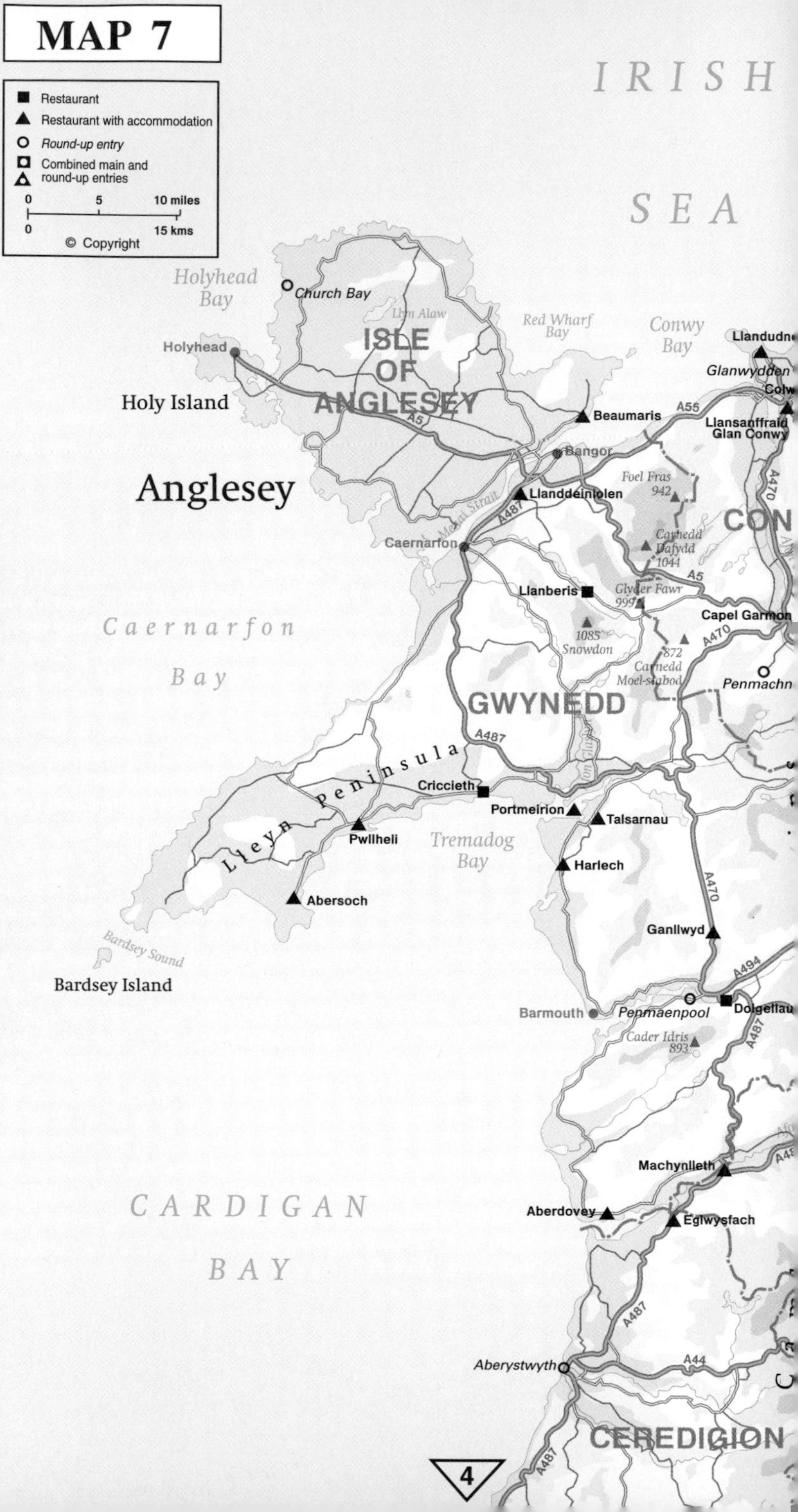
MAP 7
Restaurant
Restaurant with accommodation
Round-up entry
Combined main and round-up entries
0
5
10 miles
0
15 kms
© Copyright
IRISH SEA
Holyhead Bay
Church Bay
Llyn Alaw
ISLE OF ANGLESEY
Red Wharf Bay
Conwy Bay
Holyhead
Holy Island
A5
Beaumaris
A55
Llansanffraid Glan Conwy
Glanwydden
Bangor
Anglesey
Foel Fras 942
Llanddeiniolen
Menai Strait
A487
Caernarfon
Carnedd Dafydd 1044
A5
Llanberis
Glyder Fawr 999
Capel Garmon
A470
Caernarfon Bay
1085 Snowdon
872 Carnedd Moel-siabod
Penmachno
GWYNEDD
A487
Lleyn Peninsula
Criccieth
Portmeirion
Talsarnau
Pwllheli
Tremadog Bay
Harlech
Abersoch
A470
Ganllwyd
Bardsey Sound
Bardsey Island
A494
Barmouth
Penmaenpool
Dolgellau
Cader Idris 893
A487
Machynlleth
CARDIGAN BAY
Aberdovey
Eglwysfach
A487
A44
Aberystwyth
CEREDIGION
A487
4

MERSEYSIDE
GTR
MANCHESTER
CHESHIRE
FLINTSHIRE
DENBIGHSHIRE
WREXHAM
SHROPSHIRE
POWYS
Southport
Wrightington
Coppull Moor
Ormskirk
Skelmersdale
Wigan
Bolton
Wallasey
Liverpool
Birkenhead
St Helens
Warrington
Widnes
Runcorn
Prestatyn
Rhyl
R. Mersey
R. Weaver
Chester
Hawarden
Denbigh
Ruthin
Broxton
Worleston
Crewe
Nantwich
Wrexham
Whitchurch
Llandrillo
Llanarmon Dyffryn Ceiriog
Oswestry
L. Vyrnwy
Llanfyllin
Llanwddyn
R. Severn
Shrewsbury
Dorrington
Norton
Worfield
Pontdolgoch
Montgomery
Newtown
Llanfair Waterdine
Bromfield
Ludlow
Brimfield
Llyn Brenig
Bala Lake
8
5

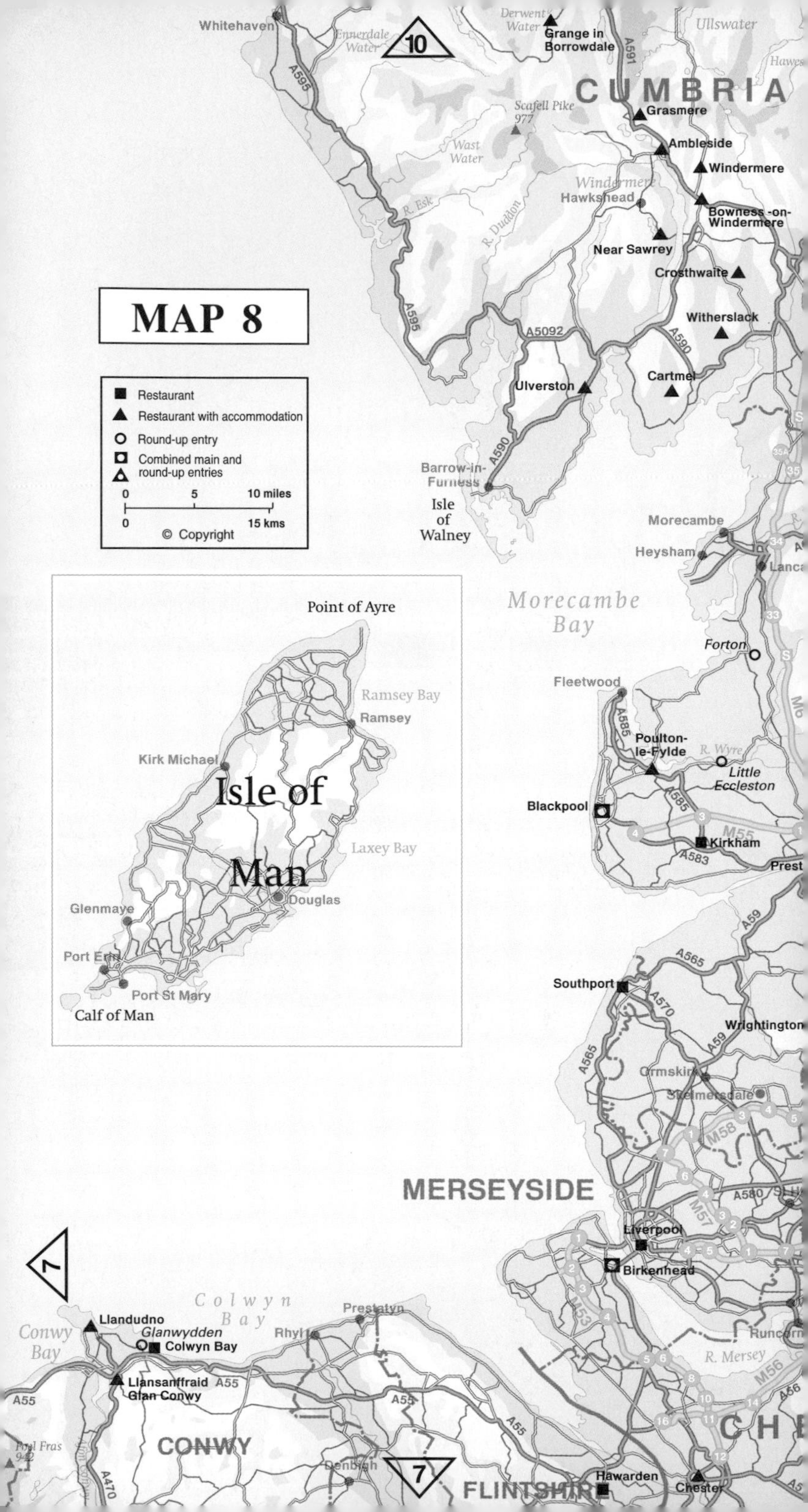
MAP 8
Restaurant
Restaurant with accommodation
Round-up entry
Combined main and round-up entries
0 5 10 miles
0 15 kms
© Copyright
10
7
7
CUMBRIA
Whitehaven
Ennerdale Water
Derwent Water
Grange in Borrowdale
Ullswater
Scafell Pike 977
Wast Water
Grasmere
Ambleside
Windermere
Hawkshead
Bowness-on-Windermere
Near Sawrey
Crosthwaite
Witherslack
R. Esk
R. Duddon
A595
A591
A5092
A590
Ulverston
Cartmel
Barrow-in-Furness
Isle of Walney
Morecambe
Heysham
Morecambe Bay
Forton
Fleetwood
A585
Poulton-le-Fylde
R. Wyre
Little Eccleston
Blackpool
M55
Kirkham
A583
Isle of Man
Point of Ayre
Ramsey Bay
Ramsey
Kirk Michael
Laxey Bay
Douglas
Glenmaye
Port Erin
Port St Mary
Calf of Man
A59
A565
A570
Southport
Wrightington
Ormskirk
Skelmersdale
M58
MERSEYSIDE
A580
M57
Liverpool
Birkenhead
M53
R. Mersey
M56
Runcorn
Colwyn Bay
Conwy Bay
Llandudno
Glanwydden
Colwyn Bay
Prestatyn
Rhyl
Llansanffraid Glan Conwy
A55
A470
CONWY
Denbigh
Hawarden
FLINTSHIRE
Chester

10
Barnard Castle
A66
Yarm
R. Tees
A685
Moulton
Richmond
A19
Northallerton
Leyburn
Yorkshire
East Witton
6
R. Swale
Masham
West Tanfield
A1
A61
NORTH
Dales
Asenby
R. Ure
A168
Arncliffe
Ramsgill
A65
A687
YORKSHIRE
Wath-in-
Nidderdale
Boroughbridge
Low Laithe
Ripley
Ferrensby
R. Nidd
A1(M)
Burnsall
Hetton
Bolton
Abbey
A59
Harrogate
A682
Skipton
R. Hodder
R. Ribble
Ilkley
A661
Boston
Spa
Sawley
R. Wharfe
Linton
Clitheroe
A6068
A650
NCASHIRE
A6120
A64
Longridge
Haworth
Leeds
A63
Langho
M65
Burnley
Bradford
M621
Accrington
A646
WEST
Shelf
R. Aire
Halifax
Todmorden
Brighouse
Dewsbury
Millbank
Wakefield
A666
YORKSHIRE
Cheesden
Huddersfield
Ramsbottom
Golcar
Newmillerdam
Rochdale
M62
M66
Heywood
Marsden
A629
Roydhouse
Honley
Bolton
Lydgate
Barnsley
A628
GREATER
SOUTH
M60
MANCHESTER
A616
A580
Eccles
Manchester
M67
YORKSHIRE
M62
Salford
Sale
Rotherham
Derwent Res.
Altrincham
Stockport
Birch Vale
Sheffield
Ladybower Res.
M56
M6
A6
Wilmslow
A52
Ridgeway
Prestbury
A556
Nether
Alderley
A623
A537
Buxton
Baslow
Chesterfield
A619
A617
Ashford
Bakewell
A34
A54
5
DERBYSHIRE

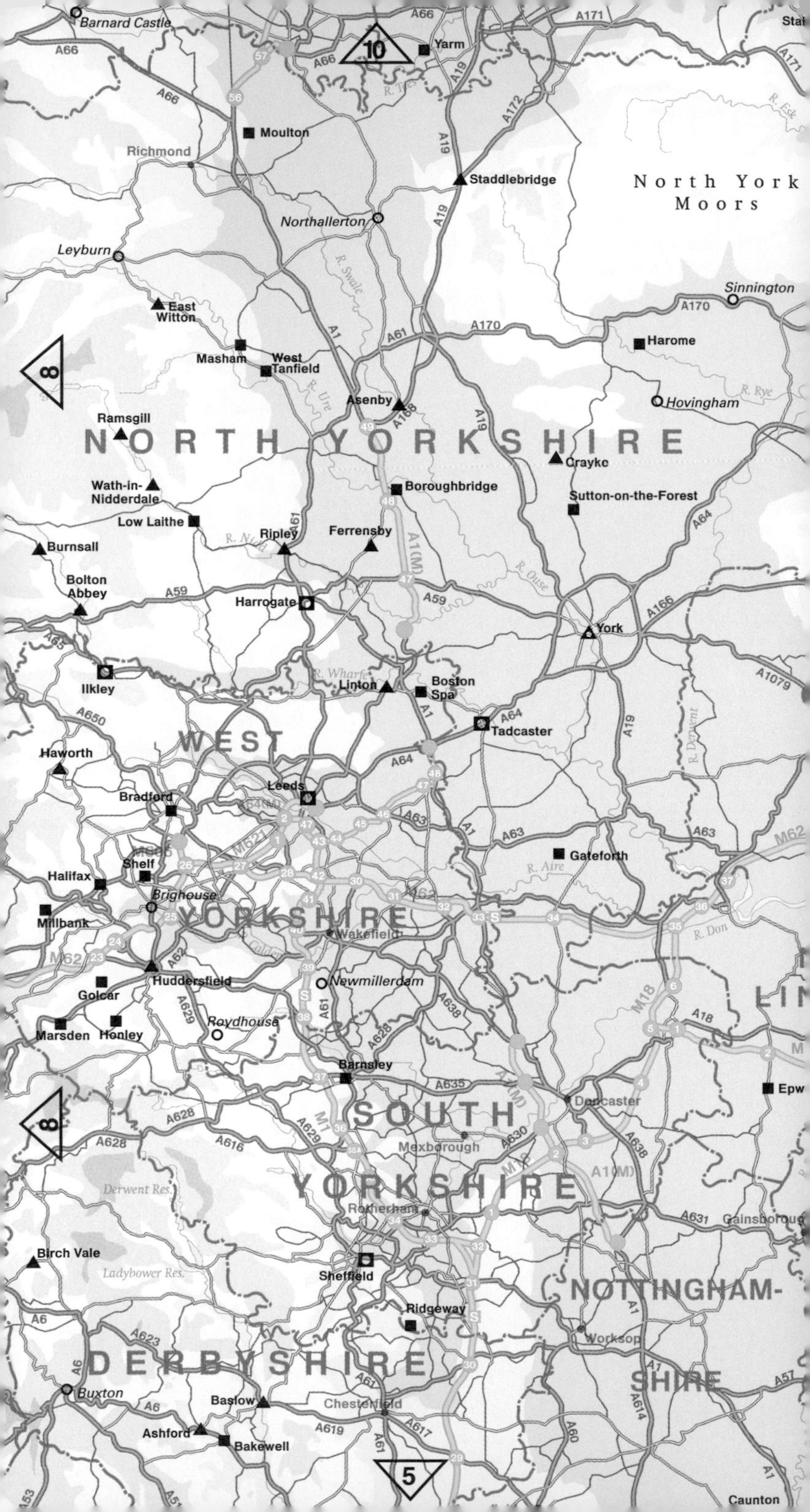

10
8
8
5
Barnard Castle
Yarm
Moulton
Richmond
Staddlebridge
North York Moors
Northallerton
Leyburn
Sinnington
East Witton
Harome
Masham
West Tanfield
Asenby
Hovingham
NORTH YORKSHIRE
Ramsgill
Crayke
Wath-in-Nidderdale
Boroughbridge
Sutton-on-the-Forest
Low Laithe
Ripley
Ferrensby
Burnsall
Bolton Abbey
Harrogate
York
Ilkley
Linton
Boston Spa
Tadcaster
WEST YORKSHIRE
Haworth
Leeds
Bradford
Gateforth
Shelf
Halifax
Brighouse
Millbank
Wakefield
Huddersfield
Newmillerdam
Golcar
Marsden
Honley
Roydhouse
Barnsley
SOUTH YORKSHIRE
Doncaster
Epw
Mexborough
Derwent Res.
Rotherham
Gainsborough
Birch Vale
Sheffield
Ladybower Res.
NOTTINGHAMSHIRE
Ridgeway
Worksop
DERBYSHIRE
Buxton
Baslow
Chesterfield
Ashford
Bakewell
Caunton
R. Tees
R. Esk
R. Swale
R. Ure
R. Rye
R. Nidd
R. Ouse
R. Wharfe
R. Derwent
R. Aire
R. Don
A1(M)
M62
M18
M1

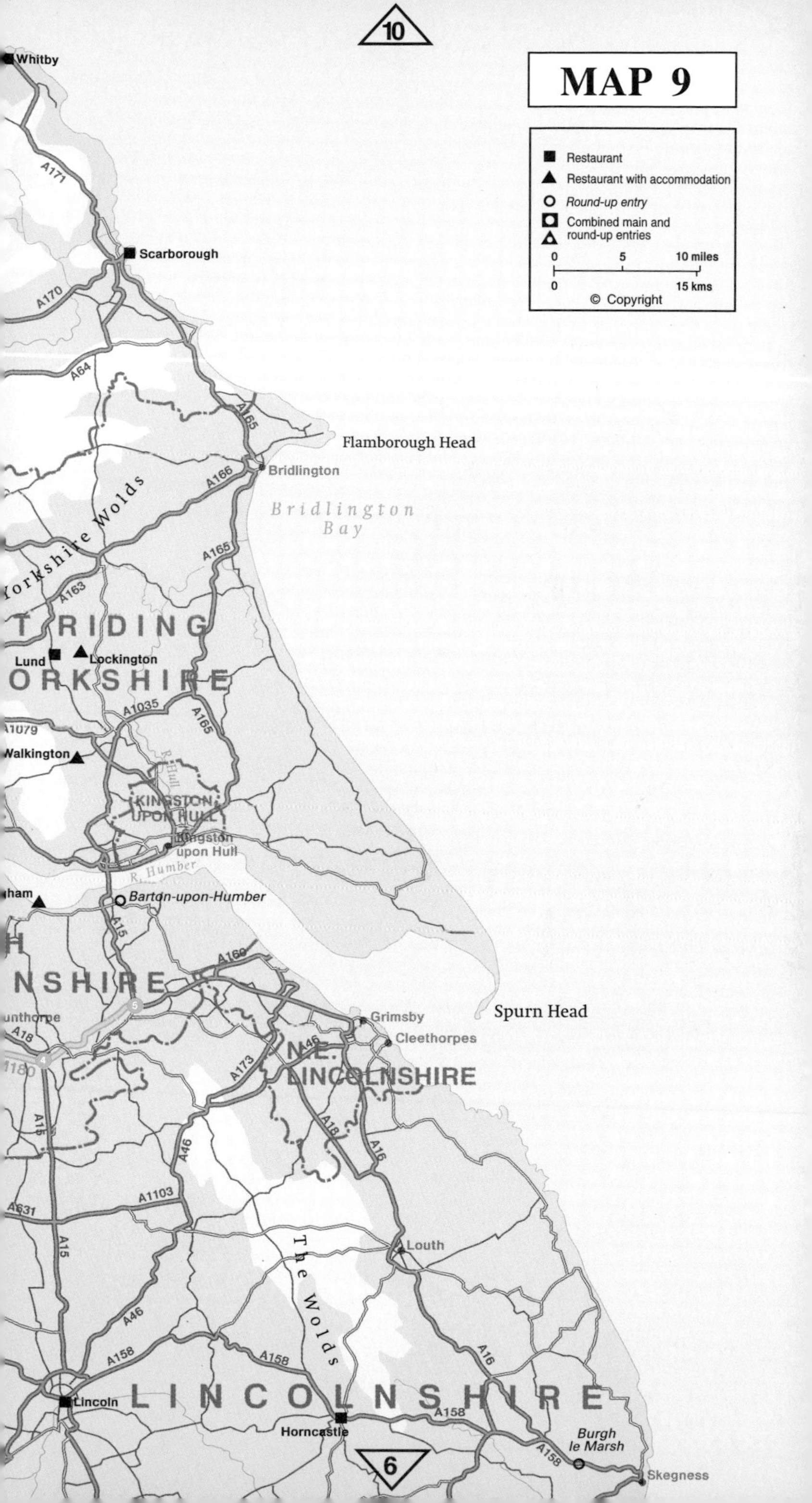

10
MAP 9
Restaurant
Restaurant with accommodation
Round-up entry
Combined main and round-up entries
0
5
10 miles
0
15 kms
© Copyright
Whitby
A171
Scarborough
A170
A64
A165
Flamborough Head
Bridlington
A166
Bridlington Bay
Yorkshire Wolds
A165
A163
RIDING
Lund
Lockington
ORKSHIRE
A1035
A165
A1079
Walkington
R. Hull
KINGSTON UPON HULL
Kingston upon Hull
R. Humber
ham
Barton-upon-Humber
A15
NSHIRE
A160
unthorpe
A18
Spurn Head
Grimsby
Cleethorpes
A173
N.E. LINCOLNSHIRE
A46
A18
A16
A15
A46
A1103
A631
A15
Louth
The Wolds
A46
A16
A158
A158
LINCOLNSHIRE
Lincoln
A158
Horncastle
Burgh le Marsh
A158
6
Skegness

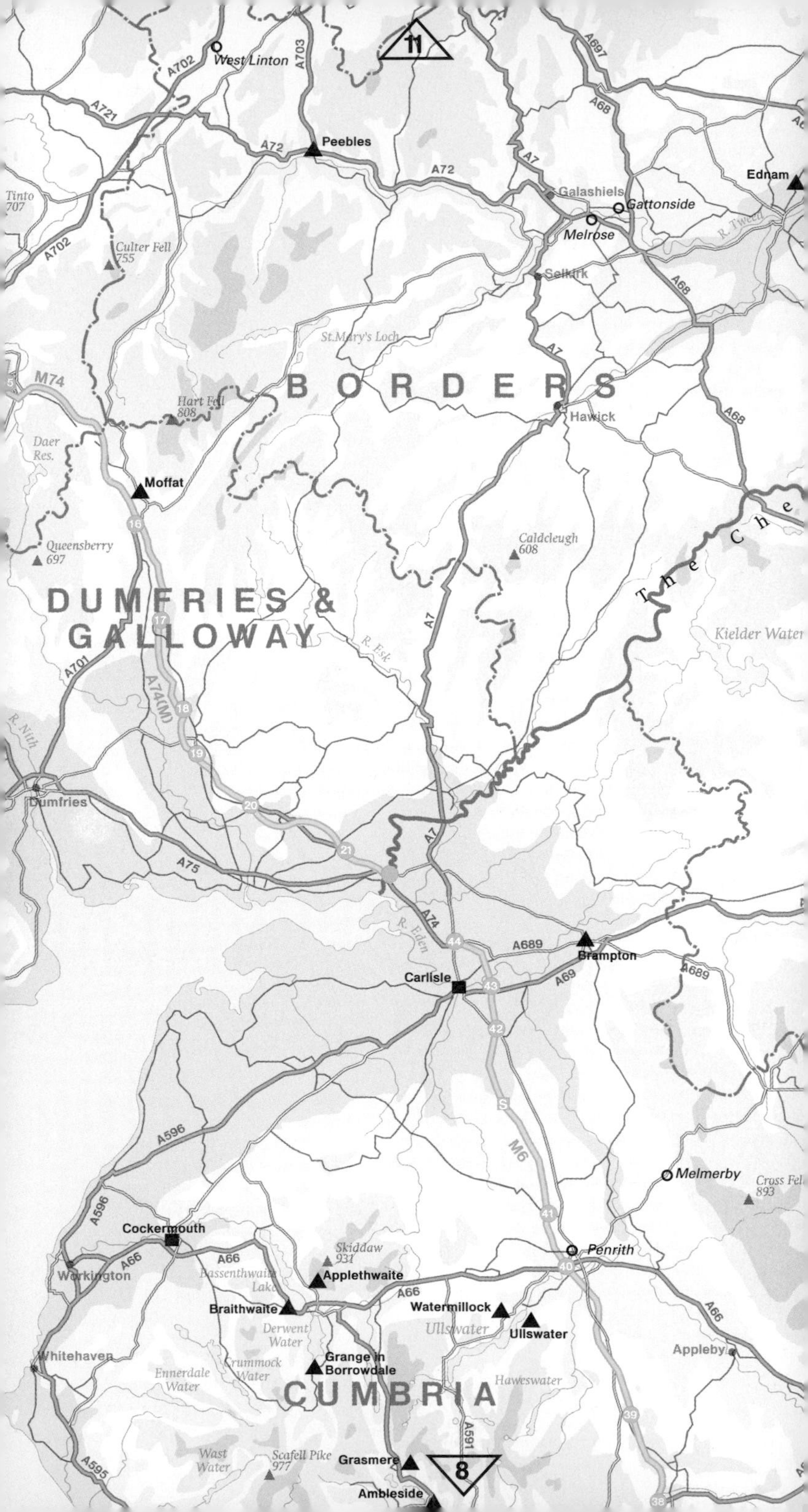

11
West Linton
A702
A703
A697
A721
A72
Peebles
A68
A7
Ednam
Tinto
707
Galashiels
Gattonside
Melrose
R. Tweed
A702
Culter Fell
755
Selkirk
St.Mary's Loch
M74
BORDERS
Hart Fell
808
Hawick
Daer
Res.
Moffat
16
Queensberry
697
Caldcleugh
608
DUMFRIES &
GALLOWAY
17
A701
A74(M)
18
R. Nith
19
R. Esk
A7
Kielder Water
Dumfries
20
21
A75
A74
R. Eden
44
A689
Brampton
Carlisle
43
A69
A689
42
M6
A596
Melmerby
Cross Fell
893
41
Cockermouth
A596
A66
Skiddaw
931
Penrith
40
Workington
A66
Bassenthwaite
Lake
Applethwaite
A66
Braithwaite
Watermillock
Ullswater
Ullswater
A66
Derwent
Water
Appleby
Whitehaven
Crummock
Water
Grange in
Borrowdale
Ennerdale
Water
Haweswater
CUMBRIA
A591
39
West
Water
Scafell Pike
977
Grasmere
8
A595
Ambleside
38

MAP 10
11
9
Restaurant
Restaurant with accommodation
Round-up entry
Combined main and round-up entries
0 5 10 miles
0 15 kms
© Copyright
Berwick-upon-Tweed
Holy Island
Farne Is.
The Cheviot 815
Alnwick
Alnmouth
NORTHUMBERLAND
Ponteland
Matfen
Great Whittington
Corbridge
Newcastle upon Tyne
Tynemouth
TYNE & WEAR
Gateshead
Stanley
Consett
Carterway Heads
Chester-le-Street
Derwent Res.
Durham
Willington
DURHAM
Hartlepool
HARTLEPOOL
Tees Bay
Redcar
STOCKTON-ON-TEES
Middlesbrough
REDCAR
Yarm
Romaldkirk
Barnard Castle
R. Aln
R. Coquet
R. Blyth
R. Pont
R. Tyne
R. Tees
A1
A697
A1068
A189
A19
A696
A68
A69
A692
A194(M)
A167
A688
A689
A179
A1(M)
A66
A171
A172

MAP 11

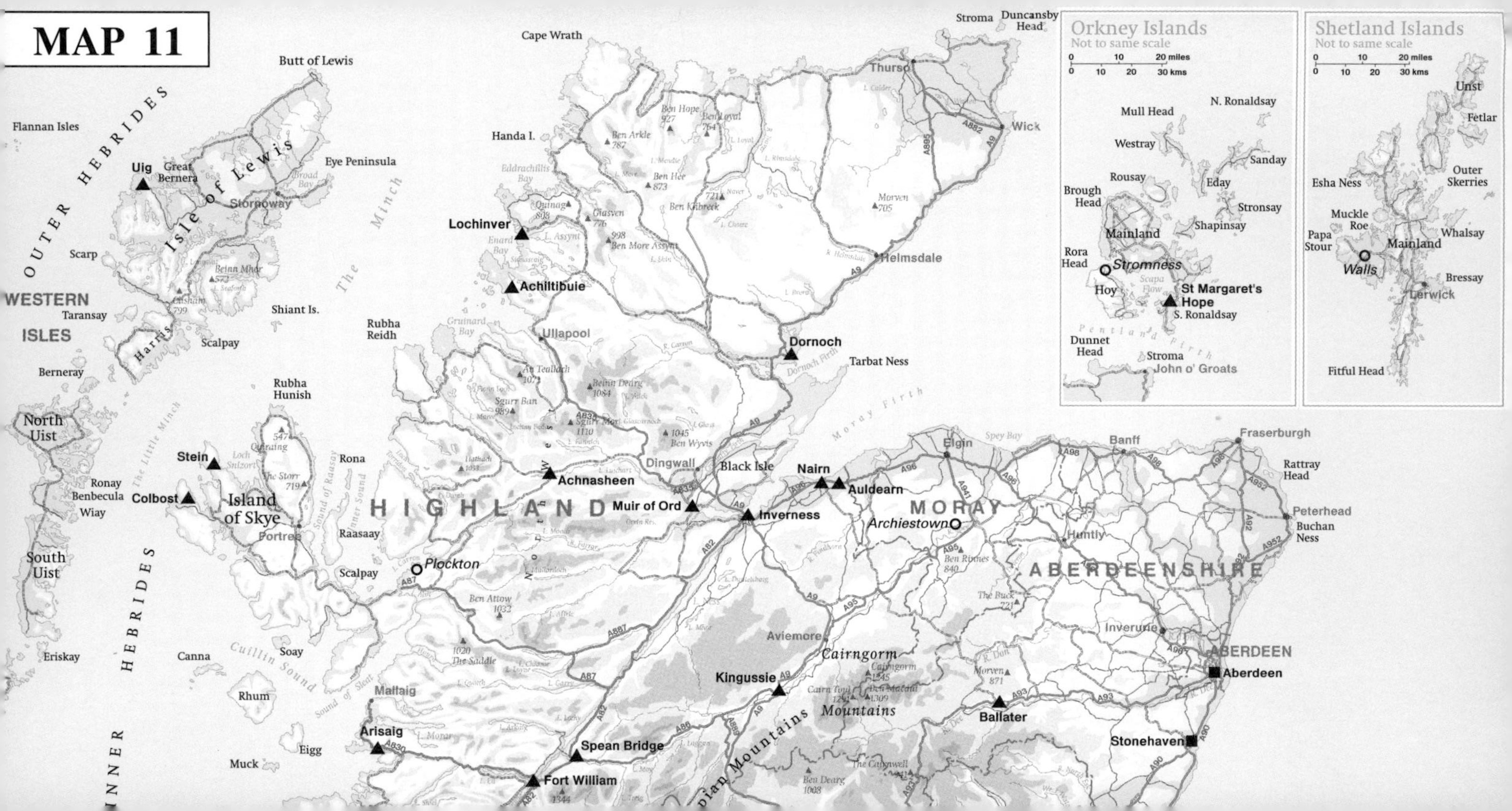

OUTER HEBRIDES
WESTERN ISLES
INNER HEBRIDES
Flannan Isles
Butt of Lewis
Uig
Great Bernera
Isle of Lewis
Stornoway
Eye Peninsula
Scarp
Taransay
Harris
Scalpay
Shiant Is.
Berneray
North Uist
Ronay
Benbecula
Wiay
South Uist
Eriskay
The Minch
The Little Minch
Rubha Hunish
Rubha Reidh
Stein
Colbost
Island of Skye
Portree
Rona
Raasaay
Scalpay
Soay
Canna
Rhum
Eigg
Muck
Cuillin Sound
Sound of Sleat
Cape Wrath
Handa I.
Lochinver
Achiltibuie
Ullapool
Achnasheen
Plockton
Mallaig
Arisaig
Spean Bridge
Fort William
HIGHLAND
Dingwall
Black Isle
Muir of Ord
Inverness
Nairn
Auldearn
Dornoch
Tarbat Ness
Moray Firth
Helmsdale
Thurso
Wick
Stroma
Duncansby Head
Aviemore
Cairngorm Mountains
Kingussie
MORAY
Archiestown
Elgin
Spey Bay
Banff
Fraserburgh
Rattray Head
Peterhead
Buchan Ness
Huntly
ABERDEENSHIRE
Inverurie
ABERDEEN
Aberdeen
Ballater
Stonehaven
Orkney Islands
Not to same scale
0 10 20 miles
0 10 20 30 kms
Mull Head
N. Ronaldsay
Westray
Sanday
Rousay
Eday
Brough Head
Stronsay
Mainland
Shapinsay
Rora Head
Stromness
Hoy
Scapa Flow
St Margaret's Hope
S. Ronaldsay
Pentland Firth
Dunnet Head
Stroma
John o' Groats
Shetland Islands
Not to same scale
0 10 20 miles
0 10 20 30 kms
Unst
Fetlar
Outer Skerries
Esha Ness
Muckle Roe
Whalsay
Papa Stour
Mainland
Walls
Bressay
Lerwick
Fitful Head

Restaurant
Restaurant with accommodation
Round-up entry
Combined main and round-up entries
0 20 miles
0 20 kms
© Copyright
10
PERTHSHIRE & KINROSS
ARGYLL & BUTE
STIRLING
FIFE
EAST LOTHIAN
MIDLOTHIAN
WEST LOTHIAN
NORTH LANARKSHIRE
SOUTH LANARKSHIRE
NORTH AYRSHIRE
EAST AYRSHIRE
SOUTH AYRSHIRE
DUMFRIES & GALLOWAY
BORDERS
NORTHUMBERLAND
CUMBRIA
DURHAM
Southern Uplands
Eriska
Oban
Kilchrenan
Clachan-Seil
Crinan
Cairndow
Inveraray
Balquhidder
Crieff
Auchterarder
Dunkeld
Kinclaven
Perth
Kinfauns
Dundee
Arbroath
Cupar
Peat Inn
Anstruther
Fife Ness
Kirkcaldy
Dunfermline
Stirling
Falkirk
Linlithgow
Edinburgh
Leith
Gullane
Glasgow
Greenock
Paisley
Motherwell
Kilmarnock
Fairlie
Dalry
Troon
Ayr
Annbank
Brodick
Isle of Arran
Isle of Bute
Bowmore
Islay
Jura
Colonsay
Oronsay
Gigha
Island of Mull
Iona
Staffa
Lismore
Mull of Kintyre
Mull of Oa
West Linton
Peebles
Galashiels
Melrose
Gattonside
St Boswells
Swinton
Ednam
Berwick-upon-Tweed
Holy Island
Farne Is.
Alnmouth
Hawick
Moffat
Dumfries
Crossmichael
Kirkcudbright
Newton Stewart
Stranraer
Mull of Galloway
Burrow Head
Luce Bay
Solway Firth
Firth of Forth
Ochil Hills
Lammermuir Hills
The Cheviot Hills
Carlisle
Brampton
Haydon Bridge
Great Whittington
Matfen
Ponteland
Corbridge
Newcastle upon Tyne
Gateshead
Carterway Heads
Consett
Durham
Willington
Hartlepool
Melmerby

Greater London
BARNET
Stanmore
Finchley
Rani
Two Brothers
Vrisaki
Wood Green
Le Cadre
Hendon
Gourmet Garden
HARROW
Village Bistro
Parsee
Cafe Japan
WEMBLEY
Willesden
Sushi-Say
Sabras
Hampstead
See Map 13
CAMDEN
BRENT
William IV
A40(M)
HAMMERSMITH AND FULHAM
See Map 15
Ealing
Parade
Acton
Gilbey's
Alastair Little Lancaster Road
Orsino
CITY OF WEST-MINSTER
Esarn Kheow
Balzac Bistro
Chez Moi
Anglesea Arms
Patio
Brackenbury
Havelock Tavern
Adams Café
Chinon
Cotto
KENSINGTON AND CHELSEA
See Map 14
Riso
Thai Bistro
Bush
Snows on the Green
Popeseye
La Trompette
Chiswick
Azou
Brentford
HAMMERSMITH
Gate
Le Potiron Sauvage
Blue Elephant
Ransome's Dock
Riva
River Café
Salisbury Tavern
Chutney Mary
Stepping Stone
Metrogusto
Sonny's
Fulham
Café Spice Namaste
Redmonds
Phoenix
Putney Bridge
Lavender
So.uk
Enoteca Turi
Del Buongustaio
Brady's
Crowthers
RICHMOND
Wandsworth
Ditto
Pizza Metro
Le Gothique
WANDSWORTH
Twickenham
3 Monkeys
Sarkhel's
Chez Bruce
Kastoori
Radha Krishna Bhavan
Streatham
Utah
Light House
Wimbledon
Merton
Kingston upon Thames
Morden
Mitcham
Mirch Masala
KINGSTON UPON THAMES
Malden
MERTON
M1
A1
A5109
A109
A111
A1000
A410
A5
A406
A504
A4
A4140
A4008
A404
A40
A41
A4020
A315
A307
A306
A205
A3205
A316
A3
A24
A217
A214
A218
A23
A216
A308
A236

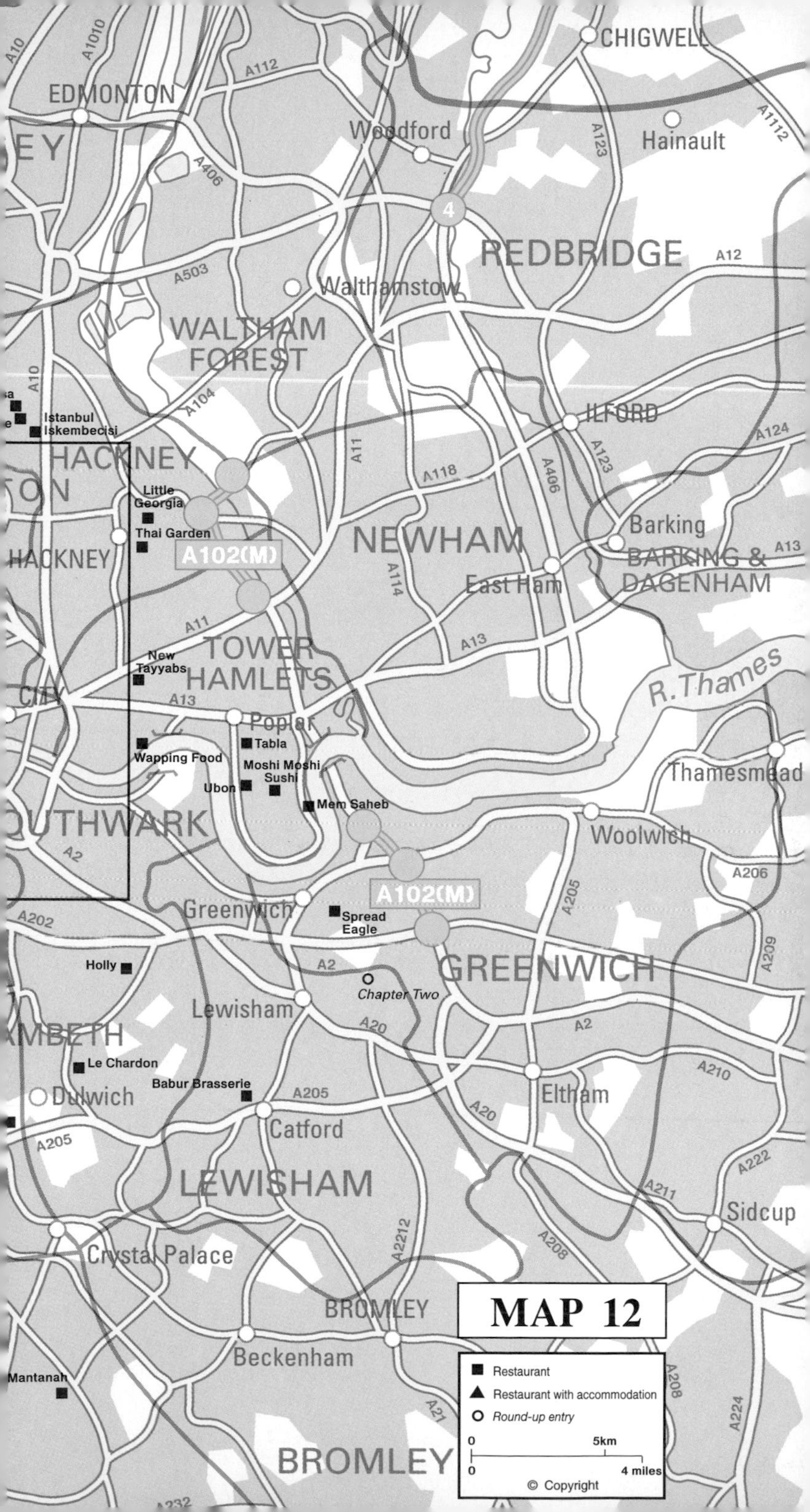
CHIGWELL
EDMONTON
Woodford
Hainault
REDBRIDGE
Walthamstow
WALTHAM FOREST
ILFORD
Istanbul Iskembecisi
HACKNEY
Little Georgia
Thai Garden
A102(M)
NEWHAM
Barking
BARKING & DAGENHAM
East Ham
TOWER HAMLETS
New Tayyabs
CITY
Poplar
Tabla
Wapping Food
Moshi Moshi Sushi
Ubon
Mem Saheb
R. Thames
Thamesmead
Woolwich
SOUTHWARK
Greenwich
Spread Eagle
GREENWICH
Holly
Chapter Two
Lewisham
LAMBETH
Le Chardon
Babur Brasserie
Dulwich
Eltham
Catford
LEWISHAM
Sidcup
Crystal Palace
MAP 12
BROMLEY
Beckenham
Mantanah
Restaurant
Restaurant with accommodation
Round-up entry
0 5km
0 4 miles
© Copyright

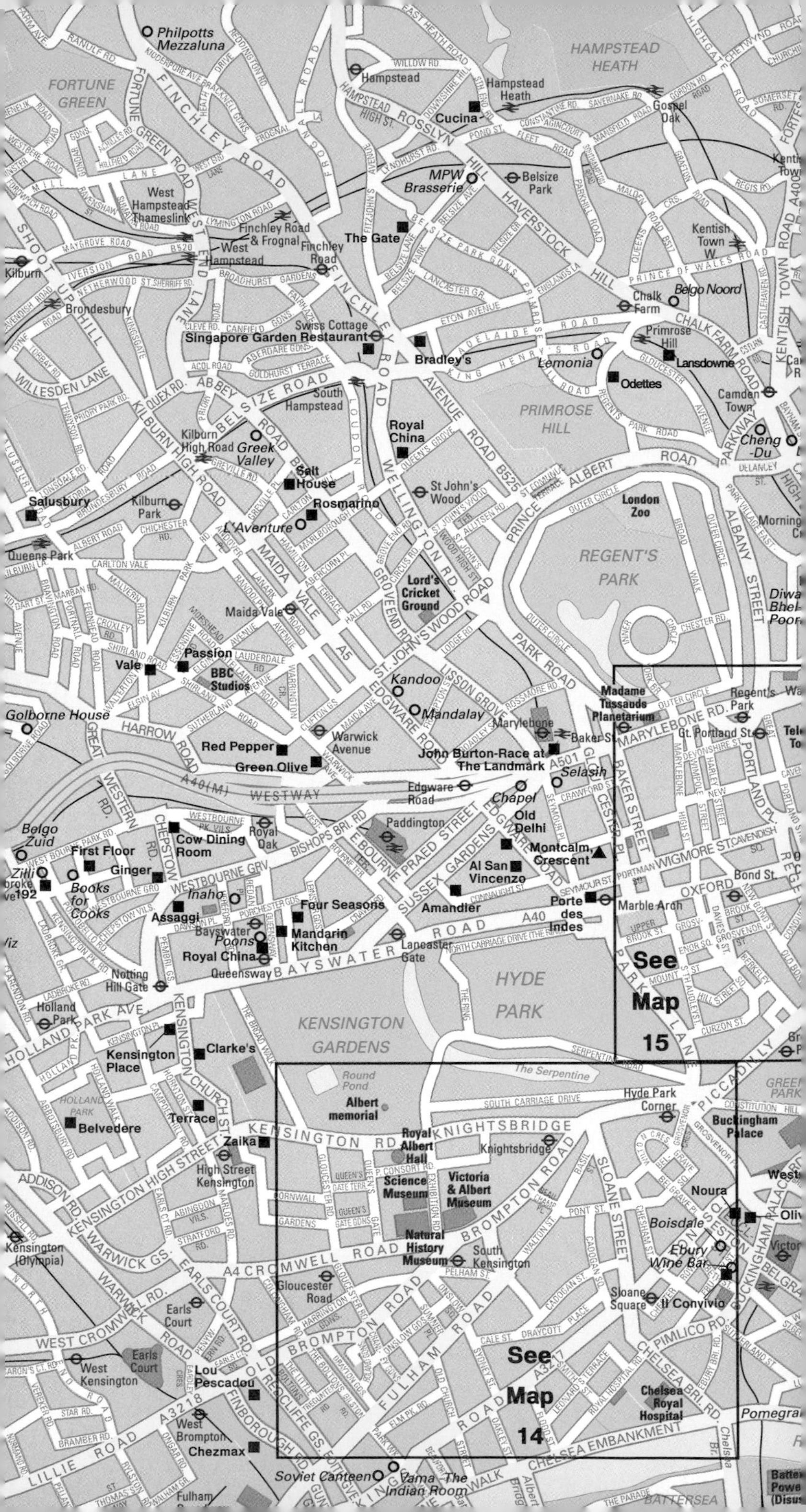

Philpotts Mezzaluna
FORTUNE GREEN
HAMPSTEAD HEATH
Hampstead
Hampstead Heath
Cucina
Gospel Oak
FINCHLEY ROAD
HAMPSTEAD HIGH ST.
ROSSLYN HILL
MPW Brasserie
Belsize Park
HAVERSTOCK HILL
Kentish Town
Kentish Town W.
West Hampstead Thameslink
Finchley Road & Frognal
West Hampstead
Finchley Road
The Gate
Kilburn
Brondesbury
Belgo Noord
Chalk Farm
PRINCE OF WALES ROAD
KENTISH TOWN ROAD
Swiss Cottage
Singapore Garden Restaurant
Bradley's
Lemonia
Primrose Hill
Lansdowne
Odettes
CHALK FARM ROAD
Camden Town
South Hampstead
BELSIZE ROAD
WILLESDEN LANE
PRIMROSE HILL
Cheng-Du
Kilburn High Road
Greek Valley
Royal China
AVENUE ROAD
PRINCE ALBERT ROAD
Salt House
St John's Wood
Salusbury
Rosmarino
L'Aventure
Kilburn Park
London Zoo
Queens Park
REGENT'S PARK
Morning
Lord's Cricket Ground
MAIDA VALE
Maida Vale
ALBANY STREET
Diwana Bhel-Poori
Vale
Passion
BBC Studios
Kandoo
Mandalay
Madame Tussauds Planetarium
Regent's Park
Golborne House
HARROW ROAD
Marylebone
Baker St.
Warwick Avenue
Red Pepper
Green Olive
John Burton-Race at The Landmark
Selasih
Gt. Portland St.
MARYLEBONE RD.
A40(M) WESTWAY
Edgware Road
Chapel
BAKER STREET
Belgo Zuid
Cow Dining Room
Royal Oak
Paddington
Old Delhi
Zilli
First Floor
Ginger
Montcalm, Crescent
WIGMORE ST.
192
Books for Cooks
Al San Vincenzo
Bond St.
OXFORD
Inaho
Four Seasons
Amandier
Marble Arch
Porte des Indes
Assaggi
Bayswater
Poons
Mandarin Kitchen
BAYSWATER ROAD
Lancaster Gate
Royal China
Queensway
HYDE PARK
See Map 15
Notting Hill Gate
Holland Park
HOLLAND PARK AVE.
KENSINGTON GARDENS
Kensington Place
Clarke's
Round Pond
The Serpentine
Albert memorial
Hyde Park Corner
Belvedere
Terrace
HOLLAND PARK
GREEN PARK
PICCADILLY
Buckingham Palace
Zaika
KENSINGTON RD
KNIGHTSBRIDGE
Royal Albert Hall
Knightsbridge
High Street Kensington
KENSINGTON HIGH STREET
Science Museum
Victoria & Albert Museum
BROMPTON ROAD
SLOANE STREET
Noura
Olivo
Kensington (Olympia)
Boisdale
Natural History Museum
South Kensington
Ebury Wine Bar
Victoria
A4 CROMWELL ROAD
Gloucester Road
Sloane Square
Il Convivio
Earls Court
WEST CROMWELL ROAD
PIMLICO RD.
West Kensington
Earls Court
See Map 14
Lou Pescadou
FULHAM ROAD
Chelsea Royal Hospital
West Brompton
LILLIE ROAD
Chezmax
CHELSEA EMBANKMENT
Soviet Canteen
Yama - The Indian Room
Fulham
BATTERSEA

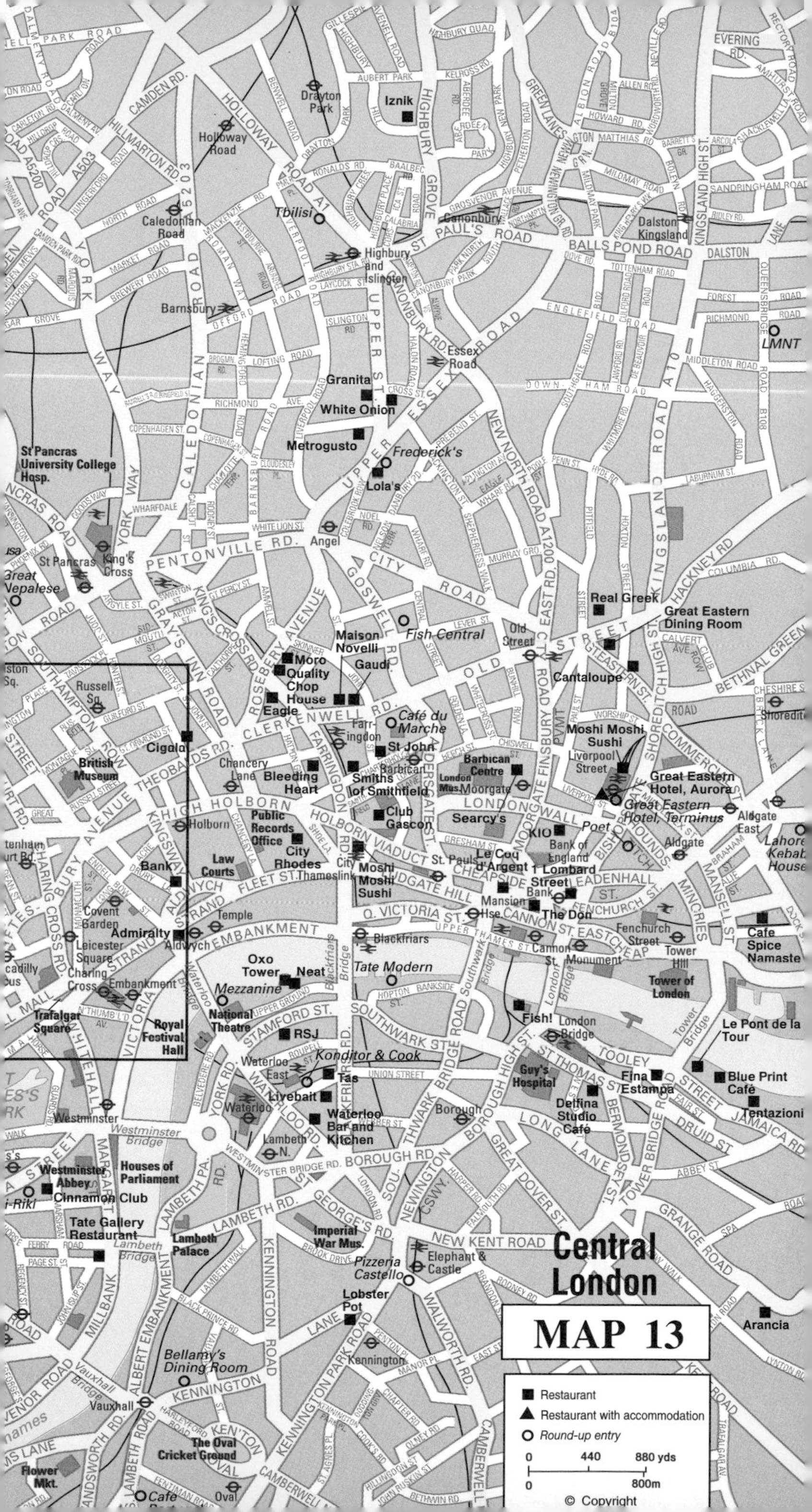

Central London
MAP 13
Restaurant
Restaurant with accommodation
Round-up entry
0
440
880 yds
0
800m
© Copyright
Iznik
Tbilisi
Granita
White Onion
Metrogusto
Frederick's
Lola's
LMNT
Real Greek
Great Eastern Dining Room
Cantaloupe
Fish Central
Maison Novelli
Moro
Quality Chop House
Gaudi
Eagle
Café du Marche
St John
Bleeding Heart
Smiths of Smithfield
Club Gascon
Barbican Centre
London Mus.
Searcy's
Moshi Moshi Sushi
Great Eastern Hotel, Aurora
Great Eastern Hotel, Terminus
Poet
KIO
Le Coq d'Argent
1 Lombard Street
The Don
Cigala
British Museum
Public Records Office
City Rhodes
Law Courts
Bank
Moshi Moshi Sushi
Admiralty
Oxo Tower
Neat
Mezzanine
Tate Modern
National Theatre
RSJ
Royal Festival Hall
Konditor & Cook
Tas
Livebait
Waterloo Bar and Kitchen
Fish!
Guy's Hospital
Fina Estampa
Delfina Studio Café
Blue Print Café
Tentazioni
Le Pont de la Tour
Cafe Spice Namaste
Tower of London
Lahore Kebab House
Westminster Abbey
Cinnamon Club
Houses of Parliament
Tate Gallery Restaurant
Lambeth Palace
Imperial War Mus.
Pizzeria Castello
Lobster Pot
Arancia
Bellamy's Dining Room
The Oval Cricket Ground
Flower Mkt.
St Pancras University College Hosp.
Great Nepalese
Trafalgar Square

MAP 14

Central London: South West

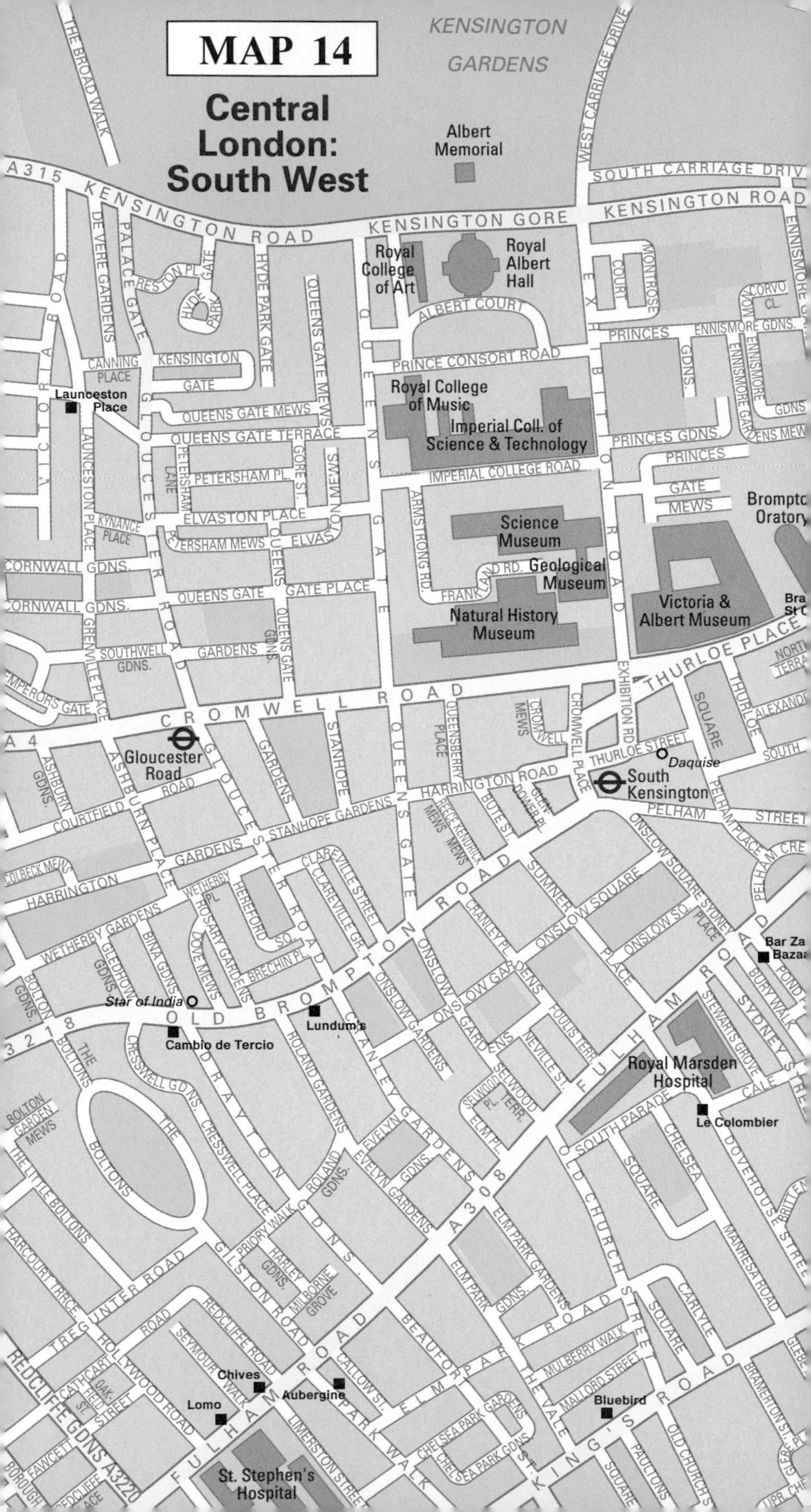

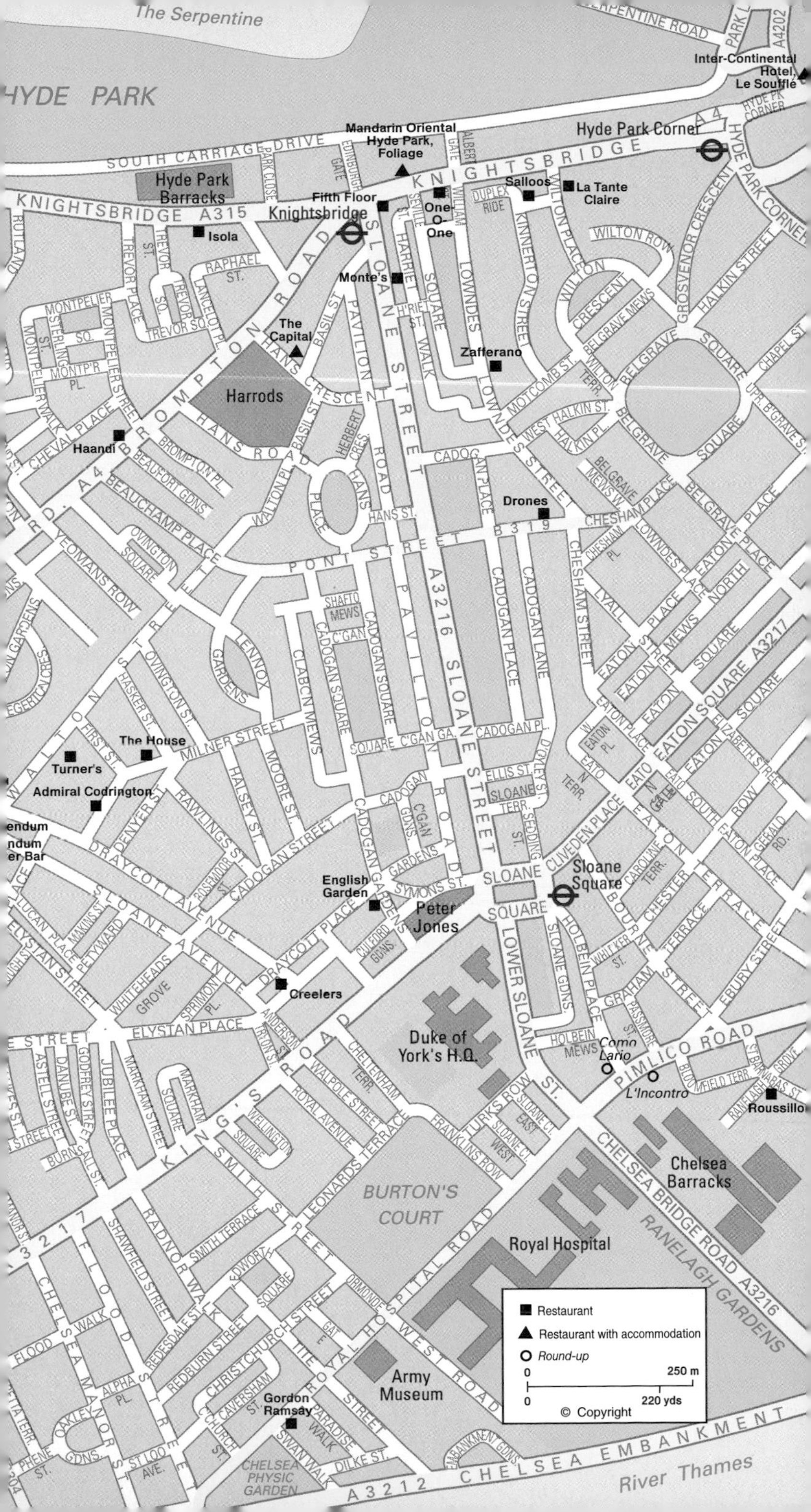
The Serpentine
HYDE PARK
SERPENTINE ROAD
Inter-Continental Hotel, Le Soufflé
Hyde Park Corner
HYDE PK CORNER
Mandarin Oriental Hyde Park, Foliage
SOUTH CARRIAGE DRIVE
KNIGHTSBRIDGE
KNIGHTSBRIDGE A315
Hyde Park Barracks
Fifth Floor
Knightsbridge
One-O-One
Salloos
La Tante Claire
Isola
Monte's
WILTON ROW
WILTON CRESCENT
GROSVENOR CRESCENT
HALKIN STREET
The Capital
Zafferano
Harrods
BROMPTON ROAD
HANS CRESCENT
HANS ROAD
Haandi
BELGRAVE SQUARE
MOTCOMB ST.
LOWNDES STREET
SLOANE STREET
Drones
CHESHAM PLACE
PONT STREET
BEAUCHAMP PLACE
A3216 SLOANE STREET
PAVILION ROAD
CADOGAN PLACE
CADOGAN LANE
CADOGAN SQUARE
EATON SQUARE A3217
EATON PLACE
LENNOX GARDENS
WALTON STREET
MILNER STREET
The House
Turner's
Admiral Codrington
DRAYCOTT AVENUE
CADOGAN STREET
SLOANE AVENUE
English Garden
Peter Jones
Sloane Square
SLOANE SQUARE
LOWER SLOANE ST.
HOLBEIN PLACE
BOURNE STREET
CHESTER ROW
Creelers
ELYSTAN PLACE
KING'S ROAD
Duke of York's H.Q.
Como Lario
L'Incontro
PIMLICO ROAD
Roussillon
Chelsea Barracks
CHELSEA BRIDGE ROAD A3216
RANELAGH GARDENS
BURTON'S COURT
ROYAL HOSPITAL ROAD
Royal Hospital
SMITH STREET
FLOOD STREET
CHELSEA MANOR STREET
Army Museum
Gordon Ramsay
CHELSEA PHYSIC GARDEN
CHELSEA EMBANKMENT
River Thames
A3212
Restaurant
Restaurant with accommodation
Round-up
0 250 m
0 220 yds
© Copyright

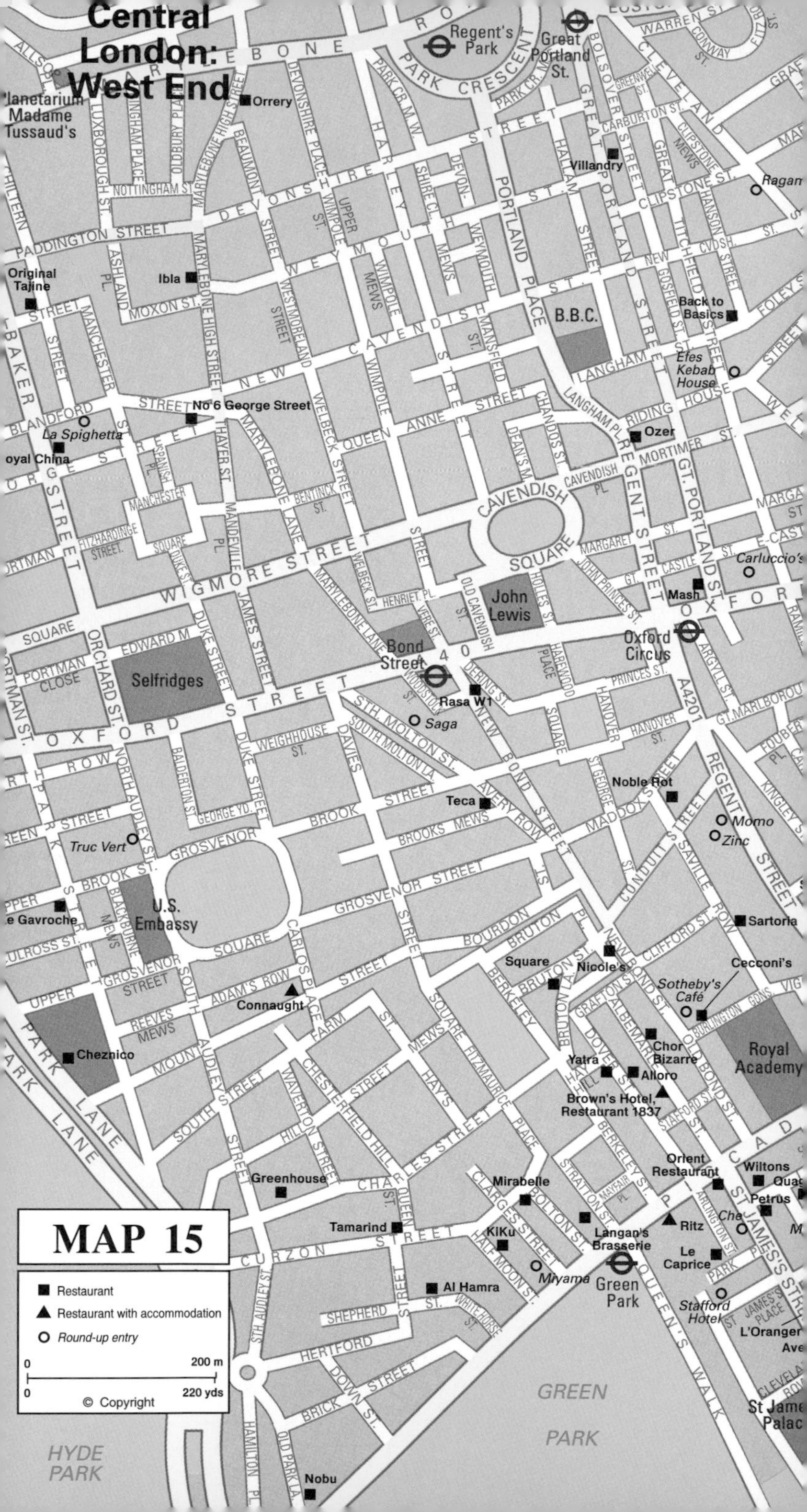
Central London: West End
MAP 15
Restaurant
Restaurant with accommodation
Round-up entry
0 200 m
0 220 yds
© Copyright
Orrery
Planetarium
Madame Tussaud's
Regent's Park
Great Portland St.
Villandry
Ragam
Original Tajine
Ibla
Back to Basics
B.B.C.
Efes Kebab House
No 6 George Street
La Spighetta
Royal China
Ozer
Carluccio's
Mash
John Lewis
Oxford Circus
Bond Street
Selfridges
Rasa W1
Saga
Teca
Noble Rot
Momo
Zinc
Truc Vert
U.S. Embassy
Le Gavroche
Sartoria
Square
Nicole's
Cecconi's
Sotheby's Café
Connaught
Cheznico
Chor Bizarre
Yatra
Alloro
Royal Academy
Brown's Hotel, Restaurant 1837
Orient Restaurant
Wiltons
Petrus
Greenhouse
Mirabelle
Tamarind
KiKu
Langan's Brasserie
Ritz
Le Caprice
Miyama
Green Park
Al Hamra
Stafford Hotel
L'Oranger
Green Park
Hyde Park
Nobu
St James's Palace
Oxford Street
Wigmore Street
Regent Street
Piccadilly
Park Lane
Curzon Street
Grosvenor Square
Cavendish Square
Portland Place

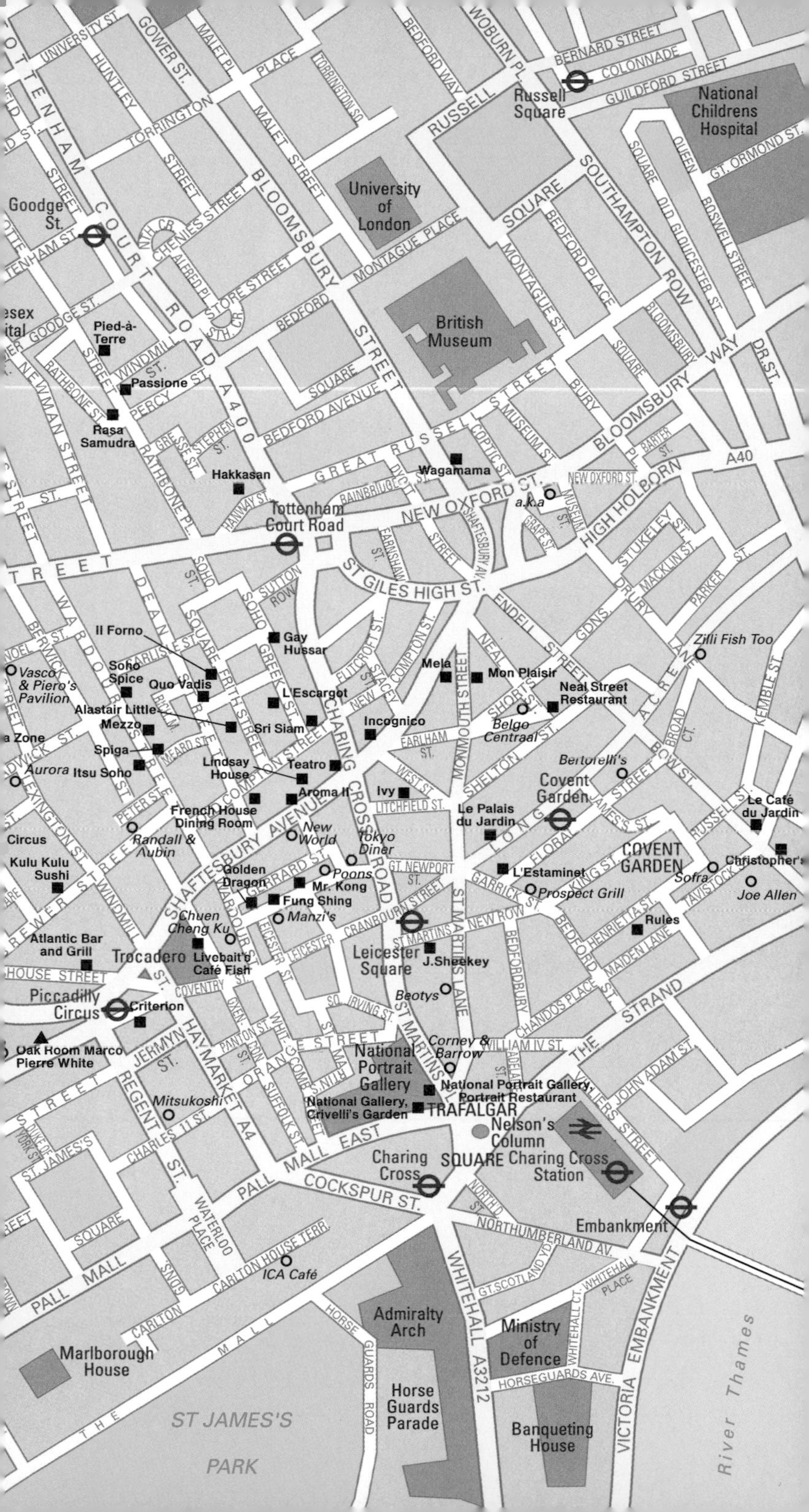

University St.
Gower St.
Malet Pl.
Place
Torrington Sq.
Bedford Way
Woburn Pl.
Bernard Street
Colonnade
Russell Square
Guildford Street
National Childrens Hospital
Tottenham
Huntley
Torrington
Malet Street
Russell
Gt. Ormond St.
Queen Square
Goodge St.
Court Road A400
Chenies Street
Bloomsbury
University of London
Montague Place
Square
Southampton Row
Old Gloucester St.
Boswell Street
Alfred Pl.
Store Street
Bedford Place
Montague St.
British Museum
Bloomsbury Square
Bloomsbury Way
Dr. St.
Goodge St.
Pied-à-Terre
Windmill St.
Passione
Percy St.
Rathbone St.
Newman Street
Rasa Samudra
Rathbone Pl.
Stephen St.
Bedford Avenue
Great Russell Street
Museum St.
Coptic St.
Bury Pl.
Barter St.
A40
Wagamama
Hakkasan
Hanway St.
Tottenham Court Road
Rainbridge St.
Dyott St.
New Oxford St.
a.k.a
Grape St.
High Holborn
Stukeley St.
Macklin St.
Parker St.
Street
Soho St.
Dean
Sutton Row
St Giles High St.
Earnshaw St.
Shaftesbury Av.
Endell Street
Drury Lane
Gdns.
Il Forno
Gay Hussar
Soho Square
Greek St.
Carlisle St.
Wardour
Berwick
Vasco & Piero's Pavilion
Soho Spice
Quo Vadis
Alastair Little
Mezzo
Spiga
Aurora
Itsu Soho
L'Escargot
Sri Siam
Frith Street
Flitcroft St.
New Compton St.
Charing Cross Road
Mela
Mon Plaisir
Neal Street Restaurant
Neal St.
Monmouth Street
Shorts Gdns.
Belgo Centraal
Incognico
Earlham St.
Zilli Fish Too
Kemble St.
Broad Ct.
Bow St.
Acre
Meard St.
Old Compton Street
Teatro
Lindsay House
Aroma II
Ivy
West St.
Litchfield St.
Shelton St.
Bertorelli's
Covent Garden
Le Palais du Jardin
James's St.
Long Acre
Floral St.
Russell St.
Le Café du Jardin
Lexington St.
Peter St.
French House Dining Room
Randall & Aubin
Shaftesbury Avenue
New World
Tokyo Diner
Gt. Newport St.
L'Estaminet
Garrick St.
King St.
Covent Garden
Christopher's
Sofra
Tavistock St.
Joe Allen
Circus
Kulu Kulu Sushi
Brewer Street
Golden Dragon
Gerrard St.
Poons
Mr. Kong
Fung Shing
Manzi's
Prospect Grill
Cranbourn Street
St. Martins Lane
New Row
Henrietta St.
Rules
Maiden Lane
Atlantic Bar and Grill
Chuen Cheng Ku
Livebait's Café Fish
Trocadero
Leicester Sq.
Leicester St.
Leicester Square
J.Sheekey
Bedfordbury
Bedford St.
Chandos Place
The Strand
House Street
Coventry St.
Piccadilly Circus
Criterion
Irving St.
Beotys
Haymarket
Jermyn St.
Oak Room Marco Pierre White
Panton St.
Orange Street
National Portrait Gallery
Corney & Barrow
William IV St.
Adelaide St.
Villiers Street
John Adam St.
Regent St.
Mitsukoshi
National Portrait Gallery, Portrait Restaurant
National Gallery, Crivelli's Garden
Trafalgar Square
Nelson's Column
Charing Cross Station
Charles II St.
Suffolk St.
Pall Mall East
Duke of York St.
St. James's Square
Charing Cross
Cockspur St.
Northumberland Av.
Embankment
Waterloo Place
Carlton House Terr.
ICA Café
Pall Mall
Gt. Scotland Yd.
Whitehall Pl.
Whitehall Ct.
Carlton
Horse Guards Road
Admiralty Arch
Whitehall A3212
Ministry of Defence
Horseguards Ave.
Victoria Embankment
River Thames
Marlborough House
The Mall
St James's Park
Horse Guards Parade
Banqueting House

MAP 16

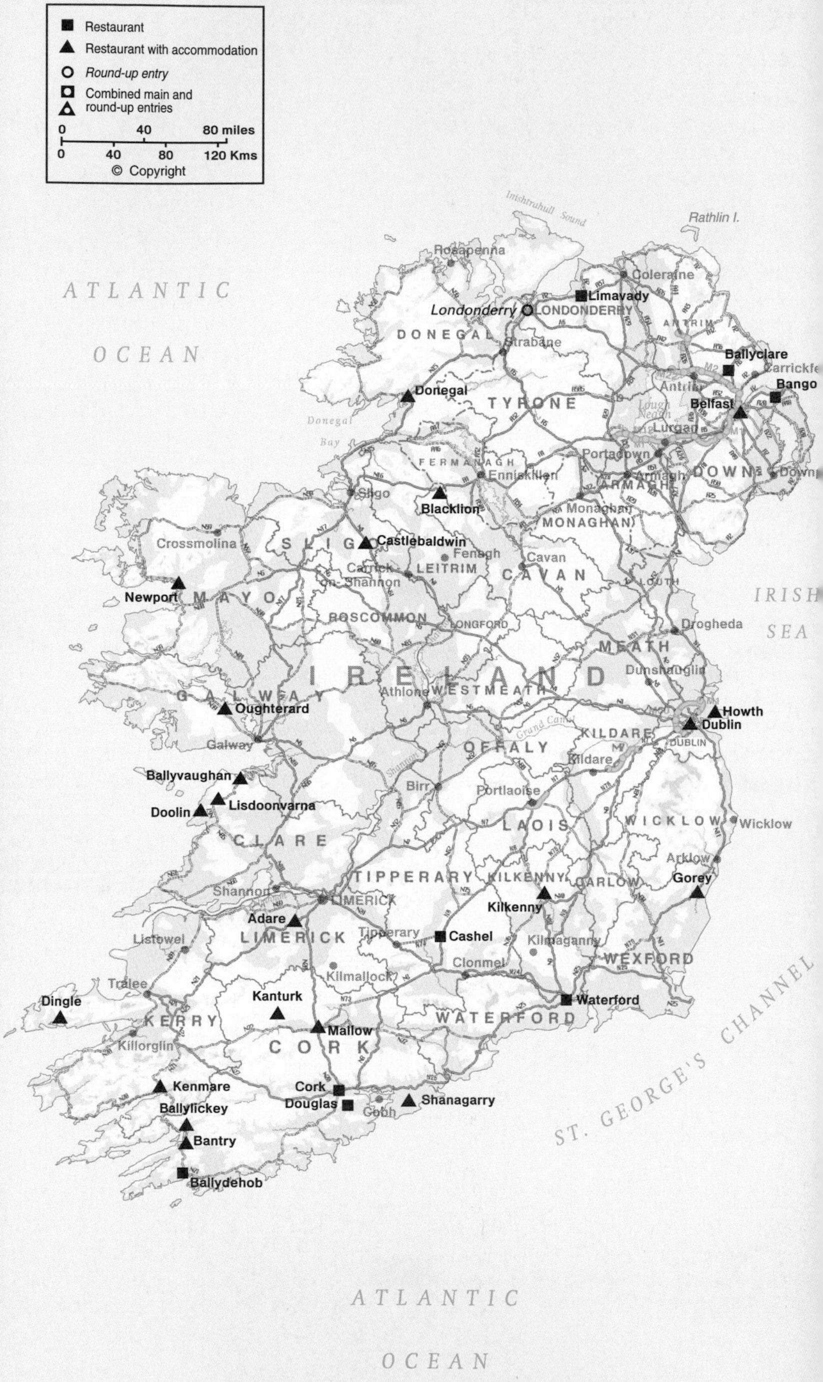
Restaurant
Restaurant with accommodation
Round-up entry
Combined main and round-up entries
0 40 80 miles
0 40 80 120 Kms
© Copyright
ATLANTIC OCEAN
IRISH SEA
ST. GEORGE'S CHANNEL
ATLANTIC OCEAN
IRELAND
Rathlin I.
Rosapenna
Coleraine
Limavady
Londonderry
LONDONDERRY
ANTRIM
DONEGAL
Strabane
Ballyclare
Carrickfe
Bango
Antrim
Belfast
Donegal
TYRONE
Lurgan
Portadown
Armagh
DOWN
Downp
FERMANAGH
Enniskillen
ARMAGH
Sligo
Blacklion
Monaghan
MONAGHAN
Crossmolina
SLIGO
Castlebaldwin
Fenagh
Cavan
LEITRIM
Carrick-on-Shannon
CAVAN
Newport
MAYO
LOUTH
ROSCOMMON
LONGFORD
Drogheda
MEATH
Dunshaughlin
Athlone
WESTMEATH
GALWAY
Oughterard
Howth
Dublin
Galway
KILDARE
DUBLIN
OFFALY
Kildare
Ballyvaughan
Birr
Portlaoise
Lisdoonvarna
Doolin
LAOIS
WICKLOW
Wicklow
CLARE
Arklow
TIPPERARY
KILKENNY
CARLOW
Gorey
Shannon
LIMERICK
Kilkenny
Adare
Tipperary
Cashel
Listowel
LIMERICK
Kilmaganny
Clonmel
WEXFORD
Kilmallock
Tralee
Dingle
Kanturk
Waterford
KERRY
Mallow
WATERFORD
Killorglin
CORK
Kenmare
Cork
Douglas
Cobh
Shanagarry
Ballylickey
Bantry
Ballydehob

LEWDOWN Devon map 1

▲ Lewtrenchard Manor

Lewdown EX20 4PN
TEL: (01566) 783256 FAX: (01566) 783332
EMAIL: stays@lewtrenchard.co.uk
WEB SITE: www.lewtrenchard.co.uk
off A30 Okehampton to Launceston road, turn left at Lewdown

COOKING **5**
MODERN BRITISH
£28–£50

The Victorian hymnist Sabine Baring Gould created Lewtrenchard in a mixture of architectural styles with the appearance of great age, although its dark panelling and old oil paintings now contrast markedly with the lively, contemporary cooking of Jason Hornbuckle, formerly of Tyddyn Llan (see entry, Llandrillo, Wales). What strikes most is the food's freshness and intensity of flavour, for example in a triple-layered terrine of peppers in traffic-light colours interspersed with slices of aubergine, accompanied by a chunky avocado salsa. Presentation is a strong suit – as seen in a 'minestrone' of clear, vegetable-laden broth wearing a frilly mobcap of pasta filled with melting goats' cheese – but visual artistry is not allowed to get the upper hand.

Dishes work because they are carefully considered: as in roast squab pigeon with asparagus risotto and beetroot sauce, or a more conventional dish of beef medallions with dauphinois potatoes and glazed carrots in a rich red wine reduction. Fine balancing of flavours is evident in desserts too, including a chocolate tart served warm with orange and cardamom ice cream, and a banana and passion fruit sorbet to accompany a crème brûlée with a slice of caramelised pineapple at the bottom. Neatly attired waiting staff operate with deftness and efficiency. Originality and enthusiasm mark out a wine list that opens with classic clarets and burgundies, some in good mature vintages, and then offers commendable choice in other regions and styles, with a strong focus on South Africa: house selections kick off with a half-dozen from there, starting at £11.

CHEF: Jason Hornbuckle PROPRIETORS: James and Sue Murray OPEN: all week 12 to 1.30, 7 to 9 MEALS: Set L Mon to Sat £32, Set L Sun £19.50, Set D £32. Bistro menu available Mon to Sat L SERVICE: not inc, card slips closed CARDS: Amex, Delta, Diners, MasterCard, Switch, Visa DETAILS: 30 seats. 30 seats outside. Private parties: 8 main room, 16 and 60 private rooms. Car park. Children's helpings. Children under 8 by arrangement. No smoking in dining room. Wheelchair access (also WC). Music ACCOMMODATION: 9 rooms, all with bath/shower. TV. Phone. B&B £90 to £175. Children under 8 by arrangement. Fishing (*The Which? Hotel Guide*)

LIDGATE Suffolk map 6

Star Inn

The Street, Lidgate CB8 9PP
TEL: (01638) 500275
on B1063, 6m SE of Newmarket

COOKING **1**
MEDITERRANEAN
£24–£43

On the face of it the Star looks like an old-fashioned English country pub, an impression confirmed by its bare wooden tables, simple chairs and settles, and huge open fireplaces. There is even a traditional bar, where you can sit and enjoy a pint of the local Greene King ale. Food, however, is anything but the usual pub grub and draws large, mostly appreciative crowds. Lengthy blackboard menus have something of a Spanish flavour, thanks to the influence of owner Maria Teresa Axon, who hails from Catalonia. Paella Valenciana and hake à la Vasca are popular stalwarts, and pigs' trotters, boquerones (anchovies), grilled cod and swordfish have also appeared. A short selection of wines of the month introduces the main list of some 60 bins, including a wide Spanish range. House wines are £12 a bottle, £2.50 a glass.

CHEF/PROPRIETOR: Maria Teresa Axon OPEN: all week L 12 to 2 (2.30 Sat and Sun), Mon to Sat D 7 to 10 CLOSED: 25 and 26 Dec, 1 Jan MEALS: alc Mon to Sat (main courses £10.50 to £15.50). Set L Mon to Sat £10.50 (2 courses), Set L Sun £14.50 SERVICE: not inc, card slips closed CARDS: Amex, Delta, MasterCard, Switch, Visa DETAILS: 50 seats. 20 seats outside. Private parties: 24 main room, 24 private room. Car park. Children's helpings. No smoking in dining room. Occasional music (£5)

LIFTON Devon map 1

▲ Arundell Arms

Lifton PL16 0AA
TEL: (01566) 784666 FAX: (01566) 784494 COOKING **5**
EMAIL: reservations@arundellarms.com MODERN BRITISH/FRENCH
just off A30, 3m E of Launceston £30–£57

Anybody wanting to catch an angler could be sure of finding one here, where they congregate in season beside the banks of five rivers (including the Tamar) to which the old, creeper-covered coaching inn has fishing rights. They rise, no doubt, to the bait of stone-flagged floors, well-appointed bar, elegant chandeliered dining room, and the opportunity to alternate between bar snacks and two-, three- or four-course meals. Recent refurbishment and general smartening up do not detract from the solidly comfortable and 'timeless atmosphere' of the place, and the kitchen's pride in local materials gets the cooking off to a flying start.

Naturally raised beef and lamb (perhaps roast rack with a mint crust), and organic vegetables, are treated with due respect, and seafood is a strong suit: Helford oysters with browned onions and saffron hollandaise, or a casserole of monkfish, brill, sea bass and lobster. Seasonal input is evident in St Enodoc asparagus in April and May, either cold with lemon mayonnaise, or grilled with Parmesan, and such classical treatments and saucing help to give the cooking its identity. Simplicity and tradition define desserts – perhaps a gratin of strawberries with sweet wine sabayon, or lemon curd sponge pudding with clotted cream – and service is friendly, helpful and smiley. There is plenty for traditionalists on the wine list too, although choice under £20 is more than fair, helped by a handful by the (large) glass.

CHEFS: Philip Burgess and Nick Shopland PROPRIETOR: Anne Voss-Bark OPEN: all week 12.30 to 2, 7.30 to 9.30 CLOSED: 24 and 25 Dec, D 26 Dec MEALS: Set L £18 (2 courses) to £22, Set D £30 to £37.50. Bar menu available SERVICE: not inc CARDS: Amex, Diners, MasterCard, Switch, Visa DETAILS: 70 seats. 30 seats outside. Private parties: 80 main room, 30 private room. Car park. Vegetarian meals. Children's helpings. No smoking in dining room. Wheelchair access (also WC). Music ACCOMMODATION: 27 rooms, all with bath/shower. TV. Phone. B&B £46.50 to £117. Baby facilities. Fishing (*The Which? Hotel Guide*) (£5)

LINCOLN Lincolnshire map 9

Wig & Mitre

30 Steep Hill, Lincoln LN2 1TL
TEL: (01522) 535190 FAX: (01522) 532402
EMAIL: reservations@wigandmitre.co.uk

COOKING **3**
MODERN BRITISH
£20–£49

This characterful place in the old heart of Lincoln serves food all day, taking in breakfast and snacks as well as more substantial fare, its many different-sized rooms enabling it to cater for varied needs at the same time. Rustic chairs and red paper napkins give a slightly pubby feel, but the menu has greater ambition. Soups both traditional (tomato and basil) and not-so (crab, lemon grass and coconut) have earned high praise, as has baked cod on leek and potato mash with beurre blanc. A roast fillet of rarely encountered gurnard is served with crisp-fried cabbage and a mustard butter sauce, and fine pork sausages and mash with onion gravy are 'nearly as good as home-made'. A little racier is duck breast with Thai red curry sauce and a jasmine rice cake. Tempting desserts run to glazed citrus tart with raspberry sorbet, and toffee-filled profiteroles with toffee and pecan sauce. Service is mostly efficient and courteous. A French-based wine list features a range of good producers; house French is £10.50.

CHEFS: Paul Vidic and Peter Dodd PROPRIETORS: Valerie and Michael Hope, and Paul Vidic OPEN: all week 8 to 11 MEALS: alc (main courses £6 to £17). Set L £9 (2 courses) to £12. Breakfasts, sandwiches and light meals also available SERVICE: not inc CARDS: Amex, Delta, Diners, MasterCard, Switch, Visa DETAILS: 135 seats. Private parties: 65 main room, 20 private room. Vegetarian meals. Children's helpings. No smoking in dining room. No music (£5)

LINTON West Yorkshire map 8

▲ Wood Hall

Trip Lane, Linton LS22 4JA
TEL: (01937) 587271 FAX: (01937) 584353
EMAIL: woodhall@arcadianhotels.co.uk
WEB SITE: www.arcadianhotels.co.uk
from Wetherby take A661 N for ½m, turn left for Sicklinghall and Linton, then left to Linton and Wood Hall, turn right in Linton opposite Windmill pub, continue 2m along single-track road

COOKING **2**
MODERN EUROPEAN
£23–£69

Corporate hospitality and 'health and leisure' facilities are important at this eighteenth-century house set in gentle countryside, where well-spaced tables and fine views contribute to the dining room's appeal. A sensible menu (apart from a surfeit of supplements on the set price version) offers scallops with smoked bacon, a chicken liver and haggis parfait, and a generous piece of just-firm cod fillet topped with a thick layer of Welsh rarebit. Flavours come through well, for example in a tomato and basil soup, and Sunday's roast Aberdeen Angus beef with Yorkshire pudding and onion gravy wins support. Vegetables and coffee need improving, but cheeses are well kept, and desserts have included a successful apple and rhubarb crumble with custard. The wine list aims high. Look to South America for a selection under £20, or choose from the eight house wines.

CHEF: Phillip Pomfret PROPRIETOR: Arcadian Hotels OPEN: Sun to Fri L 12 to 3, all week D 7 to 10 MEALS: alc D (main courses £12 to £21.50). Set L £15.95, Set L Sun £14.50, Set D £24.95. Bar menu available SERVICE: not inc, card slips closed CARDS: Amex, Delta, Diners, MasterCard, Switch, Visa DETAILS: 80 seats. Private parties: 110 main room, up to 25 private rooms. Car park. Vegetarian meals. Children's helpings. No smoking in dining room. Wheelchair access (also WC). Music ACCOMMODATION: 42 rooms, all with bath/shower. TV. Phone. Room only £60 to £125. Rooms for disabled. Swimming pool. Fishing (*The Which? Hotel Guide*) (£5)

LITTLE BEDWYN Wiltshire **map 2**

Harrow Inn

NEW ENTRY

Little Bedwyn SN8 3JP
TEL: (01672) 870871
EMAIL: dining@harrowinn.co.uk
WEB SITE: www.harrowinn.co.uk
off A4, 4m SW of Hungerford

COOKING **4**
MODERN BRITISH
£40–£61

There aren't any locals to be found propping up the bar and drinking pints at this old pub in a thatched village by the Kennet and Avon canal. Antique red walls dominate the fresh, clean décor, and large wine glasses and photographs of fish and shellfish announce the serious culinary intent. Daily-changing menus reflect the seasons, and fish features prominently: you might see Tor Bay crab, Cornish lobster, scallops, crevettes, John Dory, cod and wild salmon. Innovative treatment and presentation might team wild sea bass with scallop won ton and a sweet chilli and aubergine dressing, while meat options have taken in rack of Welsh lamb with rosemary and garlic, and medallions of Welsh black beef with watercress and horseradish.

Desserts range from a familiar lemon tart to more exotic chilled tropical fruit terrine with mango ice cream. Service is friendly and efficient, while impeccable cheeses and incidentals add worthy support. Passion for wine is evident on the list, which makes a feature of Riojas from Lopez de Heredia in vintages dating back to 1942. A serious dessert section is attached to the pudding and cheese list, the highlight of which is Canada's Inniskillin Ice Wine (pricing reflects its rarity). For a more accessible dip into sweet wines, try tasting glasses of 'museum' releases of mature Yalumba wines. French house red and white start at £13.

CHEF: Roger Jones PROPRIETORS: Sue and Roger Jones OPEN: Tue to Sun L 12 to 2, Tue to Sat D 7 to 9 CLOSED: 2 weeks Christmas and New Year, 3 weeks Aug MEALS: alc (main courses £14 to £18) SERVICE: not inc, card slips closed CARDS: Amex, Delta, MasterCard, Switch, Visa DETAILS: 40 seats. 36 seats outside. Private parties: 50 main room. No smoking in dining room. Wheelchair access (also WC). No music

Subscribers to Which? Online can access The Good Food Guide *on www.which.net.*

(£5) *indicates that the restaurant has elected to participate in the* Good Food Guide *voucher scheme. For full details, see page 6.*

LITTLE SHELFORD Cambridgeshire map 6

Sycamore House

1 Church Street, Little Shelford CB2 5HG
TEL: (01223) 843396

COOKING 4
MODERN BRITISH
£32–£39

This quiet, detached corner property is one of the more intimate restaurants in the Guide. He cooks, she serves, and décor in the two small dining areas has an unfussy and domestic feel: a small fireplace housing a vase of flowers, a dresser lined with old bottles, and a few bright prints adding colour. The monthly-changing menu favours simple, straightforward dishes described in no-nonsense fashion: for example, blackened salmon with sweet chilli sauce, or pork rillettes with red onion marmalade, followed by steamed smoked haddock with poached egg and watercress sauce, or rack of lamb with creamy onion and garlic sauce.

Occasionally, Michael Sharpe indulges in a flight of fancy: spicy tomato, aubergine and apricot soup, say, or avocado and lettuce crêpe with salsa verde. His inventive side also shows in desserts of blackcurrant and orange trifle, and mincemeat and mascarpone tart with nutmeg ice cream. Wines major on France (house wines £9.95) but also pick out value from around the world. Reasonable prices and a diversity of styles make for a lively, approachable range.

CHEF: Michael Sharpe PROPRIETORS: Michael and Susan Sharpe OPEN: Tue to Sat D 7.30 to 9 CLOSED: 25 Dec MEALS: Set D £23.50 SERVICE: not inc, card slips closed CARDS: Delta, MasterCard, Switch, Visa DETAILS: 24 seats. Private parties: 24 main room. Car park. Vegetarian meals. No children under 12. No smoking in dining room. No music (£5)

LIVERPOOL Merseyside map 8

Becher's Brook

29A Hope Street, L1 9BQ
TEL: (0151) 7070005 FAX: (0151) 7087011

COOKING 3
GLOBAL
£24–£85

The restaurant is decorated with Inuit, Cree and and Haida art, one of Canadian David Cooke's passions, and his food is highly individual too. Ingredients such as lamb sweetbreads, shiitake jus, sea urchin and soya butter might all appear on the menu. Although recent reports note some inconsistency in the cooking, and less than accurate timing, the kitchen still turns out some impressive dishes, including a starter of smoked salmon and leek rösti with roast lobster on a bed of lemon grass cappuccino and salmon roe.

Less exotic, perhaps, but equally convincing, has been a tender, flavourful fillet of Welsh Black beef with foie gras and an intense Madeira jus. Desserts are a strong point; the Grand Plat offers a selection of five pudlets, each 'a class act, and to have them all on one plate was sheer bliss and indulgence'. The shortish wine list, arranged by price and style, trawls Old and New Worlds for interesting, food-friendly choices from £12.95. By the time the Guide appears, the set lunch will probably have been replaced by tapas ranging from £2.95 to £8.95.

CHEF: David Cooke PROPRIETORS: Becher's Brook Restaurants Ltd OPEN: Mon to Fri L 12 to 2.30, Mon to Sat D 5 to 10 MEALS: alc (main courses £15.50 to £30). Pre-theatre 12 to 2 and 5 to 6.45 £11.50 (2 courses) to £14.95. Tapas menu also available L SERVICE: not inc CARDS: Amex, Delta, MasterCard, Switch, Visa DETAILS: 38 seats. Private parties: 38 main room. Vegetarian meals. No smoking in dining room. Music (£5)

Chung Ku

NEW ENTRY

Columbus Quay, Riverside Drive,
Liverpool L3 4DB — COOKING **4**
TEL: (0151) 726 8191 FAX: (0151) 726 8190 — CHINESE
WEB SITE: www.chungkurestaurant.co.uk — £17–£70

The two-storey dining area's glass frontage allows panoramic views of the Mersey. Tables are closely spaced, but high ceilings diffuse some of the background noise, and the upstairs section is more peaceful. Five chefs from China have been recruited since the opening in 2000, and a senior Chinese inspector found their cooking and presentation exceptional. The 70-strong list of dim sum in English takes in impressively light noodle rolls filled variously with scallops, or grouper, as well as the usual prawns and pork; and chiu chow dumplings with spicy minced pork, coriander and peanuts.

Barbecue meats are equally commended. So are such main dishes as salt and chilli king prawn, stewed belly pork with salt preserved cabbage, grouper fillet with mange tout and Chinese mushrooms, and – best of all – beautifully crisp yet tender choi sum, pungent with garlic. These are from the Chinese-language-only special menu, so try to persuade the willing (if sometimes hard-pressed) staff of your interest in real Chinese food, and discuss the menu with them. Prices, though not low, are justified by the ambience as well as by the cooking. House wines are £9.50

CHEF: Au Tung PROPRIETOR: Mrs T.L. Shum OPEN: all week, noon to 11 (9.30 Sun and bank hols) CLOSED: 25 Dec MEALS: alc (main courses £7.50 to £30). Set L (till 2.30) £9.50, Set D £18 to £28 (min 2 to 4) SERVICE: not inc CARDS: Amex, Delta, MasterCard, Switch, Visa DETAILS: 400 seats. Private parties: 200 main room. Car park. Vegetarian meals. Wheelchair access (also WC). Music. Air-conditioned

Shangri-La

37 Victoria Street, Liverpool L1 6BQ — COOKING **2**
TEL: (0151) 255 0708 and 227 2707 — CHINESE
FAX: (0151) 236 6560 — £25 – £49

This is an archetypal city-centre Chinese restaurant, traditionally decorated, seating hundreds on various levels. The menu offers a few concessions to occidentals, and more than a few treats for Chinese experts. Dim sum, traditionally eaten until the late afternoon, are described on the menu as 'stimulants to your amicable conversation' and include deep-fried vegetable won ton, deep-fried scallops with yam pastry, and a special steamed dim sum combination for at least two people, ideal for those venturing into this territory for the first time. You are invited to 'take your strength from the concentrated goodness' of soups, including shark's fin with chicken, and beef and tomato. Special seafood dishes feature crab, lobster, sea bass and Dover sole, and hotpots take in fried oyster with ginger and spring onion, as well as braised sea slugs and fish lips. House wines are £9.80.

CHEF: Mr Chan PROPRIETOR: Mr Ho OPEN: all week 12 to midnight CLOSED: 25 Dec MEALS: alc (main courses £5.50 to £24). Set L 12 to 2.30 £5.30, Set D 2.30 onwards £14 to £24 (min 2) SERVICE: not inc, card slips closed CARDS: Amex, Delta, Diners, MasterCard, Switch, Visa DETAILS: 400 seats. Private parties: 200 main room, 100 private room. Vegetarian meals. Music. Air-conditioned

Simply Heathcotes

NEW ENTRY

Beetham Plaza, 25 The Strand, L2 0XL
TEL: (0151) 2363536 FAX: (0151) 2363534
EMAIL: liverpool@simplyheathcotes.co.uk
WEB SITE: www.heathcotes.co.uk

COOKING **3**
MODERN ENGLISH
£25–£48

Paul Heathcote has hit the expansion trail with a vengeance. His original restaurant at Longridge has now spawned a litter of Simply Heathcotes, this one (opposite the Liver and Cunard buildings) joining the branches in Preston and Manchester (see entries). It flaunts its modern credentials with a curved plate-glass frontage, Chinese granite floors, a solid cherrywood bar and Philippe Starck chairs, while the menu makes much of Lancashire ingredients. Black pudding 'hash brown', Goosnargh chicken and duckling, and ice cream made with Liverpool's own Cain's bitter, are supported by internationalist briagde of polenta, brandade and risottos.

Raw materials are good-quality, and if the format seems 'straightforward brasserie', most dishes have a touch of class, producing for example a salmon terrine (combining smoked and poached) well complemented by sharp horseradish and sweet beetroot, and a carefully timed daily-special hake fillet, simply served on a bed of spinach with hollandaise and new potatoes. Vegetarian dishes are as flavourful as the rest, and desserts might include fluffy-light baked cheesecake with sweet apple and cinnamon compote, or a chocolate and peanut brownie with that beer-flavoured ice-cream. A world-wide wine list kicks off with proprietary French blends at £11.50.

CHEF: Andrew McGuinness PROPRIETOR: Paul Heathcote OPEN: all week 12 to 2.30, 7 to 10 (6 to 11 Sat) CLOSED: 24 to 26 Dec, 1 Jan, bank hol Mon MEALS: alc exc Sun L (main courses £12 to £17). Set L £13.50 (2 courses) to £15.50. Brunch menu available Sun SERVICE: 10% (optional), card slips closed CARDS: Amex, Delta, Diners, MasterCard, Switch, Visa DETAILS: 75 seats. Private parties: 75 main room, 28 private room. Vegetarian meals. Children's helpings. No cigars/pipes in dining room. Wheelchair access (also WC). Music. Air-conditioned

60 Hope Street

60 Hope Street, Liverpool L1 9BZ
TEL: (0151) 707 6060 FAX: (0151) 707 6016
EMAIL: info@60hopestreet.com
WEB SITE: www.60hopestreet.com

COOKING **4**
MODERN EUROPEAN
£24–£57

This trendy, pacesetting combination of ground-floor restaurant and basement café-bar has struck a winning chord on Merseyside. Polished wood floors, and blue and orange walls, cut a striking minimalist edge in the double-fronted Georgian terraced house, where wooden tables are simply laid with starched napkins. It all expresses a relaxed confidence, and service is knowledgeable, chatty and attentive without getting in the way. A regularly changing carte (bolstered by daily specials) relies more on skill and invention than on luxury ingredients, with sound materials laying a firm foundation: in a starter of seared tuna on a bed of diced Mediterranean vegetables, or a winning combination of guinea fowl with black pudding, roast sweet potatoes, caramelised apple segments and wilted rocket.

Other well reported dishes include cumin-seared scallops with zaalouk (answers on a postcard, please) and pomegranate dressing; wild sea bass with boulangère potatoes and creamed leeks; and a raspberry brûlée with shortbread. But the star finish is undoubtedly a deep-fried jam sandwich with Carnation milk ice cream, an adult take on the 'ultimate in nursery food from a bygone era'. A classically styled list offers a selection of wine-friendly ideas to match a variety of dishes. Prices remain fair throughout, and effort has been made to provide reds, whites and even sparklers under £13, although those marked out as house wines start at £13.50.

CHEF: Steven McCabe PROPRIETORS: Colin, Holly and Gary Manning OPEN: Mon to Fri L 12 to 2.30, Mon to Sat D 7 to 10.30 CLOSED: 25 and 26 Dec, bank hols MEALS: alc (main courses £14 to £18.50). Set L £10.95 (2 courses) to £13.95 SERVICE: not inc, 10% for parties of 8 or more CARDS: Delta, MasterCard, Switch, Visa DETAILS: 90 seats. Private parties: 90 main room, 30 private room. Children's helpings. No-smoking area. Occasional music. Air-conditioned

Tai Pan £

W.H. Lung Building, Great Howard Street, L5 9TZ
TEL: (0151) 207 3888 FAX: (0151) 207 0100
WEB SITE: www.taipan.co.uk

NEW CHEF
CHINESE
£17–£65

It was all change at this clean, bright restaurant above a supermarket, with the arrival of new owners and a new chef as the Guide went to press. No new menus were available (the previous one listed steamed scallop dumplings, fried cuttlefish cakes, and brisket casserole) but Tommy Chan was listed last year at New Emperor in Manchester, so he is no stranger to large restaurants, cosmpolitan brio, or a busy repertoire designed for both Chinese and English customers. Reports please.

CHEF: Tommy Chan PROPRIETOR: Office Might Ltd OPEN: all week, noon to 11.30 MEALS: alc (main courses £6.50 to £30). Set L Mon to Fri 12 to 2 £5.45 (2 courses) to £8.45, Set D £14 to £25 (all min 2) SERVICE: not inc CARDS: Amex, Delta, MasterCard, Switch, Visa DETAILS: 370 seats. Private parties: 280 main room, 90 private room. Car park. Vegetarian meals. Wheelchair access (also WC). Music. Air-conditioned

Ziba

15–19 Berry Street, Liverpool L1 9DF
TEL: (0151) 708 8870 FAX: (0151) 707 9926

COOKING **5**
MODERN ENGLISH
£26–£49

This smartly converted car showroom on the edge of Europe's oldest Chinatown is reached through a glass atrium and open metal staircase. A long bar, windows down two sides, and girders supporting the sloping ceiling provide a dramatic backdrop for some equally stimulating modern cooking. A carte changes seasonally, the prix-fixe week by week, and their combined range and allure keep at least one reporter returning time and again. The food's 'great intensity and definition of flavour' is evident in seared scallops with pancetta and a butternut squash risotto, and in an assiette of fish combining grey mullet, salmon, sea bass and turbot with linguine, mayonnaise and slivers of garlic.

Vegetarians might opt for polenta cake with ratatouille and parsley purée, while others might waver between Goosnargh chicken breast with sage and roast sweet potato, or loin of lamb with goats' cheese tortellini and basil purée. Puddings have a distinct northern demotic slant: custard tart with caramelised banana, say, or a peanut-butter and jam ice cream sandwich. Wines, listed by style, have largely been sourced for their value and lively character; most are under £20, although a few stunners, like Sassicaia, command dizzier prices.

CHEF: Glenn Futter PROPRIETORS: Martin and Helen Ainscough OPEN: Mon to Sat 12 to 2, 6 (6.30 Sat) to 10 (10.30 Sat) CLOSED: 25 and 26 Dec, bank hols (exc Good Fri) MEALS: alc (main courses £13.50 to £15). Set L and D £13 (2 courses) to £16.50 SERVICE: not inc, 10% for parties of 10 or more CARDS: Amex, Delta, MasterCard, Switch, Visa DETAILS: 120 seats. Private parties: 120 main room, 12 private room. Car park. Vegetarian meals. No cigars/pipes throughout; no smoking in 1 dining room. Wheelchair access (also WC). Occasional music (£5)

LLANFAIR WATERDINE Shropshire map 5

▲ Waterdine

Llanfair Waterdine LD7 1TU
TEL: (01547) 528214 FAX: (01547) 529992

COOKING **4**
MODERN BRITISH
£24–£43

Standing across from the church, the sixteenth-century long house was originally built as a drovers' inn, the River Teme at the bottom of the garden marking the English–Welsh border at this point. It still has the feel of a pub, serving well-kept real ales from local brewers, and the candlelit dining room (there is also a beamed taproom and a bright bistro) has impressive and peaceful views of sheep and rolling hills. Dinner is three courses, the style an appealing mix that might take in starters of chestnut soup, Roquefort soufflé, or a piece of moist monkfish wrapped in Parma ham, set beside a pile of soft provençale vegetables.

Accurate timing is a feature, producing crisp-skinned fillet of brill on a well-judged potato galette surrounded by a large quantity of creamy leeks, and a generous-sized, pink, flavourful breast of duck (with bacon, celeriac and morels) in a plentiful rich gravy. Pastry is another strength, filled with tasty tomato flesh and a round of melting goats' cheese to start, and appearing as an individual warm lemon tart to finish. Alternatively, there might be a soft-poached pear in red wine, served with a scoop of clotted cream. Bread is good, service is welcoming and relaxed, and breakfast is worth staying for, not least for those who have taken advantage of the astute selection of fairly priced wines. These avoid the usual lazy options in favour of enterprising drinking and good value from around the world. House red and white by the glass are £2.25.

CHEF/PROPRIETOR: Ken Adams OPEN: Sun L 12.15 to 1.45, Tue to Sat D 7.15 to 9.15 CLOSED: 1 week Nov to Dec, 1 week Jan to Feb MEALS: Set L £15, Set D £25. Light L available Tue to Sat. Bar menu available Tue to Sat D SERVICE: not inc, card slips closed CARDS: Delta,

MasterCard, Switch, Visa DETAILS: 40 seats. 16 seats outside. Private parties: 12 main room, 12 private room. Car park. No children under 8 in dining room. No smoking in dining room. No music ACCOMMODATION: 3 rooms, all with bath/shower. TV. B&B £40 to £70. No children

LOCKINGTON East Riding of Yorkshire map 9

▲ Rockingham Arms

52 Front Street, Lockington YO25 9SH COOKING **4**
TEL: (01430) 810607 FAX: (01430) 810734 MODERN EUROPEAN-PLUS
off A164, between Beverley and Driffield £42–£50

Still looking like an old village pub, and charming with it, Rockingham Arms strikes a confident air, its cavernous, brick-walled, candle-lit barn of a dining room furnished with wicker chairs and polished wooden tables. It uses fine ingredients in a straightforward but imaginative menu: six choices for each of the three courses, perhaps taking in spiced crab cake with sweet chilli sauce, or calf's liver with beetroot and apple confit, sage beignets and veal jus.

But the daily specials board seems the best bet, judging by one visitor's haul: a fresh-tasting starter of prawns in a citrus sauce with fennel, a 'seriously good' steak cooked pink as requested, and a fine piece of halibut, set about with potatoes, lentils, scallions and tomatoes in a dill sauce. The finishing line (the place is named after a racehorse) sees treacle tart with clotted-cream ice cream, and a soft meringue roulade with Muscat-poached fruits and praline. Alternatively, an international trio of cheeses comes with medjool dates and pepper crackers. Around 75 skilfully selected wines, starting at £12.95 and staying mostly under £25, mix classic European names and New World offerings; if in doubt, take a chance on a name you don't recognise.

CHEFS: Sue Barker and Simon Stevenson PROPRIETORS: David and Sue Barker OPEN: Tue to Sat D 7 to 10 CLOSED: Christmas, bank hols MEALS: Set D £24.95 (2 courses) to £28.95 SERVICE: not inc CARDS: Amex, Delta, MasterCard, Switch, Visa DETAILS: 54 seats. Private parties: 14 main room. Car park. Vegetarian meals. Music ACCOMMODATION: 3 rooms, all with bath/shower. TV. B&B £85 to £110. No children (£5)

LONG CRENDON Buckinghamshire map 2

▲ Angel Restaurant

47 Bicester Road, Long Crendon HP18 9EE COOKING **3**
TEL: (01844) 208268 FAX: (01844) 202497 SEAFOOD/PACIFIC RIM
on B4011, 2m NW of Thame £30–£62

Set on the outskirts of a well-kempt village, this sixteenth-century former pub provides an attractive venue for Trevor Bosch's contemporary cookery. Diners start off in the beam-laden bar, then young well-practised staff direct them to stripped-pine tables in one of a series of dining areas including a light conservatory and (in summer) a patio. Though meat eaters and vegetarians are catered for (partridge in port and redcurrant sauce, or wild mushroom and asparagus mille-feuille, for instance) it's the fish dishes, chalked above the bar, that dominate.

The fusion approach might take in a pavé of salmon on champ with spicy mussels, dressed with competing creamy and sweet chilli sauces, but most flavour combinations are simple and sensible. The quality of ingredients shines through, too: in an intensely savoury cream of haddock and saffron soup, and in a fine specimen of grilled lemon sole with herb butter and niçoise-style salad. A fitting finale is a plate of taster-sized portions of five popular puds ranging from lemon meringue pie to crème brûlée with strawberries marinated in vodka. Trevor Bosch has made an effort to balance wine styles on his list, especially among fish-friendly whites, which range from fresh and fruity Sauvignons and Muscadets to rich, buttery Chardonnays. For those who prefer red, some good Australian names provide value. House wines change monthly, and start at £13.95.

CHEFS: Trevor Bosch and Donny Joyce PROPRIETOR: Angela Good OPEN: all week L 12 to 2.30 (3 Sun), Mon to Sat D 7 to 10 MEALS: alc exc Sun L (main courses £12.50 to £21.50). Set L Sun £14.95 (2 courses) to £17.95 SERVICE: not inc CARDS: Delta, MasterCard, Switch, Visa DETAILS: 75 seats. 32 seats outside. Private parties: 30 main room, 6 to 30 private rooms. Car park. Vegetarian meals. Children's helpings. No smoking in 1 dining room. Music. Air-conditioned ACCOMMODATION: 3 rooms, all with bath/shower. TV. Phone. B&B £55 to £65. Baby facilities (*The Which? Hotel Guide*) (£5)

LONG MELFORD Suffolk **map 6**

Scutchers Bistro

Westgate Street, Long Melford CO10 9DP COOKING **3**
TEL: (01787) 310200 FAX: (07000) 785443 MODERN BRITISH
WEB SITE: www.scutchers.com £28–£52

It may feel more gastro-pub than bistro, but this is still a very pleasant place. Wood panelling, pine tables, trellises and flagstone floors create a comforting feel, enhanced by a log fire in winter. The menu choice is wide, as is the range of influences: from sauté foie gras on rösti with mushy peas, haggis and caramelised shallots, to rather simpler toasted goats' cheese crostini with red pepper tapénade.

Roast loin of lamb scores highly, perhaps served with root vegetables and a thyme gravy, or there may be strips of Dover sole with a light curry sauce, and perhaps a vegetarian risotto with a poached egg. Desserts include a trio of home-made ice creams in a tuile basket (well-reported), and bread-and-butter pudding with apricot coulis. 'Service,' says one report, 'unfailingly achieves that difficult balance between friendliness and professionalism.' The wine list, sourced from Lay and Wheeler, has many fine bottles, but prices are stiffish; a 15-strong 'Scutchers Selection', opening with South African red and white at £11.50, offers some relief.

CHEFS: Nicholas Barrett and Guy Alabaster PROPRIETORS: Nicholas and Diane Barrett OPEN: Tue to Sat 12 to 2, 7 to 9.30 CLOSED: 4 days Christmas, first week Jan, last week Aug MEALS: alc (main courses £10 to £17) SERVICE: not inc CARDS: Amex, Delta, MasterCard, Switch, Visa DETAILS: 75 seats. 45 seats outside. Private parties: 75 main room. Car park. Vegetarian meals. Children's helpings. No cigars/pipes in restaurant. Wheelchair access (also WC). No music. Air-conditioned (£5)

The Guide's top-rated restaurants are listed near the front of the book.

LONGRIDGE Lancashire map 8

Paul Heathcote's

104–106 Higher Road, Longridge PR3 3SY
TEL: (01772) 784969 FAX: (01772) 785713
EMAIL: longridge@heathcotes.co.uk
from Preston, follow Town Centre signs, drive uphill though centre of Longridge, then turn left, following signs for Jeffery Hill

NEW CHEF
MODERN BRITISH
£26–£95

Three small interlinked stone cottages on the edge of Longridge stand at the hub of a small entrepreneurial empire, with branches of Simply Heathcotes in Preston, Manchester and now Liverpool (see entries). Matthew Harris arrived just as the Guide went to press, too late for us to receive any feedback. Initial plans, however, seemed to involve no great change of style, which owes an equal debt to both classical French cooking and the northern larder, taking in Reg Johnson's highly rated Goosnargh poultry, and perhaps a dish of black pudding embedded in hash brown potatoes with Lancashire cheese. Wines aim for the high ground, with some fine bottles to their credit, although prices hardly favour modest drinkers. French and Chilean house wines at £13.50 are blended specially for the restaurant.

CHEF: Matthew Harris PROPRIETOR: Paul Heathcote OPEN: Wed to Fri and Sun L 12 to 2.15, Wed to Sun D 7 to 9.30 MEALS: alc D (main courses £18 to £24). Set L £16.50, Set D £38 to £65 SERVICE: 10% (optional), card slips closed CARDS: Amex, Delta, Diners, MasterCard, Switch, Visa DETAILS: 60 seats. Private parties: 60 main room, 16 private room. Car park. Vegetarian meals. Children's helpings. No smoking in dining room. Wheelchair access (not WC). Music (£5)

LOOE Cornwall map 1

Trawlers

Buller Quay, East Looe PL13 1AH
TEL: (01503) 263593

COOKING **2**
CAJUN/PROVENÇALE SEAFOOD
£27–£45

Trawlers is located smack on the quayside, the daily catch ties up right outside and the town's thriving fish market is just a net-cast away. Seafood is indeed at the heart of its operation; walls are covered with fishing pictures, photographs and nets, while laminate-topped tables and simple wooden chairs characterise the unpretentious interior. Chef Todd Varnedoe, who hails from New Orleans, adds spice to proceedings with classic southern-states and provençale cooking: Creole crab cakes, Cajun spiced breast of chicken, and pan-fried king prawns and monkfish with garlic, tomatoes and capers. Desserts hit a more familiar note with chocolate marquise and vanilla sauce perhaps heading up the bill. Service is 'characterful and efficient', while the short, good-value wine list offers six by the half-bottle and French house wine at £9.25 (£2.30 a glass).

CHEF: Todd Varnedoe PROPRIETORS: Roger Stamp and Cathy Styche OPEN: Tue to Sat (Mon July and Aug) D only 6.30 to 9.30 CLOSED: Jan MEALS: alc (main courses £12 to £16.50). Set D £14.75 (2 courses) SERVICE: not inc CARDS: Amex, MasterCard, Switch, Visa DETAILS: 30 seats. Private parties: 30 main room. Vegetarian meals. Children's helpings. No children under 6. No smoking in dining room. Wheelchair access (not WC). Occasional music (£5)

Water Rail

NEW ENTRY

Lower Market Street, East Looe PL13 1AX
TEL/FAX: (01503) 262314

COOKING **2**
SEAFOOD
£25–£53

'What a find!' enthused one report of this restaurant in a seventeenth-century building down a narrow side street off the harbour. Inside, it is small and characterful, with white walls, beams and cottagey dark-wood furniture. The welcome is warm, and service is keen and friendly. Richard Maior-Barron learnt his skills around the Mediterranean fishing regions, which shows in the wide choice of simple dishes built on supplies fresh from the quay. They are used in nightly specials, perhaps crab and anchovy cakes with yoghurt, garlic and cucumber sauce, or skewered monkfish grilled and served in an uncomplicated parsley, garlic and tomato sauce. Simple excellence marks out desserts too: of classic chocolate mousse or homely spotted dick. A short wine list provides inexpensive drinking from £8.95, with most bottles well under £20.

CHEF: Richard Maior-Barron PROPRIETORS: Richard and Denise Maior-Barron OPEN: Wed to Mon D only 7 to 10 MEALS: alc (main courses £9.50 to £24.50). Set D £13.95 (2 courses) SERVICE: not inc CARDS: Delta, MasterCard, Switch, Visa DETAILS: 38 seats. Private parties: 20 main room, 12 private room. Vegetarian meals. No children under 10. No smoking in 1 dining room. Music (£5)

LOWER SLAUGHTER Gloucestershire map 5

▲ Lower Slaughter Manor

Lower Slaughter GL54 2HP
TEL: (01451) 820456 FAX: (01451) 822150
EMAIL: lowsmanor@aol.com
WEB SITE: www.lowerslaughter.co.uk
off A429, at sign 'The Slaughters'

COOKING **4**
ANGLO-FRENCH
£31–£73

Sheltered grounds, manicured lawns, and serried rows of roses and begonias contribute to a serene setting; built of warm golden stone, the house itseslf dates back to 1658, its interior packed with deep sofas and chairs, and deep pink and red fabrics. The formula is a set-price menu of classic European cooking, and although dinner is a grander affair than lunch, it might well open with a retro appetiser of prawn cocktail with a fishcake. Alongside straightforward dishes, such as beef carpaccio with herb dressing, might be a more ambitious way with Orkney crab, combining tortellini and samosas dressed with a frothy basil sauce.

Although dishes can be complex, they generally hang together, as in a main course plate of new season's lamb, combining roast saddle, a cutlet, a chunk of sweetbread and slices of liver, all atop a stack of layered vegetables, with a pool of stock-based Madeira sauce, the whole garnished with deep-fried herbs.

Desserts, such as rhubarb crumble soufflé with a flavourful yoghurt and custard ice cream, are well executed too. Formally dressed staff, many of them French, are attentive and courteous, and the wine list has a classic bent, with much attention given to France, but more modern styles do get an airing. The extensive halves selection offers, again, mainly French choices, including the occasional mature vintage. Six house wines from all corners of the wine-producing world start at £13.25.

CHEF: Jonathon Baron PROPRIETORS: Roy and Daphne Vaughan OPEN: all week 12.30 to 2, 7.30 to 9.30 (10 Sat) MEALS: Set L £12 (2 courses) to £40, Set D £45. Light L available SERVICE: not inc CARDS: Amex, Delta, Diners, MasterCard, Switch, Visa DETAILS: 34 seats. Private parties: 34 main room, 20 private room. Car park. No children under 12. Jacket and tie. No smoking in dining room. Occasional music ACCOMMODATION: 16 rooms, all with bath/shower. TV. Phone. B&B £175 to £400. Rooms for disabled. No children under 12. Swimming pool (*The Which? Hotel Guide*)

▲ Washbourne Court **NEW ENTRY**

Lower Slaughter GL54 2HS
TEL: (01451) 822143 FAX: (01451) 821045 — COOKING **3**
EMAIL: washbourne@msn.com — MODERN EUROPEAN
WEB SITE: www.washbournecourt.co.uk — £31–£67

Well-trained, courteous and professional staff, and a 'stylish and witty' restaurant manager get things off to a good start at this part-seventeenth-century, honey-coloured Cotswold-stone hotel set alongside the River Eye. Its traditional English appearance is helped by polished wood-veneer tables and mock antique chairs, against a backdrop of deep pink, reproduction Canalettos and views over the gardens.

By contrast, the ambitious cooking has a modern edge, offering sound combinations such as seared scallops with shellfish risotto and cauliflower purée on a scallop roe bisque. At the same time, expect a few formalities (the cloche treatment) and an elaborate approach to dishes: in roast cannon of Cotswold lamb in a brioche and herb crust, for example, served with courgette charlotte, roast garlic and juniper berry jus.

Deep-fried rice pudding with apricot and prune 'morceaux' and fudge ice cream comes recommended by staff, although an assiette of desserts may prove a stronger attraction. Extras include canapés, appetiser, inter-course sorbet and petits fours, so pace yourself. A smart collection of predominantly French wines does extend to the less ordinary, but pricing reflects the venue. French country wines, and the house selection beginning at £20 a bottle, provide more affordable drinking options.

CHEF: Sean Ballington PROPRIETORS: Roy and Daphne Vaughan OPEN: all week 12.30 to 2, 7 to 9 MEALS: Set L Mon to Sat £16.75 (2 courses) to £19.75, Set L Sun £22, Set D £42. Bar menu available SERVICE: not inc CARDS: Amex, Delta, Diners, MasterCard, Switch, Visa DETAILS: 60 seats. Private parties: 60 main room, 20 private room. Car park. Vegetarian meals. No children under 12 in dining room. No smoking in dining room. Wheelchair access (not WC). Occasional music ACCOMMODATION: 28 rooms, all with bath/shower. TV. Phone. D,B&B £145 to £270. Rooms for disabled (£5)

LOW LAITHE North Yorkshire map 9

Dusty Miller

Low Laithe, Summerbridge HG3 4BU — COOKING **5**
TEL: (01423) 780837 FAX: (01423) 780065 — ANGLO-FRENCH
on B6165, 2m SE of Pateley Bridge — £34–£61

Just the pavement separates the Dennisons' modest restaurant from the B-road through the village. There's a drawing of a rustic miller on the cover of the menu; otherwise 'Dusty' gives way to colourful pictures of French rural life in the tiny dining room, which has a cared-for, old-fashioned feel, with white table linen, cream-painted flock wallpaper and a ticking grandfather clock. Brian Dennison's Anglo-French repertoire is appealingly unpretentious, although nobody could accuse it of being bang up-to-date, given pâté Beaujolais, melon with ham, and tournedos Rossini among the offerings.

Raw materials are first-rate (freshly landed fish from Whitby, Loch Fyne oysters, and local meats), while the accomplished cooking is helped along by impressive saucing: spring lamb with rosemary jus delivered exactly as described but with a sauce boat of extra 'top-class' jus. A set-price menu and a couple of daily dishes support the carte, while starters might take in cannelloni of prawns and haddock, and desserts fresh fruit sorbets, or tarte Tatin. Elizabeth Dennison is a warm, friendly and calm host, while the short wine list has a page of French fine wines and offers more modest drinking from £12.90.

CHEF: Brian Dennison PROPRIETORS: Brian and Elizabeth Dennison OPEN: Tue to Sat D only 6.30 to 11 CLOSED: 25 and 26 Dec, 1 Jan, 2 weeks Aug to Sept MEALS: alc (main courses £18 to £20). Set D £24 SERVICE: not inc, card slips closed CARDS: Amex, MasterCard, Visa DETAILS: 44 seats. Private parties: 30 main room, 14 and 16 private rooms. Car park. Vegetarian meals. Children's helpings. No children under 9. No smoking in dining room. Wheelchair access (not WC). Occasional music

LUDLOW Shropshire map 8

▲ Dinham Hall

NEW ENTRY

Dinham, Ludlow SY8 1EJ
TEL: (01584) 876464 FAX: (01584) 876019 — COOKING **3**
EMAIL: info@dinhamhall.co.uk — FRENCH
WEB SITE: www.dinhamhall.co.uk — £42–£50

This attractive Palladian building dating from 1792 is opposite the Castle, its deep-pink dining room (elaborately draped, with white linen-covered tables) overseen by attentive, if rather formal, staff. If Olivier Bossut's menu – in French with English translations – didn't disclose his heritage, the presentation might, with its little appetisers, mid-meal sorbet, 'fussy bits and bobs' and other decorative flourishes.

Many dishes are based on upmarket ingredients, some with intriguing flavour combinations, such as nutty scallops served in a mesclun salad with beetroot juice, or paupiette of sea bass and foie gras with an aniseed beurre blanc. Even desserts explore this vein: hot chocolate and raspberry pudding comes with aniseed ice cream and pistachio sauce. Other dishes take a more familiar route, perhaps in the form of rack of lamb with creamy Savoy cabbage and raspberry vinegar sauce, or tarte Tatin made the old-fashioned way with apples. The wine list, with some well-priced house recommendations at £13.50, combines classic French regions with selections from Spain, the New World and Herefordshire, emphasising reasonable prices rather than fancy names; there is plenty under £25.

CHEF: Olivier Bossut PROPRIETORS: J.P. and J.E. Mifsud OPEN: all week 12.30 to 2, 7 to 9 CLOSED: 26 Dec, 1 Jan L MEALS: Set L £24 (2 courses) to £28.50, Set D £24 (2 courses) to £28.50. Light L menu also available SERVICE: not inc, card slips closed CARDS: Amex, Delta, Diners, MasterCard, Switch, Visa DETAILS: 25 seats. 30 seats outside. Private parties: 34 main room, 10 and 24 private rooms. Car park. Children's helpings. No children under 8. No smoking in dining room. No music ACCOMMODATION: 15 rooms, all with bath/shower. TV. Phone. B&B £70 to £170 (*The Which? Hotel Guide*)

Hibiscus

17 Corve Street, Ludlow SY8 1DA — COOKING **6**
TEL: (01584) 872325 FAX: (01584) 874024 — FRENCH
£38–£72

Extensive wood panelling, stone walls and a welcome lack of clutter produce an 'elegantly minimalist' feel to this narrow terraced house. Well-spaced tables, padded chairs and gentle lighting create a calm environment in which to study a sensibly short yet lively menu that teams pan-fried foie gras with liquorice and William pear, and flavours turbot with coffee and cardamom. 'Outstanding' raw materials include langoustine tails, served with roast white peach and a rather domineering peanut butter sauce, and a terrine of 'almost raw' wild salmon, bound with aubergine purée, served with a garlicky smoked crème anglaise. Many supplies come from France; in June Périgord lamb (it has been Welsh at other times) was sliced into pink rashers and served with a jumble of green vegetables 'in the best possible condition', along with roasted lemon and garlic.

Portions are well-judged, and attention to detail enables technically demanding dishes to be pulled off with assurance. But complexity does not rule out robust flavours; one soup was served in three layers: a base of hollandaise, then shaved melted Parmesan, then an earthy wild mushroom soup heady with truffle. Not everything is perfect, but much is (including timing), and the cooking's bravura lifts it out of the ordinary. Ice creams are a feature of desserts, ranging from hedgerow flavours such as hawthorn (served with a whole peach, skinned and caramelised) to star anise (with warm chocolate tart). Impeccable extras include 'the best' bread, made from roasted flour. Service from Claire Crosby finds the right balance between formal and casual, and wines, divided into France and the Rest, are sharply chosen, though prices are highish; house wines are £14.

CHEF: Claude Bosi PROPRIETORS: Claude Bosi and Claire Crosby OPEN: Wed to Sat L 12.30 to 1.30, Mon to Sat D 7.30 to 9.30 (Sun D 15 Apr to 1 Oct) CLOSED: 2 weeks Jan, 1 week Aug MEALS: Set L £19.50 (2 courses) to £25, Set D £32.50 to £45 SERVICE: not inc, card slips closed CARDS: MasterCard, Switch, Visa DETAILS: 26 seats. Private parties: 26 main room. Car park. Children's helpings. No smoking in dining room. Wheelchair access (not WC). No music

Use the lists towards the front of the book to find suitable restaurants for special occasions.

Merchant House

Lower Corve Street, Ludlow SY8 1DU
TEL: (01584) 875438

COOKING **8**
MODERN BRITISH
£34–£48

In a small town thick with good places to eat, Merchant House is top of the heap. Don't expect decorative or culinary frills; this is 'the most understated restaurant I have encountered', its lack of pretension evident in beams and bare wooden tables whose sole apparent purpose is 'not to distract from the food'. Lunch has been streamlined to just three choices per course, its price reduced to compensate, while dinner offers four choices. If that doesn't sound much, bear in mind that this is a tiny operation, with just one man preparing everything. The cooking – immediate, approachable, unadorned – lays bare the prime quality of materials: fresh, sweet, firm local asparagus, served as a starter with artichoke, mushroom duxelles and an indulgently eggy but fresh-tasting basil sabayon, or lobster in a beautifully balanced broth of lentils and coriander.

Anything that doesn't need to be on the plate just isn't there, as in a starter of veal sweetbread, fully exploiting the contrast of crisp outside and soft inside, served on a cake of mashed potato and olive, with just enough sauce to moisten it. Since their main items remain centre stage – fine, plump, pink squab pigeon with a spring vegetable risotto for example – dishes retain a focus and sense of purpose. Fish, expertly timed to be 'semi-translucent', might appear as grilled sea bass with a refreshingly light basil and crème fraîche sauce, or as a joyous bourride of turbot, monkfish and prawn, pungent with garlic, saffron and a hint of curry spice.

Traditional skills count for more than showmanship in deserts too: as in apricot tart with amaretto ice cream, or a simply poached peach served with exemplary pistachio ice cream (none of that green paste here). Bread is first-rate, and service from Anja Hill and helper is efficient, friendly and unassuming, not in the least effusive or flamboyant. No service charge is made, which adds to the operation's sense of honesty and integrity. Wines combine quality, value and interest within a small compass, starting with Italian house wines at £13.50 and £15.50 and branching out to the great estates of France and Spain.

CHEF: Shaun Hill PROPRIETORS: Shaun and Anja Hill OPEN: Fri and Sat L 12.30 to 1.45, Tue to Sat D 7 to 8.45 CLOSED: 1 week Christmas, 1 week spring MEALS: Set L £25, Set D £31 SERVICE: net prices, card slips closed CARDS: Delta, MasterCard, Switch, Visa DETAILS: 24 seats. Private parties: 8 main room. No smoking in dining room. Wheelchair access (not WC). No music

▲ Mr Underhill's

Dinham Weir, Ludlow SY8 1EH
TEL: (01584) 874431
WEB SITE: www.mr-underhills.co.uk

COOKING **7**
MODERN EUROPEAN
£40–£48

Underneath the castle ramparts, beside Dinham Weir on the fast-flowing River Teme, Mr Underhill's location exposes it to the possibility of flooding, and the worst happened (twice) over last autumn and winter, a fine way to celebrate 20 years in the business (16 of them, as some readers may recall, at Stonham in Suffolk). All is now back to normal in the long, airy and attractive dining room.

The dinner format, with no choice at all before dessert, is relatively unusual these days, at least among more cosmopolitan restaurants, but the menu is discussed beforehand, and if this arrangement allows the kitchen to perform at its best, then who can doubt its wisdom?

A sense of economy is also evident in favoured sauces, such as champagne and chive beurre blanc, which is applied variously to warm asparagus salad, or to a pair of light, crisp fishcakes (made with smoked haddock, cod and salmon). It also surrounded an inspector's lightly textured broad bean risotto pancake, topped with asparagus spears and a Parmesan crisp. Dishes are attractively presented without seeming contrived, and deftly handled, successfully contrasting textures, flavours and colours. Rose-pink breast of Barbary duck, for example, might come flavoured with cinnamon and cumin and arranged around a beguiling display of root vegetables, with tiny pools of sweet, pungent quince jelly; or else thinly sliced over caramelised onions, griddled aubergine and courgette, with a creamy parsley sauce.

Skilful desserts – lemon tart, or bread-and-butter pudding – are as good as ever, and the gooey, pastry-less warm chocolate 'tart' (more of a mousse) is mentioned in dispatches too, along with poached pear with pistachio ice cream. Bread is first-class, and sushi has appeared among the appetisers. Judy Bradley (or Mrs Underhill, as she has also been called) is a natural and accomplished hostess, who runs front-of-house like a well-oiled machine, so meals are well paced and regulated. Classic French wines, and great names from Italy and Spain such as Gaja and Vega Sicilia, share the characterful list with good-value offerings, notably from southern France. House French reds and whites start at £12.50.

CHEF: Christopher Bradley PROPRIETORS: Christopher and Judy Bradley OPEN: Wed to Mon D only 7.30 to 8.30 (L by arrangement) MEALS: Set D £30 SERVICE: not inc CARDS: MasterCard, Switch, Visa DETAILS: 24 seats. 36 seats outside. Private parties: 8 main room. Car park. Children's helpings. No smoking in dining room. No music ACCOMMODATION: 6 rooms, all with bath/shower. TV. B&B £75 to £105. Phone. Fishing (*The Which? Hotel Guide*)

▲ Overton Grange 🍷

Hereford Road, Ludlow SY8 4AD
TEL: (01584) 873500 FAX: (01584) 873524
EMAIL: overton@shrewsburynet.com
WEB SITE: www.overtongrangehotel.co.uk
on B4361, 1½m S of Ludlow

COOKING **5**
ANGLO-FRENCH
£33–£57

A mile or so out of town, the comfortably furnished oak-panelled house stands in its own grounds overlooking gardens and fields, and a friendly welcome starts the ball rolling. Menus trade off choice against price: at dinner the cheaper version offers no choice at all, while the other runs to about four alternatives per course. The kitchen prefers to stay with its favourite items, from moist breast of quail in thin pasta with broad beans and ceps, to several ways with seared scallops: sitting on little potato discs surrounded by pea purée and bacon, or perhaps with vichyssoise and a deep-fried oyster as impressively light as air ('I could have eaten a whole bucketful').

Turbot is a favourite fish, typically flavourful and well timed – served in a saffron nage for one reporter, in a winey sauce for another – while game has included rare roast venison, and hare with choucroute. The 'beautifully arranged but gastronomically irrelevant trimmings' don't dampen enthusiasm, and desserts excite without straying too far from familiar partnerships: hot chocolate cup with pistachio ice cream, or roast pineapple with coconut ice cream and black pepper caramel. Bread, amuse-gueules and pre-dessert are also appreciated. As ever, star Californian and, especially, Spanish wines distinguish the list. Few come in under £25, and house wines start at around £16, reflecting the up-market ambience.

CHEF: Wayne Vickerage PROPRIETOR: Grange Hotels Ltd OPEN: Sun to Fri L 12.15 to 1.45, all week D 6.45 to 9.30 MEALS: Set L Mon to Fri £25, Set L Sun £18.50 to £28.50, Set D £22.50 to £32.50 SERVICE: not inc, card slips closed CARDS: Delta, MasterCard, Switch, Visa DETAILS: 30 seats. Private parties: 40 main room, 30 private room. Car park. Children's helpings. Wheelchair access (not WC). No music ACCOMMODATION: 14 rooms, all with bath/shower. TV. Phone. B&B £60 to £135

LUND East Riding of Yorkshire map 9

Wellington Inn 🍷

19 The Green, Lund YO25 9TE COOKING **3**
TEL: (01377) 217294 FAX: (01377) 217192 MODERN BRITISH
£29–£47

The warmth of this old pub's traditional décor, to say nothing of the warmth from its log fires, makes a suitable backdrop for a menu lighter than the Yorkshire norm. Fresh queen scallop and chorizo tart with red pepper sauce, or a salad of fresh crab, asparagus and quails' eggs with Bloody Mary dressing, may be a good way to start. Clever spins on conventional ideas have produced spinach and blue cheese dumplings to accompany lightly charred calf's liver, and a basil and chilli oil sauce for ribeye steak with garlic and cherry tomatoes.

Desserts maintain the 'light' theme – chocolate and honeycomb cheesecake, for example, or raspberry crème brûlée – although those with sturdier appetites are catered for too: sticky toffee pudding comes with warm butterscotch and vanilla ice cream. Alternatively there may be a Port and Stilton toastie with apple and grape salad. An astutely chosen, well-annotated list of 60 wines, including eight by the glass, is very fairly priced from £9.95 per bottle. Don't miss the wine of the month page, which introduces something more unusual or expensive, and offers the chance to try it at a 'knock-down price'.

CHEFS: Sarah Jeffery and Toby Greensides PROPRIETORS: Russell and Sarah Jeffery OPEN: Tue to Sat D only 7 to 9.30 MEALS: alc D (main courses £13 to £17). Bar menus available Tue to Sun L and Tue to Sat D SERVICE: not inc, card slips closed CARDS: Delta, MasterCard, Switch, Visa DETAILS: 45 seats. Private parties: 30 main room. Car park. No children under 14. Music

The Guide is totally independent, accepts no free hospitality, and survives on the number of copies sold each year.

The 2003 Guide will be published before Christmas 2002. Reports on meals are most welcome at any time of the year, but are particularly valuable in the spring (no later than June). Send them to The Good Food Guide, *FREEPOST, 2 Marylebone Road, London NW1 4DF. Or email your report to goodfoodguide@which.net*

LYDFORD Devon map 1

Dartmoor Inn

Lydford EX20 4AY
TEL: (01822) 820221 FAX: (01822) 820494

COOKING **4**
MODERN BRITISH-PLUS
£24–£49

It may look ordinary from the outside, but this sixteenth-century pub has been much improved since Karen and Philip Burgess took over in 1998. By offering excellent value for money and sourcing high-quality supplies locally and seasonally (blackboards list the farms where the meat was reared), they have managed to build up a loyal, appreciative following. The foot-and-mouth crisis of 2001 hit this part of Devon hard, and business suffered; but, like so many others, the Burgesses redoubled their efforts. Latest initiatives include theme nights (such as stir-fry suppers and warm Madras nights), and members of their diners' club are offered discounts and exclusive monthly dinners.

Regular menus, in modern country pub mould, include such traditional fare as roast rump of lamb with rosemary and root vegetables, as well as a variety of more contemporary global dishes: risotto of asparagus and peas with Parmesan, for example, or pan-fried crab cakes with tarragon and a curried cream sauce. Staff, overseen by Karen Burgess, are 'helpful and courteous', and wines on the short list are reasonably priced, starting at £9.75 and staying mostly under £20.

CHEFS: Philip Burgess and Ian Brown PROPRIETORS: Karen and Philip Burgess, Anne Voss-Bark OPEN: Tue to Sun L 12 to 2.15, Tue to Sat 6.30 to 10 MEALS: alc (main courses £10 to £18.50). Set L £13 (2 courses) to £15.75 SERVICE: not inc, card slips closed CARDS: Delta, MasterCard, Switch, Visa DETAILS: 65 seats. 25 seats outside. Private parties: 20 main room, 20 private room. Car park. Vegetarian meals. Children's helpings. No children under 5 Fri and Sat D. No smoking in dining room. Music

LYDGATE Greater Manchester map 8

▲ White Hart

GREATER MANCHESTER GFG 2002 COMMENDED

51 Stockport Road, Lydgate OL4 4JJ
TEL: (01457) 872566 FAX: (01457) 875190
EMAIL: booking@thewhitehart.co.uk
WEB SITE: www.thewhitehart.co.uk
on A6050, 3m E of Oldham

COOKING **5**
ANGLO-FRENCH
£23–£52

This handsome 200-year-old stone inn on a hill overlooking Oldham combines old-world charm with twenty-first-century credentials: bar, brasserie, restaurant and bedrooms. On the ground floor, the brasserie has burgundy and brick walls and rustic appeal, and there's still space for a busy bar and a couple of snug-like rooms for regulars. The brasserie menu sizzles with a great selection of sausages made on the premises – chicken and black pudding, spicy pork and leek, or lamb and mint (all served with various mash combinations) – alongside cosmopolitan offerings such as deep-fried crab soufflés with home-made lime pickle, and tempura of haddock with minted peas and fried potatoes.

By contrast, the restaurant is in a new extension with vibrant yellow walls, wooden floor and contemporary seating. Here the repertoire has added sophistication and luxury ingredients: confit of rabbit saddle with seared foie gras and Madeira jus to start, then Welsh Black beef fillet with sauté sweetbreads, girolles and asparagus, or roast monkfish tail with mussel broth. Finish with a rich chocolate and cherry fondant tart with vanilla ice cream, or tian of poached figs and ginger snap with lemon and tonic sorbet. Good home-made breads, friendly professional service and sound British cheeses provide worthy support, and the global wine list has plenty of drinking under £20 (including 33 by the glass and house from £11) to keep everyone happy.

CHEF: John Rudden PROPRIETORS: Charles Brierley and John Rudden OPEN: all week 12 to 2.30, 6 to 10 (1 to 8 Sun and bank hols) CLOSED: 1 to 3 Jan MEALS: Set L £10.75 (2 courses) to 13.75, Set L Sun £16, Set D Sun to Fri 6 to 6.45 £10.75 (2 courses) to 13.75 SERVICE: not inc, card slips closed CARDS: Amex, Delta, MasterCard, Switch, Visa DETAILS: 125 seats. Private parties: 70 main room, 24 to 70 private rooms. Car park. Vegetarian meals. No smoking in 1 dining room. Wheelchair access (also WC). Music. Air-conditioned ACCOMMODATION: 12 rooms, all with bath/shower. TV. Phone. Room only £62.50 to £110. Baby facilities (*The Which? Hotel Guide*) (£5)

LYNDHURST Hampshire **map 2**

▲ Le Poussin at Parkhill

Beaulieu Road, Lyndhurst SO43 7FZ
TEL: (023) 8028 2944 FAX: (023) 8028 3268
EMAIL: sales@lepoussinatparkhill.co.uk
WEB SITE: www.lepoussin.co.uk
from Lyndhurst take B3056 towards Beaulieu; Le Poussin is on the right after 1m (signposted)

COOKING **6**
MODERN BRITISH
£27–£61

This well-appointed self-styled 'restaurant-with-rooms' in extensive grounds in the New Forest is a comfortable place, with homely and 'sensible' furnishings, where the food relies on exceptional ingredients rather than peculiar combinations for its impact. Dishes may appear simple, but only because the skill is disguised: a tomato tarte Tatin with a fillet of sea bass looks easy enough to make at home, but the crisp flaky pastry, high-quality tomato and fine fish combine to lift it way above the ordinary. Careful timing is an integral part of the cooking's success, for example in a starter of three large and accurately griddled scallops with leek purée, or breast of poussin stuffed with foie gras, the leg boned and stuffed with chicken and wild mushroom mousse.

A sense of balance and restraint enables Alex Aitken to bring off some complex dishes, such as a trio of main-course meats: rare herb-crusted fillet of beef, pink lamb cutlet with provençale vegetables, and a slice of venison saddle with red cabbage. Soufflés (and not just passion fruit, the house speciality) come in for high praise, as do lemon tart with passion fruit sorbet, and chocolate fondant with poached pear. The cheese course is unusual in that it pairs small quantities of four cheeses ('in beautiful condition') with four small glasses of wine, the result 'perfect'. The two-course set lunch is considered good value, and French staff are pleasant and helpful. An extensive and well-researched list wine list kicks off with a selection from the main body that helpfully presents characterful, well-priced options. Opening up scope for experimentation is a wide-ranging group of 30 wines by the glass, plus more than 25 half-bottles. Prices start at £10.90.

CHEF: Alex Aitken PROPRIETORS: Alex and Caroline Aitken OPEN: all week 12 to 2, 7 to 9.30 CLOSED: first 2 weeks Jan MEALS: Set L £15 (2 courses), Set D £29.50 (2 courses) to £37 SERVICE: 10% (optional), card slips closed CARDS: Amex, Delta, MasterCard, Switch, Visa DETAILS: 50 seats. 20 seats outside. Private parties: 100 main room, 25 to 40 private rooms. Car park. No smoking in dining room. Wheelchair access (not WC). No music ACCOMMODATION: 20 rooms, all with bath/shower. TV. Phone. B&B £30 to £150. Baby facilities. Swimming pool. Fishing (*The Which? Hotel Guide*)

MADINGLEY Cambridgeshire **map 6**

Three Horseshoes

High Street, Madingley CB3 8AB
TEL: (01954) 210221 FAX: (01954) 212043
off A1303, 2m W of Cambridge, close to M11 junction 13

COOKING **4**
MEDITERRANEAN/GLOBAL
£25–£54

This picturesque, white-painted thatched inn in a peaceful village operates a similar policy to other establishments in the Huntsbridge Group (the Falcon Inn, Fotheringhay, the Old Bridge Hotel, Huntingdon, and the Pheasant Inn, Keyston; see entries), whereby an autonomous owner/chef runs an easy-going setup: eat from the same menu in the bar, or in the attractive and slightly more formal conservatory dining room, and expect colourful, cosmopolitan food, much of it with a strong Italian bias. Nibble on a bowl of warm olives or pork scratchings and survey a choice that might take in rare tuna nori rolls with nuoc cham and green mango salad, or a riceless risotto (made with grain-shaped pasta), enriched with truffle oil, mascarpone and Parmesan.

There may be a lot going on in dishes, but it all seems to be under control and effective, be it a busy salad combining leek, potato, rocket, chorizo, soft-boiled egg and bottarga, or pan-fried halibut served with mashed peas, broad beans and a sprinkling of black olives, the plate slicked with mint oil and tapénade. Desserts don't let the side down, judging by a commendably silky pannacotta served with dark cherries, and a summery plate of crescent-shaped wedges of maroon-coloured melon marinated in Valpolicella. Value, range and rarity are key elements of the wine list. Over 30 bottles appear in a '£20 and Under' section, and 16 house wines start at £11 a bottle. The list is full of interest, and sherry and sweet wines are specialities.

CHEF: Richard Stokes PROPRIETOR: Huntsbridge Ltd OPEN: all week L 12 to 2, Mon to Sat D 6.30 to 9.30 MEALS: alc (main courses £7.50 to £16.50) SERVICE: 10% (optional), card slips closed CARDS: Amex, Diners, MasterCard, Switch, Visa DETAILS: 90 seats. 40 seats outside. Private parties: 60 main room. Car park. Vegetarian meals. No smoking in dining room. Wheelchair access (not WC). No music

Report forms are at the back of the book; write a letter if you prefer; or email us at goodfoodguide@which.net

All details are as accurate as possible at the time of going to press, but chefs and owners often change, and it is wise to check by telephone before making a special journey. Many readers have been disappointed when set-price bargain meals are no longer available. Ask when booking.

MAIDENCOMBE Devon **map 1**

▲ Orestone Manor

Rockhouse Lane, Maidencombe TQ1 4SX
TEL: (01803) 328098 FAX: (01803) 328336
EMAIL: enquiries@orestone.co.uk
WEB SITE: www.orestone.co.uk
on A379 between Torquay and Teignmouth

COOKING **2**
MODERN ENGLISH
£24–£46

Despite its English Riviera outlook – the sea, barely a mile away, is visible through the trees – this brick and ochre-painted country-house hotel adopts a colonial pose. The elephant motif on fabrics, shelves, walls, curtains and tables is ingeniously varied, and the elaborate Indian carving is evocative too, although the dining room's trellising and wicker chairs prefer country-garden mode. Dinner is the main business, organised around a carte that might take in wild mushroom risotto, a fine chunk of cod, or carefully handled duck with a stock reduction. Meats are accurately cooked and rested, vegetables are copious, seasoning varies considerably, and desserts appear to be a highlight, judging by first-rate lemon tart, and a successful coffee and praline parfait with rum sauce. Service might be better co-ordinated, while wines are varied and reasonably priced, starting with house red and white at £9.75.

CHEF: Anthony Hetherington PROPRIETORS: Peter Morgan and F. Etessami OPEN: all week 12.30 to 2, 7 to 9 MEALS: alc L (main courses £8 to £14). Set L £15.95, Set D £30 SERVICE: not inc, card slips closed CARDS: Amex, Delta, MasterCard, Switch, Visa DETAILS: 45 seats. 20 seats outside. Private parties: 65 main room. Car park. Vegetarian meals. No smoking in dining room. Wheelchair access (also WC). Occasional music ACCOMMODATION: 12 rooms, all with bath/shower. TV. Phone. B&B £50 to £160. Rooms for disabled. Baby facilities. Swimming pool (£5)

MAIDSTONE Kent **map 3**

Soufflé

31 The Green, Bearsted, Maidstone ME14 4DN
TEL/FAX: (01622) 737065

COOKING **3**
ANGLO-FRENCH
£28–£56

Head a few miles out from the centre of Maidstone to the heart of elegant, well-heeled suburbia to find this sixteenth-century house, appropriately subtitled 'the restaurant on the green'. Outside, a pretty patio is a popular spot in summer, while in the beamed dining room no expense has been spared to create an up-market impression, the tone set by cream and burgundy tapestry curtains, crisp white table linen, and white candles in glass holders. The food likewise aims to make an impact with its sophistication, but does so in more cosmopolitan fashion, calling on plenty of modern themes. Roast pumpkin ravioli with oregano, tiger prawns with sweet chilli sauce, and pavé of salmon with béarnaise and parsnip gnocchi illustrate the kitchen's willingness to reach far and wide for ideas, while puddings might take in mango tart with pineapple sorbet, or chocolate terrine. Major French regions dominate the wine list, and prices tend to reflect this, though there is fair choice under £20, starting with a pair of house vins de pays at £12.50.

CHEF: Nick Evenden PROPRIETORS: Nick and Karen Evenden OPEN: Tue to Fri and Sun L 12 to 2, Tue to Sat D 7 to 9.30 MEALS: alc Tue to Sat (main courses £16 to £17.50). Set L £13.50 (2 courses) to £16.50, Set D Tue to Fri £22.50 SERVICE: 10% (optional), card slips closed CARDS: Amex, Delta, MasterCard, Switch, Visa DETAILS: 60 seats. 20 seats outside. Private parties: 55 main room, 23 private room. Car park. Vegetarian meals. Children's helpings Sun L. No children under 10 Sat D. No cigars/pipes in dining room. Wheelchair access (also men's WC). Music (£5)

MALMESBURY Wiltshire — map 2

▲ Old Bell

Abbey Row, Malmesbury SN16 0AG
TEL: (01666) 822344 FAX: (01666) 825145 — COOKING **4**
EMAIL: info@oldbellhotel.com — MODERN BRITISH
WEB SITE: www.oldbellhotel.com — £26–£48

Inns don't come much more venerable than this: it was originally built in the twelfth century for visitors to the abbey next door. While part of that is now a picturesque ruin, the Old Bell, dressed in grey Cotswold stone, is a small warren of bars and lounges with a high-ceilinged dining room that is both comfortable and imposing: thanks to coats of arms, ornately framed portraits, and a pair of stone fireplaces. Customers are casually dressed, and staff are formally trained (courteous, charming, observant) yet easy going.

Michael Benjamin looks to the Mediterranean for ideas – a tomato and polenta tart with goats' cheese and basil, for instance – but mostly stays in more general European mode, offering brill with saffron risotto, and a layer of white crabmeat sandwiched between crème fraîche and crisp, minutely diced vegetables, surrounded by splodges of carrot and ginger sauce. A tendency to make dishes more elaborate than they need to be does not do them any favours: in the case of this crab starter, it could have managed without the deep-fried aubergine skin, cherry tomato, pink grapefruit, olive purée, radish, cucumber, sprigs of mint and basil and so forth with which it was adorned. Another sandwich – of pistachio mousse between layers of chocolate sponge – has come with a scoop of well-made chocolate sorbet. Bread is first class, and wines, although often good, hardly bother to make an effort under £20.

CHEF: Michael Benjamin PROPRIETORS: Nicholas Dickinson and Nigel Chapman OPEN: all week 12.30 to 2, 7 to 9.30 MEALS: Set L £11.75 (2 courses) to £15, Set L Sun £18, Set D £21.75 to £28. Bar menu available SERVICE: not inc, card slips closed CARDS: Amex, Delta, Diners, MasterCard, Switch, Visa DETAILS: 60 seats. 20 seats outside. Private parties: 80 main room, 12 to 24 private rooms. Car park. Vegetarian meals. Children's helpings. No children at D. No smoking in dining room. Wheelchair access (not WC). No music ACCOMMODATION: 31 rooms, all with bath/shower. TV. Phone. B&B £68 to £190. Rooms for disabled. Baby facilities (*The Which? Hotel Guide*)

Net prices *in the details at the end of an entry indicates that the prices given on a menu and on a bill are inclusive of VAT and service charge, and that this practice is clearly stated on menu and bill.*

'For friendliness, smiles and chat, I'd rather have an Aeroflot check-in lady any day.'
(On eating in London)

MALVERN WELLS Worcestershire map 5

Croque-en-Bouche

221 Wells Road, Malvern Wells WR14 4HF
TEL: (01684) 565612 FAX: (0870) 7066282
EMAIL: mail@croque-en-bouche.co.uk
WEB SITE: www.croque-en-bouche.co.uk
on A449, 2m S of Great Malvern

COOKING **8**
MODERN EUROPEAN-PLUS
£43–£65

Occupying an unremarkable Victorian end of terrace (formerly a shop), this is a 'treasured experience' that 'never fails to impress'; one couple has been unable to recall a single poor dish in over 20 years of visiting. The secret lies not in a large kitchen brigade, nor in a sharp-suited hierarchy of greeter, maître d' and sommelier, but in the hands of the two dedicated owners. The format remains as ever: for those going the whole hog, a soup, then a choice of three intermediate and three main courses followed by a salad, then cheese and around half a dozen desserts.

Soups vary from simple lettuce, or summer vegetables, to one of cannellini beans, wild celery and leek, and tend to be vegetable-based, although a smoked haddock and lovage version has also gone down well. The next course typically offers a selection of Japanese items that might include ginger-pickled salmon and sea vegetable, seared tuna, tofu roll, duck egg omelette, and a cucumber and shiitake pickle. Fish, generally sourced from Cornwall, is an alternative, and given typically interesting treatment: perhaps taking in skate with claytonia leaves and a mango and coriander salsa, or cod with tapénade on peperonata with wild rocket.

Main courses centre on fine-quality meats, from honey-glazed duck (with split green pea purée, mint and walnut pesto, and an expertly made stock sauce), to roast leg of Welsh Marches lamb, perhaps marinated Tunisian-style and served with couscous, pickled lemon, and harissa-spiced gravy. These are accompanied by a fine potato gratin, and followed by an excellent salad: the garden is a source of leaves, herbs and vegetables. A delicately flavoured blue cheesecake was the highlight of the next course for one couple, and the Joneses might use their own herbs to marinate goats' cheese, or serve local Lightwood or Charlie Westhead cheeses.

Finally, dessert allows the option to indulge in a simple glass of Vin Santo with cantucci biscuits for dunking, or a rich chocolate fudge bread pudding (combining home-made panettone and Valrhona chocolate) served with a small tower of vanilla yoghurt sherbet. Although eating here may not be cheap by Worcestershire standards, reporters appear to have no reservations about either the food or its value, especially on Thursday. Robin Jones is a charming, unpretentious, efficient and entertaining host, happy to discuss food and wine, or leave you to it; meals are gently paced and everything runs smoothly providing you turn up on time. All he asks is a bit of enthusiasm in return. 'You didn't even say thank you,' he admonished one departing couple, who had nevertheless found everything 'simply superb'.

Wine is sold as passionately as ever and the full list is immense, covering regions large and small in great detail, with great names butting up against more value-conscious labels. Red Rhône is still a speciality, but more from outside

France is now offered than from within, including some mature Australian reds. Wine lovers can request a list by email in advance to peruse at leisure, but choice on the day is made simpler by a much-abbreviated 'wines by style' list, featuring its own suggestions from £13.50.

CHEF: Marion Jones PROPRIETORS: Marion and Robin Jones OPEN: Thur to Sat D only 7 to 9.30 CLOSED: 1 week May, 1 week Sept MEALS: Set D Thur £27 to £33, Set D Fri and Sat £34 to £40 SERVICE: net prices, card slips closed CARDS: Delta, MasterCard, Switch, Visa DETAILS: 22 seats. Private parties: 6 main room, 6 private room. No smoking in dining room. Wheelchair access (not WC). No music

Planters

191–193 Wells Road, Malvern Wells WR14 4HE — COOKING **3**
TEL: (01684) 575065 — SOUTH-EAST ASIAN
£28–£44

The flower-decked white frontage, tiny higgledy-piggledy rooms and homely décor give no clue that the cooking is South-east Asian, with dishes from Sri Lanka, Malaysia, Singapore and Indonesia. Starters include dhal soup, Sri Lankan vadai (lentil rissoles with coconut and yoghurt sauce), and a range of satays: pork, chicken, prawn, vegetarian, or mixed. Singaporean main dishes take in deep-fried fish in a sweet red ginger sauce, and sweet-and-sour duck breast, while Indonesian hot and spicy noodles with king prawns can be happily accompanied by side dishes of krupuk udang (prawn crackers), achar (pickled vegetables), or sayur tumis (stir-fried fresh ones). The undecided can settle for the £17.50 rijstafel – served per table: many small dishes coming at once with rice – or the £28.50 gourmet feast. Desserts (free to those ordering first and main courses à la carte) are less esoteric: a simple mango Pavlova, perhaps. An interesting list of 40 assorted wines starts at £9 for house Muscadet or Corbières.

CHEF: Chandra de Alwis PROPRIETOR: Sandra Pegg OPEN: Tue to Sat D 7 to 9 (9.30 Sat) CLOSED: 25 and 26 Dec, 1 Jan, Tues in winter MEALS: alc D (main courses £9 to £9.50). Set D £17.50 (1 course) to £28.50 SERVICE: not inc, card slips closed CARDS: MasterCard, Switch, Visa DETAILS: 34 seats. Private parties: 26 main room. Vegetarian meals. No cigars/pipes in dining area. Wheelchair access (not WC). No music

MANCHESTER Greater Manchester — **map 8**

Bridgewater Hall, Charles Hallé Restaurant

Lower Mosley Street, Manchester M2 3WS — COOKING **3**
TEL: (0161) 950 0000 FAX: (0161) 950 0001 — MODERN EUROPEAN
WEB SITE: www.bridgewater-hall.co.uk — £27–£33

Bridgewater Hall is a striking monument to one of Manchester's most famous musical sons and is home to both the orchestra and the restaurant that bear his name. The operation is geared up for corporate entertaining but also welcomes ordinary diners for meals before or after (but not during) the concert. The dining room, overlooking the Rochdale Canal, is both stylish and comfortable, done out in cool blues and greys and sensitively lit.

Menus show an appealing creative streak, adding inventive twists to a broad-based modern European style: pan-fried red mullet with saffron and crab pilaff and pea velouté, for example, or skate wing with crispy brown Morecambe Bay shrimps, beurre noisette and asparagus. To start there may be potage Yehudi Menuhin (anything Nellie Melba can do. . .), or Serrano ham with figs, red wine-spiced pear and Roquefort dressing. Desserts might include chocolate and orange marquise, or almond rice brûlée with a compote of peach, melon and apricot. The short wine list keeps prices mostly below £20, kicking off with a pair of house selections at £10.50.

CHEF: Robert Kisby PROPRIETOR: Hallogen Ltd OPEN: all week D only 5.30 to 10.30 CLOSED: 25 Dec MEALS: Set D £15.75 (2 courses) to £19.50 SERVICE: not inc, card slips closed CARDS: Amex, Delta, Diners, MasterCard, Switch, Visa DETAILS: 45 seats. Private parties: 150 main room, 20 private room. Vegetarian meals. No smoking in dining room. Wheelchair access (also WC). Occasional music. Air-conditioned

Chiang Rai

1st Floor, 762–766 Wilmslow Road, M20 2DR
TEL: (0161) 448 2277 FAX: (0161) 438 0695

COOKING **2**
THAI
£15–£38

The minimally decorated first-floor restaurant in what was once a Co-op store is a busy place, with many customers matching the youth of the waiters. The knowledgeable chef-patron takes your orders from a shorter than usual Thai menu, offering only 60 dishes, mostly from the northern region. Among more unusual starters are curried noodles with rich coconut cream and turmeric, and fried beef balls. A reporter praises fish cakes, 'firm but not dry, with underlying chilli heat'; and sliced large fried sausage, also slightly hot with powerful garlic. Tempura with fresh-tasting king prawns, al dente carrots, aubergines and courgettes are crisp and ungreasy, and another highlight is spatchcocked trout with a sweet-sour dressing of peppers, chilli, pineapple and coriander. A separate vegetarian menu offers another 30 dishes, and there are intelligently chosen set meals of both types.

CHEF/PROPRIETOR: Mrs Parkhouse OPEN: Tue to Fri 12 to 2.30, Tue to Sun D 6 to 10.30 (10 Sun) CLOSED: bank hols MEALS: alc (main courses £7.50 to £10). Set L £5 to £9, Set D £42.50 (min 2) to £87.30 (4 people). Sun 6 to 7 £7.50 (2 courses) SERVICE: 10%, card slips closed CARDS: Amex, MasterCard, Switch, Visa DETAILS: 85 seats. Private parties: 100 main room. Vegetarian meals. Music

▲ Crowne Plaza Midland, French Restaurant

Peter Street, Manchester M60 2DS
TEL: (0161) 236 3333 FAX: (0161) 932 4100
EMAIL: sales@basshotels-uknorth.co.uk
WEB SITE: www.manchester-themidland.crowneplaza.com

COOKING **3**
FRENCH
£43–£84

Located in a grand Edwardian hotel built in 1903, and reached through a vast high-ceilinged lobby covered with acres of deep-pile carpet, the oval-shaped dining room is decorated with carved wood panelling, and pink stripy wallpaper and fabrics. Not for nothing is it called the French Restaurant, dealing as it does in squab pigeon breast with foie gras and a truffle mousse, and chateaubriand (for two) with bordelaise sauce.

But there is more to the cooking than simple Gallic luxury, as the kitchen also picks up on livelier ideas, such as hake rarebit with a warm piccalilli dressing, Cornish crab with crispy won ton and a spicy mango relish, and lightly smoked venison served with a steamed pudding of pancetta, onion and field mushrooms in a thyme gravy. Finish perhaps with a tart: chocolate with espresso ice cream, maybe, or passion fruit with lemon and lime jelly. Wines are grouped by style, and prices are rather high for the quality, although there are some under £20, including house vin de pays at £13.50.

CHEF: Simon Holling PROPRIETOR: Bass Hotels and Resorts OPEN: Mon to Sat D only 7 to 10.30 (11 Fri and Sat) CLOSED: bank hols MEALS: alc (main courses £20 to £30). Set D £29 to £38 SERVICE: not inc CARDS: Amex, Delta, Diners, MasterCard, Switch, Visa DETAILS: 40 seats. Private parties: 60 main room. Vegetarian meals. Children's helpings. No cigars/pipes in dining room. Wheelchair access (also WC). Music. Air-conditioned ACCOMMODATION: 303 rooms, all with bath/shower. TV. Phone. Room only £160 to £225 Rooms for disabled. Baby facilities. Swimming pool (*The Which? Hotel Guide*) (£5)

Great Wall £

NEW ENTRY

52A Faulkner Street, M1 4EE
TEL: (0161) 237 5979 and 5664

COOKING **1**
CHINESE
£24–£44

The Wall is in a pleasantly airy basement, its off-white walls and dark wood complementing the rich red lacquer round the bar. Unusually for Manchester (indeed for the whole country), it specialises in northern Chinese cooking, although its 250 dishes include Szechuan and Cantonese ones too. There are plenty of Hong Kong favourites to enjoy, but the Peking items are even more exciting. After deep-fried delicacies – crispy squid, pork and vegetable dumplings, and onion pancakes – the highlight of one meal was a chef's special, 'stuffed with prawn meat combinations' including green pepper, aubergine and 'exquisitely creamy' bean curd. Another northern speciality is hand-made noodles, while real Peking Duck is offered as 'just duck' or in a gourmand three-course version including soup. The modestly priced wine list offers 30 well-chosen bottles, plus house wines at £8.95.

CHEF: Yoyo Leung PROPRIETOR: Q.I. Leung OPEN: all week 12 to 11.45 (12.45 Sat) MEALS: alc (main courses £6.50 to £18). Set meals also available SERVICE: 10% CARDS: Delta, MasterCard, Switch, Visa DETAILS: 60 seats. Vegetarian meals. Music. Air-conditioned

Greens £

43 Lapwing Lane, West Didsbury, M21 9LX
TEL: (0161) 434 4259 FAX: (0161) 448 2098

COOKING **1**
GLOBAL VEGETARIAN
£13–£27

An awning shades a few fair-weather tables outside, while the small, unpretentious, pale blue dining room has bare floorboards, wooden tables (some converted sewing-machines) and bentwood chairs. Service is efficient and pleasant, and the place is often busy, perhaps a little noisy, but relaxed and informal. A resourceful menu combines materials and styles from around the world: 'We are magpies in the kitchen, searching for new ingredients, combinations and influences,' they say. Evocative of the style are baked goats' cheese rolled in honey, sesame seeds, chilli and mint and served on a mango coulis, followed by spicy Vietnamese egg noodle salad with watercress, aubergine, peanuts and bean sprouts. More familiar desserts range from well-reported rhubarb crème brûlée to chocolate and ginger pudding with chocolate sauce. Greens is unlicensed, so most bring their own (no corkage).

CHEFS: Simon Connolly, Simon Rimmer and Darren Chapmam PROPRIETORS: Simon Connolly and Simon Rimmer OPEN: Wed to Fri and Sun L 12 to 2 (2.30 Sun), all week D 5.30 to 10.30 CLOSED: Christmas, bank hols MEALS: alc (main courses £7 to £10). Set L £6.95 (2 courses), Set D Tue to Sat 5.30 to 7 (Sun and Mon all night) £10.95 SERVICE: not inc, card slips closed CARDS: Delta, MasterCard, Switch, Visa DETAILS: 36 seats. 8 seats outside. Private parties: 36 main room. Vegetarian meals. Children's helpings. No cigars/pipes in dining room. Music

Koreana £

40A King Street West, M3 2WY — COOKING **2**
TEL: (0161) 832 4330 FAX: (0161) 832 2293 — KOREAN
£12–£52

This basement now has a warmer, softer look, helped by a new carpet, upholstered black chairs, recessed lighting and more Korean screens and artefacts. Page fourteen of the complicated menu explains the choice between dining traditionally, with everything arriving at the same time, or course by course, as in the £17.50 banquet. Vegetables and 'fresh and good' cod in a broth tasting of the sea were the best parts of an inspector's seafood casserole, although the shellfish rather disappointed. Also enjoyable is a wide selection of side dishes, including the essential 'fierce and garlicky' kim-chee (on its own and in patties with pork). Cod and courgette tempura is crisp and ungreasy, and vegetable delicacies include pickled green chillies, preserved lotus root and seaweed 'redolent of the sea'. Finish perhaps with an attractively presented plate of fresh fruit. A fairly priced list has house wines at £7.95, while Korean drinks include lager, soju and ginseng liqueur.

CHEFS: Cheung Hong and Mrs H. Kim PROPRIETOR: Koreana Ltd OPEN: Mon to Fri L 12 to 2.30, Mon to Sat D 6 to 10.30 (5.30 to 11 Sat) CLOSED: 25 and 26 Dec, 1 Jan, bank hol L MEALS: alc L and D (main courses £6.50 to £14). Set L £3.95 to £7 (all 2 courses), Set D £9.90 (2 courses) to £17.50 SERVICE: not inc, card slips closed CARDS: Amex, Delta, Diners, MasterCard, Switch, Visa DETAILS: 60 seats. Private parties: 60 main room. Vegetarian meals. Children's helpings. Music (£5)

Kosmos Taverna £

248 Wilmslow Road, Fallowfield,
Manchester M14 6LD — COOKING **2**
TEL: (0161) 225 9106 FAX: (0161) 256 4442 — GREEK
WEB SITE: www.kosmos-taverna.co.uk — £17–£42

The popularity of this long-established Greek Cypriot taverna owes much to the warm hospitality of chef-patronne Loulla Astin. Décor and staff contribute to the Mediterranean ambience, and the fare rarely changes. But if the menu's grills, stews, salads and familiar starters seem predictable, consider specials like rabbit casserole with onions in red wine and vinegar, chargrilled poussin (marinated with cumin, coriander and garlic), or red mullet fillet in lemon and orange sauce.

The long à la carte is supplemented by three mezethes menus. The meat one includes loukanika sausage, stifado stewed beef and (oddly) grilled baby squid; the fish one takes in whitebait, sardines, prawns and halibut in ouzo sauce, and the vegetarian version offers, among other things, revithia (chickpeas, spinach, cumin and coriander in tomato sauce). For dessert there's semeli (semolina cake with yoghurt, syrup and almonds) or Greek trifle. Greek and Cypriot wines include retsina and house wines at £12 per litre.

CHEF: Loulla Astin PROPRIETORS: Stewart and Loulla Astin OPEN: all week D only 6 (5 Sun) to 11.30 MEALS: alc D (main courses £7 to £14.50). Set D £9.90 SERVICE: not inc CARDS: Amex, Delta, MasterCard, Switch, Visa DETAILS: 90 seats. Private parties: 50 main room. Vegetarian meals. Children's helpings. No cigars/pipes in dining room. Wheelchair access (not WC). Music. Air-conditioned (£5)

Lime Tree

8 Lapwing Lane, West Didsbury,
Manchester M20 2WS — COOKING **2**
TEL: (0161) 445 1217 FAX: (0161) 445 8166 — GLOBAL
WEB SITE: www.thelimetree.com — £28–£47

The setup is 'nothing fancy' – an old house on a corner site with a conservatory addition overlooking the street – but an artful combination of remnants of stained glass and sash window frames, together with gold paint, bare wood and terracotta, makes it all look smart and feel casual. Both the busy, friendly ambience and homely food go down well with reporters (not least the good-value set-price options), and the wide-ranging menu runs from broccoli and Brie soup, via organic Cajun salmon with wilted greens, to pork chop with mustard mash.

Although some dishes may seem oddly conceived – a fine and well-timed roast mallard breast accompanied by spatchcocked quail with a sage and onion stuffing – an earthy quality pervades the food at its best: a rustic chicken liver parfait for one visitor, a thick Tuscan broth of cannellini beans and vegetables spiked with smoky bacon for another. Among desserts, sticky toffee pudding, and chocolate mousse cake are worthy of note, service is switched on and caring, and the wine list is equally clued up. Colourful in both appearance and content, it notably features lively, good-value bottles from the south of France, southern Italy and Spain. House wines, from France and Chile, are £10.95.

CHEFS: Jason Parker and Jason Dickinson PROPRIETOR: Patrick Hannity OPEN: Tue to Fri and Sun L 12 to 2.30, all week D 6 to 10.15 (10 Sun) CLOSED: bank hol Mons MEALS: alc (main courses £10 to £14.50). Set L Tue to Fri £10.95 (2 courses), Set L Sun £12.95, Set D 6 to 7 £10.95 (2 courses) SERVICE: not inc, 10% for parties of 6 or more CARDS: Amex, Delta, MasterCard, Switch, Visa DETAILS: 85 seats. 15 seats outside. Private parties: 35 main room. Vegetarian meals. Children's helpings. No smoking in 1 dining room. No cigars/pipes in dining room. Wheelchair access (not WC). Music

indicates that there has been a change of chef since last year's Guide, and the Editor has judged that the change is of sufficient interest to merit the reader's attention.

Lincoln

1 Lincoln Square, M2 5LN — COOKING **2**
TEL: (0161) 834 9000 FAX: (0161) 834 9555 — GLOBAL
£26–£63

So impressive is the décor at this modern city-centre restaurant that most diners seem to dress up for the occasion. The smart setting certainly creates an elegant impression, but the atmosphere is relaxed and lively, and attentive yet unobtrusive service helps put customers at ease. Food also tries hard to impress; the ambitious global cooking style takes in everything from pan-fried foie gras with onion tarte Tatin, caramelised pears and rocket, to Korean honey-marinated duck breast with Thai sweet potato dauphinoise and a plum and chilli sauce. Somewhere in between you may encounter homelier options of beer-battered fish and chips with tartare sauce and 'Manchester caviar', or even gammon and poached eggs with parsley sauce. Occasionally the more unusual ideas don't quite come off, but the overall success rate is high. Wines, well-chosen and reasonably priced, start at £11.

CHEF: Jem O'Sullivan PROPRIETORS: Fred and Nicole Done OPEN: Sun to Fri L 12 to 3 (4 Sun), Mon to Sat 6 to 10.30 (11 Fri and Sat) MEALS: alc Mon to Sat (main courses £12.50 to £20). Set L £14.50 (2 courses) to £16.50, Set L Sun £16.95, Set D Mon to Sat 6 to 7 £14.50 (2 courses) to £16.50, Set D Mon £22.95 SERVICE: 10% (optional), card slips closed CARDS: Amex, Delta, MasterCard, Switch, Visa DETAILS: 90 seats. Private parties: 90 main room. Vegetarian meals. Children's helpings. Wheelchair access (also WC). Music. Air-conditioned

Little Yang Sing

17 George Street, M1 4HE — COOKING **2**
TEL: (0161) 228 7722 FAX: (0161) 237 9257 — CHINESE
WEB SITE: www.littleyangsing.co.uk — £19–£55

Previously 'attractive, well decorated, and comfortable', Little Yang Sing has none the less been refurbished and enlarged, though too close to publcation for any reports to filter through in time. Scheduled improvements included attention to disabled customers' needs, and a no-smoking area. The Cantonese menu, less encyclopaedic than some, takes in unusual vegetarian dishes, such as dim sum and starters of steamed spicy nut dumpling, crispy curried pancake, beancurd waffle with spicy vegetable and deep-fried almond, and potato burger. Omnivore exotica include minced curried beef samosa, chicken roll in black pepper sauce, and steamed soup dumpling (as opposed to dumplings in soup). Set meals are conventional but a reporter was impressed by his carefully served £11 lunch of dim sum and seaweed, thickened chicken soup, chicken with vegetables and fried rice, and Chinese tea. Thirty reasonably priced wines start at £9.95.

CHEF: T.B. Phuong PROPRIETOR: L.Y.S. Ltd OPEN: all week noon to 11.15 (12.30 Fri, 1.30 Sat) CLOSED: 25 Dec MEALS: alc (main courses £7.50 to £12.50). Set L 12 to £10, Set D £16 (min 2) SERVICE: 10% CARDS: Amex, Delta, MasterCard, Switch, Visa DETAILS: 90 seats. Private parties: 100 main room. Vegetarian meals. Children's helpings. Music. Air-conditioned

London restaurants by cuisine are listed near the front of the book.

Livebait

NEW ENTRY

22 Lloyd Street, Albert Square, M2 5WA
TEL: (0161) 817 4110 FAX: (0161) 817 4111
WEB SITE: www.santeonline.co.uk

COOKING **2**
SEAFOOD
£22–£63

The Livebait formula (see London entries) seems to have plugged a gap in Manchester's city-centre eating options. Its 'crisp and sterile' ambience is not unwelcome in this vaulted Victorian building just off Albert Square, and the no-nonsense food is appreciated too. Successes have included a smoked haddock fishcake with tartare sauce ('all fish and no padding'), and tender, spicy-battered squid with a trio of dips (sweet plum, salsa verde and a kind of rouille).

Livebait platters are so generously loaded as to obscure one's companion at a tiny twosome table, but single-fish dishes are by no means run-of-the-mill: spicy monkfish cheeks (seldom seen) come with couscous and harissa, and pan-fried Dover sole is agreeably partnered with a minted pea purée (mushy gone posh?). A real paella (including chicken and chorizo as well as seafood) is also worth celebrating. Fine English cheeses offer an alternative to desserts such as properly gooey peach Tatin with top-drawer vanilla ice cream. Service is confident and friendly, and the stylistically grouped wine list starts with Vins de Pays d'Oc at £10.50.

CHEF: Stephen Dray PROPRIETOR: Groupe Chez Gerard OPEN: Mon to Sat 12 to 3, 5.30 to 11 (all-day dining Sat) MEALS: alc (main courses £8 to £16). Set L £9.95 (2 courses) to £12.95, Set D 5.30 to 7 £9.95 to £12.95 SERVICE: 10% (optional), card slips closed CARDS: Amex, Delta, Diners, MasterCard, Switch, Visa DETAILS: 130 seats. Private parties: 34 main room. Vegetarian meals. Children's helpings. No smoking in 1 dining room. Wheelchair access (also WC). Music. Air-conditioned

Moss Nook

Ringway Road, Manchester M22 5WD
TEL: (0161) 437 4778 FAX: (0161) 498 8089
on B5166, 1m from Manchester Airport

COOKING **6**
CLASSIC ENGLISH
£28–£79

It may be only a mile away from Manchester Airport, but Moss Nook is a world away from hustle and bustle. An air of well-heeled opulence pervades the warm red tones of the dining room, its stained glass, cut glass and comfortable low-slung chairs, and, despite the odd spot of formation dome-lifting, there is a welcome lack of stuffiness in the approach. Kevin Lofthouse has been cooking here for nigh on 20 years, and the weight of experience shows in both consistency of quality and the nerveless treatment of raw materials, which are often left to speak for themselves in disarmingly simple preparations: a first-course soufflé is made with Swiss cheese and chives and sauced with Stilton, while sauté scallops are served with asparagus and a dressing of sesame and pumpkin seed oils.

Straightforward treatments illustrate the confidence, as Dover sole may be grilled or sautéed, beef fillet is given an old-school cream and mushroom sauce, and breast of chicken is stuffed with vegetables and sauced with white wine and garlic. You may need to throw dietary caution to the winds for desserts such as Amaretto-soaked strawberries folded into whipped cream and topped with buttery shortcake, or the medley of miniature chocolate creations. The wine list opens in classic regions of France, but explores non-European countries in heartening depth too. Prices are by no means giveaway, but there is fair choice below £25. House wines from Australia open the bidding at £14.

CHEF: Kevin Lofthouse PROPRIETORS: Pauline and Derek Harrison OPEN: Tue to Fri L 12 to 1.30, Tue to Sat D 7 to 9.30 CLOSED: 2 weeks Christmas MEALS: alc (main courses £19.50 to £28). Set L £18.50, Set D £31.50 (both whole tables only) SERVICE: not inc, card slips closed CARDS: Amex, Delta, MasterCard, Switch, Visa DETAILS: 65 seats. 20 seats outside. Private parties: 55 main room. Car park. No children under 12. Jacket and tie. No pipes in dining room. No music

New Emperor

52–56 George Street, M1 4HF
TEL: (0161) 228 2883 FAX: (0161) 228 6620 — COOKING **2**
EMAIL: reservation@newemperor.co.uk — CHINESE
WEB SITE: www.newemperor.co.uk — £16–£54

Staff are friendly and attentive even when the restaurant is packed, notes an inspector, who also approved the general standard of cooking under a new chef. The menu includes classic dishes plus crossovers such as Spanish fried rice and 'very competent' spicy nut dumplings. Other tasty dumplings are steamed pork and prawn siu mai, and fried beef war tip, while salt and chilli spare ribs are 'sweet and tender'. Seafood (both cooking and sourcing) is a major strength, as demonstrated by plump and tasty prawns with ginger and spring onion. Brisket casserole, with plenty of lean and fat but little gristle, has a fine flavour and texture. Less common dishes include fresh and dried squid, and special stuffed duck with prawn meat sauce. Note the 10 per cent service charge is disguised as an 'eat-in charge', and that credit card slips are left open. House wines are £10.50, and there are six by the glass.

CHEF: Mr Fong PROPRIETOR: Johnny Lee OPEN: all week noon to midnight (1am Sat) MEALS: alc (main courses £6.50 to £10). Buffet L Mon to Fri 12 to 3 £6.50. Set L and D £16.50 to £32.50 (all min 2) SERVICE: 10% CARDS: Amex, Delta, Diners, MasterCard, Switch, Visa DETAILS: 300 seats. Private parties: 280 main room, 20 private room. Vegetarian meals. Wheelchair access (also WC). Music. Air-conditioned

Nico Central

Mount Street, Manchester M60 2DS
TEL/FAX: (0161) 236 6488 — COOKING **1**
EMAIL: manchester@nicocentral.com — MODERN EUROPEAN
WEB SITE: www.trpplc.com — £24–£50

Attractive surroundings, reasonable prices and an interesting menu (and perhaps live jazz on Fridays) are what draw reporters to this outpost of the Restaurant Partnership. Mock art nouveau décor dominates the pale yellow, high-ceilinged dining room, and the brasserie feel is reflected in a menu that embraces sun-dried tomato risotto, a light leek and Camembert tart in crisp filo pastry, and chargrilled ribeye steak with Boursin glaze and lyonnaise potatoes. Although some dishes seem to have one ingredient too many (steamed orange pudding with Cointreau ice cream, raspberries and chocolate sauce, for example), the kitchen has made a fair fist of medallions of moist Parma-wrapped monkfish in a cream and mustard sauce, and pink duck breast with a dark stock reduction. Service was efficient for one reporter, but 'poor and unfriendly' for another. A 50-strong wine list caters reasonably well for moderate spenders; house vins de pays are £13.30.

CHEF: Ryan Jackson PROPRIETOR: The Restaurant Partnership OPEN: Sun to Fri L 12 to 2.30, all week D 6 (5.30 Sat) to 10.30 (11 Fri and Sat, 10 Sun) CLOSED: bank hols, exc 25 Dec MEALS: alc (main courses £9.50 to £16). Set L £10.95 (2 courses) to £12.95, Set D 6 to 7 £10.95 (2 courses) to £12.95. Bar menu available SERVICE: 12.5% (optional), card slips closed CARDS: Amex, Delta, Diners, MasterCard, Switch, Visa DETAILS: 110 seats. Private parties: 110 main room. Vegetarian meals. Children's helpings. No-smoking area. Wheelchair access (also WC). Music. Air-conditioned (£5)

Ocean Treasure £

Greenside Way, Middleton, M24 1SW
TEL: (0161) 653 6688 FAX: (0161) 653 3388

COOKING **2**
CHINESE
£15–£59

Having its own supermarket underneath gives this quite luxurious restaurant access to every ingredient, however unlikely, and to fresh meat and vegetables. There are also sea-water tanks to keep seafood alive. Specialities in that section extend to three varieties of crab (green, velvet and Canadian). These, however, are not on the normal menu, which depends to an extraordinary degree on stir-fries (even in set meals, these constitute four of five main dishes in a £23-per-head banquet for four). Birds' nests may contain shredded fillet steak and king prawn, or stir-fried scallops and honey peach. Daily blackboard seafood specials might run to fresh scallops, razor shells or other clams, or bargain-price lobsters. Four Duboeuf house wines start at £8.90, and there's only one item over £20 (except in the patron's fine wine selection).

CHEF: Alex Sin PROPRIETORS: Stuart Yip and Jack Lui OPEN: all week noon to 11 MEALS: alc (main courses £7 to £11). Set L £4.30 (1 course) to £7.80, Set D £16 to £29 (all min 2) SERVICE: 10% CARDS: Amex, Delta, MasterCard, Switch, Visa DETAILS: 300 seats. Private parties: 320 main room, 12 to 12 private rooms. Car park. Vegetarian meals. Occasional music. Air-conditioned

Pacific

58–60 George Street, Manchester M1 4HF
TEL: (0161) 228 6668 FAX: (0161) 236 0191
EMAIL: enquiries@pacific-restaurant-manchester.co.uk
WEB SITE: www.pacific-restaurant-manchester.co.uk

COOKING **2**
CHINESE/THAI
£18–£65

Here there are two restaurants: Chinese on the first floor, Thai on the second. Their modern feng-shui-ed décor blends ivory-white (table cloths, chairs and walls) with colourful abstract paintings and potted palms.

The Thai menu is a long carte, the focus of which is a list of main ingredients (king prawn to beef to duck) and a choice of different-strength sauces; put them together and you might get an 'impeccably sweet' lobster with yellow curry, or anise-flavoured chicken red curry. Staples such as tom-yam gai (hot and sour chicken soup) and spring rolls are well rendered.

The Chinese menu operates the same way, taking in choice dim sum, and chef's specials such as stuffed scallop with prawn meat, fresh oysters in black pepper sauce casserole, and near legendary unicorn sea bass. The long wine list starts with house bottles from £9.90, and is fairly priced, even when it reaches three-figure classics in the 'connoisseur list'.

CHEF: Tim Wong (China) Mrs Renée Kitruksa (Thailand) PROPRIETOR: Special Charms Ltd OPEN: all week: (China) 12 to 11.30, (Thailand) 12 to 3, 6 to 11.30 MEALS: alc (main courses (China) £7.50 to £11.50, (Thailand) £6.90 to £14.90). Set L £5.50 (2 courses) to £9.50. Set L and D (China) £18.50 to £35, (Thailand) £20 to £38; (some min 2, others single-person supplement). Buffet menu available L (Thailand) SERVICE: 10% CARDS: Amex, Delta, Diners, MasterCard, Switch, Visa DETAILS: 270 seats. Private parties: 120 main room, 40 private room. Vegetarian meals. No children under 3. No smoking in dining room. No-smoking areas. Wheelchair access (also WC). Music. Air-conditioned

Le Petit Blanc £

NEW ENTRY

55 King Street, M2 4LQ
TEL: (0161) 832 1000 FAX: (0161) 832 1001
WEB SITE: www.lepetitblanc.com

COOKING **3**
MODERN FRENCH
£24–£50

The newest member of this chain (see entries for Oxford, Cheltenham and Birmingham) is plusher than the Oxford original but offers the same classily presented brasserie staples at reasonable prices. The ground floor of a 1960s city-centre bank, stylishly renovated, provides a modern space with white tiled floors, white walls, lavish flower arrangements and Wenge wood tables. One reporter approves 'the diversity of the menu, with vegetarian options, children's menus and identification of French regional dishes'. Alcohol-, lactose-, dairy-, gluten- and nut-free menus are available, vegetarians and vegans are well catered for, and service is attentive and helpful, if sometimes slow.

Among starters might be crisp, fresh-tasting, deep-fried crab cakes with green onion risotto, or unctuous foie gras and chicken liver parfait with red onion marmalade. Main courses might include gamey, tender roast breasts of wild pigeon with cabbage and chestnuts, or meltingly soft lamb shank with pea and mint risotto. French standards like floating islands 'Maman Blanc', and caramel and Armagnac soufflé, feature among desserts. The short wine list favours France, but has good New World bottles too; house wines start at £10.65.

CHEF: Steve Nash PROPRIETOR: Raymond Blanc OPEN: all week 12 to 3, 5.30 to 11. Light menu also available 11 to 7 MEALS: alc (main courses £8.50 to £15.95). Set L and D £12.50 (2 courses) to £15. SERVICE: 10% (optional) CARDS: Amex, Diners, MasterCard, Switch, Visa DETAILS: 130 seats. 16 seats outside. Private parties: 65 main room, 12 to 12 private rooms. Vegetarian meals. Children's helpings. Wheelchair access (also WC). Music. Air-conditioned

The Restaurant Bar & Grill

NEW ENTRY

14 John Dalton Street, M2 6JR
TEL: (0161) 839 1999 FAX: (0161) 835 1886

COOKING **2**
BAR AND GRILL
£26–£47

This newcomer has created a very attractive, modern environment, with glass partitions, black leather chairs, Wenge wood tables and quality glassware. The menu reflects influences from the Far East, Middle East, Mediterranean and

USA, although the cooking is generally seen as more creditable than inspired. Starters include crisp crab cakes filled with white and brown meat with a coriander and lime dipping sauce, and fried chilli squid with Thai noodle salad. There is a large selection of pasta and risotto, as well as fish and meat dishes, such as grilled fillet steak, or skewered lamb fillets with cumin and garlic. To finish, a well-flavoured dark chocolate pudding comes with chocolate sauce and creamy vanilla ice cream. Service balances relaxed informality and efficiency, and the brief wine list has some decent bottles (from £10.95) at restrained mark-ups.

CHEF: James Gingell PROPRIETOR: Metropolitan Restaurant Group OPEN: Sun to Fri 12 to 3, 6 to 11, Sat noon to 11 MEALS: alc (main courses £7 to £15). Bar and Sun brunch menus also available SERVICE: not inc CARDS: Amex, Delta, Diners, MasterCard, Switch, Visa DETAILS: 140 seats. Private parties: 12 main room. Vegetarian meals. Children's helpings. Music. Air-conditioned

Rhodes & Co

Waters Reach, Trafford Park,
Manchester M17 1WS
TEL: (0161) 868 1900 FAX: (0161) 868 1901
EMAIL: rhodesmanchester@sodexho-uk.com

COOKING **4**
MODERN BRITISH
£25–£54

Looking like a sleek American-style diner, this branch of the Rhodes empire (see also Scotland Round-ups, Edinburgh) is efficiently run by pleasant staff and serves well-prepared brasserie-style food, much of it with a distinctly modern British flavour, and with a high comfort rating. The updating of traditional ideas is a Gary Rhodes trade mark, applied with a will to deep-fried fish and chips, salmon fishcakes with lemon butter sauce, and braised cured ham hock with parsley mash and pickled apples. Other brasserie staples might include Caesar salad, and poached egg Benedict, but there is input from around Europe too, taking in caramelised onion tart with a Roquefort dressing, and prawn, tomato and pea linguine. Even an unlikely-sounding crossover dish – macaroni cheese pie – contrives to make 'an interesting combination'.

Children get their own short menu, featuring Heinz tomato soup, grilled chicken sticks with barbecue sauce, and profiteroles with chocolate sauce, although rhubarb, jelly and custard is on the adults' menu, along with lemon rice pudding, and a banana and chocolate ice cream 'pie' with fudge sauce: if that is not indulgent, we don't know what is. Prices on the youthful, global wine list start at £12.50, and there are eight wines by the large glass.

CHEFS: Gary Rhodes and Ian Morgan PROPRIETORS: Sodexho and Gary Rhodes OPEN: Mon to Fri L 12 to 2.30, all week D 6.30 (6 for reservations) to 9.30 MEALS: alc (main courses £8 to £14.50). Set L £12.50 (2 courses) to £15 SERVICE: 10% (optional), card slips closed CARDS: Amex, Delta, Diners, MasterCard, Switch, Visa DETAILS: 85 seats. Car park. Vegetarian meals. Children's helpings. Music. Air-conditioned (£5)

The Guide relies on feedback from its readers. Especially welcome are reports on new restaurants appearing in the book for the first time. All letters to the Guide are acknowledged.

Simply Heathcotes

Jacksons Row, M2 5WD
TEL: (0161) 835 3536 FAX: (0161) 835 3534
EMAIL: manchester@simplyheathcotes.co.uk
WEB SITE: www.heathcotes.co.uk

COOKING **2**
MODERN ENGLISH
£25–£54

This branch of Simply Heathcotes (there are others in Preston and now Liverpool, see entries) is situated just off Deansgate in the heart of the city. It features rather elegant well-spaced tables, some clothed, some not, on a blond wood floor under a constellation of ceiling spotlights. Dave Aspen cooks to the now familiar Heathcote formula of solid north-country ingredients brushed with a touch of Mediterranean class.

A moist and chunky terrine of ham hock, black pudding and Lancashire cheese brings together some trademark materials, and accurately cooked fillet steak, either fired with cracked pepper or tempered with béarnaise, is a hearty size. Fish eaters might start with smoked haddock, served with celeriac rémoulade and a poached egg, before grilled sea bass simply served with lemon and garlic. There is bread-and-butter pudding to finish, or baked egg custard racily scented with rosewater. Courteous and professional service helps things along, and wines are good, although prices – opening at £11.50 but soaring to £42.50 for a St Emilion and a Meursault – may add significantly to the bill.

CHEF: Dave Aspen PROPRIETOR: Paul Heathcote OPEN: all week 11.45 to 2.30, 5.30 (6 Sun) to 10 (11 Sat, 9 Sun) CLOSED: bank hol Mons MEALS: alc exc Sun L (main courses £12 to £17). Set L and D 5.30 to 7 £13.50 (2 courses) to £15.50 SERVICE: 10% (optional), card slips closed CARDS: Amex, Delta, Diners, MasterCard, Switch, Visa DETAILS: 170 seats. Private parties: 170 main room, 60 private room. Vegetarian meals. Children's helpings. No cigars/pipes in dining room. Wheelchair access (also WC). Music. Air-conditioned (£5)

Tai Pan £

Brunswick House, 81–97 Upper Brook Street,
Manchester M13 6TW
TEL: (0161) 273 2798 FAX: (0161) 273 1578

COOKING **4**
CHINESE
£20–£49

This spacious eating hall above a Chinese supermarket has quite pleasant décor and furnishings, but the real attraction is the cooking. Dim sum, or at least some of them, now appear on the English-language menu: among successful steamed dumplings are shui mai, scallop, prawn and chive, and beef with ginger and spring onion. Approval has also greeted fried prawns in rice paper, cuttlefish cakes, and Vietnamese spring rolls. Service does not always match the cooking, which sets high standards, in both simple dishes (roast duck, char sui and crispy belly pork) and more elaborate ones such as sliced chicken with straw mushrooms, or two embodiments of noodles: vermicelli Singapore style, or ho fun – flat ones – with seafood. Menus for two or more people run from a dinner at £14.50 per head to the seafood banquet at £30; the latter includes smoked fish, fried oyster with black pepper, mussels Szechuan style, lobster tails with garlic butter, steamed fresh scallop, and then the main course, which by tradition has one more dish than the number of diners. Forty-odd wines are graded from dry to sweet for whites and light to heavy for reds, and include one from China.

Prices stay mainly below £20, with the unspecified house three at £8.20. Or drink Tsing Tao or Ginseng beer.

CHEF: Hon Sun Woo PROPRIETOR: Tai Pan Restaurant Ltd OPEN: all week 12 to 12.30, 3 to 11 MEALS: alc (main courses £5 to £10). Set L £5.45 (2 courses) to £9.45, Set D £14.50 to £30 SERVICE: not inc, card slips closed CARDS: Amex, Delta, Diners, MasterCard, Switch, Visa DETAILS: 300 seats. Private parties: 110 main room, 110 private room. Car park. Vegetarian meals. Wheelchair access (also WC). Music. Air-conditioned

Yang Sing 🍷

34 Princess Street, Manchester M1 4JY — COOKING **5**
TEL: (0161) 236 2200 FAX: (0161) 236 5934 — CANTONESE
WEB SITE: www.yang-sing.com — £27–£60

Harry Yeung has clocked up a quarter-century in the kitchens of the restaurant his father started in 1977. The large basement dining area (there's a smaller ground-floor room too) now has frescoes, sculptures, and one wall is a waterfall running over slate. A window display of roast meats fronts the open kitchen. Harry's menu encompasses a vast collection of stir-fries, Cantonese favourites (the salt and pepper pork chop is applauded), barbecue dishes, and a sizeable vegetarian section including stir-fried mangetout with fresh lily bulb and preserved olive leaf.

Dim sum are among the highlights, particularly 'Harry specials' of fusion cuisine: crisp, lemony deep-fried chicken and sweetcorn pancake, or the light, clean flavours of fresh and dry scallop dumplings. Among main dishes, a first-rate seafood hotpot containing aubergine, delicate prawns and squid in spicy Szechuan sauce has triumphed over comparatively disappointing sweet and sour pork, and one guest, treated to a banquet, enthused over its steamed turbot centrepiece. Under Harry's brother Gerry, waiting staff are 'relaxed yet involved'. Wines, listing heavily to France (just six reds and six whites come from the New World), are awash with vibrancy and value; a good range under £25 includes five house offerings at £10.95 (£2.30 a glass).

CHEF: Harry Yeung PROPRIETOR: Yang Sing Ltd OPEN: all week noon to approx 11.15 (11.45 Fri and Sat, 10.15 Sun) CLOSED: 25 Dec MEALS: alc (main courses £6 to £11). Set L and D £16.50 (min 2) SERVICE: 10%, not inc CARDS: Amex, Delta, MasterCard, Switch, Visa DETAILS: 250 seats. Private parties: 250 main room, 36 to 250 private rooms. Vegetarian meals. Wheelchair access (also WC). Music. Air-conditioned

MARSDEN West Yorkshire — **map 8**

▲ Olive Branch

Manchester Road, Marsden HD7 6LU
TEL: (01484) 844487
EMAIL: reservations@olivebranch.uk.com — COOKING **2**
WEB SITE: www.olivebranch.uk.com — MODERN ENGLISH
on A62, between Slaithwaite and Marsden — £24–£50

The stone-built pub a mile from the village – essentially an informal restaurant-with-rooms and a bar – welcomes with a series of small open-plan areas decorated with pine tables, bench seats, and racks of empty wine bottles. Order from a blackboard over the bar, remembering also to check the many squares of paper fastened to the walls for extra dishes; it all adds up to a lot of choice, not least when it comes to seafood. Queen scallops arrive in their shells with garlicky butter and melted Gruyère, sauté squid comes in a lightly chillied tomato salsa, and line-caught sea bass has been served with grilled aubergine and fennel. Meat eaters might opt for rump of venison, or lamb shank on creamy mash with a carefully reduced sauce, while desserts run to rhubarb and ginger trifle. Young staff can set a cracking pace, and a globetrotting wine list is considerate to those on a modest budget, with over half the bins priced under £20. French red and white house wines provide particularly impressive value at £10.50.

CHEFS: Paul Kewley and John Lister PROPRIETORS: John and Ann Lister OPEN: Wed to Fri L 12 to 1.45, Mon to Sat D 6.30 to 9.30, Sun 1 to 8.30 CLOSED: 26 Dec, first 2 weeks Jan, second week Aug MEALS: alc (main courses £9.50 to £17). Set L £14.95, Set D 6.30 to 7.30 Mon to Thur £14.95 SERVICE: not inc, card slips closed CARDS: Delta, MasterCard, Switch, Visa DETAILS: 70 seats. 24 seats outside. Private parties: 40 main room. Car park. Vegetarian meals. Children's helpings. No smoking in 1 dining room. Music ACCOMMODATION: 3 rooms, all with bath/shower. TV. Phone. B&B £45 to £60 (*The Which? Hotel Guide*) (£5)

MARSH BENHAM Berkshire **map 2**

Red House

Marsh Benham RG20 8LY
TEL: (01635) 582017 FAX: (01635) 581621

COOKING **2**
FRENCH-PLUS
£32–£56

This thatched, red-brick, pub/restaurant proved 'a real discovery' for one reporter who had not visited since it used to be the Water Rat. The emphasis is more on food than beer, and the same menu obtains throughout: in the red-painted bar, in the library-style dining room, and on the terrace whenever al fresco eating is possible. A generous choice covers traditional French items such as sirloin steak with béarnaise, and pan-fried foie gras (is there anywhere that doesn't serve this now?), as well as other European options of Serrano ham with rocket salad, and wild mushroom risotto. Then there's a whole host of dishes from around the globe including lamb with couscous, curried chicken marinated in lime, coconut and ginger, and Cajun salmon with Creole sauce. Among seasonal items are desserts such as jellied summer fruits, and a crème brûlée with blackberries, both enjoyed in August. A short wine list (not the restaurant's greatest strength) begins with house South African at £11.95, and eight other recommendations under £20.

CHEF: Jerry Monmessin PROPRIETOR: T. Gwyn-Jones OPEN: Tue to Sun L 12 to 2.15 (2.30 Sun), Tue to Sat D 7 to 10.15 CLOSED: 25 and 26 Dec MEALS: alc (main courses £11 to £17.50) Bar menu available L SERVICE: not inc CARDS: Amex, Delta, MasterCard, Switch, Visa DETAILS: 92 seats. 30 seats outside. Private parties: 60 main room. Car park. Vegetarian meals. Children's helpings. No children under 8 in dining room. No smoking in dining room. Wheelchair access (also WC). Music

indicates that smoking is either banned altogether or that a separate dining room (not just an area) is maintained for non-smokers.

MASHAM North Yorkshire **map 9**

Floodlite £

7 Silver Street, Masham HG4 4DX
TEL: (01765) 689000

COOKING **5**
ANGLO/FRENCH
£19–£46

Looking more like 'an old haberdasher's premises', with its unlikely décor, the Floods' idiosyncratic restaurant in an unspoiled Yorkshire market town boasts crystal chandeliers and a long-case clock in the dining room, and, in the basement bar, a glass-fronted wood-effect fire and seating upholstered in burgundy crushed velour. Charles Flood's cooking is, reassuringly perhaps, not quite as odd as the surroundings, but delivers plenty of flavour in the form of some tried-and-true European dishes.

Quenelles of pike with lobster sauce might have stepped straight off the pages of Escoffier, and asparagus hollandaise, salmon with sorrel, and roast saddle of roe deer with bacon, shallots and wild mushrooms in red wine sauce will strike some familiar chords too. Ingredients are well-sourced, and one regular visitor rhapsodises over the 'rich terrines, superbly fat moules, well-timed fish, pink lamb, and banana mousse with toffee sauce'. Other ways to finish might be chocolate marquise with raspberry coulis, or a plate of English cheeses with celery and grapes. Though strong on France, the wine list nips briskly about among other regions too, and the half-dozen house wines from Australia and France all cost less than £10.

CHEF: Charles Flood PROPRIETORS: Charles and Christine Flood OPEN: Fri to Sun L 12 to 2, Tue to Sat D 7 to 9 MEALS: alc (main courses £9.50 to £17.50). Set L £10.50 (2 courses) to £12.50, Set D £12.50 (2 courses) to £15 SERVICE: not inc, card slips closed CARDS: Amex, MasterCard, Visa DETAILS: 36 seats. Private parties: 28 main room. Vegetarian meals. Children's helpings. Occasional music (£5)

MATFEN Northumberland **map 10**

▲ Matfen Hall

Matfen NE20 0RH
TEL: (01661) 886500 FAX: (01661) 886055
EMAIL: info@matfenhall.com
WEB SITE: www.matfenhall.com

NEW CHEF
MODERN ENGLISH
£27–£53

As the Guide went to press sous-chef Craig McMeeken was promoted to the top job at the Blackett family seat: a Regency mansion transformed into an opulent country-house hotel. His lively style, down-to-earth yet up-to-date, offers smoked haddock with bubble and squeak to start, or a sweetcorn and spirng onion risotto, followed perhaps by roast sea bass with chive crème fraîche. There are farmhouse cheeses, as well as desserts such as glazed orange tart with citrus syrup. France and the New World, with a few Spanish and Italian bottles between, form the foundations of the wine list. House vins de pays, Syrah and Sauvignon, are £13.45.

CHEF: Craig McMeeken PROPRIETORS: Sir Hugh and Lady Blackett OPEN: Sun L 12 to 2.30, all week D 7 to 9.30 MEALS: alc (main courses £9.50 to 18.50). Set L Sun £15.95, Set D £19.95 SERVICE: not inc, card slips closed CARDS: Amex, Delta, MasterCard, Switch, Visa DETAILS: 70 seats. Private parties: 50 main room, 120 private rooms. Car park. Vegetarian meals. Children's helpings. No smoking in dining room. Wheelchair access (also WC). Music. Air-conditioned ACCOMMODATION: 31 rooms, all with bath/shower. TV. Phone. B&B £95 to £205. Rooms for disabled. Baby facilities (*The Which? Hotel Guide*) (£5)

MELBOURN Cambridgeshire **map 6**

Pink Geranium

25 Station Road, Melbourn SG8 6DX
TEL: (01763) 260215 FAX: (01763) 262110 COOKING **4**
EMAIL: bookings@pinkgeranium.co.uk MODERN BRITISH
WEB SITE: www.pinkgeranium.co.uk £30–£81

'I have not seen décor like this since a stay 15 years ago at a seaside guesthouse,' volunteered one reporter of this rose-smothered, pink, thatched cottage in a small garden. In fact it has all been toned down a bit, and now simple white tablecloths and china are set against blackened panelling and a mahogany fireplace, while jazz (in the lounge) has replaced the classical background music. Mark Jordan sets his cap at a stylish, modestly inventive kind of cooking. It takes in a starter of accurately timed seared scallop with lemon butter sauce, and a well constructed patchwork terrine of lamb shoulder and sweetbreads, set about with soft boiled quails' eggs and spoonfuls of sauce gribiche.

Timings are generally sound, producing pink meats where appropriate, and main courses can be quite robust, as in a lavish dish of duck breast with a gingery poached half-peach on puréed butternut squash. To finish, check out the hot bitter chocolate soufflé with coconut mille-feuille, or a compote of strawberries with champagne jelly. Service from young men in white shirts and black trousers is a little untutored. Starting at £12, and with plenty of halves, the wine list majors on France but covers America and the Antipodes as well.

CHEF: Mark Jordan PROPRIETOR: Lawrence Champion OPEN: Tue to Sun L 12 to 2, Tue to Sat D 7 to 9.30 CLOSED: 25 and 26 Dec, 1 Jan MEALS: alc exc Sun L (main courses £19.50 to £25). Set L Mon to Fri £14 (2 courses) to £18, Set L Sat and Sun £19.50, Set D Tue to Fri £30 to £55 (latter for whole table only) SERVICE: 10% (optional), card slips closed CARDS: Amex, Delta, MasterCard, Switch, Visa DETAILS: 60 seats. Private parties: 50 main room, 6 and 14 private rooms. Car park. Children's helpings. No smoking in dining room. No music (£5)

▲ Sheene Mill

Station Road, Melbourn SG8 6DX
TEL: (01763) 261393 FAX: (01763) 261376 COOKING **2**
EMAIL: mail@stevensaunders.com GLOBAL
WEB SITE: www.stevensaunders.com £24–£67

Instantly recognisable as an old mill, complete with stream, pond and ducks (plus a lot of publicity about owner Steven Saunders), this is a delightful and 'semi-formal' restaurant with a sunshine-yellow and royal-blue dining room where modern brasserie food is simply and attractively presented. One of the chefs is Thai, which may explain the presence of Thai chicken soup, if not the sweet chilli dressing that accompanies a deep-fried filo parcel of goats' cheese, while native ideas run to braised shank of lamb with garlic mash and onion gravy. Desserts tend to be syrupy, offering pain perdu with maple syrup, and saffron-poached pear with chocolate mousseline and roast chestnut syrup. Service can leave a lot to be desired, and wines are arranged in broad groups according to their suitability for fish and shellfish, beef, game and so on. Prices start at £10.95.

CHEFS: Richard Salt, Steven Saunders, Chris Driver and Siri Sirisang PROPRIETORS: Steven and Sally Saunders OPEN: all week L 12 to 2.30 (3.30 Sun), Mon to Sat D 7 to 10 (10.30 Sat) CLOSED: 26 Dec MEALS: alc (main courses £13 to £23.50). Set L Mon to Fri £10.50 (2 courses) to £14.50, Set L Sat £14.50 (2 courses) to £18.50 (not always available – phone to check), Set L Sun £19.50 SERVICE: 10% (optional), card slips closed CARDS: Amex, Delta, MasterCard, Switch, Visa DETAILS: 120 seats. 25 seats outside. Private parties: 120 main room, 12 private room. Car park. Vegetarian meals. Children's helpings. No smoking before 3 at L, 9.30 at D. Wheelchair access (not WC). Music. Air-conditioned ACCOMMODATION: 9 rooms, all with bath/shower. TV. Phone. B&B £65 to £110 (*The Which? Hotel Guide*) (£5)

MIDDLESBROUGH Middlesbrough map 10

Purple Onion

80 Corporation Road, Middlesbrough TS1 2RF — COOKING **3**
TEL: (01642) 222250 — MODERN EUROPEAN
EMAIL: thepurpleonion@hotmail.com — £23–£55

Finding a French-style brasserie in the centre of Middlesbrough is almost as unexpected as the Claes Oldenburg bottle sculpture that stands nearby, but here it is, occupying the ground floor of a former department store. The décor shows an eye for detail, effectively recreating a French ambience with touches of art nouveau and jazz. A few Gallic overtones are also evident in the cooking, though the modern brasserie style knows no boundaries, offering spiced fishcakes with Thai-style shellfish sauce, alongside wild mushroom risotto with sorrel, Madeira and Parmesan.

Among main courses are some inventive, cosmopolitan twists on classic themes, as in a loin of venison with duck and orange sausage and a vegetable and pearl barley sauce, or spiced duck breast with brandy-soaked apricots, chilli won tons and a lentil sauce. Portions are on the hearty side, and presentation tends towards the 'rough and ready', but it is all wholesome and satisfying. The short wine list covers a fair range of styles and countries, and represents fair value. Prices start at £10.95.

CHEFS: Tony Chapman and Darren Allen PROPRIETORS: John and Bruno McCoy OPEN: all week 12 to 2.30, 7 to 10 MEALS: alc (main courses L £6.50 to £10.50, D £11 to £17), Set L Sun £10.95 (2 courses) to £12.95 (3 courses), Mon to Sat 5 to 7 pre-theatre specials available SERVICE: not inc, card slips closed CARDS: MasterCard, Switch, Visa DETAILS: 80 seats. Private parties: 80 main room. Vegetarian meals. Children's helpings. Wheelchair access (also WC). Music. Air-conditioned (£5)

If a restaurant is new to the Guide this year (did not appear as a main entry in the last edition), NEW ENTRY *appears opposite its name.*

MIDHURST West Sussex map 3

Maxine's

Elizabeth House, Red Lion Street,
Midhurst GU29 9PB
TEL: (01730) 816271
EMAIL: maxines@lineone.net

COOKING **2**
EUROPEAN
£24–£42

In an out-of-the-way street, Maxine's occupies a single room in an old half-timbered house; the décor harks back to an era when lacy curtains and tasselled lamps were as indelibly English as the nearby South Downs. The menu too is a long-running production (the de Jagers have been here since 1982), but readers praise the consistency and charm of the place with powerful conviction. Among commendations are broccoli and almond soup, fillets of red mullet with mustard sauce, and shanks of lamb ('outstanding, lean, rich meat') with roast potatoes and creamed turnips. Dutch apple pie (served perhaps with walnut ice cream) is also praised, or there may be a straightforward rhubarb brûlée. French house wines are £10.95.

CHEF: Robert de Jager PROPRIETORS: Robert and Marti de Jager OPEN: Wed to Sun L 12 to 1.30, Wed to Sat D 7 to 9 CLOSED: 2 weeks Jan MEALS: alc (main courses £11 to £17). Set L and D (exc Sat D) £16.95 SERVICE: net prices, card slips closed CARDS: Amex, Delta, MasterCard, Switch, Visa DETAILS: 24 seats. Private parties: 30 main room. Children's helpings. No smoking in dining room. No music

MILFORD ON SEA Hampshire map 2

Rouille

69–71 High Street, Milford on Sea SO41 0QG
TEL/FAX: (01590) 642340
EMAIL: rouille@ukonline.co.uk
WEB SITE: www.rouille.co.uk

COOKING **6**
MODERN FRENCH
£26–£66

Quite possibly named after the paprika-coloured façade, Rouille has an uncluttered dining room and feels relaxed and unpretentious, but it is by no means casual: the dedication of the Hollombys ensures that both food and customers are treated with the respect they deserve. Lui Hollomby is picky about supplies, sourcing them from all over the place: poultry from Somerset, beef and shellfish from Scotland, Kentish lamb, Wiltshire pork, and fish from Brixham. Local growers also get a look-in, supplementing fruit and vegetables from Rungis and Covent Garden markets, so that items such as spinach, leeks and rhubarb are picked to order.

All this careful shopping produces a marked freshness 'of every single item on the plate', and while ideas tend not to stray far from well-established norms, dishes are well considered. Glazed Quantock duck comes with a black cherry sauce, and Aberdeen Angus fillet with chanterelles and Madeira sauce, although there are occasional excursions further afield: crispy tiger prawns with curried coconut sauce, or seared scallops with lemon grass and coriander sauce, for example.

The less expensive fixed-price menu of three choices per course, still something of a bargain, can be extended to twice the length with price supplements for extra dishes: perhaps for Cornish fish soup (with rouille, naturellement), roast turbot with rosemary sauce, or a warm apple tart with gingerbread ice cream. The classic vein that runs through the repertoire is evident among desserts of plum clafoutis, chocolate mousse, and poached pear with cinnamon rice pudding. A short, sensibly chosen and stylistically arranged wine list starts with Vin de Pays d'Oc at £12.

CHEF: Lui Hollomby PROPRIETORS: Nicola and Lui Hollomby OPEN: Thur and Fri L 12 to 2 (bookings only), Tue to Sat D 7 to 9.30 MEALS: Set L and D Tue to Fri £14.95 to £25.95, Set D Sat £21.95 (2 courses) to £25.95 SERVICE: not inc, card slips closed CARDS: Amex, Delta, Diners, MasterCard, Switch, Visa DETAILS: 24 seats. Private parties: 30 main room. Children's helpings. No smoking in dining room. Occasional music. Air-conditioned (£5)

MILL BANK West Yorkshire **map 9**

YORKSHIRE GFG 2002 COMMENDED

Millbank £

NEW ENTRY

Mill Bank HX6 3DY
TEL: (01422) 825588 FAX: (01422) 822080
EMAIL: millbankph@ukonline.co.uk

COOKING **4**
MODERN EUROPEAN
£22–£43

Claiming to be a 'country inn with a city edge', Millbank is a characterful brick-built former pub on the edge of the Pennines with great views, a warm welcome and reasonable prices. It bridges the opposite poles by combining log-burning stoves, flag floors and old wooden church pew seating with contemporary colours, modern furniture, and patio doors that lead to some smart decking. All is astutely packaged, and Stephen Smith (last seen in the Guide at Restaurant 19 in Bradford) has taken well to the format of a new-wave gastro-pub, serving up a generous slab of savoury wood pigeon terrine with a not-too-sweet chutney, and a simple but well-executed salad of plump olives, tart goats' cheese and sweet tomatoes, all coated in pungent olive oil with good bread to mop it up.

The contemporary European style has also taken in a thick slice of pink calf's liver with creamy sage mash, a trio of stuffed peppers, and moist, skinless salmon fillet with herb tagliatelle and tapénade. Although this is Yorkshire, and rhubarb and ginger crumble is a hit, traditional puddings don't have it all their own way: expect to see pannacotta with strawberries, or elderflower and grape jelly with a honey bun. Service from the owners is informal yet professional, and a short, well-considered, stylistically arranged wine list starts helpfully below £10.

CHEF: Stephen Smith PROPRIETORS: Paul and Christine Halsey OPEN: Wed to Sun L 12 to 2 (12.30 to 3.30 Sun), Tue to Sat D 6.30 to 9.30 CLOSED: 1 to 15 Oct, Mar MEALS: alc (main courses £8 to £14). Set L Wed to Sat £10.95 (2 courses inc wine). Set L Sun £10.50 (2 courses). Bar menu available D SERVICE: not inc CARDS: Delta, MasterCard, Switch, Visa DETAILS: 35 seats. 30 seats outside. Private parties: 32 main room. Vegetarian meals. No smoking in dining room. Music

---

Dining rooms where music, either live or recorded, is never played are signalled by No music *in the details at the end of an entry.*

MILTON ERNEST Bedfordshire map 6

Strawberry Tree

BEDFORDSHIRE GFG 2002 COMMENDED

3 Radwell Road, Milton Ernest MK44 1RY — COOKING **6**
TEL: (01234) 823633 FAX: (01234) 825976 — MODERN BRITISH
5m N of Bedford on A6 towards Kettering — £41–£57

'With the sad demise of the French Partridge' over the border in Northamptonshire, whose owners retired after nearly 40 years, 'this is now the outstanding small restaurant in the area', commented one visitor. The well-kept and efficiently run thatched cottage has also had a makeover, resulting in more space in the sitting room, a plainer dining room with fewer fussy ornaments, and a generally lighter and more pleasing aspect. There is a lightness to the food too, exemplified by the 'juicy, fresh Mediterranean flavours' of a gâteau of skinned aubergines, peppers and tomatoes pressed into a round cake, surrounded by pesto-flavoured goats' cheese.

The Bonas combine their own seasonal supplies of vegetables, leaves and herbs with organic meat, some of it from rare breeds, and take care in both the composition and presentation of dishes: for example, in a pressed terrine of partridge served with a small cone of sweet-sour, tangy-tasting jelly set with pieces of pear and medlar. Desserts win equal praise, taking in a notably light rendition of bread-and-butter pudding imbued and sauced with apricots, and a tube of crisp chocolate filled with rich chocolate ganache, served with a chocolate sorbet and armagnac ice cream. Extras range from high-quality appetiser soups (including lightly curried sweetcorn) to estimable petits fours. Service is rather formal but unobtrusive, and the short wine list has something for most tastes and pockets, starting with commended French blends at £12.

CHEFS: Jason and Andrew Bona PROPRIETOR: John Bona OPEN: Wed to Fri and Sun L 12 to 1.30, Wed to Sat D 7 to 8.30 MEALS: alc L Wed to Fri (main courses £15 to £18). Set D £34 SERVICE: not inc, card slips closed CARDS: Delta, MasterCard, Switch, Visa DETAILS: 22 seats. Private parties: 18 main room, 8 private room. Car park. Children's helpings. No smoking in dining room. Wheelchair access (not WC). Occasional music £5

MORETON-IN-MARSH Gloucestershire map 5

Annie's

3 Oxford Street, Moreton-in-Marsh GL56 0LA — COOKING **2**
TEL/FAX: (01608) 651981 — ANGLO-FRENCH
EMAIL: anniesrest@easicom.com — £35–£55

Annie's is a welcome antidote to the plush, expansive country-house style of eating so prevalent in the Cotswolds. The scale is small, the floors flagged, the ceiling beamed and the pictures familial, with support coming from tourists and locals alike. David Ellis takes a country-cooking route that will be familiar to all those who holiday in France – asparagus soup, duck confit, lambs' kidneys with a wholegrain mustard sauce – while also incorporating a bit of variety in the form of filo-wrapped tiger prawns with chilli sauce. Main-course fish varies by the day, and puddings are as traditional as meringues or treacle tart. A French-oriented 50-strong wine list (including a dozen half-bottles) starts with four house wines at £12.50 (£2.50 a glass).

CHEF: David Ellis PROPRIETORS: David and Anne Ellis OPEN: Mon to Sat D 7 to 9.30 (L by arrangement) MEALS: alc (main courses £15.50 to £20) SERVICE: not inc, card slips closed CARDS: Amex, Delta, Diners, MasterCard, Switch, Visa DETAILS: 30 seats. Private parties: 30 main room. Vegetarian meals. No smoking while others eat. Music (£5)

Marsh Goose

High Street, Moreton-in-Marsh GL56 0AX
TEL: (01608) 653500 FAX: (01608) 653510 — COOKING **3**
EMAIL: info@marshgoose.com — MODERN BRITISH
WEB SITE: www.marshgoose.com — £29–£56

With a café and deli-cum-kitchen shop taking up space at the front, the downsized restaurant now fits into a couple of small linked dining rooms at the rear, their stone and plaster walls covered with collectable modern paintings. The cooking is founded on respectably sourced materials including organic chicken and Gloucester Old Spot pork, although there have been some disappointments over the past year, with reporters (and an inspector) noting that some of the zing and freshness, as well as the bright ideas and thoughtful partnerships, appear to have evaporated.

Nevertheless there are still some decent dishes, including foie gras and chicken liver parfait, and a generous slab of briefly seared tuna topped by a scoop of chickpea mixture, with a couple of slices of grilled Parma ham and sweet peppers. Desserts, meanwhile, have included a fine passion fruit soufflé, and a well-timed baked peach, halved and stoned, the cavity filled with a blob of vanilla-flavoured mascarpone. Wines include important names from the New and Old Worlds, like Jeffrey Grosset, the Hess Collection and Gaja, and at reasonable cost. Six diverse house wines are £12.50 (£3.25 a glass), and on the rest of the list there are many more bottles under £20 offering both variety and value.

CHEF: Sonya Kidney PROPRIETORS: Sonya Kidney, Leo Brooke-Little and Gordon Campbell Gray OPEN: Wed to Sun L 12.30 to 2.30, Tue to Sat D 7.30 to 9.30 MEALS: alc (main courses £10 to £18). Set L Wed to Sat £18.50, Set L Sun £26.50 SERVICE: not inc CARDS: Amex, Delta, Diners, MasterCard, Switch, Visa DETAILS: 45 seats. Private parties: 22 main room. Vegetarian meals. Children's helpings. No smoking in dining room. Wheelchair access (also WC). No music

MORSTON Norfolk — **map 6**

▲ Morston Hall

Morston NR25 7AA
TEL: (01263) 741041 FAX: (01263) 740419
EMAIL: reception@morstonhall.com — COOKING **6**
WEB SITE: www.morstonhall.com — MODERN BRITISH
on A149, 2m W of Blakeney — £32–£57

In March 2002 the Blackistons celebrate their first decade at this outsized brick and flint house, to which their warm hospitality seems particularly well suited. It is comfortable and stylish without being pompous, its mustard-yellow walls and red velvet drapes sitting comfortably beside an inglenook fireplace, flagstone floors and sewing machine tables. Dinner is four courses, and the menu's only choice is between cheese and dessert (likes and dislikes are checked when booking). The second course – after perhaps a slab of foie gras sitting on a walnut and sultana brioche, well partnered by an intense Muscat jelly – is typically fish: at one meal a piece of first-class, dense yet tender salmon cooked slowly in duck fat and served just warm.

Skill and dedication are part of the package, applied to well-sourced materials that might take in live Scottish scallops, locally smoked eel, and cod caught off the north Norfolk coast. Main courses allow red meats to shine: perhaps milk-fed lamb from Devon with broad beans, or a fine, tender, roast loin of venison with cabbage, potatoes and a seriously concentrated sauce. Portions are considered 'just right', allowing room for desserts of raspberry sablé with white chocolate ice cream, or a zesty lemon and lime tart, made with good shortcrust pastry, served with an Earl Grey tea sorbet. Service is attentive and caring, and the ungreedy operation extends to providing jugs of tap water on the table, and closing credit card slips. Intelligently selected wines from around the world are arranged by grape variety, but 'should you be confused by this layout please do not hesitate to ask for guidance', says the list. Ten wines by the glass, plus monthly recommendations, prompt exploration. Mark-ups are reasonable, and house wines are £12.

CHEFS: Galton Blackiston and Samantha Wegg PROPRIETORS: Tracy and Galton Blackiston OPEN: Sun L 12.30 for 1 (1 sitting), all week D 7.30 for 8 (1 sitting) CLOSED: 25 and 26 Dec, 1 Jan to 1 Feb MEALS: Set L £23, Set D £37 SERVICE: not inc, card slips closed CARDS: Amex, Delta, Diners, MasterCard, Switch, Visa DETAILS: 40 seats. Private parties: 16 private room. Car park. Children's helpings. No smoking in dining room. Wheelchair access (also men's WC). No music ACCOMMODATION: 6 rooms, all with bath/shower. TV. Phone. D,B&B £110 to £220. Baby facilities (*The Which? Hotel Guide*)

MOULSFORD Oxfordshire map 2

▲ Beetle & Wedge

Ferry Lane, Moulsford OX10 9JF
TEL: (01491) 651381 FAX: (01491) 651376 COOKING **5**
WEB SITE: www.thebeetle&wedge.co.uk ANGLO-FRENCH
off A329, down Ferry Lane to river £34–£68

Set right on the Thames, where willows weep, 'The Beetle' has two restaurants. The bustling Boat House, with its terrace by the jetty, is casual, the Dining Room in the main building more sedate. Tautology-spotters noticed that last year we flagged the cooking here as 'Anglo-English' (inaugurating a school of ultra-nationalist cuisine); what we meant to indicate was the cross-Channel theme that Richard Smith has always pursued. Organic fruit and vegetables, grass-fed beef hung and butchered in-house, the freshest fish and local game are the mainstays.

Such materials might produce a palate-cleansing starter of three eloquently fresh scallops with olive and tomato salsa and a heap of lamb's lettuce, perhaps followed by Gressingham duck breast, served classically with a green peppercorn sauce and gratin dauphinoise on the side. Those who hanker for luxuries may find a foie gras and truffle sauce partnering a simple onion tart, while main-course pheasant breast could come with ceps, cognac and cream.

Try to leave room for warm, 'gooey' chocolate pudding with almond milk ice cream, or fresh fruit pavlova with raspberry and champagne sorbet. Service can get flustered at busy sessions. Wines are mainly classic French and Italians, with oversized claret bottles meriting a page, and 'fine wines bought at auction' getting two. Towards the end, 'wines from other areas' canter swiftly from Corbières to Cloudy Bay. House wines (three white, four red) from Australia, Spain and southern France are £15 (£3.75 a glass).

CHEFS: Richard Smith and Olivier Bouet PROPRIETORS: Richard and Kate Smith OPEN: Dining room Tue to Sun L 12 to 2, Tue to Sat D 7 to 10; Boat House all week 12 to 1.45, 7 to 9.45 MEALS: alc (main courses Dining Room £14.50 to £21.75; Boat House £10.50 to £18.50). Sun Set L (Dining Room) £37.50. Cover £1 (Boat House) SERVICE: not inc CARDS: Amex, Delta, Diners, MasterCard, Switch, Visa DETAILS: Dining Room 30 seats; Boat House 65 seats. 50 seats outside (Boat House). Private parties: 35 (Dining Room), 50 (Boat House) main room, 64 private room. Car park. Vegetarian meals. No smoking in dining room. Wheelchair access (also WC). Occasional music ACCOMMODATION: 10 rooms, all with bath/shower. TV. Phone. D,B&B £95 to £165. Rooms for disabled. Baby facilities (*The Which? Hotel Guide*)

MOULTON North Yorkshire **map 9**

Black Bull Inn

Moulton DL10 6QJ
TEL: (01325) 377289 FAX: (01325) 377422 COOKING **4**
EMAIL: sarah@blackbullinn.demon.co.uk SEAFOOD
1m SE of Scotch Corner £24–£62

The Black Bull continues to impress visitors for its consistency and value. There is always a lively crowd in the bar, and the building itself has bags of atmosphere and character, looking every inch the old-fashioned English village inn. On top of that, one of the dining rooms is a converted opulent railway carriage dating from 1932. Fish is a strong suit. An extensive list of hot and cold starters ranges from simple platters of oysters, via queen scallops in garlic with a Wensleydale and thyme crumb topping, to a salad of prawns, salmon, crab, herring, anchovies and mussels. Main courses, meanwhile, might take in grilled halibut on spinach with chilli jam, or Dublin Bay prawn curry.

Meat eaters will not be disappointed either, with options typically including roast herbed rack of lamb on ratatouille and couscous, and whole roast grouse with bread sauce and game chips. Vegetarians have their own imaginative menu. On the wine list of around 100 bottles, house recommendations', chosen for good value and popularity with customers, range from an aged Rioja to an unoaked Australian Chardonnay: all bar the champagne offered are under £20. Prices remain friendly throughout the list, sometimes surprisingly low, like a 1993 Dom Pérignon for under £70. House reds, whites and a rosé are available at £9.50.

CHEF: Paul Grundy PROPRIETOR: A.M.C. Pagendam OPEN: Mon to Fri L 12 to 2, Mon to Sat D 6.45 to 10.15 CLOSED: 24 to 26 Dec MEALS: alc (main courses £15.50 to £26). Set L £15.50. Bar L menu available SERVICE: not inc CARDS: Amex, Delta, Diners, MasterCard, Switch, Visa DETAILS: 100 seats. 20 seats outside. Private parties: 10 main room, 12 and 30 private rooms. Car park. Vegetarian meals. No children under 7. No music

NANTWICH Cheshire **map 7**

Peppers ✱ £

Mill Street, Nantwich CW5 5ST
TEL: (01270) 629100 FAX: (01270) 629688

COOKING **2**
MODERN EUROPEAN
£15–£48

This Grade II listed Georgian town house is just off the high street, though it feels secluded thanks to its garden terrace overlooking a bowling green. In its time it has been a private home, a bank and a club, and the elegant dining room retains something of the club feel, with plenty of plants, bare floorboards and bare wooden tables. The pared-down country-house style of cooking offers plenty to entice: a sausage of chicken and bacon with braised green peas is a typical starter, while around a dozen main courses might run from traditionally served sirloin steak to breast of duckling on a risotto of pearl barley, broad beans and red onions. Light meals and snacks, served all day, range from hot filled baguettes to risotto of chorizo, spring onions and tomatoes. Finish with something like toffee and banana crumble with butterscotch sauce. A short wine list covers good ground, prices starting at £9.80. Six house selections are available by the glass from £2.75.

CHEF: Andy Hollinshead PROPRIETOR: Mike Williams OPEN: Tue to Sun L 11 to 3, Tue to Sat D 6 to 9.30 MEALS: alc Tue to Sat (main courses £8 to £17). Set L Sun £12.95. Light L menu available Tue to Sat 11 to 7, Sun 12 to 2.30 SERVICE: not inc, card slips closed CARDS: Amex, Delta, MasterCard, Switch, Visa DETAILS: 90 seats. 65 seats outside. Private parties: 70 main room, 20 and 50 private rooms. Car park. Vegetarian meals. Children's helpings. No smoking in dining room. Wheelchair access (not WC). Music (£5)

NAYLAND Suffolk **map 6**

▲ White Hart

11 High Street, Nayland CO6 4JF
TEL: (01206) 263382 FAX: (01206) 263638
EMAIL: nayhart@aol.com
WEB SITE: www.whitehart-nayland.co.uk

NEW CHEF
MODERN EUROPEAN
£21–£52

This comfortable, cleanly scrubbed pub/restaurant-with-rooms belongs to Michel Roux of the Waterside Inn (see entry, Bray); and one of his protégés, who has also spent some time cooking in Paris, took over the kitchen just as the Guide went to press. It is likely that the varied menu will remain, taking in southern European ideas such as a ravioli of Jerusalem artichoke with a black olive 'beurre blanc', alongside gutsier dishes of beef cheek and oxtail in a red wine sauce with winter vegetables. Good producers feature on the sharply chosen wine list, although prices are highish for the style of restaurant. Twenty come by the glass, from £3.10.

CHEF: Carl Shillingham PROPRIETOR: Michel Roux OPEN: Tue to Sun 12 to 2.30, 6.30 to 9.30 (also open bank hol Mons) CLOSED: 26 Dec to 4 Jan MEALS: alc (main courses £9 to £16). Set L Tue to Sat £11 (2 courses) to £18.25, Set L Sun £9.50 (1 course) to £18.25, Set D Tue to Fri £16.50 (2 courses) to £20.50. Light lunch menu also available SERVICE: 12.5% (optional), card slips closed CARDS: Amex, Delta, Diners, MasterCard, Switch, Visa DETAILS: 50 seats. 40 seats outside. Private parties: 70 main room, 36 private room. Car park. Vegetarian meals. Children's helpings. Wheelchair access (not WC). Music ACCOMMODATION: 6 rooms, all with bath/shower. TV. Phone. B&B £57.50 to £95. Baby facilities (*The Which? Hotel Guide*) (£5)

NEAR SAWREY Cumbria map 8

▲ Ees Wyke

Near Sawrey LA22 0JZ
TEL/FAX: (015394) 36393
EMAIL: eeswyke@aol.com
WEB SITE: www.smoothhound.co.uk/hotels/eeswyke.html
on B5285 2m S of Hawkshead

COOKING **2**
BRITISH
£32–£39

This 'elegant shimmering white Georgian house' in Beatrix Potter's home hamlet is a comfortable country-house hotel, run like a family home. After pre-dinner drinks with other guests at seven, well-spaced white-and-pink-clothed tables await in an airy, non-smoking dining room. Although the five-course menu has many favourites of yesteryear avocado and prawns with marie-rose sauce perhaps, or calf's liver with Dubonnet and orange sauce – John Williams is not closed to new ideas, turning out a colourful, well-flavoured caramelised onion and feta cheese tartlet with roast pepper salsa. The second (no-choice) course might offer a soufflé, or Thai-style crab cakes, and dishes of help-yourself vegetables are left on the table to accompany mains of grilled halibut with parsley butter, or roast rack of English lamb. Hot cherries with vanilla ice cream provide a breather before trying the seven cheeses, all in 'excellent condition, especially the runny Brie'. Sixty decently priced wines start with five house selections at £10.50 (£3 a glass).

CHEF: John Williams PROPRIETORS: John and Margaret Williams OPEN: all week D only 7 to 7.30 CLOSED: Jan and Feb MEALS: Set D £24 (£15 for residents) SERVICE: not inc, card slips closed CARDS: Amex DETAILS: 18 seats. Private parties: 24 main room. Car park. No children under 8. No smoking in dining room. No music ACCOMMODATION: 8 rooms, all with bath/shower. TV. D,B&B £65 to £130 (*The Which? Hotel Guide*)

▲ Sawrey House

NEW ENTRY

Near Sawrey LA22 0LF
TEL: (015394) 36387 FAX: (015394) 36010
EMAIL: mail@sawreyhouse.com
WEB SITE: www.sawreyhouse.com
on B5285 S of Hawkshead

COOKING **4**
MODERN BRITISH
£35–£42

Set in extensive gardens, Sawrey House stands high on a hill with magnificent views across Esthwaite Water. It's a friendly place, 'not grand, but homely, without airs and graces', with a comfortable lounge and bar where an upright piano – redolent of pre-war afternoon teas – plays by itself throughout dinner: 'keys going up and down, pedals moving, but no Liberace'. The kitchen, meanwhile, eschews the mundane country-house route in favour of interesting, imaginative and ambitious ideas, helped along by a varied contemporary larder of girolles, chorizo, tamarind, black pudding, chilli oil, pickled walnuts and the like.

Dinner is six courses, typically starting with a soup or fish option – maybe red mullet with mango salsa – followed perhaps by a busy bruschetta of goats' cheese with a pile of aubergine caviar, pistachios, tomato jam and rocket leaves. One country-house idiom it does share is the mid-meal sorbet (perhaps rhubarb) before bacon joint with butterbeans, or a Mediterranean-inspired dish of sea bass with tomatoes, olives, mussels, pesto and sauce vierge. Leave room for banana and saffron parfait with mango, paw paw and coconut sorbet, plus coffee with petits fours. Service is pleasant, while a rather compact wine list trots the globe; prices start at £10.50 and stay mostly under £20.

CHEF: Nigel Skinkis PROPRIETORS: Colin and Shirley Whiteside OPEN: all week D only 7 to 8 MEALS: Set D £29.50 SERVICE: net prices, card slips closed CARDS: Amex, Delta, Diners, MasterCard, Switch, Visa DETAILS: 32 seats. Private parties: 40 main room. Car park. Vegetarian meals. No children under 8. No smoking in dining room. Music. Air-conditioned ACCOMMODATION: 11 rooms, all with bath/shower. TV. Phone. D,B&B £65 to £150. Rooms for disabled. No children under 8 (*The Which? Hotel Guide*) (£5)

NETHER ALDERLEY Cheshire **map 8**

The Wizard

Macclesfield Road, Nether Alderley SK10 4UB
TEL: (01625) 584000 FAX: (01625) 585105

COOKING **3**
MODERN BRITISH
£21–£48

Rugged and rustic looking, and surrounded by woods and fields, this converted roadside pub has a lot more to offer than outward appearance suggests. Open-plan dining areas retain the informality of the building's former incarnation, while eschewing twee 'Olde English' pub effects. Instead, the impression is of serene, relaxed simplicity: scrubbed wooden tables are set off with white candles and tall-stemmed flowers, and off-white walls are hung with tasteful framed pictures and cartoons.

The food likewise creates an impression of sophistication and flair, while remaining down to earth and wholesome-sounding. Baked goats' cheese with roast peppers, chorizo and an haricot bean dressing is typical, as are pan-seared scallops with cranberry chutney and coriander. Main courses are in similar vein, ranging from silver mullet topped with tapénade on baby vegetables with a pesto dressing, to roast breast of Goosnargh duck with fondant potato, honey-roast parsnips and red wine sauce. Desserts tend to be variations on classic themes, such as passion fruit crème brûlée with shortbread biscuits. Wines are a decent selection arranged by style, with good choice below £20. House recommendations start at £10.50.

CHEF: Mark Wilkinson PROPRIETOR: Ainscoughs OPEN: Tue to Sun L 12 to 2, Tue to Sat D 7 to 9.30 MEALS: alc (main courses L £7 to £11, D £9 to £16). Set L Tue to Sat £10.50 (2 courses) to £13.50, Set L Sun £12.95 (1 course) to £18.95 SERVICE: not inc, card slips closed CARDS: Amex, Delta, MasterCard, Switch, Visa DETAILS: 90 seats. 20 seats outside. Private parties: 40 main room, 20 and 40 private rooms. Car park. Vegetarian meals. Children's helpings. No smoking in 1 dining room. No pipes in dining room. Wheelchair access (also men's WC). Music

NEWBURY Berkshire map 2

▲ Newbury Manor

London Road, Newbury RG14 2BY
TEL: (01635) 528838 FAX: (01635) 523406
EMAIL: enquiries@newbury-manor-hotel.co.uk
WEB SITE: www.newbury-manor-hotel.co.uk

COOKING **7**
MODERN EUROPEAN
£35–£95

Water meadows, woodlands and the rivers Lambourn and Kennet form part of the backdrop to this Georgian manor house. Dramatically designed, with high ceilings, vibrant colours and rich fabrics, all dominated by massive paintings, it sports a conservatory bar (a model of 'everything but restraint') and a swagged and pelmetted dining room with gilded mirrors and starched napkins, both attended by a florist who 'probably spends with more abandon than Elton John'. David Sharland has left, but the broadly modern European style continues.

The cooking is beguiling, since it not only has a firm grasp of essentials – timing is accurate, and textures 'just so' – but also takes an intelligent approach to the design and construction of each dish, in which both balance and contrast are carefully managed. This is evident, for example, in a starter of three plump, just stiffened scallops on a swirl of cauliflower purée, whose creaminess contrasts with the crispness of tiny, thinly battered cauliflower fritters, and in another of paper-thin crisp cannelloni, more like a spring roll than pasta, filled with moist shredded duck and accompanied by pan-fried foie gras and creamed potato.

Fish and game are also likely to feature, perhaps in the form of poached fillet of brill, on a raft of crab-filled ravioli in a light crème fraîche sauce, or moist, pink squab pigeon breast on a bed of Puy lentils, the boned and stuffed legs standing to attention, served with a light sherry vinegar sauce and a scattering of tiny golden chanterelles. Desserts generally display equally skilful handling, for example in a hot apple and honey soufflé served with a doll's house portion of apple crumble, and in a tower of thin hazelnut-encrusted biscuit filled with rhubarb cream, paired with a light mascarpone sorbet. House recommendations from £13.50 to £25.50 head the wine list, taking in Pinot Grigio from Italy, Australian Shiraz and burgundy. Prices can get lofty in some sections, pushed up by big names and highly rated vintages, but a strong range under £25 is at hand for characterful drinking, with southern Italy providing much of the charm.

CHEF: Nicholas Evans PROPRIETOR: Bob Rae OPEN: all week L 12 to 1.45 (2 Sun), Mon to Sat D 7 to 9.30 MEALS: alc (main courses £17.50 to £20.50). Set L Mon to Sat £16.50 (2 courses) to £25, Set L Sun £14.50 (2 courses) to £19.50, Set D £36 to £65 SERVICE: not inc, card slips closed CARDS: Amex, Delta, MasterCard, Switch, Visa DETAILS: 80 seats. 25 seats outside. Private parties: 100 main room, 8 to 45 private rooms. Car park. Children's helpings. Jacket and tie. No smoking in dining room. Wheelchair access (also WC). Music. Air-conditioned ACCOMMODATION: 33 rooms, all with bath/shower. TV. Phone. B&B £95 to £165. Rooms for disabled. Baby facilities. Fishing

See inside the front cover for an explanation of the symbols used at the tops of entries.

NEWCASTLE UPON TYNE Tyne & Wear map 10

Café 21

NEW ENTRY

19–21 Queen Street, Princes Wharf, Quayside,
Newcastle upon Tyne NE1 3UG
TEL: (0191) 222 0755 FAX: (0191) 221 0761

COOKING **6**
MODERN EUROPEAN
£24–£60

The Northeast's premier restaurant, 21 Queen Street, closed its doors just as the last edition of the Guide went to press, signalling the end of an era. As the waterfront developed over the years, so the restaurant paradoxically outgrew its location. After a dozen years the place just didn't fit any more, and the premises were turned over to become another in the small, successful chain of Café 21s (other branches, and entries, are in Ponteland, Durham and Sunderland). Many of the staff remain the same, but the style is now much less formal. The food has been simplified, and prices lowered, but the quality remains 'outstanding' for such relaxed eating.

A kitchen that was accustomed to turning out foie gras with lentils, or an elaborate dish of duck prepared five different ways, now directs its attention to blue cheese fritters, fishcakes with a herb butter sauce on a bed of spinach and chips, and lemon risotto with grilled prawns. In truth, Terence Laybourne was never much into folderol, and his common-sense approach serves the new populist style just as well as the old. Reporters, likewise, appreciate that a good vegetable tempura with sweet chilli sauce, or a properly done sirloin steak with herb butter and chips are more than a match for fancier stuff. Daily blackboard specials keep in touch with the seasons (coming up with jugged hare in January), and there is also a vegetarian blackboard.

Desserts interleave standards of the repertoire – such as bitter chocolate marquise with espresso ice cream, or a light, steamed lemon sponge pudding with lemon-curd ice cream – with a few interesting variants: rhubarb and Sauternes trifle, for example. Forty-plus wines suit the circumstances, with plenty of interest under their £25 ceiling, helped by a dozen more expensive fine wines. House Duboeuf is £10.50.

CHEF: Christopher Dobson PROPRIETOR: Terence Laybourne OPEN: Mon to Sat 12 to 2.30, 6 to 10.30 CLOSED: Christmas, bank hols MEALS: alc (main courses £9.50 to £19.50). Set L £12 (2 courses) to £14.50 SERVICE: not inc CARDS: Amex, Delta, Diners, MasterCard, Switch, Visa DETAILS: 60 seats. Private parties: 24 main room. Vegetarian meals. Children's helpings. No smoking in 1 dining room. No pipes in dining room. Wheelchair access (not WC). Music

Fisherman's Lodge

Jesmond Dene, Jesmond, Newcastle upon
Tyne NE7 7BQ
TEL: (0191) 281 3281 FAX: (0191) 281 6410
WEB SITE: www.fishermanslodge.co.uk

COOKING **4**
SEAFOOD
£33–£98

Surrounded by woods, a couple of miles from the city centre, this old Victorian lodge combines a modern bar with a dark green dining room whose low lighting and absence of pictures can make it feel a bit sombre. A choice of both à la carte and set-price menus is a generous gesture, further extended by specials which are individually priced. Fish, the longest suit, is given varied treatment ranging from king prawn tempura with chilli jam, via grilled red mullet fillets with couscous, to seared scallops with Barolo vinaigrette and truffled cauliflower purée.

Sauces can tend to overwhelm, and flavours may not always be as positive as they should, but sound materials have included chargrilled king prawns in curry sauce, Dover sole boned at table, and shank of flavourful lamb with Savoy cabbage. Other non-fishy items might run to roast saddle of rabbit, duck leg confit, and a dish combining pig's trotter and veal sweetbreads. Stilton and fresh figs is one of the simpler desserts, or there may be a bitter chocolate and walnut terrine with caramel ice cream. Service is prompt and friendly, although there have been communication difficulties. A well-balanced wine list offers ten recommendations under £20, four of them available by the glass.

CHEFS: Steven Jobson and Paul Amer PROPRIETORS: Tom and Jocelyn Maxfield OPEN: Mon to Fri L 12 to 2, Mon to Sat D 7 to 10.30 CLOSED: Christmas, bank hols MEALS: alc (main courses £16.50 to £36.50). Set L £19.50, Set D Mon to Fri £34.50 SERVICE: not inc CARDS: Amex, Delta, MasterCard, Switch, Visa DETAILS: 70 seats. Private parties: 60 main room, 8 to 40 private rooms. Car park. Vegetarian meals. No smoking in dining room. Wheelchair access (also WC). Music

NEW MILTON Hampshire **map 2**

▲ Chewton Glen

Christchurch Road, New Milton BH25 6QS
TEL: (01425) 275341 FAX: (01425) 272310
EMAIL: reservations@chewtonglen.com
WEB SITE: www.chewtonglen.com
from A35 follow signs to Walkford and Highcliffe; take second turning on left after Walkford down Chewton Farm road

COOKING **5**
MODERN EUROPEAN
£35–£97

For those who like to work up an appetite, Chewton Glen is the place. It has a gymnasium, sauna, steam room, spa pool, two swimming pools, three tennis courts, a snooker room, croquet lawn, and a nine-hole golf course. It also has service from friendly and helpful staff that is 'immaculate from start to finish... we felt at home within five minutes'. Pierre Chevillard's role in keeping this most cosseting of hotels afloat – he has been here for 23 years – should not be underestimated either. Given the clientele, the food has to be soothing and comforting, and indeed it is: from predictably rich twice-baked Emmental cheese soufflé with fondue sauce to foie gras terrine (one of a number of dishes carrying a supplement).

Occasional excursions may seem bold in the context, such as the pairing of pork and shellfish – in an 'intensely flavoured' trio of langoustines, scallops and pork confit, served with a cep and parsley risotto – but the kitchen's particular skill is that it can make familiar dishes stand out, be it tender beef tournedos with gratin dauphinois and horseradish sauce, or a particularly light and crispy version of bread-and-butter pudding. To accompany dessert, sweet wines from a variety of regions are suggested and offered by the glass from £6. Bottles don't come cheap on the resplendent list, reflecting the setting and stellar names, and wines under £20 are scarce. House wines, from France and New Zealand, come in just below £20.

CHEF: Pierre Chevillard PROPRIETORS: Martin and Brigitte Skan OPEN: all week 12.30 to 1.45, 7.30 to 9.30 MEALS: alc L (main courses £8.50 to £14.50). Set D £47.50 SERVICE: 10%, card slips closed CARDS: Amex, Delta, Diners, MasterCard, Switch, Visa DETAILS: 120 seats. 24 seats outside. Private parties: 120 main room, 6 to 120 private rooms. Car park. Vegetarian meals. No children under 6. Jacket and tie. No smoking in dining room. Wheelchair access (also WC). No music. Air-conditioned ACCOMMODATION: 62 rooms, all with bath/shower. TV. Phone. Room only £250 to £695. Rooms for disabled. No children under 6. Swimming pool (*The Which? Hotel Guide*)

NEWTON LONGVILLE Buckinghamshire **map 3**

Crooked Billet

2 Westbrook End, Newton Longville MK17 0DF
TEL: (01908) 373 936 FAX: (01908) 631 979
EMAIL: johngilchrist@the-crooked-billet-pub.co.uk
WEB SITE: www.the-crooked-billet-pub.co.uk

COOKING **3**
MODERN BRITISH
£23–£55

A sixteenth-century thatched building in an unusually attractive Home Counties village, the Crooked Billet is an exemplary country pub with a weekly-changing range of hand-pumped ales. It also has Emma Sexton's seasonal menus sourced from the inn's own garden as well as a network of well-chosen local suppliers. You may find baked gem squash with wild mushroom and thyme cream, or crispy sea bass with Indian-style spinach and potato, tomato chutney and a spot of Spanish chorizo for good measure. Or there may be lamb fillet and black pudding with green beans and a red wine sauce: the cooking obviously pays allegiance to no particular style. Simpler things are not overlooked, though: try watercress soup, a sirloin steak with garlic butter and chips, and chocolate marquise to finish. The 270 wines available by the glass, along with over 45 half-bottles, offer a dramatic range of choice. World-class names abound on the list, but the selection of more modest ones is impeccable. Pays d'Oc varietals start at only £11, and many a lively style is offered under £20.

CHEF: Emma Sexton PROPRIETORS: John Gilchrist and Emma Sexton OPEN: Tue to Sun L 12 to 2 (2.30 Sun), Tue to Sat 7 to 10 CLOSED: 25 and 26 Dec, first 2 weeks Jan, first week Sept MEALS: alc (main courses L £7.50 to £16, D £9 to £20) SERVICE: not inc, card slips closed CARDS: Delta, Diners, MasterCard, Switch, Visa DETAILS: 50 seats. 50 seats outside. Private parties: 8 main room. Car park. Vegetarian meals. Children's helpings. No children in restaurant. No smoking in dining room. Wheelchair access (also WC). No music (£5)

NORTON Shropshire **map 5**

▲ Hundred House Hotel

Bridgnorth Road, Norton TF11 9EE
TEL: (01952) 730353 FAX: (01952) 730355
EMAIL: hundredhouse@lineone.net
WEB SITE: www.hundredhouse.co.uk
on A442, 6m S of Telford

COOKING **3**
MODERN EUROPEAN
£26–£71

Highly individual and full of character, this creeper-clad roadside inn with beautiful gardens is 'one of those rare all-rounders' where dedicated hard work from the owners has ensured that everything is just as it should be. The relaxed and informal bar is the heart of the operation, but there is also a separate dining area offering an interesting brasserie menu, plus a blackboard of daily specials. Quality of ingredients and care in preparation mark out Stuart Phillips's cooking. Start perhaps with confit leg of Hereford duck on a salad of rocket, tomato and chorizo, before moving on to venison sausages with braised celery, spring onion mash and a juniper-flavoured jus, or a whole pan-fried plaice with fennel beurre blanc. Finish with one of 'Sheila's home-made sweets', such as pear and mascarpone trifle with white chocolate ice cream. Good real ales and farmhouse cider are served in the bar, and an ambitious wine list opens with a dozen house selections from £12.50; all are available by the large or extra-large (250ml) glass.

CHEF: Stuart Phillips PROPRIETORS: the Phillips family OPEN: all week 12 to 2.30 (2 Sun), 6 to 9.30 (7 to 9 Sun) MEALS: alc (main courses £11 to £28). Set L Sun £16.95. Bar menu available SERVICE: not inc CARDS: Delta, MasterCard, Switch, Visa DETAILS: 80 seats. 20 seats outside. Private parties: 40 main room, 40 private room. Car park. Vegetarian meals. Children's helpings. No smoking in 1 dining room. Wheelchair access (not WC). Occasional music ACCOMMODATION: 10 rooms, all with bath/shower. TV. Phone. B&B £75 to £125 (*The Which? Hotel Guide*) (£5)

NORWICH Norfolk — map 6

Adlard's

79 Upper St Giles Street, Norwich NR2 1AB
TEL: (01603) 633522 FAX: (01603) 617733
EMAIL: bookings@adlards.co.uk
WEB SITE: www.adlards.co.uk

COOKING **4**
MODERN BRITISH
£32–£63

A couple of hundred yards from the city centre, Adlard's is a comfortable, unstuffy place that strikes a balance between the relaxed and smart-formal ends of the spectrum. Its calm, cream-coloured décor is enlivened with large abstract oil paintings, its menu with some appealing ideas, such as roast scallops with apple and ginger purée, and squab pigeon with white bean casserole. First-class materials underpin the operation, and reporters have enjoyed roast pheasant, and tender chump of lamb with chargrilled vegetables, although the main-course tortellini of wild mushrooms has conspicuously not met with approval.

The carte offers a choice of four items per course (the set-price lunch has two options, set-price dinner is no choice) that might also take in a Jerusalem artichoke risotto, or red mullet with sauté shallots, and although component items are generally good, some combinations are deemed inappropriate, and timing and seasoning are not always carefully managed. Finish perhaps with banana tarte Tatin, or prune and armagnac soufflé. Service is 'excellent, no other word for it'. Stars from around the world, and more modestly priced wines, both offer diversity and value. Wine and food pairing recommendations are useful, and over 30 half-bottles encourage experimentation. House wines are £14 a bottle.

CHEF: Roger Hickman PROPRIETOR: David Adlard OPEN: Tue to Sat L 12.30 to 1.45, Mon to Sat D 7.30 to 10.30 CLOSED: Christmas week MEALS: alc (main courses £16 to £19.50). Set L £15 (2 courses) to £19, Set D Mon to Fri £25 SERVICE: not inc CARDS: Amex, Delta, Diners, MasterCard, Switch, Visa DETAILS: 40 seats. Private parties: 40 main room. Vegetarian meals. Wheelchair access (not WC). No music. Air-conditioned

Marco's

17 Pottergate, Norwich NR2 1DS
TEL: (01603) 624044

COOKING **2**
ITALIAN
£27–£49

Occupying a brick-fronted house in a cobbled street, with awnings over the windows and a bell to ring to gain admission, Marco's wins for 'honest food' with no pretensions or flummery, just good cooking by the owner: you can hear the sizzling while he works. He serves ample portions at reasonable prices (the set lunch offers particularly good value) in time-hallowed Italian style, producing home-made gnocchi with pesto, vividly sauced fettucine, and chicken breast cooked in white wine and tomato. When it comes to seafood, prawns appear in various guises: in a pancake with tomato and garlic, in a fish soup, and sauté alla livornese (with onion, garlic, tomato and lemon juice). Vegetables include courgette slices fried in olive oil, and 'unusually good' sauté potatoes, while desserts run from zabaglione via ices and sorbets to Marco's own version of bread-and-butter pudding. A sensible list of Italian wines is grouped by region, starting with house Soave and Valpolicella from Bolla at £12.50.

CHEF/PROPRIETOR: Marco Vessalio OPEN: Tue to Sat 12 to 2, 7 to 10 MEALS: alc (main courses £12.50 to £17). Set L £16 SERVICE: not inc, card slips closed, 10% for parties of 8 or more CARDS: Amex, Diners, MasterCard, Visa DETAILS: 22 seats. Private parties: 10 main room. Vegetarian meals. No smoking in dining room. Wheelchair access (not WC). Occasional music

NOTTINGHAM Nottinghamshire map 5

Hart's

1 Standard Court, Park Row,
Nottingham NG1 6GN
TEL: (0115) 911 0666 FAX: (0115) 911 0611
EMAIL: ask@hartsnottingham.co.uk
WEB SITE: www.hartsnottingham.co.uk

COOKING **6**
MODERN ENGLISH
£24–£58

The word 'polished' applies to most things at this popular and stylish city-centre brasserie, from its wooden floor, via glassware and cutlery, to atmosphere, service and food. It is a classy, modern and highly professional operation that addresses a generally affluent and self-confident crowd, and is 'always reliable'. The food is deceptively simple, with no unnecessary fuss or trimmings, just high-quality materials lightly and confidently handled. An appealing menu offers a choice of fish options, two or three vegetarian dishes, plus excursions into game, as well as the more usual beef sirloin, roast chicken and so forth: firm-fleshed brill, for example, is served with buttery juices, crisp rösti and a sprinkling of wild mushrooms.

It is assured cooking, turning out velvety, flavourful parsnip soup, and a 'light-as-air' chicken liver and foie gras terrine, as well as highly commended vegetarian dishes such as grilled halloumi cheese with roasted aubergine and vegetable fritters. Complementary tastes and textures are evidence of sound conception and execution, sauces are rich yet subtle – an 'exquisite' jus to accompany honey-glazed breast and crisp-skinned leg of guinea fowl – and vegetables (from mash to sugar snap peas) are properly handled.

Among desserts, spicy baked apple charlotte with nutmeg ice cream, and chocolate pudding with chocolate sauce and white chocolate ice cream come commended, the set-price lunch gets the thumbs up, and the smooth running of the highly praised service is largely attributable to the informative and helpful Eddie Hart. A short but resourceful wine list keeps prices in check and delivers good value by the glass. Bottle prices start at £11.50.

CHEF: Mark Gough PROPRIETOR: Tim Hart OPEN: all week 12 to 2, 7 (6 for pre-theatre menu; bookings only) to 10.30 MEALS: alc (main courses £9.50 to £15). Set L Mon to Sat £11 (2 courses) to £14.95, Set L Sun £18, Set D Sun £15 SERVICE: 10%, card slips closed CARDS: Amex, Delta, MasterCard, Switch, Visa DETAILS: 80 seats. 20 seats outside. Private parties: 84 main room, 14 to 50 private rooms. Car park at D. Vegetarian meals. Children's helpings. No-smoking area. No cigars/pipes in dining room. Wheelchair access (also WC). No music

Sonny's

3 Carlton Street, Hockley, Nottingham NG1 1NL
TEL: (0115) 947 3041 FAX: (0115) 950 7776

COOKING **3**
MODERN BRITISH
£23–£49

The bright, contemporary cooking offered at this city-centre venue is clearly a hit with Nottingham folk. Crowds regularly fill the spacious dining room, which is decorated in modern minimal style with pale colours. There is plenty to entice on the menu, with around eight choices per course covering a broad spectrum of styles. Starters range from a rustic and earthy-sounding salad of air-dried pork, celeriac and borlotti beans, to a classic fish soup with rouille, Gruyère and croûtons. Similar variety is offered by Provençal- and Mediterranean-influenced main courses, as in grilled sea bass with ratatouille and a warm tomato and basil dressing, or roast chicken breast with tarragon gnocchi, morels and broad beans. To finish, there may be lemon tart with blueberry compote, or lime bavarois with caramelised pineapple and chocolate shortbread. A lively bunch of wines is offered on the short list, all at reasonable prices and with many available by the glass. A pair of vins de pays at £10.45 (£2.85 a glass) open each section.

CHEF: David Hodgins PROPRIETOR: Rebecca Mascarenhas OPEN: all week 12 to 2.30, 7 to 10.30 (11 Fri and Sat, 9.30 Sun) CLOSED: Christmas, bank hols MEALS: alc (main courses £10 to £15.50). Set L Mon to Fri £10 (2 courses) to £13.95, Set L Sun £15 (2 courses) to £17.50 SERVICE: 10% (optional), card slips closed CARDS: Amex, Delta, MasterCard, Switch, Visa DETAILS: 80 seats. Private parties: 60 main room, 30 private room. Vegetarian meals. Children's helpings Sun L only. No-smoking area. Music. Air-conditioned (£5)

World Service

NOTTINGHAMSHIRE NEWCOMER OF THE YEAR

NEW ENTRY

Newdigate House, Castle Gate,
Nottingham NG1 6AF
TEL: (0115) 8475587 FAX: (0115) 8475584
WEB SITE: www.worldservicerestaurant.com

COOKING **5**
FRENCH/PACIFIC RIM
£21–£55

This new restaurant is housed in the gracious Georgian home of the Nottingham United Services Club, which has moved to the upper floors. The décor fuses colonial grandeur (panelled walls, fireplaces, tiled floors) with sumptuous Indonesian styling (dark wood, plain polished tables, subdued lighting, tribal masks). The entrance is like a walled oriental garden, and servers wear Indonesian-inspired garb.

Chefs Nick Aiello, formerly at Hambleton Hall (see entry, Hambleton), and Chris Elson serve 'classic French cuisine with a touch of Pacific Rim influence', and do it admirably. In fact, most dishes are European-based – such as a starter of fresh, creamy, green pea and mint soup with Parmesan mousse and morel mushrooms ('just taste, taste, taste') – though some – like a main course of Japanese-styled seared tuna with pickled ginger and white radish salad – go further afield. Still others are closer to 'fusion' cuisine: for example, a perfectly braised turbot fillet with shiitake mushrooms and chive sauce. Overall, the cooking is marked by good-quality ingredients, impressive Oriental-style presentation and brilliant accompaniments. Desserts, like banana crème brûlée, or roast apple pancake with caramel sauce and vanilla ice cream, are relatively straightforward.

A page each of whites, reds and halves chart the wine globe, with plenty under £20 (house Argentines are £9.90), and a fine-wine section offers French classics for bigger spenders. Six wines by the glass, from £2.65, open up choice throughout the meal, and a focus on saké adds interest.

CHEFS: Nick Aiello and Chris Elson PROPRIETORS: Ashley Walter, Philip Morgan and Nick Aiello OPEN: all week 12 to 2.30 (3.30 Sun), 7 to 10.30 (9 Sun) MEALS: alc (main courses £11 to £17). Set L £12.50 (2 courses) to £17, Set Sun D £9.50 (2 courses) to £13 SERVICE: not inc CARDS: Amex, Delta, Diners, MasterCard, Switch, Visa DETAILS: 75 seats. 30 seats outside. Private parties: 36 main room, 14 and 36 private rooms. Car park. Vegetarian meals. Children's helpings. No smoking in dining room. Music (£5)

OLD BURGHCLERE Hampshire map 2

Dew Pond

Old Burghclere RG20 9LH COOKING **5**
TEL: (01635) 278408 FAX: (01635) 278580 ANGLO-FRENCH
off old A34, 3m W of Kingsclere £40–£54

Although not far from a main road, the pale custard-coloured house makes the most of its peaceful views: two linked dining rooms decorated in 'English bourgeois' fashion look out over fields, hills and downs, one of them Watership Down. Keith Marshall adopts a generally conservative approach, his country cooking taking in a salad of goats' cheese and roasted provençale vegetables, or calf liver with black pudding and Colcannon potatoes. Ideas tend to be straightforward rather than exciting, although good materials provide a firm foundation: white crab meat mixed with avocado and mushrooms, placed on a crouton, and surrounded by a thin trail of tomato sauce, or saddle of roe deer on a powerfully flavoured celeriac purée, served with rösti and a heavily reduced stock-based sauce.

Desserts run to crème brûlée and sticky toffee pudding, while crusty bread and fine pastry indicate the kitchen's professionalism, although at inspection a marked lack of flavour in too many items shows that skills are patchy. Service leaves much to be desired, but the wine list, broken up into broad style groups, offers characterful bottles at modest prices; many are available under £20, and only two in the succinct halves section exceed £10. House reds and whites (French and Australian) are £11.95.

CHEF: Keith Marshall PROPRIETORS: Keith and Julie Marshall OPEN: Tue to Sat D 7 to 10 MEALS: Set D £28 SERVICE: not inc, 10% for parties of 8 or more CARDS: Delta, MasterCard, Switch, Visa DETAILS: 45 seats. Private parties: 50 main room, 25 private rooms. Car park. Children's helpings. No children under 5. No smoking in dining room. Wheelchair access (not WC). Occasional music (£5)

OMBERSLEY Worcestershire map 5

Venture In

Main Road, Ombersley WR9 0EW COOKING **2**
TEL/FAX: (01905) 620552 MODERN BRITISH/FRENCH
£26–£48

Fortnightly special fish dinners remain popular at this refurbished half-timbered inn just off the Worcester to Kidderminster road. One visitor enjoyed steamed sea bass fillet partnered by fennel and saffron ravioli in a tarragon sauce, followed by fillet of cod on potato and spinach rösti with a crab and chilli oil dressing. The rest of Toby Fletcher's French-inspired food is sometimes overlaid with modern ideas too, taking in anything from a straightforward twice-baked Roquefort soufflé (on a pear and rocket salad), to a chicken version of bourride served with saffron potatoes. Poultry and game are also likely to surface, perhaps as a pressed guinea fowl terrine, or venison medallions with Puy lentils and wild mushrooms. Among desserts, look out for a cream cheese ice cream in a chocolate cone, served with a warm, port-infused apple and pear compote. Most of the three dozen varied wines stay commendably under £20, supplemented by a few more expensive classics. Five house wines at £10.95 set the ball rolling.

CHEF/PROPRIETOR: Toby Fletcher OPEN: Tue to Sun L 12 to 2, Tue to Sat D 7 to 9.45 MEALS: Set L Tue to Sat £14.95 (2 courses) to £17.95, Set L Sun £18.95, Set D £27.95 SERVICE: not inc, card slips closed CARDS: Delta, MasterCard, Switch, Visa DETAILS: 34 seats. Private parties: 34 main room, 14 and 18 private rooms. Car park. Vegetarian meals. No children under 9. No smoking in dining room. No music. Air-conditioned

ORFORD Suffolk map 6

▲ Crown and Castle, Trinity

Orford IP12 2LJ
TEL: (01394) 450205 FAX: (01394) 450176 COOKING **2**
EMAIL: info@crownandcastlehotel.co.uk MODERN BRITISH
WEB SITE: www.crownandcastlehotel.co.uk £25–£50

Eating seems to happen all over the place in this converted pub, whose plank floor, wooden beams and utilitarian polished tables are livened up by a varied collection of pictures. Options include a casual bar menu, afternoon tea, a kids' menu, and a carte of commendable simplicity that might feature oak smoked salmon with horseradish cream, a buffalo mozzarella, tomato and olive salad, or jazzed up oysters at £1.10 apiece. Some items, such as jerk squid or flavourful crab cake, can be taken as either a starter or main course, and while results are variable they have produced an enjoyable bruschetta of red peppers and grilled artichokes, as well as succulent slow-roast belly pork with buttered kale and mustard mash, and high-quality pink flavourful breast of duck in a vegetable broth. Finish perhaps with a pot of creamy glazed lemon curd, or a slice of tasty frangipane tart. Service could do with sharpening up, but the varietally arranged wine list provides plenty of choice from Chardonnay to Vernaccia, from Gamay to Corvina, much of it around the £20 mark. House Sicilian is available by the glass, half-litre, litre, and bottle (£10.20).

CHEF: Brendan Ansbro PROPRIETORS: David and Ruth Watson OPEN: all week 12 to 2, 7 to 9.30 (May to Sep L 12 to 2.30, D 6.30 to 10). MEALS: alc (main courses £9.50 to £13.50). Set L Mon to Sat £13.50 (2 courses) to £17.50. Bar menu available SERVICE: not inc CARDS: Delta, MasterCard, Switch, Visa DETAILS: 48 seats. 40 seats outside. Private parties: 12 main room, 12 private room. Car park. Vegetarian meals. Children's helpings. Wheelchair access (not WC). No music ACCOMMODATION: 18 rooms, all with bath/shower. TV. Phone. D,B&B £85 to £150. Rooms for disabled (£5)

OSWESTRY Shropshire map 7

▲ Sebastians

45 Willow Street, Oswestry SY11 1AQ
TEL: (01691) 655444 FAX: (01691) 653452
EMAIL: sebastians.rest@virgin.net
WEB SITE: www.sebastians-hotel.co.uk

COOKING **3**
FRENCH
£37–£49

Occupying a sixteenth-century house with oak beams, panelled walls, and oil lamps on the tables, Sebastians goes in for a fairly traditional style of French cooking: duck leg confit is served on a cassoulet bean base, garlic mushrooms come in a cream and Roquefort sauce, and a crisp filo pastry parcel has been filled with a well-flavoured mix of goats' cheese and cranberry. Fish is claimed as a speciality, yielding salmon with choucroute, and firm, fresh red mullet in a fish broth accompanied by deep-fried leeks. Good-quality meats, meanwhile, have included lamb with a rösti cake and lentils, and tender duck breast in a pleasantly sharp blackcurrant sauce. Desserts run from a parfait of tiramisù glacé to a crisp-topped trio of custards – coffee, vanilla, and wild thyme – and service is attentive yet unfussy. France also predominates on the wine list, although the New World gets a look in too, and prices (starting at £11.50) are realistic.

CHEF: Mark Sebastian Fisher PROPRIETORS: Michelle and Mark Sebastian Fisher OPEN: Tue to Sat D only 6.30 to 9.45 CLOSED: 25 and 26 Dec, 1 Jan MEALS: Set D £22 (2 courses) to £26 SERVICE: not inc, card slips closed CARDS: Amex, Delta, MasterCard, Switch, Visa DETAILS: 35 seats. 25 seats outside. Private parties: 40 main room. Vegetarian meals. Children's helpings. No smoking in dining room. Wheelchair access (not WC). Music ACCOMMODATION: 8 rooms, all with bath/shower. TV. Phone. Room only £40 to £50. Rooms for disabled. Baby facilities (£5)

£ *means that it is possible to have a three-course meal, including coffee, half a bottle of house wine and service for £25 or less per person, at any time the restaurant is open, i.e. at dinner as well as lunch. It may be possible to spend considerably more than this, but by choosing carefully you should find £25 or less achievable.*

The Guide always appreciates hearing about changes of chef or owner.

OXFORD Oxfordshire map 2

▲ Al-Shami £

25 Walton Crescent, Oxford OX1 2JG COOKING **2**
TEL: (01865) 310066 FAX: (01865) 311241 LEBANESE
WEB SITE: www.al-shami.co.uk £19–£39

A Victorian back street in Oxford's student haven of Jericho accommodates this well-liked Lebanese brasserie. Chandeliers, potted plants and Middle Eastern paintings decorate the bright interior, but it's the good-value choice of 39 hot and cold meze that draws custom from academia and beyond. Hummus topped with crisp strips of lamb receives praise aplenty, and the 'very fresh' tabbouleh also finds favour. More unusual offerings include mohammara bil-jawz, a vibrantly red blend of crushed nuts, capsicum, olive oil and spices. Main courses comprise grilled meats such as kibbeh bil-siniyeh (a baked disc of ground lamb and crushed wheat stuffed with pine kernels and onions) and some fish and vegetarian dishes: okra, garlic and tomatoes on rice, for instance. Lebanese pastries, pointed out by 'charming, very welcoming' staff, make a fitting finale. The short drinks list has Lebanese house wine at £9.99, arak and various vintages of Château Musar.

CHEF: Mimo Mahfouz PROPRIETOR: Al-Shami Cuisine OPEN: all week 12 to 12 MEALS: alc (main courses £6.50 to £12). Set L and D £15. Cover £1 SERVICE: not inc, 10% for parties of 6 or more CARDS: MasterCard, Switch, Visa DETAILS: 50 seats. Private parties: 50 main room, 50 private room. Vegetarian meals. Wheelchair access (also WC). Music ACCOMMODATION: 12 rooms, all with bath/shower. TV. Phone. B&B £35 to £45 (£5)

Cherwell Boathouse

50 Bardwell Road, Oxford OX2 6ST
TEL: (01865) 552746 FAX: (01865) 553819 COOKING **3**
EMAIL: info@cherwellboathouse.co.uk MODERN ENGLISH/FRENCH
WEB SITE: www.cherwellboathouse.co.uk £25–£33

Down a quiet lane off the Banbury Road, overlooking the river, the Boathouse does not hide its origins: bare brick walls have an oar as decoration, and the floor is well-used parquet. An outside dining 'deck' has been added, and 'restrained expansion' of restaurant and kitchen is planned for early 2002.

Good timing of high-quality (often local) ingredients characterises the regularly changing fixed-price menus. Pan-fried pigeon breast with crispy bacon salad has been a highlight among starters, or you might try warm wild mushroom tartlets, followed by baked mackerel with rhubarb compote. Breast of guinea fowl with red cabbage earns praise for the quality of the meat and accompanying garlic jus, and sticky date and walnut cake might round things off. Staff are young, laid-back and engaging, though not infallible. Proprietor Anthony Verdin's background at Morris and Verdin assures vinous value and variety, with leanings to Burgundy and to the Riesling grape. The many and various house selections start at £9 (£2.50 a glass) for a fruit-filled southern French, and low pricing permeates the list, even extending to Cloudy Bay Sauvignon Blanc at £22.

CHEF: Wayne Cullen PROPRIETOR: Anthony Verdin OPEN: all week L 12 to 2, Mon to Sat D 6.30 to 10 (10.30 Fri and Sat) MEALS: Set L Mon to Fri £9.75 (2 courses) to £18.50, Set L Sat and Sun £19.50, Set D £20.50 SERVICE: not inc, 10% for parties of 6 or more CARDS: Amex, Delta, Diners, MasterCard, Switch, Visa DETAILS: 60 seats. 100 seats outside. Private parties: 20 main room, 80 in marquee in summer. Car park. Vegetarian meals. Children's helpings. No smoking in dining room. Wheelchair access (also WC). No music (£5)

La Gousse d'Ail

NEW ENTRY

268 Woodstock Road, Oxford OX8 1AS
TEL: (01865) 311936 FAX: (01865) 516613
EMAIL: info@lagoussedail.co.uk
WEB SITE: www.lagoussedail.com

COOKING **6**
MODERN FRENCH
£31–£165

Since the last edition of the Guide, this large 1930s villa, about a mile and a half from the city centre, has been extensively refurbished in bright modern colours, turning from a brasserie (it was called the Lemon Tree) into a serious and sophisticated cosmopolitan restaurant. An elegant and airy feel predominates, helped by skylights, French windows looking on to a small courtyard garden, and modern art on the walls. Readers who may remember Jonathan Wright from his days at Le Manoir aux Quat' Saisons (he was last listed there in 1999; see entry) will not be surprised to find that his cooking is firmly in the mould of modern French haute cuisine.

Luxuries are conspicuous by their presence – as in a ravioli of crab and langoustine topped with morels and truffles – but dishes rely equally on dedicated workmanship and skilful handling for effect: for example, in a main course of 'lamb every which way', including a tiny, exquisitely braised shoulder, pink kidneys on a pea sauce, a 'square' of pink muscle, and sweetbread beignets, all served with a 'memorably good' gravy, or jus niçoise as the menu has it. This is not dyed-in-the-wool stuff, and there are brave combinations to prove it: such as a croustillant of melting, pan-fried foie gras and sweet roasted mango, accompanied by coffee praline and jasmine tea sauce. Even more surprising, perhaps, is how effective such a partnership turns out to be.

Bitter flavours seem to be a hallmark, of pan-frying, and of desserts such as an opulently rich chocolate fondant with espresso sauce, tempered by a sweet pistachio ice cream. Service under the guidance of Jayne Wright is generally professional, although an air of 'contrived dignity' can pervade. There is nothing wrong with the wine list that more amenable prices could not fix, although ten house selections are available by the glass from £4.50 to £8.

CHEF: Jonathan Wright PROPRIETORS: Jonathan and Jayne Wright OPEN: Tue to Sun L 12 to 2.30, Tue to Sat D 6 (7 Sat) to 10.30 CLOSED: first 2 weeks Jan, first 2 weeks Aug MEALS: alc (main courses £22 to £26). Set L Tue to Sat £16.50 (2 courses) to £19.50, Set L Sun £28, Set D Tue to Fri £22 (2 courses) to £85, Set D £55 to £85 SERVICE: 10% (optional), card slips closed CARDS: MasterCard, Switch, Visa DETAILS: 75 seats. 28 seats outside. Private parties: 90 main room, 24 private room. Car park. Vegetarian meals. No smoking in 1 dining room. Wheelchair access (also WC). No music

All entries, including Round-ups, are fully indexed at the back of the Guide.

▲ Parsonage Restaurant & Bar

1 Banbury Road, Oxford OX2 6NN — COOKING **2**
TEL: (01865) 310210 FAX: (01865) 311262 — ENGLISH/MEDITERRANEAN
£30–£46

Looking suitably ancient, the seventeenth-century weathered stone building used to be the parsonage for nearby St Giles's church. Handy for the centre of town, it opens into a couple of informal bar areas, is comfortable and reliable, and deals in plain fare to suit casual eating: wild mushroom tart, salmon fishcakes, or twice-baked spinach and Parmesan soufflé. More substantial appetites might favour pan-fried calf's liver and bacon with sage and onion mash, or chargrilled quail on potato rösti. To finish, sorbets and ice creams share the billing with chocolate tart and baked Alaska. Sound, moderately priced wines start with Australian Chardonnay (£12.60) and Spanish Tempranillo (£13.20); around a dozen come by the glass.

CHEF: Alison Watkins PROPRIETOR: Jeremy Mogford OPEN: all week 12 to 2.30, 6 to 10.30 CLOSED: 24 to 29 Dec MEALS: alc (main courses £10 to £13) SERVICE: not inc CARDS: Amex, Delta, Diners, MasterCard, Switch, Visa DETAILS: 33 seats. 24 seats outside. Private parties: 13 main room. Car park. Vegetarian meals. Children's helpings. No cigars/pipes in dining room. Music. Air-conditioned ACCOMMODATION: 30 rooms, all with bath/shower. TV. Phone. B&B £140 to £200. Baby facilities (*The Which? Hotel Guide*)

Le Petit Blanc

71–72 Walton Street, Oxford OX2 6AG — COOKING **4**
TEL: (01865) 510999 FAX: (01865) 510700 — FRENCH
WEB SITE: www.petit-blanc.com — £24–£47

Although the brasserie market has become increasingly crowded in recent years, the first of the Petit Blanc chain (see also entries in Birmingham and Cheltenham) holds its own with a consistent level of cooking. Tables have no cloths, floors have no carpets, and a lot of the walls are glass, so expect a bit of a hubbub at busy times: the light, casual style of food is an adjunct to socialising as much as an end in itself. French bourgeois dishes recalling M. Blanc's home background – skate grenobloise, or roast wild pigeon with cabbage and chestnuts – are only part of the story, as the seasonally changing menu appeals to a broader spectrum with coconut, coriander and lime soup, and salmon and haddock fishcake.

Caesar salad deserves 'special mention' for both its gargantuan proportions and freshness, risotto comes out well (flavoured with Parma ham, peas, lemon and Parmesan for one lunchtime visitor) and a smooth, firm, flavourful foie gras and chicken liver parfait shows that classics are handled properly. A relatively short dessert selection takes in treacle tarte (sic), and pistachio soufflé with chocolate ganache. Service is willing, and a varietally arranged globetrotting wine list (which includes Viognier and Tempranillo) keeps its feet on the ground as far as prices are concerned. House Marsanne and Grenache are £10.65.

CHEF: Martin White PROPRIETOR: Raymond Blanc OPEN: all week 12 to 3 (3.30 Sat and Sun), 6 to 11 (10 Sun) CLOSED: 25 Dec MEALS: alc (main courses £8.50 to £16), Set L 12 to 3 and D 6 to 7 and 10 to 11 (available all evening on Sun) £12.50 (2 courses) to £15. Light L menu available Mon to Fri 12 to 7 SERVICE: not inc, 10% (optional) for parties of 8 or more CARDS: Amex, Delta,

Diners, MasterCard, Switch, Visa DETAILS: 150 seats. Private parties: 85 main room, 20 private room. Car park Sat and Sun L. Vegetarian meals. Children's helpings. No smoking in 1 dining room. Wheelchair access (also WC). Music. Air-conditioned (£5)

White House

2 Botley Road, Oxford OX2 0AB
TEL: (01865) 242823 FAX: (01865) 793331
EMAIL: thewhitehouseoxford@btinternet.com

COOKING 1
MODERN BRITISH
£29–£49

This large pub, a former toll-house near Oxford railway station, probably wouldn't win any gongs for interior design, but it does take food quite seriously. The restaurant is at the rear of the pub and during summer months diners can take full advantage of the wonderful walled garden. The tendency is towards hearty fare; food is served on large white plates and comes in huge portions. Starters might include sizzling red mullet with spring onion and ginger, or simple fettucine and pesto. Mains might turn up escalope of salmon with red onion raita, or leek and butter bean gratin with Dijon mustard. Vegetarian dishes are helpfully picked out with a 'smiley' face. The wine list is priced just right for a pub, with some interesting bottles from France, Italy and the New World. There is plenty of choice between £15 and £20.

CHEF: Christopher Bland PROPRIETOR: John Martin OPEN: all week 12 to 2.30, 6.30 to 9.30 CLOSED: 25 and 26 Dec MEALS: alc (main courses £9.50 to £15). Bar menu available Mon to Sat L and Mon to Fri D 6 to 7.30 SERVICE: not inc CARDS: Delta, MasterCard, Switch, Visa DETAILS: 70 seats. 60 seats outside. Private parties: 50 main room. Car park. Vegetarian meals. Children's helpings. Wheelchair access (also WC). No music (£5)

PADSTOW Cornwall map 1

Brock's

The Strand, Padstow PL28 8AJ
TEL: (01841) 532565 FAX: (01841) 533199
EMAIL: brockx@compuserve.com

NEW CHEF
MODERN BRITISH
£28–£58

There is plenty going on in Padstow, as one can see from a window table over the street at this sunny yellow first-floor restaurant, and there has been some activity inside too, as Shane Young took over the kitchens just before the Guide went to press. The lively emphasis on fish looks like remaining, in the form of lemon sole with ginger and lemon-grass butter, and monkfish Marsala with toasted coconut, while desserts are likely to include grilled figs with blueberry compote and mascarpone cream. The short wine list opens with a Chilean Merlot at £12.95. Reports please.

CHEF: Shane Young PROPRIETORS: Tim and Hazel Brocklebank OPEN: Tue to Sat 12.15 to 2, 7 to 9.30 (10 Fri and Sat) CLOSED: 5 Jan to 5 Feb MEALS: alc (main courses L £7 to £12, D £10 to £17.50). Set D £19.50 (2 courses) to £23.50 SERVICE: not inc CARDS: Delta, MasterCard, Switch, Visa DETAILS: 60 seats. Private parties: 40 main room, 30 private room. Vegetarian meals. Children's helpings. No smoking in dining room. Occasional music

Margot's

11 Duke Street, Padstow PL28 8AB
TEL: (01841) 533441 — COOKING **2**
EMAIL: oliveradrian@hotmail.com — MODERN BRITISH
WEB SITE: www.margots.co.uk — £26–£40

Though Margot died in 1998, Adrian Oliver keeps his former employer's name on the frontage of the small, brightly decorated restaurant that he and his wife now own. Some fans feel he should step forward into the limelight he deserves for his thoughtful approach to cooking and its commendable results. His style is unpretentious and uncomplicated, and menus change daily, reflecting the availability and seasonality of local produce. Fish and seafood show particularly well, perhaps mussels and clams with coriander and ginger, or cod baked with garlic, anchovies and parsley served on olive oil mash; non-fish options might include confit of duck with red wine and thyme sauce and spring onion mash. Desserts might take in caramelised lemon tart with clotted cream, and a short wine list (supplemented by wines of the month listed on a blackboard) includes five house selections from £9.95.

CHEFS: Adrian Oliver and Matthew Cortis PROPRIETORS: Adrian and Julie Oliver OPEN: Thur to Sun L 12 to 2, Wed to Sun D 7 to 9.30 CLOSED: late Nov, Jan; limited opening Dec MEALS: alc L (main courses £9 to £13). Set D £19.95 (2 courses) to £24.95 SERVICE: not inc CARDS: Amex, Delta, MasterCard, Switch, Visa DETAILS: 25 seats. Private parties: 25 main room. Vegetarian meals. Children's helpings. No smoking in dining room. Wheelchair access (not WC). Music (£5)

▲ Number 6 Art & Seafood Café

6 Middle Street, Padstow PL28 8AP — COOKING **4**
TEL/FAX: (01841) 532093 — SEAFOOD-PLUS
£35–£55

The starting point at Number 6 – which proclaims itself 'the other seafood restaurant in Padstow' – is high-quality local produce, notably daily supplies of outstanding Cornish seafood, but also locally grown herbs and salad leaves, and even ostrich farmed in Camelford. Karen Scott's cooking brings in influences from the Mediterranean and the Pacific rim to produce starters of seared scallops with a sweet chilli dressing alongside locally smoked salmon with corn cakes and avocado salad. Loin of blue-fin tuna with lemon grass, coriander, coconut and black Thai rice comes from one end of the main-course spectrum, while Cornish cod with Spanish potatoes, chorizo, watercress salad and balsamic dressing is at the other.

Décor in the dining room is predominantly white, with cream door and window frames, a black and white tiled floor, and potted plants to add colour; plenty of windows let in the light. Wines are from Christopher Piper of Ottery St Mary, and the list has been chosen well in respect of both quality and price. Four house selections are £11.50 a bottle, £4 a glass.

CHEF: Karen Scott PROPRIETORS: Karen and Peter Scott OPEN: Wed to Mon D only 7 to 9.30 (6.30 to 10.30 Fri and Sat in summer) MEALS: alc (main courses £16). Set D £19.50 (2 courses) to £24.50 SERVICE: not inc CARDS: none DETAILS: 40 seats. 6 seats outside. Private parties: 40 main room. No smoking in dining room. Music ACCOMMODATION: 2 rooms, both with bath/shower. TV. B&B £40 to £70. No children (*The Which? Hotel Guide*) (£5)

▲ Rick Stein's Café

10 Middle Street, Padstow PL28 8AP
TEL: (01841) 532700 FAX: (01841) 532942 COOKING **2**
EMAIL: reservations@rickstein.com GLOBAL/SEAFOOD
WEB SITE: www.rickstein.com £24–£39

This is a good place to 'sample some of the delights of the Stein team at sensible prices', though some feel 'bistro' would be a more appropriate designation than 'café'. Arrive early for lunch (no lunch bookings are taken, and trade is always brisk); for a more leisurely meal, dinner is a better bet. Unfortunately popularity has its downside, and several reporters have experienced lengthy delays and harassed service.

The Stein name is synonymous with bold, modern fish cookery, evident in starters of mussels with cream, curry, cognac and saffron, and in Thai fishcakes with sweet-and-sour cucumber and onion dressing. Main courses on the short dinner menu, meanwhile, might run to lemon sole with ciabatta crumb crust and salsa verde mayonnaise, or grilled Pollock with Irish-style mash. The short and sensibly priced wine list has nothing under £10 or over £20.

CHEF: Julian Lloyd PROPRIETORS: Rick and Jill Stein OPEN: Mon to Sat 12 to 2.30, 7 to 9.30 CLOSED: 23 to 26 Dec, 1 May MEALS: alc (main courses L £5.50 to £7, D £10). Set D £18 SERVICE: not inc CARDS: Delta, MasterCard, Switch, Visa DETAILS: 43 seats. 10 seats outside. Private parties: 16 main room. Children's helpings. Vegetarian meals. No smoking in dining room. Music ACCOMMODATION: 3 rooms, all with bath/shower. TV. Phone. B&B £70 to £90. Baby facilities

▲ St Petroc's Bistro

4 New Street, Padstow PL28 8EA
TEL: (01841) 532700 FAX: (01841) 532942 COOKING **2**
EMAIL: reservations@rickstein.com BISTRO
WEB SITE: www.rickstein.com £32–£48

Light, bright and breezy, with lots of wood and a fair amount of noise, this is the dining room of a white painted hotel just above the harbour and the crowds. The first offshoot of the Seafood Restaurant (see entry below), it continues to offer relatively unfussy dishes like squid (sautéed with Greek salad, or deep fried with aïoli), poached skate wing with black butter, or pan-fried lemon sole (fresh as can be) with lemon-grass butter. Non-fishy options have included a just-runny rocket risotto, and well-timed sirloin steak. Some items that should not be difficult to produce (from toast to chips to chowder) have been below par, but plain accompaniments – just boiled new potatoes perhaps – are appreciated for their straightforwardness. Desserts run to chocolate mousse with whisky and crème fraîche, and a well-judged Bakewell tart. Young, sassy, suntanned staff can seem very pleased with themselves at times, but are deemed attentive and efficient, and most of the two dozen sharply chosen wines stay accommodatingly below £20.

CHEF: Alistair Clive PROPRIETORS: Nick and Jill Stein OPEN: Tue to Sun 12 to 2, 7 to 9.30 CLOSED: 17 to 26 Dec, 1 May MEALS: alc (main courses £12 to £14.50) SERVICE: not inc CARDS: Delta, MasterCard, Switch, Visa DETAILS: 56 seats. 10 seats outside. Private parties: 12 main room, 6 private room. Children's helpings. No smoking in dining room. Music. Air-conditioned ACCOMMODATION: 13 rooms, all with bath/shower. TV. Phone. B&B £95 to £150. Baby facilities

▲ Seafood Restaurant

Riverside, Padstow PL28 8BY
TEL: (01841) 532700 FAX: (01841) 532942 — COOKING **6**
EMAIL: reservations@rickstein.com — SEAFOOD
WEB SITE: www.rickstein.com — £46–£99

The Rick Stein experience now includes a cookery school (also available for private dinner parties), a gift shop, a new deli, more rooms at St Edmund's House next door, and a mail-order service, in addition to the Café and St Petroc's (see entries above). The jewel in the crown, however, remains the Seafood Restaurant. Many people seem to come expecting it to be the best fish restaurant in the country and, although opinions divide, most reporters go away happy. It certainly looks a worthy cosmopolitan venue, the stark white dining room brightened by vividly coloured paintings (for sale) and sharp spotlighting, and relaxed customers generate enough buzz to make it always seem like a special occasion.

The spectrum runs from sauté squid salad with chilli, mint and coriander, via bourride with a biting aïoli, to puffy poached quenelles of gurnard, light and bouncy, served with a nutmeggy lobster sauce. A small but generous starter plate of fruits de mer scores for variety and freshness, and other commendably straightforward treatments include cod with chips and tartare sauce, and two tail fillets of fresh and accurately timed sea bass, their skin heavily salted, with just a tomato and olive oil dressing flecked with herbs.

Desserts are on a par with everything else: a creamy, wobbly, vanilla-speckled pannacotta, for example, with two accurately poached plums in syrup and a crunchy biscuit. Those on a tight budget might query some of the cost, but most reporters are happy about value for money. The wine list is packed with a variety of styles perfectly geared to the fruits of the sea, headed by a lively personal selection. House white vin de pays and red Côtes du Rhône come in at £14.95 and £18.75 respectively, reflecting the fairly hefty mark-ups.

CHEFS: Rick Stein and Stephan Delowme PROPRIETORS: Rick and Jill Stein OPEN: all week 12 to 2, 7 to 10 CLOSED: 17 to 26 and 31 Dec, May bank hol MEALS: alc (main courses £16.50 to £39), Set L £33.50, Set D £39 SERVICE: not inc CARDS: Delta, MasterCard, Switch, Visa DETAILS: 109 seats. Private parties: 16 main room. Vegetarian meals. Children's helpings. No children under 3. Occasional music. Air-conditioned ACCOMMODATION: 19 rooms, all with bath/shower. TV. Phone. B&B £95 to £170. Baby facilities (*The Which? Hotel Guide*)

'The sole had been fed steroids by the size of it, but the red mullet resembled an anorexic sardine.' (On eating in London)

PAINSWICK Gloucestershire map 2

▲ Painswick Hotel

Kemps Lane, Painswick GL6 6YB
TEL: (01452) 812160 FAX: (01452) 814059
EMAIL: reservations@painswickhotel.com
WEB SITE: www.painswickhotel.com

COOKING **5**
BRITISH
£27–£63

Redecoration and refurbishment continue apace at this former rectory, hemmed in by grey-stone houses on the narrow road that runs through the village. It is 'pure, genteel Gloucestershire, all fine linen and polished this and that', although its stone fireplaces, carved ceilings and large gilt mirrors are on a pleasingly small scale. Sourcing materials is a serious business, taking in Trelough ducks and Gloucester Old Spot pork, venison and game birds from nearby estates and shoots, and West Country fish such as sea bass from day boats, and dived scallops. Despite such obviously foreign dishes as shredded duck and Landes foie gras with Sauternes jelly, a strong British vein runs through the cooking, exemplified by rump of Cotswold lamb with pease pudding.

A lightness of touch is evident too, not least when it comes to saucing: a chicken jus to accompany Cornish turbot with lobster tortellini and grilled asparagus, or an oyster cappuccino served with a dish of sea bass paired with leek and bacon risotto. Regional cheeses (such as Cerney goats' and unpasteurised Cheddar) offer an alternative to desserts such as hot chocolate fondant with Malteser ice cream. Service is swift and well informed, and the list of soundly chosen wines, with France in the ascendancy, picks off many a fine producer. The first few pages give a steer to those on more modest budgets, with the house selection starting at £13.50.

CHEF: Kevin Barron PROPRIETORS: Gareth and Helen Pugh OPEN: all week 12 to 2, 7 to 9.30 MEALS: alc D (main courses £18.50 to £22.50). Set L Mon to Sat £13 (2 courses) to £16, Set L Sun £17.50, Set D £24 (2 courses) to £27.50. Light L menu available SERVICE: not inc, card slips closed CARDS: Amex, Delta, MasterCard, Switch, Visa DETAILS: 30 seats. 20 seats outside. Private parties: 60 main room, 18 private room. Car park. Vegetarian meals. Children's helpings. No smoking in dining room. Occasional music ACCOMMODATION: 19 rooms, all with bath/shower. TV. Phone. B&B £75 to £180. Baby facilities (£5)

PAULERSPURY Northamptonshire map 5

▲ Vine House

100 High Street, Paulerspury NN12 7NA
TEL: (01327) 811267 FAX: (01327) 811309
off A5, 2m SE of Towcester

COOKING **3**
MODERN EUROPEAN
£38–£48

Occupying an attractive 300-year-old building in a pretty rural village, Vine House serves three-course meals (the same price at lunch and dinner) in a broadly European style, taking in Cornish mackerel pâté, calf's liver with a sweet potato variation on bubble and squeak, and roast wood pigeon with white bean purée. Timings and seasoning do not please all reporters, but successes have included a well-judged spinach, pine nut and basil risotto, herb gnocchi with smoked haddock, and crisp-skinned, moist-fleshed sea bream with lentil purée. Desserts are a high point, judging by one visitor's lemon pannacotta served with honey-poached strawberries and crushed almond praline. Vegetarians are required to give 24 hours' notice. Although service may lack polish, there is a willingness to please, and a French-dominated wine list opens with a brace of house wines at £11.25.

CHEFS/PROPRIETORS: Marcus and Julie Springett OPEN: Wed to Fri L 12 to 1.45, Mon to Sat D 7 to 9.30 MEALS: Set L and D £25.95 SERVICE: not inc CARDS: MasterCard, Visa DETAILS: 33 seats. Private parties: 33 main room, 10 private room. Car park. Vegetarian meals with 24 hours' notice. No smoking in dining room. No music ACCOMMODATION: 6 rooms, all with bath/shower. TV. Phone. B&B £49 to £79 (*The Which? Hotel Guide*) (£5)

PAXFORD Gloucestershire **map 5**

▲ Churchill Arms £

Paxford GL55 6XH — COOKING **5**
TEL: (01386) 594000 FAX: (01386) 594005 — MODERN EUROPEAN
EMAIL: churchill-arms@hotmail.com — £22–£44

Although this aims to be a pub with food rather than a restaurant with beer, it has a 'very Cotswold atmosphere' and food that few pubs could match. At least the yellow Cotswold-stone building near the church looks the part, with trestle tables out front, and sepia prints, old pews, and bare tables and floors within. Some of the dishes sound pubby too, including cottage pie, and honey-roast ham with egg and chips, but there may also be John Dory with red wine risotto, or braised lamb shank with a casserole of haricot beans and chorizo. While staying with generally familiar ideas, the style remains gently inventive, producing dishes such as saffron-marinated mackerel with cucumber sauce, and loin of rabbit with spiced aubergine and lentils.

For those counting the pennies, some of the starters might make a substantial enough meal in themselves: ox tongue and crisp sweetbreads are served with diced beetroot and Cumberland sauce, and breast of pigeon comes with roast onion and celeriac purée. Desserts, meanwhile, run from pannacotta with orange and nutmeg parfait, to iced pistachio terrine with raspberry coulis. Service might be more enthusiastic. A short roving wine list starts with eight house wines under £10, and much of the rest stays commendably under £20.

CHEF: Ivan Reid PROPRIETORS: Sonya and Leo Brooke-Little OPEN: all week 12 to 2, 7 to 9 MEALS: alc (main courses £6.50 to £14) SERVICE: not inc CARDS: Delta, MasterCard, Switch, Visa DETAILS: 60 seats. 60 seats outside. Private parties: 30 main room. Vegetarian meals. Wheelchair access (not WC). No music ACCOMMODATION: 4 rooms, all with bath/shower. TV. Phone. B&B £40 to £70 (*The Which? Hotel Guide*)

The text of entries is based on unsolicited reports sent in by readers, backed up by inspections conducted anonymously. The factual details under the text are from questionnaires the Guide sends to all restaurants that feature in the book.

NEW CHEF *is shown instead of a cooking mark where a change of chef occurred too late for a new assessment of the cooking.*

PENZANCE Cornwall map 1

Harris's

46 New Street, Penzance TR18 2LZ
TEL: (01736) 364408 FAX: (01736) 333273
EMAIL: harriss.restaurant@lineone.net

COOKING **3**
ANGLO-FRENCH/SEAFOOD
£37–£66

Consistency is the watchword here, as well it might be for a restaurant with not far short of 30 years under its belt. A fiercely loyal customer base, the freshest fish and seafood from the Newlyn catch, not to mention an unforgettable shimmering pink interior, have kept it deservedly popular, as has Roger Harris's confident way with classic preparations. Smoked salmon stuffed with crabmeat on balsamic-dressed leaves is a substantial starter, and the fish soup is highly recommended too. Daily specials, always worth consulting, might run to grilled sea bream with red pepper sauce, while the main menu trendily offers roast monkfish with wild mushroom risotto. Carnivorous appetites are catered for as well, with correctly timed medallions of lamb on roasted fennel delivering satisfaction at a June meal. The same occasion produced a fittingly seasonal summer pudding ('moist, firm and with a hint of sharpness'), or there may be chocolate-cased iced lemon soufflé. The wine list, which leads with France and nods towards other regions, starts at £12.50.

CHEF: Roger Harris PROPRIETORS: Roger and Anne Harris OPEN: Tue to Sat noon to 7 CLOSED: 3 weeks winter, 25 and 26 Dec MEALS: alc (main courses £12.50 to £25). Light lunch menu also available SERVICE: 10%, card slips closed CARDS: Amex, MasterCard, Switch, Visa DETAILS: 40 seats. Private parties: 20 main room. No smoking in 1 dining room. Music

PETERSFIELD Hampshire map 2

JSW

NEW ENTRY

1 Heath Road, Petersfield GU31 4JE
TEL: (01730) 262030

COOKING **5**
MODERN BRITISH
£27–£45

J.S. Watkins opened this town-centre restaurant in June 2000. Pale beige walls are hung with some of his sister's line drawings of male figures; long-stemmed crystal glasses add to the understated elegance; and a bunch of riotously coloured flowers lends the only splash of colour. The same simple menu – four dishes per course and not a supplement in sight – operates at lunch and dinner, though the fixed prices are different. The direct style of cooking is characterised by depth and richness of flavour, for example in a mosaic of quail and wild mushrooms, and sauté foie gras with lentils and bacon. Main courses operate on similarly robust lines, and although seasoning may not always be absolutely spot on, dishes are well constructed, as in a loin of veal with broad beans, truffles and a creamy mash of yellow-fleshed potatoes.

Materials are well sourced, taking in Bresse chickens, and fish from Newlyn: perhaps cod, roasted and served with ratatouille and asparagus on a chive-strewn crème fraîche sauce. Desserts eschew the hackneyed in favour of pear poached in red wine with rice pudding, or a jelly of blood orange and pink champagne; ice creams, breads and pasta are all made in-house. The wide-ranging wine list prices both reds and whites fairly (from £13.50) and, refreshingly, starts with the New World. Although great names are scattered through the list (including one or two mature vintages), there is choice aplenty under £20, plus a mix of styles offered in large glasses from £3.50, and more in half-bottles.

CHEF/PROPRIETOR: J.S. Watkins OPEN: Tue to Sat 12 to 2, 7 to 10 CLOSED: first 2 weeks Jan MEALS: Set L £12.50 (2 courses) to £15.50, Set D £22.50 (2 courses) to £25.50 SERVICE: not inc CARDS: Delta, MasterCard, Switch, Visa DETAILS: 22 seats. Private parties: 28 main room. Vegetarian meals. No music (£5)

PETER TAVY Devon map 1

Peter Tavy Inn £

Peter Tavy PL19 9NN
TEL: (01822) 810348 FAX: (01822) 810835
EMAIL: peter.tavy@virgin.net
off A386, 3m NE of Tavistock

COOKING **2**
MODERN EUROPEAN
£18–£35

With its low ceilings, beams, open fireplaces and flagstone floors, this ancient inn 'oozes atmosphere' and achieves unusually high standards in all areas. Utterly obliging staff go out of their way to make visitors feel welcome, and provide efficient, friendly service even when the place is heaving – which is often. Food has also come in for high praise from reporters. Choice is wide and varied, starters ranging from scallop and bacon salad to prawn Orly with lemon and ginger sauce, main courses encompassing everything from fillet steak Rossini to seafood créole on spicy pineapple, and lemon and coriander duck with rice pancakes. Portions are designed to suit the heartiest appetites, so it pays to arrive hungry. Leave room for desserts, which may include apple and almond crumble, or treacle tart, 'both served with one of the best custards we have tasted'. Around three dozen good-value wines help to keep the bill under control. Four house selections are £7.95.

CHEF: Steve Byrne PROPRIETORS: Graeme and Karen Sim OPEN: all week 12 to 2, 7 (6.30 Fri and Sat) to 9 CLOSED: 25 Dec MEALS: alc (main courses L £4.50 to £9, D £7 to £13) SERVICE: not inc, card slips closed CARDS: Delta, MasterCard, Switch, Visa DETAILS: 76 seats. 100 seats outside. Private parties: 44 main room. Car park. Vegetarian meals. Children's helpings. No children in bar area. No smoking in 1 dining room. Music (£5)

PETWORTH West Sussex map 3

Soanes Restaurant

Grove Lane, Petworth GU28 0HY
TEL/FAX: (01798) 343659
WEB SITE: www.soanes.co.uk

COOKING **4**
MODERN EUROPEAN
£45–£60

Look out across undulating country to the South Downs, pre-dinner drink in hand, before moving to the timbered dining room of this mostly seventeenth-century (conservatory extension excepted) grey-stone farmhouse. The trappings of fine dining range from canapés, via an intermediate sorbet, to home-made petits fours, and lengthy menu descriptions accurately summarise what is to be put before you. An essentially classical style underpins the cooking, which might offer crab soup with garlic croûtons to start, or sauté calf's liver and smoked bacon on toasted dill and onion bread.

Meats tend to be lightly cooked – chump of lamb, for example, with creamed parsnips and a port and thyme sauce – while fish often gets robust treatment: fillets of John Dory, perhaps, teamed with thyme-roasted potatoes, pickled white cabbage and a wholegrain mustard sauce. Bailey's liqueur goes into both an ice cream and a sauce for hot chocolate soufflé, while lemon parfait makes a lighter accompaniment for pears poached in red wine and cinnamon. Considerate service and a French-led wine list complete the traditionalist approach. House wines (Chilean) are £14.

CHEFS: Gregory Laskey and Allison St Quintin PROPRIETORS: Gregory Laskey, Allison and Gillian St Quintin OPEN: Tue to Sat D 7 to 9.30 (also Sun L once a month) CLOSED: 2 weeks Jan MEALS: alc (main courses £17 to £20) SERVICE: not inc CARDS: Delta, Diners, MasterCard, Switch, Visa DETAILS: 26 seats. Private parties: 38 main room. Car park. Vegetarian meals. Children's helpings. No children under 7 at D. No smoking in dining room. Wheelchair access (not WC). No music. Air-conditioned

PLUMTREE Nottinghamshire **map 5**

Perkins

Old Railway Station, Plumtree NG12 5NA
TEL: (0115) 937 3695 FAX: (0115) 937 6405 COOKING **2**
EMAIL: perkinsrestaurant@supanet.com MODERN BRITISH/FRENCH
off A606, 2m S of Nottingham £22–£42

Apart from a conservatory tacked on to the back, and a brick kitchen to one side, this country halt probably looks much as it did when steam trains stopped here. Inside is a different matter, with French prints, wooden tables and a display cabinet of desserts, 'a sort of trolley without wheels'. The menu changes every four to five weeks, blackboards list daily specials, and the European-based repertoire takes in wild mushroom omelette, chicken liver and pork pate with plum chutney, and deep-fried salt cod fritters with a marinated anchovy salsa. Dishes are generally treated straightforwardly, along the lines of seared red mullet on crab risotto, or entrecote steak with red pesto, while desserts have included butterscotch and walnut tart with ginger ice cream, and strawberry meringue roulade. Modest pricing is a feature of the short globe-trotting list, which includes six French country wines under £12, and four house bottles at £10.25.

CHEFS: Hugh Cocker, Lisa Pickering and Marco Smeeth PROPRIETORS: Tony and Wendy Perkins OPEN: Tue to Sun L 12 to 2 (2.30 Sun), Tue to Sat D 6.45 to 9.45 MEALS: alc Tue to Sat L and Tue to Sun D (main courses £8 to £11.50). Set L Tue to Sat £9.75 (2 courses), Set L Sun £12.50 (2 courses) to £15.95, Set D Tue to Thur and Sun £15.95 SERVICE: not inc CARDS: Amex, Delta, Diners, MasterCard, Switch, Visa DETAILS: 73 seats. 24 seats outside. Private parties: 12 main room, 30 private room. Car park. Vegetarian meals. No smoking in 1 dining room. Wheelchair access (not WC). Occasional music. Air-conditioned

denotes an outstanding wine cellar; denotes a good wine list, worth travelling for.

PLYMOUTH Devon map 1

Chez Nous 🍷

13 Frankfort Gate, Plymouth PL1 1QA
TEL/FAX: (01752) 266793

COOKING **4**
FRENCH COST
£46–£55

An unlikely setting it may be, in a pedestrian square near the covered market, but this fiercely Gallic enterprise makes no concessions to its surroundings: there is not even a cheap lunch to tempt in the shoppers. It is a small, friendly restaurant with neat tables, French prints, and a red, white and blue colour scheme, serving determinedly French food. Shellfish, game and offal are as likely to appear as beef fillet or chicken breast, the repertoire taking in scallops in a light creamy ginger-infused sauce, oxtail in red wine, and medallions of venison. Primary materials are well sourced and properly treated, and fish is a highlight, be it thick flakes of cod with a crisp pistou topping, or fillets of turbot with caper berries, a dish whose simplicity confirms the kitchen's skill and justified confidence. Accompanying vegetables and salads are well rendered too.

Dessert choices seem half-hearted in comparison with the rest, many involving sorbets, ice creams, iced nougat and the like, although the one that most reporters choose – a sablé biscuit with raspberries, matching sorbet and clotted cream – comes in for praise. Service is personable and efficient. A French bias has been brought to bear on the choice of wines. A good representation of burgundies and other regional styles complements the cooking, and 20-plus half-bottles and six wines by the glass open up variety. Sensible prices balance the cost of a meal, with six house wines, not all French, at £12.50 a bottle.

CHEF: Jacques Marchal PROPRIETORS: Jacques and Suzanne Marchal OPEN: Tue to Fri L 12.30 to 1.30, Tue to Sat D 7 to 10.30 CLOSED: 3 weeks Feb, 3 weeks Sep, bank hols MEALS: Set L and D £33 SERVICE: not inc CARDS: Amex, Diners, MasterCard, Switch, Visa DETAILS: 28 seats. Private parties: 32 main room. No children under 8. Wheelchair access (not WC). Music

PONTELAND Northumberland map 10

Café 21 £

35 The Broadway, Darras Hall,
Ponteland NE20 9PW
TEL/FAX: (01661) 820357

COOKING **4**
MODERN EUROPEAN
£21–£51

The Ponteland outpost of the Terence Laybourne gastronomic empire (see also entries in Durham, Newcastle upon Tyne and Sunderland) is set in a converted shop in a leafy and affluent area. No great expense has been lavished on décor: table covers are paper, menus are on blackboards, and the wooden chairs are not the most comfortable ever designed, but this is a place where simplicity rules. The food is equally straightforward, showing respect for the high quality of its ingredients, and sensitivity to achieving the right balance of flavours and textures. Examples include a starter terrine of duck and green peppercorns, and a main course of slow-cooked shoulder of lamb with purple broccoli and thyme jus. Other options might run to Cheddar and spinach soufflé, or simply grilled fillet of halibut with herbed Jersey Royals. A slice of plum and almond tart, or banana parfait with bitter chocolate ice cream, rounds things off nicely. Most of the wines on the short, varied list are under £20, with Duboeuf house wine opening the bidding at £10.50.

CHEF: Michael Waugh PROPRIETOR: Terence Laybourne OPEN: Sat L 12 to 2, Mon to Sat D 5.30 to 10 CLOSED: bank hols MEALS: alc (main courses £9.50 to £18). Set L and D 5.30 to 7 £11.50 (2 courses) to £13 SERVICE: not inc CARDS: Amex, Delta, Diners, MasterCard, Switch, Visa DETAILS: 68 seats. Private parties: 70 main room. Vegetarian meals. Children's helpings. Wheelchair access (also WC). Music

POOLE Dorset map 2

▲ Mansion House

Thames Street, Poole BH15 1JN
TEL: (01202) 685666 FAX: (01202) 665709
EMAIL: dining@themansionhouse.co.uk
WEB SITE: www.themansionhouse.co.uk

COOKING **3**
MODERN BRITISH
£26–£44

In a side road off Poole quay, this hotel's gold-topped railings and creeper-clad brick façade make a handsome sight. The dining room has prints of old boats on the walls, and an abundance of fresh flowers raises the spirits. Gerry Godden's cooking revolves around tried-and-true culinary principles, producing home-cured salmon in gravad lax fashion with a honey and mustard dressing, and partnering a baked mackerel and potato terrine with 'dazzlingly fresh' scallops and tomato chutney. Accurately timed sea bass gets fashionable Thai treatment, steamed with pak choi and sauced with coconut milk and lemon grass, while duck breast comes with a sauce of calvados and green peppercorns, and herb-crusted rack of lamb with one of red wine and rosemary. Desserts have been more variable, although a passion fruit crème brûlée with passion fruit ice cream has been a resounding success. West Country cheeses arrive with grapes and walnut bread, and professional, friendly service does the place proud. House 'recommendations' (from £12.95) are arranged in price order on the tripartite wine list, as are the stylistically grouped 'wines from around the world' (all under £30); fine wines and halves complete the inventory.

CHEF: Gerry Godden PROPRIETORS: Robert Leonard, and Jackie and Gerry Godden OPEN: Sun to Fri L 12 to 2, Mon to Sat D 7 to 9.30 MEALS: alc Mon to Fri L (main courses £9 to £10). Set L £17.50, Set D £19.75 (2 courses) to £27.20 SERVICE: not inc CARDS: Amex, Delta, Diners, MasterCard, Switch, Visa DETAILS: 85 seats. Private parties: 100 main room, 14 to 36 private rooms. Car park. Vegetarian meals. No children under 5 exc Sun L. No smoking in 1 dining room. Occasional music. Air-conditioned ACCOMMODATION: 32 rooms, all with bath/shower. TV. Phone. B&B £65 to £120. Baby facilities (*The Which? Hotel Guide*) (£5)

Prices quoted in the Guide are based on information supplied by restaurateurs. The prices quoted at the top of each entry represent a range, from the lowest meal price to the highest; the latter is inflated by 20 per cent to take account of likely price rises during the year of the Guide.

PORLOCK WEIR Somerset map 1

▲ Andrews on the Weir

NEW ENTRY

Porlock Weir TA24 8PB
TEL: (01643) 863300 FAX: (01643) 863311
EMAIL: information@andrewsontheweir.co.uk
WEB SITE: www.andrewsontheweir.co.uk

COOKING **5**
MODERN BRITISH
£24–£53

A Victorian villa overlooking the old harbour houses a lively, youthful operation. The dining room's theatrical décor – a Louis XV/Old Vic hybrid with gold-effect chairs and damask curtains – prepares visitors for some glamorous cooking, starting with fine breads and an amuse-bouche of frothy lobster and lemon-grass bisque. Ideas may be familiar from metropolitan menus, but attention to detail, accurate seasoning, and optimum use of local materials sets them apart here. Even apparently simple assemblies make a forceful impression, judging by a stack of aubergine, courgette, beef tomato and goats' cheese with dressings of olive oil and red pepper coulis.

The kitchen is adept at rich and substantial dishes, including a terrine of duck – breast, confit and liver – with celeriac rémoulade, but fish stands out, not least for freshness: whether sea bass on garlicky crushed potatoes, or skate wing with capers and spinach on 'elastic mash' full of butter and boiled double cream. Exmoor lamb, perhaps with ravioli of sweetbreads and tarragon jus, is equally beguiling, and rhubarb cheesecake, filled with irresistible 'fibrous goo', is enhanced by custard ice cream and cardamom-scented juices. Savoury finishes include Welsh rarebit with smoked salmon, Avruga caviare and a fried quail's egg, and top-drawer British cheeses. Wines from around the world, listed by style, are fairly priced and include unusual discoveries: a Californian Carignan-Grenache at £13.95 and an aromatic Greek white for £14.20, for example. Seven house wines start from £10.25.

CHEF: Andrew Dixon PROPRIETORS: Andrew Dixon and Rodney Sens OPEN: Tue to Sun L 12.15 to 2.30, Tue to Sat D 7.15 to 9.30 CLOSED: second and third weeks Jan and Nov MEALS: alc (main courses £18). Set L Tue to Sat £10.50 (2 courses) to £14, Set D £18.50, Set D Tue to Fri £18 SERVICE: not inc CARDS: Amex, Delta, Diners, MasterCard, Switch, Visa DETAILS: 25 seats. Private parties: 25 main room. Car park. Vegetarian meals. No children under 12. No smoking in dining room. Wheelchair access (not WC). Music ACCOMMODATION: 5 rooms, all with bath/shower. TV. B&B £50 to £100. No children under 12 (*The Which? Hotel Guide*) (£5)

PORTHLEVEN Cornwall map 1

▲ Critchards

Harbourside, Porthleven TR13 9JA
TEL: (01326) 562407 FAX: (01326) 564444
EMAIL: stevecritchard@aol.com
WEB SITE: www.critchards.com

COOKING **1**
SEAFOOD
£27–£62

This quayside restaurant is in a former grain mill about three hundred years old. Its fish (from Newlyn market) and lobsters (off the Porthleven boats) get a wide range of treatments. Some dishes are simple, even homely: oysters, grilled lobster, Dover sole or hot shellfish platter (plus steak or pork for unrepentant carnivores). But another facet of the menu shows in a paw-paw, mango and poppy seed cocktail, in John Dory sautéed with vanilla, or in red gurnard Thai style. A reporter's Thai-style mussels in a well-balanced broth, and smoked haddock and pine nuts wrapped in spinach and baked a lattice pastry case, showed 'real flair'. Daily-changing desserts range from lemon tart with flaked almonds and clotted cream to home-made Italian-style banana and Strega ice cream. House wines are £11.95, and there are interesting organic bottles.

CHEF: Jo Critchard PROPRIETORS: Steve and Jo Critchard OPEN: Mon to Sat (occasionally Sun) D 6.30 to 9 MEALS: alc (main courses £8 to £26) SERVICE: not inc, card slips closed CARDS: MasterCard, Switch, Visa DETAILS: 44 seats. Vegetarian meals. Children's helpings. No children under 5. No smoking in dining room. Occasional music ACCOMMODATION: 2 rooms, both with bath/shower. TV. B&B £49 to £59. No children under 6 (£5)

PORTREATH Cornwall map 1

Tabb's

Tregea Terrace, Portreath TR16 4LD
TEL: (01209) 842488

COOKING 2
MODERN BRITISH-PLUS
£23–£48

A little way from the harbour, Tabb's has a rustic feel. A raffia screen separates a small lounge, with bay window and garden-style furniture, from the stone-walled dining room hung with local artists' paintings. The set menu offers two or three choices per course, the carte six or seven, and there may be a daily special too. Much of the cooking has a homely feel, with good materials well treated and particularly well timed: hake given a Mediterranean treatment, for example, or duck with a smoked bacon sauce. Supplies are augmented by Gloucester Old Spot pork and Cornish mutton (perhaps baked with onions and lentils), and desserts are as good as everything else: from chocolate marquise, via syrup sponge, to iced pistachio parfait with caramel sauce. Service is capably overseen by Melanie Tabb, and a modest wine list starts with house French at £9.95.

CHEF: Nigel Tabb PROPRIETORS: Nigel and Melanie Tabb OPEN: Sun L 12.15 to 1.45, Wed to Mon D 7 to 9 CLOSED: 2 weeks Nov, 2 weeks Jan MEALS: alc D (main courses £10.50 to £19). Set Sun L £13.50, Set D £16.50 SERVICE: not inc, card slips closed CARDS: Delta, MasterCard, Switch, Visa DETAILS: 30 seats. Private parties: 33 main room. Vegetarian meals. Children's helpings. No smoking in dining room. Wheelchair access (not WC). Music (£5)

POULTON-LE-FYLDE Lancashire map 8

▲ River House

Skippool Creek, Thornton-Le-Fylde, Poulton-le-Fylde FY5 5LF
TEL: (01253) 883497 FAX: (01253) 892083
EMAIL: enquiries@theriverhouse.org.uk
WEB SITE: www.theriverhouse.org.uk
from roundabout junction of A585 and B5412 follow signs to Skippool Creek

COOKING 4
FRENCH-PLUS
£34–£60

After 40 years, Bill Scott's restaurant beside a tidal creek shows no sign of flagging. Glossy, dark green walls and a vivid white ceiling make the dining room 'inviting and pleasant', and while some dishes are long stayers – 'soufflé suissesse, sauté of chicken livers and salmon angélique must be overdue their silver jubilee award' – roast ostrich ambled in more recently. The latest innovation is design-it-yourself main courses: select your meat or fish, then partner it with your choice from 14 sauces (maximum 6 per table!) from hollandaise and béarnaise to coconut and ginger, or port and blueberry. 'One way for customers to ruin dinners with inappropriate choices', perhaps, though coconut and ginger went well with our inspector's beef schnitzel, and honey, lemon and thyme complemented a chicken breast stuffed with lemon-scented olives. A fish of the day appears alongside the ever-present poached salmon. Finish with apple and cinnamon sponge pudding of exemplary lightness, or crème brûlée with hazelnut biscuits. The wine list is short on detail but will delight lovers of France, claret particularly; house wines are £12.50.

CHEF/PROPRIETOR: Bill Scott OPEN: Mon to Sat 12 to 2, 7.30 to 9.30 CLOSED: 25 and 26 Dec, 1 Jan MEALS: alc (main courses £16 to £22). Set L and D £25 (4 courses) SERVICE: not inc CARDS: Delta, MasterCard, Switch, Visa DETAILS: 40 seats. Private parties: 40 main room. Car park. Vegetarian meals. No children under 7. Music ACCOMMODATION: 4 rooms, all with bath/shower. TV. Phone. B&B £70 to £90 (*The Which? Hotel Guide*) (£5)

PRESTBURY Cheshire **map 8**

▲ White House

The Village, New Road, Prestbury SK10 4DG
TEL: (01625) 829376 FAX: (01625) 828627
EMAIL: mail@thewhitehouse.uk.com
WEB SITE: www.thewhitehouse.uk.com
on A538, 4m N of Macclesfield

COOKING **2**
MODERN BRITISH
£25–£66

The White House, though appropriately named, is not what its setting in a picturesque village might suggest, representing instead an enclave of free-thinking cosmopolitanism in an area not known for its gastronomic abandon. Ryland Wakeham's cooking is nothing if not ambitious and innovative: starters range from home-smoked wood pigeon breast with tarte Tatin and cassis jus, to pan-seared scallops on an aromatic coulis of cauliflower and mango with chilli salsa. Main courses, meanwhile, take in 'restyled old favourites' such as crispy confit duck leg on gratin potatoes and Puy lentils, as well as more up-to-date offerings like pan-fried cod on champ with chorizo, leek and warm tomato dressing. Desserts are a forte: arborio rice crème brûlée with tropical fruit soup, for example. More than 50 wines are featured in an unorganised but well-chosen wine list; prices start at £13.95 for house French vins de table.

CHEFS: Ryland Wakeham and Mark Cunniffe PROPRIETORS: Ryland and Judith Wakeham OPEN: Tue to Sun L 12 to 2, Mon to Sat D 7 to 10 CLOSED: 25 Dec MEALS: alc (main courses £12.50 to £18). Set L £13.95, Set D Mon to Fri £15.50 (2 courses) to £18.50 SERVICE: not inc, card slips closed CARDS: Amex, Diners, MasterCard, Switch, Visa DETAILS: 75 seats. 12 seats outside. Private parties: 80 main room, 8 to 40 private rooms. Car park. Vegetarian meals. Children's helpings. Wheelchair access (not WC). Music ACCOMMODATION: 11 rooms, all with bath/shower. TV. Phone. Room only £40 to £120. No children under 10 (*The Which? Hotel Guide*)

PRESTON Lancashire map 8

Simply Heathcotes

23 Winckley Square, Preston PR1 3JJ
TEL: (01772) 252732 FAX: (01772) 203433 COOKING **3**
EMAIL: preston@simplyheathcotes.co.uk BRASSERIE
WEB SITE: www.heathcotes.co.uk £32–£43

This was the first of Paul Heathcote's Simply siblings to branch out from his central operation in Longridge (see entry; see others In Liverpool and Manchester). Smartly decorated in minimal modern style, it is in the Georgian heart of Preston near Avenham Park. A basement café-bar serves lighter meals, but the main business takes place above, where Matthew Nugent cooks in what aficionados will recognise as the Heathcote idiom. That means smoked mackerel, Lancashire cheese, black pudding, rhubarb, Goosnargh duckling and lamb chop cooked with finesse and some delicacy, and interspersed with southern European ideas. A spinach and mascarpone pasty with braised lentils is a neat compromise between the two styles, while dishes that receive praise include fillet of red mullet topped with aubergine caviar on spiced and raisined couscous, and homely carrot and walnut cake served with crème fraîche. The same wine list offered at the other branches applies here too, with the £20 line just about dividing it across the middle. House wines from the Loire are £11.50.

CHEF: Matt Nugent PROPRIETOR: Paul Heathcote OPEN: Mon to Fri 12 to 2.30, 7 to 10, Sat 5 to 10.30, Sun 11.30 to 3, 6 to 9.30 CLOSED: 25 and 26 Dec, 1 Jan, bank hol Mons MEALS: alc (main courses £13.50 to £15). Bar and bistro menus available SERVICE: 10% (optional, max £20), card slips closed CARDS: Amex, Delta, Diners, MasterCard, Switch, Visa DETAILS: 80 seats. Private parties: 50 main room, 80 private room. Vegetarian meals. Children's helpings. No cigars/pipes in dining room. Wheelchair access (not WC). Music. Air-conditioned

RAMSBOTTOM Greater Manchester map 8

GREATER MANCHESTER GFG 2002 COMMENDED

Ramsons

18 Market Place, Ramsbottom BL0 9HT COOKING **4**
TEL: (01706) 825070 FAX: (01706) 822005 ITALIAN
off A56/M66, 4m N of Bury £21–£52

Chris Johnson never seems to stand still, having reinvented the old Village premises many times over, rejigging the components of wine cellar, deli, coffee bar and restaurant as times and circumstances have changed. The current set-up consists of a small, ground-floor restaurant with church pew seating, and a basement café bar modelled on an Italian enoteca, with its own menu of bruschette, salads, cured meats and other light dishes. His long-time partner Ros Hunter has been forced into retirement by severe disability, and a new team is injecting some of the vitality back into the cooking.

One thing that has remained constant is the search for first-class produce, which takes in both local ingredients and (despite the food miles) much from Italy, specifically Milan market. Results are striking, from tomatoes 'the like of which I can scarcely recall', to top-quality, accurately timed scallops with finely shredded mange-tout and a gently peppery rocket sauce. Seasoning is minimal and well judged, flavours work well both independently and together, and the uncompromisingly brief cooking of beef tournedos (on a bed of young asparagus tips and stir-fried mushrooms) produces first-class results. It is also worth taking up the menu's suggestion to eat a plate of vegetables separately, before the main course.

Despite billing itself as 'slow food' (with considerable justification), simple preparation is at the heart of the operation, producing small pieces of tempura monkfish with Mediterranean vegetables, and poached apricots with a honeyed, creamy filling of mascarpone and toasted pine nuts. Chris Johnson runs front-of-house with customary evangelical zeal and, although the wine cellar has had to be drastically reduced, it offers a short, accessible house selection of mostly Italian wines (prices start at £9.75 for Pinot Grigio and Merlot from Veneto), as well as a list of finer French bottles.

CHEF: Naz Naseem PROPRIETORS: Ros Hunter and Chris Johnson OPEN: all week L 12 to 2 (1 to 3.30 Sun), Tue to Sat D 7 (6.15 for early-bird) to 9.30 (7 for early-bird) CLOSED: 1 Jan MEALS: alc Mon to Sat (main courses £8.50 to £15.50). Set L Mon to Sat and D 6.15 to 7 £9.95 (2 courses) to £12.95, Set L Sun £13.95 (2 courses) to £16.95 SERVICE: not inc, card slips closed CARDS: Amex, Delta, MasterCard, Switch, Visa DETAILS: 36 seats. Private parties: 30 main room, 12 private room. Vegetarian meals. Children's helpings. No smoking in dining room. Music (£5)

RAMSGILL North Yorkshire **map 8**

▲ Yorke Arms

Ramsgill HG3 5RL
TEL: (01423) 755243 FAX: (01423) 755330 COOKING **7**
EMAIL: enquiries@yorke-arms.co.uk MODERN BRITISH
WEB SITE: www.yorke-arms.co.uk £33–£60

Fires, beams, polished brass and flag floors are all in keeping with the long, rough-stone, creeper-covered building in a quiet corner of the Dales. The pub side of the trade has gone, and it now styles itself a restaurant with rooms: lots of them, including an 'old and comfy' lounge, and a dining room whose bare wooden floor and tables convey a solid, traditional, uncluttered impression. An al fresco eating area has been added at the back, a garden is planned for vegetables and herbs, and staff are smart, well trained, knowledgeable and courteous. Nothing is posh or grand, yet everything appears relaxed, friendly and generous.

Flavours are big, bold and clear, without frills or folderol, and dishes have a habit of being 'endlessly interesting', thanks to their combination of fine materials, professional workmanship, and the culinary intelligence that pulls them together. One example is a variation on the 'duck with orange sauce' theme: small slices of pink, juicy breast with blistery skin are set next to slices of tightly textured duck sausage wrapped in its skin, and served with unctuous mash, a whole, small, globe artichoke bottom, tiny heads of pak choi, and an impeccably judged, stock-based, citrus-flavoured sauce. And there was nothing there that didn't belong.

The food is more than just technically accomplished. Frances Atkins seems to have something of a 'magic touch' in her free-spirited combination of quite ordinary ingredients with more luxurious items. It takes inspiration to conjure up something as 'indecently decadent' as a sweetcorn version of hummus and combine it with 'outstandingly fresh' lobster (flesh and claw), set about with leaves and herbs. Rice pudding and rhubarb may not, on the face of it, sound particularly thrilling, but that is just what they become when a cone of cool, wobbly, creamy rice pudding is buttressed by wafers of roast strawberry, lightly brûlée, and served with a translucent rhubarb syrup containing two-inch sticks of rhubarb, candied to a sweet frazzle. Wines play fair by a wide range of pockets and tastes, starting with eight house wines under £15 available by the glass.

CHEF: Frances Atkins PROPRIETORS: Gerald and Frances Atkins OPEN: all week L 12 to 2, Mon to Sat D 7 to 9 (Sun D residents only) MEALS: alc (main courses £12 to £16.50). Light L available SERVICE: not inc CARDS: Amex, Delta, Diners, MasterCard, Switch, Visa DETAILS: 70 seats. 25 seats outside. Private parties: 40 main room, 10 and 12 private rooms. Car park. Vegetarian meals. No children under 12. No smoking in dining room. Wheelchair access (not WC). Occasional music ACCOMMODATION: 14 rooms, all with bath/shower. TV. Phone. D,B&B £85 to £300. Baby facilities (*The Which? Hotel Guide*) (£5)

REIGATE Surrey map 3

Dining Room

59A High Street, Reigate RH2 9AE
TEL/FAX: (01737) 226650

COOKING **5**
MODERN BRITISH
£28–£56

Decorated in creamy yellow, with plenty of fresh flowers and paintings on food themes, this bright, modern, first-floor restaurant is where Tony Tobin oversees a frequently changing menu that deals in upstanding flavours and uncomplicated preparations. Among the lively ideas, seared tuna might be given a lime crust and served with oven-dried cherry tomatoes, or there might be sticky chilli chicken with coconut rice. Although standards can waver, pleasing earthy textures and flavours characterised one lunch that went from smoked salmon and new potato terrine with wasabi vinaigrette, to roast duck leg on mustard-spiked onions, followed by a palate-refreshing trio of lemon desserts that comprised a tart, a mousse and a scoop of ice cream. Spiced plum crumble with cinnamon clotted cream is a more indulgent way to finish.

Cheeses are prime British specimens, and incidentals are up to snuff, although service appears not to pay much attention to detail. Wines – mostly French and classic, yet almost all below £20 – are presented on a single page with short notes, backed up by a supplementary list of fine wines, and four Chilean house wines at £11.95 (£4.50 a glass). There is a second branch, Dining Room 2, in Haywards Heath.

CHEF: Tony Tobin PROPRIETOR: Elite Restaurants Ltd OPEN: Sun to Fri L 12 to 2.30, Mon to Sat D 7 to 10 CLOSED: 1 week Christmas, Easter, first 2 weeks Aug MEALS: alc (main courses £16.50). Set L Mon to Fri £13 (2 courses) to £16.50, Set L Sun £25, Set D £16.95 (2 courses) SERVICE: 12.5% (optional), card slips closed CARDS: Amex, Delta, Diners, MasterCard, Switch, Visa DETAILS: 50 seats. Private parties: 50 main room. Children's helpings. No smoking in dining room. Occasional music. Air-conditioned (£5)

▲ *means accommodation is available.*

RICHMOND Surrey map 3

Burnt Chair

5 Duke Street, Richmond TW9 1HP
TEL: (020) 8940 9488 COOKING **3**
EMAIL: connect1@burntchair.com GLOBAL
WEB SITE: www.burntchair.com £35–£57

Weenson Oo has been here ten years now, and although time has in no way dimmed his enthusiasm, he leaves much of the cooking these days to Emmanuel Vollmar. Delicate lighting and distantly tinkling classical music provide a gentle background for some wide-ranging ideas. One reported starter involved a welter of crab, roast peppers, soba noodles, green beans and chopped nuts in an 'oil-free dressing': a generous heap that tantalised with a multiplicity of flavours. Fruity accompaniments are favoured, pairing quail with pineapple and lychees, and lime-marinated sea bream with a banana and lentil salad and pepper salsa. Or you could pick something tried-and-tested, like sliced 'wild' beef with roast red onions and horseradish cream.

The hit at inspection was a properly oozing warm chocolate fondant with smooth, intensely flavoured lemon sorbet; otherwise there may be roast pineapple with coconut ice cream and raspberry coulis. The cellar stays faithful to America's good, great and downright interesting, with prices in this half of the list from £24 to around £100. The other half offers classic French bottles, plus a handful from elsewhere. House Sonoma bottlings provide the value, at £14.75 (£3.75 a glass).

CHEFS: Emmanuel Vollmar and John Goodall PROPRIETOR: Weenson Oo OPEN: Tue to Sat D only 6 to 11 (lunch parties by arrangement) CLOSED: 1 week Christmas, 10 days August MEALS: alc (main courses £11.50 to £18.50). Set D 6 to 7 £15 (2 courses). Cover £1 SERVICE: not inc CARDS: Delta, MasterCard, Switch, Visa DETAILS: 36 seats. Private parties: 36 main room. Children's helpings. No smoking in dining room. Music (£5)

Chez Lindsay £

11 Hill Rise, Richmond TW10 6UQ COOKING **1**
TEL: (020) 8948 7473 FAX: (020) 8332 0129 BRETON
£19–£62

Although the menu has expanded of late in certain departments, notably in the fruits de mer section, Lindsay Wotton's business is still very much the neighbourhood restaurant and crêperie on which she has built a solid local following over the past 13 years. Buckwheat flour is milled to a special formula by her supplier to ensure that the pancakes turn out thin and sheer, the better to show off their fillings of perhaps egg, cheese and ham, or smoked salmon with lemon and chive cream. Main courses for the heartier appetite might include a scallop and bacon brochette served with a thyme-flavoured red wine sauce and rice, or perhaps braised lamb shank with gratin dauphinois. Desserts centre on sweet versions of the crêpes, with honey and almonds a possible filling, chocolate and banana another. With the exception of one Spanish red and an Australian fizz, the wine list is entirely French, and prices are fair, house wines starting at £10.95. Otherwise, good Breton cider is the house speciality.

CHEFS: Lindsay Wotton, Franck Rivallain and Ivo De Jesus PROPRIETOR: Lindsay Wotton OPEN: Mon to Sat 11 to 3, 6 to 11, Sun 12 to 10; crêperie menu available only Mon to Sat 3 to 6 MEALS: alc (main courses £5 to £18.50). Set L Mon to Sat (exc bank hols) £5.99 (2 courses) to £10.99, Set D Sun to Fri £10.99 SERVICE: not inc CARDS: Delta, MasterCard, Switch, Visa DETAILS: 48 seats. Private parties: 50 main room, 36 private room. Vegetarian meals. Children's helpings. No cigars/pipes while others eat. Wheelchair access (not WC). MusicRichmond (£5)

RIDGEWAY Derbyshire **map 9**

Old Vicarage

Ridgeway Moor, Ridgeway S12 3XW
TEL: (0114) 247 5814 FAX: (0114) 247 7079
EMAIL: eat@theoldvicarage.co.uk
WEB SITE: www.theoldvicarage.co.uk
from A616, ¾m NW of Mosborough, turn W on B6054/B6388; in Ridgeway, turn S; restaurant is ½m on L, nearly opposite village church

COOKING **6**
MODERN BRITISH-PLUS
£48–£70

The kitchen garden, on view from the car park, is a good sign. This handsome stone house has had its hall, lobby and dining rooms refurbished with new oak floors and light colours. Unchanged, though, is Tessa Bramley's modern British cuisine – three- or four-course menus built on sound classical techniques – her own produce adding to that from local farms and suppliers. At its best it combines simple flavours in novel ways, drawing on ideas and techniques from Europe and Asia, often brought together on the same plate. Among starters might be char-griddled loin of tuna on oriental stir-fried vegetables with pak choi and lemon grass, or pan-fried sea bass on saffron risotto cake with mango salsa and sherry-vinegar sauce.

Main courses go in for easy-to-eat fillets: from brill with a coconut crust (in a lightly curried sauce with cockles and baby leeks) to a triumphantly simple sirloin steak with red cabbage and horseradish mash. Puddings might feature warm chocolate brownie with pistachio ice cream and coffee-bean sauce, or a trio of English strawberry desserts. Or try the cheeses, Golden Cross, Cashel Blue and Swaledale among them. An 80-strong, stylistically organised wine list is sourced as much from the southern hemisphere as from classic French regions. Prices run from a £16.50 vins de pays to £100-plus for mature vintages of prized clarets and burgundies, but there is choice enough under £25.

CHEFS: Tessa Bramley, Nathan Smith and Andrew Gilbert PROPRIETOR: Tessa Bramley OPEN: Tue to Fri L 12.30 to 2.30, Sun L 12 to 2.30, Tue to Sat D 7 to 10 CLOSED: 26 Dec, 31 Dec–1 Jan MEALS: Set L and D £33 to £43 SERVICE: not inc, card slips closed CARDS: Amex, Delta, Diners, MasterCard, Switch, Visa DETAILS: 50 seats. 16 seats outside. Private parties: 54 main room, 28 private room. Car park. Vegetarian meals. Children's helpings. No smoking in dining room. Wheelchair access (not WC). No music

The Guide office can quickly spot when a restaurateur is encouraging customers to write recommending inclusion. Such reports do not further a restaurant's cause. Please tell us if a restaurateur invites you to write to the Guide.

RIPLEY North Yorkshire map 9

▲ Boar's Head

Ripley HG3 3AY
TEL: (01423) 771888 FAX: (01423) 771509
EMAIL: reservations@boarsheadripley.co.uk
WEB SITE: www.ripleycastle.co.uk

COOKING **3**
MODERN BRITISH
£22–38

An ancestor of the present owners rescued Edward III from a boar that tried hunting him; the ancestor got a knighthood, and the boar, eaten at the ensuing banquet, got its head on the family crest. Hence the name of this handsome, slightly Gothic, grey-stone inn. A bistro meets the needs of many who come to visit the castle (next door), serving up Cumberland sausage with black olive mash, and grilled beef fillet with red onion marmalade, while the earthy-coloured dining room lays on more serious fare: here the beef is likely to come with foie gras and lyonnaise potatoes, and chicken might be turned into a 'jambonette' and served with black pudding and veal sweetbreads.

There is lightness too, though, and plenty of variety: in Thai duck spring rolls, in seasonal asparagus with a light, frothy sabayon hollandaise, and in a lunchtime variation on cheese on toast using mozzarella, ciabatta, and black and white pudding. A properly tart fruit crumble of strawberries, blackberries and redcurrants has also pleased at lunch. 'Young, keen-to-please staff instil confidence', and wines are good value, with many bins under £20 and claret from £11.75. A solid assortment of classic French offerings is buttressed by a diversity of other styles, including Chilean house wines for £12.75.

CHEF: Jason Main PROPRIETORS: Sir Thomas and Lady Ingilby OPEN: all week 12 to 2 (2.30 summer), 7 to 9.30 (10 summer) MEALS: Set L Mon to Sat £10 (2 courses) to £14, Set L Sun £14.95, Set D £18.50 to £23.50. Bar/bistro menu available SERVICE: not inc CARDS: Amex, Delta, Diners, MasterCard, Switch, Visa DETAILS: 80 seats. 80 seats outside. Private parties: 40 main room, 15 to 66 private rooms. Car park. Vegetarian meals. Children's helpings. No cigars/pipes. Wheelchair access (also WC). Music ACCOMMODATION: 25 rooms, all with bath/shower. TV. Phone. B&B £99 to £140. Rooms for disabled. Baby facilities. Fishing (*The Which? Hotel Guide*)

RIPLEY Surrey map 3

Michels

13 High Street, Ripley GU23 6AQ
TEL: (01483) 224777 FAX: (01483) 222940
off A3, 4m SW of Cobham

COOKING **5**
MODERN FRENCH-PLUS
£32–£70

Occupying a large house in the middle of Ripley, with flowery wallpaper, wooden shutters, and a sunken bar area for drinks before and after, Michels takes a modern approach to French cooking. This is not a kneejerk style that follows the crowd, however, but an individual one betraying both skill and imagination. Starters have included puff pastry discs interleaved with casseroled cos lettuce and cep mousseline, and the main course vegetarian option might be a ravioli of horseradish with spring vegetables and sage butter sauce. If the food is labour intensive, it seems to be in proportion, with most effort being expended on main courses: gurnard fillets, for example, bound together to resemble the body of a fat fish, served with a filo pastry tartlet of courgette slices, and a blob of aïoli.

The surprise four-course menu is considered relatively good value: one visitor began with a strong-tasting haddock soufflé, followed by quail on pommes purée interspersed with tortellini of quail liver, then cheese, finishing with passion fruit sorbet accompanied by a brochette of fresh fruits and a rum baba. Other desserts have included a layered pile of vanilla cream and crisp apple slices served with apple sorbet, and an unusual chilled version of bread-and-butter pudding. Well-chosen wines on the stylistically arranged list find something for most pockets, starting with five house wines under £15.

CHEF: Erik Michel PROPRIETORS: Erik and Karen Michel OPEN: Tue to Fri and Sun L 12.30 to 1.30, Tue to Sat D 7.30 to 9 (7 to 9.30 Sat) CLOSED: early Jan MEALS: alc (main courses £18 to £23). Set L £21, Set D Tue to Fri £23 to £33 (latter inc wine) SERVICE: not inc, 10% for groups of 6 or more CARDS: Amex, Delta, MasterCard, Switch, Visa DETAILS: 45 seats. Private parties: 12 main room, 12 private room. Car park. Vegetarian meals. Children Sun L only. No smoking while others eat. Wheelchair access (not WC)

ROADE Northamptonshire map 5

NORTHAMPTONSHIRE GFG 2002 COMMENDED

▲ Roade House

16 High Street, Roade NN7 2NW
TEL: (01604) 863372 FAX: (01604) 862421 COOKING **5**
WEB SITE: www.roadehousehotel.co.uk MODERN BRITISH
off A508, 4m S of Northampton £26–£47

This could be considered a model of its kind. Alongside the restaurant the Kewleys run a small hotel, and the well-managed operation offers just the sort of hospitality and good food that both travellers and locals appreciate. The scale is personable, and because ambition is just right, results are invariably successful. Behind such broad-ranging ideas as spiced lamb patty with couscous and a mint and yoghurt dressing, or tagliatelle with mussels, lemon, chilli and Parmesan, lies a sound grasp of essentials. Reporters are impressed by the accuracy of timing, which makes the most of good materials, not least when it comes to game and poultry: pink partridge on a bed of Savoy cabbage and bacon, for example, or pigeon breasts on a disc of polenta surrounded by halved Brussels sprouts and chestnuts in a strong reduction.

Meals that have begun with a lightly curried fish stew, a well-dressed salad of baked goats' cheese and olives, or a wintry dish of slow-cooked, herb-perfumed belly pork, have ended with apple and almond tart, fine crème brûlée, and a rhubarb mille-feuille served with ice cream and peach compote. One couple who 'couldn't fault the service' had 'no complaints about the bread' either, and the food is also commended for its value for money. Wine prices on the 80-strong list are sensible, beginning with two French and two South African house wines at £10.75.

CHEFS: Chris Kewley and Steve Barnes PROPRIETORS: Chris and Sue Kewley OPEN: Tue to Fri and Sun L 12.30 to 1.45, Mon to Sat D 7 to 9.30 MEALS: alc D (main courses £14.50 to £17). Set L Tue to Fri £15 (2 courses) to £16.50, Set L Sun £18 SERVICE: not inc, card slips closed CARDS: Amex, Delta, MasterCard, Switch, Visa DETAILS: 50 seats. Private parties: 58 main room. Car park. Children's helpings. No smoking in dining room. Wheelchair access (also WC). Occasional music. Air-conditioned ACCOMMODATION: 9 rooms, all with bath/shower. TV. Phone. B&B £55 to £79. Rooms for disabled. Baby facilities

ROCHDALE Greater Manchester **map 8**

After Eight

2 Edenfield Road, Rochdale OL11 5AA
TEL/FAX: (01706) 646432

COOKING **4**
ANGLO-FRENCH
£26–£44

Ensuring that a successful formula remains successful requires a great deal of hard work, so the continuing efforts of Geoffrey and Anne Taylor deserve applause. Their nineteenth-century wool merchant's house on the Blackburn road is a popular venue, largely thanks to the proprietors' hands-on approach, which gives the place a welcoming, homely atmosphere. Dining areas also have a domestic feel, with patterned blue wallpaper, tapestry-upholstered chairs and white-shuttered windows. Cooking is mostly Anglo-French in origin, albeit with a few novel twists such as a pithiviers containing tiger prawns in a cheese sauce.

Results have included an accomplished, tender rack of lamb with a well-flavoured crust of thyme and mustard, served on a large mound of garlicky mash, with a rich gravy containing sherry and small pieces of lamb's kidney. Although dishes can be complicated, and timing occasionally suffers, ancillaries are generally sound, as in a blackcurrant sauce and exemplary lyonnaise potatoes to accompany a filo parcel of duck breast stuffed with duck liver. Finish with a selection of top-quality regional English cheeses, or maybe butterscotch and pecan pudding. Prices start at £10.90 on the wine list, which remains good value throughout its broad global selection.

CHEF: Geoffrey Philip Taylor PROPRIETORS: Geoffrey Philip and Anne Taylor OPEN: Tue to Sat D only 7 to 10 (L party bookings only) CLOSED: 26 Dec, 1 Jan, Easter Mon MEALS: alc (main courses £10 to £16) SERVICE: not inc CARDS: Amex, Delta, Diners, MasterCard, Switch, Visa DETAILS: 45 seats. Private parties: 30 main room, 18 and 30 private rooms. Vegetarian meals. Children's helpings. No smoking in dining room. Wheelchair access (not WC). Music (£5)

ROMALDKIRK Co Durham **map 10**

▲ Rose & Crown

Romaldkirk DL12 9EB
TEL: (01833) 650213 FAX: (01833) 650828
EMAIL: hotel@rose-and-crown.co.uk
WEB SITE: www.rose-and-crown.co.uk
on B6277, 6m NW of Barnard Castle

COOKING **2**
TRADITIONAL ENGLISH
£21–£45

Styling itself a traditional inn, with an oak-panelled dining room featuring candles and starched tablecloths, the Rose & Crown serves up food to match. Four-course dinners are the kitchen's showcase (although there are bar lunches and suppers too), and meat tends to be in the ascendancy among main courses, from roast fillet of Teesdale Fell lamb with béarnaise sauce, to chargrilled calf's liver and bacon. In season, there is a preponderance of game from nearby shooting estates: perhaps breast of grouse with juniper and pan haggerty, or braised partridge with Savoy cabbage and pancetta. Meals might start with a smoked haddock soufflé, or mushroom and aubergine risotto, the second course is soup, and desserts of baked vanilla cheesecake, or banana and toffee tart draw things to a close: unless you prefer English cheeses to finish. A varietally arranged and generally affordable wine list starts with Chilean house wines at £9.95.

CHEFS: Christopher Davy and Dawn Stephenson PROPRIETORS: Christopher and Alison Davy OPEN: Sun L 12 to 1.30, Mon to Sat D 7.30 to 9 CLOSED: 24 to 26 Dec MEALS: Set L £13.95, Set D £25. Bar menu available SERVICE: not inc, card slips closed CARDS: MasterCard, Switch, Visa DETAILS: 24 seats. Private parties: 30 main room. Car park. Vegetarian meals. No children under 6. No smoking in dining room. Wheelchair access (not WC). No music ACCOMMODATION: 12 rooms, all with bath/shower. TV. Phone. B&B £62 to £100. Rooms for disabled. Baby facilities (*The Which? Hotel Guide*) (£5)

ROMSEY Hampshire **map 2**

Old Manor House

21 Palmerston Street, Romsey SO51 8GF
TEL: (01794) 517353

COOKING **6**
ITALIAN
£30–£52

The ancient brick and timber building has a comfortably domestic lounge (the decorative skulls are from deer that have fallen in the name of gastronomy) and a seriously beamed dining room. If the dark oak, white tablecloths and huge log fireplace make it all seem very English, then the food is by contrast extremely Italian. The style is deceptively simple, right from the easy-to-understand menu itself (no fancy verbiage here) to what is on the plate, which disguises an awful lot of behind-the-scenes effort.

This is a kitchen that works with quiet confidence, making it feel as if the food is produced 'by people who really know about, and love, food'. Mauro Bregoli is a hunter-gatherer, and smoker and curer of meats, as much as a chef, offering home-produced bresaola, wild boar ham with pickled cherries, and smoked venison that can be cut with a fork. His kitchen also stands testimony to the idea that less is more: instead of frills and fancies, expect prime materials sensitively treated, including palpably fresh cod with a crisp herb topping, and slices of porchetta (roast piglet stuffed with fennel and thyme), its vibrantly garlicky and caper-laden salsa verde acting as a corrective to the richly fatty meat.

Desserts are out of the same no-nonsense mould, taking in a light chocolate sponge ('simplicity itself'), and tiramisù 'as it should be'. Great whites and reds from France and Italy constitute the core of the wine list, and although bottles under £25 are scant, value is provided by a page of house choices, which include a Chilean white and red at £11.50.

CHEF: Mauro Bregoli PROPRIETORS: Mauro and Esther Bregoli OPEN: Tue to Sun L 12.15 to 2, Tue to Sat D 7.15 to 9.30 MEALS: alc (main courses £14.50 to £18.50). Set L £19.50 SERVICE: not inc CARDS: Amex, Delta, MasterCard, Switch, Visa DETAILS: 28 seats. Private parties: 28 main room. Car park. No cigars/pipes in dining room. No music

ROSS-ON-WYE Herefordshire **map 5**

The Pheasant at Ross

52 Edde Cross Street, Ross-on-Wye HR9 7BZ
TEL: (01989) 565751 FAX: (01989) 763069

COOKING **3**
COUNTRY COOKING
£37–£47

After changing its name a time or two – last year it was called 'Faisan Doré (and Pheasants Too)' – Eileen Brunnarius has settled on good old-fashioned 'Pheasant', as it was originally called. And instead of trying to split herself into a restaurant and brasserie to please all comers, she has reverted to a single menu with straightforward pricing. One thing has remained constant: the country-cooking style, evident in chicken liver terrine with cornichons, and well-trimmed, tender rack of lamb with buttery new potatoes. The enterprise is backed up by a mix of local and specialist materials, taking in Gressingham duck breast with roast parnsips, and orange roughy poached in lemon oil, while desserts have embraced such traditional ideas as plum brown Betty with clotted cream, and buttered apple shortbread.

Service may be on the slow side, but splendid sherries will lend a note of cheer. An individual and instructive wine list roams the byways (and some highways) of the world to bring flavourful, uncommon and food-friendly wines to table at very reasonable prices; search it by style, grape variety or accompanying food. You can also try before buying; drink by the glass, course by course; and even reseal leftovers to take home.

CHEF/PROPRIETOR: Eileen Brunnarius OPEN: Thur to Sat D (Tue and Wed D, bookings only) 7 to 9.30 CLOSED: 23 Dec to 2 Jan MEALS: alc D (main courses £15) SERVICE: not inc CARDS: Amex, Delta, MasterCard, Switch, Visa DETAILS: 20 seats. Private parties: 20 main room, 8 private room. Vegetarian meals. Children's helpings. No smoking in dining room. Wheelchair access (not WC). Music (£5)

ROTHERFIELD PEPPARD Oxfordshire **map 2**

Greyhound

NEW ENTRY

Gallowtree Lane, Rotherfield Peppard RG9 5HT
TEL: (0118) 9724822 FAX: (0118) 9722227
EMAIL: hotgreyhound@cs.com
WEB SITE: www.greyhoundinn.com

COOKING **1**
MODERN BRITISH
£24–£47

Near the village crossroads, off the B481 south-west of Henley, this ancient brick-and-timber building has a timbered barn for a dining room, its white walls decorated with large oil paintings, its tightly packed tables making service difficult for staff. The short carte is restaurant-pub (rather than plain pub), with starters at dinner ranging from fresh pea and ham soup, to fried squid with mustard and chilli oil. Main courses might include grilled herbed salmon with dill mash and pesto, rump of lamb with minted ratatouille, or pork fillet with herb mash and grain mustard cream. Sticky toffee pudding comes light and generously drizzled with sauce. Of five house wines from £11.95, only one is French, which reflects the makeup of the shortish, decently priced list.

CHEF: Damian Yelland PROPRIETORS: Desiree Van Reeuwijk and Raymond Argyle OPEN: Tue to Sun L 12 to 2.30, Tue to Sat D 7 to 9.45 MEALS: alc (main courses £7.50 to £16) SERVICE: not inc CARDS: Delta, Diners, MasterCard, Switch, Visa DETAILS: 40 seats. 40 seats outside. Private parties: 30 main room, 50 private room. Car park. Vegetarian meals. Children's helpings. No-smoking areas. Wheelchair access (also WC). Music. Air-conditioned

ROWDE Wiltshire map 2

George & Dragon

High Street, Rowde SN10 2PN COOKING **4**
TEL: (01380) 723053 FAX: (01380) 724738 SEAFOOD
EMAIL: gd-rowde@lineone.net £21–£50

In a corner spot in the centre of the village, the George & Dragon appears like a local pub: rustic-feeling, with lots of character, bare tables and paper napkins. The menu (supplemented by a blackboard) focuses on fish. There is no doubting the quality and freshness of supplies, and the cooking is thankfully not over-ambitious: grilled skate might come with pesto, lemon sole is grilled whole, and roast hake has been served with chargrilled peppers and aïoli. With one exception, though, reporters and inspectors feel the food is not what it was, and the cooking seems to have lost its edge.

Nevertheless, there are still good dishes to be had: a generous salad of white crab meat at one meal, and baked turbot fillets paired with stickily soft scallops and a tasty lobster and brandy sauce. Desserts have produced a generous deep wedge of flavourful lemon tart, and sticky toffee pudding with toffee sauce, both served with clotted cream. Service has been 'rushed' and 'sullen' for one reporter, 'pleasant' and 'friendly' for another. An intelligently chosen wine list offers lots of interest at fair prices, starting with £9.50 house varietals from Domaine Virginie.

CHEFS: Tim Withers, Hannah Seal and Kate Phillips PROPRIETORS: Tim and Helen Withers OPEN: Tue to Sat 12 to 2, 7 to 10 MEALS: alc (main courses £9 to £17.50). Set L £10 (2 courses) to £12.50 SERVICE: not inc, card slips closed CARDS: Delta, MasterCard, Switch, Visa DETAILS: 40 seats. 20 seats outside. Private parties: 12 main room. Car park. Vegetarian meals. Children's helpings. No smoking in dining room. No music

RYE East Sussex map 3

Landgate Bistro £

5–6 Landgate, Rye TN31 7LH COOKING **4**
TEL: (01797) 222829 MODERN BRITISH
WEB SITE: www.landgatebistro.co.uk £21–£38

Occupying a couple of small, plain shop units in an old street by one of the ancient fortified gateways into Rye, the bistro opens into a bar and a long, thin dining room, with a pleasantly rustic décor of timber, brickwork and basic furnishings. Choice is generous and the variety appealing, taking in onion and feta tart, baked sea bass with hollandaise, and lambs' kidneys with a grain mustard sauce. Romney Marsh lamb and Gloucester Old Spot pork are among the well-sourced materials, and sensitive treatment has produced commendable dishes of moist salmon and salt-cod fishcakes with a lemon and parsley dressing, and slices of pink Gressingham duck breast with a light jus. Vegetables, an optional extra, are simple and plentiful, while desserts run to damson fool, and chocolate truffle loaf. Service is relaxed, friendly and reasonably efficient (although it might be better acquainted with details of the food), and the wine list combines diversity and interest with fair prices, starting at £8.90. Eight wines are served by the glass, none of them over £3.

CHEF: Toni Ferguson-Lees PROPRIETORS: Nick Parkin and Toni Ferguson-Lees OPEN: Tue to Sat D only 7 to 9.30 CLOSED: 2 weeks Christmas, 2 weeks autumn MEALS: alc (main courses £9 to £13). Set D Tue to Thur £16.90 SERVICE: net prices, card slips closed CARDS: Amex, Delta, Diners, MasterCard, Switch, Visa DETAILS: 30 seats. Private parties: 10 main room. Vegetarian meals. Children's helpings. No smoking in dining room. Music (£5)

ST IVES Cornwall **map 1**

Porthminster Beach Café

Porthminster Beach, St Ives TR26 2EB	COOKING **4**
TEL/FAX: (01736) 795352	GLOBAL
below St Ives railway station	£18–£44

This place exploits its enviable position, on the edge of one of the area's finest beaches, with picture windows looking across Carbis Bay. The bright dining room has colourful paintings by local artists, and the covered terrace makes this a popular venue on warm summer evenings. By day, it *is* a beach café, with a list of teas, coffees and cakes, and a range of light lunch dishes, such as crab sandwich or chargrilled St Ives Bay mackerel with couscous.

The evening menu is more sophisticated, mainly Mediterranean-influenced but with Far Eastern touches, and the cooking does not compromise the quality of daily-delivered local fish and seafood. Wok-fried squid with chilli, ginger, lime and coriander, and grilled scallops with garlic, white wine and parsley are typical starters. Main courses run from grilled John Dory with mussel risotto dumplings, to pan-fried salmon steak with steamed pak choi and roasted red peppers, while meat eaters may find crispy duck laksa, and more choice on a daily specials board. The wine list, brief and uncomplicated, stays under £20; house white (Chilean) and red (Spanish) are £9.50.

CHEF: Simon Morgan, Simon Pellow and Andy Grant PROPRIETORS: W.J. Woolcock, D.N. Fox and R. and T. Symons OPEN: all week 12 to 4, 6.30 to 10 CLOSED: Jan to Feb MEALS: alc (main courses L £4 to £9, D £9 to £15) SERVICE: not inc CARDS: Delta, MasterCard, Switch, Visa DETAILS: 58 seats. 60 seats outside. Car park. Vegetarian meals. Children's helpings. No smoking in dining room. Music (£5)

Restaurateurs justifiably resent no-shows. If you quote a credit card number when booking, you may be liable for the restaurant's lost profit margin if you don't turn up. Always phone to cancel.

All entries in the Guide are re-researched and rewritten every year, not least because restaurant standards fluctuate. Don't rely on an out-of-date Guide.

ST KEYNE Cornwall map 1

▲ Well House

St Keyne PL14 4RN
TEL: (01579) 342001 FAX: (01579) 343891
WEB SITE: www.wellhouse.co.uk
on B3254, 3m S of Liskeard; at end of village near church follow sign to St Keyne Well

COOKING **4**
COST
£40–£54

Reached along winding country lanes, Well House rewards with sweeping views, a small bar, and a cheerful honey-coloured dining room with bay windows and well-spaced tables. It is a quiet, relaxing place with its feet firmly planted in the Southwest, sourcing fish from Looe, local game, and regional beef, lamb and pork. There are no concessions to anyone seeking a cheap lunch, the emphasis being placed instead on a contemporary menu with plenty of touchstone ideas and a sensible, unfussy approach.

Veal sweetbreads come with black olive gravy to start, and game appears in the form of roast squab pigeon, partridge, or venison fillet with lentils, while seafood options have included seared scallops with herb risotto, and roast sea bass served with asparagus, salsify and a lime velouté. Cheeses hail from Cornwall, Devon and Somerset, and among commended desserts are a Grand Marnier soufflé, and an apple and calvados tart with star anise ice cream. France's domination of the wine list makes other regions appear almost an afterthought, but these other sections are notable for a spread of grape varieties and modest prices. England is represented too. Three house wines, from Chile and Australia, are £10.50 a bottle, £2.50 a glass.

CHEF: Mathew Corner PROPRIETORS: Nick Wainford and Ione Nurdin OPEN: all week 12.30 to 1.30, 7 to 9 MEALS: Set L and D £25.50 (2 courses) to £33.50 SERVICE: not inc, card slips closed CARDS: Delta, MasterCard, Switch, Visa DETAILS: 32 seats. 20 seats outside. Private parties: 26 main room. Car park. Vegetarian meals. Children's helpings. No children under 8 at D. No smoking in dining room. Wheelchair access (also WC). No music ACCOMMODATION: 9 rooms, all with bath/shower. TV. Phone. B&B £75 to £160. Baby facilities. Swimming pool (*The Which? Hotel Guide*)

ST MARGARET'S AT CLIFFE Kent map 3

▲ Wallett's Court

Westcliffe, St Margaret's at Cliffe CT15 6EW
TEL: (01304) 852424 FAX: (01304) 853430
EMAIL: wc@wallettscourt.com
WEB SITE: www.wallettscourt.com
on B2058, off A258 Dover to Deal road, 3m NE of Dover

COOKING **2**
ANGLO-FRENCH
£30–£65

Set in seven acres near Dover's white cliffs, Wallett's Court combines ancient and modern in its Romanesque exercise pool, fitness room, four-poster beds and seventeenth-century dining room. Seasonal menus offer generous choice (ten main-course options at dinner, for example), and the repertoire ranges from duck liver parfait with Sauternes jelly, to a mix of tiger prawns, monkfish and scallops in coconut milk (flavoured with chillies and lime leaves) served with

Thai fragrant rice. Regional materials might include rack of Romney Marsh lamb served with sweetbreads and a bean casserole. Not all reporters have enjoyed the food, but vegetarians, who normally get a choice of two main courses, may find themselves choosing a wild mushroom and spinach mille-feuille with a goats' cheese gratin and poached egg. Finish with roast peanut parfait on a dark chocolate sauce, or hot gingerbread soufflé. A heavily annotated wine list majors on France and starts with Burgundian Aligoté (£14) and Pinot Noir (£15).

CHEF: Stephen Harvey PROPRIETORS: the Oakley family OPEN: Sun to Fri L 12 to 2, all week D 7 to 9 MEALS: Set L £13.50 (2 courses) to £17.50, Set D £27.50 (2 courses) to £40 SERVICE: not inc, 10% for parties of 8 or more CARDS: Amex, Delta, Diners, MasterCard, Switch, Visa DETAILS: 70 seats. 10 seats outside. Private parties: 40 main room, 15 to 40 private rooms. Car park. Vegetarian meals. Children's helpings. No children under 8 after 8pm. No smoking in dining room. Occasional music ACCOMMODATION: 17 rooms, all with bath/shower. TV. Phone. B&B £75 to £150. Baby facilities. Swimming pool (*The Which? Hotel Guide*) (£5)

ST MARTIN'S Isles of Scilly **map 1**

▲ St Martin's on the Isle

Lower Town, St Martin's TR25 0QW
TEL: (01720) 422092 FAX: (01720) 422298 COOKING **5**
EMAIL: stay@stmartinshotel.co.uk MODERN EUROPEAN
WEB SITE: www.stmartinshotel.co.uk £43–£52

Just a short flight from Land's End, the Scilly Isles are a magnet for lovers of warm summer weather and sandy beaches. 'The setting of this hotel and restaurant is, of course, idyllic, with superb views of the sea and other islands', says one reporter. Since last year, bedrooms and the dining room have been redecorated, with the latter now painted marine blue and bright yellow. Windows give on to magnificent views to Tresco. Head chef Stewart Eddy, new since last year, focuses on locally caught fish and shellfish, with a few luxury ingredients such as foie gras and wild mushrooms, and perhaps a few Mediterranean influences thrown in, too.

The short dinner menu might turn up such starters as pan-fried red mullet with ratatouille and aubergine caviar, or perhaps Serrano ham with quail's eggs, Gorgonzola and grapes. Main courses have included seared sea bream with herb risotto and mussels on bouillabaisse jus, and maize-fed chicken with roasted garlic and crispy sage stuffing with thyme jus. Desserts remain well-considered and well-executed, taking in caramelised peach with a Florentine biscuit and vanilla ice cream, and chocolate mousse with kumquat sauce and chocolate sorbet. Breads, ice creams, sorbets and petits fours are all home-made. Reporters enthuse about 'friendly and hospitable staff', and the extensive wine list offers a good selection of New World wines as well as bottles from France and Italy. Prices start at £13.50.

CHEF: Stewart Eddy PROPRIETOR: Peter Sykes OPEN: all week D only 7 to 9 CLOSED: Nov to Mar inclusive MEALS: Set D £32.50 SERVICE: not inc, card slips closed CARDS: Amex, Delta, Diners, MasterCard, Switch, Visa DETAILS: 60 seats. 60 seats outside. Private parties: 100 main room. Vegetarian meals. Children's helpings. No children under 12. No smoking in dining room. Occasional music ACCOMMODATION: 30 rooms, all with bath/shower. TV. Phone. D,B&B £85 to £320. Rooms for disabled. Baby facilities. Swimming pool. Fishing (*The Which? Hotel Guide*)

ST MAWES Cornwall **map 1**

▲ Rising Sun

The Square, St Mawes TR2 5DJ
TEL: (01326) 270233 FAX: (01326) 270198
EMAIL: therisingsun@btclick.com

COOKING **3**
MODERN ENGLISH
£20–£42

The conservatory-style frontage offers a ringside seat overlooking the summer crowds that gather in front of this ordinary-looking hotel – it is only a few yards from the harbour wall – while the spacious interior is tastefully done out in wood and eau-de-nil paint. A daily-changing card lists four or five cosmopolitan options per course: smoked kedgeree cake with a quail's egg centre, perhaps, followed by thickly sliced duck breast in a red wine sauce. Fish is first rate (sea bass for one, John Dory for another), and dishes can be rather busy: successfully so in the case of a trio of mousses (smoked salmon, cucumber and brown crabmeat), less so when side plates of vegetables are added to those already on the plate. Desserts are a highlight, judging by silky-textured chocolate terrine, oatmeal meringue with raspberry and blueberry compote, and 'inspired' lavender-flavoured pannacotta with rose cream. Service has generally been a 'mixture of well-trained formality and sloppiness', the latter applying too often to wine service, although the useful, globetrotting list is considerate on price: five house wines come in under £10.50.

CHEF: Ann Long PROPRIETOR: R.J. Milan OPEN: Sun L 12 to 1.45, all week D 7 to 9 MEALS: Set L Sun £12.95, Set D £23 (2 courses) to £27. Bar menu available SERVICE: not inc, card slips closed CARDS: Delta, MasterCard, Switch, Visa DETAILS: 50 seats. 50 seats outside. Private parties: 50 main room. Car park. Vegetarian meals. Children's helpings. No children under 5. No smoking in dining room. Wheelchair access (also WC). No music ACCOMMODATION: 8 rooms, all with bath/ shower. TV. Phone. B&B £49.50 to £69.50 (*The Which? Hotel Guide*)

▲ Tresanton Hotel

Lower Castle Road, St Mawes TR2 5DR
TEL: (01326) 270055 FAX: (01326) 270053
EMAIL: info@tresanton.com
WEB SITE: www.tresanton.com

COOKING **5**
MEDITERRANEAN
£31–£55

About a quarter of a mile from the centre, Tresanton overlooks the bay and St Anthony Lighthouse, which provides one of the hotel's decorative leitmotifs. The terrace is a good spot for lunch in fine weather, while the wood-panelled, ivory-white dining room provides an unfussily smart setting for a well-balanced menu. Despite the location, fish does not predominate, although its straightforward presentation appeals: brill comes with warm olive sauce, for example, and roast Dover sole is served with bay and oregano.

Pasta and rice dishes extend to pappardelle with crab and chorizo, and a rich creamy risotto of roast pumpkin and goats' cheese, while meat options have yielded a substantial and satisfying dish of slow-cooked lamb shank, convincingly tasty, and timed so that its gelatinous parts were just the right soft texture, served with kale and borlotti beans. Simplicity has been shown to be a virtue: for example, in a plum crumble tartlet using thin, sweet pastry, fat and tasty plums, and an oatmealy topping. Service is both friendly and more often on the ball than not, and Italian wines are well represented on an intelligently constructed list, although prices are not gentle. House Rosso Conero is £15.50 and Arpeggio Bianco £12.

CHEF: Peter Robinson PROPRIETOR: Olga Polizzi OPEN: all week 12.30 to 2.30, 7 to 9.30 MEALS: Set L £15 (2 courses) to £20, Set D £33 SERVICE: not inc, card slips closed CARDS: Amex, Delta, MasterCard, Switch, Visa DETAILS: 48 seats. 60 seats outside. Private parties: 50 main room, 50 private room. Car park. Vegetarian meals. Children's helpings. No music ACCOMMODATION: 26 rooms, all with bath/shower. TV. Phone. B&B £195 to £265. Baby facilities (*The Which? Hotel Guide*)

Victory Inn

NEW ENTRY

Victory Hill, St Mawes TR2 5DQ
TEL: (01326) 270324 FAX: (01326) 270238

COOKING **3**
SEAFOOD
£42–£51

Formerly a fishermen's local, just a stone's throw from the harbour, the Victory now has the subtitle 'Cornish seafood pub and restaurant' to designate its change of emphasis following the arrival of Rob Dawson. His commitment to local seafood is, he claims, uncompromising, and his philosophy is summed up by the mantra: 'Keep it fresh, keep it simple.' The traditional bar offers a straightforward menu of modern seafood dishes, while in the brightly decorated first-floor dining room – predominantly white, with paintings by local artists – the menu is a fixed-price three-course affair in more ambitious style.

The signature dish of Spanish-style roast cod on chorizo, pepper and potato stew has been well received, and the range extends from 'grissini-style' crab and crayfish spring rolls (moist filling, crisp casing) with chilli and soy dipping sauces, to a sweet and savoury combination of accurately timed monkfish on spiced aubergines with carrot and star anise syrup. Grand Marnier crème brûlée with caramelised orange has been a triumphant dessert, while the list of around 25 wines shows a predictable bias towards whites but none the less offers good variety. Prices start at £12.95.

CHEF: Rob Dawson PROPRIETOR: Inn Partnership OPEN: Wed to Sun D only 7 to 9.30 CLOSED: 25 and 26 Dec, last 2 weeks Feb MEALS: Set D £24.95 (2 courses) to £29.95. Bar menu available SERVICE: not inc CARDS: Delta, MasterCard, Switch, Visa DETAILS: 30 seats. Private parties: 30 main room. No smoking in dining room. Music (£5)

SALE Greater Manchester **map 8**

Hanni's

4 Brooklands Road, Sale M33 3SQ
TEL: (0161) 973 6606

COOKING **2**
EASTERN MEDITERRANEAN
£23–£50

This busy, friendly restaurant in a shopping parade offers food from the eastern Mediterranean (here extended to the Maghreb for couscous Fez with meatballs). Some familiar-sounding names may mislead: chicken chawourma is pieces of pan-fried fowl; Tunisian mergaz is not spiced sausage but charcoal-grilled meatballs in hot, fresh chilli sauce; and chalet is Iranian chelow, its lamb transmuted to beef. For a party of at least 15 and with seven days notice, a whole lamb can be stuffed with rice and mixed nuts and roasted. More modestly, the happy hour two-course menu offered until seven on weekdays is a good deal. Meze – à la carte or assorted, and taken as starter or main course – may include borek (filo pastry stuffed with soft cheese, egg and parsley); hummus comes plain or with aubergine or meat. Only one wine exceeds £20 in a world-wide list that includes Greek, Moroccan, Lebanese, Israeli and Turkish bottles; house Corsicans are £11.95.

CHEF: Mr Hoonanian PROPRIETORS: Mohamed Hanni and Al-Taraboulsy OPEN: Mon to Sat D only 6 to 10.30 (11 Fri and Sat) CLOSED: 25 and 26 Dec, Good Fri, Easter Mon, last 2 weeks Aug MEALS: alc (main courses £10.50 to £14). Set D Mon to Fri 6 to 7 £10.95 (2 courses) SERVICE: not inc CARDS: Amex, Delta, MasterCard, Switch, Visa DETAILS: 50 seats. Private parties: 50 main room. Vegetarian meals. Children's helpings. Wheelchair access (not WC). Occasional music. Air-conditioned

SALFORD Greater Manchester map 8

▲ Lowry Hotel, The River Room Marco Pierre White

NEW ENTRY

50 Dearmans Place, Chapel Wharf,
Salford M3 5LH
TEL: (0161) 827 4000 FAX: (0161) 827 4001
EMAIL: enquiries@thelowryhotel.com
WEB SITE: www.rfhotels.com

COOKING **5**
FRENCH
£25–£57

A new international convention centre, and the 2002 Commonwealth Games, are bringing boom times to Manchester, regeneration spreading to Salford, long its poor relation. Rocco Forte opened this five-star hotel overlooking the Irwell in spring 2001, and the gastronomic hub of this temple of 'third millennium modernism' is The River Room Marco Pierre White, with big windows, booth tables and a profusion of staff. David Woolf, who has worked at Le Petit Blanc (see entry, Manchester), majors in sophisticated French cuisine. Classic soups such as gratinée normande and vichyssoise, or chou farci braisé a l'ancienne, cock a snook at current urban food fashion, and an uncommonly straightforward approach marks a 'menu gourmand' that includes sole with tartare sauce, spring lamb with thyme jus, and chocolate tart with milk ice cream.

Technique is reassuringly sound; one diner trying the stuffed cabbage found it wrapping a 'dense, garlicky filling of minced pork'. Well-timed fish dishes are ably supported by their accompaniments – white haricots and clams in the case of cod à la dieppoise – and a separate vegetarian menu offers four choices per course. Any Marco menu has lemon tart – 'rich, sharp custard on a paper-thin pastry base' – or there may be prune and armagnac ice cream, or the Granny Smith version of crème brûlée. The wine list canters through French regions, southern Europe and the New World, odd bargains popping up among the pricier bottles; house varietals are £10.50.

CHEF: David Woolf PROPRIETOR: Rocco Forte OPEN: all week 12 to 2.30, 6.30 to 10 (6 to 10.30 Fri to Sun) MEALS: alc (main courses £12.50 to £16.50). Set L Mon to Sat £12 (2 courses) to £15, Set D £22 to £33 (all Set Ds for whole table only). Bar menu also available SERVICE: 10% (optional), card slips closed CARDS: Amex, Delta, Diners, MasterCard, Switch, Visa DETAILS: 100 seats. 25 seats outside. Private parties: 8 main room, 20 private room. Car park. Vegetarian meals. Children's helpings. No smoking in 1 dining room. Wheelchair access (also WC). Music. Air-conditioned ACCOMMODATION: 164 rooms, all with bath/shower. TV. Phone. Room only £185 to £1,000. Rooms for disabled. Baby facilities (£5)

SANDGATE Kent map 3

▲ Sandgate Hotel, La Terrasse

The Esplanade, Sandgate CT20 3DY COOKING **7**
TEL: (01303) 220444 FAX: (01303) 220496 FRENCH
WEB SITE: www.sandgatehotel.com £35–£72

The sea is just across the road, and France is just across the Channel, so this skilfully modernised, four-storey building already has a Gallic orientation. And, just like the average French hotel, although the accommodation is fine it is the food that makes it a 'little gem'. A small yet uncramped dining room, smartly turned out with stained-glass panels and lots of yellow, displays pictures of the Loire, whence Samuel Gicqueau hails. Although his speciality is fish and shellfish, sourced from Folkestone or Boulogne, foie gras sometimes appears to run them a close second: a warm escalope with roast pear and kumquat marmalade, for example, or a ballottine with a truffle-oiled green bean salad.

Whatever is not foie gras, among starters, tends to be shellfish: a croustillant of pan-fried langoustines infused with lime leaf, or three scallops, each stuffed with a piece of truffle and sitting on sliced ratte potatoes, all in a truffle sauce. Main-course fish might feature sea bass with braised chicory, roast turbot with ceps, or a fricassee of eels served with crushed potatoes mixed with garlic and artichoke. Meat is not neglected, however. Beef is Aberdeen Angus, lamb is from Romney Marsh, and the repertoire also runs to pink duckling with griotte cherries, and plump, tender pigeon served with sweet potato purée, roast almonds, grapes and small turnips in a red wine jus.

The style throughout is both precise and classical, evident in desserts such as a large, beautifully risen raspberry soufflé, and a flat circle of what looks like chocolate cake but turns out to be a light mousse, accompanied by coffee ice cream and a coffee and almond sauce. French service is attentive and friendly without being too familiar; 'when we congratulated the waiter on the dessert he duly explained how to make it and then produced a printed recipe'. Wines have a predictably French bias, and offerings from the Loire are especially bountiful and varied. Prices are mostly above £20, although a lively house French red and white are £14 a bottle, £3.50 a glass.

CHEF: Samuel Gicqueau PROPRIETORS: Zara and Samuel Gicqueau OPEN: Wed to Sun L 12.15 to 1.30, Tue to Sat D 7.15 to 9.15 CLOSED: 4 weeks Jan, 10 days Oct MEALS: alc (main courses £17 to £23). Set L and D Mon to Fri £22, Set L Sat and Sun £31 SERVICE: not inc CARDS: Amex, Delta, Diners, MasterCard, Switch, Visa DETAILS: 18 seats. Private parties: 26 main room. Car park. Children's helpings. No smoking in dining room. Wheelchair access (not WC). Music ACCOMMODATION: 14 rooms, all with bath/shower. TV. Phone. B&B £45 to £76. Baby facilities (*The Which? Hotel Guide*)

London Round-ups listing additional restaurants that may be worth a visit can be found after the main London section.

SAWLEY Lancashire map 8

Spread Eagle £

Sawley BB7 4NH
TEL: (01200) 441202 FAX: (01200) 441973
WEB SITE: www.thespreadeagle.co.uk
off A59, 4m NE of Clitheroe

COOKING **2**
MODERN BRITISH
£18–£44

Picture windows look out over the daffodil-bordered and duck-strewn River Ribble to the Pennines, and the relaxed, comfortable and spacious dining room sets off Greg Barnes's appealing country cooking; he stayed on when ownership changed just after the last Guide appeared. The gamut runs from a sustaining soup (a successful marriage of smoked haddock and celery for one visitor) to a well-handled tuna steak with a 'Chinese salsa' of tomato, red onion, chilli, spring onion, garlic, soy sauce and rice wine vinegar.

More mainstream main courses have included pork fillet with split-pea purée, and slow cooked shoulder of lamb with a lentil and red wine jus. For dessert, coffee ice cream counterpoints a rich terrine of dark chocolate, and honeycomb toffee, nougat and hazelnuts goes into a soft parfait with an intense raspberry coulis. Staff 'couldn't have made us feel more welcome'. A short, sensible, generously priced wine list opens with Duboeuf house wines at £9.95, and there is a fine selection of single malts.

CHEFS: Greg Barnes PROPRIETORS: Nigel and Ysanne Williams OPEN: Tue to Sun L 12 to 2.15, Tue to Sat D 6 to 9 MEALS: alc (main courses £8.50 to £13.50). Set L £8 (2 courses) to £10.25, Set D £12.95 (2 courses) to £14.95 SERVICE: not inc, card slips closed CARDS: Amex, MasterCard, Switch, Visa DETAILS: 80 seats. Private parties: 150 main room, 30 private room. Car park. Vegetarian meals. Children's helpings. No smoking in dining room. Music (£5)

SCARBOROUGH North Yorkshire map 9

Lanterna

33 Queen Street, Scarborough YO11 1HQ
TEL/FAX: (01723) 363616
WEB SITE: www.lanterna-ristorante.co.uk

COOKING **3**
ITALIAN
£30–£63

Giorgio and Rachel Alessio describe their food as Italian, not Anglo-Italian as indicated last year. Seasonality is respected, with daily specials featuring fresh asparagus between March and June, and porcini in autumn. White truffle dishes in winter range from £12 for starters to £22 as mains, and fish from the harbour might include mullet (red and grey), sole (lemon and Dover) or Scarborough woof.

If prawn cocktail, steak Diane, and veal with Marsala, mushrooms and cream strike an old-fashioned note, that is because they have been kept in the repertoire from long ago (the restaurant was already 25 years old when the Alessios took over five years ago) to please regulars; they are highlighted on the menu in red. Italian style sweets include pannacotta, and cassata (home-made ice cream with candied fruits, nuts and masala). Re-decoration of the dining area was planned for October 2001. Wines travel the length and breadth of Italy on the good-value list, though a few French and a Portuguese bins are offered too. House red and white are £10.50.

CHEF: Giorgio Alessio PROPRIETORS: Rachel and Giorgio Alessio OPEN: Mon to Sat D 6.30 to 11 CLOSED: 2 weeks Oct and Nov, 25 and 26 Dec, 1 Jan MEALS: alc (main courses £12 to £22) SERVICE: not inc, card slips closed CARDS: Delta, MasterCard, Switch, Visa DETAILS: 30 seats. Private parties: 35 main room. Vegetarian meals. Children's helpings. No children under 2. Consideration of other diners. Wheelchair access (not WC). Music. Air-conditioned

SELLACK Herefordshire map 5

HEREFORDSHIRE NEWCOMER OF THE YEAR

Lough Pool Inn £

NEW ENTRY

Sellack HR9 6LX
TEL: (01989) 730236 FAX: (01989) 730462
off A49, 3m W of Ross-on-Wye

COOKING **4**
MODERN EUROPEAN
£21–£37

After selling his London restaurants, Stephen Bull (a native of Abergavenny) has returned to the Marches, where he runs this country pub. Londoners may think that something of a comedown, whereas country folk know it is a wise move. He hasn't changed the feel of the place – it still has its flag floor, beams and chunky wooden tables – and he still caters for local drinkers, although his horizons are wider: the M50 isn't far away. As for the food (Roger Gorman moved here from London too), the Bull style suits a pub well: it has always been down to earth, parsimonious in the best sense (using humble materials to good effect) and unfussy. And so it continues, with an onion, courgette and saffron tart, and black pudding fritters with a first-class beetroot chutney.

The skill level is high – notable in a fine carrot and cardamom soup, and in nuggets of seared pink lamb in a dark cumin-infused broth of lentils and chickpeas – and local supplies are being explored, supported by a few imports such as Brixham fish (cod, perhaps, simply sauced with herbs and lemon). Desserts are substantial enough to suit pub appetites, ranging from sticky date pudding to pecan tart with clotted cream and maple syrup. A separate bar menu was due to come into effect as the Guide went to press. The wine list was due for a revamp too, although its emphasis on value under £20 (starting at £9.50 for Vin de Pays Colombard) is an encouraging start, and cider will get its own list.

CHEF: Roger Gorman PROPRIETOR: Stephen Bull OPEN: all week 12 to 2.30, 6.30 to 9.30 (12 to 5 Sun 1 Oct to 1 Mar) CLOSED: 25 Dec MEALS: alc (main courses £6.50 to £12). Bar menu available SERVICE: not inc, card slips closed CARDS: Delta, MasterCard, Switch, Visa DETAILS: 80 seats. 50 seats outside. Private parties: 30 main room. Car park. Vegetarian meals. Children's helpings. No children under 14 in bar. No smoking in dining room. Wheelchair access (not WC). No music

---

£ *means that it is possible to have a three-course meal, including coffee, half a bottle of house wine and service for £25 or less per person, at any time the restaurant is open, i.e. at dinner as well as lunch. It may be possible to spend considerably more than this, but by choosing carefully you should find £25 or less achievable.*

The Guide's top-rated restaurants are listed near the front of the book.

SHEFFIELD South Yorkshire **map 9**

Carriages

NEW ENTRY

289 Abbeydale Road South, Dore,
Sheffield S17 3LB
TEL: (0114) 2350101
EMAIL: info@carriagesrestaurant.co.uk
WEB SITE: www.carriagesrestaurant.co.uk

COOKING **3**
MODERN BRITISH
£34–£51

Out of town on Sheffield's south-western fringe, Carriages is stationed in tastefully converted shop premises with large picture windows. Pastel-coloured walls, pale linen blinds and greenery give a light, modern air to the square dinning room, with its tightly packed tables, upholstered chairs and starched linen tablecloths and napkins. Quality fresh ingredients and skilful presentation are high points of a contemporary repertoire enlivened with Mediterranean influences. A starter of pan-seared scallops comes with sweet chilli jam, rocket and crème fraîche, and smoked haddock fishcakes with smoked salmon cream and tomato salsa. Mains might include bang-bang chicken, or pan-fried halibut with chips, pea purée, tartare sauce and home-made ketchup, while a cannon of lamb is teamed with chargrilled vegetables provençale and rosemary jus. Down-to-earth desserts run the gamut from sticky toffee pudding with caramel ice cream to glazed lemon tart with fresh blueberries and raspberry sorbet. Service by a young team is more willing than skilled, with 'few smiles, no chattiness'. The compact, well-chosen wine list has a strong French influence but covers Old World and New; house wines are £10.90.

CHEFS: Cary Brown and Richard Burden PROPRIETORS: Cary Brown, Richard Burden and Aran Wilkinson OPEN: Tue to Sat D 7 to 10 CLOSED: bank hols MEALS: alc D (main courses £11 to £17). SERVICE: not inc CARDS: Delta, MasterCard, Switch, Visa DETAILS: 50 seats. Private parties: 60 main room. Car park. Wheelchair access (also WC). Music

Rafters

220 Oakbrook Road, Nether Green,
Sheffield S11 7ED
TEL/FAX: (0114) 230 4819
WEB SITE: www.raftersrestaurant.co.uk

COOKING **4**
MODERN BRITISH
£35–£45

The entrance in a side-street off Oakbrook Road makes this restaurant hard to find, but loyal followers claim the atmosphere is 'always relaxed and welcoming', and the food 'excellent'. Both entrance hall and upstairs dining room are hung with framed testimonials, where colourful, arty designer lighting contrasts with the rather more traditional bistro atmosphere. The menu, too, indicates an upmarket bistro. A lot of items – including fine bread, ice creams and sorbets – are made in-house: in a starter of wild boar sausages on sauerkraut with charred tomato sauce, both the sausages and the sauerkraut are home-made.

Satisfaction also stems from the skill with which many dishes are handled, as when three small cutlets of rosemary-roasted Derbyshire lamb, with a good crust of fat, are set off by an unctuously textured parcel of lentil and aubergine.

Desserts are decidedly homey: pecan pie with vanilla ice cream, or chocolate fudge cake with hot chocolate sauce and caramel ice cream. Timing is sometimes imprecise, and some dishes may lack punch, but in most cases flavours and textures are well judged. The French-leaning wine list has plenty under £20; house wines start at £9.50.

CHEFS: Jamie Bosworth and Marcus Lane PROPRIETORS: Jamie and Joanne Bosworth OPEN: Mon to Sat D only 7 to 10 CLOSED: 25 Dec, 1 week Jan, 2 weeks Aug, bank hols, MEALS: Set D £24.95 SERVICE: not inc, card slips closed CARDS: Amex DETAILS: 40 seats. Private parties: 40 main room. Vegetarian meals. Children's helpings. No children under 7. No cigars/pipes in dining room. Music

Thyme

32–34 Sandygate Road, Crosspool,
Sheffield S10 5RY
TEL: (01142) 666096

COOKING **6**
BISTRO
£21–£61

The extra number in the address of the former Smiths of Sheffield reflects expansion and relaunch. Wooden floors, high-backed chairs and undressed tables give it a bright city-brasserie feel, but what remains unchanged is the aim to produce simple but polished food using fine British regional produce: Orkney beef, Mull mussels, and rhubarb and Whitby cod from closer to home.

Post-refurbishment, the kitchen is very much on song, dealing adroitly with a wide range of materials. Goats' cheese appears threefold in a starter – a warm filo tartlet, a roulade coated in herbs and dressing, and a creamy ice cream – while Gressingham duck is turned into a first-class pressed terrine, aromatic with Eastern spicing, accompanied by sweet chilli jam and crème fraîche. Diversity is a strength, as dishes range from half a dozen big, chunky, firm, accurately timed scallops with crisp pancetta and minted pea purée, to a retro chargrilled beef fillet served with chips, grilled tomato, button mushrooms and two sauces: red wine and béarnaise. Deliberately sweet sauces rather than familiar stock reductions are favoured, and generally work well. Note that vegetables and nibbles are charged extra.

Desserts include a highly commended banoffi crumble with rum and raisin ice cream, and a crème brûlée notable for its accompaniment of puréed and whole raspberries and intense raspberry sorbet. An intelligently compiled wine list, balancing Old World and New, has lively, young, drinkable styles at its core. It starts with cheerful house wines from £10, stays affordable throughout, and ends with a short, interesting 'cellar selection'.

CHEFS: Richard Smith and Scott Wade PROPRIETORS: Richard and Victoria Smith OPEN: all week 12 to 2, 6.30 to 9.30 (10 Sat) MEALS: alc (main courses L £7.50 to £14, D £11 to 18). Set L £12.50. Set D 7 to 9.30 £12.50 SERVICE: not inc, card slips closed CARDS: Amex, Delta, MasterCard, Switch, Visa DETAILS: 70 seats. 10 seats outside. Private parties: 60 main room, 24 private room. Vegetarian meals. No smoking in 1 dining room. Wheelchair access (also WC). Music. Air-conditioned

Although the cuisine style noted at the top of entries has in most cases been suggested to the Guide by the restaurants, some have been edited for brevity or appropriateness.

SHELF West Yorkshire **map 8**

Bentley's

12 Wadehouse Road, Shelf HX3 7PB
TEL: (01274) 690992 FAX: (01274) 690011
EMAIL: bentleys@btinternet.com
WEB SITE: www.bentleys-foodandwine.co.uk

COOKING **3**
MODERN BRITISH
£18–£47

There's not much to Shelf (basically a pit-stop on the Bradford to Halifax road) but it does boast the Bentleys' small terraced restaurant. 'Cosy and chintzy' was how one reporter described its atmosphere. Apart from the carte, a fixed-price menu is offered at lunchtimes. Start perhaps with a small omelette filled with smoked wild mushrooms and asparagus, topped with chervil hollandaise, before tackling one of the lengthily described main courses. These might take in Cornish sea bass on a stir-fry of vegetables, squid and noodles with a crab and prawn spring roll and plum and ginger dressing, or breast of Gressingham duck served with a thyme-flavoured red onion 'tarte Tatin', olive oil mash and a red onion glaze. Yorkshire rhubarb goes into a crumble with a honey and ginger sabayon for pudding, or there is a trio of home-made ices served in a tuile basket with a fruit coulis. Service is friendly and informal, and a soundly chosen wine list keeps most of its prices below £20, starting with house French at £9.95 or Australian at £12.95.

CHEFS: Paul Bentley and Anthony Bickers PROPRIETORS: Paul and Pamela Bentley OPEN: Tue to Fri L 12 to 2, Tue to Sat D 6.30 to 9 (9.30 Sat) CLOSED: 25 to 31 Dec MEALS: alc (main courses £10 to £16.50). Set L £8.25 (2 courses) to £9.95 SERVICE: not inc, card slips closed CARDS: Delta, MasterCard, Switch, Visa DETAILS: 65 seats. Private parties: 25 main room, 25 private room. Car park. Vegetarian meals. No smoking in dining room. Music. Air-conditioned

SHEPTON MALLET Somerset **map 2**

▲ Bowlish House

Coombe Lane, Shepton Mallet BA4 5JD
TEL/FAX: (01749) 342022
on A371 to Wells, ¼m from town centre

COOKING **4**
MODERN FRENCH/BRITISH
£36–£48

The candlelit dining room of this immaculately kept Georgian mansion, set just back from the traffic, is decorated in pale primrose, with a huge mirror over the fireplace, and French windows giving on to a conservatory. In this elegant setting, Deirdré Forde's cooking amiably combines traditional British and French elements, taking in twice-baked Stilton and celery soufflé, and ballottine of foie gras in Sauternes jelly with truffle and artichoke rémoulade.

A sense of timing and balance is at the heart of things, producing a main course of monkfish with squid-ink pasta, roasted garlic and a rich red wine sauce, and suckling pig is agreeably partnered by roasted apple and celeriac mash. Showboating desserts have included iced ginger bombe garnished with stem ginger and syrup, and a highly successful revival of Black Forest gâteau. Wines have been carefully sourced for value and interest, with plenty of choice for a range of budgets: from Tuscany's Ornellaia to well-priced classic clarets and value options from the rest of the world. There are nearly 30 half-bottles, and four each of house reds and whites at £10.95 (£3 a glass).

CHEF: Deirdré Forde PROPRIETORS: John and Deirdré Forde OPEN: Tue to Sat D only 7 to 9.30 (L by arrangement) MEALS: Set D £21 (2 courses) to £25 SERVICE: not inc, card slips closed CARDS: Delta, MasterCard, Switch, Visa DETAILS: Private parties: 45 main room, 30 private room. Car park. Vegetarian meals. Children's helpings. No smoking in dining room. Occasional music ACCOMMODATION: 3 rooms, all with bath/shower. TV. B&B £50 to £65. Baby facilities

▲ Charlton House, Mulberry Restaurant

Shepton Mallet BA4 4PR
TEL: (01749) 342008 FAX: (01749) 346362
EMAIL: enquiry@charltonhouse.com COOKING **6**
WEB SITE: www.charltonhouse.com MODERN BRITISH
1m from Shepton Mallet on A361 towards Frome £30–£86

The house acts as a showcase for the Mulberry range of furnishings and fabrics, but the result – described by one reporter as an 'opulent-but-faded-well-established-antiquey look' – is discreet and restful rather than hard sell. Although the dining room's 'deck chairs' seem designed more for the eye than for the posterior, shirtsleeved customers add to the sense that this is a refreshingly unstuffy country-house hotel. Nevertheless, luxury materials are conspicuous by their presence – truffle oil, champagne sauce, foie gras, sevruga caviar – and dishes often appear busy and complex, but they are not overworked. This is a professional kitchen that knows what it is doing.

Technical accomplishment is impressive, and Mediterranean ideas seem to have the upper hand: for example, in an intelligently composed sharp-sweet feta and red pepper terrine accompanied by bruschetta and salsa, and in a main course of four well-timed scallops served with ricotta-filled pasta, diced pancetta, spinach and grilled artichoke. Other pasta accessories have included a brace of pumpkin-filled ravioli served beside a pinky-red pigeon breast in a cep nage. Although desserts may not always hit quite the same high notes, it is not for want of trying: chocolate mousse comes with brandy-steeped cherries and a scoop of kriek (cherry beer) sorbet, and pineapple tarte Tatin is served with coconut ice cream and a brûlée-style chilli-topped fluffy mousse. Rich pickings are on offer for the serious wine drinker with equally serious funds. Those looking to spend under £20 will have to make do with the varied choice of half-bottles and the lively, lengthy selection by the glass. Bottle prices start at £14.

CHEF: Adam Fellows PROPRIETORS: Mr and Mrs R.J. Saul OPEN: all week 12.30 to 1.45, 7.30 to 9.30 MEALS: alc L (main courses £8 to £18). Set L £12.50 (2 courses) to £16.50, Set D £38.50 to £55. Light L available SERVICE: not inc CARDS: Amex, Delta, Diners, MasterCard, Switch, Visa DETAILS: 80 seats. 20 seats outside. Private parties: 80 main room, 20 and 40 private rooms. Car park. Vegetarian meals. Children's helpings. No smoking in dining room. Wheelchair access (also WC). Music ACCOMMODATION: 16 rooms, all with bath/shower. TV. Phone. B&B £112.50 to £315. Baby facilities. Swimming pool. Fishing (*The Which? Hotel Guide*)

All entries, including Round-ups, are fully indexed at the back of the Guide.

SHERE Surrey map 3

Kinghams

Gomshall Lane, Shere GU5 9HE
TEL: (01483) 202168
just off A25 Dorking to Guildford road

COOKING **4**
MODERN ENGLISH
£29–£57

Looking like a tea room, with its small, oak-beamed rooms and an open fire, this pretty little restaurant is a popular lunch venue. The good-value set-price menu is partly responsible, offering three uncomplicated but varied choices per course. One summer lunch, for example, began with a neat dome of diced melon and paw-paw on a mint-infused lemon syrup, while main-course roast loin of lamb has featured a generous portion of sweet and tender meat on a bed of nutty brown lentils with a robust caper and onion sauce.

The carte, meanwhile, features plenty of fish (see also the daily specials), starters typically including a 'mini bouillabaisse', or smoked haddock fishcake topped with a poached quail's egg. A more complex style is evident in main courses of wild venison saddle wrapped in an oatmeal pancake with apple and damson relish and an orange glaze, and to finish there may be lemon torte with roasted plums and rhubarb topped with 'caramel shards'. Service is on the ball. Wines are wide ranging and generally good value; house selections are £11.95 a bottle, £3 a glass.

CHEF/PROPRIETOR: Paul Baker OPEN: Tue to Sun L 12 to 2.15, Tue to Sat D 7 to 9.30 CLOSED: 25 Dec to 3 Jan MEALS: alc exc Sun (main courses £11 to £20.50). Set L Tue to Sat £13.95 (2 courses), Set L Sun £14.50 (2 courses) to £18, Set D Tue to Thur £15.95 (2 courses) SERVICE: not inc CARDS: Amex, Delta, Diners, MasterCard, Switch, Visa DETAILS: 50 seats. 20 seats outside. Private parties: 32 main room, 20 and 30 private rooms. Car park. Vegetarian meals. No children Sat D. No smoking in dining room. Wheelchair access (not WC). Music (£5)

SHIPHAM Somerset map 2

▲ Daneswood House

Cuck Hill, Shipham BS25 1RD
TEL: (01934) 843145 FAX: (01934) 843824
EMAIL: info@daneswoodhotel.co.uk
WEB SITE: www.daneswoodhotel.co.uk
S of Bristol off A38 towards Cheddar; hotel is on left as you leave the village

COOKING **3**
MODERN BRITISH
£30–£49

A four-square Edwardian building sitting in trees and gardens on a small plateau up a steeply winding lane near Cheddar, Daneswood was originally a homeopathic hydro. Conservatory extensions and spacious, wood-panelled dining-rooms with William Morris wallpaper aspire to create a sense of grand luxe that the cooking seeks to reinforce. Dinner runs from amuse-bouche to petits fours with coffee, and much of the food is original and technically accomplished: a crisp pasty, lined with spinach, containing a whole pigeon breast covered with foie gras is a novel idea.

Main-course show-stoppers have included a correctly timed roast fillet of sea bass with langoustine risotto and a 'mild and unobtrusive' herbed butter sauce, and loin of Mendip lamb with dauphinoise and a béchamel-free version of moussaka. Desserts, an embarrassment of riches, may include a thin and crumbly rhubarb tart with a fine matching ice cream, or a two-tone chocolate, walnut and mascarpone torte with an admirably strong bitter chocolate sorbet. A classical French-based wine list ascends into three figures, but there is a good choice of halves, and 14 house wines start with a £9.95 Gascon white.

CHEFS: Heather Matthews and Elise Hodges PROPRIETORS: David and Elise Hodges OPEN: all week 12 to 2, 7 to 9.30 CLOSED: 24 Dec to 5 Jan MEALS: Set L Mon to Sat and D all week £23.95 (2 courses) to £29.95. Light lunch (inc Sun) £19.95 SERVICE: not inc, card slips closed CARDS: Amex, Delta, Diners, MasterCard, Switch, Visa DETAILS: 50 seats. Private parties: 35 main room, 10 to 35 private rooms. Car park. Vegetarian meals. Children's helpings. No smoking in dining room. Wheelchair access (also WC). Music ACCOMMODATION: 17 rooms, all with bath/shower. TV. Phone. B&B £89.50 to £150. Baby facilities (*The Which? Hotel Guide*) (£5)

SHIPSTON ON STOUR Warwickshire **map 5**

▲ Chavignol **NEW ENTRY**

8 Mill Street, Shipston on Stour CV36 4AW COOKING **7**
TEL: (01608) 663888 FAX: (01608) 663188 MODERN EUROPEAN
EMAIL: chavignol@virginbiz.com £35–£112

Chavignol moved from Chipping Norton (that site has now become Brasserie Chavignol; see entry) into a huge old custard-coloured mill near the bridge over the River Stour, and opened in summer 2001. Several months of sympathetic restoration, bringing out the best in a naturally beautiful old building, have left it looking smart, uncluttered and restrained. Now that it has accommodation as well, the two linked dining rooms (one of them a conservatory) are open all week, and menu options allow a choice between indulgence and moderation.

The cooking itself has a rather 'baroque' character, and some dishes sail pretty close to the wind in terms of complexity; at least that is the impression given by a poached duck's egg on buttered spinach in a globe artichoke, glazed with hollandaise and accompanied by tuna beignets and a beetroot syrup. On the whole, though, things just about manage to stay focused, for example in a herby-flavoured, lightly mustardy mousse surrounded by diced, crisply fried ox tongue, accompanied by cauliflower and truffle purée and a rich stock-based sauce given bite from a dash of raspberry vinegar. What is also impressive is that all the items in a dish are well rendered: a meaty, flavourful roast sea trout, for example, and its accompaniments of first-class pesto-dressed tagliatelle, finely diced ratatouille, a rough-textured Parmesan twist, and fresh peas in a rich tomato purée; oh, and there was also an accurately timed chargrilled scallop sitting on a mound of tangled cucumber filaments.

Desserts are no less labour-intensive, and no less appealing: a square of creamy, gently honey-flavoured iced parfait is well contrasted with toasted brioche and a roasted sesame tuile, and partnered by spicy figs and a pineapple sabayon. A charming, affable and intelligent Mark Maguire greets and takes orders, while helpers do the rest. He has made efforts to source wines from less-fashionable regions, picking out some producers for their innovation and smaller-scale production, though popular classics feature as well. The Infinitus Argentinian Malbec-Syrah at £23, and Viogniers from the South of France at £19, are characterful examples from the former category. Otherwise, bottles under £25 are few, though house wines start at £14.

CHEF: Marcus Ashenford PROPRIETOR: Mark Maguire OPEN: all week 12 to 2, 7 to 10 MEALS: Set L £18 to £25, Set D £27 to £85 (inc wine) SERVICE: not inc CARDS: Amex, Delta, MasterCard, Switch, Visa DETAILS: 35 seats. Private parties: 30 main room. Car park. Vegetarian meals. Children's helpings. No smoking in dining room. Wheelchair access (also WC). No music ACCOMMODATION: 5 rooms, all with bath/shower. TV. Phone. B&B £150 to £280

SHREWSBURY Shropshire map 5

Sol

82 Wyle Cop, Shrewsbury SY1 1UT
TEL: (01743) 340560 FAX: (01743) 340552

COOKING **5**
INTERNATIONAL
£28–£52

Wyle Cop is one of Shrewsbury's more characterful streets, partly thanks to Sol itself: the Mexican décor makes it hard to miss. The warm tones are echoed by the welcome and service from Debbie Williams and helpers, and reporters find the cooking 'consistently good'. It is based on sound supplies, from Cornish fish (perhaps pan-fried and served with creamed fennel tart), to French foie gras, poultry and wild mushrooms. John Williams is a talented chef, making veal and smoked bacon sausage (served with celeriac rémoulade), and partnering roast breast of local pigeon with beetroot terrine and a spiced foie gras bon bon to impressive effect.

The food keeps its feet on the ground, adding enough spice to provoke interest without overpowering: capers here, herb oils there, a mustard jus with Gressingham duck breast, and horseradish cream with a ballottine of Shetland salmon. Accompanying vegetables get the thumbs-up (layered winter vegetables and sculpted roast potato for one visitor). There may be no choice on the set lunch menu, but value is good and the three courses 'perfectly balanced', according to a reporter who enjoyed haddock mousse with tomato brandade, a satisfying duck confit, and tart and tasty poached plums with fromage frais. Five house wines at £9.95 head a good-value list, its unshowy but thoughtful range encompassing a good variety of grapes and styles.

CHEF: John Williams PROPRIETORS: John and Debbie Williams OPEN: Tue to Sat 12.30 to 2, 7 to 9.30 CLOSED: 1 week Christmas, 1 week autumn MEALS: alc L (main courses £10 to £15). Set D £28.50 to £33 SERVICE: not inc, card slips closed CARDS: Delta, MasterCard, Switch, Visa DETAILS: 45 seats. Private parties: 20 main room, 20 private room. Vegetarian meals. No children under 8. No smoking in dining room. Wheelchair access (not WC). Music

SKIPTON North Yorkshire map 8

Le Caveau

86 High Street, Skipton BD23 1JJ
TEL/FAX: (01756) 794274

COOKING **2**
ANGLO-FRENCH COST
£22–£40

Plumb in the middle of Skipton, this centuries-old building has in its time housed a grain store and a prison, but is now more upliftingly home to Le Caveau, a cellar restaurant, as its name announces. The very tall might mind their heads on standing, but limited space is used well and there are ample staff to ensure everyone feels looked after. The food is as modern in outlook as can be;

for example goats' cheese and caramelised red onion tart, with thin, short pastry, served with redcurrant vinaigrette. Main courses tend to richness: a corpulent chicken breast stuffed with well-seasoned wild mushroom and bacon mousse, perhaps, or salmon en croûte in a sauce containing pink peppercorns and dill. End things on a high note with rhubarb and orange crumble served with proper custard, or sticky toffee pudding with hot toffee sauce and a toffee-flavoured ice cream. It is all thought to represent fine value, as does the varied and usefully annotated wine list. House wines from Georges Duboeuf are £9.50.

CHEF: Richard Barker PROPRIETORS: Brian Womersley and Richard Barker OPEN: Tue to Sat 12 to 2, 7 to 9.30 MEALS: alc (main courses £9.50 to £14). Set L £6.95 (2 courses), Set D Tue to Thur £13.95 SERVICE: not inc CARDS: Amex, Delta, MasterCard, Switch, Visa DETAILS: 28 seats. Private parties: 16 main room. Vegetarian meals. No smoking in dining room. Music (£5)

SOUTHALL Greater London map 3

Brilliant

72–76 Western Road, Southall UB2 5DZ COOKING **3**
TEL: (020) 8574 1928 FAX: (020) 8574 0276 INDIAN
WEB SITE: www.brilliantrestaurant.com £24–£58

The Anand family's confidence and enthusiasm has grown over the 25 years since relocating from Kenya to Southall. Panoramic windows ensure it stands out in the street, and most customers are seated at long communal tables, which adds to the jolly, bustling atmosphere. A huge flat-screen TV on one wall may offer sport or other entertainment. Most items come in copper dishes over copper pots with candle heaters. Brilliant's African roots show in mogo-spiced cassava chips, and in tilapia fish dishes: either marinated Kenyan style and cooked in a tandoor, or served in a rich, spicy masala sauce. Daily specials might turn out tandoori lamb: tender and accurately cooked, still pink in the middle. Aloo tikka (potato cutlet with chickpeas, yoghurt and tamarind sauces) cleverly balances flavours, textures and colours, while a mixed vegetable curry includes deep-flavoured aubergine, peas, potatoes and cauliflower. Generous portions of mainly conventional lamb and chicken 'special meals' are suggested for three or five people (but could satisfy more than that). House wines are £9, but beer or lassi are better bets.

CHEF: D.K. Anand PROPRIETORS: K.K. and D.K. Anand OPEN: Tue to Fri L 12 to 2.30, Tue to Sun D 6 to 11 CLOSED: first 3 weeks Aug MEALS: alc (main courses £6 to £11). Set L and D £17.50 SERVICE: not inc, card slips closed CARDS: Amex, Delta, Diners, MasterCard, Switch, Visa DETAILS: 240 seats. Private parties: 120 main room, 120 private room. Car park. Vegetarian meals. Children's helpings. No smoking in 1 dining room. Wheelchair access (also WC). Music. Air-conditioned (£5)

Occasional music *in the details at the end of an entry means live or recorded music is played in the dining room only rarely or for special events.* No music *means it is never played.*

New main entries and restaurant closures are listed near the front of the book.

SOUTHPORT Merseyside map 7

Warehouse Brasserie

NEW ENTRY

30 West Street, Southport PR8 1QN
TEL: (01704) 544662 FAX: (01704) 500074
EMAIL: info@warehousebrasserie.co.uk
WEB SITE: www.warehouse-brasserie.co.uk

COOKING **2**
GLOBAL
£17–£54

One block back from the seafront, and occupying two floors, the Warehouse has put Southport back on the gastronomic map. Popular, buzzy, friendly and contemporary, the ambience is warm and welcoming with a relaxed enthusiasm. Mirrored panelling, Dali prints, wooden floorboards and modern seating set the tone, and a modern brasserie repertoire – divided into 'Small Dishes', 'Large Dishes', 'Side Orders' and 'Puddings', plus pastas and salads at dinner – is enlivened with trendy trips to the Mediterranean and beyond.

Typical starters might see spiced aubergine and tomato tart with tahini sauce, or confit duck spring roll with mango and coriander relish. Pastas have featured fettucine with sun-dried tomatoes, garlic and basil, while mains may surprise with Hawaiian monkfish partnered by roasted sweet potatoes and tropical fruit salsa; or there is homely fish and chips with mushy peas. Among puddings that have pleased are a cleverly executed milk chocolate and orange tiramisù. Lunch is good value, the set-price menu particularly so, as is the early-evening deal, while the compact, well-chosen wine list is simply classified by colour. Four house wines roll out at £9.95 to £13.95.

CHEF: Marc Vérité PROPRIETOR: Paul Adams OPEN: Mon to Sat 12 to 2, 5.30 to 10.30 CLOSED: 25 and 26 Dec, 1 Jan MEALS: alc (main courses £5 to £15.50). Set L £6.95 (2 courses) to £8.95, Set D Mon 5.30 to 10.30 and Tue to Thur 5.30 to 7.30 £9.95 (2 courses) to £11.95 SERVICE: not inc, 10% for parties of 10 or more CARDS: Amex, Delta, MasterCard, Switch, Visa DETAILS: 110 seats. Private parties: 74 main room, 45 private room. Occasional music. Air-conditioned

SOUTHWOLD Suffolk map 6

▲ Crown Hotel

High Street, Southwold IP18 6DP
TEL: (01502) 722275 FAX: (01502) 727263

COOKING **1**
MODERN BRITISH-PLUS
£27–£42

This Georgian hotel/restaurant/pub is owned by local brewer and wine-merchant Adnams, so the jewel in this Crown is its wine list. None the less, a cosmopolitan repertoire of well-presented, modern dishes offers fair support. Informal eating from a bar menu strong on seafood might take in tapas, sushi, or cod tempura with sweet potato chips and tartare. The restaurant shifts up a gear, to chargrilled beef sirloin with horseradish dauphinois and Portobello pancakes, and seared sea bass with celeriac and anchovy rémoulade, although results can prove patchy. Most agree that service is friendly and efficient. A well-priced, interest-packed wine list includes young, fruit-filled wines under £15, and starts with French country reds from £9.50 (among them 1996 Mas de Daumas Gassac at £26.95), but there are contemporary classics from elsewhere too, including Yarra Yerring's Dry Red No 1, and Ridge Vineyards' Geyserville.

CHEF: Chris Coubrough PROPRIETOR: Adnams Hotels OPEN: all week 12.30 to 2, 7.30 to 9.30 MEALS: restaurant Set L £16.50 (2 courses) to £19.50, Set D £22 (2 courses) to £27; bar alc (main courses £8 to £24) SERVICE: not inc, card slips closed CARDS: Amex, Delta, Diners, MasterCard, Switch, Visa DETAILS: 25 seats. 14 seats outside. Private parties: 20 main room. Car park. Vegetarian meals. Children's helpings. No smoking in dining room. Occasional music ACCOMMODATION: 14 rooms, all with bath/shower. TV. Phone. B&B £57 to £82 (*The Which? Hotel Guide*)

STADDLEBRIDGE North Yorkshire — map 9

▲ McCoy's Bistro

Cleveland Tontine, Staddlebridge DL6 3JB
TEL: (01609) 882671 FAX: (01609) 882660
WEB SITE: www.mccoysatthetontine.co.uk
6m NE of Northallerton, at junction of A19 and A172

COOKING **5**
BISTRO
£23–£52

This is not a posh place, rather a relaxing and civilised one for those who approach it in the right spirit: don't expect country-house splendour, or even matching furniture, but do enjoy an oddly sited stone-built house with a laid-back atmosphere and a sharp sense of priorities. One of its strengths, for a regular visitor at least, is that there isn't much chance of finding it restyled, or of the food being anything other than consistently good. Since the restaurant is open only on Saturday evenings, most visitors eat in the basement bistro, where a long menu revels in variety, taking in roasted vegetables with chive aïoli, curried smoked haddock soup with spicy rouille, and braised shin of beef with colcannon mash.

Many dishes don't seem to have a real home, except on the plate: crumbly and subtly spiced black pudding, for example, served with caramelised onions, a quail's egg and chargrilled focaccia, or spiced roast duck breast with a tiny duck sausage. The skill seems to lie in a sound grasp of essentials, the kind that produce tender, pink rack of lamb with a 'big wobbly blob' of exemplary béarnaise, or desserts such as a generously deep custard tart with rhubarb purée and matching ice cream, or a small but rich and dense tart 'made with the best chocolate', accompanied by pistachios and maple syrup ice cream. Service (something else that doesn't change) hits the spot, and around 40 well-chosen wines focus largely on France and the southern hemisphere, starting with house Chardonnay and Merlot at £12.95.

CHEF: Marcus Bennett PROPRIETORS: the McCoy brothers OPEN: bistro all week 12 to 2, 7 to 9.30; restaurant Sat D only 7 to 9.30 CLOSED: 25 and 26 Dec MEALS: bistro alc (main courses L £9 to £13, D £15.50 to £18). Set L £10.95 (2 courses) to £12.95, Set D Sun to Thu 7 to 8 £14.95 (2 courses) to £16.95, Set D Sat in restaurant £29.50 SERVICE: not inc CARDS: Amex, Delta, Diners, MasterCard, Switch, Visa DETAILS: 120 seats. Private parties: 50 main room, 15 and 23 private rooms. Car park. Vegetarian meals. Music. Air-conditioned ACCOMMODATION: 6 rooms, all with bath/shower. TV. Phone. B&B £75 to £95

'The menu also had a nut warning - ''all dishes contain nuts'' – which sounds like something the insurance company asked them to print.' (On eating in London)

STAITHES North Yorkshire map 9

▲ Endeavour

1 High Street, Staithes TS13 5BH
TEL: (01947) 840825

COOKING **2**
SEAFOOD
£27–£46

'Where to go for a weekend by the sea?' wondered one couple. They ended up in this little restaurant-with-rooms in a converted fisherman's cottage in Staithes, which exercises a powerful pull. After eating lemon sole with a coriander hollandaise, and monkfish on leeks and celeriac, they were well satisfied. A strong point of the menu is that it offers less frequently encountered fish, such as gurnard, octopus, sea urchin, whiting and dab. Nor are the treatments necessarily the obvious ones: skate might have a pink peppercorn and lemon sauce instead of black butter and capers. There are meat dishes, if you want. Meals end with something simple like lemon tart, or – for show-offs – a crêpe filled with whipped cream, crushed meringue and Cointreau-soaked strawberries, served with a raspberry and mango sauce. A short, sensible wine list covers the world in brief, opening with Chardonnay and Cabernet-Merlot vins de pays at £8.95.

CHEF/PROPRIETOR: Lisa Chapman OPEN: Tue to Sat 11.45 to 2, 6.45 to 9 MEALS: alc (main courses £10 to £17) SERVICE: not inc CARDS: none DETAILS: 45 seats. Private parties: 30 main room, 10 to 30 private rooms. Small car park. Vegetarian meals. No smoking in dining room. No music ACCOMMODATION: 3 rooms. 2 with bath/shower. TV. B&B £55 (*The Which? Hotel Guide*)

STANTON Suffolk map 6

Leaping Hare Vineyard Restaurant

Wyken Vineyards, Stanton IP31 2DW
TEL: (01359) 250287 FAX: (01359) 252372
signposted from A143, 8m NE of Bury St Edmunds

COOKING **1**
MODERN BRITISH
£25–£42

'The Leaping Hare must be one of the pleasantest places to dine in the English countryside.' This massive grey barn on the Wyken Hall Estate, with its profusion of oak beams and numerous leaping hare paintings, provides the backdrop for modern British fare that changes daily according to availability. It champions the use of the freshest of foods from garden and countryside: game and mushrooms from the estate woods, lamb from the rare breeds herd, and organic dairy produce provide the inspiration. Start with plump Suffolk asparagus in season, or their own bresaola cured in Wyken red wine and served with truffle oil and Parmesan. Follow that with pan-fried breast of wood pigeon with celeriac rösti and spring greens, and finish with zesty lemon and lime pie, or rhubarb mille-feuilles. Service is pleasant, there's a café and gift shop, and wines include six whites and a red from the Wyken Vineyard (from £9), plus 20-odd from round the world.

CHEF: Steven Jessop PROPRIETORS: Kenneth and Carla Carlisle OPEN: all week L 12 to 3, Fri and Sat D 7 to 9.30 CLOSED: 24 Dec to 7 Jan MEALS: alc (main courses £9 to £15). Light lunches also available SERVICE: not inc, card slips closed CARDS: Delta, MasterCard, Switch, Visa DETAILS: 50 seats. Private parties: 60 main room. Car park. Children's helpings. No smoking in dining room. Wheelchair access (also WC). No music (£5)

STOCKCROSS Berkshire **map 2**

▲ Vineyard at Stockcross

Stockcross RG20 8JU
TEL: (01635) 528770 FAX: (01635) 528398
EMAIL: general@the-vineyard.co.uk
WEB SITE: www.the-vineyard.co.uk
just off A4, 2m W of Newbury on B4000

COOKING **5**
ANGLO-FRENCH
£36–£117

Named in honour of the owner's Californian winery, this is a suitably lavish expression of the hospitality industry at full throttle. A comfortable, light, luxurious, airy dining room overlooks an imposing and 'bizarre' pool dotted with flames, while unobtrusive and largely impeccable country-house service is delivered by smartly dressed formal staff. There is no shortage of indulgent gestures on Billy Reid's menu either, which takes in a lobster, potato and truffle salad, and escalope of foie gras with pear chutney. Loins, suprêmes and fillets of meat and fish dominate the raw materials, although these are balanced to a degree by a beignet of black pudding with scalded scallop, and spaghetti of cockles with chorizo among starters.

Enthusiasm for sunny southern flavours is evident in a terrine of Mediterranean vegetables with olive and basil dressing, and the food is impeccably presented, served up with colourful and artistic flair at the right temperature: confit of duck with a glossy golden crisp skin, accompanied by chestnut-spiked mashed potato, finishing with custard tart, or well-timed poached pear with crème fraîche and dark chocolate ice cream. Most reporters are happy, although there are accounts of fish not appearing as fresh as it should be, varying standards throughout a meal, some service errors, and extras that can bump up the bill. California understandably features prominently on the sharply chosen wine list (with Viognier, Pinot Grigio and Marsanne among the more usual Chardonnays), and although there is little under £20, quality is high – there are plenty of big names such as Ch. Latour and Sassicaia for those who want them – and value remains commendable throughout. House wines start at £12.

CHEF: Billy Reid PROPRIETOR: Sir Peter Michael OPEN: all week 12 to 2, 7 to 10 MEALS: alc (main courses £21 to £27). Set L £17 (2 courses) to £22, Set D £47 to £85 SERVICE: not inc CARDS: Amex, Delta, Diners, MasterCard, Switch, Visa DETAILS: 74 seats. Private parties: 55 main room, 40 and 60 private rooms. Car park. Vegetarian meals. Children's helpings. Wheelchair access (also WC). Music. Air-conditioned ACCOMMODATION: 31 rooms, all with bath/shower. TV. Phone. B&B £211 to £587. Rooms for disabled. Baby facilities. Swimming pool (*The Which? Hotel Guide*)

Subscribers to Which? Online can access The Good Food Guide *on www.which.net.*

STOKE BRUERNE Northamptonshire map 5

Bruerne's Lock

5 The Canalside, Stoke Bruerne NN12 7SB
TEL: (01604) 863654 FAX: (01604) 863330
EMAIL: bruernlock@aol.com
WEB SITE: www.bruerneslock.co.uk
off A508, 3½m from M1 junction 15

COOKING **2**
COST
£28–£57

Red brick outside and terracotta colours inside give this Georgian building beside a flight of seven locks on the Grand Union Canal a warmth that is echoed in the service: the menu is explained in some detail, and a leisurely pace is maintained by cheerful staff. The kitchen's broad brush produces a wide range of dishes, including spinach and watercress velouté, marinated sardine fillets topped with crumbled goats' cheese, and chicken in a Thai curry cream, although the Mediterranean is a favourite source of ideas: red snapper comes with salsa, and rack of lamb is rolled in provençale herbs. Sound materials and careful timing characterise the cooking, from one reporter's 'garlic field mushroom assembly' to flavourful roast chicken breast, and well-reported desserts have included passion fruit crème brûlée, and sticky toffee pudding with butterscotch sauce. Thirty-plus wines are grouped by weight and style, with house Cortese and Barbera varietals from Piedmont at £14.25.

CHEF: Nick Collingwood PROPRIETOR: H.F.T. Leisure Ltd OPEN: Tue to Fri and Sun L 12.15 to 2.15, Tue to Sat D 7.15 to 9.30 CLOSED: 1 week Oct, 26 Dec to 10 Jan, 1 week Mar MEALS: alc D (main courses £14.50 to £20.50). Set L Tue to Fri £14.50 (2 courses) to £17, Set L Sun £18, Set D Tue to Fri £17 SERVICE: not inc CARDS: Amex, Delta, MasterCard, Switch, Visa DETAILS: 54 seats. 20 seats outside. Private parties: 54 main room, 14 private room. Car park. Vegetarian meals. Children's helpings. No smoking in dining room. Wheelchair access (not WC). Music

STOKE SUB HAMDON Somerset map 2

Priory House Restaurant

NEW ENTRY

1 High Street, Stoke sub Hamdon TA14 6PP
TEL/FAX: (01935) 822826

COOKING **7**
MODERN EUROPEAN
£31–£50

After covering himself in glory at Ockenden Manor in West Sussex, Martin Hadden (and wife Michele) took over a former bistro in this sprawling village just a couple of miles from the National Trust's Montacute House. With 'more taste than money', they have turned it into a classy restaurant, decorated in restrained blue and beige, and set out their stall with a short, contemporary and very appealing European-based menu. Simplicity is a keynote, evident in full-flavoured pesto risotto with asparagus and Parmesan shavings, a goats' cheese raviolo with red pepper coulis, and fillet of beef with horseradish and red wine gravy.

If the food appears to play safe, however, it is certainly not lacking in character. Technical skills can be taken for granted, but dishes are also put together with great care, as in a main course consisting of slices of pan-fried sweetbread, each on a bed of thick tomato- and basil-flavoured mayonnaise, alternating with a mix of salad potatoes, browned onion and green peppercorns, all surrounding a samosa-type basket of lightly dressed leaves. 'I can't imagine sweetbreads being prepared with greater finesse,' confessed our inspector.

Items are also arranged with 'mathematical precision', for example in a starter of pan-fried, tarragon-glazed chicken livers, set on a thin ring of potato slices, themselves sitting on a criss-cross grid of French beans, looking 'like soldiers on parade' and dressed with hazelnut oil. If only the pepper grinder and coarse sea salt were further out of reach in the kitchen, the balance would be even more impressive. Arty presentation reaches a climax with desserts, where chunks of strawberry, dressed in an intense purée of the same, have been separated by scoops of mascarpone, and set around a dramatic eggy biscuit tower containing a champagne sorbet. Prices on the 60-strong, pleasingly varied wine list soon hop over the £20 barrier, but half a dozen house wines under £18 are also available by the glass from £4.

CHEF: Martin Hadden PROPRIETORS: Martin and Michele Hadden OPEN: Tue to Sat 12 to 2, 7 to 9 CLOSED: 2 weeks Christmas, 2 weeks Aug MEALS: Set L £14 (2 courses) to £28, D £24 (2 courses) to £28 SERVICE: not inc, card slips closed CARDS: Delta, MasterCard, Switch, Visa DETAILS: 30 seats. Private parties: 8 main room. Vegetarian meals. No smoking in dining room. Wheelchair access (not WC). No music

STORRINGTON West Sussex **map 3**

Fleur de Sel

Manleys Hill, Storrington RH20 4BT COOKING **6**
TEL: (01903) 742331 FAX: (01903) 740649 FRENCH
£31–£64

The Bargate-stone building may be very English, with a garden for summer drinks, but everything else about this operation is seriously French, starting with a name that commemorates the coarse salt produced in the marshes of Noirmoutier on the Atlantic coast, Michel Perraud's home territory. Decorated to a high standard, with a bright bar and a pair of elegant dining rooms, it is a welcoming place with smiling, efficient and unobtrusive service overseen by Bernadette Perraud. Another consequence perhaps of the chef's origins is the concentration on fish and shellfish, which might feature juicy Cornish crab cake (virtually all crab), surrounded by langoustine tails and a herb butter sauce, or a salad of opalescent scallops, arranged in a circle on a bed of wild rocket, topped with generous slices of perfumed summer truffle, and given a lightly sweet verjuice dressing.

Elsewhere foie gras is likely to make an appearance, maybe pan-fried with elderberry sauce, while main-course meats have included sweetbread with artichoke and wild mushroom ragoût, and chunky nuggets of flavourful lamb with a rosemary sauce. Integral vegetables receive their share of attention, taking in courgette stuffed with a macedoine of peppers, and aubergine so finely chopped as to be almost a salsa, while desserts bring out the kitchen's best. Mango Tatin comes with a thrilling, bittersweet, fluffy balsamic sorbet, and a standard-setting crème brûlée is subtly infused with almonds, accompanied by a roast peach topped with a sharp lime sorbet. Lovers of fine French wine will not be disappointed by the 100-strong list, and a short selection under £20 helps the less extravagant.

CHEF: Michel Perraud PROPRIETORS: Bernadette and Michel Perraud OPEN: Tue to Fri and Sun L 12 to 2, Tue to Sat D 7 to 10 MEALS: Set L £14.50 (2 courses) to £33, Set D Tue to Thur £18.50 (2 courses) to £33, Set D Fri and Sat £28 (2 courses) to £33 SERVICE: 12.5% (optional), card slips closed CARDS: Amex, Delta, MasterCard, Switch, Visa DETAILS: 50 seats. Private parties: 20 main room. Car park. No children under 12. No smoking in dining room. Wheelchair access (not WC). Music

STOWMARKET Suffolk map 6

Tot Hill House

NEW ENTRY

Tot Hill, Stowmarket IP14 3QH
TEL/FAX: (01449) 673375

COOKING **2**
MODERN EUROPEAN
£31–£46

This charming and substantial country house, beside the busy A14 on the outskirts of Stowmarket, is nevertheless peaceful, welcoming and hospitable. Deep-blue carpets, peach and terracotta walls, and subdued lighting contribute to a serenely comfortable ambience, helped along by smart, friendly service. Menus incorporate plenty of appealing combinations: avocado and smoked haddock in a coarse grain mustard crème fraîche with Avruga caviar, and toasted goats' cheese on a salad of sweet crisp leaves with butter beans, garlic croûtons and walnut dressing.

Care extends to a light, crisp batter for monkfish medallions, served with a creamy mushroom sauce, and other main course options might run to breast of Gressingham duck with apple and horseradish stuffing, or rump of lamb with roasted Mediterranean vegetables. Desserts generally include a brandy-snap basket filled with ice cream: perhaps honeycomb ice with chocolate sauce. Since the location makes driving necessary, the wine list could do with a few more half-bottles, but still represents a varied range. Prices start at £13.50.

CHEFS: Christopher Bruce and Daniela Bruce-Foster PROPRIETORS: Christopher and Mary Bruce OPEN: Wed to Fri and Sun L 12 to 1.30, Wed to Sat D 7 to 8.30 (9 Sat) CLOSED: 2 weeks Jan, 1 week late summer MEALS: Set L Wed to Fri £20 (2 courses) to £25, Set L Sun £14.95 (2 courses) to £17.95, Set D £20 to £25 SERVICE: not inc CARDS: Delta, MasterCard, Switch, Visa DETAILS: 40 seats. Private parties: 40 main room. Car park. Children's helpings. No smoking in dining room. Wheelchair access (also WC). No music

STOW-ON-THE-WOLD Gloucestershire map 5

▲ The Royalist

NEW ENTRY

Digbeth Street, Stow-on-the-Wold GL54 1BN
TEL: (01451) 830670 FAX: (01451) 870048
EMAIL: info@theroyalisthotel.co.uk
WEB SITE: www.theroyalisthotel.co.uk

COOKING **4**
MODERN BRITISH
£23–£54

In 2000 the Thompsons forsook their Fulham Road eatery for this venerable timbered building opposite a tiny triangular green in Stow. With its end-walls in exposed Cotswold stone, the long, narrow, beamed dining room (named AD947: this is England's oldest inn) makes a fine setting for some grandiose cooking. The menu changes seasonally; to weightier winter starters, spring adds chargrilled squid with fondant tomatoes and wilted rocket, together with a Japanese seafood platter dressed in ginger and soy.

Much skill is discernible, though at times the lily may be gilded to the limit: pinkly cooked, thinly sliced venison fillet of prime quality, for example, is served on a bed of sauerkraut and bacon, with a pear sitting on a pastry case alongside it. Celeriac mash and a Madeira jus, however, make apposite partners for pot-roasted shank of lamb. Complexity continues into desserts, which might include chewy chocolate fondant with poached cherries and liquorice ice cream, or 'brambly' apple tart Tatin with ginger and honey ice. The wine list, striking a good balance between regions, offers some varied drinking under £20; six French house wines, filed towards the end, are £12.50.

CHEF: Alan Thompson PROPRIETORS: Alan and Georgina Thompson OPEN: Tue to Sun L 12 to 2.30, Tue to Sat D 7 to 9.30 MEALS: alc (main courses £13 to £17). Set L Wed to Sat £9.50 (2 courses) to £12.50 SERVICE: 10%, card slips closed CARDS: Amex, Delta, MasterCard, Switch, Visa DETAILS: 35 seats. Private parties: 16 main room. Car park. Vegetarian meals. Children's helpings. No children under 6. No smoking in dining room. Wheelchair access (also WC). No music ACCOMMODATION: 8 rooms, all with bath/shower. TV. Phone. B&B £52.50 to £170 (*The Which? Hotel Guide*) (£5)

STRATFORD-UPON-AVON Warwickshire map 5

Russons

NEW ENTRY

8 Church Street, Stratford-upon-Avon CV37 6HB
TEL: (01789) 268822

COOKING **2**
GLOBAL
£23–£42

This bistro's owners used to run a pub, which may account for the flexibility here. There is a full à la carte menu, but nobody minds if you order just bangers and mash, and early opening hours and 'fast, friendly' service please theatre-goers. Separate rooms for smokers and non-smokers are simply furnished, with flag flooring and dried hops on the ceiling beams. A list of daily fresh seafood items almost outnumbers the rest of the monthly-changing menu, and strong international influence shows in Thai curried king prawns, and Cajun salmon with lime and coriander salsa. Black pudding and bacon with mild English mustard sauce works extemely well, and a whole lemon sole, grilled with citrus and dill butter and dusted with paprika, constituted a 'perfect marriage' or one visitor. Finish with bread-and-butter pudding with vanilla custard sauce, or crème brûlée with fruits. Fairly priced wines start with house Chileans at £10.25.

CHEF: N. Garcia PROPRIETORS: Mr and Mrs Russon OPEN: Tue to Sat 11.30 to 1.45, 5.30 to 9.45 CLOSED: 1 week Christmas to New Year, 1 week Easter, 2 weeks end Aug MEALS: alc (main courses £7 to £15) SERVICE: not inc, card slips closed CARDS: Amex, MasterCard, Switch, Visa DETAILS: 50 seats. Private parties: 8 main room. Vegetarian meals. No children under 5 after 7.30. No smoking in 1 dining room. Music

indicates that smoking is either banned altogether or that a separate dining room (not just an area) is maintained for non-smokers.

STRETE Devon map 1

Laughing Monk

Totnes Road, Strete TQ6 0RN
TEL: (01803) 770639
5m S of Dartmouth, just off A379

COOKING **2**
MODERN EUROPEAN-PLUS
£22–£41

The atmosphere is welcoming at this converted school, where meals are hosted by the 'friendly and chatty' Trudy Rothwell, with husband David at the stove. Décor runs on unashamedly red lines, with walls, ceiling, napkins, seat cushioning and carpet all setting off the pine tables, chairs, settles and floor. The kitchen makes the best of local produce, with fish and shellfish from Brixham; scallops are given a dressing of coriander, chives and chilli and served on a bed of guacamole, while crab might appear as a soufflé with spring onions to start. Locally sourced meats might feature venison accompanied by thyme, port and roasted onions with celeriac mash. Vegetables arrive on tiered stands, while cholesterol-challenging desserts, from apricot and cream roulade to fruit-studded fudge cake, are paraded by trolley. The modest wine list offers a white from Devon's Sharpham Estate. Five house selections run from £9.45 to £11.45.

CHEF: David Rothwell PROPRIETORS: David and Trudy Rothwell OPEN: Sun L on last Sun of month 12 to 2, Tue to Sat D 7 to 9.30 MEALS: alc D (main courses £11 to £15). Set L £14.95 SERVICE: not inc, card slips closed CARDS: Diners, MasterCard, Switch, Visa DETAILS: 50 seats. Private parties: 60 main room, 30 private room. Car park. Children's helpings. No children under 7. No smoking in dining room. Wheelchair access (also women's WC). Occasional music

STUCKTON Hampshire map 2

▲ Three Lions

Stuckton SP6 2HF
TEL: (01425) 652489 FAX: (01425) 656144
EMAIL: the3lions@btinternet.com
½m SE of Fordingbridge, off A338 but not signposted from it: take the turn just S of Fordingbridge and follow a sign down a narrow country lane

COOKING **7**
ANGLO-FRENCH
£39–£58

Light, clean, airy, neat and tidy, this family-run restaurant 'makes you feel welcome and valued'. It is attractively decorated with pottery and brass ornaments, polished wooden tables and starched napkins, and staff deliver attentive and cheery service under the tutelage of Jane Womersley. Availability of produce determines the menu, which typically relies on fish from local day boats, fruit and vegetables from small local growers, and seasonal game supplemented by such things as locally gathered wild mushrooms.

Michael Womersley's transparently honest style of cooking is resourceful and imaginative without feeling the need to be wildly inventive, producing seafood highlights such as a splendid crab bisque, fresh, firm turbot, and a starter of four medium-sized, fresh-tasting scallops, each sliced in two and accurately griddled, with a Thai dressing. He deals even-handedly with mainstream meats, turning out tender loin of fatless lamb, paired with a mound of chopped leeks and diced bacon bound together with cream, and well-hung, tasty fillet steak served with two sauces: one of ground black pepper, one of creamed garlic. At the same time the menu invariably takes the opportunity to divert with an egg, bacon and cep salad, a main course of wild boar, or perhaps an offal first course such as rösti with chopped liver underneath, pink kidneys on top and a rich brown sauce around.

Vegetables (charged separately) might include creamy dauphinois potato, swede purée, and spring and red cabbages, while desserts run to lemon posset, and a hot chocolate pudding, crisp outside and with a dark gooey centre, served with vanilla ice cream and custard. The compact, predominantly French wine list is headed by a ten-strong house selection, from £12.75 to £19.50, which takes in increasingly popular styles from the Mediterranean, including a Corsican red. The rest of the list stays mainly above £20, but takes in a useful page of half-bottles.

CHEF: Michael Womersley PROPRIETORS: Mr and Mrs Michael Womersley OPEN: Tue to Sun L 12 to 2, Tue to Sat D 7 to 9.30 (10 Sat) CLOSED: last 2 weeks Jan, first week Feb MEALS: alc (main courses £13.50 to £17). Set L Tue to Fri £14.50 (2 courses) SERVICE: not inc CARDS: Delta, MasterCard, Switch, Visa DETAILS: 60 seats. 12 seats outside. Private parties: 70 main room, 30 private room. Car park. Vegetarian meals. Children's helpings. No smoking in dining room. Wheelchair access (not WC). No music ACCOMMODATION: 3 rooms, all with bath/shower. TV. B&B £59 to £85. Rooms for disabled (*The Which? Hotel Guide*) (£5)

STURMINSTER NEWTON Dorset map 2

▲ Plumber Manor

Sturminster Newton SP7 0QF
TEL: (01258) 472507 FAX: (01258) 473370
EMAIL: book@plumbermanor.com
A357 to Sturminster Newton, take first left to Hazelbury Bryan, on left-hand side after 2m

COOKING **2**
ANGLO-FRENCH
£28–£50

At the end of a chestnut-lined drive, the Manor is a solid, grey-stone pile, home of the Prideaux Brune family since it was built in the seventeenth century. Brian of that ilk cooks to a comfortably old-fangled Anglo-French formula, offering 'scallops Gauloise' (not tobacco-fumigated, but teamed with leek purée and basil), salmon and sole roulade sauced with champagne and saffron, and roast loin of venison served with red cabbage, a poached pear and a sauce of gin and juniper. Gargantuan portions of vegetables are perhaps more Anglo than French. The large selection from a dessert trolley usually includes the likes of chocolate truffle torte, lime and passion fruit mousse, and almond pavlova with black and green grapes in a welter of cream. Pleasant service 'takes care of you'. The largely French wine list open with Pays d'Oc varietals at £11.50.

CHEF: Brian Prideaux Brune PROPRIETOR: Richard Prideaux Brune OPEN: Sun 12.30 to 1.30, all week 7 to 9.30 MEALS: Set L £17.50, Set D £23 to £29 SERVICE: net prices, card slips closed CARDS: Amex, Diners, MasterCard, Switch, Visa DETAILS: 65 seats. Private parties: 45 main room, 14 to 65 private rooms. Car park. Vegetarian meals. Children's helpings. No smoking in dining room. Wheelchair access (also WC). No music ACCOMMODATION: 16 rooms, all with bath/shower. TV. Phone. B&B £80 to £155. Rooms for disabled. Baby facilities (*The Which? Hotel Guide*)

SUDBURY Suffolk map 6

Red Onion Bistro £

57 Ballingdon Street, Sudbury CO10 2DA
TEL: (01787) 376777 FAX: (01787) 883156

COOKING **1**
MODERN EUROPEAN
£16–£37

Informality and low prices are two of the primary attractions of this popular brasserie. Red-checked curtains and green-checked tablecloths give the dining room an old-fashioned French feel, while the cooking is modern and European, encompassing Cajun-crusted squid and avocado salad, roast chump of lamb on sweet potato champ with a chorizo jus, and chargrilled marinated chicken on fettucine with tomato and Parmesan sauce. That said, daily specials might be as down to earth and traditional as steak and Guinness pie. A short and fairly priced wine list opens with house vins de pays at £9 a bottle, £2 a glass.

CHEFS: Stuart Mott and Gary Farthing PROPRIETOR: Red Onion Bistro Ltd OPEN: all week L 12 to 2, Mon to Sat D 6.30 to 9.30 MEALS: alc (main courses £7 to £11). Set L Mon to Sat £7.50 (2 courses) to £9.50, Set L Sun £12.75, Set D £9.50 (2 courses) to £12 SERVICE: not inc, card slips closed CARDS: Amex, Delta, MasterCard, Switch, Visa DETAILS: 65 seats. 25 seats outside. Private parties: 60 main room, 10 private room. Car park. Vegetarian meals. Wheelchair access (not WC). No music (£5)

SUTTON GAULT Cambridgeshire map 6

▲ Anchor Inn

Sutton Gault CB6 2BD
TEL: (01353) 778537 FAX: (01353) 776180
EMAIL: anchorinnSG@aol.com
WEB SITE: www.anchor-inn-restaurant.co.uk
off B1381 Sutton to Earith road, just S of Sutton, 6m W of Ely

COOKING **2**
MODERN BRITISH
£27–£47

Surrounded by fens, this modest-looking whitewashed inn was built around 1650 to accommodate the men who dug the local swamp-draining rivers: old oak ceiling beams and a large black stove give it a convincingly old world look. Martin Russell, who has cooked at the Old Bridge Hotel in Huntingdon (see entry), brings a lively approach to the food, offering up roast spicy chump of lamb with couscous and minted yoghurt salad, and wild boar and apple sausages with green beans and onion gravy. A high comfort rating is apparent in poached smoked haddock with spinach, poached egg and mustard sauce, and interesting vegetarian options might include beetroot risotto with herb fromage frais. Desserts are a strong point, featuring old favourites of bread-and-butter pudding alongside Arabian orange cake with chocolate ice cream. Service is informal, relaxed and friendly. Wines on the varied and fairly priced list are helpfully classified according to weight (reds) and dryness (whites).

CHEF: Martin Russell PROPRIETORS: Robin and Heather Moore OPEN: all week 12 to 2, 7 to 9 (6.30 to 9.30 Sat) CLOSED: 26 Dec MEALS: alc (main courses £10 to £15). Set L Mon to Fri £7.95 (2 courses), Set L Sun £16.50 SERVICE: not inc CARDS: Amex, Delta, MasterCard, Switch, Visa

DETAILS: 70 seats. 30 seats outside. Private parties: 30 main room. Car park. Vegetarian meals. Children's helpings. No smoking in dining room. Wheelchair access (also WC). No music ACCOMMODATION: 2 rooms, both with bath/shower. TV. Phone. B&B £50 to £95 (£5)

SUTTON-ON-THE-FOREST North Yorkshire **map 9**

Rose & Crown

NEW ENTRY

Main Street, Sutton-on-the-Forest YO61 1DP
TEL: (01347) 811333 FAX: (01347) 811444
EMAIL: reserve@rosecrown.co.uk
WEB SITE: www.rosecrown.co.uk
on B1363, 8m N of York

COOKING **6**
MODERN BRITISH
£25–£53

The old pub has been tastefully converted, its beams, wooden floors and fireplaces chiming well with the pastel colours, candles, and starched linen that give it its classy feel. So thorough has been the transformation that it now feels like a plush modern restaurant, helped by uniformly clad staff who are both friendly and professional, and of course by Stephen Harper, who has previously worked at the Chester Grosvenor (see entry). A blackboard of daily dishes (including fish) supplements the printed menus, whose modest descriptions belie the skills involved: salmon and king prawn ravioli, for example, expertly made with fine pasta, the purée filling both fresh and richly flavoured, accompanied by stir-fried tiger prawns and julienne vegetables.

The straightforwardness of the cooking, which makes the most of flavours and textures, stems from its confidence, evident in well-trimmed, tender rump of Dales lamb served with provençale potatoes and two sets of contrasting, wilted green leaves – spinach and aromatic basil – and nothing more than an olive oil 'jus' to moisten the dish. The style, meanwhile, hops nimbly from a Chinese-style sweet chilli duck leg to braised lamb shank, while desserts have included a twice-baked apricot and pistachio soufflé, and hot orange sponge with lemon ice cream and a bitter caramel sauce. Anyone counting the pennies might consider the set-price 'Hobson's Choice' dinner option. The half-dozen house wines at £10.95 presage a sympathetically priced, 50-strong, round-the-world collection.

CHEF: Stephen Harper PROPRIETOR: Ralph Magee OPEN: Wed to Sun L 11.45 to 2 (4 Sun), Wed to Sat D 6.30 to 9 CLOSED: first 3 weeks Jan MEALS: alc (main courses £10 to £18). Set L Wed to Sat £9.50 (1 course) to £15.50, Set L Sun £12.50 (2 courses) to £15.95, Set D £21.50. Sandwich menu available L SERVICE: not inc CARDS: MasterCard, Switch, Visa DETAILS: 50 seats. 12 seats outside. Private parties: 50 main room. Car park. Vegetarian meals. Children's helpings. No smoking in dining room. Wheelchair access (also WC). Music (£5)

The Guide relies on feedback from its readers. Especially welcome are reports on new restaurants appearing in the book for the first time. All letters to the Guide are acknowledged.

The Good Food Guide *is a registered trade mark of Which? Ltd.*

SWAFFHAM Norfolk **map 6**

▲ Strattons

4 Ash Close, Swaffham PE37 7NH
TEL: (01760) 723845 FAX: (01760) 720458
EMAIL: strattonshotel@btinternet.com
WEB SITE: www.strattons-hotel.co.uk

COOKING **4**
MODERN EUROPEAN
£43–£51

Well hidden down an alleyway off Swaffham's marketplace, Strattons is a rambling old house set in lovely tranquil gardens. Environmental awareness is acute here: waste is recycled; most produce is locally sourced, and much is organic. After drinks upstairs in a lounge with baroque flourishes, diners are led to the ground-floor restaurant, where grey-green-panelled walls and garden views encourage a feeling of serenity. Vanessa Scott's set-price, daily-changing menu is concise – only three main courses – but highly enticing. Among top-quality ingredients have been cod, intelligently paired with a risotto and gravy, both made from earthy wild mushrooms, and impressively roast loin of Duroc pork, served with rosemary-crushed potatoes, sprouting broccoli, sun-dried tomato and sweet red cabbage.

First courses have included an 'appetising, if unnervingly hearty' soup of lamb flavoured with lemon and tarragon, and the well-kept cheeseboard might include a Brie-like Norfolk White Lady made from sheep's milk. Tradition is given a tweak for dessert: rhubarb bread-and-butter pudding, for instance. Les Scott runs front-of-house with infectious enthusiasm, although service can get overstretched at busy times. The lengthily annotated wine list features a wide choice, ordered by style, with bottles from £10.50 (red) and £8.50 (white).

CHEFS: Vanessa Scott and Margaret Cooper PROPRIETORS: Les and Vanessa Scott OPEN: all week D only 7 to 9 (7 Sun) CLOSED: Christmas MEALS: Set D £32 SERVICE: not inc, card slips closed CARDS: Amex, Delta, MasterCard, Switch, Visa DETAILS: 20 seats. Private parties: 12 main room. Car park. Vegetarian meals. Children's helpings. No smoking in dining room. Occasional music ACCOMMODATION: 6 rooms, all with bath/shower. TV. Phone. B&B £80 to £160. Baby facilities (*The Which? Hotel Guide*)

TADCASTER North Yorkshire **map 9**

Singers

16 Westgate, Tadcaster LS24 9AB
TEL: (01937) 835121
WEB SITE: www.singersrestaurant.co.uk

COOKING **2**
MODERN EUROPEAN
£19–£34

Singers is a warm, friendly, informal local, with plenty of smiles and a lively buzz of conversation providing the backing track to its musical theme. Song sheet-covered walls and a musical-styled wine list (soprano whites, tenor or baritone reds) develop the motif, though wooden tables are tiny and tightly packed and the décor looks a shade tired. The menu runs on modern lines with forays towards the Mediterranean: tarte Tatin of red onions and tomato drizzled with olive oil, or a salad of goats' cheese and beetroot with balsamic vinegar to start, followed perhaps by a successful roast chump of lamb with mustard mash, roast garlic and thyme gravy. Desserts have a familiar ring, among them perhaps sticky toffee pudding with butterscotch sauce, or apple and raisin crumble with vanilla ice cream. During the week there's a good-value early-evening menu, while the compact wine list offers house French at £9.95 (£2 a glass).

CHEFS: David Lockwood and Jonathan Wilson PROPRIETORS: Philip Taylor and Guy Vicari OPEN: Tue to Sat D only 6 to 9.30 CLOSED: 1 week Feb, 1 week Aug MEALS: Set D Tue to Fri 6 to 7 £11.95, Set D Tue to Thur £9.95 (1 course) to £17.95, Set D Fri and Sat £17.95 SERVICE: not inc, card slips closed CARDS: Delta, MasterCard, Switch, Visa DETAILS: 38 seats. Private parties: 38 main room. Vegetarian meals. No smoking in dining room. Wheelchair access (not WC). Music

TADWORTH Surrey map 3

Gemini

28 Station Approach, Tadworth KT20 5AH
TEL/FAX: (01737) 812179

COOKING **3**
FRENCH/MODERN EUROPEAN
£25–£53

Refurbishment of the dining room over the past year followed redecoration of the bar, so an equal stylishness now prevails throughout and the dining chairs are a little comfier these days than veterans may remember. Robert Foster still cooks in bright southern European mode, with assorted fish and shellfish appearing on open ravioli with asparagus and creamed leeks, while buffalo mozzarella is wrapped in Parma ham and served with a spiced tomato relish.

That star turn of Yorkshire fish, Whitby cod, appears on a bed of crushed cannellini beans with mussels and Taleggio, but there are oriental influences too, as in breast of Gressingham duck with pak choi, and sticky belly pork in a sauce of lentils and coriander. Pink fruit jelly with a contrasting sorbet of blue Curaçao is a visually ostentatious way to conclude, and the ubiquitous spiced poached pear comes with creamed Roquefort. Service is friendly and helpful, and the wine list offers a whirlwind tour of the vinous globe at mostly manageable prices. Eight house wines span a range from £10.95 to £12.95.

CHEF/PROPRIETOR: Robert Foster OPEN: Tue to Fri and Sun L 12 to 2.30, Tue to Sat D 7 to 9.30 CLOSED: 2 weeks Christmas MEALS: alc Tue to Fri L and D (main courses £14 to £16.50). Set L Sun £9.50 (1 course) to £15.50, Set D Sat £29.50 SERVICE: not inc CARDS: Amex, Delta, Diners, MasterCard, Switch, Visa DETAILS: 50 seats. 15 seats outside. Private parties: 50 main room. Children's helpings. No children under 12 at D. No smoking in dining room. Wheelchair access (not WC). Music (£5)

TAPLOW Berkshire map 3

▲ Cliveden, Waldo's

Taplow SL6 0JF
TEL: (01628) 668561 FAX: (01628) 661837
EMAIL: reservations@clivedenhouse.co.uk
WEB SITE: www.clivedenhouse.co.uk
off A4, 2m N of Taplow on Cliveden road

NEW CHEF
MODERN EUROPEAN
£78–£127

Country houses don't come much grander than this National Trust property, with its formal gardens, wooded grounds dropping down to the Thames, and much carved wood and stone inside. Last year's chef John Wood departed for Dubai, and Peter Mark Dodson was due to take over the kitchen in October

2001. For the past dozen years he has been head chef at the Waterside Inn (see entry, Bray), practising a refined version of French haute cuisine. No menus were available as the Guide went to press, but his track record suggests that, whatever he cooks, Waldo's will be well worth a visit. Reports please.

CHEF: Peter Mark Dodson PROPRIETOR: Destination Hotels and Resorts OPEN: Tue to Sat D only 7 to 9.30 CLOSED: Christmas MEALS: Set D £58 to £84. Cover £3 SERVICE: not inc CARDS: Amex, Delta, Diners, MasterCard, Switch, Visa DETAILS: 95 seats. Private parties: 60 main room, 14 to 60 private rooms. Car park. No children under 12. Jacket and tie. No smoking in dining room. Wheelchair access (also women's WC). No music. Air-conditioned ACCOMMODATION: 39 rooms, all with bath/shower. TV. Phone. Room only £305 to £460. Rooms for disabled. Baby facilities. Swimming pool

TAUNTON Somerset **map 2**

Brazz

Castle Bow, Taunton TA1 1NF
TEL: (01823) 252000 FAX: (01823) 336066
EMAIL: reception@the-castle-hotel.com
from M5, follow directions for town centre and Castle Museum/Hotel

COOKING **2**
MODERN BRITISH
£25–£52

Colourful and classy, the original Brazz (another is in Exeter – see entry – and there are plans for more) delights the eye with its fibre-optic dome and tank of silver dollar fish, and offers simple, good-value sustenance. It hits the vernacular with enthusiasm, happy to serve prawn cocktail, burger and chips, Caesar salad, and fish and chips with tartare sauce: lack of highfalutin ambition saves Brazz from becoming too serious. The food is generally successful, but this branch seems to lack its own chef (Richard Guest is head chef at Castle Hotel, see entry below), which may explain the variability. And, regulars say, service can let the side down. Informality and willingness to please show in pasta and salads offered in small or large portions, comforting puddings (such as rhubarb Bakewell tart with proper custard) and a fairly priced wine list starting with ten by the glass.

CHEF: Richard Guest PROPRIETORS: the Chapman family OPEN: all week 11.30 to 3, 6.30 to 10.30 (11 Fri and Sat) MEALS: alc (main courses £7 to £15) SERVICE: 10% (optional), card slips closed CARDS: Amex, Delta, Diners, MasterCard, Switch, Visa DETAILS: 100 seats. Private parties: 50 main room. Car park. Vegetarian meals. Children's helpings. Wheelchair access (also WC). Music. Air-conditioned

▲ Castle Hotel

Castle Green, Taunton TA1 1NF
TEL: (01823) 272671 FAX: (01823) 336066
EMAIL: reception@the-castle-hotel.com
WEB SITE: www.the-castle-hotel.com

COOKING **6**
MODERN BRITISH
£32–£76

The Castle cocoons with its ancient stones, bricks and timber, and although the dining room hardly sets the pulse racing (all the design energy seems to have gone into Brazz; see entry above), a few fabrics and tapestries lend richness and style to the public rooms. While the menu embodies something of Kit

Chapman's eternal quest for modern British food – potted head cheese with creamed horseradish and capers, for example – it also covers other bases in the shape of duck liver Chantilly with Muscatel and vanilla reduction.

One example of sound British cooking successfully combines two old-fashioned elements – a steamed suet pudding filled with well-cooked mutton – while elsewhere the style runs from a homely leek and potato broth supporting a couple of fillets of John Dory, to an accomplished pyramid of clear, jellied tomato consommé on a base of white crabmeat. In general, flavours might be bolder, and greater accuracy and attention to detail would help, but the kitchen can turn on the gutsy charm with, for example, a first-class dark, sticky, deep-flavoured pig's trotter, stuffed with pork belly and apricots, in a lake of intensely reduced sauce.

Rhubarb and custard sounds an ordinary enough finish, but this novel version comes as a cold rhubarb jelly on a crumbly biscuit, surmounted by vanilla-speckled cream, and decked with thin brittle strands of semi-dried rhubarb. Service, mostly male and French, seems less sharp than in previous years, though the wine list has a user-friendly feel, with nine house recommendations that will suit most tastes, starting at £15.50. Prices can be high, reflecting the surroundings, but value is found in most regional groupings and styles.

CHEF: Richard Guest PROPRIETORS: the Chapman family OPEN: all week 12.30 to 2, 7 to 9.30 MEALS: Set L £14.95 (2 courses) to £17.95, Set D £24.95 (2 courses) to £31 SERVICE: 10% (optional), card slips closed CARDS: Amex, Delta, Diners, MasterCard, Switch, Visa DETAILS: 65 seats. Private parties: 90 main room, 8 to 90 private rooms. Car park. Vegetarian meals. Children's helpings. No smoking in dining room. Wheelchair access (not WC). No music ACCOMMODATION: 44 rooms, all with bath/shower. TV. Phone. B&B £98 to £240. Rooms for disabled. Baby facilities

TAVISTOCK Devon map 1

▲ Horn of Plenty

Gulworthy, Tavistock PL19 8JD
TEL/FAX: (01822) 832528
EMAIL: enquiries@thehornofplenty.co.uk
WEB SITE: www.thehornofplenty.co.uk
3m W of Tavistock on A390, turn right at Gulworthy Cross

COOKING 6
GLOBAL
£28–£64

Under the same ownership as Carved Angel (see entry, Dartmouth) and overlooking the wooded Tamar Valley, the creeper-covered house has a fountain out front, modest dimensions, and a soothing, tranquil yet well-kept feel. It also has a conservatory dining room bolted on to the side, and a menu that is equally at home with tempura fish, spicy Thai dressings, herby polenta, and foie gras on a potato and parsnip pancake served with fresh figs. Ideas are carefully considered and skilfully handled, as for example in a starter of scallops, thinly wrapped not in bacon but in more appropriate smoked salmon, seared on their ends, perfectly timed, with a chive and saffron sauce.

Peter Gorton's menus take a loosely seasonal approach; partridge in October is fine (two boneless breasts and two legs in a black pepper sauce), although asparagus among the vegetables on the same plate seemed rather out of synch. Lamb is well received (perhaps roast loin glazed with an orange and mint syrup), and desserts run to glazed lemon tart, and chocolate raviolis with pistachio ice cream. The pace of service continues to be leisurely (an hour between arriving and ordering for one couple) although it has been 'exemplary' for another. Wines tend to be chosen for their prestige, and prices are not helpful (Cloudy Bay Chardonnay at nearly £50 is nothing short of greedy), but there are plenty of good bottles on offer. Ten house wines start at £14.

CHEF: Peter Gorton PROPRIETORS: Paul and Andie Roston, and Peter Gorton OPEN: Tue to Sun L 12 to 2, all week D 7 to 9 CLOSED: 24 and 25 Dec MEALS: Set L £18.50 to £23.50, Set D £40 SERVICE: not inc CARDS: Amex, Delta, MasterCard, Switch, Visa DETAILS: 60 seats. 12 seats outside. Private parties: 60 main room, 16 private room. Car park. Vegetarian meals. Children's helpings. No children under 10 at D. No smoking in dining room. Wheelchair access (also WC). Music ACCOMMODATION: 10 rooms, all with bath/shower. TV. Phone. B&B £85 to £200. Rooms for disabled. Baby facilities (*The Which? Hotel Guide*)

TEFFONT EVIAS Wiltshire **map 2**

▲ Howard's House

Teffont Evias SP3 5RJ
TEL: (01722) 716392 FAX: (01722) 716820
EMAIL: enq@howardshousehotel.com
WEB SITE: www.howardshousehotel.com
off B3089, W of Dinton and 9½m W of Salisbury, signposted Chicksgrove

COOKING **5**
MODERN BRITISH-PLUS
£26–£56

In a quintessential English village setting, this 'Homes and Gardens'-style seventeenth-century dower house is surrounded by box hedges, lawns and cottage flowers. Warm yellows and bold fabrics in the sitting room give way to a blue carpet and white tablecloths in the small, oblong dining room, where service is friendly, welcoming and well-informed. It all makes a tranquil, idyllic and perhaps unlikely backdrop to Paul Firmin and Boyd Mackintosh's sophisticated and adventurous cuisine. Their busy modern style shows in starters of seared scallops with spicy rocket salad, lemon-grass couscous and fresh basil oil, and in grilled goats' cheese with caramelised apples, fresh figs and garlic croûtons in a walnut and balsamic dressing.

Freshness and quality of raw materials are keynotes, and clear flavours point to their skilful handling: black olive mash, fennel confit and a watercress sauce might accompany pan-fried fillet of cod, and char-seared loin of venison has been partnered by braised Savoy cabbage and a rosemary and redcurrant glaze. Hot pistachio soufflé with milk chocolate sauce and praline ice cream might be among desserts. Canapés, bread, petits fours and a well-priced table d'hôte all appeal, and the French-slanted wine list offers fine support; it is strong in Burgundy and Bordeaux, and includes a good selection of halves and six house wines from £9.95 to £13.50.

CHEFS: Paul Firmin and Boyd Mackintosh PROPRIETOR: Paul Firmin OPEN: Sun L 12.30 to 1.45, all week D 7.30 to 9 CLOSED: 24 to 27 Dec MEALS: alc D (main courses £14 to £19). Set L £18.50, Set D £19.95 SERVICE: not inc, card slips closed CARDS: Amex, Diners, MasterCard, Switch, Visa DETAILS: 30 seats. Private parties: 38 main room. Car park. Vegetarian meals. Children's helpings. No smoking in dining room. Wheelchair access (not WC). Occasional music ACCOMMODATION: 9 rooms, all with bath/shower. TV. Phone. B&B £85 to £155. Baby facilities (*The Which? Hotel Guide*)

TETBURY Gloucestershire map 2

GLOUCESTERSHIRE NEWCOMER OF THE YEAR

Trouble House

NEW ENTRY

Cirencester Road, Tetbury GL8 8SG
TEL: (01666) 502206 FAX: (01666) 504508

COOKING **5**
MODERN BRITISH
£25–£43

After the last edition of the Guide appeared, Michael Bedford left the bright lights and big brigade of City Rhodes (see entry, London) for the charms of rural Gloucestershire. He and wife Sarah took over a rustic, stone-built, white-painted Wadworth's pub, where a low-ceilinged bar and a couple of small dining rooms contribute to the Hardyesque village atmosphere. There is nothing city slick about the menus or food either. Everything is utterly simple, ideas are good, materials impeccable, and techniques sound: indeed, one jaded inspector's faith in humanity was restored by a pale slab of warm smoked haddock sitting on a bed of cold asparagus (both wild and cultivated) and green beans, all fresh, al dente and lightly dressed in mayonnaise.

The lack of garnish, coupled with 'perfect combinations, perfectly executed', is indicative of the refreshingly simple and direct style of cooking: for example, in a successful partnership of thinly sliced duck breast and a small locally made merguez sausage, served on a loose bed of haricot beans and lentils drifting in a silky, deep-flavoured stock-based sauce. Desserts are no less enjoyable, judging by a fresh, fragrant and creamy cone of nougat glacé, thickly studded with praline, topped with ribbon-like pineapple rings and surrounded by deep-red strawberries in an unsweet red wine sauce. It all smacks of a decent and honest operation, with service overseen by Sarah Bedford: a service charge is not included, but then you are exhorted to order at the bar anyway. A short, sensibly priced wine list starts with six house wines (from France, Chile and Australia) under £10.

CHEF: Michael Bedford PROPRIETORS: Michael and Sarah Bedford OPEN: Tue to Sun 12 to 2, 7 to 9.30 CLOSED: 25 Dec MEALS: alc (main courses £8 to £16) SERVICE: not inc CARDS: Amex, Delta, MasterCard, Switch, Visa DETAILS: 60 seats. 30 seats outside. Private parties: 20 main room. Car park. Vegetarian meals. Children's helpings. No smoking in 1 dining room. Wheelchair access (not WC). Music

TETSWORTH Oxfordshire map 2

Swan at Tetsworth

NEW ENTRY

High Street, Tetsworth OX9 7AB
TEL: (01844) 281182 FAX: (01844) 281770
EMAIL: restaurant@theswan.co.uk
WEB SITE: www.theswan.co.uk

COOKING **4**
MODERN EUROPEAN
£28–£50

The antiques trade may take up most of the Swan's capacious interior – over 80 dealers display stock in this ancient former inn – but the restaurant, occupying a ground-floor wing, deserves its own acclaim. Creaking oak floorboards, enormous fireplaces and old beams attest to the age of the dining room. The food, however, is anything but staid, and features strikingly good raw materials. The menu encompasses modern assemblies – of grilled goats' cheese, pak choi and mango salsa perhaps – before caramelised guinea fowl with orange and celeriac. Roasted sea bass with sauce vierge might be among the daily fish specials.

One meal began with a starter-sized portion of a main course – faultless seared scallops with pea purée and smoked bacon – followed by rump of lamb with thyme, peppers and courgettes, notable also for the quality of its accompanying rösti and lightly grilled vegetables. Dinner might conclude with a pannacotta and raspberry coulis 'bursting with flavour'. Service (headed by an enthusiastic, considerate manageress) is another highlight, although 'frightful' Muzak can be a drawback to some. The wine list, divided by style and concisely annotated, contains several New World options. House wines are £11.95.

CHEF: Naseem Salam PROPRIETOR: Swan Holdings Ltd OPEN: all week L 12 to 2.15 (3.30 Sun), Tue to Sat D 7 to 9.15 (9.45 Sat) CLOSED: 25 and 26 Dec MEALS: alc (main courses £9.50 to £16.50) SERVICE: not inc, 10% for parties of 10 or more CARDS: Delta, MasterCard, Switch, Visa DETAILS: 55 seats. 20 seats outside. Private parties: 55 main room, 14 private room. Car park. Vegetarian meals. Children's helpings. No-smoking area. No cigars/pipes in dining area. Wheelchair access (also WC). Music (£5)

THAME Oxfordshire **map 2**

▲ Old Trout

29–30 Lower High Street, Thame OX9 2AA
TEL: (01844) 212146 FAX: (01844) 212614 COOKING **2**
EMAIL: mj4trout@aol.com MODERN EUROPEAN
WEB SITE: www.theoldtrouthotel.co.uk £24–£58

The door from the street leads straight into the dining-room of this endearing restaurant-with-rooms (cobbled together from sixteenth-century cottages) which has low ceilings and flagged floors. A seafood skewer on crab risotto makes a generous starter (the single scallop winning praise), and there may be a pasta dish that can be a first or main course, such as linguini with prawns, chorizo and tomato. Most mains will suit hearty appetites: blackened swordfish with jambalaya, or accurately timed peppered ribeye steak, for example. Extra charges for vegetables are an annoyance, but the generosity and richness of desserts such as raspberry parfait with shortcakes and a matching candy-floss-light sorbet go some way to compensate. Unassuming service gets the job done. An extensive list of high-quality bottles, grouped by style, opens with house wines at £13.50.

CHEFS: Mark Jones and Ben Clarke PROPRIETORS: Mr and Mrs M.E. Jones OPEN: Mon to Sat 12 to 2.30, 6.30 to 10 CLOSED: 2 weeks from 25 Dec MEALS: alc (main courses £10.50 to £20). Set L £12.50 SERVICE: not inc, card slips closed CARDS: Delta, Diners, MasterCard, Switch, Visa DETAILS: 70 seats. 30 seats outside. Private parties: 30 main room, 16 and 30 private rooms. Car park. Vegetarian meals. No smoking in 1 dining room. Music ACCOMMODATION: 7 rooms, all with bath/shower. TV. Phone. B&B £60 to £85 (£5)

'For an establishment that staunchly resists children below twelve, it was odd to be greeted on arrival by a waiter who looked about ten or eleven.' (On eating in Yorkshire)

TITLEY Herefordshire map 5

▲ Stagg Inn

Titley HR5 3RL
TEL: (01544) 230221 FAX: (01544) 231390
EMAIL: reservations@thestagg.co.uk
WEB SITE: www.thestagg.co.uk
on B4355 between Kington and Presteigne

COOKING **5**
MODERN BRITISH
£25–£45

The Stagg doubles comfortably as both a restaurant and a country inn, complete with real fires and antique furniture. Wooden tables in the bar sit beneath a collection of jugs dangling from the beams, and the dining room is hardly much grander. Blackboards list regular and special dishes, based on free-range poultry (perhaps duck breast with a sweet-sour rhubarb sauce), organic pork (with a bacon and sherry vinaigrette), and Herefordshire beef (with celeriac purée and red wine sauce). The food is praised for its 'dead simple presentation', evident in seared scallops, sometimes served with creamed leeks, sometimes with buttery Swiss chard and strong black pepper oil, and in a rack of young, pink, soft-textured local lamb served with fennel and garlic purée and a trickle of red wine sauce. Vegetables come in traditional style – lots of them in a separate dish – notable among which have been swede purée and red cabbage.

Steve Reynolds's classical background (he has worked at Le Gavroche; see entry, London) underpins the style, not least among desserts, from creamed rice pudding with cinnamon ice cream, to the top-class vanilla custard surrounding one visitor's trio of ice creams: honey and whisky, caramel, and prune and armagnac. Regional cheeses are unpasteurised, bread is praised, and an enterprising and fairly priced wine list takes in a Reichensteiner from nearby Bodenham, and eight colourful house wines in a wide range of styles all impressively under £10.

CHEF: Steve Reynolds PROPRIETORS: Steve Reynolds and Nicola Holland OPEN: Tue to Sun 12 to 2, 6.30 to 10 (7 to 9 Sun) CLOSED: first 2 weeks Nov MEALS: alc exc Sun L (main courses £9.50 to £16). Set L Sun £11.50. Bar menu available SERVICE: not inc, card slips closed CARDS: Delta, MasterCard, Switch, Visa DETAILS: 70 seats. 20 seats outside. Private parties: 32 main room, 16 to 32 private rooms. Car park. Vegetarian meals. Children's helpings. No smoking in dining room. No music ACCOMMODATION: 2 rooms, both with bath/shower. TV. B&B £30 to £70

TODMORDEN West Yorkshire map 8

Old Hall

Hall Street, Todmorden OL14 7AD
TEL: (01706) 815998 FAX: (01706) 810669

COOKING **2**
MODERN EUROPEAN
£19–£48

Although parts of the stone-built Grade II listed building date back to 1294, most of it is Elizabethan and – given the dark wooden panelling and stone fireplace with its elaborately carved wooden surround – feels like it. The menu reassures with some familiar ideas: from salmon and crab fishcakes with hollandaise, via slow-roast shank of lamb, to roast guinea fowl with smoked bacon and Savoy cabbage. At the same time it generates interest with starters of goats' cheese and potato tart, and a lively-sounding salad of black pudding with chorizo and poached egg served with a roast nectarine and red onion chutney. A straightforward line in desserts, meanwhile, has produced a winter berry pavlova, and tarts of lemon or hot apple. The two-course lunch sounds a bargain, although it has not always been up to scratch. A short wine list commendably stays mostly under £20, starting at £9.95 for South African Chenin Blanc.

CHEF: Chris Roberts PROPRIETORS: Nick and Madeleine Hoyle OPEN: Tue to Sun L 12 to 2 (2.30 Sun), Tue to Sat D 7 to 9.30 CLOSED: 25 and 26 Dec, first week Jan MEALS: alc (main courses £9 to £16). Set L Tue to Sat £7.50 (2 courses), Set L Sun £10.95 (2 courses) to £13.95 SERVICE: not inc CARDS: Delta, Diners, MasterCard, Switch, Visa DETAILS: 70 seats. 30 seats outside. Private parties: 26 main room, 18 to 26 private rooms. Vegetarian meals. Children's helpings. No smoking in dining room. Music

TORQUAY Devon map 1

No 7 Fish Bistro

NEW ENTRY

Beacon Terrace, Inner Harbour,
Torquay TQ1 2BH
TEL/FAX: (01803) 295055

COOKING **1**
FISH
£25–£48

This small family-run bistro just up from the harbour is awash with the fruits of the sea. Cream walls are decorated with fishy plaques, prints and posters, while tables, with attractive navy and cream thick plastic covers, are set on polished-wood floors. It's all very homely, unpretentious and honest, just like the cooking. Fish and shellfish from local boats and markets are simply roasted or grilled, with timing accurately judged; Brixham plaice, Star Point crab, lobster from local pots, or Dover sole. Blackboard specials add to the haul: perhaps fillets of cod and plaice tempura, monkfish baked with black pepper and sea salt, shellfish platters, or John Dory, red mullet and lemon sole. Puddings play second fiddle but might include apple tart, perhaps flamed with calvados, or raspberry crème brûlée. Service is efficient and pleasant, while the compact wine list offers fish-friendly drinking with plenty of bottles under £20. House wines start at £10.

CHEFS: G.J., J.I. and O.J. Stacey PROPRIETORS: G.J. and J.I. Stacey OPEN: Wed to Sat L 12.45 to 1.45, all week D 6 to 10.15 (7 to 9.45 winter) CLOSED: Sun and Mon D winter, first week Nov, Christmas and New Year, 2 weeks Feb MEALS: alc (main courses £10 to £17) SERVICE: not inc CARDS: Amex, MasterCard, Switch, Visa DETAILS: 38 seats. Private parties: 20 main room. Vegetarian meals. Children's helpings. Music. Air-conditioned (£5)

TUNBRIDGE WELLS Kent map 3

▲ Hotel du Vin & Bistro

Crescent Road, Tunbridge Wells TN1 2LY
TEL: (01892) 526455 FAX: (01892) 512044
EMAIL: reservations@tunbridgewells.hotelduvin.com
WEB SITE: www.hotelduvin.com

COOKING **4**
BISTRO
£34–£54

Comfort is the watchword here. As at siblings in Winchester and Bristol (see entries), everything is geared to enjoying life's finer things, especially wine. The walls of the bare-boarded dining room are covered with oenophilia (from cartoons to case ends), and the encyclopaedic wine list seemingly spans the viticultural world (Canada, Israel and Thailand included). France is well represented, including its better-value southern fringes, and house Merlot and Chardonnay at £11.50, set the tone of a moderate pricing policy.

Graham Ball took over the kitchen in late 2000, and his refined, modern bistro-style cooking ranges wide. Starters take in delicate, creamy Cullen skink, and a contemporary rare-grilled tuna on a lively salsa of tomato, mint and chilli. Among main courses, roast fillet of cod has impressed with its timing and accompanying wild mushroom lasagne and rich red-wine sauce, while tender calf's liver layered with a fine onion tart pleased another reporter. Portions can overwhelm, though (the liver was enough for two), and Sunday lunch may not catch the restaurant at its best. Pleasing desserts include a wobbly, vanilla-flecked pannacotta, served with a generous helping of raspberries in a syrupy jus. Waiting staff are polite, efficient, professional and 'obviously well trained'.

CHEF: Graham Ball PROPRIETOR: Hotel du Vin Ltd OPEN: all week 12 (12.30 Sun) to 1.45 (2 Sun), 7 to 9.45 MEALS: alc (main courses £10 to £15) SERVICE: not inc CARDS: Amex, Delta, Diners, MasterCard, Switch, Visa DETAILS: 80 seats. 30 seats outside. Private parties: 75 main room, 14 private room. Car park. Vegetarian meals. Children's helpings. No cigars/pipes in dining room. Wheelchair access (also WC). No music ACCOMMODATION: 32 rooms, all with bath/shower. TV. Phone. Room only £80 to £145. Baby facilities (*The Which? Hotel Guide*)

TWICKENHAM Greater London map 3

McClements

2 Whitton Road, Twickenham TW1 1BJ COOKING **6**
TEL: (020) 8744 9610 FAX: (020) 8744 9598 FRENCH
EMAIL: johnmac21.aol.com £31–£51

This neighbourhood venue gives diners the impression of attending an extremely civilised dinner party. In spring 2001 it had a make-over of the interior and a few tweaks to the menu. Gutsier ingredients, such as the offal for which John McClements is known, remain in the repertoire, which now offers more fish and some lighter sauces. 'The food is complex, and the restaurant favours elongated crockery which allows the different elements to sit a comfortable distance from each other,' wrote a reporter; a starter of foie gras, guinea fowl terrine, rabbit and ham gelée, pork rillettes and stuffed pig's trotter 'seemed like an object lesson in the different and inventive ways in which meat can be extracted, stuffed, pressed and moulded.'

Curiosity led an inspector to order the veal chop in coffee-flavoured jus, which proved to be a confident, subtle creation. Other dishes might include a starter of caramelised scallops with pea purée and pancetta-infused sauce, or a main course of pot-roast sucking pig with fondant potato and cauliflower cream. Desserts might turn up the likes of baked lime and rhubarb mousse with strawberry sorbet, or almond and amaretti tart with pistachio ice cream. France accounts for more than half the solid wine list, which starts at £12.75. As the Guide went to press, building work was under way to move McClements' sister restaurant, TW1, to 6 Whitton Road, two doors away from McClements.

CHEFS: John McClements and Carlos Mosca PROPRIETOR: John McClements OPEN: all week L 12 to 2.30, Mon to Sat D 6.30 to 11 MEALS: Set L £18 (2 courses) to £20, Set D £25 (2 courses) to £30 SERVICE: 10% (optional), card slips closed CARDS: Amex, Delta, MasterCard, Switch, Visa DETAILS: 40 seats. Private parties: 40 main room, 20, 80 private rooms. Car park. Vegetarian meals. Children's helpings. No smoking in 1 dining room. Wheelchair access (also WC) (£5)

ULLSWATER Cumbria map 10

▲ Sharrow Bay

Lake Ullswater CA10 2LZ
TEL: (01768) 486301 FAX: (01768) 486349
EMAIL: enquiries@sharrow-bay.com
WEB SITE: www.sharrow-bay.com COOKING **7**
2m from Pooley Bridge on E side of lake, on road signposted Howtown and Martindale ENGLISH £44–£66

The setting wows visitors with views across the lake to towering mountains 'so picturesque it's almost unreal'. Equally unchanging baroque décor takes in antique ornaments, ornate fireplaces and candelabras, and a dining room with starched linen napkins and polished glasses. And the menu still offers four- and five-course meals with generous choice. If there are changes, they are marked by a response to smaller appetites and a move towards lighter food.

The cooking doesn't aim for undue sophistication or complexity, but it gets the essentials right; prime materials run from local lamb, beef and poultry to Scottish scallops, perfectly timed, served with an orange sauce and a salad heady with lemon and basil. Foie gras as good as it gets may be served with sweet apple, tangy poached rhubarb and a calvados sauce. Many dishes have been simplified, although main-course twinning is still apparent: beef fillet comes with braised oxtail, noisette of venison with a casserole of venison in a pastry case, and tender breast of honey-marinated Lunesdale duckling with a crisp filo parcel containing duck confit, cabbage and lentils.

Between starter and main course come the 'compulsory' items: a well-flavoured sorbet at lunch, at dinner a soup or fish (maybe firm-textured poached brill with choucroute and a sweet and sour sauce), then sorbet. Desserts – with cold ones in the ascendant – although hardly insubstantial, are perhaps the biggest casualty of the drive for smaller portions: perhaps a syllabub with fine shortbread, a banana and butterscotch tart, and a warm, sugary, sticky pineapple Tatin with a light custard.

Service, from a mix of confident and relaxed old hands and younger recruits, is at its best friendly and 'professional without being pretentious'. The Sharrow Selection of wines by bottle or glass is helpfully annotated to aid pairing food and drink. The main list – thick and especially deep in claret and burgundy – goes from £13.50 to the stratosphere and is prefaced by sommelier James Payne, highlighting some of the great vintages and styles within.

CHEFS: Juan Martin and Colin Akrigg PROPRIETOR: Brian Sack OPEN: all week 1 to 1.30, 8 to 8.30 CLOSED: Early Dec to early March MEALS: Set L £36.25, Set D £47.25 SERVICE: net prices, card slips closed CARDS: Delta, MasterCard, Switch, Visa DETAILS: 65 seats. Private parties: 35 main room. Car park. No children under 13. Jacket and tie. No smoking in dining room. Wheelchair access (also WC). No music. Air-conditioned ACCOMMODATION: 26 rooms, all with bath/shower. TV. Phone. D,B&B £115 to £210. Rooms for disabled. No children under 13 (*The Which? Hotel Guide*)

ULVERSTON Cumbria **map 8**

▲ Bay Horse

Canal Foot, Ulverston LA12 9EL
TEL: (01229) 583972 FAX: (01229) 580502
EMAIL: reservations@thebayhorsehotel.co.uk
WEB SITE: www.thebayhorsehotel.co.uk
off A590; just before centre of Ulverston, follow signs to Canal Foot

COOKING **4**
ENGLISH COUNTRY-HOUSE
£28–£54

Once a staging post for coaches crossing Morecambe Bay, this eighteenth-century inn overlooking the Leven Estuary is now a destination in its own right. The hallmarks of part-owner John Tovey are evident: slick professional service; a comfortable, conservatory dining room with green-velvet-upholstered chairs and fresh flowers on tables; and menus firmly in the country-house mould that is almost synonymous with his name.

This means a wide-ranging if fairly safe cooking style, based on good materials and hearty portions. Starters might include tomato and mozzarella salad with basil vinaigrette, or devilled mushrooms on a peanut butter croûton. Main courses run from poached smoked haddock on a bed of leeks and prawns with herb cream sauce, to pan-fried chicken with chillies, spring onion and ginger, glazed with honey, calvados and raspberry vinegar. Typically calorific desserts include rich chocolate mascarpone cheesecake or tipsy trifle. One part of the extensive wine list is devoted to South Africa, the other covers France and the rest of the world; both start at £15.50.

CHEFS: Robert Lyons and Esther Jarvis PROPRIETORS: John Tovey and Robert Lyons OPEN: Tue to Sat L 12 to 1.30, all week D 7.30 for 8 (1 sitting) SERVICE: 10%, card slips closed CARDS: MasterCard, Switch, Visa DETAILS: 50 seats. Private parties: 50 main room. Vegetarian meals. No children under 12. No smoking in dining room. Wheelchair access (also WC). Music. Air-conditioned ACCOMMODATION: 9 rooms, all with bath/shower. TV. Phone. B&B £90 to £170. No children under 12 (*The Which? Hotel Guide*)

UPPER SLAUGHTER Gloucestershire **map 5**

▲ Lords of the Manor

Upper Slaughter GL54 2JD
TEL: (01451) 820243 FAX: (01451) 820696
EMAIL: lordsofthemanor@btinternet.com
WEB SITE: www.lordsofthemanor.com
turn W off A429, 3m S of Stow-on-the-Wold

COOKING **8**
MODERN FRENCH
£36–£107

A short gravel drive leads to secluded buildings of honey-coloured Cotswold stone: in front, an expanse of lawn with croquet mallets; behind, gently terraced gardens with outdoor seating. Despite a flower-arranger's efforts the dining room is not exciting, but tables are well-spaced and generously sized, and exhilaration aplenty comes on the plate.

John Campbell cooks like a man obsessed, playing with ideas to extract every ounce of potential. Savoury ice creams, for example, play an integral and recurring role: a mustard sherbet with smoked haddock risotto to start, parsnip ice cream with chocolate fondant to finish. In between comes 'a study in stickiness' provided by beef fillet. The beef is cooked slowly – 'at 59°, not one degree more nor less, I was told' – and served juicy and rare throughout; stickiness comes from the dribble of oxtail sauce, the unctuous mash topped with a slice of fragrant white truffle, and luscious browned-onion ice cream. 'Nothing, but nothing, was superfluous'.

Dishes are complex, but coherence unites their various components to create satisfaction: for example in a starter of stiff John Dory fillets sitting on wafer-thin slices of pickled lamb's tongue, on a bed of watercress and sliced shiitake mushrooms, all in a pool of impeccable, frothy red wine emulsion. Technical excellence can be taken for granted (though bread appears to have missed out here) without drawing attention to itself; for 'the most distinctive sweet-savoury combination ever,' try the whole pear, its skin caramel-coated, sitting in a caramelised puff pastry cup, sharing the plate with a Roquefort ice cream and streaks of honey syrup and balsamic.

Service matches the food ('committed is an understatement'); bookings are staggered, and meals progress at a sedate pace. Fine French wines dominate a list, as weighty as its prices, that mixes stellar names from around the world with occasional characterful, good-value bottles from south-west France, though even outlying regions don't offer much under £20. Nine wines by the glass (from £5) and ten 'sommelier's favourites' make realistic starting points. French house wines are £15.95 a bottle.

CHEF: John Campbell PROPRIETOR: Empire Ventures OPEN: all week; 12.30 to 2, 7 to 9.30 MEALS: alc (main courses £19.50 to £26). Set L £16.95 (2 courses) to £19.95, Set D £79 (Bar/terrace L menu also available) SERVICE: 12.5%, card slips closed CARDS: Amex, Delta, Diners, MasterCard, Switch, Visa DETAILS: 50 seats. 20 seats outside. Private parties: 50 main room, 8 to 30 private rooms. Car park. Vegetarian meals. No children under 7. No smoking in dining room. No music. Air-conditioned ACCOMMODATION: 27 rooms, all with bath/shower. TV. Phone. B&B £99 to £299. Rooms for disabled. Baby facilities. Fishing (*The Which? Hotel Guide*)

VIRGINSTOW Devon — map 1

DEVON GFG 2002 COMMENDED

▲ Percy's

Virginstow EX21 5EA
TEL: (01409) 211236 FAX: (01409) 211275
EMAIL: bookings@percys.co.uk
WEB SITE: www.percys.co.uk
follow signs to Percy's from Gridley corner on A388, or from B3218 at Metherell Cross junction

COOKING **5**
MODERN BRITISH
£42–£57

In many ways Percy's is a model of its kind. Dedicated to using some of its own organic materials, so that the food reflects seasonal gluts and shortfalls, it maintains a degree of contact with the land that is as rare as it is welcome. The 130 acres include wildlife ponds, new woodland, sheep, geese, chickens, horses and a kitchen garden that supplies herbs, salads and vegetables, while the 400-year-old house now has a stylish extension with oak floors, a zinc bar and an airy breakfast room. The garden's role and a direct daily link with the fish auctions at

Looe are immediately apparent in an impressive home-cured mackerel salad, the gravlax-style fish shaved in thin slices over a pile of perky, peppery leaves.

Themes tend to run through a meal: beetroot may be served as crisps to nibble at the bar, and as a main-course vegetable, while rosemary has turned up in the orange sauce accompanying home-reared pink-cooked goose breast, and again in an ice cream served with a first-class creamy-textured lemon tart. Spices also produce interesting taste combinations, from curry- and cumin-flavoured fig chutney that partners chicken liver parfait, to the assertive cardamom flavour in a custardy crème brûlée. Tina Bricknell-Webb's sound technique is well complemented by husband Tony's amiable front-of-house presence, and a short wine list, with around ten by the glass, is cannily chosen and sensibly priced, starting at £12.

CHEF: Tina Bricknell-Webb PROPRIETORS: Tony and Tina Bricknell- Webb OPEN: all week 12 to 2, 6.30 to 9 MEALS: Set L and D £32.50 to £37. Bar L available SERVICE: not inc CARDS: Amex, MasterCard, Switch, Visa DETAILS: 50 seats. 30 seats outside. Private parties: 26 main room, 12 to 26 private rooms. Car park. Vegetarian meals. No children under 12 in dining room. No smoking in dining room. Wheelchair access (also WC). No music ACCOMMODATION: 8 rooms, all with bath/shower. TV. Phone. B&B £69.50 to £145. Rooms for disabled. No children under 12 in accommodation. Fishing (*The Which? Hotel Guide*) (£5)

WALKINGTON East Riding of Yorkshire **map 9**

▲ Manor House

Northlands, Newbold Road,
Walkington HU17 8RT
TEL: (01482) 881645 FAX: (01482) 866501
EMAIL: info@the-manor-house.co.uk
WEB SITE: www.the-manor-house.co.uk
off B1230 towards Beverley from Walkington

COOKING **2**
MODERN BRITISH
£26–£67

Just outside Walkington and not far from the historical town of Beverley, this Victorian mansion has a secluded feel, being set in substantial gardens and surrounded by parkland. It has a domestic yet opulent feel, combining lavish furnishings and décor with old-fashioned Yorkshire hospitality. Derek Baugh searches far and wide for culinary ideas, enhancing his traditional French cooking with influences from the Far East and pretty much everywhere else in between. The four-course menu – 'thirty pounds and no pence', as the menu states, but with some supplements – offers plenty of choice: among starters might be poached baby skate wings with a piccalilli and spring onion bouillabaisse, or shredded rabbit and leek confit with grape chutney and a Thai dipping sauce. Next comes a sorbet or soup, then main courses ranging from halibut with asparagus and fennel in a butter sauce to gigot of lamb with sage and onion couscous with minted jus. Desserts look pretty but are not up to the same standard. The list of more than 250 wines also shows a leaning towards France, with plenty under £20, including house wines at £13.95.

CHEF: Derek Baugh PROPRIETORS: Derek and Lee Baugh OPEN: Mon to Sat D only 7 to 9.15 CLOSED: 25 Dec to 1 Jan, bank hol Mons MEALS: Set D Mon to Fri £15, Set D Mon to Sat £30 SERVICE: not inc, card slips closed CARDS: Delta, MasterCard, Switch, Visa DETAILS: 56 seats. Private parties: 36 main room. Car park. Vegetarian meals. No children under 12. Music ACCOMMODATION: 7 rooms, all with bath/shower. TV. Phone. Room only £70 to £110

WARMINSTER Wiltshire map 2

▲ Bishopstrow House

Warminster BA12 9HH
TEL: (01985) 212312 FAX: (01985) 216769
EMAIL: enquiries@bishopstrow.co.uk
WEB SITE: www.slh.com/bishopst
on B3414, 1m E of Warminster

COOKING **4**
MODERN ENGLISH
£32–£75

English roses and cottage garden flowers surround the four-square, creeper-covered, stone-built house. While indoor and outdoor pools, a gym, spa, tennis courts, massage and therapy treatments all point to athletic preoccupations, the comfortable leather and velvety sofas in the lounge and library suggest solace at the end of it. Dinner is the main business – not cheap, with a few price supplements, vegetables extra, and an 'optional' 15 per cent service charge on top – and the slowly changing repertoire has a penchant for some bright flavours: chargrilled scallops and asparagus with sweet chilli jam, or tuna carpaccio with soy mustard dressing. At the same time it soothes with old favourites, from a Cornish crab and prawn cocktail to Angus ribeye steak with béarnaise, from melting chocolate sponge to sticky toffee pudding. Wines are well chosen but not sympathetically priced, with the exception of a couple of Argentinian house wine blends at £14.

CHEF: Chris Suter PROPRIETORS: Simon Lowe, Howard Malin and Andrew Leeman OPEN: all week 12 to 2 and 7 to 9 (9:30 Fri and Sat) MEALS: alc L 12.30 to 2 (main courses £8.50 to £14). Set D £38, Bar menu available all week 12 to 6 SERVICE: 15% (optional), card slips closed CARDS: Amex, Delta, Diners, MasterCard, Switch, Visa DETAILS: 70 seats. 40 seats outside. Private parties: 70 main room, 15 and 27 private rooms. Car park. Vegetarian meals. Children's helpings. No smoking in dining room. Wheelchair access (also men's WC). Music ACCOMMODATION: 32 rooms, all with bath/shower. TV. Phone. B&B £99 to £330. Rooms for disabled. Baby facilities. Swimming pool. Fishing (*The Which? Hotel Guide*)

WARWICK Warwickshire map 5

Findons

7 Old Square, Warwick CV34 4RA
TEL: (01926) 411755 FAX: (01926) 400453
EMAIL: rosemary@findons-restaurant.co.uk
WEB SITE: www.findons-restaurant.co.uk

COOKING **2**
MODERN BRITISH
£24–£62

Wedged into a corner where two streets meet, Findons is on the ground floor of a well-maintained eighteenth-century house with a smart green and white frontage. Meat from an award-winning local butcher, fresh fish from the Birmingham market, and French cheeses shipped directly from Paris are the mainstays of a dynamic and trend-conscious menu. Some idea of the range can be gauged from starters of baby squid with fine green beans in a lobster and Sambuca broth; and chicken livers given the Far Eastern treatment with mango, spring onion, coriander and a dressing of soy, ginger and sesame. Main courses keep up the pace with minted mascarpone and roast garlic to accompany chump of lamb, and orange and oregano for sea bass. A 'stack' is a favoured way of presentation: in a starter of aubergine, plum tomato and red pepper for example,

and in a dessert such as 'tiramisù stack with black cherries'. Service is informed, smiling and attentive, and the fairly priced wine list includes a few mature clarets and a pair of vintage Madeiras. House French and Spanish are £10.95.

CHEFS: Sean Rouse and Michael Findon PROPRIETOR: Findon & Williams Ltd OPEN: Mon to Fri L 12 to 2, Mon to Sat D 7 to 9.30 CLOSED: 26 Dec to 2 Jan, bank hols MEALS: alc (main courses £11 to £19). Set L £4.95 (1 course) to £13.95, Set D £15.95 SERVICE: not inc, 10% for parties of 8 or more CARDS: Amex, Delta, Diners, MasterCard, Switch, Visa DETAILS: 45 seats. 25 seats outside. Private parties: 36 main room, 14 and 36 private rooms. Vegetarian meals. No children under 8. Wheelchair access (not WC). Music (£5)

WATERHOUSES Staffordshire — map 5

▲ Old Beams

Leek Road, Waterhouses ST10 3HW — COOKING **6**
TEL: (01538) 308254 FAX: (01538) 308157 — MODERN BRITISH
on A523, 7m SE of Leek — £30–£62

Fancy a whirl on the Waltzer before dinner? This restaurant-with-rooms on the edge of the Peak District national park is ten minutes' drive from Alton Towers. Choose between beamed dining-room, with open fire in winter, or light-filled conservatory extension looking over the garden. 'If this were France,' writes one visitor, 'this would be a great find.' It is anyway, and all the better for the engaging charm of Ann Wallis and son out front.

Of course, Nigel's cooking contributes, too, for he takes great pains with everything from incidentals to main dishes. A starter of haddock risotto with curry velouté – fat flakes of fish and moist but not sloppy risotto impeccably complementary – demonstrates his technique. Also delicate is a main course of lemon sole filled with seafood mousseline on lobster sauce with new season's asparagus, each flavour ringing clear and true. Meatier dishes work well too, witness one reporter's grilled duck breast on cabbage cooked in port with olive-oiled potatoes and red wine reduction. Among desserts, try a prune and armagnac duo of hot soufflé and ice cream, or the crème brûlée with toasted brioche marinated in Grand Marnier.

Listed on two sides of an A3 card, the wines focus on value; prices start at £14.50, and the minority costing over £30 are well priced for their maturity. Characterful alternatives to French classics include a Côtes du Frontonnais and a Fitou, and a Chardonnay from Beaujolais, not to mention the non-Europeans.

CHEF: Nigel Wallis PROPRIETORS: Nigel and Ann Wallis OPEN: Fri, Sun L 12 to 1.30, Tue to Sat D 7 to 9 CLOSED: Jan MEALS: alc D (main courses £16.50 to £20.50). Set L £23 SERVICE: none, card slips closed CARDS: Amex, Delta, Diners, MasterCard, Switch, Visa DETAILS: 40 seats. Private parties: 40 main room. Car park. Vegetarian meals. No smoking in dining room. Occasional music ACCOMMODATION: 5 rooms, all with bath/shower. TV. Phone. B&B £65 to £120. Baby facilities (*The Which? Hotel Guide*)

indicates that there has been a change of chef since last year's Guide, and the Editor has judged that the change is of sufficient interest to merit the reader's attention.

WATERMILLOCK Cumbria map 10

▲ Rampsbeck Country House Hotel

Watermillock, Ullswater CA11 0LP
TEL: (017684) 86442 FAX: (017684) 86688
EMAIL: enquiries@rampsbeck.fsnet.co.uk
WEB SITE: www.rampsbeck.fsnet.co.uk
on A592 Penrith to Windermere road

COOKING **3**
ANGLO-FRENCH
£36–£62

'As we arrived, a duck was snuggling up to the wheel of a 4x4'; that shows how close to Ullswater this charming eighteenth-century country-house is. Pastel pink and green combine in the décor of both lounge and dining room, where Andrew McGeorge draws on the pick of local suppliers for some ingenious cookery: perhaps a lasagne of strongly flavoured roast quail and woodland mushrooms with fried quails' eggs to start, the meat juices forming the sauce. Soup or sorbet then precedes rich main courses involving a variety of cooking methods: baked feuilleté of crab with grilled langoustines, roasted asparagus and a crab and coriander sauce is one example. But there are simpler preparations too: say, curried parsnip soup, or rack of lamb with potato rösti and a port sauce. Lush desserts might encompass a hot passion fruit soufflé – 'well-risen and gladdening to the eye' – with vanilla ice cream and passion fruit sorbet. A stylistically presented list mixes classic French wines with new-wave European and interesting global styles at fair prices; many bins are under £20, including 11 house wines from £11.25.

CHEF: Andrew McGeorge PROPRIETORS: Tom and Marion Gibb, and Mrs M. J. MacDowall OPEN: all week 12 to 1 (booking essential), 6.45 to 8.15 CLOSED: early Jan to mid-Feb MEALS: Set L £27, Set D £30 to £41. Bar L available SERVICE: not inc, card slips closed CARDS: Delta, MasterCard, Switch, Visa DETAILS: 45 seats. Private parties: 70 main room, 15 private room. Car park. Children's helpings. No children under 7. No smoking in dining room. No music ACCOMMODATION: 20 rooms, all with bath/shower. TV. Phone. B&B £60 to £200 (*The Which? Hotel Guide*)

WATH-IN-NIDDERDALE North Yorkshire map 8

▲ Sportsman's Arms

Wath-in-Nidderdale, Pateley Bridge HG3 5PP
TEL: (01423) 711306 FAX: (01423) 712524
off B6265, 2m NW of Pateley Bridge

COOKING **4**
ANGLO-FRENCH
£26–£52

Cross an ancient packhorse bridge to reach this seventeenth-century inn of mellow sandstone that is now an elegant hotel and restaurant, set among grouse moors and hiking country. The Carters' kitchen makes the most of its setting, sourcing game from within a three-mile radius, and buying fish directly from the Whitby boats.

The cooking puts a modern spin on its resolutely Anglo-French approach, producing a starter plate of caramelised red onion, roasted peppers, walnut oil and balsamic with warm goats' cheese, while chicken breast is marinated in coriander and lemon and served on a mildly curried risotto. The signature Sportsman's salad with hazelnut dressing is considered especially good value. Olives, artichokes and wild mushrooms might accompany peppered beef fillet, and prunes and oranges figure among the traditionally fruity garnishes for a breast of Gressingham duckling.

Finish with a meringued fool made with rhubarb from the garden, apple pie served with a piece of crumbly Wensleydale, or summer pudding. Regulars find the team 'as professional and helpful as always'. House recommendations bring value to the fore on an already keenly priced wine list, starting at £11.90 and including a fruity red from celebrated Italian producer Antinori. Italy is well represented on the main list, on which lively French country and southern hemisphere bottles follow smart clarets and burgundies in good vintages.

CHEFS: Ray and James Carter, and Seth Marsland PROPRIETORS: Ray and Jane Carter OPEN: Sun L 12 to 2.15, Mon to Sat D 7 to 9.30 CLOSED: 25 Dec MEALS: alc D (main courses £10 to £18). Set L Sun £17.80. Bar menu available SERVICE: not inc, card slips closed CARDS: Delta, MasterCard, Switch, Visa DETAILS: 80 seats. 50 seats outside. Private parties: 50 main room, 12 private room. Car park. Vegetarian meals. Children's helpings. No smoking in dining room. Wheelchair access (not WC). No music ACCOMMODATION: 13 rooms, all with bath/shower. TV. Phone. B&B £45 to £90. Fishing (*The Which? Hotel Guide*)

WELLS Somerset **map 2**

Ritcher's

5 Sadler Street, Wells BA5 2RR
TEL: (01749) 679085 FAX: (01749) 673866
WEB SITE: www.ritchers.co.uk

COOKING **2**
FRENCH
£20–£36

Ritcher's is down an alleyway off the market square, and in clement weather the first you see of it is tables on the patio. Within, there's an informal ground-floor bistro and a burgundy-hued, more intimate restaurant above. The owners are into their second decade here, their style constant despite Nick Hart relinquishing the stoves to his sous-chef of five years. Duos and trios are a feature of the cooking, and don't be surprised to find several sauces on one plate: a Dijon mustard cream, and a balsamic and truffle jus, with roast rack of tasty English lamb for example.

The comparatively static menu – which might take in a bowl of soup under a pastry crust, or chargrilled fillet steak with wild mushrooms, Stilton, cider gravy and 'big chips' – is supplemented by daily fish and shellfish specials: perhaps scallops with streaks of pesto, beetroot and roast tomato dressings. Reporters have praised desserts such as tarte Tatin with a mini-crumble of rhubarb, and the classic crème brûlée. A serviceable wine list opens with eight interesting house wines from £9.95.

CHEF: Jason Porter PROPRIETORS: Kate Ritcher and Nick Hart OPEN: all week 12 to 2, 7 to 9 (10 Sat) CLOSED: 26 Dec, 1 Jan MEALS: Set L £7.50 (1 course) to £11.50, Set D £17.50 (2 courses) to £20.50 SERVICE: not inc, card slips closed CARDS: Delta, MasterCard, Switch, Visa DETAILS: 40 seats. 12 seats outside. Private parties: 22 main room. Vegetarian meals. No children under 10 at D. Wheelchair access (not WC). Music. Air-conditioned

All entries in the Guide are re-researched and rewritten every year, not least because restaurant standards fluctuate. Don't rely on an out-of-date Guide.

WELLS-NEXT-THE-SEA Norfolk **map 6**

▲ Rococo at the Crown

The Buttlands, Wells-next-the-Sea NR23 1EX
TEL: (01328) 710209 FAX: (01328) 711432
EMAIL: rococorest@aol.com
WEB SITE: www.rococoatthecrown.co.uk

COOKING **6**
MODERN BRITISH
£44–£64

Since the last edition of the Guide the Andersons have upped sticks from King's Lynn, where they spent a decade, and have taken over the Crown Hotel in this north Norfolk seaside town. Usually, when restaurants move, their owners take the opportunity to refurbish, have a rethink, maybe change the menu. In the Andersons' case, although they have added a brasserie called Jewel, it is more or less business as usual: they have brought their co-chef and restaurant manager with them, and even the dining room is the same mustard colour as before.

Rococo itself is now open only for dinner, but menus offer the same contemporary slant as before. Regional materials find a niche, perhaps in the shape of smoked Brancaster mussels, served with an open ravioli of roasted smoked salmon, or roast Norfolk squab pigeon with dauphinois potatoes and a thyme jus. Flavours are often pointed up by bright relishes and accompaniments: pickled ginger and a coriander and chilli dressing, for example, with a crispy squid salad on peppery leaves, and preserved lemons with olives and a gingery saffron jus to accompany chump of lamb. Fish takes a prominent place among main courses – steamed fillet of black bream on herb couscous, or monkfish and tiger prawns with pak choi and jasmine rice – while vegetarians might be offered a roast vegetable and cheese flan.

Soothing desserts run from iced liquorice parfait, via caramelised rice pudding, to a dark chocolate and sultana sticky pudding with a praline centre. Careful sourcing has brought to the wine list a variety of choice under £25. The occasional star, whose price shoots up considerably, adds depth to the lively, easy-drinking styles and to the well-priced, more serious bottles from around the globe.

CHEFS: Nick Anderson and Alec Howard PROPRIETORS: Nick and Anne Anderson OPEN: Rococo all week D only 7 to 9.30; Jewel all week 12 to 2, 6 to 9 MEALS: Rococo Set D £25.50 (2 courses) to £35.50; Jewel alc (main courses £6 to £12) SERVICE: not inc, card slips closed CARDS: Amex, Delta, MasterCard, Switch, Visa DETAILS: Rococo: 36 seats. Private parties: 24 main room. Vegetarian meals. Music. Jewel: 50 seats. 30 seats outside. Private parties: 24 main room. Vegetarian meals. Children's helpings. No-smoking area. Wheelchair access (not WC). Music. Car park ACCOMMODATION: 11 rooms, all with bath/shower. TV. Phone. B&B £55 to £130. Baby facilities (£5)

The 2003 Guide will be published before Christmas 2002. Reports on meals are most welcome at any time of the year, but are particularly valuable in the spring (no later than June). Send them to The Good Food Guide, *FREEPOST, 2 Marylebone Road, London NW1 4DF. Or email your report to goodfoodguide@which.net*

WELWYN GARDEN CITY Hertfordshire map 3

▲ Auberge du Lac 🍷

Brocket Hall, Lemsford, Welwyn Garden City AL8 7XG
TEL: (01707) 368888 FAX: (01707) 368898 COOKING **5**
EMAIL: aubergedulac@brocket-hall.co.uk MODERN FRENCH-PLUS
off B653 2m W of Welwyn £28–£74

This eighteenth-century hunting lodge on the Brocket Hall estate sets off Pascal Bréant's innovatively inspired cooking. There is a weekly-changing lunch menu and a set dinner menu of three courses (four, if you want what is, in effect, a second starter: say, pistachio-crusted foie gras with caramelised rhubarb and quince, or crab ravioli in a crustacean-based saffron cream). Terrines of one sort or another (perhaps lobster en persillé sauced with tomato and tarragon) crop up as starters, while main courses offer extraordinary choice, from spiced monkfish tail with chicken liver in red wine, to a more mainstream saddle of venison with celeriac purée, roasted pear, red berries and a balsamic sauce.

The odd oriental note is sounded, in a Szechuan-style duck breast on cabbage stir-fried with sesame seeds and lemon grass, although, perhaps in view of the ambitious style, not everything comes off equally well. Favourite desserts take in crème brûlée with bitter chocolate ice cream, and glazed lemon tart with blackberry sorbet. The burgundies and Bordeaux that take up much the wine list include a fair sprinkling over 15 years old, providing plentiful mature drinking, and wines from the rest of the world are a serious bunch too. Although prices rarely dip below £20 – house white starts at £21.50, house red at £25 – a broad selection is offered by the glass (from £6), ranging from a fresh Western Australian Verdelho to a Californian Pinot Noir.

CHEF: Pascal Bréant PROPRIETOR: CCA International OPEN: Tue to Sun L 12 to 2.30, Tue to Sat D 7 to 10 MEALS: Set L £25, Set D £38 to £45 SERVICE: 10%, card slips closed CARDS: Amex, Delta, Diners, MasterCard, Switch, Visa DETAILS: 70 seats. 70 seats outside. Private parties: 70 main room, 2 to 16 private rooms. Vegetarian meals. Car park. Children's helpings. No cigars/pipes in dining room. Wheelchair access (not WC). Music. Air-conditioned ACCOMMODATION: 16 rooms, all with bath/shower. TV. Phone. B&B £145 to £170. Rooms for disabled. Baby facilities

WEST BAY Dorset map 2

Riverside Restaurant

West Bay DT6 4EZ
TEL: (01308) 422011 COOKING **2**
WEB SITE: www.riverside-restaurant.co.uk SEAFOOD
off A35, 1m S of Bridport £23–£57

The Riverside, approached by a walkway over the river, fits the popular image that serious seafood restaurants are down amid the sights and sounds of the sea. It is bright, cheerful and informal, with bare floorboards and wooden tables, and the Watsons' philosophy is to let the basic ingredients (high-quality fish) do the talking, so this is no place for bizarre combinations. Daily specials and a main menu offer, among other things, seared scallops with mixed leaves, lardons, pine nuts and croûtons; Atlantic oysters with shallot vinegar; turbot with hollandaise; and deep-fried cod in Guinness batter with mushy peas and chips. Desserts lean towards the homely, perhaps treacle tart with ice cream or knickerbocker glory. Service is easy-going and efficient, and the global wine list (mostly priced at flat rates: £10, £15, £20, etc.) offers a good selection of halves, and house wines at £10.

CHEFS: Paul Morey, Will Longman and Nic Larcombe PROPRIETORS: Arthur and Janet Watson OPEN: Tue to Sun L 12 to 2.15, Tue to Sat D 6.30 to 9 (open Sun D and Mon L/D at bank hols; D hours vary Feb to Apr and Oct/Nov, phone to check); booking advisable CLOSED: 1 Dec to mid-Feb MEALS: alc (main courses £8.50 to £19.50). Set L Feb to Apr and Oct and Nov weekdays £12.50 (2 courses) to £15 SERVICE: not inc, card slips closed CARDS: Delta, MasterCard, Switch, Visa DETAILS: 90 seats. 30 seats outside. Private parties: 100 main room, 20 private room. Vegetarian meals. Children's helpings. No smoking in dining room. Wheelchair access (also women's WC). Occasional music

WEST ILSLEY Berkshire map 2

The Harrow

West Ilsley RG20 7AR
TEL: (01635) 281260 FAX: (01635) 281139
1½m off A34, 10m N of Newbury

COOKING **3**
MODERN BRITISH
£29–£45

This seventeenth-century inn overlooking the village duck pond and cricket field nowadays is, some might argue, more restaurant than pub – at least on a Saturday night – though the interior is still dominated by pictures of hunting scenes, and the plain wooden tables and chairs are definitely pubby. The menu typically offers seven or eight starters, among which reporters have enjoyed black pudding and poached egg on spinach and bacon, and twice-baked Stilton soufflé. Main courses are supplemented by three or four daily specials on a board, and approval comes for chicken with morels, and roast duck with ginger and rösti. To follow, you might choose such home-made desserts as passion fruit mousse with raspberry sorbet, or hot chocolate fondant with pistachio custard and vanilla ice cream; or else the selection of five appetisingly described fine British cheeses. Seven wines are offered by the glass (£2) or bottle (£11.95), and 20 others listed are all below £20 a bottle; Somerset Royal Cider Brandy is available too.

CHEF: Scott Hunter PROPRIETORS: Emily Hawes and Scott Hunter OPEN: Tue to Sun L 12 to 2, Tue to Sat D 7 to 9 (open Sun D and Mon March to Nov) MEALS: alc (main courses £9.50 to £14) SERVICE: not inc, card slips closed, 10% for parties of 8 or more CARDS: Delta, MasterCard, Switch, Visa DETAILS: 65 seats. 40 seats outside. Car park. No smoking in dining room. Occasional music. Air-conditioned

▲ *means accommodation is available.*

Prices quoted in the Guide are based on information supplied by restaurateurs. The prices quoted at the top of each entry represent a range, from the lowest meal price to the highest; the latter is inflated by 20 per cent to take account of likely price rises during the year of the Guide.

WEST TANFIELD North Yorkshire map 9

▲ Bruce Arms

Main Street, West Tanfield HG4 5JJ
TEL: (01677) 470325 FAX: (01677) 470796

COOKING **4**
MODERN ENGLISH
£23–£41

Stone fireplaces, piles of logs and exposed beams give the Bruce the air of a traditional village inn. A glance at the blackboard menu shows a kitchen striving for a degree of local and seasonal input – roast loin of Dales lamb comes with a mushroom 'parcel' and tarragon sauce – but it is the sensibly modernist approach that strikes most forcibly. This is down to earth rather than fanciful cooking, taking in calf's liver with smoked bacon and mash, and fillet of sea bass with ginger and sesame couscous. Among the salsas, risottos and truffle oil there may also be an exotic note (chicken breast with banana, smoked ham, coconut and mild curry sauce), and a comfort element in the shape of salad of black pudding with poached egg and hollandaise, or soft chocolate cake with mascarpone and coffee sauce. The wine list takes a brisk trot around the world, staying mostly below £15. Besides five house wines by the small (£1.70) and large (£2.50) glass, a half-dozen 185ml 'small bottles' at £3.15 allow 'a fresh wine every time'.

CHEF: Geoff Smith PROPRIETORS: Amanda Donkin and Geoff Smith OPEN: Wed to Sun L 12 to 2, Tue to Sat D 6.30 to 9.30 CLOSED: 31 Dec and 1 Jan; first week in Feb, June and Nov MEALS: alc (main courses L £5 to £15.50, D £9 to £15.50). Set L Sun £9.50 (1 course) to £14.50. Light L available Wed to Sat SERVICE: not inc, card slips closed CARDS: Delta, MasterCard, Switch, Visa DETAILS: 42 seats. 16 seats outside. Private parties: 26 main room. Car park. Vegetarian meals. Music ACCOMMODATION: 3 rooms, all with bath/shower. TV. B&B £37.50 to £55

WETHERSFIELD Essex map 6

Dicken's ✱ £

The Green, Wethersfield CM7 4BS
TEL: (01371) 850723 FAX: (01371) 850727

COOKING **2**
MODERN BRITISH
£25–£55

John Dicken's 12-year-old restaurant underwent a refurbishment in October 2000. Gone is the pink-painted frontage, replaced by a handsome deep blue, while the front dining area is a lighter cornflower blue, its walls adorned with gastro-paintings and gastro-aphorisms (sample: 'Age is only important if you are a cheese'). At one bound, the restaurant has become a brasserie, and the menu reflects the transformation. A pairing of brasserie pâtés (one coarse-textured, the other smooth) comes with apricot chutney and sweet piccalilli, triple sausage and squeak is self-explanatory, and green Thai curry is made with cashew nuts and served on coconut rice. All these dishes, and a dozen others, may be had in starter or main course size. More traditionally, there are grills, such as sirloin steak with mushrooms and onion rings, or cod fillet with herb butter, and crêpes suzette or pears poached in grenadine with rice pudding to finish. The smart, polite service copes well under pressure, and a listing of speciality beers might well draw attention away from the short but serviceable wine list. House Vin de Pays d'Oc is £9.95.

CHEF/PROPRIETOR: John Dicken OPEN: all week 12 to 2, 6.30 to 9.30 CLOSED: phone to check over Christmas MEALS: alc (main courses £9 to £20) SERVICE: not inc CARDS: Amex, Delta, Diners, MasterCard, Switch, Visa DETAILS: 40 seats. Private parties: 40 main room, 16 private room. Car park. Children's helpings. No smoking in dining room. Wheelchair access (also WC). Music

WHITBY North Yorkshire **map 9**

Magpie Café £

14 Pier Road, Whitby YO21 3PU
TEL: (01947) 602058 FAX: (01947) 601801 COOKING **2**
EMAIL: ian@magpiecafe.co.uk SEAFOOD
WEB SITE: www.magpiecafe.co.uk £17–£46

The Magpie Café – a striking mid-eighteenth century building that has been a seafood restaurant for more than 60 years – makes the best of its position between the fish market and the harbour: lobsters come straight off the boats as they land at the quayside opposite, and the ever-present queues of hungry seafood enthusiasts often have to make way for twice daily deliveries that ensure the fish is always as fresh as possible. Traditional fish and chips with tartare sauce and a side order of mushy peas exemplifies the largely old-fashioned cooking style; also regularly on offer are favourites such as Whitby kippers with brown bread; mussels in wine, cream and garlic; lobster thermidor; and grilled skate wing with black butter, lemon and capers. There are also several meat dishes, a long list of hot and cold desserts, and two dozen good-value wines, priced from £9.95.

CHEFS: Ian Robson and Paul Gildroy PROPRIETORS: Ian Robson and Alison McKenzie-Robson OPEN: all week 11.30 to 9 (6.30 Sun Nov to Mar) CLOSED: 24 and 25 Dec, 1 Jan, mid-Jan to mid-Feb MEALS: alc (main courses £4.50 to £17) SERVICE: not inc, card slips closed CARDS: Amex, Delta, MasterCard, Switch, Visa DETAILS: 100 seats. Private parties: 50 main room. Vegetarian meals. Children's helpings. No smoking in dining room. Occasional music. Air-conditioned (£5)

WHITCHURCH Hampshire **map 2**

Red House

21 London Street, Whitchurch RG28 7LH COOKING **2**
TEL: (01256) 895558 GLOBAL
£19–£43

This sixteenth-century inn – part informal restaurant, part pub – isn't red at all, but white. The pub and dining areas are quite distinct, the latter having large arched mirrors and plain wooden tables and floors. In addition to printed menus, daily specials are chalked on a board. Shannon Wells is not one to mince his flavours, so expect some fairly bold cooking, with plenty of herbs, salt and garlic. Raw materials are sound, and timing is well judged, producing effective dishes such as pan-fried scallops with bacon and Parmesan stuffing, and lamb fillet wrapped in Parma ham with thyme potatoes and red wine reduction. Although on the dessert side lemon tart has failed to please, other options might run to bread-and-butter pudding with butterscotch sauce, chocolate brownies, or coffee brûlée. Service is young, enthusiastic and well-informed, and the annotated and reasonably priced wine list has ten house bottles from £9.95, seven available by the glass.

CHEFS: Shannon Wells and Peter Nash PROPRIETORS: Shannon and Caroline Wells OPEN: all week 12 to 2, 6.30 (7 Sun) to 9.30 MEALS: alc (main courses L £5 to £14.50, D £8 to £16.50). SERVICE: not inc, card slips closed CARDS: MasterCard, Switch, Visa DETAILS: 40 seats. 50 seats outside. Private parties: 27 main room. Car park. Vegetarian meals. No children at D. No smoking in dining room. No music

WHITSTABLE Kent map 3

Sportsman

NEW ENTRY

Faversham Road, Seasalter, Whitstable CT5 4BP
TEL: (01227) 273370
take Whitstable exit from A299 and follow signs for Seasalter; pub at far end of village

COOKING 3
MODERN EUROPEAN
£30–£45

'A really civilised place in a strange location' was how one impressed visitor summed up the appeal of this upmarket dining pub. It stands seemingly in the middle of nowhere – sea on one side, marshland on the other – and first impressions are of a fairly ordinary weather-beaten old pub. Inside, however, the appearance is tasteful and modern: cream-painted walls, bare floorboards, contemporary lighting and chunky tables.

Stephen Harris – co-proprietor and self-taught chef – has an admirably down-to-earth philosophy: to do simple things well, and to use only local produce. His 'short and sweet' blackboard menu offers a modern version of country cooking. A recommended starter is a platter of antipasti for two, incorporating (among other things) bresaola, fresh anchovies, hard-boiled quails' eggs and oysters topped with chorizo. Main courses, meanwhile, might include local turbot braised in Vin Jaune with morels, or a heartier, well-flavoured rump of lamb with a large portion of boulangère potatoes and a richly flavoured gravy made with the roasting juices. Properly made tarte Tatin is a dessert speciality. Alongside well-kept Shepherd Neame beers are around a dozen wines from £9.95; five are available by the glass.

CHEFS: Stephen Harris, Dan Flavell and Joel Groves PROPRIETORS: Stephen, Philip and Damian Harris OPEN: Tue to Sun L 12 to 2, Tue to Sat D 7 to 9 MEALS: alc (main courses £11 to £16) SERVICE: not inc, card slips closed, 10% for parties of 6 or more CARDS: Delta, Diners, MasterCard, Switch, Visa DETAILS: 40 seats. Private parties: 12 main room, 20 private room. Car park. Children's helpings Sun L. No children in bar area. No smoking in 1 dining room. Wheelchair access (not WC). Music

Report forms are at the back of the book; write a letter if you prefer; or email us at goodfoodguide@which.net

The Guide always appreciates hearing about changes of chef or owner.

WICKHAM Hampshire map 2

▲ Old House

The Square, Wickham PO17 5JG
TEL: (01329) 833049 FAX: (01329) 833672
EMAIL: enq@theoldhousehotel.co.uk
2 ½m N of Fareham, at junction of A32 and B2177

COOKING 2
MODERN BRITISH
£29–£55

This handsome, wisteria-clad Georgian building, dating back to 1715, overlooks Wickham's attractive, broad square. At the front is a lounge with a large fireplace and comfy sofas, and there are two dining rooms: a small wood panelled one, and a rather formal, high-ceilinged one with generously sized tables covered in starched white tablecloths. Menus apply an English country-house spin to the modern British approach, delivering roundels of duck and foie gras to start (the duck wrapped in Savoy cabbage and poached), or pan-fried squid stuffed with basil risotto served with crayfish sauce. Main courses can be substantial, and flavoured mashed potato seems to be a recurring theme: pan-fried breast of corn-fed duck might come with chive mash served with creamy mushroom sauce, while chargrilled monkfish and scallops arrive atop a coriander version with saffron and ginger broth. A dessert of pear tarte Tatin hit the spot for one reporter, or there might be a selection of cheeses. Wines are listed by style and give good choice below the £20 marker, starting at £10.95 (£2.75 a glass).

CHEF: Anthony Guichard PROPRIETORS: John and Gloria Goodacre OPEN: Tue to Sun L 12 to 2, Mon to Sat D 7 to 9.30 CLOSED: 26 Dec to 5 Jan MEALS: alc (main courses £14 to £18.50). Set L £15 (2 courses) to £18.50, Set D £18.50 (2 courses) to £21 SERVICE: not inc CARDS: Amex, Delta, Diners, MasterCard, Switch, Visa DETAILS: 45 seats. Private parties: 40 main room, 14 private room. Car park. Vegetarian meals. No smoking in dining room. Wheelchair access (not WC). Occasional music ACCOMMODATION: 9 rooms, all with bath/shower. TV. Phone. B&B £65 to £90. (£5)

WILLITON Somerset map 2

▲ White House

11 Long Street, Williton TA4 4QW
TEL: (01984) 632777

COOKING 6
ENGLISH/MEDITERRANEAN
£86–£57

'A wonderful place to stay and to eat,' enthused one visitor to this attractive, well-maintained Georgian-style building, run by 'exceptionally kind' Kay and Dick Smith since 1967. Décor is both artistic and rustic, with dark bare stone walls in the dining room, and the civilised atmosphere is undisturbed by music or smoking. It is an appropriate setting for the slightly old-fashioned and utterly simple cooking that reporters enjoy.

A typical dinner opens with tarragon and potato soup, followed by a choice of perhaps Brixham crab tart, or a classic soufflé suissesse, before the main event. This usually includes a fish option, maybe a bourride of turbot and red mullet in a rich sauce of saffron, tomato and wine with rouille and aïoli, while meat dishes have taken in grilled noisettes of local spring lamb with parsnip purée and cooking juices. Among desserts might be hazelnut meringue cake with strawberries. Wines are an inspired, mostly European, collection, full of adventurous styles at good prices. Particular interest comes from the south of France, which features Domaine de Trévallon reds back to 1991 and a variety of Bandols back to 1987. Two pages of reds and whites singled out for interest provide an alternative to house wines at around £12.

CHEFS/PROPRIETORS: Kay and Dick Smith OPEN: all week D only 7 to 8.30 CLOSED: Nov to mid-May MEALS: Set D £34 SERVICE: not inc CARDS: none DETAILS: 22 seats. Private parties: 6 main room. Car park. Children's helpings. No smoking in dining room. Wheelchair access (not WC). No music ACCOMMODATION: 10 rooms, all with bath/shower. TV. Phone. D,B&B £83 to £172. Rooms for disabled. Baby facilities

WILMINGTON East Sussex **map 3**

▲ Crossways

Lewes Road, Wilmington BN26 5SG
TEL: (01323) 482455 FAX: (01323) 487811
EMAIL: dine@crosswayshotel.co.uk COOKING **4**
WEB SITE: www.crosswayshotel.co.uk MODERN BRITISH
on A27, 2m W of Polegate £40–£51

Looking down on this Georgian hotel from the hillside is the famous Neolithic chalk carving known as the Long Man of Wilmington. Though Crossways has not been around for as long, it deserves its reputation as an attraction in its own right. An elegant décor of pink carpets and drapes, and abundant fresh flowers, make for a welcoming dining room, and service, overseen by the owners, is attentive. Given the inventive modern cooking as well, it is hard to see how anyone could fail to enjoy coming here.

Four-course menus change monthly to keep up with the seasons, and make good use of local produce, notably beef and lamb. Starters tend to include a few novelties, such as Camembert ice cream with spiced oranges, or an unlikely sounding prawn and banana basket. Soup follows, then main courses, which generally stick to more familiar territory: roast rack of spring lamb with red wine, rosemary and redcurrant sauce, for example, or roast Gressingham duck with pink grapefruit and elderflower sauce. A quartet of English wines, including a champagne-style sparkler, opens the list; the rest are a well-chosen and fairly priced selection, starting at £11.95.

CHEFS: Juliet Anderson and David Stott PROPRIETORS: David Stott and Clive James OPEN: Tue to Sat D only 7.30 to 8.30 CLOSED: 24 Dec to 24 Jan MEALS: Set D £29.95 SERVICE: not inc, card slips closed CARDS: Amex, Delta, MasterCard, Switch, Visa DETAILS: 24 seats. Private parties: 6 main room. Car park. No children under 12. No smoking in dining room. Wheelchair access (not WC). Occasional music ACCOMMODATION: 7 rooms, all with bath/shower. TV. Phone. B&B £50 to £80

The Guide is totally independent, accepts no free hospitality, and survives on the number of copies sold each year.

NEW CHEF *is shown instead of a cooking mark where a change of chef occurred too late for a new assessment of the cooking.*

WILMSLOW Cheshire map 7

Bank Square

4–6 Bank Square, Wilmslow SK9 1AN
TEL: (01625) 539754 FAX: (01625) 539813

COOKING 3
MODERN EUROPEAN
£20–£54

An elaborately gabled red-brick façade topped with a balustraded dome and clock face gives strong indication – if the name hadn't already – that these premises once housed a bank. The interior refurbishment leaves such grandeur and stolidity behind, though, in favour of cool, undulating lines and a display of spotlit wine bottles on a white wall. Similarly, there is nothing old-school about Glen Barry's cooking, which makes the most of local suppliers to offer gutsy modern dishes. Among them might be a starter of black and white puddings with new potatoes braised in Guinness (along with crisp-fried cabbage and a devilled sauce), followed perhaps by bacon-wrapped cannon of lamb with sweet pea purée.

A certain level of complexity is actively courted, which brings on the likes of peppered loin of venison with spinach, potato rösti, a compote of pimentos and a kumquat sauce; but the kitchen is also proud to draw attention to its lobster thermidor. Finish with the house speciality of steamed black cherry sponge with cherry syrup, or passion fruit bavarois with mango coulis. A suitably modern wine list offers plenty of bright New World flavours to balance French classics, opening with South African house wines at £12.90.

CHEF: Glen Barry PROPRIETORS: David and Janet Rivett OPEN: Mon to Sat 12 to 2, 6.30 to 10 MEALS: alc (main courses £10 to £18). Set L £9.95, Set D Mon to Fri £9.95. Bar menu available SERVICE: 10% (optional) CARDS: Amex, Delta, MasterCard, Switch, Visa DETAILS: 55 seats. Private parties: 60 main room, 36 private room. Vegetarian meals. Children's helpings. No cigars/pipes in dining room. Occasional music. Air-conditioned (£5)

WINCHCOMBE Gloucestershire map 5

▲ Wesley House

High Street, Winchcombe GL54 5LJ
TEL: (01242) 602366 FAX: (01242) 609046
EMAIL: enquiries@wesleyhouse.co.uk
WEB SITE: www.wesleyhouse.co.uk

COOKING 2
ANGLO-FRENCH
£25–£61

Wesley House is terribly ancient, even by Cotswold standards. Though named after the founder of Methodism, who is believed to have stayed here in 1779, it predates even him by a couple of hundred years, and has beams, roughly plastered walls and a giant red-brick hearth to show for it. Front-of-house, Matthew Brown, remains his usual chatty, amiable self, but a new regime has been installed in the kitchen.

The menu format of three courses for a fixed price is unchanged (two-course menus are available too, and à la carte at lunch), although the style is somewhat simpler than before. Its range is demonstrated by a fine piece of marinated chargrilled salmon, served with Thai noodles in a sharp, clear-tasting dressing, and by a generous portion of roast chump of lamb with a properly made wild mushroom risotto and sauté girolles. Old-fashioned desserts have included poached strawberries set on calvados-flavoured crème fraîche with shortbread. South Africa continues to be the focus of the wine list, and a special feature is made of Veenwouden Estate, which produces a small quantity of claret-like blends. Classic French and carefully selected New World wines provide a backdrop, and house recommendations kick off with a South African Chardonnay at £11.50.

CHEFS: Alex Breach and Richard Upton PROPRIETOR: Matthew Brown OPEN: all week L 12 to 2, Mon to Sat and bank hol Sun D 6.45 to 9 MEALS: alc L (main courses £7 to £18.50). Set L £10 (2 courses) to £14.50, Set D Mon to Fri 6.45 to 7.45 £18.50 (2 courses) to £21, Set D Mon to Fri £26 (2 courses) to £31, Set D Sat £31 SERVICE: not inc CARDS: Amex, Delta, MasterCard, Switch, Visa DETAILS: 55 seats. 20 seats outside. Private parties: 65 main room. Vegetarian meals. Children's helpings. No smoking in dining room. Wheelchair access (not WC). Occasional music ACCOMMODATION: 6 rooms, all with bath/shower. TV. Phone. B&B £40 to £80. Baby facilities (*The Which? Hotel Guide*) (£5)

WINCHESTER Hampshire **map 2**

Bertie's

5 Jewry Street, Winchester SO23 8RZ
TEL: (01962) 860006 FAX: (01962) 866129

COOKING **3**
MODERN BRITISH
£21–£47

This blue-fronted restaurant (formerly Hunters), in a narrow terraced building on a busy street near the shopping precinct, has undergone a complete refurbishment to go with its name change. 'A Lucinda Lambton fantasy' was how one returnee described the new interior, with its pastel colours, small murals of flowers, food and Mediterranean landscapes, and red-tiled floor.

Simon Lakey cooks equally vivid modern dishes, with the emphasis on straightforward combinations based on sound raw materials. Three fat scallops come arranged around a mound of rocket leaves with a ribbon of lemon and saffron cream sauce, and roast rump of lamb 'bursting with flavour and juiciness' is served with swede purée, dauphinois potatoes and veal stock. Alternatives might run to bruschetta topped with sweet peppers and mozzarella, or confit duck leg glazed with honey and ginger. Not everything pleases (lemon tart didn't exactly raise the rafters at inspection), but other choices might include prunes and armagnac in the crème brûlée, or hot fudge sauce with chocolate brownie. Service is full of 'theatrical gestures' but gets the job done. France and the New World dominate the capacious wine list, which opens with Chilean house wines at £11.50.

CHEF: Simon Lakey PROPRIETORS: David and Martin Birmingham OPEN: Mon to Sat 12 to 2, 6.30 to 10 CLOSED: bank hol Mons MEALS: alc (main courses L £5 to £9, D £10 to £15). Set L £8.95 (2 courses) to £11.95, Set D Mon to Fri £11.95 (2 courses) to £14.95 SERVICE: not inc, 10% for parties of 6 or more CARDS: Amex, Delta, Diners, MasterCard, Switch, Visa DETAILS: 65 seats. Private parties: 24 main room. Vegetarian meals. Music (£5)

To find a restaurant in a particular area use the maps at the centre of the book.

Chesil Rectory

1 Chesil Street, Winchester SO23 OHU
TEL: (01962) 851555 FAX: (01962) 869704

COOKING **6**
MODERN BRITISH
£39–£67

Claiming to be the oldest house in the city, the fifteenth-century Rectory wears its age on its sleeve (even though it has dropped the 'Old' from its name) in the form of heavy, iron-bound wooden doors, uneven varnished board floor and leaded windows. Front-of-house is unstuffy, well-informed and professional, and Philip Storey's highly accomplished cooking is both classical and innovative. Choice commodities (from Loch Fyne oysters to Valrhona chocolate) supplement the fine local supplies that otherwise underpin his menus. These change seasonally, despite a few long stayers such as twice-baked cheese soufflé, and a pairing of pork and black pudding served with mustard mash and an apple butter sauce.

Among highlights have been a 'totally gorgeous' wild mushroom risotto, followed by a generously sized skate fillet with lemon confit, asparagus and mashed potato. Beef fillet has been given the Rossini treatment, topped with foie gras and sauced with madeira, on a disc of crisp rösti and shredded Savoy cabbage. Bright fruit flavours are mobilised to give point to desserts: rhubarb soup is garnished with strawberries, and soft mango sorbet accompanies a well-risen passion fruit soufflé. Presentation, right through to plentiful petits fours, is impeccable. The pedigree wine list is full of delights, helpfully arranged by style, although mark-ups cast a shadow over proceedings. A house selection built around a dozen reds and whites from Italy, France and California occupies a range between £15 and £20.

CHEF: Philip Storey PROPRIETORS: Philip and Catherine Storey OPEN: Tue to Sat 12 to 1.45, 7 to 9.15 (9.45 Sat) MEALS: Set L £20 (2 courses) to £25, Set D £30 (2 courses) to £40 SERVICE: not inc, 12.5% for parties of 6 or more CARDS: Amex, Delta, Diners, MasterCard, Switch, Visa DETAILS: 50 seats. Private parties: 40 main room, 8 to 40 private rooms. Vegetarian meals available on request. Children's helpings. No smoking in 1 dining room. Music (£5)

▲ Hotel du Vin & Bistro

Southgate Street, Winchester SO23 9EF
TEL: (01962) 841414 FAX: (01962) 842458
EMAIL: info@winchester.hotelduvin.com
WEB SITE: www.hotelduvin.com

COOKING **4**
MODERN EUROPEAN
£31–£54

The original outlet of a steadily growing chain (see also entries in Bristol, Tunbridge Wells and Birmingham) is a lively, enjoyable place that successfully blends an informal setting with a serious approach to food and wine. Beiges, creams and yellows light up the airy dining room, polished floors and comfortable antique leather upholstered chairs add a touch of old-school elegance, and service from traditionally dressed French waiters and waitresses is 'professional, polite and helpful'.

Gareth Longhurst's bistro cooking covers both classic and contemporary modes, from a generous starter of non-greasy duck rillettes with well-made celeriac rémoulade, to a light variation on the tarte Tatin theme containing beetroot and goats' cheese. Main courses mostly revisit old ideas: crisp tempura of fresh-tasting haddock on flavourful pea purée (chips available as a side dish for £2 extra), or tasty, pink pan-fried calf's liver with a mound of mash containing pieces of bacon, set in a glossy brown gravy. Desserts range from old-fashioned spotted dick and custard to marmalade jelly with bitter chocolate sorbet.

Wines are chosen with an eye to some less familiar viticultural regions, including Galilee in Israel, and even Thailand, which provide contrast to the smart selection of traditional European bottles. Prices are sensible, although they occasionally slip into three-figure territory. Own-label house wines start at £13, and there is a daily specials list from £11.95.

CHEF: Gareth Longhurst PROPRIETOR: Hotel du Vin Ltd OPEN: all week 12 to 1.45, 7 to 9.45 MEALS: alc exc Sun L (main courses £10 to £15). Set L Sun £22.50 SERVICE: not inc CARDS: Amex, Delta, Diners, MasterCard, Switch, Visa DETAILS: 65 seats. 20 seats outside. Private parties: 12 and 48 private rooms. Car park. Vegetarian meals. Children's helpings. No cigars/pipes in dining room. Wheelchair access (not WC). No music ACCOMMODATION: 23 rooms, all with bath/shower. TV. Phone. Room only £95 to £185. Rooms for disabled. Baby facilities (*The Which? Hotel Guide*)

▲ Wykeham Arms

75 Kingsgate Street, Winchester SO23 9PE — COOKING **2**
TEL: (01962) 853834 FAX: (01962) 854411 — MODERN BRITISH/MEDITERRANEAN
£22–£40

The setting, amid narrow streets of fine old houses, is evocative, the small dining room an oasis of calm just off the crowded fire-warmed bars. This is the sort of pub-restaurant 'that you dream of having at the end of your street', a place where visitors feel very much at home. There is nothing pretentious about the cooking, which might take in a pigeon, bacon and potato salad, Aberdeen Angus steaks (peppered or plain), and steamed plaice fillets filled with smoked salmon and herb mousse. 'Being very old, we have joined the "two starters and a pud" brigade,' confided one couple, who rated a first-class coarse pork pâté the highlight. Others may be tempted by one of the eight specials on offer each day. Management is quiet and efficient, service is charming, attentive and friendly, and wines are listed in brief for those who know what they like and want to get at it fast, or with full notes colourfully illustrated for experimenters. A quick scan brings up plenty of choice under £20, with house wines starting at £10.95.

CHEFS: Nicola Saunders and Gary Stickland PROPRIETOR: George Gale & Co. Ltd OPEN: Mon to Sat 12 to 2.30, 6.30 to 8.45 CLOSED: 25 Dec MEALS: alc (main courses L £5.50 to £13, D £10 to £13.50) SERVICE: not inc, card slips closed CARDS: Amex, Delta, Diners, MasterCard, Switch, Visa DETAILS: 85 seats. Car park. Vegetarian meals. No children under 14. No smoking in 3 dining rooms. No music ACCOMMODATION: 14 rooms, all with bath/shower. TV. Phone. B&B £45 to £117.50. No children under 14 (*The Which? Hotel Guide*)

The cuisine styles noted at the tops of entries are only an approximation, often suggested to us by the restaurants themselves. Please read the entry itself to find out more about the cooking style.

WINDERMERE Cumbria map 8

▲ Gilpin Lodge

Crook Road, Windermere LA23 3NE
TEL: (015394) 88818 FAX: (015394) 88058
EMAIL: hotel@gilpin-lodge.co.uk
WEB SITE: www.giplin-lodge.co.uk
on B5284, 2m SE of Windermere

NEW CHEF
MODERN BRITISH
£27–£61

Set on a hillside surrounded by woodland, this Victorian house takes an accommodating approach to visitors and, under its new chef, an exciting approach to its food. Working within a classical framework, Sam Carswell partners roast Bresse pigeon with fried ox tongue, and puts together combinations such as tournedos of wild salmon with foie gras, spiced lentils, and an apple and fig chutney. As if that were not enough, meals might finish with a rhubarb and tangerine parfait accompanied by a salt tuile and raspberry beignets. Reports on results are particularly welcome. Wines dutifully cover the globe, picking up good names along the way, and moderate pricing makes a fair proportion of them accessible, helped by half a dozen wines by the glass under £3.50.

CHEF: Sam Carswell PROPRIETORS: John and Christine Cunliffe OPEN: all week 12 to 2.30, 7 to 9 MEALS: alc L Mon to Sat (main courses £7.50 to £12). Set L Sun £17.50, Set D £35 SERVICE: not inc CARDS: Amex, Delta, Diners, MasterCard, Switch, Visa DETAILS: 55 seats. 18 seats outside. Private parties: 22 main room, 13 and 28 private rooms. Car park. Vegetarian meals. No children under 7. No smoking in dining room. Wheelchair access (not WC). Music ACCOMMODATION: 14 rooms, all with bath/shower. TV. Phone. B&B £80 to £210. Rooms for disabled. No children under 7 (*The Which? Hotel Guide*) (£5)

▲ Holbeck Ghyll

Holbeck Lane, Windermere LA23 1LU
TEL: (015394) 32375 FAX: (015394) 34743
EMAIL: stay@holbeckghyll.com
WEB SITE: www.holbeck-ghyll.co.uk
from A591, 3m N of Windermere turn E (Holbeck Lane, signposted Troutbeck), hotel is ½m on left

COOKING **5**
MODERN FRENCH
£37–£67

Reached up a steep little lane, this place demonstrates how ravishing Cumbria can be; from both of the lounges and the dining room, the view over Windermere to the fells beyond is sublime. Holbeck Ghyll itself is a small stone-built manor house, whose panelled dining room and black-aproned staff lend it a period feel.

David McLaughlin cooks confidently in modern French style, partnering seared foie gras with split peas and salsify, and a warm salad of langoustines and lobster with celeriac rémoulade. His impeccable timing is evident in half a dozen plump scallops (also on celeriac, mashed this time), and in a main course of sliced duck breast, cooked beyond pink but still moist and full of flavour, served with sarladaise potatoes and a Madeira jus. Fish appears to be a strong suit, judging by roast brill with a ragoût of bacon, celery and girolles, and by a highly rated sea bass with braised fennel and artichokes in a vermouth sauce.

The Gallic seam runs through to desserts, in the shape of cherry clafoutis, chocolate délice with prune and armagnac ice cream, and an individual vanilla cheesecake with a compote and sorbet of strawberries. A good selection of British and French cheeses is helpfully described on the menu. The extensive catalogue of a wine list has much mature claret and burgundy, as well as reasonable selections from the New World, but prices are pretty stiff. Six house wines begin at £16.50 (£4 for a glass) for an Australian Semillon-Chardonnay.

CHEF: David McLaughlin PROPRIETORS: David and Patricia Nicholson OPEN: all week 12.30 to 2, 6.45 to 9.30 MEALS: Set L £25, Set D £42.50 SERVICE: not inc, card slips closed CARDS: Amex, Delta, Diners, MasterCard, Switch, Visa DETAILS: 50 seats. 20 seats outside. Private parties: 65 main room. Car park. Vegetarian meals. No children under 9. Wheelchair access (also WC). No music ACCOMMODATION: 20 rooms, all with bath/shower. TV. Phone. D,B&B £110 to £320. Baby facilities (*The Which? Hotel Guide*) (£5)

Jerichos

Birch Street, Windermere LA23 1EG — COOKING **5**
TEL/FAX: (015394) 42522 — ENGLISH
EMAIL: enquiries@jerichos.co.uk — £31–£50

Easy to find down a side street, Jerichos greets with a flagged terrace, a smart aubergine colour scheme, and a short, weekly-changing menu that describes dishes in some detail. Choice is sensibly geared to what is basically a one-man kitchen, and a degree of ingenuity is brought to bear on some essentially mainstream ideas, from the vinaigrette of dark soy, honey and grain mustard applied to a confit duck leg, to the Parmesan and cep risotto that comes with another starter of own-smoked chicken. Plainer still might be a creamy parsnip and cauliflower soup, or thick, tasty asparagus combined with locally smoked salmon, a poached egg and a first-rate mustardy mayonnaise.

Even complicated dishes work well, however, judging by a poached fillet of firm baby halibut served on buttered, dill-glazed, crumbled new potatoes, with black sardine paste and an aniseed- and dill-flavoured sauce. Herbs and spices are well deployed, not least in a vegetarian main course of variously marinated, grilled and roast thyme-scented vegetables on tomato provençale couscous, with grilled goats' cheese and balsamic vinegar. Generally the cooking is 'brimful of flavour', and if puddings seem to lack the panache of the rest of the menu, bread (straight from the oven) is a highlight. The well-researched wine list, with food-matching suggestions, offers plenty of style and value: try the whites from Western Australia's Vasse Felix and Cape Mentelle at £19 and £16.50 respectively. Eight house wines from around the world are £12.

CHEFS: Chris Blaydes and Sarah Connolly PROPRIETORS: Chris and Jo Blaydes OPEN: Tue to Sun D only 6.45 to 9.30 CLOSED: 24 to 26 Dec, 1 Jan, last 2 weeks Nov MEALS: alc (main courses £13 to £16.50) SERVICE: not inc CARDS: Delta, MasterCard, Switch, Visa DETAILS: 36 seats. Private parties: 25 main room, 14 and 25 private rooms. Vegetarian meals. No children under 12. No smoking in dining room. Music

'The crab salad came with a fish knife; the sirloin with a knife so blunt that it made no difference whether one used the top edge or the cutting edge.' (On eating in Wiltshire)

▲ Miller Howe 🍷 £✶

Rayrigg Road, Windermere LA23 1EY
TEL: (015394) 42536 FAX: (015394) 45664
EMAIL: lakeview@millerhowe.com
WEB SITE: www.millerhowe.com
on A592, between Windermere and Bowness

COOKING **6**
ENGLISH COUNTRY HOUSE
£29–£64

'It would be hard to find a nicer setting,' summed up one visitor, eyeing the views of Langdale Pikes, Bow Fell, Crinkle Crags and Swirl How from the light and airy conservatory. A friendly welcoming atmosphere tends to raise the spirits further. The no-choice menu, established long ago in John Tovey's era, remains in vestigial form: five courses (one of them typically a sorbet) with no choice before dessert. But there is also a separate list of 'alternatives' to extend options. However odd this arrangement may seem, the cooking is characterised by skilful combinations of fine ingredients, sometimes injected with a degree of flair and originality: for example in vanilla tagliatelle with feta cheese, pine nuts and black truffle.

Flavours are generally well balanced, and fish has been noteworthy: monkfish wrapped in prosciutto has come on a bed of Puy lentils with Noilly Prat beurre blanc. Although vegetable accompaniments may sound excessive – fondant potato with mustard, spinach with juniper, and cauliflower with blue cheese sauce, for example, all to partner roast fillet of lamb – they are well executed and induce a sense of satisfaction. Indeed, the generally bold flavours confirm that there is 'nothing wishy-washy about the cooking', judging by gamey-tasting venison with a smear of intense dark chocolate and red wine sauce, accompanied by cumin-roast potatoes, spiced red cabbage, and celeriac and horseradish rémoulade.

Desserts run to a 'sublime' sticky toffee pudding, bread is well reported, and wines include both big names from the world's elite and surprises such as a rosé from South Africa. Classical European sections are preceded by often less usual New World offerings. Mark-ups are fair, although house wines are £17.50.

CHEF: Susan Elliott PROPRIETOR: Charles Garside OPEN: all week 12.30 to 1.30, 8 (1 sitting) CLOSED: 6 to 19 Jan MEALS: Set L Mon to Sat £17.50, Set L Sun £19.95, Set D £39.50 SERVICE: not inc, card slips closed CARDS: Amex, Diners, MasterCard, Switch, Visa DETAILS: 64 seats. Private parties: 64 main room. Car park. Vegetarian meals. No children under 8. No smoking in dining room. Wheelchair access (also WC). Occasional music. Air-conditioned ACCOMMODATION: 12 rooms, all with bath/shower. TV. Phone. D,B&B £170 to £270 (double room). No children under 8 (*The Which? Hotel Guide*) (£5)

WINKLEIGH Devon map 1

Pophams £✶

Castle Street, Winkleigh EX19 8HU
TEL: (01837) 83767

COOKING **5**
MODERN BRITISH
£30–£43

With just three tables, and just three openings a week, it would be surprising if Pophams were not full most of the time. But given a simple and honest approach to the food as well, it is apparent that getting a table is never going to be easy.

And while many a chef has taken a bold leap into the big time, only to come unstuck with a bigger kitchen and more staff and customers, Melvyn Popham and Dennis Hawkes stick resolutely and commendably to their small-scale operation.

A few seasonal vegetables from the village, and meat from a nearby butcher, add to the sense of domestic enterprise, and unfussy treatment accounts for another large part of its success. Warm crab tart comes with no more than a blob of crème fraîche, and salmon fishcake might be given a curry cream sauce. Main courses offer just a couple of alternatives: perhaps beef fillet with a port and red wine sauce, or chicken breast stuffed with smoked ham, basil and mozzarella, with a Noilly Prat cream sauce. Cream may be a clue to the old-fashioned nature of the cooking, but at least there is enough left over for desserts of rich lemon ice cream with strawberry compote, or sticky ginger pudding with a ginger wine sauce and clotted cream.

CHEF: Melvyn Popham PROPRIETORS: Melvyn Popham and Dennis Hawkes OPEN: Wed to Fri L only 11.45 to 2.30 CLOSED: Feb MEALS: alc (main courses £15 to £17). Unlicensed but BYO (no corkage) SERVICE: not inc CARDS: none DETAILS: 10 seats. Private parties: 10 main room. No children under 14. No smoking in dining room. Air-conditioned

WINTERINGHAM North Lincolnshire map 9

▲ Winteringham Fields

RESTAURANT OF THE YEAR GFG 2002

Winteringham DN15 9PF
TEL: (01724) 733096 FAX: (01724) 733898
EMAIL: wintfields@aol.com
WEB SITE: www.winteringhamfields.com

COOKING **9**
PROVINCIAL FRENCH/SWISS
£42–£121

Situated at the crossroads in an unassuming village near the Humber Bridge, the converted farmhouse has open fires, wooden beams, low ceilings, antiques, curios and deep settees all of which are distributed between a busily decorated drawing room and a flower-filled conservatory. Meanwhile, all creature comforts are catered for in the refurbished dining room: it has lots of elbow room, comfortable chairs 'large enough for a rugby forward', tables heavily draped with fabric and crisp linen, each with a painted ostrich egg, the whole intimate, formal and discreet.

If first impressions count for anything, then Winteringham is already on to a winner with its succession of memorable appetisers. This is a mini-industry in its own right, whose production line has impressed equally with clear soups – from beef consommé to rhubarb with Avruga caviar – and small crisp cromesquis of liquid foie gras and truffle. The food is inventive, materials often luxurious, and as well as some local produce (Lincolnshire Marsh duckling, for example) the kitchen's own gardens contribute herbs and vegetables. Dishes are the result of sheer hard labour coupled with technical excellence and sometimes a dash of inspiration: for example, a world-class and 'truly great dish' of crispy veal sweetbreads served with a ravioli of egg yolk 'that seemed to almost defy science'.

The cooking is exciting, artistic and, at its best, as good as any you will find, which is to say that above all it is supremely enjoyable: for example, a 'masterful' two-part starter of foie gras – an accurately cooked tranche, and a slice of smooth, rich terrine – which would have been outstanding on its own, was rendered exceptional by a stunning quince and fig chutney, the whole exhibiting 'harmony, poise and balance'. Other 'impeccable' combinations have included pan-fried langoustine with a crisp tuile pipe of aubergine marmalade, and steamed fillet of turbot served with foie gras, a vanilla pod, and morels stuffed with a delicate fish mousse. Those in search of something simpler have raved about the sea bass baked in salt, served with a small copper pan of sauce Choron (tomato-flavoured béarnaise).

Dessert is preceded by another painstaking offering: for instance, a passion-fruit soufflé into which is inserted a tiny cone of caramel ice cream, an incidental of such effort and artistry that it confirms a kitchen 'dedicated to true gastronomy'. The assiette of miniature desserts might offer samples of a trompe l'oeil artist's palette of sorbets, a classic crème brûlée, meringue baked with soft caramel (with mascarpone ice cream), and a hot pyramid of dark chocolate and Glayva coulant wrapped in flaky white chocolate crème pâtissière. Staff are sharply dressed, highly experienced, knowledgeable, professional, unobtrusive, and immensely helpful; if one of them has to be singled out, it must be the man who explains the remarkable cheese trolley, his wares as extensive as they are in prime condition, constituting probably the best cheese selection of any restaurant in the UK. Winteringham's 'genuine warmth' is overseen by the ever-hospitable Annie Schwab, 'with a smile that lit up Lincolnshire' for one visitor. Although the sommelier's help is praised too, the ambitious wine list is not geared towards bargains; indeed its unfriendly prices constitute the only real cloud on the horizon. Nevertheless, six house wines come in under £18.50.

CHEF: Germain Schwab PROPRIETORS: Germain and Annie Schwab OPEN: Tue to Sat 12 to 1.30, 7 to 9.30 CLOSED: 2 weeks Christmas, last week Mar, first week Aug, last week Oct MEALS: alc (main courses £25 to £35). Set L £22 (2 courses) to £28, Set D £35 to £65 SERVICE: not inc, card slips closed CARDS: Amex, Delta, MasterCard, Switch, Visa DETAILS: 42 seats. Private parties: 10 main room, 10 private room. Car park. No smoking in dining room. Wheelchair access (not WC). No music ACCOMMODATION: 10 rooms, all with bath/shower. TV. Phone. B&B £75 to £165. Rooms for disabled. No children under 8 exc babies (*The Which? Hotel Guide*)

WITCHFORD Cambridgeshire **map 6**

▲ Needhams **NEW ENTRY**

186 Main Street, Witchford CB6 2HT
TEL/FAX: (01353) 661405

COOKING **2**
MODERN EUROPEAN
£23–£47

In an area not overrun with decent restaurants, Needhams is in a large, characterful, brick-built, one-time farmhouse in a fens dormitory village close to Ely. Though the bar is beamed, the décor is resolutely modern, neat and comfortable (if a touch uncharismatic), a theme continued in the beige dining room with its plum tablecloths and napkins. The menu runs on innovative modern lines, with tempura of squid on a bed of cucumber and spring onions with sweet chilli and garlic sauce, or pan-fried sea bass with Moroccan vegetable tagine and couscous. Among dishes to have pleased are expertly cooked wild boar on fondant potato with pink peppercorn sauce and parsnip crisps, and a subtle Irish whiskey and orange brûlée. Coffee, elegantly served in the conservatory, comes with 'really good' chocolate truffles. The compact wine

list, based mainly in France and the New World, kicks off with two South African house wines at £9.50.

CHEF: Luke Pearson PROPRIETORS: Verity Lowe and Luke Pearson OPEN: Tue to Sun L 12 to 2 (2.30 Sun), Tue to Sat D 7 (6.30 Sat) to 9.30 CLOSED: 1 to 14 Jan MEALS: alc exc Sun L (main courses £9 to £16.50). Set L Sun £15.95 SERVICE: not inc CARDS: Amex, Delta, MasterCard, Switch, Visa DETAILS: 50 seats. Private parties: 22 main room, 85 private room. Car park. Vegetarian meals. Children's helpings. No smoking in dining room. Wheelchair access (also WC). Music ACCOMMODATION: 2 rooms. B&B £35 to £50

WITHERSLACK Cumbria map 8

▲ Old Vicarage

Church Road, Witherslack LA11 6RS
TEL: (015395) 52381 FAX: (015395) 52373
EMAIL: hotel@oldvicarage.com
WEB SITE: www.oldvicarage.com
off A590, take first left in village to church

COOKING **3**
MODERN BRITISH/FRENCH
£26–£54

In a quiet backwater, unsurprisingly next to a church, the Old Vicarage feels comfortable, warm and lived in. Its unassuming nature is matched by the kitchen's seriousness of intent: materials include line-caught sea bass and Winster Valley pigeon, and among suppliers are Woodall's of Waberthwaite (for bacon and pork) and Howbarrow Organic Farm at Cartmel (for vegetables). French, Scandinavian, British and Eastern influences are brought to bear, and although James Brown aims to keep his cooking simple, that doesn't stop him serving grilled lemon sole fillets on citrus mash with root vegetable crisps, accompanied by seared scallops and a lemon, dill and tarragon beurre blanc. In February he has paired Winster pigeon with Holker Estate venison (both lightly oak-smoked) and served them with fondant potato, roasted vegetables, ale-braised pearl barley and a damson jus.

Desserts are a little closer to most people's idea of simplicity, taking in Westmorland curd tart, and spiced rhubarb sponge with custard. Service is invariably pleasant, and wines are civilly priced. House wines set the scene, starting at £9.50 for youthful, southern French red and white, and the rest are presented under stylistic headings with guidelines for food matching.

CHEF: James Brown PROPRIETORS: Jill and Roger Brown, and Stanley and Irene Reeve OPEN: Sun L 12 to 2, all week D 6 (7 Sat) to 9 MEALS: alc D (main courses £14 to £18). Set L Sun £12.50 (2 courses) to £15.50, Set D Sun to Fri 6 to 7 £12.50 (2 courses) to £15.50. Light L menu available Mon to Sat SERVICE: not inc, card slips closed CARDS: Amex, Delta, MasterCard, Switch, Visa DETAILS: 40 seats. Private parties: 20 main room, 12 private room. Car park. Vegetarian meals. Children's helpings. No smoking in dining room. Wheelchair access (not WC). Music ACCOMMODATION: 14 rooms, all with bath/shower. TV. Phone. D, B&B £80 to £200. Rooms for disabled. Baby facilities (*The Which? Hotel Guide*) (£5)

Although the cuisine style noted at the top of entries has in most cases been suggested to the Guide by the restaurants, some have been edited for brevity or appropriateness.

WOKINGHAM Berkshire **map 3**

Rose Street

6 Rose Street, Wokingham RG40 1XU
TEL: (0118) 978 8025 FAX: (0118) 989 1314

COOKING **4**
MODERN ANGLO-FRENCH
£30–£64

Number 6 Rose Street is a charming building of some antiquity standing shoulder to shoulder with similarly attractive cottages in the centre of Wokingham. It operates as a wine bar and restaurant and can get quite busy: as well as three small, beamed dining rooms there is a conservatory, used mainly for overspill. The cooking adds some imaginative modern twists to an otherwise largely traditional style, and fish and seafood are abundant on both the carte and the 'lunch de jour' (sic) menus. A starter of white crabmeat wrapped in smoked salmon with tomato, avocado and mango, coriander juice and pain d'épices exemplifies the inventive side, while Caesar salad is a more familiar offering.

Among main courses might be thyme-roasted chicken breast on tagliatelle with asparagus, leeks, spinach and a Champagne sauce, or grilled sea bass with rosemary fondant potatoes accompanied by seared scallops, baby fennel and vanilla cream. For dessert, one diner was particularly impressed with a juniper flavoured cheesecake with mirabelles: 'delicate, runny and to be eaten very slowly.' One or two problems have been encountered with service but reporters remain generally content. A predominantly French wine list includes a few more interesting New World bottles; prices start at £13.75.

CHEF: Paul Scott PROPRIETORS: John Read and Paul Scott OPEN: Mon to Sat 12 to 2.30, 7 to 10 CLOSED: 25 and 26 Dec, 1 Jan, MEALS: alc (main courses £13 to £21.50). Set L £14.95 (2 courses) to £18.95 SERVICE: not inc, 12.5% for parties of 8 or more CARDS: Delta, MasterCard, Switch, Visa DETAILS: 44 seats. Private parties: 18 main room, 10 to 18 private rooms. Vegetarian meals. Children's helpings. No smoking in 1 dining room. Wheelchair access (also women's WC). Music (£5)

WOODBRIDGE Suffolk **map 6**

Captain's Table £

3 Quay Street, Woodbridge IP12 1BX
TEL: (01394) 383145 FAX: (01394) 388508
WEB SITE: www.captainstable.co.uk

COOKING **4**
MODERN EUROPEAN
£20–£38

A short walk from Woodbridge quayside, handy for both the railway station and the theatre, the Pommiers' simply decorated restaurant boasts an enclosed patio for summer dining. The focus of the menus is classic European food, but with as many ingredients as possible sourced locally. Fillet of cod with a parsley cream sauce, or chicken breast with baby onions, mushrooms and Madeira sauce might provide the main business, following perhaps a straightforward salad of artichoke, red onion, green bean, red pepper and quails' eggs. Samosas of ham, black pudding and apple with a lentil dressing are one of the more unusual starters. Daily specials are chalked up on a board, and meals end lightly enough with the likes of fromage frais mousse with blackberries, or poached pear with ginger ice cream. Service is friendly – nothing appears too much trouble – and an up-to-date, agreeably varied wine list comes at manageable prices from £8.95.

CHEF: Pascal Pommier PROPRIETORS: Jo and Pascal Pommier OPEN: Tue to Sun L 12 to 2 (3 Sun), Tue to Sat D 6.30 to 9.30 (10 Fri and Sat) CLOSED: 2 weeks Jan MEALS: alc (main courses £5.50 to £11.50) SERVICE: not inc, card slips closed CARDS: Delta, MasterCard, Switch, Visa DETAILS: 50 seats. 30 seats outside. Private parties: 34 main room, 19 and 20 private rooms. Car park. Vegetarian meals. Children's helpings. No smoking in dining room. Wheelchair access (not WC). No music

WOODSTOCK Oxfordshire map 2

▲ Feathers Hotel

Market Street, Woodstock OX20 1SX
TEL: (01993) 812291 FAX: (01993) 813158 COOKING 4
EMAIL: enquiries@feathers.co.uk MODERN EUROPEAN
WEB SITE: www.feathers.co.uk £33–£85

Just a few minutes' walk from the entrance to Blenheim Palace, the restaurant and hotel share the seventeenth-century building with a popular, stylish bar that is open for snacks, aperitifs and coffee. Walk past Johan, the African Grey parrot, into one of three inter-connecting dining rooms with rag-rolled yellow walls and a few antique-style pictures, where a modern, luxury-based menu remains little changed in style from the previous regime.

Foie gras and truffles might appear together (with a main-course beef fillet), and oysters and caviar have come together in a vichyssoise with cucumber, but most dishes, on the carte at least, have a seductive quality about them even when using humbler materials: roast veal with pancetta-spiked rösti and morel jus, for example. Accurate timing, honest flavours and proper textures are apparent in al dente penne served with baby vegetables and Parmesan shavings, and in calf's liver topped with a slice of well-cooked streaky bacon, on a bed of steamed Asian greens, in a rich red wine sauce.

Hazelnut parfait with summer fruits comes recommended, or there may be an equally eye-catching yellow peach consommé with peach sherbet. Prestigious names pepper the French section of the wine list, and much of the rest offers decent drinking under £30. Around ten wines are available by the large glass for under £5.

CHEF: Darren Prideaux PROPRIETOR: Empire Ventures Ltd OPEN: all week 12.30 to 2.15, 7.30 to 9.15 (9.30 Sat) MEALS: alc (main courses £17 to £24.50). Set L Mon to Sat £15.50 (2 courses) to £19.50, Set L Sun £20.50 SERVICE: 12.5% (optional), card slips closed CARDS: Amex, Delta, Diners, MasterCard, Switch, Visa DETAILS: 50 seats. Private parties: 50 main room. Vegetarian meals. Children's helpings. No smoking in dining room. Music. Air-conditioned ACCOMMODATION: 21 rooms, all with bath/shower. TV. Phone. B&B £90 to £290. Baby facilities (*The Which? Hotel Guide*) (£5)

Dining rooms where music, either live or recorded, is never played are signalled by No music *in the details at the end of an entry.*

Use the lists towards the front of the book to find suitable restaurants for special occasions.

WORCESTER Worcestershire map 5

Brown's

24 Quay Street, Worcester WR1 2JJ COOKING **3**
TEL: (01905) 26263 FAX: (01905) 25768 ANGLO-FRENCH
£26–£50

Within sight of the cathedral, Brown's occupies a substantial nineteenth-century red-brick mill near the bridge over the River Severn. Winter floods wreaked havoc in 2001, but now that it is above water again all is back to normal. A set-price menu of five or six options per course revolves around essentially straightforward techniques: roasting of duck (with apricots) or squab pigeon (with foie gras), grilling (herring with mustard mash), and chargrilling (thick fillet steak, with a choice of herb butter or red wine sauce, chips or mash) for a couple of lunchers who found everything just to their liking.

Good buying and proper handling ensure that the lettuce and croûtons in a lightly dressed Caesar salad are properly crisp, and that the roast sea bass (on a cucumber salad) is accurately timed and well flavoured. Cheeses are well described and in good condition, and desserts have taken in moist baklava topped with grilled figs, mascarpone and raspberries. Efficient and friendly service is included in the price, which contributes to the good value, and a traditionally styled French wine list is fleshed out with a few wines from elsewhere, notably Australia. Prices start at £11.95.

CHEFS: W.R. Tansley and L. Jones PROPRIETORS: W.R. and P.M. Tansley OPEN: Tue to Fri L 12.30 to 1.45, Tue to Sat D 7.30 to 9.45 MEALS: Set L £20.50, Set D £36 SERVICE: net prices, card slips closed CARDS: Amex, Delta, MasterCard, Switch, Visa DETAILS: 100 seats. Vegetarian meals. No children under 8. No-smoking area. Wheelchair access (also WC). No music

WORFIELD Shropshire map 5

▲ Old Vicarage

Worfield WV15 5JZ
TEL: (01746) 716497 FAX: (01746) 716552
EMAIL: admin@the-old-vicarage.demon.co.uk COOKING **2**
WEB SITE: www.oldvicarageworfield.com MODERN EUROPEAN
off A454, 3m E of Bridgnorth £31–£64

Apart from a conservatory extension at the back, much of this red-brick Edwardian vicarage feels original, with parquet floors, floral-print curtains, shiny antique tables, and walls full of pictures. New owners arrived in 2001, although Blaine Reed's food continues in the same vein as before, with meals priced according to the main course, the most expensive option being chargrilled Hereford beef fillet with foie gras and wild mushroom jus. Good raw materials have included a starter of three accurately griddled scallops (oddly partnered by red pepper ratatouille, blobs of mayonnaise and a mango coulis), and chargrilled venison fillet on sweet braised red cabbage.

Dishes may not always correspond exactly with their menu description, seasoning can be overdone, extra vegetables come on a side plate, and presentation can be finicky. Cheeses are taken seriously, and desserts might run to a first-class iced banana parfait with banana fudge ice cream and glazed banana. Meals come with good bread, and old-fashioned service is friendly and helpful. Intelligently sourced mature clarets start off a wine list characterised by fair pricing and interesting finds, like South Australia's Maglieri Shiraz at £19.75. The halves section is plump and wide-ranging, and house wines, which have dipped in price, now starting at £13.50, fill a whole page with youthful styles.

CHEFS: Blaine Reed and Richard Arnold PROPRIETORS: David and Sarah Blakstad OPEN: Sun to Fri L 12 to 2, all week D 7 to 9 MEALS: Set L £18.50, Set D £22 to £37.50 SERVICE: not inc CARDS: Amex, Delta, Diners, MasterCard, Switch, Visa DETAILS: 42 seats. Private parties: 42 main room, 12 and 14 private rooms. Car park. Vegetarian meals. Children's helpings. No smoking in dining room. Wheelchair access (also WC). Occasional music ACCOMMODATION: 14 rooms, all with bath/shower. TV. Phone. B&B £75 to £175. Rooms for disabled. Baby facilities (*The Which? Hotel Guide*)

WORLESTON Cheshire **map 5**

▲ Rookery Hall

Worleston CW5 6DQ
TEL: (01270) 610016 FAX: (01270) 626027
EMAIL: rookery@arcadianhotels.co.uk
WEB SITE: www.rookeryhall.co.uk
on B5074, 2½m N of Nantwich

COOKING **3**
MODERN EUROPEAN
£30–£66

A time-warp nineteenth-century pile in the Cheshire countryside, with large sitting rooms, comfortable sofas, log fires and a beautiful panelled dining room, Rookery Hall has all the atmospheric credentials a country house needs. A busy menu takes quite a few risks, some of which work better than others: curry smoked lamb comes with an aubergine bavarois, aubergine wafers, and an apple, raisin and pine kernel dressing, while a main-course fillet of beef is simmered in Madeira consommé and served with saffron potato gnocchi, spring greens and wild mushrooms. Not all visitors are equally impressed, but successes have included baked sea bass on a vanilla and bourbon risotto. Among desserts a citrus fruits soufflé (with grapefruit sorbet and a zingy sauce) has won acclaim. Service is well oiled, and this is one of the last remaining outposts of dome-lifting. Relatively few wines on the standard global list stay under the £20 barrier (Sauvignon Blancs from Chile and New Zealand are among them). House wine is £15.50.

CHEF: Craig Grant PROPRIETOR: Hand Picked Hotels and Arcadian OPEN: Mon to Fri and Sun L 12 to 2, all week D 7 to 9.45 MEALS: Set L £19.50, Set D £27 to £37.50. SERVICE: not inc CARDS: Amex, Delta, Diners, MasterCard, Switch, Visa DETAILS: 36 seats. 10 seats outside. Private parties: 60 main room, 60 private rooms. Car park. Vegetarian meals. Children's helpings. No smoking in dining room. Wheelchair access (also WC). Occasional music ACCOMMODATION: 45 rooms, all with bath/shower. TV. Phone. B&B £85 to £180. Rooms for disabled. Baby facilities. Fishing (*The Which? Hotel Guide*)

The Guide's longest-serving restaurants are listed near the front of the book.

WRIGHTINGTON Lancashire map 8

Mulberry Tree

NEW ENTRY

9 Wrightington Bar, Wrightington WN6 9SE
TEL/FAX: (01257) 451400
take Parbold exit from M6 junction 27 then first right down Mossy Lea road

COOKING 5
MODERN BRITISH
£24–£49

Mark Prescott, who has cooked at Le Gavroche in London, and more recently at the White Hart in Nayland, Suffolk (see entries), brings classically trained skills to this converted pub on a corner of the main street. The open-plan space has a contemporary feel, with soft colours, light beech furniture, a mulberry-tree motif and a few pub touches. Dining room and bar menus run on similar lines, the latter offering an added range of speciality sandwiches. There's also a wide choice of daily-changing blackboard specials: lobster, perhaps spicy Thai fishcakes with cucumber and chilli relish, or breast of wood pigeon with wild mushrooms and red wine sauce.

Superior skills shine through in food that displays a 'lightness of touch and good presentation', helped along by good-quality local produce. Well-received starters have included a pressed ham hock and foie gras terrine with black truffle, and a warm brioche with marinated salmon, a poached egg and hollandaise. Mains might offer roast rump of lamb with basil and tomato jus, or roast fillet of cod saltimbocca. Warm melting chocolate pudding with vanilla ice cream makes a fine finish. Terrific breads, pickles and chutneys are all home-made, and vegetables are well judged. Service, by a young team, is pleasant and attentive. A compact global list delivers Australian house wine at £9.50 (£2.50 a glass) and plenty of drinking under £20.

CHEF: Mark Prescott PROPRIETORS: James Moore and Mark Prescott OPEN: Tue to Sun 12 to 2 (3 Sun), 6 to 9 (10 Fri and Sat) CLOSED: first week Nov, D 25 Dec, 26 Dec, first 2 weeks Jan, last week May MEALS: alc exc Sun L (main courses £8.50 to £17.50). Set L Sun £15.95. Bar menu available SERVICE: not inc CARDS: Delta, MasterCard, Switch, Visa DETAILS: 70 seats. 16 seats outside. Private parties: 120 main room. Car park. Vegetarian meals. Children's helpings. No smoking in dining room. Wheelchair access (not WC). Music (£5)

WYE Kent map 3

▲ Wife Of Bath

4 Upper Bridge Street, Wye TN25 5AF
TEL: (01233) 812540 FAX: (01233) 813630
EMAIL: reservations@wifeofbath.com
WEB SITE: www.wifeofbath.com

COOKING 3
MODERN EUROPEAN
£26–£46

A Chaucerian theme predominates in John Morgan's small, elegantly decorated village restaurant, which feels like a private home. Old prints of the village and photos of the owner's daughter add to that impression, and Robert Hymers, now in his twelfth year in the kitchen, cooks in posh domestic fashion. A wide fixed-price menu choice takes in celery soup with Stilton and black pepper croûtons, smoked salmon pancakes with herb butter sauce, with maybe grilled sea bass with fennel, or roast pheasant breast classically partnered with apples and calvados, to follow. Sweetbreads and lamb are both praised by one reader, who also gave thanks for the printed menu that has replaced the verbal recitation of puddings: home-made ice creams and sorbets are the principal draw. It is all served by knowledgeable and personable staff. The wine list, opening with house vins de pays at £13.75, contains a good showing of New World bottles too.

CHEF: Robert Hymers PROPRIETOR: John Morgan OPEN: Tue to Sat 12 to 1.45, 7 to 9.45 CLOSED: 25 Dec to 2 Jan MEALS: alc L (main courses £10 to £16). Set L £11 (2 courses), Set D £25.75 SERVICE: not inc CARDS: Amex, Delta, Diners, MasterCard, Switch, Visa DETAILS: 50 seats. Private parties: 50 main room. Car park. Vegetarian meals. No pipes in dining-room. Wheelchair access. No music ACCOMMODATION: 5 rooms, all with bath/shower. TV. Phone. B&B £45 to £95. Rooms for disabled (*The Which? Hotel Guide*)

WYMONDHAM Leicestershire **map 5**

Berkeley Arms **NEW ENTRY**

59 Main Street, Wymondham LE14 2AG COOKING **2**
TEL: (01572) 787587 MODERN EUROPEAN
£26–£35

The Berkeley Arms, a kitchen-centred pub-restaurant of honey-coloured stone and pantiles, stands on Wymondham's main street with picnic tables in front and a garden behind. Its pine furniture, beams and exposed stone are simple yet tasteful, and beyond the global influences and voguish presentation lies some talent, ambition, and realistically priced food. Lunch might bring starters of parsnip soup, or a potato and Stilton tart with a sweet-sour vegetable garnish, followed perhaps by chicken tikka salad with a light chilli kick. The longer dinner menu has more elaborate dishes: maybe pan-fried breast of pigeon on bubble and squeak to begin, then Lincolnshire sausage on mustard and leek mash with onion gravy. Lemon tart is a homely, crumbly version, and chocolate truffle suitably bitter. Service is courteous. As well as real ales at the bar, there is a tiny wine list, uninspiring but keenly priced, starting at £8.

CHEF: Nick McGeown PROPRIETORS: Nick and Cathy McGeown OPEN: Tue to Sun L 12 to 2, Tue to Sat D 7 to 9 CLOSED: no food on bank hol Mons MEALS: alc (main courses £9.50 to £12.50) SERVICE: not inc, card slips closed CARDS: MasterCard, Switch, Visa DETAILS: 25 seats. 40 seats outside. Private parties: 25 main room. Car park. Vegetarian meals. Children's helpings. No smoking in dining room. Wheelchair access (also WC). Music

YARM Stockton-on-Tees **map 10**

Chadwick's

104B High Street, Yarm TS15 9AU COOKING **4**
TEL: (01642) 788558 FAX: (01642) 788344 MODERN EUROPEAN
WEB SITE: www.chadwicksrestaurant.com £23–£45

This 'modern brasserie/bistro-style' restaurant (as it describes itself) is very twenty-first-century, with subtle grey and silver décor contributing to an informal ambience in which to enjoy serious food. The word 'eclectic' might have been coined for the menu, with starters taking in Serrano ham and tomato tostada; antipasto of Italian meats; crispy duck salad with mandarins, watercress and soy; potiquet de moules farcies; Loch Fyne smoked salmon; and spanna koppita with Greek salad. Pasta and risotto are dual-priced as starters or mains.

Fish dishes include grilled salmon with fresh pasta and asparagus velouté, bourride of cod and mussels, and homely smoked haddock with Savoy cabbage, lemon and nut-brown butter. A rare ethnic starter is twice-baked Swiss cheese soufflé, while a meat option, again with singular ethnic origins, is ribeye steak, BBQ butter, south-western fries and onion rings. Masham Black Sheep ale vies with Belgian Trappist beers; wines are catholic too, with French from £10.95, and Spanish, Italian and Greek bottles jostling Californian, Chilean, South African and Antipodean.

CHEF: Phil Vaux PROPRIETOR: David Brownless OPEN: Tue to Sat; 12 to 2.30, 5.30 to 9.30 CLOSED: 16 to 23 Oct, 25 and 26 Dec, 1 Jan, bank hols MEALS: alc (main courses L £7 to £9.50, D £11 to £17). Tue to Fri 5.30 to 6.30 alc (main courses £6 to £9) SERVICE: not inc CARDS: Delta, MasterCard, Switch, Visa DETAILS: 70 seats. Private parties: 74 main room. Vegetarian meals. Children's helpings. No smoking in 1 dining room. Music

YARMOUTH Isle of Wight map 2

▲ George Hotel 🍷

Quay Street, Yarmouth PO41 0PE
TEL: (01983) 760331 FAX: (01983) 760425
EMAIL: res@thegeorge.co.uk
WEB SITE: www.thegeorge.co.uk

COOKING **3**
MODERN BRITISH
£35–£68

Right on the water's edge, with its own small, private pebbly beach, the George certainly has 'location, location, location' in its favour. As well as a club-like bar, there are two dining rooms: a formal red restaurant and a cheerful yellow brasserie with a friendly, laid-back atmosphere. We have included and marked the main restaurant in previous entries, but since all reports this year are for the brasserie, it would appear to be the most useful one to describe for our readership.

Ambition is sensibly kept in check, as the half a dozen or more choices per course run to glazed tomato tart, Thai crab soup, warm lambs' tongue salad, and perhaps a skinless 'sausage' of chicken mousse and black pudding served with a grain mustard sauce. The kitchen may not always fully exploit the seasons, serving braised oxtail with root vegetables in late May, but it handles the essentials competently: for one visitor a moist halibut steak served with endive and buttery sliced potatoes, followed by blueberry and almond gâteau with a blueberry sorbet. Service is generally well informed and professional, and a short, well-chosen wine list is organised by colour and price band, with a good selection under £20, including a number at £12.50. Choices take in smart and fruity new styles from Spain and France.

Food in the main restaurant, for the record, is of a different order of sophistication, dinner at £45 taking in pigeon with ox tongue and white-bean sauce, and sea bass fillet with poached oyster, girolles and polenta crisps.

CHEF: Kevin Mangeolles PROPRIETORS: Jeremy and Amy Willcock, and John Illsley OPEN: brasserie all week 12 to 3, 7 to 10; restaurant Tue to Sat D only 7 to 10 MEALS: brasserie alc (main courses £12.50 to £16); restaurant Set D from £45 SERVICE: none, card slips closed CARDS: Amex, MasterCard, Switch, Visa DETAILS: brasserie 80 seats. 150 seats outside. Private parties: 20 main room, 20 private room. Children's helpings. Wheelchair access (not WC). No music; restaurant 40 seats. Private parties: 20 main room, 20 private room. No children under 10. No music. Air-conditioned ACCOMMODATION: 17 rooms, all with bath/shower. TV. Phone. B&B £115 to £205 (*The Which? Hotel Guide*)

YATTENDON Berkshire map 2

▲ Royal Oak NEW ENTRY

The Square, Yattendon RG18 0UG
TEL: (01635) 201325 FAX: (01635) 201926 COOKING **2**
EMAIL: theroyaloakhotel@hotmail.com MODERN EUROPEAN
off B4009, 5m W of Pangbourne £31–£55

In this 300-year-old inn, casually set dining areas offer a brasserie-style carte and a separate vegetarian menu, while the more formal dining room serves a £35 set meal of three courses, plus amuse-bouche, coffee and petit fours. New chef Jason Gladwin has come from the Vineyard at Stockcross (see entry) and lifted standards. Many dishes now use lots of ingredients, but the complexity usually works. Restaurant starters may include 'fish delight' – tempura-fried prawns with crispy spinach, honey-roast salmon and Scottish smoked salmon with dressed leaves – or ravioli of chicken with morels. Main courses come complete with vegetables: pan-roasted tournedos of salmon and sea bass on spinach, perhaps, with a shellfish velouté and cocotte potatoes. A neat and colourful terrine of wild berries set in champagne, with passion fruit sorbet and vanilla syrup, made a 'fresh and clean-tasting finish' to an inspection meal. Service is friendly, and wines (organised by price from £11) include some from good Old and New World producers.

CHEF: Jason Gladwin PROPRIETOR: Corus & Regal Hotels OPEN: Sun L 12 to 2.30, Mon to Sat D 7 to 9.30 (10 Fri and Sat) MEALS: alc (main courses £11 to £19). Set D £35. Bar/brasserie menu also available SERVICE: 10% (optional), card slips closed CARDS: Amex, Delta, Diners, MasterCard, Switch, Visa DETAILS: 60 seats. 40 seats outside. Private parties: 28 main room, 10 private room. Car park. Vegetarian meals. Children's helpings. No smoking in 1 dining room. No music ACCOMMODATION: 5 rooms, all with bath/shower. TV. Phone. Room only £100 to £130. Baby facilities (*The Which? Hotel Guide*)

YORK North Yorkshire map 9

Melton's

7 Scarcroft Road, York YO23 1ND COOKING **5**
TEL: (01904) 634341 FAX: (01904) 635115 MODERN BRITISH
WEB SITE: www.meltonsrestaurant.co.uk £22–£42

With plain dark wood floors, magnolia walls, undressed tables and sober blue upholstery, this brasserie-style restaurant doesn't pursue trendiness. What the owners call their 'no-nonsense approach' favours simplicity and good value, to the point of including own-brand bottled water, filter coffee and service as complimentary items. The cooking, too, is simple, though technically accomplished and based on excellent raw materials.

The menu changes every couple of months, and seafood is an important element, with starters such as mussel broth with chervil, and mains of roast halibut with five-spice, sweet pepper and tomato vinaigrette, as well as a daily fish special. There's an Italian influence here, too, showing perhaps in poached egg on polenta with Jerusalem artichoke shavings, bitter leaves and truffle oil, or in cannelloni of crab and fresh herbs. Straightforward but intensely flavoured passion fruit soufflé is one way to finish, or try walnut and brandy tart.

Despite some uninspiring halves, the wine list has a refreshingly modern approach and includes some well-chosen producers. The enlightened policy of low mark-ups is praiseworthy; prices start at £10.80, and you can drink very well for under £20, from classic claret to fruit-filled southern Italian reds. The Hjorts, obviously on to a winning formula, plan another branch, Melton's Too, scheduled to open in autumn 2001.

CHEFS: Adam Holliday and Michael Hjort PROPRIETORS: Michael and Lucy Hjort OPEN: Tue to Sun L 12 to 2, Mon to Sat D 7 to 10 (early dinner 5.30 to 6.15) CLOSED: 1 week August, 3 weeks from 24 Dec MEALS: alc (main courses £10.90 to £15.95). Set L and D 5.30 to 6.15 £16.50 SERVICE: none, card slips closed CARDS: Delta, MasterCard, Switch, Visa DETAILS: 27 seats. Private parties: 36 main room, 16 private room. Vegetarian meals. Children's helpings. No smoking in 1 dining room. Wheelchair access (not WC). Music. Air-conditioned (£5)

▲ Middlethorpe Hall

Bishopthorpe Road, York YO23 2GB
TEL: (01904) 641241 FAX: (01904) 620176
EMAIL: info@middlethorpe.com
WEB SITE: www.middlethorpe.com

COOKING **3**
MODERN BRITISH
£30–£63

Few old houses get such sympathetic handling as those owned by Historic House Hotels (see other entries Bodysgallen Hall, Llandudno, and Hartwell House, Aylesbury), this one decked out on a grand scale with well-maintained gardens, gilded mirrors, chandeliers, moulded ceilings and wood panelling. If comfort and opulence appeal, this is the place to come. A similar country-house aura suffuses the food, which goes in for labour-intensive dishes such as poached quail consommé with mushroom ravioli, and luxuries from foie gras terrine to upmarket fish such as sea bass with pak choi and Chinese mushrooms.

At the same time there are earthy braises of oxtail, or pork knuckle with herb gnocchi, and squab pigeon, perhaps served with Savoy cabbage. The cooking is 'sound in most respects', making up in simple accomplishment what it may lack in flair or sparkle: a centrepiece paupiette of salmon in a champagne sauce from one visitor's fixed-price three-course lunch, for example. Desserts soothe with warm Black Forest pudding, or a selection of chocolate puddings. Luxury permeates the wine list, which is filled with elegant, though slightly high-priced delights, and is rather indulgent in champagne. Characterful house wines, starting from £14.50, are a much-needed saving grace for those on a modest budget.

CHEF: Martin Barker PROPRIETOR: Historic House Hotels Ltd OPEN: all week 12 to 1.45, 7 to 9.45 CLOSED: 25 and 31 Dec (open for residents) MEALS: Set L Mon to Sat £16 (2 courses) to £19, Set L Sun £22, Set D £36 to £45 SERVICE: net prices, card slips closed CARDS: Delta, MasterCard, Switch, Visa DETAILS: 60 seats. Private parties: 50 private rooms. Car park. Vegetarian meals. No children under 8. Jacket and tie. No smoking in dining room. Wheelchair access (not WC). No music ACCOMMODATION: 30 rooms, all with bath/shower. TV. Phone. Room only £109 to £325. No children under 8 in accommodation. Swimming pool (*The Which? Hotel Guide*)

Scotland

ABERDEEN Aberdeen **map 11**

Silver Darling

Pocra Quay, North Pier, Aberdeen AB11 5DQ
TEL/FAX: (01224) 576229

COOKING **4**
SEAFOOD
£33–£57

Although it is a fair hike from the city centre, Silver Darling has bagged a fine location down by the harbour entrance. Given the name as well (a reference to herring) there can be no doubting what drives the kitchen. For some 16 years Didier Dejean has put Aberdeen's fishy harvest through his native culinary mill and come up with a wide range of often enticing dishes, from the utterly straightforward (half a dozen oysters on ice) to the largely traditional (monkfish bourride), by way of the enterprisingly variational (steamed skate roulade with black butter and ravigote dip).

His raw materials include North Sea turbot, red snapper, sea bass, salmon (of course) and sometimes a fresh-water interloper – fillets of zander and river trout in red wine sauce – while treatments extend from a humble mussel and cockle soup, to scallop and tuna tartare with coriander and lime. There are a few land-based items, such as ravioli of foie gras and wild mushrooms, and sirloin steak with sarladaise potatoes, plus desserts of fromage blanc tart with raspberry sorbet, or iced cocoa mousse with chocolate syrup. Wines are mostly French and not outrageously priced. Two house varietals from Haut Poitou are £11.50.

CHEF/PROPRIETOR: Didier Dejean OPEN: Mon to Fri L 12 to 2, Mon to Sat D 7 to 9.30 MEALS: alc (main courses £16.50 to £19.50). Set L £19.90 (2 courses) to £24 SERVICE: not inc, card slips closed CARDS: Amex, Delta, Diners, MasterCard, Switch, Visa DETAILS: 52 seats. Private parties: 14 private room. Wheelchair access (also WC). Music

---

The 2003 Guide will be published before Christmas 2002. Reports on meals are most welcome at any time of the year, but are particularly valuable in the spring (no later than June). Send them to The Good Food Guide, *FREEPOST, 2 Marylebone Road, London NW1 4DF. Or email your report to goodfoodguide@which.net*

Card slips closed *in the details at the end of an entry indicates that the total on the slips of credit cards is closed when handed over for signature.*

ACHILTIBUIE Highland map 11

▲ Summer Isles Hotel

Achiltibuie IV26 2YG
TEL: (01854) 622282 FAX: (01854) 622251
EMAIL: summerisleshotel@aol.com
WEB SITE: www.summerisleshotel.co.uk
take A835 to Drumrunie, 10m N of Ullapool, then single-track road for 15m; hotel 1m past Achiltibuie on left

COOKING **5**
MODERN EUROPEAN
£23–£56

After a long drive on a single-track road through an apparent wilderness, you deserve a good view. But this one surpasses most expectations, and the ringside seat provided by the sunset-facing dining room of this white-painted house makes the panorama little short of breathtaking. Given the remoteness, it is not surprising to find the local environment playing its part in the operation. Lobster might come with a vermouth and butter sauce, and turbot from Lochinver has been grilled and served with capers and lime. The kitchen also busies itself smoking duck breast, to serve with poached figs and a berrymeal loaf, and stuffing home-made pasta with local crab or mussels.

Dinner is five courses, with a good balance between meat and fish – goujons of monkfish, followed by roast rib of Aberdeen Angus beef at one meal, for example – and there is no choice before dessert: chocolate hazelnut meringue, maybe, a tangy lemon flan, or steamed syrup pudding. Then cheese brings everything to a savoury conclusion. After a roll call of outstanding claret-years, the wine list divides its time between the rest of France and other global greats; the better names can be tried for less money in the 50-plus half-bottle selection. Bottle prices start at around £12.50, and eight wines, including champagne, are served by the glass.

CHEF: Chris Firth-Bernard PROPRIETORS: Mark and Gerry Irvine OPEN: all week 12.30 to 2, 8pm (1 sitting D) CLOSED: mid-Oct to Easter MEALS: alc L (main courses £9 to £25). Set D £40 SERVICE: net prices, card slips closed CARDS: MasterCard, Switch, Visa DETAILS: 28 seats. Private parties: 8 main room. Car park. Children's helpings. No children under 6. No smoking in dining room. No music ACCOMMODATION: 13 rooms, all with bath/shower. Phone. B&B £69 to £220. No children under 6. Fishing (*The Which? Hotel Guide*)

ACHNASHEEN Highland map 11

▲ Loch Torridon Hotel

Loch Torridon, by Achnasheen IV22 2EY
TEL: (01445) 791242 FAX: (01445) 791296
EMAIL: enquiries@lochtorridonhotel.com
WEB SITE: www.lochtorridonhotel.com

COOKING **3**
MODERN BRITISH
£50–£63

The magnificent untamed Highland setting, miles from anywhere, and the presence of stag's head trophies on the walls should give some idea of what this Victorian baronial-style hotel is all about. In the grand, sumptuous dining room, panelled walls, an antique sideboard, damask tablecloths and high-backed Jacobean-style chairs serve to reinforce the impression that this is a place with a history. The menu, on the other hand, has at least one foot firmly in the present.

The emphasis is on fresh produce, including some from the hotel's own gardens, and other local supplies, particularly of fish and game. These are given a variety of modern treatments, from carpaccio of tuna, or tomato tart with rocket salad and Parmesan crackling, to main courses of grilled salmon on buttered spinach with rösti, oyster beignet and vermouth cream; or rump of lamb with Bishop Kennedy cheese gratin and a Madeira sauce. Wines are predominantly French, including a page of 'fine and rare' bottles, and prices are mostly over £20, although eight house selections start at £14.

CHEF: Neil Dowson PROPRIETORS: David and Geraldine Gregory OPEN: all week 12 to 2 for light lunches, D 7.15 to 8.30. MEALS: light lunch menu, Set D £38 SERVICE: not inc CARDS: Amex, Delta, Diners, MasterCard, Switch, Visa DETAILS: 40 seats. Private parties: 40 main room, 14 private room. Car park. Children's helpings. No smoking in dining room. Wheelchair access (not WC). No music ACCOMMODATION: 20 rooms, all with bath/shower. TV. Phone. B&B £55 to £286. Rooms for disabled. Baby facilities. Fishing

ANNBANK South Ayrshire map 11

▲ Enterkine House £ **NEW ENTRY**

Annbank, Ayr KA6 5AL
TEL: (01292) 521608/520580
FAX: (01292) 521582
EMAIL: mail@enterkine.com
WEB SITE: www.enterkine.com
5m east of Ayr on B742

COOKING **3**
FRENCH/ITALIAN
£25–£52

Sitting in a commanding position overlooking rolling Ayrshire countryside, Enterkine was built as a private house in the 1930s and still feels most unlike a conventional hotel. It has no big signs advertising its presence, and no formal reception, while soft furnishings in soothing colours produce a sedate feel. Lunch is three courses, dinner four (the second perhaps tomato soup) and a short monthly-changing menu typically adopts a Franco-Italian approach, producing a classically executed leek and Parmesan risotto with a poached egg, and fine-quality organic lamb cutlets, cooked pink as requested, with accomplished provençale vegetables. Fish (from nearby Troon) has included first-rate monkfish in a light, crisp tempura-style batter with coarse pea purée.

Desserts pander to sweet-tooth Scots in the form of an 'indelicately large' portion of rich Grand Marnier parfait with citrus fruit salad, and melting malted chocolate mousse set over a yielding poached pear, enriched by a gungey toffee sauce. Appetisers are particularly good, service is efficient and unobtrusive, and varied and reasonably priced wines start with four house recommendations at £13.95.

CHEF: Douglas Smith PROPRIETOR: Oswald Browne OPEN: Wed to Sat L 12 to 2.30, all week D 7 to 9.15 MEALS: Set L £15.50, Set D £32.50 SERVICE: not inc, card slips closed CARDS: Amex, Delta, MasterCard, Switch, Visa DETAILS: 38 seats. Private parties: 28 main room, 14 private room. Car park. No smoking in dining room. Wheelchair access (also WC). No music ACCOMMODATION: 6 rooms, all with bath/shower. TV. Phone. D, B&B £120 to £150. Rooms for disabled. No children under 7. Fishing (£5)

denotes an outstanding wine cellar; denotes a good wine list, worth travelling for.

ANSTRUTHER Fife map 11

Cellar

24 East Green, Anstruther KY10 3AA
TEL: (01333) 310378

COOKING **6**
MODERN SEAFOOD
£26–£69

After many years looking just the same, with rough stone walls and sewing machine tables, the Cellar is to be extended with a new reception area. But the fundamentals remain unchanged, as Peter Jukes observes the seasons, serving mussels in winter, and crabs from May to September. Much of the repertoire may be familiar – a creamy Finnan haddock omelette, perhaps, or lobster thermidor – but the kitchen also takes on board some bright flavours, such as seared tuna with cracked coriander and black pepper, and pesto-crusted cod.

The freshness and quality of supplies is evident in 'some of the best fish I have eaten in my life' for a reporter who dined on halibut resting on a bed of cabbage with bacon and pine kernels. Prime species are the norm, along the lines of turbot paired with Isle of Mull scallops, served with leeks and a white wine sauce, and salmon appears in a number of guises: in a quiche, as a pairing of hot-smoked and cold-smoked, and blackened and spiced, accompanied by sun-dried tomato couscous. Non-fish eaters might be offered Scotch beef fillet with wild mushrooms, and desserts tend to be simple but effective affairs such as vanilla ice cream with soft fruits and a matching sauce.

On the wine list, heavyweights sit beside well-selected bottles at more approachable prices from the major wine-growing regions, with seafood-friendly whites from Alsace receiving fair attention. Almost 30 mainly French halves are offered, encouraging changeovers throughout the meal, and house German white is £15.

CHEF: Peter Jukes PROPRIETORS: Peter and Susan Jukes OPEN: Wed to Sun L 12.30 to 1.30, all week D 6.30 to 9.30 MEALS: Set L £14.50 (2 courses) to £16.50, Set D £24.50 (2 courses) to £45 SERVICE: not inc, card slips closed CARDS: Amex, Delta, Diners, MasterCard, Switch, Visa DETAILS: 40 seats. Private parties: 40 main room. Children's helpings. No children under 8. No smoking in dining room. Occasional music

ARISAIG Highland map 11

▲ Arisaig House

Beasdale, by Arisaig PH39 4NR
TEL: (01687) 450622 FAX: (01687) 450626
EMAIL: arisaighse@aol.com
WEB SITE: www.arisaighouse.co.uk,
www.arisaighouse.com
on A830, 3m E of Arisaig

COOKING **6**
FRANCO-SCOTTISH
£39–£80

Giant American redwoods feature among the garden's 20 acres of arboreal treasures, and although the stone-built house is Victorian – with walled gardens, including one for fruit and vegetables – an extensive pre-war renovation gives the house more of a 1930s atmosphere. The dining room has a rather formal feel, and the kitchen's efforts are concentrated on four-course dinners, the second a choice of sorbet, soup (from asparagus to Cullen skink), or salad. Local materials and French ideas combine to produce a range of dishes that don't stray far from classical territory, taking in jambonette of quail, braised guinea fowl with sauerkraut, and veal with artichoke barigoule.

Fish often gets a Mediterranean treatment (sea bass, for example, served with 'basil-scented' potatoes, black olives and sauce vierge), while Highland venison might come with more native creamed celeriac and juniper game jus. The appealing variety of savoury dishes is echoed in desserts that might take in a hot soufflé with Baileys and chocolate chips, and glazed poached pear with eau de vie sorbet. Wines under £20 are in the minority, but quality on the largely French list is convincing, and five house wines from £14.50 set the ball rolling.

CHEF: Duncan Gibson PROPRIETORS: Ruth, John and Andrew Smither OPEN: all week 12.30 to 2, 7.15 to 8.45 CLOSED: 1 Dec to 28 Feb MEALS: alc light L menu (main courses £4.50 to £12.50). Set L £25, Set D £32.50 to £55 SERVICE: not inc, card slips closed CARDS: Delta, MasterCard, Switch, Visa DETAILS: 30 seats. 10 seats outside. Private parties: 30 main room. Car park. Vegetarian meals. No children under 8 exc babies. No smoking in dining room. Wheelchair access (also WC). No music ACCOMMODATION: 12 rooms, all with bath/shower. TV. Phone. B&B £110 to £295. No children under 8 exc babies. Baby facilities (*The Which? Hotel Guide*)

AUCHMITHIE Angus map 11

But 'n' Ben £

Auchmithie DD11 5SQ COOKING **2**
TEL: (01241) 877223 FAX: (01241) 430901 SEAFOOD/TRADITIONAL SCOTTISH
on coast, 3m NE of Arbroath, off A92 £18–£47

Considered 'the epitome of homeliness', But 'n' Ben occupies a couple of simply converted cottages overlooking a rocky, weather-beaten stretch of coastline. It makes the most of its location (Arbroath is just down the road) by serving smokies in pancakes, in kedgeree, with poached egg, or just buttered. Lobsters, crabs and langoustines come direct from fishermen and are treated straightforwardly (a lemon butter sauce for lobster perhaps), and dishes are rarely anything but comforting, judging by battered, deep-fried monkfish, and fish pie with a mashed potato crust. Beef also features (they have the advantage of a local abattoir) either as a plain grilled steak or perhaps in beef bourguignon, and in order to service the breakfasts and afternoon teas the kitchen does a lot of baking, as well as making jams and chutneys. Desserts are served from a trolley. Around 30 wines are sensibly priced, starting with house vins de pays at £9.50.

CHEFS: Margaret and Angus Horn PROPRIETORS: Margaret, Iain and Angus Horn OPEN: Wed to Mon 12 to 2.30, 7 to 9.30 CLOSED: 26 Dec, 1 Jan MEALS: alc (main courses £5.50 to £19.50) SERVICE: not inc CARDS: Diners, MasterCard, Switch, Visa DETAILS: 40 seats. Private parties: 50 main room. Car park. Children's helpings. No smoking in dining room. Wheelchair access (also WC). No music (£5)

All details are as accurate as possible at the time of going to press, but chefs and owners often change, and it is wise to check by telephone before making a special journey. Many readers have been disappointed when set-price bargain meals are no longer available. Ask when booking.

AUCHTERARDER Perthshire & Kinross map 11

▲ Auchterarder House

Auchterarder PH3 1DZ
TEL: (01764) 663646 FAX: (01764) 662939
EMAIL: auchterarder@wrensgroup.com
WEB SITE: www.auchterarderhouse.com

COOKING **2**
MODERN SCOTTISH
£33–£67

Grand baronial mansions on this scale were all the rage in the early part of the nineteenth century. Though undoubtedly impressive, it can seem a little overbearing for modern tastes: the dining room, with oak-block floor, candelabras and an ornate fireplace, would be just the place to hold a banquet. Dinner is four courses with three options at each stage, except for the second which might be a 'compulsory' lavender-soaked lemon lasagne of West Coast seafood. The style is quite as elaborate as the setting, with plenty of highly wrought, labour-intensive constructions: among starters, for example, might be a ballottine of chicken, lentils and pheasant on a bed of red wine and beetroot barley risotto with glazed chestnuts, while main courses encompass Perthshire venison loin with beetroot noodles, smoked paprika cakes and tarragon. Typical among desserts might be a barbecued banana soufflé with rum and raisin sorbet and spicy tropical fruits. Bottle prices rarely dip below £24 on the wine list, and looking for something under £20 will yield no results, but for those seeking finesse whatever the cost, good names from regions classic and new should satisfy.

CHEF: Willie Deans PROPRIETOR: Wren's Hotel Group OPEN: all week 12.30 to 2, 7 to 9.30 MEALS: alc L (main courses £8 to £9.50). Set D £39.50 SERVICE: not inc CARDS: Amex, Diners, MasterCard, Switch, Visa DETAILS: 45 seats. 10 seats outside. Private parties: 60 main room, 14 and 40 private rooms. Car park. Vegetarian meals. Children's helpings. No smoking in dining room. Wheelchair access (not WC). No music ACCOMMODATION: 15 rooms, all with bath/shower. TV. Phone. B&B £135 to £295. Baby facilities

Andrew Fairlie at Gleneagles

NEW ENTRY

Gleneagles Hotel, Auchterarder PH3 1NF
TEL: (01764) 694267 FAX: (01764) 694163
EMAIL: andrew.fairlie@gleneaegles.com

COOKING **5**
MODERN FRENCH
£79–£115

Although located in the hotel, the restaurant is a separate business, signalled by a black lectern at the entrance with the letters AF intertwined: readers may remember Andrew Fairlie from One Devonshire Gardens in Glasgow. Paintings of him adorn the dining room, and he seems to have adopted Henry Ford's approach: you can have any colour of walls or menu so long as it is black. The style is uncompromisingly French, evident in a brandade of cod with a confit of provençale vegetables, and an 'assiette of pork Gascony', although a few contemporary flourishes ring the changes: rack of lamb, for example, served with breadcrumbed sweetbread and a well-cooked half-kidney 'devilled' with wasabi, on top of seasonal peas and broad beans.

Prices are not cheap, though luxuries abound. A couple of courses on the tasting menu deploy truffles: summer truffle ravioli with woodland mushrooms and a white bean sauce, and first-class truffle gnocchi to accompany roast squab pigeon with braised cabbage. Other dishes on this menu continue the theme in the shape of a marjolaine of foie gras with peach chutney, and lightly smoked tender lobster served with herb butter sauce, well complemented by its flavourful watercress salad. This menu ends with a hot chocolate pudding. Cheese comes as a generous plated selection with grapes, oatcakes and poppyseed biscuits, and desserts have included a sweet, well-flavoured hot cherry soufflé with matching sorbet.

Service is attentive – too much so for our inspector, with constant topping up and conversations interrupted – but staff are affable and cheerful. Wines are high quality but not for the faint-hearted, with little under £30 and nothing under £20, although a dozen by the glass might help the wallet if you sip slowly.

CHEF/PROPRIETOR: Andrew Fairlie OPEN: Mon to Sat D only 6.30 to 10 CLOSED: 2 weeks Jan MEALS: alc (main courses £27). Set D £75 SERVICE: not inc CARDS: Amex, Delta, Diners, MasterCard, Switch, Visa DETAILS: 40 seats. Private parties: 40 main room. Car park. Vegetarian meals. No smoking in dining room. Wheelchair access (also WC). Music. Air-conditioned

AULDEARN Highland map 11

▲ Boath House

Auldearn IV12 5LE
TEL: (01667) 454896 FAX: (01667) 455469
EMAIL: wendy@boath-house.demon.co.uk COOKING **5**
WEB SITE: www.boath-house.com FRANCO-SCOTTISH
on A96, 2m E of Nairn £37–£58

Set back from the Inverness to Aberdeen road, in 20 acres of grounds, this Grade A listed Georgian mansion looks out on a restful vista of lawns and old trees. Inside, walls are covered with work by local painters and craftsmen, and the friendly and chatty owners greet and serve. If prices appear to have escalated since last year, that is because the format has now moved to a four-course lunch and five-course dinner, with a simple two-way choice at main course and dessert stage. Ideas contrive to be both sensible and interesting, and materials appear well sourced. Chicken is maize-fed (perhaps in a warm galantine with smoked ham knuckle), scallops are dived (as part of a seafood 'medley' on braised lentils), and halibut may be from the West Coast, served at one meal with pappardelle and asparagus in a saffron and chive velouté.

Meals typically start with soup – usually with a touch of luxury such as green pea with foie gras and truffle oil – followed at dinner by salmon carpaccio with horseradish cream, before a fish or meat option, the latter taking in ribeye steak with clapshot and buttered spinach. A specific cheese – such as Bonnet goats' with green figs and beetroot relish – precedes dessert of pineapple on spiced bread with cinnamon ice cream perhaps, or chocolate truffle torte with a pumpkin sorbet. Wines on the regularly updated list major on France, but also provide a good global sampling. Prices stay mostly above £20, though six house wines (including one from Mexico) start at £12, and there are around a dozen half-bottles.

CHEF: Charles Lockley PROPRIETORS: Don and Wendy Matheson OPEN: Wed to Sun L 12.30 to 1.45, all week D 7 to 8.45 CLOSED: last 2 weeks Jan MEALS: Set L £24.95, Set D £35 SERVICE: not inc CARDS: Amex, Delta, MasterCard, Switch, Visa DETAILS: 32 seats. Private parties: 26 main room. Car park. Vegetarian meals. Children's helpings. No smoking in dining room. Wheelchair access (also WC). Music ACCOMMODATION: 7 rooms, all with bath/shower. TV. Phone. B&B £90 to £175. Rooms for disabled. Baby facilities. Fishing (*The Which? Hotel Guide*) (£5)

AYR South Ayrshire map 11

Fouters Bistro

2A Academy Street, Ayr KA7 1HS
TEL: (01292) 261391 FAX: (01292) 619323 COOKING **1**
EMAIL: qualityfood@fouters.co.uk MODERN SCOTTISH
WEB SITE: www.fouters.co.uk £20–£51

The narrow stone-flagged cellar has had a stark revamp in bright blue and white, and although it is hardly the last word in comfort it does offer a friendly welcome and a good-humoured atmosphere. Scottish materials include ultra-fresh seafood – plump West Coast scallops, and a daily special of crisp-skinned silver bream served with new potatoes – although the kitchen obviously seeks inspiration elsewhere too: chicken comes with mango salsa, and Ayrshire lamb with Moroccan-spiced couscous. Among highlights has been a crisp and buttery pastry starter with red onion confit and browned goats' cheese, while recommended desserts have included banana parfait laced with dark rum, and chocolate mousse with sweet shortbread. Some three dozen wines from France, Italy and Switzerland start around £12.

CHEFS: Laurie Black and Lewis Pringle PROPRIETORS: Laurie and Fran Black OPEN: Tue to Sat 12 to 2, 6 to 10 CLOSED: 25 to 27 Dec, 1 to 3 Jan MEALS: alc (main courses L £5 to £14, D £9 to £17) SERVICE: not inc CARDS: Amex, Delta, Diners, MasterCard, Switch, Visa DETAILS: 38 seats. Private parties: 14 main room, 14 private room. Vegetarian meals. Children's helpings. No smoking in 1 dining room. No pipes in dining room. Occasional music. Air-conditioned (£5)

BALLATER Aberdeenshire map 11

▲ Balgonie Country House

Braemar Place, Ballater AB35 5NQ
TEL/FAX: (013397) 55482
EMAIL: balgoniech@aol.com COOKING **3**
WEB SITE: www.royaldeesidehotels.com MODERN SCOTTISH
off A93, on W outskirts of Ballater £30–£52

An Edwardian house in a peaceful setting, with four acres of garden and impeccable housekeeping standards, Balgonie is well placed for some traditional Scottish pursuits, including golfing and following the Malt Whisky Trail. Traditional ideas also tend to rule in the four-course dinners that are the kitchen's main preoccupation: from mint-flavoured pea soup, via chicken liver and pheasant terrine, to roast saddle of Scottish lamb with rosemary jus. Starter salads have included pigeon breast with raspberry vinaigrette, and an enterprising one of Arbroath smokies and black pudding with lemon vinaigrette, while fish might run to herb-crusted cod with saffron risotto. Mocha fudge tart, and tiramisù torte with Tia Maria sauce show a penchant for indulgent desserts. John Finnie lists himself as chef although, according to a reporter, since he waits on tables he must have everything cooked, ready and waiting by 7.30. More than half of the 60 wines are French, the rest a varied global selection, and there is fair choice under £20.

CHEF: John Finnie PROPRIETORS: John and Priscilla Finnie OPEN: all week 12.30 to 2 (reservations only), 7 to 9 CLOSED: 5 Jan to 10 Feb MEALS: Set L £19, Set D £31 SERVICE: not inc, card slips closed CARDS: Amex, Delta, Diners, MasterCard, Switch, Visa DETAILS: 30 seats. Private parties: 30 main room. Car park. Children's helpings. No smoking in dining room. Wheelchair access (also WC). No music ACCOMMODATION: 9 rooms, all with bath/shower. TV. Phone. B&B £60 to £130. Baby facilities (*The Which? Hotel Guide*)

▲ Darroch Learg

Braemar Road, Ballater AB35 5UX
TEL: (013397) 55443 FAX: (013397) 55252
off A93 Ballater to Braemar Road at western edge of village

COOKING **6**
MODERN SCOTTISH
£27–£57

Darroch Learg is a country house of some charm, situated to the west of the village with fine views across the hills. Recent reports have found the kitchen 'firing on all cylinders' as David Mutter continues to impress reporters with his accomplished modern Scottish cooking. The foundation is assiduous attention to detail: top-quality materials carefully sourced from respected Scottish producers, including meat from a local butcher, venison ('some of the best we have ever tasted') from Balmoral estate, and locally gathered wild mushrooms; and everything from bread and pasta to chutneys and shortbread are made in-house. There is also an appealing lack of pretentiousness about his style: menus are devoid of flowery descriptions, and options on the light lunch menu are as down-to-earth as smoked salmon sandwiches, or as refined as ravioli of Loch Fyne crab with Parmesan cream and pesto.

A touch of luxury is introduced to the evening set-price menu: foie gras and truffles crop up in several dishes, the former in a terrine of ham hock served with pea purée, the latter with broad beans to accompany roast loin of veal. Fish and shellfish predominate among starters, perhaps roast fillet of cod with a mussel broth, while main courses are mostly meat-based: loin of Deeside lamb, for example, on a bed of ratatouille with puréed potatoes and a red wine sauce; or rare and tender saddle of venison accompanied by figs and black pudding, which proved 'an excellent combination' for one reporter. To finish, there may be vanilla parfait with hazelnut sponge and warm mulled fruits. If there is a down side it is that service can be slow and 'seems to disappear' towards the end of the evening. A fat wine list pays homage to the traditional regions of Europe and brings out new classic styles from the rest of the world. Prices appear fair – they hover around the £20-mark – with house wines starting at £17.10, for a New Zealand Sauvignon Blanc.

CHEF: David Mutter PROPRIETOR: the Franks family OPEN: all week 12.30 to 2, 5 to 9 CLOSED: Christmas and last 3 weeks of Jan MEALS: Set L £19.50, Set L Sun £18.50, Set D £34. Light L menu available Mon to Sat SERVICE: net prices, card slips closed CARDS: Amex, Diners, MasterCard, Switch, Visa DETAILS: 48 seats. 8 seats outside. Private parties: 62 main room. Car park. Vegetarian meals. Children's helpings. No smoking in dining room. Wheelchair access (not WC). No music ACCOMMODATION: 18 rooms, all with bath/shower. TV. Phone. Rooms for disabled. Baby facilities (*The Which? Hotel Guide*)

▲ Green Inn

9 Victoria Road, Ballater AB35 5QQ
TEL/FAX: (013397) 55701
EMAIL: info@greeninn.com
WEB SITE: www.green-inn.com

COOKING **5**
MODERN SCOTTISH
£43–£51

The dining room has been given a fresh feel with updated décor, but otherwise it's business as usual. Jeffrey Purves keeps himself busy in the kitchen while wife Carol takes charge front-of-house, creating a friendly, informal ambience. A short essay at the front of the menu sets out the philosophy behind the cooking, which places admirable emphasis on local supplies, and displays a sensitivity to environmental concerns (they serve only male lobsters and diver-caught scallops); game is from local forests and moors.

A penchant for elaborate combinations often brings together several traditional Scottish flavours in imaginative new arrangements: a labour-intensive starter of guinea fowl breast stuffed with haggis mousse, served with a Lochnagar whisky and raisin jus impressed its reporter, while another enjoyed a simpler alliance of sea bass fillet with avocado salsa. Among main courses, grilled fillet of Angus beef topped with a Strathdon blue cheese soufflé in a port jus has come in for praise; alternatives may run to roast monkfish on ratatouille with a pesto dressing, and loin of pork with black pudding and mustard cream sauce.

To finish, a first-class list of Scottish cheeses is offered, all from small specialist producers; otherwise there are inventive desserts such as iced basil soufflé with caramelised pear and peppercorn syrup, or prune and frangipane flan with Laphroaig whisky ice cream. The small but well-formed wine list offers plenty of choice under £20 (under £10 in the halves section), from Australian old-vine Grenache to white Bordeaux. Six global styles are offered by the glass, and house wines start at £11.60, for a Loire red.

CHEF: Jeffrey Purves PROPRIETORS: Jeffrey and Carol Purves OPEN: all week D only 7 to 9 CLOSED: Sun and Mon Oct to end Mar, 4 days Christmas, 2 weeks Dec MEALS: Set D £27.50 (2 courses) to £31.50 SERVICE: not inc CARDS: Amex, Delta, Diners, MasterCard, Switch, Visa DETAILS: 32 seats. Private parties: 32 main room. Vegetarian meals. Children's helpings. No smoking in dining room. Wheelchair access (not WC). Music. Air-conditioned ACCOMMODATION: 3 rooms, all with bath/shower. TV. D,B&B £70 to £119 (*The Which? Hotel Guide*) (£5)

The Guide relies on feedback from its readers. Especially welcome are reports on new restaurants appearing in the book for the first time. All letters to the Guide are acknowledged.

Net prices *in the details at the end of an entry indicates that the prices given on a menu and on a bill are inclusive of VAT and service charge, and that this practice is clearly stated on menu and bill.*

BALQUHIDDER Stirling — map 11

SCOTLAND GFG 2002 COMMENDED

▲ Monachyle Mhor

Balquhidder FK19 8PQ
TEL: (01877) 384622 FAX: (01877) 384305
EMAIL: info@monachylemhor.com
WEB SITE: www.monachylemhor.com
6m W of A84 turning at Kingshouse

COOKING **4**
MODERN SCOTTISH
£24–£50

This 'treasure in the Trossachs' merits enthusiasm not only for its scenery, but also for its hospitality – Jean Lewis remains 'the centre of social interaction' both before and after dinner – and for its approach to food. Local and organic ingredients play a part. Some are grown in the hotel's own vegetable and herb garden, grouse and venison come from the estate and trout from the loch; wild berries and mushrooms are collected, and Tom Lewis has tried his hand at curing ham.

The cooking is not complicated or ambitious but honest and unfussy – fresh, lightly grilled sardines on dressed leaves, for example, or homely red onion and tomato soup set alight by a slick of garlicky pesto – and accurate timing shows in first-rate salmon with hollandaise and thin pasta ribbons, topped with pieces of chilli squid. Desserts are equally impressive, judging by an inspector's poached plums in syrup with vanilla-speckled pannacotta. A friendly, wide-ranging wine list – briefly annotated and sensibly priced – includes six house wines, among them a Vin de Pays d'Oc Viognier and an easy-drinking Pécharmant red.

CHEF: Tom Lewis PROPRIETORS: Rob, Jean and Tom Lewis OPEN: all week 12 to 1.45, 7 to 8.45 MEALS: alc (main courses £8.50 to £12.50). Set L Sun £17.50, Set D £32.50 SERVICE: not inc, card slips closed CARDS: Delta, MasterCard, Switch, Visa DETAILS: 36 seats. 20 seats outside. Private parties: 36 main room, 10 and 12 private rooms. Car park. No children under 12. No smoking in dining room. Wheelchair access (also WC). No music ACCOMMODATION: 10 rooms, all with bath/shower. TV. Phone. B&B £55 to £95. No children under 12. Fishing (*The Which? Hotel Guide*)

BLAIR ATHOLL Perthshire & Kinross — map 11

Loft £

Golf Course Road, Blair Atholl PH18 5TE
TEL: (01796) 481377 FAX: (01796) 481511
EMAIL: theloftrestaurant@amserve.com
WEB SITE: www.theloftrestaurant.co.uk

NEW CHEF
MODERN SCOTTISH/MEDITERRANEAN
£19–£55

Occupying a former hayloft, with twisted beams, stone walls and oak flooring, this is an operation that aims to appeal across a broad spectrum of tastes. A bistro menu offers the likes of Caesar salad and Thai chicken curry, while the main dining room goes in for goats' cheese ravioli, sea bass with sauce vierge, and roast saddle of venison. There have been changes in the kitchen, but we learned of the arrival of Paul Collins, last listed in the 2000 edition of the Guide at Lucknam Park (see entry, Colerne), too late to send an inspector or receive any feedback. His track record, however, suggests that this will be a place to watch. Reports, please.

CHEF: Paul Collins PROPRIETOR: Marise Richardson OPEN: Tue to Sun L 12 to 2.30, Tue to Sat 6 to 9.30 CLOSED: Tue Nov to Mar MEALS: alc exc Sun L (main courses £6 to £16). Set L Sun £7.95 (2 courses) to £10.75, Set D £32.50 SERVICE: not inc CARDS: Amex, Delta, Diners, MasterCard, Switch, Visa DETAILS: 56 seats. 30 seats outside. Private parties: 56 main room, 22 and 34 private rooms. Car park. Vegetarian meals. Children's helpings. No smoking in dining room. Music. Air-conditioned (£5)

BLAIRGOWRIE Perthshire & Kinross map 11

▲ Kinloch House Hotel 🍷

Blairgowrie PH10 6SG
TEL: (01250) 884237 FAX: (01250) 884333
EMAIL: info@kinlochhouse.com COOKING **4**
WEB SITE: www.kinlochhouse.com SCOTTISH
on A923, 3m W of Blairgowrie towards Dunkeld £22–£72

Here is Scottish hospitality in the grand manner. The ivy-covered Victorian stone house – beautifully set in 25 acres overlooking the Lunan Burn – has panelled rooms, waiting staff formally dressed in tartans, a log fire and sumptuous antique furniture. Quality ingredients are central: the Scottish menu (there are main and vegetarian menus too) might include Highland salmon, braised shoulder of lamb, Arbroath smokies or pan-fried fillet of Aberdeen Angus, and an increasingly common 'quality assurance' declaration on the back proclaims the restaurant's dedication to fresh, local and (where possible) organic, wild and GM-free foods.

The three-course set lunch is good value. A springtime visit might yield a simple, light starter of marinated topside of Angus beef, followed by a grilled tranche of pleasingly fresh salmon with parsley and caper butter, rounded off by a light, clear pink grapefruit, orange and passion fruit terrine with mango and strawberry syrup. The annotated wine list boasts an impressive selection of classed-growth claret, and Burgundy (red and white) is another mainstay. Though its strengths lie in France, it also contains some well-chosen New World bottles and a notable selection of halves. Thirteen house wines start at £14.95.

CHEF: Bill McNicoll PROPRIETORS: the Shentall family OPEN: all week 12.30 to 2, 7 to 9.15 CLOSED: 19 to 29 Dec MEALS: Set L £12.50, Set D £25 (2 courses) to £34 SERVICE: not inc, card slips closed CARDS: Amex, Delta, Diners, MasterCard, Switch, Visa DETAILS: 55 seats. Private parties: 55 main room, 20 private room. Car park. Vegetarian meals. No children under 7 at D. Jacket and tie. No smoking in dining room at D. Wheelchair access (also WC). No music ACCOMMODATION: 20 rooms, all with bath/shower. TV. Phone. D,B&B £95 to £270. Rooms for disabled. Baby facilities. Swimming pool. Fishing (*The Which? Hotel Guide*)

Although the cuisine style noted at the top of entries has in most cases been suggested to the Guide by the restaurants, some have been edited for brevity or appropriateness.

The Guide relies on feedback from its readers. Especially welcome are reports on new restaurants appearing in the book for the first time. All letters to the Guide are acknowledged.

CAIRNDOW Argyll & Bute map 11

Loch Fyne Oyster Bar £

Clachan, Cairndow PA26 8BH
TEL: (01499) 600236 FAX: (01499) 600234
EMAIL: info@loch-fyne.com
WEB SITE: www.loch-fyne.com
on A83, at head of Loch Fyne

COOKING **2**
TRADITIONAL SEAFOOD
£20–£68

From humble beginnings some 25 years ago, Loch Fyne has become big business, currently rolling out branches across the country. The underlying philosophy is as simple as it is laudable: take fresh fish and shellfish from the loch, and serve it straight away without embellishment. Hence a menu dealing in fresh oysters (plain, or perhaps baked with Mornay sauce), lobster mayonnaise, a shellfish platter, and queen scallops with garlic butter. Smoked fish, another speciality, includes salmon in various forms, from superior cold-smoked Kinglas fillet to hot-smoked bradan rost. In practice, disregarding the ideological tussle between wild and farmed salmon ('sustainable' farming underpins this operation), the kitchen's ambition can run ahead of itself: standards seem to fluctuate, and disappointing dishes are reported. Nevertheless the bar makes a fine roadside halt for the simplest of seafood dishes, backed up by a short, serviceable wine list starting with house white at £9.95.

CHEFS: Tracy Wyatt and Rachel McCuaig PROPRIETORS: John Noble and Andrew Lane OPEN: all week 9 to 8.30 CLOSED: 25 and 26 Dec, 1 and 2 Jan MEALS: alc (main courses L £5 to £9, D £6 to £16) SERVICE: not inc CARDS: Amex, Delta, Diners, MasterCard, Switch, Visa DETAILS: 130 seats. Private parties: 45 main room. Car park. Vegetarian meals. Children's helpings. No smoking in 1 dining room. Wheelchair access (also WC). Occasional music

CLACHAN-SEIL Argyll & Bute map 11

▲ Willowburn Hotel

Clachan-Seil, By Oban PA34 4TJ
TEL: (01852) 300276 FAX: (01852) 300597
EMAIL: willowburn.hotel@virgin.net
WEB SITE: www.willowburn.co.uk
from Oban take A816 S for 8m; then take B844, following signs for Seil Island and Luing, for 7m; after hump-backed bridge Willowburn is 400 metres on left

COOKING **2**
MODERN SCOTTISH/FRENCH
£35–£45

Those in search of peace and quiet (and maybe a bit of birdwatching or otter spotting) have a lot to choose from on the West Coast, and this place is a match for any. Reached by the Clachan Bridge over the Atlantic, it stands in an acre and a half of grounds beside Clachan Sound, serves four-course dinners (the second a soup or sorbet), and makes a point of using fresh local produce. Herbs and vegetables come from the garden, wild fruits and plants are picked while walking the dogs, and home smoking takes in anything from salmon and duck to cheese and shellfish.

Fish is landed at Oban, and shellfish comes from the waters around Corryvreckan: maybe turned into lobster and scallop sausages and served on a frothy saffron sauce. Lamb, direct from the farmer, has appeared as marinated loin with a coriander, buckwheat and orange stuffing, and desserts range from a tuile basket of warm strawberries in vanilla sauce, to weightier clootie dumpling with custard, and chocolate bread-and-butter pudding. A short, varied, reasonably priced wine list starts with four or five house wines at £10.95. Those who stay for breakfast can reckon on old-fashioned bacon and free-range eggs.

CHEF: Chris Mitchell PROPRIETORS: Chris Mitchell and Jan Wolfe OPEN: all week D only 7 to 8 CLOSED: Jan and Feb MEALS: Set D £26 SERVICE: not inc, card slips closed CARDS: Delta, MasterCard, Switch, Visa DETAILS: 24 seats. Private parties: 10 main room. Car park. Vegetarian meals. Chidren's helpings. No smoking in dining room. Music ACCOMMODATION: 7 rooms, all with bath/shower. TV. D,B&B £60 to £120. Baby facilities (*The Which? Hotel Guide*) (£5)

COLBOST Highland **map 11**

▲ Three Chimneys

Colbost, Dunvegan, Isle of Skye IV55 8ZT
TEL: (01470) 511258 FAX: (01470) 511358
EMAIL: eatandstay@threechimneys.co.uk
WEB SITE: www.threechimneys.co.uk
on B884, 4m W of Dunvegan

COOKING **5**
MODERN SCOTTISH
£30–£83

A pair of crofters' cottages they may be, with bare stone walls and wooden tables, but this is a design-conscious restaurant with a degree of elegance and sophistication. Artistic endeavour does not stop at the furnishings and paintings, but imbues the simply but carefully styled food as well. Given the location, seafood is understandably a strength, evident in perfectly cooked fish from whole sole to a halibut steak on a bed of leeks and fennel with crisp rösti. Organic produce from local market gardens also features, as does Skye lamb, the grilled loin perhaps served with pearl barley risotto.

Fine ingredients given modestly inventive treatment have produced commendable starters such as a small brochette of scallops, monkfish and courgette with a fresh coriander and lime butter, and a slice of strongly flavoured but lightly textured hot crab tart, served with warm tomato vinaigrette and accompanied by a small colourful salad of green and grey leaves and blue flowers. To finish, hot marmalade pudding with Drambuie custard continues to be number-one favourite, but also to be reckoned with are an apple, apricot and treacle tart with cinnamon ice cream, and a deeply flavoured damson parfait served with slices of crisp dessert pear and damson syrup. A sound collection of styles from Europe and the New World, sprinkled with some notable producers, provides the backbone of the wine list. Opening with three house wines from £14.95, and then both sparkling and still wines from southern France, the list ends with a collection of good-value fine old bins from less-collected vintages.

CHEFS: Shirley Spear and Isabel Tomlin PROPRIETORS: Eddie and Shirley Spear OPEN: Mon to Sat L 12.30 to 2, all week D 6.30 to 9.30 CLOSED: 7 to 24 Jan MEALS: Set L £12.95 (2 courses) to £17.95, Set D £25.50 (2 courses) to £40 SERVICE: not inc CARDS: Amex, Delta, MasterCard, Switch, Visa DETAILS: 40 seats. 6 seats outside. Private parties: 20 main room, 20 private room.

Car park. Vegetarian meals. Children's helpings. No young children at D. No smoking in dining room. Wheelchair access (not WC). No music ACCOMMODATION: 6 rooms, all with bath/shower. TV. Phone. B&B £100 to £160. Rooms for disabled. Baby facilities (*The Which? Hotel Guide*) (£5)

CRINAN Argyll & Bute map 11

▲ Crinan Hotel, Westward Restaurant

NEW ENTRY

Crinan PA31 8SR
TEL: (01546) 830261 FAX: (01546) 830292
EMAIL: nryan@crinanhotel.com
WEB SITE: www.crinanhotel.com
off A816, 6m NW of Lochgilphead

COOKING **5**
MODERN SCOTTISH
£54–£65

Crinan's potential, long under-exploited, now seems to be realised under Mark Wishart (last in the Guide in 2000, with his own restaurant in Dumfries). The hotel enjoys a tranquil setting above a tiny harbour with peerless views across to the hills of Jura, the inside filled with Frances Macdonald's colourist seascapes and infused with an air of unhurried enjoyment. The two dining options – Westward and Lock 16 – are separate entities, each with its own menu. Nicolas Ryan takes charge of the latter, while Mark Wishart runs the former, serving four courses in which local and regional supplies play their part.

Despite smoked salmon and Angus beef, what Westward has on offer is far removed from tourist fodder. The beef, for example, has appeared as a splendid piece of seared, mature-flavoured fillet, 'masterfully handled', served with a zingy parsley purée and red wine reduction. Mark Wishart cooks with commendable simplicity, producing an accurately rendered risotto flavoured with chervil, chives and parsley, and a creamy ragoût of West Coast halibut, brill, monk and sole. Not everything is perfect – some temperatures, textures and flavours at inspection could have been improved with a little more care – but desserts have included a velvety bitter chocolate mousse with a perfectly poached pear, and a classic nursery rice pudding. Coffee has disappointed, but the welcome is friendly, service courteous, and the Ryans keep an eagle eye on proceedings. Wines cover a lot of ground, with something for most pockets, starting with vin de pays at £13.

CHEF: Mark Wishart PROPRIETORS: Nicolas and Frances Ryan OPEN: all week D only 7 to 9 MEALS: Set D £42.50 SERVICE: not inc, card slips closed CARDS: Amex, MasterCard, Switch, Visa DETAILS: 25 seats. 20 seats outside. Private parties: 60 main room, 20 private room. Car park. Children's helpings. No smoking in dining room. Wheelchair access (also WC). Occasional music ACCOMMODATION: 20 rooms, all with bath/shower. TV. Phone. D,B&B £75 to £220. Rooms for disabled. Baby facilities (*The Which? Hotel Guide*) (£5)

'This was way, way below the standard of my local chippie, and way, way below the standard of my work canteen, which serves 2,000 people a day and has the virtue of being free.'
(On eating in London)

CROSSMICHAEL Dumfries & Galloway map 11

Plumed Horse

SCOTLAND NEWCOMER OF THE YEAR

NEW ENTRY

Main Street, Crossmichael DG7 3AU
TEL: (01556) 670333
WEB SITE: www.plumed-horse.co.uk

COOKING **6**
MODERN EUROPEAN
£26–£59

The only unremarkable thing about the Plumed Horse is the building: an unpretentious whitewashed barn in a straggle of cottages along the road between Castle Douglas and Ayr. Space may be tight in the ground-floor dining room (there is another one upstairs), but it is comfortable, intimate and pleasingly decorated. Fish, sourced from Kirkcudbright, is a highlight. Sometimes it can be quite involved, as in a tournedos of wild salmon with langoustine tortellini, fettucine of asparagus and smoked salmon with a sauce Nantua, but one reporter, who ordered fish soup, was asked 'if I minded waiting as the fish had only arrived minutes before me'. The 'incomparable' result included sea bass, brill, salmon, scallops, a scattering of periwinkles and a topping of caviar, all in a bowl of creamy fish stock.

Painstaking presentation and diligent cooking are at the heart of the operation, evident in a dish of braised oxtail, taken off the bone and re-formed into a disc, placed on two thick pieces of seared but deeply pink Scottish beef fillet, served on a bed of mushy mash speckled with pieces of truffle, with a veal stock sauce. Another soup that has gone down well consisted of a small scoop of sorbet surrounded by peach juice in which floated strawberries and other summer fruits; 'the waiter turned up with a bottle of champagne and poured it into the peach juice so that it fizzed. I had to tell him to stop pouring as I was driving.' The set-price lunch is considered a giveaway, service from the owners in 'fancy waistcoats' is not only professional and charming but also down to earth, and a short wine list starts at £12.60. Consider, however, the sensible offer of two glasses (house red or white), plus a dry sherry aperitif or a glass of dessert wine, all for £8.75.

CHEFS: Tony Borthwick and James Pearce PROPRIETORS: Tony Borthwick and Charles Kirkbride OPEN: Tue to Fri and Sun L 12.30 to 1, Tue to Sat D 7 to 9 CLOSED: Christmas, first 2 weeks Jan, first 2 weeks Sept MEALS: alc L Tue to Fri and D (main courses £16 to £19). Set L Tue to Fri £12.95 (2 courses) to £14.95, Set L Sun £16.95 SERVICE: not inc, card slips closed CARDS: Delta, MasterCard, Switch, Visa DETAILS: 30 seats. Private parties: 25 main room, 25 private room. Car park. Vegetarian meals. No smoking in dining room. Wheelchair access (also WC). Music. Air-conditioned

CUPAR Fife map 11

Ostlers Close

25 Bonnygate, Cupar KY15 4BU
TEL: (01334) 655574
WEB SITE: www.ostlersclose.co.uk

COOKING **5**
MODERN SCOTTISH
£27–£54

After 20 years at their small stone cottage, James and Amanda Graham can consider themselves old hands at the restaurant game. But despite their longevity they claim to be as enthusiastic as ever, thanks to a loyal following and a well-established network of suppliers built up over the years. This enthusiasm is apparent not least in Amanda Graham's lively and convivial brand of hospitality.

On the food front, the kitchen maintains a balance between keeping customers happy with old favourites and evolving the style to avoid stagnation: a short yet varied and well-balanced menu follows the seasons assiduously and is centred on high-quality local produce with a distinctly Scottish accent. Roast breast of Highland grouse, for example, comes with chanterelles and smoked bacon in a game sauce, and confit free-range duck leg 'brimming with flavour' is served on a bed of carefully seasoned braised red cabbage. Fish and seafood have been impressive: at inspection, a notably fresh fillet of Pittenweem halibut served with three similarly excellent West Coast scallops and a buttery champagne sauce. Desserts have included a tripartite creation called 'oranges and lemons' comprising delicately flavoured lemon mousse, tangerine sorbet, and lemon tart. Meals are book-ended by excellent breads and appetisers and well-crafted petits fours. A full-flavoured gamut of Australian bins joins the more classic French regions which start the wine list, which focuses on value and character. Plenty of drinking is to be had under £20, with house Chilean red and white £13 and £12 respectively.

CHEF: James Graham PROPRIETORS: James and Amanda Graham OPEN: Fri and Sat L 12.15 to 1.30, Tue to Sat D 7 to 9.30 CLOSED: 25 and 26 Dec, 1 Jan, 2 weeks winter MEALS: alc (main courses L £9.50 to £13, D £16 to £18.50). Set D Nov to Apr £20 (reservations only for Set D) SERVICE: not inc, card slips closed CARDS: Amex, Delta, MasterCard, Switch, Visa DETAILS: 28 seats. Private parties: 22 main room. Children's helpings. No children under 6 at D. No music (£5)

DALRY North Ayrshire SCOTLAND RESTAURANT OF THE YEAR **map 11**

Braidwoods

Drumastle Mill Cottage, Dalry KA24 4LN
TEL: (01294) 833544 FAX: (01294) 833553
EMAIL: keithbraidwood@btconnect
WEB SITE: www.braidwoods.co.uk
1m off A737 on Dalry to Saltcoats road

COOKING **6**
MODERN SCOTTISH
£28–£53

Two whitewashed cottages, set amid fields with panoramic country views, house a couple of smart yet unpretentious dining rooms. Exposed stonework and modern paintings against a white, blue, and creamy yellow background add to the feeling that 'taste and discretion' are at work, a feeling reinforced by the kitchen, and by the knowledgeable and personable front-of-house presence of Nicola Braidwood. Given the number of covers, it makes sense to limit choice to three first and three main courses. There is plenty of variety within this framework, from lobster and herb tortellini, via a layered terrine of potato and foie gras, to a main course of sea bass and stickily translucent scallops served with a fine, light saffron sauce.

Dishes appear simple because they have a clear focus: a buttery pastry case filled with a Mediterranean mix of courgette slices, tomato flesh, pesto and goats' cheese for example, or honey roast Gressingham duck served with roast beetroot and lentils. Fine materials and a high degree of technical accomplishment might deliver a cylinder of richly flavoured yet airily textured chocolate and coffee mousse, paired with vanilla custard and cinnamon ice cream. An improved wine list combines some fine bottles from classic regions with sharply chosen examples from elsewhere. About a third of the offerings are under £20 and a short seasonally changing selection adds interest.

CHEF: Keith Braidwood PROPRIETORS: Keith and Nicola Braidwood OPEN: Wed to Sun L 12 to 1.45, Tue to Sat D 7 to 9 CLOSED: 25th Dec, first 3 weeks Jan, first 2 weeks Sept MEALS: Set L Wed to Sat £15 (2 courses) to £18, Set L Sun £22.50, Set D £30 to £32.50 SERVICE: not inc, card slips closed CARDS: Amex, Delta, Diners, MasterCard, Switch, Visa DETAILS: 24 seats. Private parties: 14 main room. Car park. Children's helpings. No children under 12 at D. No smoking in dining room. No music

DORNOCH Highland map 11

▲ 2 Quail

Castle Street, Dornoch IV25 3SN
TEL: (01862) 811811
EMAIL: goodfood@2quail.com
WEB SITE: www.2quail.com

COOKING 4
MODERN EUROPEAN-PLUS
£40–£48

Those in the know consider this compact restaurant-with-rooms 'the best for miles around'. Michael Carr cooks, while Kerensa seems to do everything else, and, sensibly, they keep the formula simple: fixed-price dinner only. The sort of dish that receives special mention from reporters is terrine of quail and foie gras, 'the soft richness of the foie gras contrasting with the firmer but succulent flesh of the quail', accompanied by a perfectly judged pear and rosemary chutney. An alternative might be a classic juxtaposition of scallops and bacon in a risotto with broad beans, followed by a choice of one fish (halibut with courgettes and sorrel and a thyme butter sauce, for example) and two meats (possibly highly commended grilled lamb noisettes served with braised Puy lentils). Fruits are used intelligently in desserts, candied kumquats adding appropriate sharpness to rich chocolate cake, and fresh raspberries doing the same for vanilla bavarois. A good selection of wines soon rises beyond the £20 mark, but opens with Pays d'Oc Chardonnay and Cabernet/Syrah at £13.

CHEF: Michael Carr PROPRIETORS: Michael and Kerensa Carr OPEN: winter Thurs to Sat and summer Tue to Sat D only 7.30 to 9.30 CLOSED: Christmas, 2 weeks Feb/Mar, bank hols MEALS: Set D £30 SERVICE: not inc CARDS: Amex, Delta, MasterCard, Switch, Visa DETAILS: 18 seats. Private parties: 10 main room, 8 and 10 private rooms. No smoking in 1 dining room. Wheelchair access (not WC). Occasional music ACCOMMODATION: 3 rooms, all with bath/shower. TV. B&B £55 to £80. No children under 10

The Guide office can quickly spot when a restaurateur is encouraging customers to write recommending inclusion. Such reports do not further a restaurant's cause. Please tell us if a restaurateur invites you to write to the Guide.

'Surely in this day and age even the most arrogant French sommelier must be distantly aware of rumours of wines from beyond his homeland, and even heard (sacre bleu!) stories, however implausible, that a few of them may be drinkable?' (On eating in the Home Counties)

'This dish was full of non-essential items, though it's a bit hard to say exactly which they should have left out. All of them, perhaps.' (On eating in Herefordshire)

DUNKELD Perthshire & Kinross map 11

▲ Kinnaird

Kinnaird Estate, by Dunkeld PH8 0LB
TEL: (01796) 482440 FAX: (01796) 482289
EMAIL: enquiry@kinnairdestate.com
WEB SITE: www.kinnairdestate.com
from A9 2m N of Dunkeld, take B898, signposted Kinnaird, for 4½m

COOKING **6**
MODERN EUROPEAN
£43–£71

Beyond the sumptuously decorated lounge the dining room is light, with spectacular views over the Tay valley, some 9,000 acres of which belong to the estate. It is a slick and consummately professional operation, which the 'vigorously hospitable' Douglas Jack runs with brisk efficiency. Despite the grand setting it is a relaxed place, offering contemporary food grounded in the abundance of regional materials, from diver-caught scallops to Angus beef three ways: fillet with truffled potato, oxtail crépinette, and salt-beef with buttered cabbage.

Classical techniques are deployed to good effect (expect Madeira and tartare sauces, for example), but there may also be herb quinoa with the breast of duck, or maple-roasted squash with the venison. Textures are well managed – a first-class terrine of smoked salmon layered with cream cheese, nicely contrasted with a pair of crab beignets, for example – and the kitchen turns its hand with equal skill to varying degrees of richness, from a foie gras 'steak' with a port sauce, via slices of lightly cooked saddle of hare sitting on braised endive in a bitter chocolate sauce, to top-quality John Dory on finely shredded cabbage with a brace of langoustines and a crisp potato galette.

Desserts are just as classy, taking in a well-risen, vividly flavoured mint soufflé into which two scoops of chocolate sorbet are placed, and a heather honey mousse served with variations on a fig theme: halved and baked, a fig crisp sandwiching a lime sorbet, and a fig sauce. Smart French properties rub shoulders with fine wines from elsewhere, although with so little under £25 the list saps enthusiasm. House wines are £18.

CHEF: Trevor Brooks PROPRIETOR: Constance Ward OPEN: all week 12.30 to 1.45, 7 to 9.30 CLOSED: Mon to Wed Jan and Feb MEALS: Set L £30, Set D £45 SERVICE: not inc, card slips closed CARDS: Amex, Delta, MasterCard, Switch, Visa DETAILS: 36 seats. Private parties: 34 main room. Car park. No children under 12. Jacket and tie at D. No smoking in dining room. Wheelchair access (also WC). No music ACCOMMODATION: 9 rooms, all with bath/shower. TV. Phone. D,B&B £225 to £475. No children under 12. Fishing (*The Which? Hotel Guide*)

EDINBURGH Edinburgh map 11

Atrium

10 Cambridge Street, EH1 2ED
TEL: (0131) 228 8882 FAX: (0131) 228 8808

COOKING **3**
MODERN EUROPEAN
£29–£60

Approached through the hallway of a modern office complex, this trendy ground-floor pace-setter gave one reporter the impression of being 'more like a ship in full sail than an atrium', with its canvas-tented ceiling and tables of polished-wood planking. Heavy metal proves another talking-point, fashioned into lights, candle holders and menu folders. Neil Forbes's focus on quality produce, seasonality, taste and simplicity shows up in a modern European repertoire that displays invention and high aspiration.

Accomplished starters have included lobster and salmon tortellini, and seared scallops with a sweet white wine and carrot butter sauce, while a fresh-tasting main-course fillet of line-caught sea bass has come with mussel and bean stew. Chocoholics should look no further than Valrhona jivara lactée chocolate mousse, while others might prefer warm peach tart with roast almond ice cream. Amuse-bouche, set-menu options and efficient and courteous service all contribute to the upbeat feel. The serious wine list takes a discerning global stroll: New Zealand Chardonnay Reserve, Sherwood Estate 1998 at £34.75 offers enjoyable drinking, while a Mourvèdre-Marsanne French double act provides an interesting house wine, priced £12.50. The choice of sherries, spirits and pudding wines is generous.

CHEF: Neil Forbes PROPRIETORS: Andrew and Lisa Radford OPEN: Mon to Fri L 12 to 2, Mon to Sat D 6.30 to 10 (longer during Edinburgh Festival) CLOSED: Christmas and New Year MEALS: alc (main courses L £11 to £12.50, D £14.50 to £20). Set L £14 (2 courses) to £18, Set D £25 SERVICE: not inc, 10% (optional) for parties of six or more CARDS: Amex, Delta, Diners, MasterCard, Switch, Visa DETAILS: 70 seats. Private parties: 90 main room. Vegetarian meals. Children's helpings. Wheelchair access (also WC). No music. Air-conditioned

▲ Balmoral Hotel, Number One

1 Princes Street, Edinburgh EH2 2EQ
TEL: (0131) 557 6727 FAX: (0131) 557 8740 — COOKING **5**
EMAIL: numberone@thebalmoral.com — MODERN EUROPEAN
WEB SITE: www.rfhotels.com — £29–£81

As basements go, this one is large and elegant, with big, immaculately laid tables set 'yards apart', a sure sign that it is not going to be a bargain basement. But five years on, Jeff Bland continues to make a fine fist of his prime materials, including seafood: from Loch Fyne oysters, to organic salmon, to Isle of Skye crab, perhaps served as a tian in summer with avocado and chilled gazpacho. Flavours and textures seem designed to soothe, helped by a few indulgent ingredients and largely familiar ideas: asparagus with hollandaise, sole fillets with capers and lemon, or potato soup with truffle oil, sprinkled with tiny shreds of crisp potato.

Some dishes undergo a degree of elaboration or 'froufrou' that may not be strictly necessary, but centrepiece fish and meats leave little doubt as to their quality: well-timed scallops with pesto and sauce vierge, for example, or pink breast of duck 'perfectly cooked and rested'. Desserts display the same sense of professional skill, producing a roast pear tart made with crisp pastry, served with a tangy-sweet lime sorbet, or a hot banana and chocolate chip soufflé. One couple expected the place to be a bit stuffy, 'but far from it': staff are friendly and relaxed. Wine prices aim high – lots in three figures, but not a single bottle of Chilean or Argentinian under £20 – which is too cynical for comfort. Nevertheless, quality is generally impressive.

CHEF: Jeff Bland PROPRIETOR: R.F. Hotels OPEN: Mon to Fri L 12 to 2, Mon to Sat D 7 to 10 (10.30 Fri and Sat) MEALS: alc (main courses £15 to £21). Set L £12.50 (2 courses) to £15.50, Set D £35 to £50 SERVICE: not inc CARDS: Amex, Delta, Diners, MasterCard, Switch, Visa DETAILS: 60 seats. Private parties: 100 main room. Children's helpings. No smoking in 1 dining room. Wheelchair access (also WC). Music. Air-conditioned ACCOMMODATION: 186 rooms, all with bath/shower. TV. Phone. Room only £175 to £260 (£5)

Blue Bar Café

10 Cambridge Street, EH1 2ED — COOKING **2**
TEL: (0131) 221 1222 FAX: (0131) 228 8808 — MODERN BRITISH
£22–£52

'Bar café' accurately encapsulates the relaxed yet lively and informal atmosphere of this spacious, glassed-in, circular room, handy for patrons of the neighbouring Traverse Theatre and Usher Hall. Children are welcome until 8pm, and help keep it busy at lunchtimes too. Until early evening, limited-choice two- and three-course menus supplement the carte, and service is 'polite and professional'. Meals might start with soup – maybe sweet potato, saffron and bacon – or perhaps crispy salmon with bean salad and guacamole, but be careful not to fill up because main courses can be generous: 'macho' smoked pork and paprika sausages for one visitor, or a huge chicken breast on mushroom risotto. Desserts have included a well-crafted creamy caramelised rice pudding with a glistening, crunchy, golden topping. A compact wine list covers most major wine-producing countries, offering innovative styles at welcomingly low prices, with house whites starting at £12.90. Though the list may be short, a dozen wines by the glass (from £3) add to its user-friendliness.

CHEF: David Haetzman PROPRIETORS: Andrew and Lisa Radford OPEN: Mon to Sat 12 to 2.45, 6 to 10.45 CLOSED: 25 and 26 Dec MEALS: alc (main courses £10 to £13.50). Set L £9 (2 courses) to £12, Set D Mon to Thur 6 to 7.30 £11 (2 courses) to £14 SERVICE: not inc, 10% for parties of 6 or more CARDS: Amex, Delta, Diners, MasterCard, Switch, Visa DETAILS: 120 seats. Private parties: 200 main room. Vegetarian meals. No children after 8pm. Children's helpings. No-smoking area. Wheelchair access (also WC). Music. Air-conditioned (£5)

▲ The Bonham

35 Drumsheugh Gardens, Edinburgh EH3 7RN
TEL: (0131) 623 9319 FAX: (0131) 226 6080 — COOKING **5**
EMAIL: restaurant@thebonham.com — MODERN EUROPEAN
WEB SITE: www.thebonham.com — £26–£50

Three late-nineteenth-century town houses have been cleverly converted into a stylish hotel and restaurant, where the combination of Victorian and contemporary takes in an oak-panelled dining room, green abstract paintings, and fruit in steel spirals. It is a tranquil and civilised oasis, where the cooking is distinguished by clean flavours and precise technique, and by a merciful absence of frills and flourishes. The menu runs the gamut from carpaccio of tuna loin with ratte potato salad, via winter vegetable lasagne with smoked paprika cream sauce, to a seasonal asparagus menu for one June visitor: lightly steamed white spears with hollandaise that was a 'frothy, buttery delight', an asparagus 'cappuccino' to accompany pan-fried guinea fowl with delicately made tagliatelle, and a dessert of asparagus and bourbon vanilla soufflé.

The freshness of seafood is notable – in a combination of translucent seared scallop and richly flavoured salmon on a brochette (a twig of rosemary), with braised baby gem lettuce – and components of a dish are well balanced, for example in the case of a meaty and flavourful duck breast, pan-fried with a 'brilliantly crisp' skin, served with spring onion mash and a lightly spicy chutney. Quantities are well judged, presentation is assured, and proficiency extends to a tangy, sweetly foamy orange and cinnamon soufflé with a crusty brown top, and an unctuous yet lightly textured chocolate fondant well partnered by lime mascarpone in a tuile basket. Bread is high quality, service is smooth and solicitous, and a short and sensible wine list offers eight by the glass. Prices start at £13.50 (£3.50 a glass).

CHEF: Michel Bouyer PROPRIETOR: Peter Taylor OPEN: all week 12 (12.30 Sun) to 2.30 (3 Sun), 6.30 to 10 CLOSED: 3 to 6 Jan MEALS: alc D (main courses £11.50 to £17). Set L £12.50 (2 courses) to £15 (Sun inc wine) SERVICE: not inc CARDS: Amex, Delta, Diners, MasterCard, Switch, Visa DETAILS: 60 seats. Private parties: 60 main room, 24 private room. Vegetarian meals. No smoking in 1 dining room. Wheelchair access (alsoWC). Music ACCOMMODATION: 48 rooms, all with bath/shower. TV. Phone. B&B £135 to £295. Rooms for disabled. Baby facilities (*The Which? Hotel Guide*) (£5)

Le Café St Honoré

34 NW Thistle St Lane, Edinburgh EH2 1EA — COOKING **1**
TEL: (0131) 226 2211 FAX: (0131) 624 7905 — MODERN BISTRO
WEB SITE: www.icscotland.co.uk/cafe-sthonore — £25–£50

Set down a secluded cobbled lane, this is a slice of fin-de-siècle France, with black and white marble floors, huge mirrors, gold curlicues and ornate lamps; in the evening soft jazz and candlelight enhance the atmosphere. A lively, informal mood, combined with bare walls and floors means the noise level can sometimes be high, but the food remains up to scratch. An inspector dined happily on a warm salad of monkfish, chorizo and prawns, followed by an exemplary sirloin steak with frites, and his meal just about sums up the modern bistro cooking style. Other options include goats' cheese and aubergine roulade, or breast of Barbary duck with red cabbage, bacon and shallots. The wide-ranging, fairly priced wine list opens with seven house selections at £10.50 a bottle.

CHEFS: Chris Colverson and Garrett O'Hanlan PROPRIETORS: Chris and Gill Colverson OPEN: Mon to Fri L 12 to 2.15, Mon to Sat D 5 (5.30 Sat) to 10 CLOSED: 3 days Christmas, 3 days New Year, spring bank hol Mon MEALS: alc (main courses L £8 to £15, D £12.50 to £19). Set D Mon to Fri 5 to 7, Sat 5.30 to 7 £9 (2 courses) to £18 SERVICE: not inc, 10% for parties of 8 or more CARDS: Amex, Delta, Diners, MasterCard, Switch, Visa DETAILS: 48 seats. Private parties: 42 main room, 16 private room. Vegetarian meals. Children's helpings. No smoking in 1 dining room. Wheelchair access (not WC). Music

indicates that smoking is either banned altogether or that a separate dining room (not just an area) is maintained for non-smokers.

Fishers 🍷

1 The Shore, Leith, Edinburgh EH6 6QW
TEL/FAX: (0131) 554 5666

COOKING **2**
INTERNATIONAL SEAFOOD
£26–£49

At one end of the Leith shoreline, this former pub is a lively venue combining an animated bar and more sedate restaurant with views across the water. Contemporary fish cookery is the kitchen's modus operandi, and the long, hand-scribbled menus offer much to entice. Here is a chef who likes to experiment, turning out pan-fried squid burger with blue cheese and Italian black-bean salsa, brochette of swordfish with feta and watermelon, and snapper fillets in a cashew nut and banana curry with rice cooked in rose-water. Those after something a bit simpler might go for pan-fried sardines with basil and anchovy pesto, or a platter of spider crab claws, West Coast langoustines and French crevettes with basil aïoli. Through intelligent sourcing and modest mark-ups, wines on Fishers' main list rarely step over the £20 mark, and house French red and white come in under £10. A fine wine list offers the chance to taste a variety of bottles from upmarket Rioja to classic Pomerol, and at reasonable cost. A new branch, on Thirtle Street opened in spring 2001; tel: (0131) 225 5109.

CHEFS: Glynn Somerville, Sally Findly, Dan Styles, Richard Hilton and Vitally Ponin PROPRIETORS: James and Tia Millar, and Graeme and Debbie Lumsden OPEN: all week 12 to 10.30 CLOSED: 25 Dec, 1 Jan MEALS: alc (main courses £12 to £19) SERVICE: not inc, 10% for parties of 8 or more CARDS: Amex, Delta, Diners, MasterCard, Switch, Visa DETAILS: 40 seats. 20 seats outside. Private parties: 30 main room. Wheelchair access (not WC). No music

(fitz) Henry

NEW ENTRY

19 Shore Place, Leith, Edinburgh EH6 6SW
TEL: (0131) 555 6625 FAX: (0131) 555 0025
EMAIL: mail@fitzhenrys.com
WEB SITE: www.fitzhenrys.com

COOKING **4**
FRENCH/BRASSERIE
£27–£51

Inhabiting a converted nineteenth-century warehouse in the revitalised dockyard area of Leith, the enigmatically named (fitz) Henry conveys a slightly medieval feel with its cast-iron chandelier and stone-flagged floors, although flowers, armchairs and velvet swags ensure a welcoming and intimate overlay. Hubert Lamort's background (he comes from south-west France) is evident in dishes such as braised pork cheeks en crépinette with pommes purée and a honey and clove jus, and cherry clafoutis, although he is not averse to serving smoked haddock fritters, or artichoke risotto either.

The food is powered by sound technique, for example in a delicate but convincing starter of warm baby artichoke barigoule with lardons and mange-tout, and an expertly timed roast pavé of sea trout with cucumber and mint vinaigrette. Offal plays its part – perhaps appearing as fried ox tongue with a salad of dried tomatoes and asparagus – while mainstream dishes show off the quality of materials, as in a well-rendered rack of lamb with stuffed tomato, fondant potatoes and jus niçoise. Desserts may not reach the same heights, but service is both efficient and relaxed, and the wine list does a conscientious job in trying to cover all the major countries, however briefly, offering just sufficient choice beneath £20 to satisfy the thrifty. Prices open at £11.50.

CHEF: Hubert Lamort PROPRIETORS: Alan Gordon Morrison and Valerie Faichney OPEN: Mon to Fri L 12 to 2.30, Mon to Sat D 6.30 to 10.30 CLOSED: 1 to 14 Jan MEALS: alc (main courses £10 to £18). Set L £9.50 (1 course) to £16.50 SERVICE: not inc, 10% for parties of 8 or more CARDS: Amex, Delta, MasterCard, Switch, Visa DETAILS: 80 seats. Private parties: 40 main room. Car park. Vegetarian meals. Wheelchair access (also WC). Music (£5)

Haldanes

39A Albany Street, Edinburgh EH1 3QY
TEL: (0131) 556 8407 FAX: (0131) 556 2662 COOKING **3**
EMAIL: dinehaldanes@aol.com MODERN SCOTTISH
WEB SITE: www.haldanesrestaurant.com £28–£57

Though close to the city centre, in the basement of a Georgian hotel, Haldanes eschews the hard-edged modern brasserie style for something more sedate and relaxing. One of its two dining areas is an intimate study-type room with an open fire, while the other is more formal and overlooks a small walled courtyard: the overall effect is 'elegant, warm and welcoming', helped along by attentive, good-humoured service. The food likewise aims for comfort and makes good use of Scotland's natural larder, coming up with a filo parcel of haggis with roasted turnips and whisky sauce among starters, which might be followed by roast saddle of Highland venison with glazed shallots, celeriac mousse and a red wine and rosemary sauce, or sea bass with spinach and saffron risotto and a tomato and white wine sauce. 'Great' dark chocolate terrine was enjoyed by one reporter, or there might be caramelised lemon tart with a raspberry sorbet. By far the majority of bottles on the wine list are above the £20 mark, but five house wines start at £12 a bottle, £3 a glass. There is also a page of half-bottles, two fine wines by the glass and a pair of burgundies of the month.

CHEF: George Kelso PROPRIETORS: George and Michelle Kelso OPEN: Mon to Sat L (reservations only) 12 to 1.30, all week D 6 to 9 (9.30 Sat and Sun) MEALS: alc (main courses £16 to £21.50). Set L £13.25 (2 courses) to £16.95 SERVICE: not inc CARDS: Amex, Delta, Diners, MasterCard, Switch, Visa DETAILS: 50 seats. 6 seats outside. Private parties: 40 main room, 14 and 20 private rooms. Vegetarian meals. Children's helpings. No smoking in dining room. Occasional music (£5)

Kalpna £

2–3 St Patrick Square, Edinburgh EH8 9EZ
TEL: (0131) 667 9890 COOKING **2**
EMAIL: kalpnarestaurant@yahoo.co.uk INDIAN
WEB SITE: www.kalpna.co.uk £12–£39

The red, white and silver colours provide a suitably cheerful backdrop for an upbeat repertoire of vegetarian fare from Punjab, Rajasthan, Kashmir, Madras and southern India, but above all Gujarat. These form the basis of thalis of five or six dishes plus rice, breads, relishes and dessert. A reporter found that their big, strong flavours and textures, with distinctive spicing, would satisfy even a committed carnivore. Other Kalpna specialities take in khoya khaju from Rajasthan (cashew nuts with reduced cream, sultanas, pistachios, nutmeg and coriander), and paneer handi (roasted home-made cheese cooked in a purée of tomatoes, honey and a touch of cream). An economical entry into this world of flavours is via the lunchtime buffet, while on Wednesday nights a gourmet version is offered. A dozen house wines run from £9.50 a bottle. The rest of the short list, and a few 'connoisseur's choices', includes some exciting New World wines.

CHEF/PROPRIETOR: Ajay Bhartdwaj OPEN: Mon to Fri L 12 to 2, all week D 5.30 to 11 MEALS: alc (main courses £4 to £7.50). Set buffet L £5 (3 courses), Set D £10.50 to £16 SERVICE: 10%, card slips closed CARDS: Visa (accepted at D only) DETAILS: 80 seats. Private parties: 80 main room. Vegetarian meals. No smoking in dining room. Wheelchair access (not WC). Music

Martins

70 Rose Street North Lane, Edinburgh EH4 3DX — COOKING 4
TEL: (0131) 225 3106 FAX: (0131) 220 3403 — MEDITERRANEAN
EMAIL: mirons@fsbdial.co.uk — £31–£61

Extensive redevelopment of this part of Edinburgh means you may have to wear a hard hat when visiting Martin and Gay Irons's back-street restaurant. However, the plainly decorated, light-green dining room – walls adorned with colourful oil paintings, tables immaculately presented with posies of flowers – is an enclave of tranquillity. The menu represents a short culinary tour of the Mediterranean, dealing in lively flavours and top-quality ingredients. This might mean starters of seared scallops and courgettes with langoustines and spiced lentils, or briefly seared chicken livers and oyster mushrooms on braised lentils and ham hock with a balsamic reduction. Among main courses, one reporter's accurately roast guinea fowl breast combined well with its accompanying Savoy cabbage, fondant potatoes, crispy bacon and tarragon jus, while another's risotto of broad beans, red peppers and wild mushrooms brought together the virtues of attractive presentation, assured technique and good flavours.

A substantial-sounding dessert of three golf-ball-sized jam doughnuts proved in practice to be both crispy and featherweight. The warm, effusive welcome and 'almost perfect' service is appreciated by reporters, and a balanced selection of styles can be found on the wine list, which features modern classics such as Cloudy Bay as well as bottlings from the new generation of Provençal producers. Try Hamilton Russell's South African Chardonnay, similar in style to a burgundy, but one of the many bottles under £20. Five house wines are all £14, or £2.30/£3.50 for small/large glass.

CHEF: David Romanis PROPRIETORS: Martin and Gay Irons OPEN: Tue to Fri L 12 to 2, Tue to Sat D 7 to 10 (Mon to Fri L 12 to 2, Mon to Sat D 6.30 to 11 during Edinburgh Festival) CLOSED: 1 month from 24 Dec, 1 week May to June, 1 week Oct MEALS: alc (main courses £9 to £21). Set L £12.50 (2 courses), Set D £25 SERVICE: not inc, 10% for parties of 6 or more CARDS: Amex, Delta, Diners, MasterCard, Switch, Visa DETAILS: 54 seats. Private parties: 30 main room, 8 and 18 private rooms. Vegetarian meals. No children under 8. No smoking in dining room. Wheelchair access (not WC). No music

Not inc *in the details at the end of an entry indicates that no service charge is made and any tipping is at the discretion of the customer.*

Restaurant Martin Wishart

54 The Shore, Leith, Edinburgh EH6 6RA
TEL: (0131) 553 3557 FAX: (0131) 467 7091 — COOKING **6**
EMAIL: info@martin-wishart.co.uk — MODERN FRENCH
WEB SITE: www.martin-wishart.co.uk — £25–£56

Edinburgh has taken enthusiastically to this ordinary-looking restaurant in modest surroundings overlooking the Water of Leith. A small, cool dining room, comfortable but by no means luxurious, with simple, clean lines and just a few tables, is the setting for some of the city's best cooking. Menus change weekly, and although lunch is a short, set-price affair with just a couple of options per course, it cuts no corners and can hardly be beaten for value: salmon confit with cauliflower cream and oyster beignet, for example, followed by blanquette of veal, then apple crumble.

A lot of effort seems to go into dishes, but they are by no means overworked and are characterised by clarity and a sense of balance. Their French roots are apparent at every turn, and despite variations on classic recipes – sole 'bonne femme' and monkfish 'Dugléré', for example – they have their own identity: cream of parsley soup with a poached egg, or roast halibut fillet with braised pig's trotter and gribiche sauce. The food itself is distinctive for its precision and intensity of flavour, as in a robust terrine of confit duck and Puy lentils, 'a great winter dish on a cold, wet night', but is also capable of subtlety, judging by one visitor's monkfish fillet in a grain mustard sauce with silky vermicelli pasta.

Cheeses (from Iain Mellis) are first-rate, and desserts might include a white chocolate mousse with praline biscuit and raspberry sorbet, or a 'pretty orgasmic' caramelised puff pastry tartlet with roasted pears and butterscotch sauce. Service from maîtresse d' Cécile Auvinet is cheerful, knowledgeable, friendly and efficient, and a concise, intelligently chosen wine list combines quality and variety without pandering to expense accounts. French house wine is £12 (£3 a glass).

CHEF/PROPRIETOR: Martin Wishart OPEN: Tue to Fri L 12 to 2, Tue to Sat D 7 to 9.30 MEALS: alc D (main courses £16.50 to £18.50). Set L £13.50 (2 courses) to £15.50 SERVICE: not inc, 10% for parties of 6 or more CARDS: Delta, MasterCard, Switch, Visa DETAILS: 35 seats. Private parties: 35 main room. No smoking before 2pm and 10pm. No cigars/pipes in dining room. Wheelchair access (also women's WC). Music

Shore

3 Shore, Leith, Edinburgh EH6 6QW
TEL/FAX: (0131) 553 5080 — COOKING **2**
WEB SITE: www.edinburgh-waterfront.com/ — SEAFOOD
edinburghrestaurants.co.uk — £21–£44

Located in what is loosely termed 'the new Leith', Shore is an affable place where white-clothed tables take up most of the available space. Seafood and game in season are the main but not exclusive preoccupations, taking in prawns with a well-judged sweet chilli dip, and lemon sole with a caper and lime butter, a simple dish featuring good fish well prepared. At the same time there are some 'pretty wild' ideas, including duck with parsnip and orange mash, and salmon with a pineapple and blue cheese cream sauce. Standards appear to vary quite a bit. Thai style mussels, and sea bass with a sauce of saffron, capers and dill have worked well, but it is probably wise to skip dessert. Around 30 serviceable wines stay mostly below £20, starting with house Côtes du Roussillon at £9.90.

CHEFS: Alison Bryant and Innes Gibson PROPRIETOR: Stuart Linsley OPEN: all week 12 to 2.30 (12.30 to 3 Sun), 6.30 to 10 CLOSED: 25 and 26 Dec, 1 and 2 Jan MEALS: alc (main courses L £6.50 to £11, D £10 to £16). Set L £13 (2 courses) to £15.95, Set D £17.15 (2 courses) to £20.70 SERVICE: not inc, 10% for parties of 8 or more CARDS: Amex, Delta, Diners, MasterCard, Switch, Visa DETAILS: 36 seats. 12 seats outside. Private parties: 36 main room. Vegetarian meals. Children's helpings. No smoking in dining room. Wheelchair access (not WC). Occasional music (£5)

Skippers

1A Dock Place, Leith, Edinburgh EH6 6LU — COOKING 2
TEL: (0131) 554 1018 FAX: (0131) 553 5988 — SEAFOOD
WEB SITE: www.skippers.co.uk — £22–£46

It would be foolish to ditch a philosophy that remains as popular today as it was 20 years ago, and so this informal bistro-style seafood restaurant remains much as it was when it first opened. The dining room is homely and welcoming, its bright red walls adorned with posters, and service is relaxed, friendly and unhurried. Chefs – and owners – have come and gone, but their purpose has been a constant: to serve fine Scottish seafood with accompaniments that accentuate rather than smother its flavour. On the whole, they are successful. Expect sauté Shetland scallops with crab and dill risotto, grilled herb-crusted sardines 'bursting with flavour', and robustly flavoured roast cod with a buttery crust, triangles of crisp bacon and a light saffron sauce. The commitment to Scottish produce extends to game and meat: maybe roast Borders lamb chops with onion mash and red wine jus. Six house wines from £9.75 a bottle open a heavily annotated list that shouldn't stretch anyone's budget too far.

CHEFS: Stuart Thrumble, Mary Walker and Matt Flitney PROPRIETORS: Gavin and Karen Ferguson OPEN: all week 12.30 to 2 (2.30 Sun), 7 to 10 CLOSED: 24 to 26 Dec, 31 Dec to 2 Jan MEALS: alc (main courses £9 to £17.50). Set L £10.50 (2 courses) to £13.50 SERVICE: not inc, 10% for parties of 6 or more CARDS: Amex, Delta, MasterCard, Switch, Visa DETAILS: 60 seats. 12 seats outside. Private parties: 35 main room, 25 private room. Wheelchair access (also WC). Music

Tower Restaurant

Museum of Scotland, Chambers Street,
Edinburgh EH1 1JF
TEL: (0131) 225 3003 FAX: (0131) 225 0978 — COOKING 2
EMAIL: mail@tower-restaurant.com — SEAFOOD/MODERN BRITISH
WEB SITE: www.tower-restaurant.com — £29–£67

Perched above the national museum, against an enviable backdrop – with stunning views of the floodlit castle and St Giles Cathedral – this top-floor dining room plies a trade in modern brasserie dishes, from smoked onion soup with parsley dumplings to calf's liver that passes the timing test 'with flying colours'. Seafood plays a major role, taking in Buckie crab with potato salad, and smoked haddock risotto, as well as a retro prawn cocktail and more up-to-the-minute salmon and tuna sushi with smoked eel and prawn sashimi. Meat eaters and vegetarians both do well, and among desserts crème brûlée is endorsed, and cheesecake is 'well above the norm'. Wines are sorted by price band, and a dozen house wines (plus fizz and stickies) are all available by the glass.

CHEF: Steven Adair PROPRIETOR: James Thomson OPEN: all week L menu 12 to 5, D menu 5 to 11 CLOSED: 25 and 26 Dec MEALS: alc (main courses L £8.50 to £18, D £12 to £24). Set D 5 to 6 and 10 to 11 £12 (2 courses) SERVICE: not inc, card slips closed CARDS: Amex, Delta, Diners, MasterCard, Switch, Visa DETAILS: 100 seats. 70 seats outside. Private parties: 100 main room, 24 and 60 private rooms. Vegetarian meals. No smoking in dining room. Wheelchair access (also WC). Music. Air-conditioned

Valvona & Crolla Caffè Bar

19 Elm Row, EH7 4AA
TEL: (0131) 556 6066 FAX: (0131) 556 1668 COOKING **2**
EMAIL: caffe@valvonacrolla.co.uk ITALIAN
WEB SITE: www.valvonacrolla.com £25–£45

This popular venue incorporates a deli where fine Italian foods are flown in weekly from Milan. In a brightly skylighted caffè bar done out in polished light wood, the business has been doing credit to the Contini family since before the war. Tables may be packed fairly close, but lunchtime queues tell the only story that matters. Zuppa di crema di pomodoro is 'creamy, smooth and sweet', according to one of its champions, the tiramisù made with fresh mascarpone and cream 'quite memorable', while another comments that 'few places do lemon tart as well as Valvona'. Before those treats, you may well have enjoyed spaghetti with octopus in a rich tomato sauce, a spicy salami and radicchio pizza, or a loin-girding stew of Shetland smoked salmon and haddock with potatoes and courgette, the last indicating that the kitchen doesn't neglect more local produce. Since cooking is largely done to order, a certain amount of patience between courses is called for. A directory of both good and positively great Italian wines dominates the hefty list. Remember the Continis are wine merchants too, and bottles can be bought in the shop attached; corkage of just £3 in the caffè bar makes the more expensive wines particularly good value. But those who wish to stick to house Montepulciano (£5.59 plus corkage) will also benefit from this outstanding policy.

CHEFS/PROPRIETORS: the Contini family OPEN: Mon to Sat L only 12 to 3, and D 6 to 9 during Edinburgh Festival CLOSED: 25 and 26 Dec, 1 and 2 Jan MEALS: alc (main courses £9 to £13) SERVICE: not inc CARDS: Amex, Delta, MasterCard, Switch, Visa DETAILS: 80 seats. Private parties: 80 main room, 40 private room. Vegetarian meals. Children's helpings. No smoking in dining room. Wheelchair access (also WC). Music. Air-conditioned

Winter Glen

3A1 Dundas Street, Edinburgh EH3 6QG COOKING **3**
TEL: (0131) 477 7060 FAX: (0131) 624 7087 MODERN BRITISH
WEB SITE: www.winterglen.co.uk £23–£47

Blair Glen and Graham Winter have been stalwarts of the Edinburgh dining scene for over five years now, no mean achievement in this volatile market. Stone walls in the basement dining room are adorned with wreaths of hops, spacious tables are dressed with white napery and candles, and chairs are capacious and sturdy. It all adds up to a high degree of comfort for diners. Menus, too, score reassuringly high on the satisfaction scale, employing quality native produce in dishes of mainly French and Italian origin. Among starters, potato and leek terrine has impressed, as have spicy crab cakes, whether served with lime dressing or a sweet-and-sour sauce. Contemporary main-course ideas might include griddled halibut steak with a tomato and chilli broth and olive mash, or medallions of Highland venison on a compote of caramelised pear and toasted barley with a redcurrant and burgundy gravy. To finish, lemon tart has been praised for its tasty filling. Service has come across as a little distracted on occasion. A thumbnail wine list opens with VDQS Chardonnay at £13.75 (£3 a glass).

CHEF: Graham Winter PROPRIETORS: Graham Winter and Blair Glen OPEN: Mon to Fri L 12 to 2, Mon to Sat D 6.30 to 10 MEALS: Set L £10 (2 courses) to £12.50, Set D £23.50 (2 courses) to £26.50 SERVICE: not inc CARDS: Amex, Delta, MasterCard, Switch, Visa DETAILS: 60 seats. Private parties: 60 main room, 28 and 35 private rooms. No smoking before 2 at L, 9 at D. Music. Air-conditioned

EDNAM Borders **map 11**

▲ Edenwater House

Ednam TD5 7QL
TEL: (01573) 224070 FAX: (01573) 226615
EMAIL: relax@edenwaterhouse.co.uk
WEB SITE: www.edenwaterhouse.co.uk
on B6461, 2m N of Kelso

COOKING **5**
MODERN BRITISH
£36–£43

Set beside a river in a tranquil village, Edenwater feels much like a retreat. Appetites are often sharpened by golfing, fishing or cycling, and on Friday and Saturday evenings guests may be joined in the candlelit dining room by non-residents for a no-choice, four-course dinner. The structure varies – it may be soup, fish and meat or, alternatively, fish, meat and cheese, before dessert – but the attention to detail, the careful sourcing of prime materials and the clever balancing of dishes are constants. A soup (perhaps celeriac and morel) might be followed by well-timed herb-crusted sole on rösti with citrus and basil beurre blanc, while praiseworthy meat dishes have included loin of Highland venison with spiced red cabbage, courgettes, asparagus and a garnish of enormous blackberries.

If cheese there be, it might well be a goats' version flavoured with single malt whisky and served grilled on an apple croustade with red pepper chutney and balsamic dressing. Dessert may be as complex as chocolate marquise accompanied by a pear and Pippin parfait and red fruit compote, or as straightforward as raspberry soufflé. The well-annotated wine list has been intelligently put together, and doesn't cater just for the top end of the market. There are some fine growers, particularly in the southern hemisphere, as well as a slate of clarets back to 1988. House French is £11 (white) and £12.50 (red).

CHEF: Jacqui Kelly PROPRIETORS: Jeff and Jacqui Kelly OPEN: Fri and Sat D only 7.30 to 8 (all week for residents) CLOSED: Christmas, first 2 weeks Jan MEALS: Set D £30 SERVICE: net prices, card slips closed CARDS: Delta, MasterCard, Switch, Visa DETAILS: 16 seats. Private parties: 16 main room. Car park. Children's helpings. No children under 10. No smoking in dining room. Wheelchair access (not WC). No music ACCOMMODATION: 4 rooms, all with bath/shower. TV. B&B £40 to £80. No children under 10 (*The Which? Hotel Guide*)

ERISKA Argyll & Bute **map 11**

▲ Isle of Eriska

Ledaig, Eriska PA37 1SD
TEL: (01631) 720371 FAX: (01631) 720531
EMAIL: office@eriska-hotel.co.uk
WEB SITE: www.eriska-hotel.co.uk
off A828, 12m N of Oban

COOKING **6**
SCOTTISH
£47–£57

'To drive to Eriska is to drive into another world,' reckoned one visitor to this privately owned island, whose seclusion makes it something of a sanctuary for wildlife. The generously proportioned, late-Victorian, baronial-style house and its grounds add to the sense of space and tranquillity. If golf and tennis don't appeal, there is always the pool or gymnasium to help work up an appetite for the six-course dinners (and no sorbet in the middle, thank you very much; this is proper food), which are heralded by a gong. Regional materials are sensitively handled and sometimes combined with rather more exotic ones for a bright effect: chicken and okra soup, for example, or a trio each of salmon and caviar with a mango and chilli salsa and beetroot dressing.

Shellfish, always a strong suit in this part of the world, might be dealt with straightforwardly, as in a brochette of scallops and langoustines on a Jerusalem artichoke purée, or given slightly more sophisticated treatment in the shape of langoustine ravioli in an oyster broth with squat lobsters. Main courses typically offer a roast (perhaps Aberdeen Angus beef, or best end of lamb, carved from a trolley) as well as poultry (crisp breast and braised leg of Gressingham duck) and fish: grilled turbot with clams, broad beans and lovage at one meal.

After desserts such as pistachio crème brûlée and hot Amaretto soufflé comes a savoury, and then the cheese trolley for those with any room left. Service is overseen by Beppo Buchanan-Smith, 'a three-star eccentric, unconvincingly self-deprecating'. Although over half the wines are from distinguished French regions, and great names are peppered throughout the list, prices are impressively low, starting under £9 for French country wines. House wines, opening at £3 a glass, take in a Chilean Cabernet Sauvignon and Louis Latour's ground-breaking Chardonnay from the Ardèche.

CHEF: Robert MacPherson PROPRIETORS: the Buchanan-Smith family OPEN: all week D only 8 to 9 CLOSED: Jan MEALS: Set D £38.50 SERVICE: not inc, card slips closed CARDS: Amex, Delta, MasterCard, Switch, Visa DETAILS: 35 seats. Private parties: 35 main room. Car park. Jacket and tie. No smoking in dining room. Wheelchair access (not WC). No music ACCOMMODATION: 17 rooms, all with bath/shower. TV. Phone. B&B £120 to £270. Rooms for disabled. Baby facilities. Swimming pool (*The Which? Hotel Guide*)

indicates that there has been a change of chef since last year's Guide, and the Editor has judged that the change is of sufficient interest to merit the reader's attention.

FAIRLIE North Ayrshire map 11

▲ Fins

Fencefoot Farm, Fairlie KA29 0EG
TEL: (01475) 568989 FAX: (01475) 568921
EMAIL: fencebay@aol.com
WEB SITE: www.fencebay.co.uk
on A78, 1m S of Fairlie

COOKING **2**
SEAFOOD
£20–£59

The speciality of this restaurant in a converted byre by the Ayrshire coast is hinted at in its name, then confirmed by its location on a fish farm and by the abundant seafood motifs that adorn its basic dining room. Supplies come from the adjacent fish shop, which incorporates a smokehouse and a delicatessen. As well as serving fine shellfish and smoked fish au naturel, the kitchen incorporates them into cooked dishes: oysters baked with spinach, garlic, crème fraîche and goats' cheese, for example, or plaice fillets stuffed with squat lobster in a Chardonnay sauce. Other options might include Cullen skink, and lemon sole with citrus herb crust, as well as token steaks. The short, largely French wine list interleaves good-value bottles with a few classier numbers; house wines are £9.80.

CHEFS: Gillian Dick, Jill Thain and Jane Burns PROPRIETORS: Jill and Bernard Thain OPEN: Tue to Sun L 12 to 2.30, Tue to Sat D 6.30 to 9.30 MEALS: alc (main courses L £8 to £21, D £11 to £23). Set L Tue to Thur £7.50 (2 courses), Set D Tue to Thur £10 (2 courses) SERVICE: not inc, card slips closed CARDS: Amex, Delta, Diners, MasterCard, Switch, Visa DETAILS: 50 seats. Private parties: 30 main room, 20 private room. Car park. Vegetarian meals. No children at D. No smoking in dining room. Wheelchair access (also WC). Music ACCOMMODATION: 2 rooms. B&B £20 to £30. Baby facilities (£5)

FORT WILLIAM Highland map 11

Crannog

Town Pier, Fort William PH33 7NG
TEL: (01397) 705589 FAX: (01397) 705026
EMAIL: allan@crannog.net
WEB SITE: www.crannog.net

COOKING **2**
SEAFOOD
£25–£47

Lovely views across Loch Linnhe are an indisputable part of the draw at this specialist seafood restaurant perched on the end of the town's pier. It is spick and span, but not fancy, marking up its offerings on a laminated menu supplemented by a blackboard. Supplies typically come direct from the boats (the enterprise was started by fishermen) and take in prime-quality oysters, fine langoustines in garlic and herb butter, diver-caught scallops, and products from their own smokehouse, a selection of which can be taken as a starter or main course. Fish from Mallaig has included baked cod with pink peppercorns, Shetland salmon might come roasted with garlic, and the Finnan haddie soup is a fine version. Vegetables are generously anointed with hollandaise, and puddings run to heather cream cheesecake, or rich dark chocolate pot. A simple wine list, mostly white and mostly under £20, suits the circumstances.

CHEF: Gary Dobbie PROPRIETOR: Finlay Finlayson OPEN: all week 12 to 2.30, 6 to 9.30 (10 in summer) CLOSED: 25 and 26 Dec, 1 Jan MEALS: alc (main courses £9 to £16.50) SERVICE: not inc CARDS: Delta, MasterCard, Switch, Visa DETAILS: 65 seats. Private parties: 35 main room. Car park. Children's helpings. No smoking in 1 dining room. Wheelchair access (also WC). Music

▲ Inverlochy Castle

Torlundy, Fort William PH33 6SN
TEL: (01397) 702177 FAX: (01397) 702953
EMAIL: info@inverlochy.co.uk
WEB SITE: www.inverlochy.co.uk
3m N of Fort William on A82

COOKING **6**
MODERN EUROPEAN
£44–£79

Exclusive, refined and stately, 'epitomising the grand Scottish hotel', Inverlochy Castle lies with its wooded lake in manicured grounds in the lee of Ben Nevis. Once a favoured haunt of Queen Victoria, it retains its magnificence; crystal chandeliers, antiques, paintings, tartans and flower arrangements typify the sumptuous, traditional surroundings.

Matthew Gray's four-course dinners (the second a no-choice soup) use quality Scottish ingredients: charcoal-grilled fillet of Angus beef for instance, with braised root vegetables, or roast loin of venison with cider fondant potatoes, caramelised apples and a peppery port sauce. The style has a sophisticated modern edge, but the essentials are straightforward; luxury items have their place, though, as illustrated by a starter of ballottine of foie gras with French bean salad and toasted brioche. Desserts offer classic staples in the form of raspberry crème brûlée, or poached pears with caramelised lemon tart and mulled wine sauce. Lunch – a lighter, three-course affair – offers three choices per course: perhaps chicken liver parfait with plum chutney, followed by pan-fried tranche of salmon with spinach and asparagus tips, finishing with a trio of sorbets (lemon, blackberry and raspberry). Wine prices reflect the grand surroundings. House wines are £20, although a few lively styles do undercut this, those in search of value should head towards the French countryside or Chile. The depth and variety of (especially French) regions is impressive, and page upon page of half-bottles should satisfy modest drinkers and expand options for others.

CHEF: Matthew Gray PROPRIETOR: Inverlochy Castle Ltd OPEN: all week 12.30 to 1.45, 7 to 9.15 CLOSED: 7 Jan to 1 Mar MEALS: Set L £25 (2 courses) to £30, Set D £45 to £50 SERVICE: not inc, card slips closed CARDS: Amex, Delta, MasterCard, Switch, Visa DETAILS: 34 seats. Private parties: 34 main room, 15 private room. Car park. Vegetarian meals. Children's helpings. Jacket and tie. No smoking in dining room. Wheelchair access (not WC). No music ACCOMMODATION: 17 rooms, all with bath/shower. TV. Phone. B&B £180 to £380. Baby facilities. Fishing (*The Which? Hotel Guide*)

NEW CHEF *is shown instead of a cooking mark where a change of chef occurred too late for a new assessment of the cooking.*

'It was appropriate that it was daylight when the £24 robbery on our bill took place.'
(On eating in the Republic of Ireland)

GLASGOW Glasgow map 11

Amaryllis

NEW ENTRY

1 Devonshire Gardens, Glasgow G12 0UX
TEL: (0141) 337 3434 FAX: (0141) 339 0047

COOKING **6**
MODERN EUROPEAN
£31–£67

Marco Pierre White left his stoves to build an empire, Gary Rhodes and Raymond Blanc are halfway to being a brand, and Gordon Ramsay is now spreading himself beyond London. It doesn't mean he's cooking here, just setting up a restaurant with a trusted lieutenant in charge. David Dempsey's command of the Ramsay repertoire, and Fiona Nairn's front-of-house skills (service is smooth, correct and plentiful), have made this a 'must eat' place since it opened in spring 2001 as an independent operation in the hotel (One Devonshire Gardens, itself in the Guide last year).

Internally, little has changed since former chef at the the hotel, Andrew Fairlie, left for Gleneagles (see entry, Auchterarder), except that there are now more tables in an expanded dining room, and a minimalist modern decorator has been 'let loose' on it. Menus offer a set-price deal which is considered good value, bearing in mind that this is both a highly skilled and very seductive and cosseting kind of cooking, heady with truffle (try the white bean velouté) and full of sensuous flavours and voluptuous textures, not forgetting foie gras. Soft-roasted scallops come with squashy herb tortellini in a rich Jerusalem artichoke velouté, and a melting chocolate fondant on a pleasingly crisp chocolate biscuit base is topped with a foaming snowdrift of white chocolate. 'I was beginning to feel like an invalid – or a baby being weaned,' confessed its eater.

Precise timings help the show along, producing accurately roast Challandais duck with edgy caramelised chicory, and tender loin of venison served with crisp red cabbage, creamy potato purée, and a sauce redolent of stock and red wine. Cheeses at inspection were not up to standard, but desserts might take in strawberry jelly with an orange blossom ice cream, or a well-judged lavender-scented crème brûlée with apple crisps. Wines are wonderful, if you have the money to pay for them; not many offer change from £20. France dominates, and classic names abound, but the New World contributes some fine bottles too.

CHEF: David Dempsey PROPRIETOR: Gordon Ramsay OPEN: Sun to Fri L 12 to 2.30, all week D 6.45 to 11 (10 Sun) MEALS: Set L Mon to Fri £18, Set L Sun £21, Set D £25 to £35 SERVICE: not inc CARDS: Amex, Delta, MasterCard, Switch, Visa DETAILS: 70 seats. Private parties: 12 to 36 private rooms. No smoking in 1 dining room. No cigars/pipes in dining room. No music

Buttery

652 Argyle Street, Glasgow G3 8UF
TEL: (0141) 221 8188 FAX: (0141) 204 4639

COOKING **2**
MODERN SCOTTISH
£32–£65

Lavish interior décor of deep carpets, dark oak panelling and heavy velvet curtains contrasts somewhat with this long-running restaurant's location in a fairly unprepossessing part of town. But despite the luxuriously old-fashioned setting – and quaint touches like soup courses and fancy little hors d'oeuvres delivered on a large plate – the wide-ranging set-price lunch and à la carte dinner menus show an understanding of prevailing trends. Fine Scottish ingredients, notably fish and seafood, are employed in modern-sounding dishes that might be as simple as warm monkfish, scallop and pancetta salad or as elaborate as saddle of venison with chicken and wild mushroom parfait wrapped in Parma ham on a tomato and tarragon sauce. No wine list was sent to us this year, but we have been told that house vins de pays is £12.50 a bottle, £2.95 a glass.

CHEF: Ian Mackie PROPRIETOR: Punch Retail Ltd. OPEN: Mon to Fri L 12 to 2.30, Mon to Sat D 7 to 10 CLOSED: 25 and 26 Dec, bank hols MEALS: alc D (main courses £15 to £20). Set L £17.50 (2 courses) to £19.50 SERVICE: 10% (optional), card slips closed CARDS: Amex, Delta, Diners, MasterCard, Switch, Visa DETAILS: 56 seats. Private parties: 50 main room, 10 private room. Car park. Vegetarian meals. Children's helpings. No children under 7. Music. Air-conditioned

Café Gandolfi £

64 Albion Street, Glasgow G1 1NY
TEL: (0141) 552 6813 FAX: (0141) 552 8911

COOKING **2**
INTERNATIONAL
£19–£38

This landmark café, located in the Merchant City area, is, after some 21 years, still open all hours for simple, good-value food. Breakfast on eggs en cocotte with cheese and toast, or maybe call in for Scottish staples of Stornoway black pudding, Arbroath smokies or haggis. There's a modern edge to the repertoire too, with linguini, New York pastrami, or rocket with pecorino and roasted pears finding their place. More choice appears on the Seasonal Menu to crank things up a gear: asparagus and strawberry salad with Parmesan and lime yoghurt dressing, chicken fajitas with 'zingingly fresh' coriander salsa, and 'top-quality' apple pie a typical medley. The atmosphere is one of informality, with a youthful buzz and arty clientele, drawn perhaps by bold Tim Stead wood furniture and John Clark stained glass. Wines and beers are keenly priced; Australian house wine is £10.50, while eight by the glass range from £2.10 to £4.

CHEF: Margaret Clarence PROPRIETOR: Seumas MacInnes OPEN: all week 9 (noon Sun) to 11.30 CLOSED: 25 and 26 Dec, 1 and 2 Jan MEALS: alc (main courses £6 to £12) SERVICE: not inc, 10% for parties of 6 or more CARDS: Amex, MasterCard, Switch, Visa DETAILS: 65 seats. Private parties: 25 main room. Vegetarian meals. No children after 8.30pm. No-smoking area. Music. Air-conditioned

Eurasia

150 St Vincent Street, Glasgow G2 5NE
TEL: (0141) 204 1150 FAX: (0141) 204 1140
EMAIL: reservations@eurasia-restaurant.co.uk

COOKING **4**
SCOTTISH/ORIENTAL FUSION
£30–£73

The name of Ferrier Richardson's big, bold city-centre restaurant – a large open space done out mainly in wood and glass – gives some indication of its split personality. The kitchen's philosophy is to take the best Scottish produce it can find and dress it up with Asian herbs and spices, sometimes in unexpected ways but always with an underlying sense of what goes well together: so loin of Scottish lamb, for example, might be accompanied by sweet chilli potatoes and a hot oriental sauce, and spiced monkfish is served with scallop mousseline and a saffron, tomato and spring onion bouillon. Salmon sushi with wasabi and pickled ginger is a more straightforwardly oriental option, while dishes from closer to home might include caramelised butternut squash risotto cake with sun-dried tomatoes, Parmesan and pesto. Those who are prepared to take chances with their dinner might opt for the four-course 'eclectic surprise' menu. Desserts are relatively straightforward creations, such as hot banana soufflé with chocolate ice cream and caramel sauce, and the wine list also stays in fairly safe territory, predominantly France. Four house selections are £14.95 a bottle, £3.75 a glass.

CHEFS: Ferrier Richardson and Steven Caputa PROPRIETOR: Ferrier Richardson OPEN: Mon to Fri L 12 to 2.30, Mon to Sat D 7 to 11.30 MEALS: Set L £14.95 (2 courses) to £17.95, Set D £29.45 (2 courses) to £35 SERVICE: not inc CARDS: Amex, Delta, Diners, MasterCard, Switch, Visa DETAILS: 160 seats. Private parties: 120 main room, 12 and 24 private rooms. Vegetarian meals. Wheelchair access (also WC). Music. Air-conditioned

Gamba

NEW ENTRY

225A West George Street, Glasgow G2 2ND
TEL: (0141) 572 0899 FAX: (0141) 572 0896
EMAIL: info@gamba.co.uk
WEB SITE: www.gamba.co.uk

COOKING **2**
SEAFOOD
£25–£60

This subterranean restaurant is quite small but doesn't feel cramped, and service is 'laid back and friendly'. Fish is the main thing: rollmop herring and sashimi are among starters, and an inspector enjoyed 'sharp but light' ginger and prawn dumplings in deeply flavoured fish soup. Saucing a whole sea bass with basil oil and a balsamic reduction gave 'sharp definable flavours', and sweet chilli salsa complemented well-timed scallops; other main dishes range from lemon sole (grilled or meunière), to halibut with lobster bisque, artichoke and shrimps. There is one meat dish, perhaps fillet of beef, although chicken and avocado salad may be among the starters. Desserts could include rhubarb crème brûlée and a selection of cheeses. House wines from £13.95 start the white-centred list.

CHEF: Derek Marshall PROPRIETORS: Alan Tompkins and Derek Marshall OPEN: Mon to Sat 12 to 2.30, 5 to 10.30 MEALS: alc L (main courses £11.50 to £20). Set L Mon to Fri £12.95 (2 courses) to £15.95, Set L Sat £15.95 (2 courses) to £18.95, Set D £29.95 to £34.95, Set D Mon to Sat 5 to 6.15 £10.95 (2 courses) to £13.95 SERVICE: not inc, 10% for parties of 6 or more CARDS: Amex, Delta, MasterCard, Switch, Visa DETAILS: 66 seats. Private parties: 66 main room. Vegetarian meals. No children under 14 after 8. Music. Air-conditioned (£5)

▲ Hilton Glasgow, Camerons

NEW ENTRY

1 William Street, Glasgow G3 8HT
TEL: (0141) 204 5511 FAX: (0141) 204 5004
WEB SITE: www.hilton.com

COOKING **2**
MODERN EUROPEAN
£39–£61

'A return to classic standards in dining' is what Camerons restaurant in this gigantic hotel is aiming at, which translates as an atmosphere of muted intimacy, widely spaced tables and faux-antique paintings. Familiarity even extends to staff persistently addressing you by name at table.

James Murphy offers a soothing style of international cuisine, based on sound Scottish materials. A warm salad of prawns and mussels with pesto-seasoned rice combines lightness and intensity of flavour, always an impressive balancing act, and a main course at the same meal boldly and effectively paired a tranche of correctly timed halibut with pea purée and a mustard sauce. More novel preparations have included smoked ostrich with focaccia and sweet pepper pesto, and Aberdeen Angus fillet in Thai spices with herbed spätzli and pak choi. 'A Taste of Scotland' at dessert stage takes in whisky brûlée; a sorbet of strawberries and Glayva; a tartlet of Blairgowrie raspberries, and more besides. More fine wines than you can shake a corkscrew at adorn the extensive list, but prices are inevitably five-star. House French Sauvignon Blanc and Merlot are £15.50.

CHEF: James Murphy PROPRIETOR: Hilton OPEN: Mon to Fri L 12 to 1.45, Mon to Sat D 7 to 9.45 CLOSED: 31 Dec, 1 and 2 Jan MEALS: Set L £19.90 (2 courses) to £24.50 (inc wine), Set D £23.50 (2 courses) to £35 SERVICE: not inc CARDS: Amex, Diners, MasterCard, Switch, Visa DETAILS: 44 seats. Private parties: 44 main room. Vegetarian meals. Children's helpings. No smoking in dining room. Wheelchair access (also WC). Music. Air-conditioned ACCOMMODATION: 319 rooms, all with bath/shower. TV. Phone. B&B £125 to £180 (double room). Rooms for disabled. Swimming pool (£5)

▲ Groucho Saint Jude's

NEW ENTRY

190 Bath Street, Glasgow G2 4HG
TEL: (0141) 352 8800 FAX: (0141) 352 8801 — COOKING **3**
EMAIL: reservations@grouchosaintjudes — GLOBAL
WEB SITE: www.grouchosaintjudes.com — £21–£54

Cool colours, large windows, banquette seating and lots of wood combine to make this ground-floor dining room feel both modern and comfortable. Despite part-ownership by London's Groucho Club, this is not a club, but a restaurant like any other. Well, not quite like any other since it has an Australian chef, but Martin Teplitzky doesn't ram Pacific Rim down everybody's throat. Ideas sometimes fuse, but combinations are intelligent and a long way from the jumble that such cooking often implies, and different food cultures also live happily side by side as he balances poached velvet crab with ginger, garlic, lime leaves, coriander and coconut against chargrilled Aberdeen Angus sirloin with baby beetroot, horseradish and Yorkshire pudding.

The common denominator is lively, tasty food, taking in chunky deep-fried paper-wrapped prawns, served with a well-judged sweet chilli dip and deep-fried egg noodles, and well-timed lamb chops with roasted tomato chutney, peppery rocket and salty feta. A first course of light, well-flavoured mushroom-filled tortellini parcels with asparagus spears and pistachio butter was an odd-sounding combination that 'worked a treat' at inspection. To finish, Gorgonzola pannacotta is not recommended, but wines are attractively varied and tolerably priced, starting with own-label Vin de Pays d'Oc red and white at £10.50.

CHEF: Martin Teplitzky PROPRIETORS: the Groucho Club plc, and Robert Paterson and Paul Wingate OPEN: Mon to Fri L 12 to 3, all week D 5.30 to 10.30 CLOSED: 25 and 26 Dec, 1 and 2 Jan MEALS: alc (main courses £9.50 to £17.50). Set L £9.50 (2 courses) to £12.50, Set D 5.30 to 7.15 £11.50 (2 courses) to £14.50. Bar menu available SERVICE: not inc, 10% for parties of 6 or more CARDS: Amex, Delta, Diners, MasterCard, Switch, Visa DETAILS: 60 seats. Private parties: 60 main room, 28 private room. Vegetarian meals. No cigars/pipes during meals. Music. Air-conditioned ACCOMMODATION: 6 rooms, all with bath/shower. TV. Phone. B&B £105 to £185

Nairns

13 Woodside Crescent, Glasgow G3 7UL
TEL: (0141) 353 0707 FAX: (0141) 331 1684
WEB SITE: www.nairns.co.uk

COOKING **3**
MODERN SCOTTISH
£24–£52

Refurbishment has given a more luxurious feel to this basement dining room, now done out in blues and purples and accessed through a glass door. The menu continues to go in for cutting-edge food that is rarely less than interesting, and wears the provenance of its materials on its sleeve – in a warm salad of Stornaway black pudding with pigeon breast, crispy 'Fifeshire' bacon and Cumberland sauce, for example – and brings together essentially simple but effective partnerships: cold poached salmon with a Thai vegetable salad, perhaps, or a warm tartlet of seafood and asparagus with curry hollandaise. Results are clear and hugely enjoyable, be they a light and summery risotto of roasted peppers and grilled goats' cheese, roast cod with a lightly piquant caviar butter sauce, or chargrilled rump of Stirlingshire lamb with roast Mediterranean vegetables. Desserts are equally well focused and well reported, including white chocolate pannacotta with espresso sauce, and glazed lemon tart with raspberry sorbet. Wines are sharply chosen and varietally organised, although choice under £25 might be more extensive. Four house wines set the ball rolling at £15.50 (£3.50 a glass).

CHEF: Derek Blair PROPRIETORS: Nick and Christopher Nairn OPEN: Tue to Sat 12 to 2, 6 to 10 CLOSED: 25 and 26 Dec, 1 and 2 Jan MEALS: Set L £9 (2 courses) to £12, Set D £29.50 SERVICE: not inc, 10% for parties of 8 or more CARDS: Amex, Delta, Diners, MasterCard, Switch, Visa DETAILS: 40 seats. Vegetarian meals. No smoking before coffee. No cigars/pipes in dining room. Music. Air-conditioned (£5)

No. Sixteen £

16 Byres Road, Glasgow G11 5JY
TEL: (0141) 339 2544

COOKING **3**
MODERN BRITISH
£20–£43

A small but dynamic restaurant in an area not exactly short of eating options, No. Sixteen offers a colourful repertoire of soundly cooked contemporary dishes, with the added attraction of a daily-changing menu. In the words of one reporter, it is 'warm and cosy' and the service 'efficient'. Starters of smoked haddock risotto, and walnut and Stilton fritters have been recommended. Main courses offer prime cuts such as saddle of rabbit, haunch of venison, and chicken breast alongside fillets of fish (perhaps brill grilled and served with tapénade and a red pepper coulis), and there is always a vegetarian option: maybe mixed mushroom ravioli with dried ceps and spinach under a Parmesan glaze. Good bets for dessert have been a rich but light-textured dark chocolate pudding with custard, and plum and almond tart with crème fraîche. A stylistically classified wine list opens with a quartet of house wines that ranges from £10.50 to £12.75.

CHEF: Rupert Staniforth PROPRIETORS: Rupert and Aisla Staniforth OPEN: Mon to Sat 12 to 2.30, 5.30 to 10 CLOSED: 2 weeks Christmas and New Year MEALS: alc (main courses L £6.50 to £8.50, D £8.50 to £14.50). Set D 5.30 to 6.30 £9.50 (2 courses) to £11.50 SERVICE: not inc, 10% for parties of 8 or more CARDS: Delta, MasterCard, Switch, Visa DETAILS: 42 seats. Private parties: 25 main room. Vegetarian meals. Children's helpings. No music

La Parmigiana

447 Great Western Road, G12 8HH — COOKING **2**
TEL: (0141) 334 0686 FAX: (0141) 357 5595 — ITALIAN
£17–£55

A reporter appreciated the white décor with 'terracotta faux roof tiling' round the cornice and trompe l'oeil windows, and found the absence of music a bonus. If ingredients are not exclusively Italian, then using fresh local produce is no hardship, and some of it helps to justify the prices. On the à la carte menu three of four pasta starters include seafood: lobster ravioli, spaghetti with mixed fish and shellfish, and tagliolini with 'plump' Dublin Bay prawns. A whole sea bass cooked in white wine and herbs has come with strips of parsnip, courgettes, carrots and potato, while roulade of beef fillet has been stuffed with prosciutto and asparagus. Desserts include pear poached in Vin Santo, while celery and pears accompany cheese. The regional Italian list's house wines start at £12.90; its twelve Tuscan reds run from Chianti Classico at £17.90 to Sassicaia at £122.

CHEF: Sandro Giovanazzi PROPRIETORS: Angelo and Sandro Giovanazzi OPEN: Mon to Sat 12 to 2.30, 6 to 11 MEALS: alc (main courses £13 to £17). Set L £9.10, Set D 6 to 7.30 £9.50 (2 courses) to £11.50 SERVICE: not inc CARDS: Amex, Delta, Diners, MasterCard, Switch, Visa DETAILS: 50 seats. Private parties: 60 main room. Vegetarian meals. Children's helpings. No music. Air-conditioned

Puppet Theatre

11 Ruthven Lane, Glasgow G12 9BG — COOKING **2**
TEL: (0141) 339 8444 FAX: (0141) 339 7666 — MODERN EUROPEAN
EMAIL: puppet@bigbeat.co.uk — £27–£71

In a busy restaurant quarter (not far from the Ubiquitous Chip and a few steps from Stravaigin 2; see entries), Puppet Theatre offers a choice of dining options: a tropical-style conservatory with cacti and rattan blinds, or a more romantic 'antique boudoir' set-up. Stephen Nye (who came from Stravaigin) offers a menu that runs from beetroot and orange soup, via clove-scented duck breast on pea and vanilla purée, to fillet steak with caramelised shallots and a red wine and mushroom jus. Mixed results characterised an early inspection, the highlights of which included lamb shank with a pleasingly edgy sauce, and an 'economically calculated' seafood ragoût with a velvety butter sauce flavoured with saffron and lemon grass. Finish perhaps with a pairing of semi-frozen raspberry and floppy chocolate mousses served with vanilla ice cream and Tia Maria syrup. Wines (mostly under £30) are divided into 'classic' and 'modern' styles, with eight house recommendations available by the glass.

CHEF: Stephen Nye PROPRIETOR: Big Beat Group Ltd OPEN: Tue to Fri and Sun L 12 to 2.30, Tue to Sun D 7 to 10.30 CLOSED: 26 Dec, 1 to 3 Jan MEALS: alc (main courses L £6.50 to £9, D £7 to £22.50) SERVICE: not inc, 10% for parties of 8 or more CARDS: Amex, Delta, MasterCard, Switch, Visa DETAILS: 65 seats. Private parties: 28 main room, 8 to 28 private rooms. Vegetarian meals. No children under 16. No smoking in 1 dining room. Wheelchair access (not WC). Music

London restaurants by cuisine are listed near the front of the book.

Rogano

11 Royal Exchange Place, Glasgow G1 3AN
TEL: (0141) 248 4055 FAX: (0141) 248 2608
WEB SITE: www.rogano.co.uk

NEW CHEF
SEAFOOD
£25–£80

Those with a sense of nostalgia will appreciate Rogano's splendid art deco dining room, and some may even remember Andrew Cummings, who cooked here a few years back. His return signals nothing more than a steady continuation of the style, subjecting fine materials to familiar treatments – fish soup with rouille, lemon sole meunière – alongside more contemporary seared scallops with black pudding. Reports are welcome. Wines are predominantly white and French, and mark-ups tend to be high. Prices start at £12.

CHEF: Andrew Cummings PROPRIETOR: Punch Retail OPEN: all week 12 to 2.30, 6.30 to 10.30 CLOSED: 25 Dec, 1 Jan MEALS: alc (main courses £17.50 to £32.50). Set L £16.50. Bar menu available SERVICE: 12.5% (optional), card slips closed CARDS: Amex, Delta, Diners, MasterCard, Switch, Visa DETAILS: 70 seats. 20 seats outside. Private parties: 70 main room, 16 and 28 private rooms. Vegetarian meals. Children's helpings. No smoking L before 2, D before 10. Wheelchair access (not WC). No music. Air-conditioned

78 St Vincent

78 St Vincent Street, Glasgow G2 5UB
TEL: (0141) 248 7878 FAX: (0141) 248 4663
EMAIL: frontdesk@78stvincent.com
WEB SITE: www.78stvincent.com

COOKING **1**
BRASSERIE
£24–£49

'Predominantly French with a Scottish flavour' is how 78 St Vincent describes its style. This applies to both cooking and the setting in what used to be the Phoenix building: modern Scottish art sits alongside art nouveau metalwork and an original marble staircase. The modern brasserie cooking also features a few Japanese and Middle Eastern ideas thrown in for good measure. This pick 'n' mix approach turns up some novel-sounding combinations: grilled goats' cheese with pickled vegetables and wasabi croûtons; a pigeon, duck and apricot terrine with cranberry coulis; and salmon with peas and herbs in a light chicken jus with gnocchi. Atmosphere, décor and service are all considered 'first class'. A decent bunch of wines opens with a page of eight house selections available by the bottle (from £12.95) and in two sizes of glass.

CHEF: Stuart Wilson PROPRIETOR: Michael Canyers OPEN: all week 12 to 3, 5 to 10.30 (10.45 Fri and Sat) CLOSED: 25 Dec, 1 Jan MEALS: alc L (main courses £7 to £12). Set D £15.50 (1 course) to £26 SERVICE: not inc CARDS: Amex, Delta, Diners, MasterCard, Switch, Visa DETAILS: 100 seats. Private parties: 66 main room, 16 private room. Vegetarian meals. Children's helpings. No smoking in 1 dining room. Wheelchair access (also WC). No music. Air-conditioned (£5)

Occasional music *in the details at the end of an entry means live or recorded music is played in the dining room only rarely or for special events.* No music *means it is never played.*

Report forms are at the back of the book; write a letter if you prefer; or email us at goodfoodguide@which.net

Stravaigin

28 Gibson Street, Hillhead, Glasgow G12 8NX
TEL: (0141) 334 2665 FAX: (0141) 334 4099 COOKING **4**
EMAIL: bookings@stravaigin.com GLOBAL
WEB SITE: www.stravaigin.com £29–£53

Colin Clydesdale would win no prizes in a competition for sitting still the longest. Not only does his lively Hillhead bar/restaurant continue to evolve in all sorts of new directions, but this year it has sprouted an offshoot called Stravaigin 2 (see below). Other recent developments have included the establishment of close ties with a Galloway farm, with the commendable aim of giving the kitchen 'total control over our product'. Eating options run to a menu of snacks and light meals served all day in the bar upstairs, while in the ground floor dining room the main carte represents an eye-catching exposition of inventive international cooking: gingered lamb carpaccio with anise chutney, wasabi, cucumber pickle and a garlic and herb wafer illustrates Colin Clydesdale's lack of fear when it comes to mixing and matching bold flavours and various styles on one plate.

There is just as much going on in main courses, such as roast breast of corn-fed chicken on pancetta and pumpkin risotto with beetroot purée and sage gravy, or in a warm spiced pear with roast pimento and walnut tortilla wrap with sour cream and an avocado and turtle bean salsa. The generally positive tone of reports suggests that such experiments mostly produce successful results, though desserts have registered one or two disappointments. Abundant notes should help when it comes to choosing a wine from the international list. Prices are fair throughout, with house French red and white opening the selection at £12.25 a bottle.

CHEF/PROPRIETOR: Colin Clydesdale OPEN: Fri and Sat L 12 to 2.30, Tue to Sun D 5 to 11 MEALS: Set L £16.95 (2 courses) to £19.95, Set D £20.95 (2 courses) to £25.95. Bar menu available SERVICE: not inc CARDS: Amex, Delta, Diners, MasterCard, Switch, Visa DETAILS: 80 seats. Private parties: 80 main room. Vegetarian meals. Children's helpings. No smoking before 10. Music. Air-conditioned (£5)

Stravaigin 2

NEW ENTRY

8 Ruthven Lane, Glasgow G12 9BG COOKING **2**
TEL: (0141) 334 7165 FAX: (0141) 357 4785 GLOBAL
WEB SITE: www.stravaigin2.com £18–£44

'Eat local, think global' is the slogan of this new branch of Stravaigin (see entry above), which repeats the formula made successful by its sibling in more confined surroundings. A warm, friendly atmosphere, and prices pitched to suit the pockets of the local university population, help to ensure that it is busy most of the time. The cooking's penchant for globetrotting shows in Scottish meatballs with coconut broth, and Indonesian shiitake nikozumo (mushrooms with chicken in a sweet wasabi and ginger sauce). At an early inspection meal, a more familiar dish of smoked haddock and salmon fishcake with home-made chutney turned out to be more successful than some of the fusion experiments, impressing for its honest wholesomeness; another highlight was an expertly made bread-and-butter pudding with plenty of juicy Muscat-soaked raisins and a crisp caramelised topping. Wines on the short list are as varied as the food. House Chilean is £11.95.

CHEF: Hector Macrae PROPRIETOR: Colin Clydesdale OPEN: all week 12 (11 Sat and Sun) to 11 CLOSED: 25 Dec, 1 Jan MEALS: alc (main courses £9.50 to £14). Set L 12 to 3 £7.95 (2 courses) to £9.95 SERVICE: not inc CARDS: Amex, Delta, Diners, MasterCard, Switch, Visa DETAILS: 75 seats. Private parties: 45 main room, 40 private room. Vegetarian meals. Children's helpings. No smoking between 12 and 2 and 5 and 10. Wheelchair access (also WC). Music. Air-conditioned (£5)

Ubiquitous Chip

12 Ashton Lane, Glasgow G12 8SJ
TEL: (0141) 334 5007 FAX: (0141) 337 1302 COOKING **4**
EMAIL: mail@ubiquitouschip.co.uk SCOTTISH
WEB SITE: www.ubiquitouschip.co.uk £29–£69

Ronnie Clydesdale celebrated 30 years of the Chip in 2001: a notable contribution to Glasgow's long-standing culinary dynamism. The white-walled, Mediterranean-style courtyard, down a cobbled mews in the heart of the West End, is overhung with trailing plants, service is 'understated but friendly', and menus are built on fresh Scottish produce with some modish touches, not all instantly familiar. 'Marag gheal' proves to be a vegetable-suet/oatmeal mix topped with a poached duck egg, while the Caledonian 80/- batter encasing salmon brandade is made from a strong Scots ale.

Blue ling, seldom seen on menus, is roasted in duck fat and served with flageolet beans in a scallop and mushroom broth, while the fat duck itself comes as a well-timed roast breast with spiced lentils, chargrilled sweet potato and superfluous pineapple garnish. An inspector found the food cumulatively rather weightier than is normal these days, and a sweet tooth is needed for such desserts as caramelised rice pudding with cinnamon shortbread, or custard-based banana tart with raisins. The well-rounded wine list, though weighted towards France's classic areas, is crammed with superb vintages from great estates across the world. Bins under £20 are hard to find, though house red, white and rosé are £13.95 (£3.50 a glass).

CHEF/PROPRIETOR: Ronnie Clydesdale OPEN: all week 12 (12.30 Sun) to 2.30 (3 Sun), 5.30 (6.30 Sun) to 11 CLOSED: 25 Dec, 1 Jan MEALS: Set L £19.95 (2 courses) to £24.95, Set L Sun £17.50, Set D £28.95 (2 courses) to £33.95. Brasserie menu available 12 to 11 SERVICE: not inc CARDS: Amex, Delta, Diners, MasterCard, Switch, Visa DETAILS: 180 seats. Private parties: 80 main room, 20 to 50 private rooms. Vegetarian meals. Children's helpings. Wheelchair access (also WC). No music

Restaurateurs justifiably resent no-shows. If you quote a credit card number when booking, you may be liable for the restaurant's lost profit margin if you don't turn up. Always phone to cancel.

'As the waiter put my pigeon before me on the table, I happened to glance out of the window where some pigeons were pecking away. He looked as well and said, ''It is rather difficult in front of the relatives, isn't it?'' ' (On eating in London)

GULLANE East Lothian map 11

▲ Greywalls

Muirfield, Gullane EH31 2EG
TEL: (01620) 842144 FAX: (01620) 842241
EMAIL: hotel@greywalls.co.uk
WEB SITE: www.greywalls.co.uk
on A198, at E end of Gullane

COOKING **4**
MODERN BRITISH
£26–£58

Greywalls is a delight to visit. The grounds are outstanding in spring and summer, the crescent-shaped Lutyens house appears timeless, and service is relaxed and unfussy. Lunch may not be up to the standard of dinner, which is a four-course affair (the second typically a soup or salad) that takes pride in regional materials and offers some straightforward yet appealing ideas: roast West Coast scallops with tomato confit, or Angus beef fillet with foie gras and garlic chips. Seasonal input might take the form of East Lothian asparagus in May, with spinach and hollandaise, or an early-summer pea and broad bean soup.

At their best, flavours and textures work effectively, for example in a moist, salty, flavourful duck confit, its fattiness countered by vinegared anchovies, all against a background of first-class sauté waxy potatoes and pesto-covered croûtons. As an alternative to desserts such as lemon bavarois, or chocolate cheesecake, there might be a savoury along the lines of roast crottin with beetroot compote, or spiced carrot salad with raisin purée and Manchego cheese. Set around bawdy limericks, the wine list starts off with exhaustive listings of classic French regions in which rarities command high prices; equally, a fair range of stylish bottlings under £20 can be found. Outside France, the US and the antipodes are looked at in some detail, and Spanish wines have been cleverlychosen. The front-page house selection starts at £13.

CHEF: Simon Burns PROPRIETORS: Giles and Ros Weaver OPEN: all week 12.30 to 1.45, 7.30 to 9.15 CLOSED: late Oct to mid-Apr MEALS: Set L Mon to Sat £15 (2 courses) to £17.50, Set L Sun £25, Set D £37.50. Light L available Mon to Sat SERVICE: not inc, card slips closed CARDS: Amex, Delta, Diners, MasterCard, Switch, Visa DETAILS: 50 seats. 20 seats outside. Private parties: 40 main room, 20 private room. Car park. Jacket and tie. No smoking in dining room. Wheelchair access (not WC). No music ACCOMMODATION: 23 rooms, all with bath/shower. TV. Phone. B&B £115 to £225. Rooms for disabled (*The Which? Hotel Guide*) (£5)

INVERKEILOR Angus map 11

▲ Gordon's

32 Main Street, Inverkeilor DD11 5RN
TEL/FAX: (01241) 830364
WEB SITE: www.gordonsrestaurant.co.uk
off A92 from Arbroath to Montrose

COOKING **4**
MODERN SCOTTISH
£28–£48

The setting for this small family-run restaurant is a nineteenth-century sandstone building, its stained glass, beams and open fire giving the dining room a traditional rustic feel. By way of a contrast, the cooking takes an impeccably modern point of view. Meat from a local butcher, fish from Aberdeen and Arbroath, locally grown fruit, and mushrooms gathered by Gordon himself provide the foundations for some enterprising constructions, ranging from ceviche of hot-smoked salmon with tabbouleh and lime crème fraîche, to a complicated main course of hare wrapped in pheasant mousse and partnered by lavender-crusted loin of venison on kiln-dried polenta with cherries and a rowan and claret jus.

On a more classical note, the short set-price menu might also offer Aberdeen Angus beef fillet with celeriac purée accompanied by dauphinois with chanterelles and a red wine reduction. To finish there may be good old sticky toffee pudding, alongside vanilla pannacotta with roasted figs and balsamic ice cream. Coffee comes with home-made tablet or petits fours. Two dozen wines lack the imagination or scope of the cooking, but prices are mostly under £20. Three house wines, from France, are £10.95 a bottle.

CHEFS: Gordon and Garry Watson PROPRIETORS: Gordon and Maria Watson OPEN: Wed to Sun L 12 to 1.45, Tue to Sat D 7 to 9 CLOSED: last 2 weeks Jan, first 2 weeks Feb MEALS: Set L £16.50 (2 courses) to £19.50, Set D £27.50 (2 courses) to £30.50 SERVICE: not inc CARDS: Delta, MasterCard, Switch, Visa DETAILS: 24 seats. Private parties: 24 main room, 20 private room. Car park. Children's helpings. No children under 6 at D. No smoking in dining room. Wheelchair access (not WC). No music ACCOMMODATION: 3 rooms, all with bath/shower. TV. B&B £45 to £100. No children under 6

INVERNESS Highland **map 11**

▲ Culloden House

Milton of Culloden, Inverness IV2 7BZ
TEL: (01463) 790461 FAX: (01463) 792181
EMAIL: info@cullodenhouse.co.uk
WEB SITE: www.cullodenhouse.co.uk
from Inverness take A96 towards Nairn, turn right after 1m, then left at Culloden House Avenue

COOKING **2**
INTERNATIONAL
£33–£56

'This is a real baronial hall,' deduced one visitor to this creeper-clad Palladian mansion, bowled over by the excess of luxury on offer. After being greeted formally, you will be led through to the impressively ornate dining room, where sparkling chandeliers, Adam plaster reliefs and (imitation) marble pillars are the order of the day: the perfect setting for a grand banquet. Dinner is an appropriately old-fashioned affair of four courses, including either soup or sorbet before the main course. Dishes such as smoked goose with orange dressing appear among starters, while main courses encompass medallions of venison with braised red cabbage and apple on a creamy green peppercorn sauce, and honey-roast duck breast with Puy lentils and a blackcurrant jus. A selection of seven wines by the glass from £3.25 opens an all-embracing global list. Bottle prices start at £14.85 but, overall, choice under £20 is somewhat limited.

CHEF: Michael Simpson PROPRIETOR: North American Country Inns OPEN: all week 12.30 to 2, 7 to 9 CLOSED: 24 to 26 Dec MEALS: alc L (main courses £12 to £19). Set D £35 SERVICE: not inc, card slips closed CARDS: Amex, Delta, Diners, MasterCard, Switch, Visa DETAILS: 60 seats. Private parties: 65 main room, 30 private room. Car park. Vegetarian meals. Children's helpings. No children under 10. No smoking in dining room. No music ACCOMMODATION: 28 rooms, all with bath/shower. TV. Phone. B&B £85 to £270. No children under 10. Baby facilities (£5)

▲ Dunain Park

Inverness IV3 8JN
TEL: (01463) 230512 FAX: (01463) 224532
EMAIL: dunainparkhotel@btinternet.com
WEB SITE: www.dunainparkhotel.co.uk
on A82 towards Fort William, 1m from town boundary

COOKING **2**
SCOTTISH
£38–£52

This secluded Georgian country house sits in six acres of beautiful gardens and woodland, including a two-acre walled kitchen garden which provides herbs, soft fruits and vegetables. Such is the degree of comfort and pampering provided by Edward and Ann Nicoll that guests are reluctant to leave at the end of their stay. As well as home-grown produce, most other materials are sourced locally, including salmon, scallops, venison and lamb. 'Scottish with a French influence' is how they describe their cooking style, taking an admirably straightforward approach that produces some satisfying results: an inspector's meal of parsnip and apple soup, followed by beef fillet on mashed potatoes with mushrooms and a red wine sauce impressed both for its attractive presentation and for the skill evident in its preparation. Desserts are set out buffet-style to help yourself, so those who are inclined can try several. The broad-ranging international wine list is fairly priced, with Chilean Merlot and New Zealand Chardonnay opening at £14.50.

CHEFS: Ann Nicoll and Justin Sharp PROPRIETORS: Edward and Ann Nicoll OPEN: all week D only 7 to 9 MEALS: alc (main courses £16 to £18) SERVICE: not inc, card slips closed CARDS: Amex, Delta, Diners, MasterCard, Switch, Visa DETAILS: 40 seats. Private parties: 10 main room. Car park. Vegetarian meals. Children's helpings. No smoking in dining room. Wheelchair access (not WC). No music ACCOMMODATION: 13 rooms, all with bath/shower. TV. Phone. B&B £138 to £198 (double room). Rooms for disabled. Baby facilities. Swimming pool (*The Which? Hotel Guide*) (£5)

KILCHRENAN Argyll & Bute **map 11**

▲ Taychreggan

Kilchrenan PA35 1HQ
TEL: (01866) 833211 or 833366
FAX: (01866) 833244
on B845, 7m S of Taynuilt

COOKING **4**
MODERN SCOTTISH
£46–£56

If the long drive to the edge of Loch Awe seems daunting, consider making a splash by taking a seaplane from Glasgow airport instead. An elegantly appointed dining room awaits, complete with well-spaced antique waxed tables and restrained flower arrangements. Even better, the short, well-judged menu fulfils its promise, taking native produce as its starting point: grilled Loch Etive mussels, roast loin of venison, or a panaché of West Coast seafood with saffron-flavoured pasta and a basil infusion. Non-meat options have included a spinach and blue cheese soufflé to start, followed by a pithiviers of oyster mushrooms with courgette provençale. Dinner is a five-course affair, incorporating a mid-meal soup or sorbet, desserts such as rum baba or coffee crème brûlée, and a selection of Scottish cheeses, and there are bar lunches too.

Wines under £20 are very much in the minority on the mainly French list, which starts with house Vin de Pays d'Oc Chardonnay and Cabernet Sauvignon at £13.25 and £14 respectively.

CHEF: Jerome Prodanu PROPRIETOR: Romantic Places/Ammie Paul OPEN: all week D only 7.30 to 8.45. Bar lunches available MEALS: Set D £35 SERVICE: not inc CARDS: Amex, Delta, MasterCard, Switch, Visa DETAILS: 40 seats. Private parties: 50 main room. Car park. Vegetarian meals. No children under 14 at D. No smoking in dining room. Music ACCOMMODATION: 19 rooms, all with bath/shower. Phone. B&B £90 to £215. No children under 14 in accommodation. Fishing (*The Which? Hotel Guide*) (£5)

KILLIECRANKIE Perthshire & Kinross **map 11**

▲ Killiecrankie Hotel

Killiecrankie PH16 5LG
TEL: (01796) 473220 FAX: (01796) 472451
EMAIL: enquiries@killiecrankiehotel.co.uk
WEB SITE: www.killiecrankiehotel.co.uk
off A9, 3m N of Pitlochry

COOKING **3**
GLOBAL
£43–£52

Not far from the site of the Battle of Killiecrankie (a Jacobite victory over Orange forces in 1689) this Victorian manse has a modestly and unpretentiously decorated dining room with a wonderful view. While the use of native materials – such as Highland venison (served perhaps with potato and leek rösti and a date and port sauce), and a Drambuie and orange dressing (on a warm salad of sautéed pigeon breast) – indicate a concern for homely matters, the kitchen seems equally at ease with roast vegetable couscous to accompany grilled sea bass, or boned stuffed quail served with mustard mash and a garlic cream sauce. Celtic cheeses, from smoked Lochaber to Cashel Blue, come after desserts of pannacotta, or dark chocolate fondant with vanilla ice cream. Bar lunches are not recommended. A few New World wines complement the European ones, the price range is reasonable, and seven of the eight house recommendations come in under £16.

CHEF: Mark Easton PROPRIETORS: Colin and Carole Anderson OPEN: all week D and L menu available 7 to 8.30 CLOSED: 3 Jan to 4 Feb MEALS: Set D £32.50. SERVICE: not inc, card slips closed CARDS: Delta, MasterCard, Switch, Visa DETAILS: 34 seats. Private parties: 16 main room. Car park. Children's helpings. No children under 5. No smoking in dining room. No music ACCOMMODATION: 10 rooms, all with bath/shower. TV. Phone. D,B&B £69 to £178. Baby facilities (*The Which? Hotel Guide*)

The Guide is totally independent, accepts no free hospitality, and survives on the number of copies sold each year.

Dining rooms where music, either live or recorded, is never played are signalled by No music *in the details at the end of an entry.*

London Round-ups listing additional restaurants that may be worth a visit can be found after the main London section.

KINCLAVEN Perthshire & Kinross map 11

▲ Ballathie House

Kinclaven, by Stanley PH1 4QN
TEL: (01250) 883268 FAX: (01250) 883396
EMAIL: email@ballathiehousehotel.com
WEB SITE: www.ballathiehousehotel.com
off B9099; take right fork 1m N of Stanley

COOKING **2**
MODERN SCOTTISH
£25–£61

Set beside the River Tay, and surrounded by lawns, this Scottish baronial hotel is tastefully furnished and decorated, with fine plasterwork ceilings, spacious and well-lit rooms, and an air of tranquillity. Lunch can be two or three courses, dinner three or four (in which case the second is soup or sorbet), and the larder combines native ingredients with foreign ones: buffalo mozzarella, anchovies and olives in a salad, rillettes of salmon (fresh, cured and smoked), and Aberdeen Angus beef for a small supplement. Advanced or minimal preparation takes care of quite a few starters – Ogen melon with purple figs and air-dried ham, for example, or pheasant terrine with sweet-and-sour plum chutney – leaving the kitchen free to devote more effort to main courses of monkfish fillet on leek mash, or honey-roast breast of duck on red onion confit. Desserts run from sticky toffee pudding to a chilled citrus tart with lemon sorbet, and wines are a selection of well-established European styles and classic New World blends and single-grapevarieties. Prices are reasonable, and an Australian red and white duo at £13 leads the Cellarman's Choice of 15 bins, mainly under £18.

CHEF: Kevin McGillivray PROPRIETOR: Ballathie House Hotel Co Ltd OPEN: all week 12.30 to 2, 7 to 9 MEALS: Set L £15 (2 courses) to £18.50, Set L Sun £19.50, Set D £33.50 to £36.50. Bar menu available Mon to Sat L SERVICE: not inc CARDS: Amex, Delta, Diners, MasterCard, Switch, Visa DETAILS: 60 seats. 20 seats outside. Private parties: 14 main room, 16 and 32 private rooms. Car park. Vegetarian meals. Children's helpings. Jacket and tie. No smoking in dining room. Wheelchair access (also WC). No music ACCOMMODATION: 42 rooms, all with bath/shower. TV. Phone. D,B&B £95 to £250. Rooms for disabled. Baby facilities. Fishing

KINGUSSIE Highland map 11

▲ The Cross

Tweed Mill Brae, Ardbroilach Road,
Kingussie PH21 1TC
TEL: (01540) 661166 FAX: (01540) 661080
EMAIL: relax@thecross.co.uk
WEB SITE: www.thecross.co.uk

COOKING **6**
MODERN SCOTTISH
£47–£57

The sympathetically restored former mill by the brae successfully integrates modern paintings and artefacts into its old stone structure, and the dining room's roughcast walls, beams and raised hearth provide a trim background for Ruth Hadley's equally neat and ordered cooking. She concentrates her efforts on primary events rather than on elaborate incidentals, the result being a sensibly well-managed operation. Dinner is five courses, the only choices being minimal ones at main-course and dessert stage, and portions are well judged. There is no attempt to extend culinary boundaries, given soups of leek and sweetcorn, or of roast parsnip, but there is a determination to get the best out of prime materials:

for example, in three fat superior scallops, perfectly timed with translucent centres, sitting in a light orange sauce.

Regional materials abound, from West Coast squat lobsters to saddle of Skye lamb, and dishes are well constructed with textural contrasts and lots of interest, yet without stealing the main item's thunder, as in a small piece of fresh flaky cod, topped with a blob of eggy emulsion, sitting on a herby flageolet bean salad. Desserts are properly executed too – first-rate crème caramel with a poached pear and caramel ice cream – sometimes with a degree of flair, as in an individual lime cheesecake (more like a well-risen small soufflé) served with poached plums and an unusual tanka bean ice cream tasting like a cross between vanilla and liquorice.

Tony Hadley is an enthusiast of the best kind. He is, in effect, the wine list, although there is a printed one as well. There are no notes to read (he talks you through what you want to know), and there are no house wines as such, but always something of interest to taste, though nothing from France. Instead, a wide range of world styles is offered at very fair prices, from £9.90, and a decent spread of half-bottles encourages experimentation.

CHEFS: Ruth Hadley and Becca Henderson PROPRIETORS: Tony and Ruth Hadley OPEN: Wed to Mon D only 7 to 8.30 CLOSED: 1 Dec to 28 Feb MEALS: Set D £37.50 SERVICE: not inc, card slips closed CARDS: Delta, MasterCard, Switch, Visa DETAILS: 24 seats. Private parties: 30 main room. Car park. No children under 8. No smoking in dining room. Wheelchair access (also WC). No music ACCOMMODATION: 9 rooms, all with bath/shower. Phone. D,B&B £95 to £115. No children under 8 (*The Which? Hotel Guide*)

LINLITHGOW West Lothian map 11

▲ Champany Inn

Champany Corner, Linlithgow EH49 7LU
TEL: (01506) 834532 FAX: (01506) 834302
EMAIL: reception@champany.com
WEB SITE: www.champany.com
2m NE of Linlithgow at junction of A904 and A803

COOKING **5**
SCOTTISH
£48–£89

A traditional stone courtyard leads into a dining room that is 'pure 1970s' with brasses, dark wood, stone walls, and patio doors through which comes the only daylight. This is a place for steak lovers with 'deep pockets and hearty appetites', its unchanging menu offering ribeye, pope's eye, porterhouse: indeed almost any cut on request. Three weeks hanging in ionised chill rooms produces impressive depth of flavour, helped by 'fantastic fat', and saucing is minimal – a choice of three with fillet steak, otherwise béarnaise with chateaubriand (for two) – so there is no question of the food being anything other than simply presented.

While it is difficult to find beef kept in better condition, downsides include cost – £29.50 for a striploin, for example – and the fact that 'eating a pound of meat is not, for me, that great an experience'. Accompaniments include French fries, baked potato, first-rate sauté wild mushrooms and, for those who find a steak not quite meaty enough, a home-made sausage. Just in case a non-meat eater wanders in by accident, there is lobster (price on application), salmon, and deep-fried cod and chips.

Starters are equally enduring: oysters, smoked salmon, prawns piri-piri (flavourful butterflied crevettes dusted with powdered chilli, not too fiercely spiced), plus a selection of soups and salads. Portions are so large that lemon cheesecake or ice cream hardly seem necessary. A wide-reaching collection of both classic and lively styles, with plenty of variety for partnering beef, from a magnificent 32,000-bottle wine cellar, unfortunately offers little under £20. Own-label house wines starting at £14.50 can help take the costly edge off other choices.

CHEFS: Clive Davidson, David Gibson and Kevin Hope PROPRIETORS: Clive and Anne Davidson OPEN: Mon to Fri L 12.30 to 2, Mon to Sat D 7 to 10 CLOSED: 25 and 26 Dec, 1 and 2 Jan MEALS: alc (main courses £17.50 to £32.50). Set L £16.75 (2 courses) SERVICE: 10%, card slips closed CARDS: Amex, Delta, Diners, MasterCard, Switch, Visa DETAILS: 50 seats. 20 seats outside. Private parties: 50 main room, 40 private room. Car park. No children under 8. Wheelchair access (also WC). No music ACCOMMODATION: 16 rooms, all with bath/shower. TV. Phone. B&B £105 to £125. Rooms for disabled (*The Which? Hotel Guide*)

LOCHINVER Highland map 11

▲ Albannach

Baddidarroch, Lochinver IV27 4LP
TEL: (01571) 844407 FAX: (01571) 844285
EMAIL: the.albannach@virginnet.co.uk

COOKING **5**
MODERN SCOTTISH
£45–£54

'Excellent service, welcoming atmosphere, superb food and wine – what more could be asked?' So concluded a contented visitor to this remote house on the shore of Loch Inver, which also enjoys magnificent views. Menus are dictated by availability of ingredients, which can be a bit of a lottery when you use only seasonal, local, wild or free-range produce. Here, however, they have the advantage of a couple of local crofters who grow vegetables and herbs and supply ducks' and hens' eggs, and some of the local fishermen deliver their catch straight to the kitchen door, while game and free-range beef and lamb come from Morayshire. Even the tableware is made in a pottery that you can see from the dining room window.

These materials are fashioned into a daily five-course no-choice menu, with a second-course soup, and cheese before dessert. The starter might be as straightforward as a warm tartlet of Loch Roe crab with tomato chutney, or as complex as pan-fried loin of hare and breast of wood pigeon with goose confit, braised red cabbage and game chocolate sauce. Main courses tend towards the more highly wrought end of the scale but do not suffer for that: pan-fried monkfish tails and seared Loch Broom scallops on saffron and seaweed rice with a champagne sabayon is typical. To finish, there may be aniseed parfait with an almond tuile basket of berries and blueberry coulis. The wine list takes a tour of the classic French regions before exploring other major wine countries in some detail. Value persists throughout, with a handful of sparkling wines under £20 and house Vin de Pays d'Oc Merlot and Chardonnay at £9.50.

CHEFS/PROPRIETORS: Colin Craig and Lesley Crosfield OPEN: Tue to Sun and bank hol Mon D only 8 (1 sitting) CLOSED: 1 Dec to 15 Mar possibly exc Christmas to New Year MEALS: Set D £36 SERVICE: not inc CARDS: MasterCard, Switch, Visa DETAILS: 16 seats. Private parties: 22 main room. Car park. No children under 12. No smoking in dining room. No music ACCOMMODATION: 5 rooms, all with bath/shower. Phone. D,B&B £87 to £117. Rooms for disabled. No children under 12 (*The Which? Hotel Guide*)

MOFFAT Dumfries & Galloway map 11

▲ Well View

Ballplay Road, Moffat DG10 9JU
TEL: (01683) 220184 FAX: (01683) 220088
EMAIL: info@wellview.co.uk
WEB SITE: www.wellview.co.uk

COOKING **4**
SCOTTISH-FRENCH
£21–£43

Overlooking the town and hills to the west, this Victorian house goes in for soft greys, greens and pinks in its high-ceilinged rooms. The deal is six courses (one an appetiser) with no choice before dessert. Other things worth knowing are that a day's notice is necessary for any meal, that the shorter lunch menu is by arrangement, that the service policy is exemplary, and that Janet Schuckardt is a busy and accomplished cook. A typical meal might begin with a vegetarian spring roll, followed by slices of smoked chicken and melon in a tarragon dressing, then a dish of cod in a tomato and basil sauce, before a main course of duck with plum sauce. If that seems a lot, rest assured that the portions and the pace of serving are 'just right'.

Other highlights have included a smoked Orkney cheese and chive soufflé, and a prawn and salmon risotto with a champagne sauce. Cheese comes with home-made chutney and oatcakes (incidentals of a high order are made in-house), and well-rated desserts include pear and apple tart, and crème brûlée. The wine list opens in classic style with food-friendly bottles from the Loire, Bordeaux and Alsace, then dips into other styles from elsewhere. Prices are moderate, and there's a fair amount under £20 (try a Clare Valley Riesling, for example), and house selections start at £13.

CHEFS: Janet and Linda Schuckardt PROPRIETORS: John and Janet Schuckardt OPEN: Sun L 12.15 to 1.15, all week D 6.30 to 8.30 (booking essential) MEALS: Set L £14, Set D £29 SERVICE: none, card slips closed CARDS: Amex, Delta, MasterCard, Switch, Visa DETAILS: 24 seats. Private parties: 24 main room, 6 private room. Car park. No children under 5 at D. No smoking in dining room. Wheelchair access (not WC). No music ACCOMMODATION: 6 rooms, all with bath/shower. TV. B&B £55 to £100. Baby facilities (*The Which? Hotel Guide*) (£5)

MUIR OF ORD Highland map 11

▲ Dower House

Highfield, Muir of Ord IV6 7XN
TEL/FAX: (01463) 870090
EMAIL: tgfg@thedowerhouse.co.uk
WEB SITE: www.thedowerhouse.co.uk

COOKING **3**
MODERN BRITISH
£47–£57

Although not far from Inverness, this ornately decorated one-storey Victorian house feels quietly out of the mainstream. Its simple format – three-course dinners with no choice – helps to maintain a domestic feel too. The Aitchisons make use of their local butcher and baker (for oatcakes, bread and shortbread), and bring in vegetables and herbs from their own garden, although their culinary horizons extend as far as aubergine and pepper salad, red wine risotto, and roast marinated quail on a bed of couscous.

They manage to avoid an overly timid approach to no-choice meals, which might centre around seared scallops with capers and lemon, chicken braised with tomato and honey, or venison fillet with herb vinaigrette. Puddings return to home base with bread-and-butter, or hot raspberry soufflé. The wine list is cheerful and uncomplicated, with prices hovering around the £20 mark. Good names from Australia sit beside bottlings from respected South African estates, but the bias is towards France. Twenty half-bottles are offered, and house French red and white come in at £16.

CHEF: Robyn Aitchison PROPRIETORS: Robyn and Mena Aitchison OPEN: all week D only 8 to 9.30 (L by arrangement) CLOSED: 25 Dec, 2 weeks Nov MEALS: Set D £35 SERVICE: not inc, card slips closed CARDS: MasterCard, Switch, Visa DETAILS: 20 seats. 6 seats outside. Private parties: 28 main room. Car park. Children's helpings. No very young children at D. No smoking in dining room. Wheelchair access (also WC). No music ACCOMMODATION: 6 rooms, all with bath/shower. TV. Phone. B&B £55 to £150. Rooms for disabled. Baby facilities (*The Which? Hotel Guide*)

NAIRN Highland **map 11**

▲ Clifton House

Nairn IV12 4HW
TEL: (01667) 453119 FAX: (01667) 452836
EMAIL: macintyre@clifton-hotel.co.uk
WEB SITE: www.clifton-hotel.co.uk
W of town roundabout on A96

COOKING **4**
MODERN SCOTTISH COST
£29–£46

J. Gordon Macintyre has lived at Clifton House all his life, and has been in charge now for 50 years. Given a house that dates back to 1874, with a decorative style to match, it is clear that tradition plays a leading role in the operation. As far as the food is concerned, this is the best kind of tradition, where provenance of materials and quiet dedication combine to produce a simple repertoire of which most French country restaurants would be proud. Not many places still serve egg mayonnaise, mushrooms à la grecque, or turbot maître d'hôtel. 'We know the source of everything we cook and serve,' they claim, from chickens and eggs to salmon, beef and lamb, and apply basic but sound techniques to deliver partridge terrine, lamb with rosemary, and monkfish provençale. In these hands such plainness becomes a virtue, notable too in puddings such as caramel custard, or meringues with cream and raspberry sauce. Great Bordeaux and Burgundy vintages and rarities dominate the wine list, and attention to serving temperatures bodes well. Prices tend to be high, but value can be found with the house wines (from £10) and a range of styles under £15.

CHEFS: J. Gordon and Charles Macintyre PROPRIETOR: J. Gordon Macintyre OPEN: all week 12.30 to 1, 7 to 9.30 CLOSED: Christmas and New Year MEALS: alc (main courses £12 to £18) SERVICE: none, card slips closed CARDS: Amex, Diners, MasterCard, Visa DETAILS: 40 seats. Private parties: 40 main room, 12 and 20 private rooms. Car park. Vegetarian meals. Children's helpings. No smoking in 1 dining room. Music ACCOMMODATION: 12 rooms, all with bath/shower. B&B £50 to £107. Baby facilities (*The Which? Hotel Guide*) (£5)

PEAT INN Fife **map 11**

▲ Peat Inn

Peat Inn KY15 5LH
TEL: (01334) 840206 FAX: (01334) 840530
EMAIL: reception@thepeatinn.co.uk
WEB SITE: www.thepeatinn.co.uk
at junction of B940 and B941, 6m SW of St Andrews

COOKING **5**
SCOTTISH
£42–£70

Although it has had something of a makeover, and has been brightened up with much reupholstering of carpets, curtains and chairs, the Peat Inn remained very much 'as we have always found it' for one pair of returnees. A concern for prime materials has traditionally been at the heart of David Wilson's cooking, long before it occurred to the cheffy world at large that such things mattered, and despite continuing problems with fishing and agriculture he still manages to lay his hands on local ingredients. Mushrooms, for example, have included morels from a wood just ten miles away, and St George mushrooms for a May visitor, accompanied by asparagus and mint.

Seafood successes run to a fresh-tasting prawn mousse with turbot and langoustine, while game (another strong suit) has yielded tender, tasty venison with a bean purée. Although David Wilson tends to eschew fusion flavours, he is not averse to serving tender, well-cooked guinea fowl with a sesame crust in a sweet-sour red wine sauce flavoured with star anise, even though he is probably not at his best with such combinations. In general the cooking is assured, with little in the way of error, although an inspection meal found a few things below par. Those who like caramel will probably make a beeline for caramelised pear with caramel ice cream and caramel sauce, or there may be a rich chocolate tart with vanilla sauce. Bread is good, and staff are professional and well trained.

David Wilson introduces and comments on the wines in a highly personal way. Classic styles from France are followed by similar ones from around the world, like the white Burgundies introducing a global Chardonnay section, which can be useful in guiding choice. Mark-ups are generally low, although (apart from house French at £16) little is below £25.

CHEFS: David Wilson and Angus Blacklaws PROPRIETORS: David and Patricia Wilson OPEN: Tue to Sat 12.30 to 1, 7 to 9.30 CLOSED: 25 Dec, 1 Jan MEALS: alc D (main courses £16 to £19.50). Set L £19.50, Set D £30 to £45 SERVICE: not inc, card slips closed CARDS: Amex, Delta, MasterCard, Switch, Visa DETAILS: 48 seats. Private parties: 24 main room, 12 to 24 private rooms. Car park. Vegetarian meals. No smoking in dining room. Wheelchair access (also WC). No music ACCOMMODATION: 8 rooms, all with bath/shower. TV. Phone. B&B £75 to £150. Rooms for disabled (*The Which? Hotel Guide*)

All entries in the Guide are re-researched and rewritten every year, not least because restaurant standards fluctuate. Don't rely on an out-of-date Guide.

(£5) *indicates that the restaurant has elected to participate in the* Good Food Guide *voucher scheme. For full details, see page 6.*

PEEBLES Borders map 11

▲ Cringletie House hotel

Eddleston, Peebles EH45 8PL
TEL: (01721) 730233 FAX: (01721) 730244
EMAIL: enquiries@cringletie.com
WEB SITE: www.cringletie.com
on A703, 2m N of Peebles

COOKING **5**
MODERN SCOTTISH
£26–£57

An imposing barony comprising 28 acres of private grounds and woodland, Cringletie makes a rather grand initial impression, quite belied in the event by the 'informal, personal welcome' that greets visitors. A working walled kitchen garden, established in the seventeenth century, supplies vegetables, fruit and herbs to Addy Daggert's team, so that summer menus are a particular treat. The cooking is not without a certain innovative flair: a confit duck leg appears as a starter on an underlay of black pudding, all hedged about by a border of red wine jelly. Shetland scallops are seared and given textural contrast by a julienne of mange-tout, with piquillo pepper salsa to cut their sweetness.

It would be an odd Scottish menu that didn't make a feature of salmon somewhere, and here it is done proud by light steaming and partnering with gingered spinach, mashed potato and a rich butter sauce. Vegetarian dishes are subjected to the same careful approach, and a crown of beetroot mousse is the regal topping for a piece of Limousin beef fillet heartily sauced with port. A nice way with fruit combinations pairs a melting flaky tartlet of banana with first-class strawberry ice cream containing whole pieces of fruit, or there may be white chocolate mousse with mocha ice cream and a sauce of Glayva. Eight house wines at a uniform price of £16 introduce a list that is strong in Bordeaux and Burgundy but gives fair prominence to the southern hemisphere as well.

CHEF: Addy Daggert PROPRIETOR: Wren's Hotel Group OPEN: all week 12.30 to 2, 7 to 9 MEALS: Set L Mon to Sat £15.95, Set L Sun £19.50, Set D £32.50 to £35. Light L menu available Mon to Sat SERVICE: not inc, card slips closed CARDS: Amex, Delta, MasterCard, Switch, Visa DETAILS: 70 seats. Private parties: 70 main room, 20 to 35 private rooms. Car park. Vegetarian meals. Children's helpings. No smoking in dining room. Music ACCOMMODATION: 14 rooms, all with bath/shower. TV. Phone. B&B £75 to £210. Rooms for disabled. Baby facilities (£5)

PERTH Perthshire & Kinross map 11

Let's Eat/Let's Eat Again

77 Kinnoull Street, Perth PH1 5EZ
TEL: (01738) 643377 FAX: (01738) 621464
33 George Street, Perth PH1 5LA
TEL: (01738) 622771 FAX: (01738) 621464
EMAIL: enquiries@letseatperth.co.uk (both)
WEB SITE: www.letseatperth.co.uk (both)

COOKING **3**
MODERN EUROPEAN
£22–£46

These two restaurants have the same owners. Tony Heath and Shona Drysdale run kitchen and front-of-house respectively at Let's Eat, while at Let's Eat Again in George Street Paul Burns mans the stoves. Both kitchens share respect for good ingredients and 'skill, timing and attention to detail'.

One enthusiast praises Shona for spreading calm and welcome and lauds the 'comfortable (but not comfort) food', including the 'flash of inspiration' of cod in brioche crumbs with aïoli, tapénade and creamy mash. Soup of the day might be fish-based, and fish specials have included a good-sized portion of grilled halibut and turbot ('we did not come away hungry'). As a change from seafood there are meaty starter salads (such as warm roasted pigeon breast with oyster mushrooms, pancetta and apple), and main courses might take in 'lamb two ways' (roast rack and braised shoulder), or chargrilled Scotch ribeye. Desserts such as 'two crème brûlées' (classic vanilla and cappuccino) round things off. Seven house wines start at £10.50, and most of the list is below £20.

Let's Eat Again offers a shorter, simpler menu, along similar lines. Starters range from west coast mussels to warm goats' cheese with beetroot salad and orange walnut oil, while main dishes take in breast of chicken with crisp vegetables and mushroom sauce, and seared sea bass fillet with polenta cake and sun-dried tomatoes. An even more modestly priced wine list is shorter but more adventurous, running from £10 to no more than £16.50.

CHEFS: Tony Heath, Tomi Burns and Malek Esmail (Let's Eat); Paul Burns (Let's Eat Again) PROPRIETORS: Tony Heath and Shona Drysdale OPEN: Tue to Sat 12 to 2, 6.30 to 9.30 (9.45 Let's Eat Again) CLOSED: 25 and 26 Dec, 1 Jan, 2 weeks Jan, 2 weeks July MEALS: alc (main courses L £8 to £12, D £9 to £16) SERVICE: not inc, card slips closed CARDS: Amex, Delta, MasterCard, Switch, Visa DETAILS: 70 seats; private parties 70 main room (Let's Eat). 36 seats; private parties 30 main room (Let's Eat Again). Vegetarian meals. Children's helpings. No smoking in dining rooms. Wheelchair access (also WC) (Let's Eat only). Music (usually in Let's Eat, occasionally in Let's Eat Again) (£5)

63 Tay Street

NEW ENTRY

63 Tay Street, Perth PH2 8NN
TEL: (01738) 441451 FAX: (01738) 441461

COOKING **2**
MODERN EUROPEAN
£24–£50

This bright, airy restaurant enjoys views across the Tay to Kinnoull Hill, and has not taken long to win the respect of reporters thanks to its food, surroundings and service. Jeremy Wares has worked at various distinguished addresses in London and Scotland, acquiring solid skills and knowledge along the way, and his food is rooted in classic techniques and combinations. Among half a dozen starters might be smoked haddock and leek risotto with herb oil, or a moist, tender pork terrine wrapped in pancetta and accompanied by onion marmalade.

The same number of main courses divide evenly between meat and fish (plus a vegetarian option): on the one hand saddle of venison with mash, stir-fried cabbage and lentil jus, and on the other crispy salmon fillet with asparagus and beurre blanc. Rhubarb tart with ginger custard, and nougat glacé with raspberries are typical desserts. Nine varied house wines from £10.95 kick off the list, which carries on under stylistic headings, providing useful annotation as it goes. Much attention has been paid to less traditional wines, although a few classic clarets still feature, and the bulk of the list stays under £25.

CHEF: Jeremy Wares PROPRIETORS: Shona and Jeremy Wares OPEN: Tue to Sat 12 to 2, 6.30 to 9 CLOSED: first 2 weeks Jan MEALS: alc (main courses L £7, D £14.50 to £20) SERVICE: not inc, card slips closed CARDS: Amex, Delta, MasterCard, Switch, Visa DETAILS: 32 seats. Private parties: 34 main room. Vegetarian meals. No smoking in dining room. Wheelchair access (also WC). No music (£5)

PORT APPIN Argyll & Bute **map 11**

▲ Airds Hotel

Port Appin PA38 4DF
TEL: (01631) 730236 FAX: (01631) 730535
EMAIL: airds@airds-hotel.com
WEB SITE: www.airds-hotel.com
2m off A828, on E shore of Loch Linnhe

COOKING **7**
MODERN BRITISH
£67–£81

Although the view from this long, white-painted hotel with its conservatory frontage and big-windowed dining room may not be stunning, it takes only a short walk down to the loch to put the situation right. Tartans, swags and a deer's head in the lounge contrast with a relatively plain dining room, where the form is four-course dinners. Residents order their food (and wine) by 6pm, from around five options per course, and the strength is well-rendered dishes that play on familiar ideas.

Fine materials are at the heart of the operation, treated with confidence, assurance and understanding, although rarely with inspiration or excitement. The thrill comes instead from invigoratingly first-class ingredients, not least fish and shellfish. Lightly cooked Lismore oysters have been combined with smoked salmon and champagne jelly, and scallops are served in a number of ways, typically with a sunny Mediterranean disposition: for example, five large pieces of sweet, succulent, accurately seared white meat, each sitting on a blob of pesto, arranged around a small pile of diced tomato and earthy aubergine, a dish that was definitely 'more than the sum of its parts'.

Second-course soups have included well-balanced creamy parsnip, and an 'unimprovable' wild leek and potato, while main courses centre on prime materials, including fish of 'exemplary freshness' – such as fillet of turbot or halibut, the latter perhaps served with onion confit, deep-fried prawns and a chervil velouté – and lamb: neatly trimmed, herb-crusted, pink-roast loin on first-class dauphinois potatoes and scattered vegetables. De-veined orange and grapefruit segments held together in a Grand Marnier jelly make a refreshing finish, although other desserts have been disappointing in comparison. Service can be 'a bit stiff', although it is unfailingly polite and friendly, and breakfast is an undoubted highlight. With little under £30, the wine list is the preserve of the well-heeled. For those who want to dig deep, there is plenty of choice between Burgundy and Bordeaux villages, a fine range of Alsace bins, and the cream of Italians, to name but a few of the areas covered. House French starts at £22.

CHEF: Steve MacCallum PROPRIETORS: the Allen family OPEN: all week D only 7.30 to 8.30 CLOSED: Christmas, 6 to 27 Jan MEALS: Set D £50. Light L available SERVICE: not inc, card slips closed CARDS: Delta, MasterCard, Switch, Visa DETAILS: 32 seats. Private parties: 32 main room. Car park. Children's helpings. No smoking in dining room. No music ACCOMMODATION: 12 rooms, all with bath/shower. TV. Phone. D,B&B £105 to £310 (*The Which? Hotel Guide*) (£5)

▲ Pierhouse

Port Appin PA38 4DE
TEL: (01631) 730302 FAX: (01631) 730400
EMAIL: pierhouse@btinternet.com
WEB SITE: www.pierhousehotel.co.uk
off A828, on E shore of Loch Linnhe, opposite Lismore ferry

COOKING **3**
SEAFOOD
£20–£58

The lochside setting is enchanting, the view from the dining room over the jetty to Lismore a delight, and the aims of the Pierhouse are admirable: to serve fresh, locally caught seafood that reflects its natural abundance. Among the offerings are lobsters, Lismore oysters, mussels marinière, plump scallops seared to pearly translucence and served with lemon butter, and firm shelled langoustines simply dressed with garlic butter. Where the cooking is uncomplicated, results are impressive: 'the best scampi any of us will ever eat' for one family, monkfish in a creamy Pernod sauce for another visitor. Outside this small arena things are less happy: bread, vegetables and puddings could all be improved, for example. It can be a bit of a crush during high season, front-of-house could do with sharpening up, and niggles have also been recorded about prices, but wines stay mostly below £20, starting with house Australian white at £11.50.

CHEF: Rita Thomson PROPRIETORS: David and Liz Hamblin OPEN: all week 12.30 to 2.30, 6.30 to 9.30 CLOSED: 25 and 26 Dec MEALS: alc (main courses L £7 to £20, D £8 to £25) SERVICE: not inc, card slips closed CARDS: Delta, MasterCard, Switch, Visa DETAILS: 70 seats. 30 seats outside. Private parties: 60 main room, 12 private room. Car park. Vegetarian meals. Children's helpings. No smoking in dining room. Wheelchair access (also WC). Music ACCOMMODATION: 12 rooms, all with bath/shower. TV. Phone. B&B £45 to £90. Baby facilities

ST MARGARET'S HOPE Orkney **map 11**

▲ Creel

Front Road, St Margaret's Hope KW17 2SL
TEL: (01856) 831311
WEB SITE: www.thecreel.co.uk
off A961, 13m S of Kirkwall, on South Ronaldsay

COOKING **7**
MODERN SCOTTISH
£37–£54

An ordinary-looking house in a dramatically beautiful setting (and more accessible now that a new car ferry stops just a few hundred yards away), the Creel is not a place at which to expect luxury, although the Craigies have built a new reception area and breakfast room with views over the bay, and brought in some local artwork (including bas-relief fish sculptures in stained copper) to brighten up the walls and dark wood. Above all, the atmosphere is relaxed and completely unpretentious, while the food remains based on local materials from inevitably small-scale suppliers. This place is not about finesse: tables are tiny, cloths plastic, and the food is simple and often homely – fishcakes with tartare sauce, or queen scallops baked with garlic butter might be among starters. Indeed, some items, such as bread, and the chocolates with coffee, are readily available locally. What makes it stand out is the main business: stunningly fresh fish, often simply treated.

Soups are a highlight (shore crab bisque containing chunks of tusk and coley), and less usual species of fish include ling (made into a brandade), and wolffish (to accompany roast John Dory). Accurate timing is essential to make the most of seafood, and Alan Craigie's in-built stopwatch serves him well, producing sweet, meaty scallops served with smooth, herby mashed potato. Other mains might typically include a few fish – perhaps pollock, scallops and organic salmon – brought together in a simple broth. Such a dish might not have been arresting but for the freshness.

This is not entirely a seafood restaurant, however, and meat features in both first and main courses: in a pressed terrine of North Ronaldsay lamb (that feeds on seaweed) served with a warm chutney; indeed, Alan Craigie is hot on his chutneys, partnering bresaola, for example, with a first-class rhubarb version. Among desserts, lemon tart pleases, ice creams are now made in-house, and the 'chef's special' – chocolate mousse, meringue and crème caramel layered in a brandy-snap basket, served with butterscotch sauce – has been singled out for praise. A short, functional wine list has the benefit of moderate pricing, starting with a pair of house wines at £9.50.

CHEF: Alan Craigie PROPRIETORS: Joyce and Alan Craigie OPEN: all week D only 6.45 to 9 CLOSED: Nov, Jan and Feb MEALS: alc (main courses £16 to £21) SERVICE: not inc, card slips closed CARDS: MasterCard, Switch, Visa DETAILS: 40 seats. Private parties: 30 main room, 14 private room. Car park. Children's helpings. No smoking in dining room. Wheelchair access (also WC). No music ACCOMMODATION: 3 rooms, all with bath/shower. TV. B&B £45 to £70. Baby facilities (*The Which? Hotel Guide*)

SPEAN BRIDGE Highland map 11

▲ Old Pines

Spean Bridge PH34 4EG
TEL: (01397) 712324 FAX: (01397) 712433
EMAIL: goodfood@oldpines.co.uk
WEB SITE: www.oldpines.co.uk

COOKING **4**
MODERN SCOTTISH
£34–£47

The standing pines that surround the homestead may indeed be old, but the pine from which it is fashioned looks new and, ahem, spruce enough. Inside is an amiable clutter of plates and scones at afternoon tea, a pleasingly random array of books everywhere, and a flag-floored open-plan dining room where tables are shared. The friendliness is not forced, but flows from the generous spirit in which the Barbers run their inimitable restaurant-with-rooms. They are an industrious team, dedicated hunter-gatherers (of leaves and fungi) as well as avid growers (salad leaves and herbs from the polytunnel), keen smokers (of bacon, salmon, cheese and duck), and canny shoppers (buying live scallops and langoustines straight off the boats).

At dinner there is no choice before dessert, and not always then, so effort is firmly concentrated on the food in hand: perhaps earthy, country dishes such as a livery pâté, or a rustic parsnip and celeriac soup. Honesty and integrity are the watchwords, yielding homely roasts such as leg of Lochaber lamb with kidney and fresh herbs, served with a barley, leek and cep risotto; vegetables can be copious. Sticky brown-sugar meringue is typical of desserts, maybe filled with grapes and kiwi fruit, and served with a kiwi and elderflower sauce. Wines are well sourced for value and given extremely modest mark-ups: almost half the bins come in under £15, with prices starting at £10.50; and half-bottles from only £6.50 expand the choice further. A few frequently changing wines are offered by the glass to complement various dishes.

CHEF: Sukie Barber PROPRIETORS: Bill and Sukie Barber OPEN: Tue to Sun L 12 to 2.30, Tue to Sat D 8pm (1 sitting, occasionally 7.30 in winter), Sun D for residents only, bank hol Mons CLOSED: 2 weeks late Nov to early Dec, 25 and 26 Dec MEALS: Set D £24.50 to £30. Set D Sun £20 (for residents only). Light meals available all day SERVICE: not inc, card slips closed CARDS: MasterCard, Switch, Visa DETAILS: 24 seats. 6 seats outside. Private parties: 30 main room. Car park. Vegetarian meals. Children's helpings. No babies or young children at D. No smoking in dining room. Wheelchair access (also WC). No music ACCOMMODATION: 8 rooms, all with bath/shower. D,B&B £65 to £160. Rooms for disabled. Baby facilities (*The Which? Hotel Guide*) (£5)

STEIN Highland **map 11**

▲ Lochbay

1–2 Macleod Terrace, Stein, Isle of Skye IV55 8GA
TEL/FAX: (01470) 592235 COOKING **2**
EMAIL: david@lochbay-seafood-restaurant.co.uk FISH
WEB SITE: www.lochbay-seafood-restaurant.co.uk £24–£56

David Wilkinson, who used to work at Arisaig House (see entry, Arisaig), took over Lochbay in September 2000, but this restaurant's star attractions – its dramatic setting in a cottage huddled against the shore, and its fresh fish and seafood – remain. In the simply decorated dining area (rough-textured white walls, a large mirror, fresh flowers), a blackboard displays dishes of the day, perhaps Cullen skink, or dressed crab. It's the quality of ingredients that most impresses, both in starters such as cephalopods ('a very tasty jumble' of cuttlefish, squid and octopus in olive oil) and simple main courses like grilled sea bass: 'gleaming white, creamy texture' with 'chunky, toasty-coloured' chips. One visitor enjoyed the conviviality here almost as much as the 'vast, incredibly fresh' prawns (served cold with mayonnaise and hot with garlic). Fill up on old-fashioned puddings such as clootie dumpling. A short wine list includes a Scottish blackberry wine, and house French by the litre (£10.50), half-litre (£5.25) and glass (£1.75).

CHEF: David Wilkinson PROPRIETORS: David and Alison Wilkinson OPEN: Mon to Fri 12 to 2.30, 6.30 to 9 CLOSED: Nov to Mar MEALS: alc (main courses £9 to £26). Light L menu available SERVICE: not inc, card slips closed CARDS: Delta, MasterCard, Switch, Visa DETAILS: 26 seats. 16 seats outside. Private parties: 26 main room. Car park. Children's helpings. No children under 10 after 8. No smoking in dining room. Wheelchair access (not WC). Occasional music ACCOMMODATION: 2 rooms, both with bath/shower. TV. B&B £39.50 to £49. Baby facilities

---

Occasional music *in the details at the end of an entry means live or recorded music is played in the dining room only rarely or for special events.* No music *means it is never played.*

STONEHAVEN Aberdeenshire map 11

Tolbooth

Old Pier, Stonehaven AB39 2JU
TEL/FAX: (01569) 762287
WEB SITE: www.tolboothrestaurant.co.uk

COOKING **3**
SEAFOOD
£27–£46

The harbourside location is a big plus for this seafood specialist, and the proximity of Aberdeen's fish market means that it can keep on top of supplies without too much difficulty. Simple availability dictates the day's menu: perhaps grilled sardines with a lemon and herb stuffing, steamed cockles and mussels in heather ale, or blackened snapper fillet with avocado salsa. Anything harvested environmentally (dived scallops) or produced organically (Loch Duart salmon, perhaps baked with a dill crust and a crab filling) is given priority, and the Chris McCarrey also collects wild mushrooms, herbs and berries in summer and autumn. Treatments are lively enough – seared fillets of John Dory, sea bass and red mullet with a red pepper coulis and pea risotto – and there are usually a couple of non-fish options, such as goats' cheese and tomato tartlet, or breast of chicken wrapped in Parma ham with a mustard and tarragon sauce. Wines are briefly annotated, fairly priced and decently varied with house red and white £9.50 a bottle.

CHEFS: Christopher McCarrey, Stuart Duncan and Peter Penman PROPRIETOR: Christopher McCarrey OPEN: Tue to Sat D 6.30 to 9.30 (5.30 to 10 Sat) CLOSED: 3 weeks from 25 Dec, 1 week Oct MEALS: alc (main courses £10.50 to £17). SERVICE: not inc CARDS: Delta, MasterCard, Switch, Visa DETAILS: 44 seats. Private parties: 40 main room. Vegetarian meals. No children under 8. No cigars/pipes in dining room. Music (£5)

STRONTIAN Highland map 11

▲ Kilcamb Lodge

Strontian PH36 4HY
TEL: (01967) 402257 FAX: (01967) 402041
EMAIL: kilcamblodge@aol.com
WEB SITE: www.kilcamblodge.co.uk
on A861, near head of Loch Sunart

COOKING **4**
MODERN SCOTTISH
£38–£45

Rich fabrics, comfortable chairs, stunning views and relaxed service all add to the welcome at this old stone house. Dinner, beginning at 7.30 without any sense of regimentation, offers a daily-changing menu of two courses or four: in the latter case the second is a soup, such as red lentil, or leek and potato. The kitchen garden contributes fruit, vegetables and herbs, and guests can join the hotel's fishing boat and catch their own dinner of fish or shellfish: otherwise seared Moray scallops might come with bacon lardons, Loch Sunart langoustines with garlic and herb butter. If first courses tend towards fish and vegetables, mains tend to be meaty – roast Grampian pork fillet with apple and chilli compote, for example, or loin of Mingarry venison with braised red cabbage and celeriac purée – while desserts are in the approachable style of raspberry parfait or glazed lemon tart. Heading the wine list is a well-sourced house selection of styles starting at £9.95, ranging from a gutsy Côtes-du-Rhône to a crisp, dry Australian Riesling. The moderately priced main list, arranged by country, has an equally balanced global view and includes over 30 halves.

CHEF: Neil Mellis PROPRIETORS: Peter and Anne Blakeway OPEN: all week D only 7.30 (1 sitting). Light L menu available CLOSED: Christmas, Jan and Feb MEALS: set D £20.50 (2 courses) to £29.50 SERVICE: not inc, card slips closed CARDS: Delta, MasterCard, Switch, Visa DETAILS: 28 seats. Private parties: 28 main room. Car park. Children's helpings. No smoking in dining room. Wheelchair access (not WC). No music ACCOMMODATION: 11 rooms, all with bath/shower. TV. Room only £48 to £130. Baby facilities. Fishing (*The Which? Hotel Guide*)

SWINTON Borders **map 11**

▲ Wheatsheaf

Swinton TD11 3JJ
TEL: (01890) 860257 FAX: (01890) 860688
EMAIL: reception@wheatsheaf-swinton.co.uk
WEB SITE: www.wheatsheaf-swinton.co.uk
on A6112, 6m N of Coldstream to Duns road

COOKING **3**
MODERN SCOTTISH
£22–£49

Standing on the edge of the village green, this modest stone-built inn has two dining areas. The newer one, a conservatory-style extension that fills with evening sun in summer, has pale wood furniture, softly coloured curtains and prints depicting French vineyards. Reporters appreciate the friendly, efficient, well-paced service. Menus offer lots of choice, with half a dozen or so items per course, plus a blackboard of specials. One dish that crops up regularly in correspondence is a crisp, crab cake starter featuring plenty of crabmeat and flavoured with coriander; another popular choice is the exemplary crème brûlée. In between, there may be 'crisp-skinned, sweet and tangy' roast Gressingham duck glazed with honey marmalade and served with rösti, or roast loin of Highland venison in a juniper berry and quince sauce with spiced poached pear. Coffee is served by the fire, and those staying for breakfast praise the top-notch porridge and kippers. A varied international wine list opens with six house selections at £10.95 a bottle (£2.45 a glass); prices throughout are fair, with plenty below £20.

CHEF: Alan Reid PROPRIETORS: Alan and Julie Reid OPEN: Tue to Sun L 12 to 2, Tue to Sat D 6 to 9.30 MEALS: alc (main courses L £6 to £14, D £8 to £14). Set L Tue to Fri £8.90 (2 courses) SERVICE: not inc, card slips closed CARDS: Delta, MasterCard, Switch, Visa DETAILS: 46 seats. 12 seats outside. Private parties: 26 main room. Car park. Vegetarian meals. Children's helpings. No smoking in dining room. Wheelchair access (not WC). No music ACCOMMODATION: 7 rooms, all with bath/shower. TV. Phone. B&B £50 to £100. Baby facilities

£ *means that it is possible to have a three-course meal, including coffee, half a bottle of house wine and service for £25 or less per person, at any time the restaurant is open, i.e. at dinner as well as lunch. It may be possible to spend considerably more than this, but by choosing carefully you should find £25 or less achievable.*

Use the lists towards the front of the book to find suitable restaurants for special occasions.

TROON South Ayrshire map 11

▲ Lochgreen House

Monktonhill Road, Southwood, Troon KA10 7EN
TEL: (01292) 313343 FAX: (01292) 318661
EMAIL: lochgreen@costley-hotels.co.uk
WEB SITE: www.costley-hotels.co.uk

COOKING **5**
FRANCO-SCOTTISH
£29–£59

The spreading Edwardian-style house on the outskirts of Troon looks spruce and well cared for, thanks not least to its billiard-table lawns and the genteel comfort of its handsomely appointed interior. It is a solid and reassuring building with fine oak, rich fabrics and floral furnishings, whose 'grandiose domestic' style doesn't daunt, just envelops. The dining room has a mock medieval air about it, with tapestries and a vaulted ceiling, while the food takes a more colloquial country-house turn. Oddly, the carte is available only at lunch, but there is no shortage of choice on any of the menus: from melting duck confit, to full-flavoured salmon and haddock chowder, to an indulgent starter of three shelled langoustines in prime condition, combined with asparagus (in October), a poached egg and well-judged hollandaise.

The food is no less comforting than the surroundings, given a characterful terrine of foie gras, richly flavoured with alcohol and truffle, served with an exotic-tasting apple compote. Skilful handling has also produced moist pan-fried turbot fillets served with a smoked bacon 'risotto' and a pesto-infused creamy sauce, and although the food may lack a personal stamp, individual components are well rendered: for example, in desserts such as a poached pear with a strongly fruity ice cream, or a thick coconut and lime mousse accompanied by a pineapple syrup and macadamia nut biscuit.

Since Lochgreen has its own hens, expect eggs to feature often: 'we had half a dozen between us (not counting hollandaise) over dinner and breakfast.' Service, from a small hierarchy of staff, is well paced, and most major wine-producing nations are represented on the wine list, with the greatest attention paid to French regions. Great drinking choice is to be had under £25, including six house reds and whites from France and Chile starting at £14.50.

CHEFS: Andrew Costley and Donald McInnes PROPRIETOR: Bill Costley OPEN: all week 12 to 2, 7 to 9 MEALS: alc L Mon to Sat (main courses £9 to £16). Set L Sun £19.95, Set D Sun to Thur £29.50 to £32.50, Set D Fri and Sat £32.50 SERVICE: not inc, card slips closed CARDS: Amex, Delta, MasterCard, Switch, Visa DETAILS: 80 seats. Private parties: 40 main room, 40 private room. Car park. Vegetarian meals. Children's helpings. No smoking in dining room. Wheelchair access (also WC). Music. Air-conditioned ACCOMMODATION: 15 rooms, all with bath/shower. TV. Phone. B&B £99 to £160. Rooms for disabled. Baby facilities (*The Which? Hotel Guide*)

MacCallums' Oyster Bar

The Harbour, Troon KA10 6DH
TEL/FAX: (01292) 319339

COOKING **3**
SEAFOOD
£23–£54

Aim for the *Seacat* terminal, and the restaurant overlooks the harbour where fishing boats tie up. The single, large, brick-built, timber-ceilinged room is a shrine to the Americas Cup, with drawings, models, pictures, and a photograph of Sir Thomas Lipton (the tea man), who was also an ardent enthusiast. Its unpretentious nature is reflected in a simple seafood carte offering grilled langoustines with garlic butter, salmon fishcake, or a special of the day, such as Thai mussel broth, or battered sole with chips and mushy peas.

Fresh supplies are paramount, much of it coming from the wholesale market opposite (co-owner John MacCallum also runs a wet-fish shop in Glasgow). Stick to fresh fish simply done and you will eat well, as one couple did, lunching on nuggets of monkfish encased in light, crisp tempura batter with sauce gribiche, and a whole, small, grilled witch sole, unadorned except for butter and parsley. Token desserts might include iced lemon mascarpone, or raspberry crème brûlée with a shortbread biscuit, and a short list of wines mostly under £20 (house wine is £9.50) is fine for the job.

CHEFS: Nicholas Wright and Stephen Smith PROPRIETORS: John and James MacCallum OPEN: Tue to Sun L 12 to 2.45 (3.45 Sun), Tue to Sat D 7 to 9.45 MEALS: alc (main courses £8 to £20.50) SERVICE: not inc CARDS: Delta, MasterCard, Switch, Visa DETAILS: 43 seats. Private parties: 43 main room. Car park. Vegetarian meals. Children's helpings. Wheelchair access (not WC). Music

UIG Western Isles map 11

▲ Baile-na-Cille

Timsgarry, Uig, Isle of Lewis HS2 9JD
TEL: (01851) 672242 FAX: (01851) 672241
EMAIL: randjgollin@compuserve.com
take B8011 to Uig, then right down track on to shore

COOKING **1**
MODERN EUROPEAN
£33–£40

This out-of-the-way restaurant inhabits 200 square miles of wilderness in the Outer Hebrides, with two dozen sandy beaches for intrepid travellers to choose from. In answer to our question 'How many people can you seat outside?', Mr Gollin replies 'This is a big island', and the car park will, of course, accommodate 'several hundred' vehicles. Baile-na-Cille might well move with the times, but since the times hardly ever move here, neither does it. Meals continue in the vein of oxtail soup, cured tongue (a butcher in Stornoway provides the raw material), and trout baked in cream, ending with bread-and-butter pudding, or plum ice cream. Special diets are catered for (among them vegan, sugar-free, gluten-free), a tie is not required (since Mr Gollin does not possess one himself), and prices are exactly the same as last year, and the year before that. Indeed, wine prices have remained unchanged since 1985: many come from Yapp Bros and are offered at either £8.50 or £12.50; just help yourself.

CHEFS/PROPRIETORS: Richard and Joanna Gollin OPEN: all week D only 7 (1 sitting) CLOSED: 11 Oct to 9 Mar MEALS: Set D £24 SERVICE: net prices, card slips closed CARDS: MasterCard, Visa DETAILS: 30 seats. Private parties: 30 main room. Car park. Vegetarian meals. Children's helpings. No smoking in dining room. No music ACCOMMODATION: 10 rooms, all with bath/shower. B&B £24 to £63. Baby facilities. Fishing

Wales

ABERDOVEY Gwynedd map 7

▲ Penhelig Arms Hotel

Terrace Road, Aberdovey LL35 0LT
TEL: (01654) 767215 FAX: (01654) 767690
EMAIL: penheligarms@saqnet.co.uk
WEB SITE: www.penheligarms.com
on A493 Tywyn to Machynlleth road, opposite Penhelig station

COOKING **2**
MODERN BRITISH
£21–£44

Locals congregate in the comfortable bar for superior pub grub, while others sit on the sea wall in fine weather, sipping drinks with their bar snacks: this is a well-run, charming roadside inn near the harbour, with views across the Dovey estuary. There have been renovations in the dining room, which is now light and airy with small colourful pictures on its pale grey walls, but the kitchen continues as before, offering a generous range of dishes with an emphasis on locally sourced fish: perhaps grilled grey mullet with a simple oil and chilli dressing, equally straightforward rare seared tuna with garlic mayonnaise, or just plain lemon sole with spring onion butter. Such lack of fuss – exactly the way to treat fish – is much appreciated.

Meat options run to pink-grilled lamb cutlets, and pork fillet with sweet-and-sour sauce, while puddings take in hot chocolate sponge, and apricot frangipane tart. Robert Hughes is a charming host with a passion for wine, his crusade ably led by champagne at £3.50 a glass. He has created a wine list rich in both grape diversity and regional breadth, taking in, for example, a Viura-Verdejo-Sauvignon from Rueda. The dozen-strong house selection, from which it comes, is tailored to suit most tastes and even the most modest budget, with the majority priced at £10 a bottle, or £2.50 a glass.

CHEF: Jane Howkins PROPRIETORS: Robert and Sally Hughes OPEN: all week 12 to 2.15, 7 to 9.30 CLOSED: 25 and 26 Dec MEALS: alc L (main courses £7 to £10). Set L Mon to Sat £9.50 (2 courses), Set L Sun £13.50, Set D £21. Bar menu available SERVICE: not inc, card slips closed CARDS: Delta, MasterCard, Switch, Visa DETAILS: 40 seats. 30 seats outside. Private parties: 26 main room. Car park. Vegetarian meals. Children's helpings. No smoking in dining room. No music. Air-conditioned ACCOMMODATION: 14 rooms, all with bath/shower. TV. Phone. D,B&B £54 to £68 (*The Which? Hotel Guide*) (£5)

All entries in the Guide are re-researched and rewritten every year, not least because restaurant standards fluctuate. Don't rely on an out-of-date Guide.

ABERSOCH Gwynedd map 7

▲ Porth Tocyn Hotel

Bwlch Tocyn, Abersoch LL53 7BU
TEL: (01758) 713303 FAX: (01758) 713538
EMAIL: porthtocyn.hotel@virgin.net
WEB SITE: www.porth-tocyn-hotel.co.uk
on minor road 2m S of Abersoch through hamlets of Sarn Bach and Bwlch Tocyn

COOKING **4**
MODERN EUROPEAN
£27–£51

Set on a headland on the Lleyn Peninsula, Porth Tocyn does an admirable job balancing the demands of seaside visitors with its own self-imposed standards. The hotel's air of laid-back sophistication centres around the outgoing personality of Nick Fletcher-Brewer, whose grandparents founded Porth Tocyn in 1948, the same year that Sharrow Bay (see entry, Ullswater) opened its doors. To produce four-course dinners with five choices per course, and change them every night so that long-stay guests don't get bored, points to the kitchen's dedication. It might help to think of the style as a version of dinner-party cooking: homely, not too ambitious, a bit conservative, but with plenty of variety. Into this category might come smoked prawn bisque, or Caesar salad with Cajun guinea fowl, followed perhaps by pork tenderloin wrapped in smoked bacon with apple compote and cider sauce.

Then it is back to the nursery for chocolate puddle pudding or banana banoffi pie. Talking of which, the hotel goes out of its way to look after families, and high tea at 5.30pm for youngsters gives parents a break. After dinner, petits fours are doled out in generous profusion on large dishes all round the place. Sunday's buffet lunch comes in for praise ('the Guide was worth buying for this gem alone'), and a varied wine list keeps its eye on value. House wines include a Chilean Chardonnay and South African Cabernet Sauvignon at £12.50.

CHEFS: Louise Fletcher-Brewer and David Carney PROPRIETORS: the Fletcher-Brewer family OPEN: Sun buffet L 12.15 to 2, all week D 7.30 to 9 (7.15 to 9.30 at busy times) CLOSED: mid-Nov to Easter MEALS: Sun buffet L £18, Set D £25.50 (2 courses) to £32 SERVICE: not inc, card slips closed CARDS: MasterCard, Switch, Visa DETAILS: 50 seats. 30 seats outside. Private parties: 50 main room. Car park. Vegetarian meals. Children's helpings. No very young children at D. No smoking in dining room. No music ACCOMMODATION: 17 rooms, all with bath/shower. TV. Phone. B&B £52.50 to £128. Rooms for disabled. Baby facilities. Swimming pool (*The Which? Hotel Guide*)

BASSALEG Newport map 4

Junction 28

Station Approach, Bassaleg NP10 8LD
TEL: (01633) 891891 FAX: (01633) 895978
from M4 junction 28 take A468 towards Caerphilly, turn right at Tredegar Arms and take first left

COOKING **1**
MODERN BRITISH
£18–£45

Diners in the colonial Pullman-type carriage bolted to one end of this converted railway station might imagine they are on a transcontinental express; this Junction is so busy that getting a table is nearly as difficult as finding a real train.

The comfortable décor is transcontinental too, with Eastern promise in the form of life-sized Thai figurines, elephants and pictures. Eastern influences don't figure on the set lunch, but the early-evening 'flyer menu' might include confit of duck on Singapore noodles with soy and crispy seaweed, alongside grilled Barnsley lamb chop, or cod with prawns. Recommendations from the long carte include grilled goats' cheese on a croûte with roasted onions and honey sauce, followed by Cajun-seasoned seared halibut with 'fiendish contrasting' avocado, tomato and coriander salsa. Gentle mark-ups are a feature of the eighty varied wines from around the world, starting with house selections at £9.95.

CHEF: Jon West PROPRIETORS: Richard Wallace and Jon West OPEN: all week L 12 to 2 (4 Sun), Mon to Sat D 5.30 to 9.30 CLOSED: 26 Dec, 1 Jan, last week July, first week Aug MEALS: alc (main courses £8 to £16). Set L Mon to Sat £6.95 (1 course) to £10.45, Set L Sun £9.95 (2 courses) to £11.95, Set D 5.30 to 7 £11.95 SERVICE: not inc, card slips closed CARDS: Delta, MasterCard, Switch, Visa DETAILS: 165 seats. Private parties: 60 main room, 12 and 60 private rooms. Car park. Vegetarian meals. No cigars/pipes in dining room. Wheelchair access (also WC). Occasional music. Air-conditioned

BEAUMARIS Isle of Anglesey map 7

▲ Ye Olde Bulls Head

Castle Street, Beaumaris LL58 8AP
TEL: (01248) 810329 FAX: (01248) 811294 COOKING **4**
EMAIL: info@bullsheadinn.co.uk MODERN EUROPEAN
WEB SITE: www.bullsheadinn.co.uk £41–£49

A mission to stay ahead of the game seems to motivate the owners of this combination pub, brasserie and restaurant. The upgrading of bedrooms follows on last year's refurbishment of both brasserie and upstairs dining room, the latter successfully marrying old cruck timbers and modern fittings. Among local materials, seafood is prominent – in a tian of crab, for example, or in sea bass served with chervil and pickled lemon – while game might appear in the form of a terrine with bitter orange chutney, and perhaps a tripartite dish of hare served with pink fir apple potatoes, pancetta and truffle jus. To balance main courses of calf's liver, Welsh beef and venison, vegetarian options have included a white asparagus risotto, and a courgette and goats' cheese crumble, while desserts have produced a homely-sounding steamed rhubarb sponge with fudge ice cream.

The brasserie goes in for pasta, salads and sandwiches alongside a few more substantial dishes and has its own short wine list, while the restaurant's list covers most regions, with a fair mixture of styles and a range of mature vintages. Prices are reasonable, and half-bottles make the better names more accessible. House wines, from South Africa, New Zealand and France, are £13.75.

CHEF: Ernst Van Halderen PROPRIETOR: Rothwell and Robertson Ltd OPEN: restaurant Mon to Sat D only 7 to 9.30; brasserie all week 12 to 2, 6 to 9 CLOSED: 25 and 26 Dec, 1 Jan MEALS: restaurant Set D £28.75; brasserie alc (main courses £4 to £14) SERVICE: not inc CARDS: Amex, Delta, MasterCard, Switch, Visa DETAILS: 45 seats. Private parties: 25 main room, 15 private room. Car park. Vegetarian meals. Children's helpings in brasserie. No children under 7 in restaurant. No smoking in dining room. No music ACCOMMODATION: 13 rooms, all with bath/shower. TV. Phone. B&B £60 to £97. Baby facilities (*The Which? Hotel Guide*)

BROAD HAVEN Pembrokeshire map 4

▲ Druidstone £

Druidston Haven, Broad Haven SA62 3NE
TEL: (01437) 781221 FAX: (01437) 781133
EMAIL: jane@druidstone.co.uk
WEB SITE: www.druidstone.co.uk
from B4341 at Broad Haven turn right at sea; after 1½m turn left to Druidston Haven; hotel ¾m on left

COOKING **2**
GLOBAL FUSION
£19–£42

The Bells have been at this clifftop hotel in the wilder reaches of west Wales since 1972: it is an eccentric, one-off place with a determinedly anti-establishment feel. Expect all kinds of people, from schoolchildren to throwbacks from the '60s, as well as improvements to the fabric and amenities during the currency of this Guide. The food tries to cover all bases, from Turkish lamb and vegetable soup to chicken jalfrezi, from lentil and aubergine lasagne to a steak, duck and seafood gumbo. Apart from soufflés (perhaps apricot and orange), desserts tend to be hearty, along the lines of chocolate fudge cake, banoffi pie, and a customised version of an Italian classic, Druimasù. Service was a let-down for one reporter, with long waits and indifference, but nearly all the 30-plus wines try to please by staying below £20.

CHEFS: Rod, Jane and Angus Bell and Jon Woodhouse PROPRIETORS: Rod, Jane and Angus Bell OPEN: Sun L 12.30 to 2.30, Mon to Sat D 7.30 to 9.30 MEALS: alc (main courses L £7 to £13, D £7 to £16) SERVICE: not inc, card slips closed CARDS: Amex, Delta, MasterCard, Switch, Visa DETAILS: 35 seats. 30 seats outside. Private parties: 70 main room, 10 private room. Car park. Vegetarian meals. Children's helpings. No smoking in dining room. Wheelchair access (also WC). Occasional music ACCOMMODATION: 9 rooms. B&B £33.50 to £80. Baby facilities (*The Which? Hotel Guide*)

CAPEL GARMON Conwy map 7

WALES RESTAURANT OF THE YEAR

▲ Tan-y-Foel

Capel Garmon, nr Betws-y-Coed LL26 0RE
TEL: (01690) 710507 FAX: (01690) 710681
EMAIL: enquiries@tyfhotel.co.uk
WEB SITE: www.tyfhotel.co.uk
take turning marked Capel Garmon and Nebo from A470 about halfway between Betws-y-Coed and Llanrwst

COOKING **5**
MODERN BRITISH-PLUS
£39–£51

The name means 'the house under the hillside', and Tan-y-Foel does indeed sit high in a tranquil valley within Snowdonia National Park. The grey-stone, family-run hotel has been refurbished in a highly individual, vibrant and sophisticated style, giving the lounge a Japanese-minimalist edge, while dinner is taken either in the modern dining room or in the conservatory at the back. The Pitmans' travels are also evident in a daily-changing three-course menu (two choices at each level), the repertoire incorporating influences from the Mediterranean, Europe and the Far East, and drawing applause for its mix of exotic and down-to-earth ideas.

Results can be stunning, as evidenced by a starter of steamed fillet of salmon set on Thai-style rice cakes with creamy coconut red curry sauce that 'thrilled with flavour and texture combination.' Char siu marinated loin of Welsh pork (well timed) is just as accomplished, set on buttered curly kale with spicy vegetable fritters, accompanied by a silky organic carrot and ginger sauce. More traditional sounding, though equally good desserts, might include pear and frangipane tart with Poire William crème anglaise. Saucing proves a high point throughout, while appetisers and breads offer top-class support. Wines, like the food, travel the continents offering a sound selection from France and the New World. Eight house wines from £15 to £16.50 are all available by the glass, and there's a good choice of half-bottles.

CHEF: Janet Pitman PROPRIETORS: P.K. and J.C. Pitman OPEN: all week D only 7.30 to 8.15 CLOSED: Christmas MEALS: Set D £25 (2 courses) to £29 SERVICE: not inc CARDS: Amex, Delta, Diners, MasterCard, Switch, Visa DETAILS: 12 seats. Car park. No children under 7. No smoking in dining room. No music ACCOMMODATION: 7 rooms, all with bath/shower. TV. Phone. B&B £70 to £150. No children under 7 (*The Which? Hotel Guide*)

CARDIFF Cardiff map 4

Armless Dragon

97–99 Wyeverne Road, Cathays, Cardiff CF24 4BG
TEL: (029) 2038 2357 FAX: (029) 2038 2055

COOKING **1**
MODERN WELSH
£17–£38

Away from the city centre, the Armless Dragon is very much a neighbourhood restaurant. Menus have a strong Welsh feel and deploy plenty of native produce, much of it organic and sourced locally. Yet Paul Lane looks beyond his own back yard for inspiration, which gives his cooking a modern, cosmopolitan flavour: laverballs are accompanied by ginger pickled vegetables; roast chicken breast comes with leeks, girolles and truffle oil; and best end of Pembrokeshire lamb is served with liver, beetroot and smoked garlic mash. To finish, Welsh cheeses or treacle tart with bara brith ice cream keep the flag flying. There are even a couple of Welsh wines, though half the listed bottles are French; eight 'wines for every day' open the list, priced from £8.90.

CHEF/PROPRIETOR: Paul Lane OPEN: Tue to Fri L 12 to 2, Mon to Sat D 7 to 9 (9.30 Fri and Sat) CLOSED: bank hols MEALS: alc (main courses £9 to £14). Set L £8 (2 courses) to £10, Set D Mon to Fri £15 SERVICE: not inc, card slips closed CARDS: MasterCard, Switch, Visa DETAILS: 46 seats. Private parties: 50 main room. Vegetarian meals. Children's helpings. No smoking in dining room. Wheelchair access (not WC). Music (£5)

Le Cassoulet

5 Romilly Crescent, Canton, Cardiff CF11 9NP
TEL/FAX: (029) 2022 1905
EMAIL: lecassoulet@ukonline.co.uk

COOKING **3**
FRENCH
£23–£54

Chefs come and go with alarming speed, but the steadying hand of Gilbert Viader remains at the helm of this bastion of traditional French catering. The brightly lit dining room has the look and feel of a late-nineteenth-century Parisian brasserie, with art nouveau prints on the walls and stained-glass windows, and service is as Gallic as can be. English translations on the menu are the only compromise to non-Francophones, and the dishes offered fit the setting perfectly: spinach tart topped with a poached egg, aubergine gâteau with goats' cheese and tomato confit, and five-spice duck breast with roasted shallots and pears in a balsamic reduction. There is even a defiantly traditional cassoulet toulousaine, and to finish the choice might be between crème brûlée, tarte Tatin and pain perdu, or the fine selection of unpasteurised French cheeses. The wine list turns up something of a surprise in this context: Viader's own-label wine is from California's Napa Valley. Apart from that, the list concentrates on Champagne, Bordeaux, Burgundy, the Loire and the Rhône, prices starting at £11.50 a bottle, £2.75 a glass.

CHEFS: Gilbert Viader and Joakim Humaran PROPRIETORS: Gilbert and Claire Viader OPEN: Tue to Sat 12 to 2, 7 to 10 (pre- and post-theatre by arrangement) CLOSED: 2 weeks Christmas, Aug MEALS: alc D (main courses £12 to £18.50). Set L £11.50 (2 courses) to £13.50 SERVICE: not inc CARDS: Amex, Delta, Diners, MasterCard, Switch, Visa DETAILS: 40 seats. Private parties: 40 main room. Vegetarian meals. Children's helpings. No cigars/pipes in dining room. Music (£5)

Le Gallois

6–10 Romilly Crescent, Canton, Cardiff CF11 9NR
TEL: (029) 2034 1264 FAX: (029) 2023 7911 — COOKING **4**
EMAIL: le.gallois@virgin.net — MODERN EUROPEAN
WEB SITE: www.legallois.co.uk — £24–£63

Is it French, or is it Welsh? The name, etched into frosted-glass windows, plays on the dual identity, while the art nouveau décor and bright sunny-yellow walls straddle the antique and modern divide. It is only when you get to the menu that the issues resolve and its real business becomes clear. This is modern food with a strong French accent (apart from fish, the bulk of it from Cornwall, much of the produce comes direct from French markets) typified by a terrine of foie gras and sweetbreads with sauce gribiche, and pot-roast pig with Alsace bacon and truffle mash.

The variety is appealing – from crispy duck cake with sweet chilli sauce, to cod and provençale mussels with a cockle and chive gravy – and despite their apparent complexity dishes still retain a clear focus. It is a confident kitchen, equally at home with a risotto of crab and brown shrimps, an oxtail broth and matching faggot with root vegetables, or desserts such as rum pannacotta with strawberries and an eight-year-old balsamic syrup. Not all reporters are happy, and prices can seem high, but enough wines of interest make it under the £20 barrier to balance some of the finer (mostly French) bottles.

CHEF: Padrig Jones PROPRIETORS: the Jones and Dupuy families OPEN: Tue to Sat 12 to 2.30, 6.30 to 10.30 (later if pre-booked) CLOSED: Christmas to New Year, 3 weeks Aug MEALS: Set L £10.95 to £13.95, Set D £18 (1 course) to £35 SERVICE: not inc, card slips closed, 10% for parties of 6 or more CARDS: Amex, Delta, MasterCard, Switch, Visa DETAILS: 60 seats. Private parties: 60 main room. Car park. Vegetarian meals. Children's helpings. No-smoking area. No cigars/pipes in dining room. Wheelchair access (also WC). Occasional music. Air-conditioned

All entries, including Round-ups, are fully indexed at the back of the Guide.

Gilby's

Old Port Road, Culverhouse Cross,
Cardiff CF5 6DN
TEL: (029) 2067 0800 FAX: (029) 2059 4437 COOKING **3**
EMAIL: reservations@gilbysrestaurant.co.uk MODERN EUROPEAN
WEB SITE: www.gilbysrestaurant.co.uk £23–£58

The interior of this large, high-roofed converted tithe barn is broken up with open woodwork screens and banisters and hung with colourful prints, making for a pleasant atmosphere. At one end of the restaurant stands a large open kitchen, where diners can see the chefs (Kathleen Morrison has been promoted from sous-chef and previously worked at Le Manoir, Great Milton and Waterside Inn, Bray; see entries) working under the watchful eye of Anthony Armelin. Even when it is busy, the place runs 'like clockwork' thanks to knowledgeable, friendly staff.

The cooking focuses on good-quality, fresh ingredients, with tastes generally robust, portions generous. Fish and shellfish are given top billing: in a starter of rock oysters and fritto misto di mare, for example, or in main courses of lobster (served three ways), simply grilled fish, or one of 'Gilby's classics', such as pan-fried turbot on dauphinoise potatoes, roast Italian onions and crispy leeks. For non-piscophiles, there are numerous meatier (sometimes Italian-influenced) alternatives, such as chicken San Remo on fresh egg pasta, or sticky glazed shank of lamb. Desserts have included straightforward vanilla crème brûlée, and the short and keenly priced wine list seldom strays above £20. House French starts at £10.95.

CHEFS: Anthony Armelin and Kathleen Morrison PROPRIETOR: Anthony Armelin OPEN: Tue to Sun L 12 to 2.30 (3.30 Sun), Tue to Sat D 5.45 to 10 CLOSED: 24 Dec to 2 Jan, first 2 weeks Sept, bank hols MEALS: alc (main courses £9 to £18). Set L Tue to Sat £9.95 (2 courses), Set L Sun £14.95, Set D Tue to Sat 5.45 to 7.15 (6.30 Sat) £13.95 SERVICE: not inc CARDS: Amex, Delta, MasterCard, Switch, Visa DETAILS: 100 seats. 28 seats outside. Private parties: 18 main room. Car park. Children's helpings. No smoking in dining room. Wheelchair access (also WC). Music (£5)

Izakaya Japanese Tavern £ NEW ENTRY

Mermaid Quay, Cardiff Bay, Cardiff CF10 5BW
TEL/FAX: (029) 2049 2939 COOKING **4**
EMAIL: info@izakaya-japanese-tavern.com JAPANESE
WEB SITE: www.izakaya-japanese-tavern.com £16–£42

On the first-floor balcony of Mermaid Quay, with views over Cardiff Bay to the new barrage, this Japanese version of a pub offers a convincingly 'authentic' and fun experience. An izakaya is an informal place with eating and drinking bars, and there are slightly more formal tatami rooms with sunken tables for shoeless dining in traditional style. The décor is colourful, and the chefs' chants of 'hai' to acknowledge orders are a distinguishing feature. Customers are expected to share 'Japanese tapas', ordering a few of the small dishes illustrated on the menu, plus perhaps a few daily specials.

What you shouldn't expect are cheap bowls of noodles in soup, or expensive sukiyaki. Sushi appears only as temaki zushi, plated ingredients ready to roll yourself. The long menu includes assorted sashimi, and five kinds of raw fish, all with 'fresh, virgin flavours'. Cooking methods include stir-fried, deep-fried and pan-fried, including impressive crispy aubergine with a 'clean' home-made sweet-sour sauce. There are baked dishes, grills, including skewered delicacies, and simmered meats and vegetables. The short, mainly New World wine list starts at £8.90, and there are fine sakés served warm or cold.

CHEFS: Peter Mansbridge and Yoshiko Evans PROPRIETORS: Iestyn and Yoshiko Evans OPEN: Mon to Sat 12 to 2, 6 to 10.30, Sun 1 to 9.30 CLOSED: 24 Dec to 2 Jan MEALS: alc (main courses £3 to £10). Set L £7 to £8.90 (2 courses) SERVICE: not inc CARDS: Amex, Delta, Diners, MasterCard, Switch, Visa DETAILS: 75 seats. 8 seats outside. Private parties: 100 main room, 12 to 24 private rooms. No children under 8 after 8. No smoking in 1 dining room. Wheelchair access (also WC). Music

▲ St David's Hotel & Spa, Tides Bar & Restaurant

Havannah Street, Cardiff CF10 5SD
TEL: (029) 2045 4045 FAX: (029) 2031 3075 — COOKING **2**
EMAIL: tides@thestdavidshotel.com — MODERN EUROPEAN
WEB SITE: www.rfhotels.com — £32–£57

Overlooking the regenerated bay, the imposing multi-storied hotel has a roof like a seagull in flight, and the dining room has panoramic views across to the docks, the National Assembly and to Penarth church high on a cliff. A modern menu deals in a few luxuries such as foie gras terrine and grilled lobster, but also takes in goats' cheese soufflé with a strong herb dressing, simple assemblies like an artichoke salad (Jerusalem and globe) with mache and herbs, and a fancy version of fish and chips ('fresh and succulent' grilled lemon sole with frites and tartare sauce). Desserts go in for high-sugared triangles, round baubles of ice cream or sorbet, and frizzes of sugary angel hair; one reporter likened it to 'eating Christmas decorations'. More down to earth is sticky toffee pudding with coffee ice cream and fudge sauce, while roast apple comes with a confident vanilla sabayon, a sorbet, and big 'butterfly-wing' biscuits. Informal service would benefit from some training. New World wines (especially whites) balance the aristocratic French ones (ten are available by the glass), prices rising from £13.50.

CHEF: Michael Kean PROPRIETOR: RF Hotels OPEN: all week 12.30 to 2.15, 6.30 to 10.15 MEALS: alc (main courses £12.50 to £18). Set L Mon to Sat £14.50 (2 courses) to £23, Sun brunch menu £23. Set D Sun to Thur £20 (2 courses) to £25 SERVICE: not inc CARDS: Amex, Delta, Diners, MasterCard, Switch, Visa DETAILS: 120 seats. 20 seats outside. Private parties: 220 main room, 12 to 220 private rooms. Car park. Vegetarian meals. Children's helpings. No smoking in dining room. Wheelchair access (also WC). Occasional music. Air-conditioned ACCOMMODATION: 132 rooms, all with bath/shower. TV. Phone. B&B £105 to £200. Rooms for disabled. Baby facilities. Swimming pool

Prices quoted in the Guide are based on information supplied by restaurateurs. The prices quoted at the top of each entry represent a range, from the lowest meal price to the highest; the latter is inflated by 20 per cent to take account of likely price rises during the year of the Guide.

Woods Brasserie

Pilotage Building, Stuart Street, Cardiff Bay,
Cardiff CF10 5BW
TEL: (029) 2049 2400 FAX: (029) 2048 1998

COOKING 4
MODERN EUROPEAN
£30–£59

With its open kitchen, blond wood and stainless steel, the look of this dockside restaurant (located in the old Pilotage Building) is clean and modern, and there is an air of smartness and efficiency about the operation. The up-to-date approach is mirrored in a short menu that includes a couple of Thai-inspired dishes such as juicy crab cakes with a spicy dipping sauce, and plump Scottish mussels in a rich broth flavoured with lemon grass, coconut milk, chilli, garlic and coriander. Running alongside is an Italian theme, producing linguini with rocket and king prawns in a dressing with a 'good shellfish smack'.

Confident and stylish cooking has also delivered a slice of light leek and Gruyere tart; rare, flavourful chump of salt marsh lamb with a dark rich gravy; and a chunky fillet of well charred monkfish with herb butter. Finish perhaps with a wedge of light, expertly made chocolate Nemesis, or a selection of unpasteurised French cheeses. The short wine list (which includes a couple of Welsh ones) is arranged by price and has fair mark-ups; bottles start at £12.95, and a dozen wines are sold by the glass.

CHEF: Martyn Peters PROPRIETORS: Martyn and Deborah Peters OPEN: Tue to Sat 12 to 2, 7 to 10 CLOSED: 25 and 26 Dec, 31 Dec to 1 Jan, bank hols MEALS: alc (main courses £8 to £20) SERVICE: not inc, 10% for parties of 6 or more CARDS: Amex, Delta, Diners, MasterCard, Switch, Visa DETAILS: 90 seats. 30 seats outside. Private parties: 55 main room, 35 and 55 private rooms. Vegetarian meals. Children's helpings. No smoking in dining room. Wheelchair access (also WC). Music. Air-conditioned

CLYTHA Monmouthshire **map 2**

▲ Clytha Arms

Clytha NP7 9BW
TEL: (01873) 840206 FAX: (01873) 840209
EMAIL: one.bev@lineone.net
off old Abergavenny to Raglan road, S of A40, 6m E of Abergavenny

COOKING 4
MODERN WELSH
£25–£47

The Clytha Arms, a former dower house with the feel of a French country hotel, fulfils the dual roles of informal pub and restaurant, equal emphasis being given to both parts. Its success is entirely down to the efforts of the Canning family, who have been running the place for over ten years: chef Andrew is ably assisted behind the scenes by daughter Sarah, while helpful and enthusiastic service is from local young women.

By keeping the cooking simple, the kitchen manages to accommodate a long list of bar snacks, a daily-changing set menu and a wide-ranging carte, as well as a specials board. Andrew Canning is clearly passionate about his work, as shown by his careful sourcing of materials and a willingness to experiment, keeping menus fresh and vibrant. His style, broadly speaking, is modern Welsh – as in leek and laverbread rissoles with beetroot chutney, or black pasta with cockles and bacon – but the scope is broader than that suggests, encompassing smoked duck and grapefruit salad, teriyaki beef fillet, Caribbean fruit curry with prawns, and a 'marvellous, gutsy' Spanish-style seafood stew. The wine list offers rich pickings from wide-ranging regions, with plenty of choice below £20: from zingy Australian Riesling to full-bodied Spanish reds. Ten house selections come at £10.95, £1.80 by the glass.

CHEFS: Andrew and Sarah Canning PROPRIETORS: Andrew and Beverley Canning OPEN: Tue to Sun L 12.30 to 2.15, Tue to Sat D 7 to 9.30 CLOSED: 25 Dec MEALS: alc (main courses £11.50 to £16). Set L and D £12.95 (2 courses) to £15.95. Bar menu available exc Sat D and Sun L SERVICE: not inc, card slips closed CARDS: Amex, Delta, Diners, MasterCard, Switch, Visa DETAILS: 70 seats. 40 seats outside. Private parties: 50 main room, 18 private room. Car park. Vegetarian meals. Children's helpings. No smoking in dining room. Wheelchair access (not WC). No music ACCOMMODATION: 4 rooms, all with bath/shower. TV. B&B £45 to £80 (*The Which? Hotel Guide*) (£5)

COLWYN BAY Conwy map 7

Café Niçoise

124 Abergele Road, Colwyn Bay LL29 7PS
TEL/FAX: (01492) 531555

COOKING **3**
FRENCH/MODERN EUROPEAN
£25–£47

A popular, friendly little bistro, Café Niçoise contrasts its modern blonde-wood flooring and terracotta walls with traditional white tablecloths. The food has a contemporary edge too, though the style remains firmly French. Local ingredients – Welsh lamb, beef, mussels and cheeses – find a place alongside more up-to-date accompaniments, producing an Oriental seafood broth, and roasted rice cake with lemon-grass and sun-dried tomato couscous. Seafood proves an enduring strength, with grilled turbot, mussels and sauté potatoes in a bouillabaisse sauce typical of the style. The cooking of main ingredients is 'spot on', although saucing may lack zing. Must tries include a memorable assiette of desserts and a fine selection of good-value cheeses. Service, led by Lynne Swift, is warm and friendly, and the set price menu touristique is good value. Wines, arranged by style, come modestly priced with a trio each of red and white house wines at £9.95, ten half-bottles and six by the glass.

CHEF: Chris Jackson PROPRIETORS: Carl and Lynne Swift OPEN: Wed to Sat L 12 to 2, Tue to Wed D 7 to 10 MEALS: alc (main courses £8 to £15). Set L and D (exc Sat D) £13.50 (2 courses) to £15.95 SERVICE: not inc, card slips closed CARDS: Amex, Delta, MasterCard, Switch, Visa DETAILS: 32 seats. Private parties: 30 main room. Children's helpings. Occasional music (£5)

CRICCIETH Gwynedd map 7

Tir-a-Môr 🍷

1–3 Mona Terrace, Criccieth LL52 0HG
TEL: (01766) 523084 FAX: (01766) 523049

COOKING **3**
MODERN WELSH/SEAFOOD
£27–£46

An informal, down-to-earth feel characterises Clare and Martin Vowell's small corner-site restaurant. Plain wooden tables and chairs and a long bar furnish the dining room, which opens on to the street. Clare plies her trade with the aid of well-sourced local produce, particularly seafood. 'She can be trusted,' as a report simply puts it. Lleyn beef shows up well, perhaps stuffed into ravioli and richly sauced with mushrooms, brandy and cream, as does local lamb, which might appear with caramelised tomatoes and rosemary. But the 'môr' part of the name means 'sea', so daily fish specials should certainly not be overlooked. These might include marinated mackerel and gurnard fillets with potato and chive salad to start, followed perhaps by grilled turbot with asparagus and hollandaise. Warm baklava or passion fruit ice cream are the kinds of desserts to expect, and Welsh and Irish cheeses are served with home-made walnut bread. The Vowells endeavour to bring interest to their wine list, and there is certainly variety and sometimes novelty to the grape types and regional styles presented. The choice under £20 is broad, with a French country bottling kicking off house wines at £10.95.

CHEF: Clare Vowell PROPRIETORS: Martin and Clare Vowell OPEN: Mon to Sat D only 7 to 9.30 CLOSED: Jan, Mon to Thur Nov to Dec and Feb to Mar MEALS: alc (main courses £10 to £16.50) SERVICE: not inc CARDS: Delta, MasterCard, Switch, Visa DETAILS: 38 seats. Private parties: 25 main room. Vegetarian meals. No children under 7. Wheelchair access (not WC). Music

CRICKHOWELL Powys map 4

▲ Bear Hotel

High Street, Crickhowell NP8 1BW
TEL: (01873) 810408 FAX: (01873) 811696 COOKING **1**
EMAIL: bearhotel@aol.com MODERN WELSH
WEB SITE: www.bearhotel.co.uk £33–£45

This venerable hostelry combines the role of traditional inn, noted for its old-fashioned virtues of hospitality and conviviality (and serving a range of real ales), with that of a restaurant, decorated in cottagey style with patterned wallpaper and lace-covered tables. Food in both parts covers a broad spectrum, from potted shrimps to lightly curried cod rillettes topped with tomato and avocado salsa, while main courses typically encompass roast loin of lamb on thyme-scented Anna potatoes, and baked hake with a hazelnut and chilli crust. Desserts have included a 'classic, unctuous' steamed treacle sponge, and a rich, fruit-packed summer pudding. Wines are competitively priced, opening with three house selections from £8.95, and around a dozen by the glass from £1.84.

CHEFS: Marion Lovell and Brian Simmons PROPRIETORS: Judy and Stephen Hindmarsh OPEN: Sun L 12 to 2, Mon to Sat D 7 to 9.30 MEALS: alc (main courses £14 to £16). Bar menu available SERVICE: not inc, card slips closed CARDS: Amex, Delta, MasterCard, Switch, Visa DETAILS: 60 seats. 30 seats outside. Private parties: 30 private room. Car park. Vegetarian meals. No smoking in 1 dining room. Wheelchair access (also WC). No music ACCOMMODATION: 34 rooms, all with bath/shower. TV. Phone. B&B £49.50 to £120. Rooms for disabled. Baby facilities (*The Which? Hotel Guide*)

£ *means that it is possible to have a three-course meal, including coffee, half a bottle of house wine and service for £25 or less per person, at any time the restaurant is open, i.e. at dinner as well as lunch. It may be possible to spend considerably more than this, but by choosing carefully you should find £25 or less achievable.*

▲ Nantyffin Cider Mill Inn

Brecon Road, Crickhowell NP8 1SG
TEL/FAX: (01873) 810775
EMAIL: info@cidermill.co.uk
WEB SITE: www.cidermill.co.uk
1m W of Crickhowell at junction of A40 and A479

COOKING **2**
MODERN WELSH-PLUS
£28–£49

The Nantyffin made its last cider in 1966, but there are still reasons enough to stop here: salt-marsh lamb, Gloucester Old Spot pork and Welsh black beef, to name but three. Behind the inn's shimmering pink façade the Bridgemans and Sean Gerrard have been doing Crickhowell proud for a decade, offering dishes such as ravioli stuffed with sweet potato, leek and goats' cheese, or pot-roast balsamic chicken on polenta with wild mushrooms, alongside more obviously home-grown fare. That lamb might come as a herb-crusted rack, with celeriac purée and a rosemary and garlic sauce, while fish eaters might pursue more exotic gingered red mullet, steamed whole and served with pak choi and a Thai dipping sauce. Round things off with traditional crème brûlée, or Drambuie pannacotta with figs marinated in port. Wine experimentation is enthusiastically encouraged, though moderate prices (mainly under £20) on the New World list offer all the incentive needed. House wines start at £11.95 for an Australian Shiraz-Cabernet. Note that the accommodation offered is in a sister establishment 500 yards away.

CHEFS: Sean Gerrard and Shaun Ellis PROPRIETORS: Sean Gerrard, Glyn and Jessica Bridgeman OPEN: Tue to Sun 12 to 2.30, 6.30 (7 Sun) to 9.30 CLOSED: 1 week Jan, Sun D from Sept to Apr MEALS: alc (main courses £8 to £16). Set L Tue to Fri £7.50 (2 courses) SERVICE: not inc, card slips closed CARDS: Amex, Delta, MasterCard, Switch, Visa DETAILS: 100 seats. 50 seats outside. Private parties: 65 main room. Car park. Vegetarian meals. Children's helpings. No smoking in dining room. Wheelchair access (also WC). No music ACCOMMODATION: 22 rooms, all with bath/shower. TV. Phone. B&B £40 to £90. Baby facilities. Swimming pool. Fishing

DOLGELLAU Gwynedd **map 7**

Dylanwad Da £

2 Ffôs-Y-Felin, Dolgellau LL40 1BS
TEL: (01341) 422870

COOKING **3**
BISTRO
£25–£39

Lacking a native Welsh-speaker on the production team, we mistranslated Dylan Rowlands's punning restaurant name last year: it means 'good influence', not 'good welcome', although the charming, youthful and helpful service would support either interpretation. This is an honest-to-goodness bistro in the grey-stone market town at the heart of Snowdonia National Park, whose warm yellow dining room is the setting for some fairly old-school cooking that pays close attention to the comfort factor. Smoked salmon and prawns are the main ingredients in a rough-textured, flavourful soup, while lamb richly casseroled in Burgundian style has 'superb depth of flavour'. More adventurous recent sightings have been a Polish cabanos sausage in a basil-dressed salad to start, and a Thai fish stew that incorporates mussels and coconut milk. Good vegetables and fine Welsh cheeses add polish to the operation, and there are carefully made desserts, such as the lemon and lime tart that impressed an inspector with its 'wonderful pastry and piquant filling'. Lively house wines starting at £9.80 open a list where plenty of choice in a range of characterful styles from around the world is available under £20. A selection of bottles from classic French and Italian areas, matured in the restaurant's cellars, is offered at good prices.

CHEF/PROPRIETOR: Dylan Rowlands OPEN: Thur to Sat (Tue to Sun summer, all week Easter and Whitsun) D only 7 to 9 (open L by arrangement) CLOSED: 6 weeks Feb to Mar MEALS: alc D (main courses £9 to £14). Set D £16 SERVICE: not inc CARDS: none DETAILS: 30 seats. Private parties: 30 main room. Vegetarian meals. Children's helpings. No smoking in dining room. Wheelchair access (not WC). Music (£5)

EGLWYSFACH Powys map 7

▲ Ynyshir Hall

Eglwysfach SY20 8TA
TEL: (01654) 781209 FAX: (01654) 781366
EMAIL: info@ynyshir-hall.co.uk
WEB SITE: www.ynyshir-hall.co.uk
off A487, 6m SW of Machynlleth

COOKING **6**
MODERN BRITISH
£32–£61

In this intimate country-house hotel – smart yet unfussy and impeccably run – deep blue settees and terracotta rugs contrast with pale wood and Rob Reen's paintings ('restrained would be the last word for his style'). New chef Les Rennie's accomplished handling of first-rate materials shows from the word go, in a starter of sating pan-fried foie gras on a bed of Puy lentils, topped with crisp won tons filled with lightly sweet-sharp tamarind marmalade. His flavour combinations and textural contrasts indicate a sharp culinary intelligence and a determination to make food simply enjoyable.

Dishes are imaginative and balanced; carbohydrate may come as Sarladaise potatoes with roast Gressingham duck breast, or tomato and rosemary tortellini with Brecon lamb cutlets. Fish and shellfish are fresh from Cardigan Bay: first-rate, crisp-skinned sea bass fillets, served with a fat seafood raviolo in a light chilli consommé thick with slivers of root vegetables. This is skilful cooking, which doesn't lose sight of the main item, and yet gives it a context in which to shine: as in a main course of tasty squab pigeon, boned and simply roasted (legs well cooked, breast rare), and set on a rösti platform, complemented by ceps and a robustly flavoured black pudding.

Nimble hands and precise technique are responsible for desserts such as an individual pear Tatin with rosemary and quince ice cream. Wines, listed by region, lean towards France, but include delights from a variety of global winemakers (Willi Opitz's Austrian dry whites, for example). Prices are mostly well above £20, but bargains can be found, and house wines start at £15.

CHEF: Les Rennie PROPRIETORS: Rob and Joan Reen OPEN: all week 12.30 to 1.30, 7 to 8.45 CLOSED: 5 to 26 Jan MEALS: Set L £22, Set D £37 SERVICE: not inc, card slips closed CARDS: Amex, Delta, Diners, MasterCard, Switch, Visa DETAILS: 30 seats. Private parties: 30 main room, 16 private room. Car park. Vegetarian meals. No children under 9. No smoking. Wheelchair access (not WC). Occasional music ACCOMMODATION: 10 rooms, all with bath/shower. TV. Phone. B&B £90 to £205. No children under 9 (*The Which? Hotel Guide*) (£5)

FELIN FACH Powys map 4

▲ Felin Fach Griffin

NEW ENTRY

Felin Fach, Powys LD3 0UB
TEL: (01874) 620111 FAX: (01874) 620120
EMAIL: enquiries@eatdrinksleep.ltd.uk
WEB SITE: www.eatdrinksleep.ltd.uk
on A470, NE of Brecon

COOKING **3**
MODERN BRITISH
£20–£43

The legendary creature referred to in the name is depicted tucked up in bed on the sign outside this tall, plain-looking inn, surrounded by green fields dotted with sheep. An open-plan layout around a central bar lends a sense of space, while old board floors, wooden tables and rough-stone terracotta walls hung with colourful prints and photographs give the place a modern and stylish feel.

The kitchen draws on small, local suppliers, often organic, to produce a monthly-changing seasonal menu. Two thick cuts of roasted brill on a bed of crunchy leeks cooked in cream, accompanied by broad beans and a circle of tip-top olive oil, made a fine and satisfying starter for one reporter. Indeed, fish is well employed among first courses: in red mullet with ratatouille and gazpacho sauce, for example, or salmon and leek tart with sun-dried tomato mayo. Ribeye of beef with chips and béarnaise is a menu stalwart, while neck end of lamb might come with chargrilled vegetables and minted salsa verde. A light touch distinguishes desserts, which range from pears poached in saffron syrup to a muted rendition of lemon tart. Good bread baked in-house underpins the quality-conscious approach, and a short, well-chosen list opens with house wines from Sicily and southwest France at £9.10.

CHEFS: Charles Inkin and Gregory Gosse PROPRIETORS: Huw Evans Bevan and Charles Inkin OPEN: Tue to Sun 12.30 to 2.30, 7 to 9.30 (9 Sun) MEALS: alc (main courses L £4.50 to £10, D £7.50 to £12) SERVICE: not inc, card slips closed CARDS: Delta, MasterCard, Switch, Visa DETAILS: 49 seats. 20 seats outside. Private parties: 40 main room, 15 and 18 private rooms. Car park. Vegetarian meals. Children's helpings. No smoking in 1 dining room. Wheelchair access (also WC). Occasional music ACCOMMODATION: 7 rooms, all with bath/shower. Phone. B&B £40 to £73. Baby facilities

FISHGUARD Pembrokeshire map 4

▲ Three Main Street

3 Main Street, Fishguard SA65 9HG
TEL: (01348) 874275 FAX: (01348) 874017

COOKING **5**
MODERN EUROPEAN
£25–£49

Those used to cosmopolitan glitz may find this series of small rooms in a Georgian town house just off the market square a mite short on vitality, but chairs and settees are comfortable, tables are immaculately set, flowers are fresh, and for one couple a visit 'makes our holiday'. Operating as a coffee house and light lunch stop during the day, it opens for two- or three-course dinners that range widely for inspiration: from scallops with crème fraîche and sweet chilli sauce, to twice-baked soufflé St Agur with red onion marmalade. The aim to be 'honest, reliable and consistent' seems to chime with most reporters.

Fish – straight from the quay – gets special mention, from a first-course seafood nage flavoured with fennel, orange, saffron and basil, to main-course monkfish in mustard sauce, and line-caught sea bass: with chicory for one visitor, on a fumet of shallot, mushroom and ham for another. Other local materials include lamb, and prime fillet of Welsh black beef, perhaps served with béarnaise. Saucing is accomplished, and highly rated vegetables (some from local gardens) are served separately. Finish with lime syllabub, Normandy apple flan, or rhubarb and ginger mousse. Service is friendly and polished without being too formal, and a fairly priced wine list delivers good variety within a short compass. Nine house wines under £15 start the ball rolling.

CHEFS: Marion Evans and Ron Smith PROPRIETORS: Inez Ford and Marion Evans OPEN: Tue to Sat 12 to 2, 7 to 9 CLOSED: Feb; phone to check during winter MEALS: alc L (main courses £7). Set D £24 (2 courses) to £30. Light L menu available SERVICE: not inc CARDS: none DETAILS: 35 seats. Private parties: 18 main room, 14 private room. Vegetarian meals. Children's helpings. No smoking in dining room. No music ACCOMMODATION: 3 rooms, all with bath/shower. TV. B&B £65 to £75 (*The Which? Hotel Guide*)

GANLLWYD Gwynedd **map 7**

▲ Plas Dolmelynllyn

Ganllwyd LL40 2HP
TEL: (01341) 440273 FAX: (01341) 440640
EMAIL: info@dolly-hotel.co.uk
WEB SITE: www.dolly-hotel.co.uk
on A470, 5m N of Dolgellau

COOKING **1**
MODERN WELSH
£36–£44

This family-run Victorian hotel is an idiosyncratic place with somewhat old-fashioned values. Reporters consider this a merit rather than a shortcoming, and appreciate the genuinely friendly atmosphere and courteous service. Patterned curtains and wall coverings in warm, deep colours give the place a domestic feel, which carries over into Joanna Reddicliffe's cooking. The success rate might be higher if the high-quality, mostly local ingredients were allowed to speak for themselves more often, but highlights have included a sturdy, well-flavoured sirloin of Welsh beef, chargrilled to perfection and served on a root vegetable crumble with a thyme-flavoured sherry gravy, and a dessert of light and frothy but intensely flavoured chocolate mousse accompanied by crisp walnut galettes. The wine list is packed with variety, mostly under £20, from new-wave French producers to lesser-known grape styles from Australia. And if extra encouragement is needed, Jonathan Barkwith gets credit for his helpful, unpretentious wine service.

CHEF: Joanna Reddicliffe PROPRIETORS: Jonathan Barkwith and Joanna Reddicliffe OPEN: all week D only 7 to 8.30 CLOSED: 1 Nov to 28 Feb MEALS: Set D £27.50. Bar menu available L SERVICE: not inc, card slips closed CARDS: Amex, Delta, Diners, MasterCard, Switch, Visa DETAILS: 30 seats. Private parties: 40 main room. Car park. Vegetarian meals. Children's helpings. No children under 10 at D. No smoking in dining room. No music ACCOMMODATION: 10 rooms, all with bath/shower. TV. Phone. B&B £50 to £125. Children under 8 by arrangement. Baby facilities. Fishing (*The Which? Hotel Guide*) (£5)

HARLECH Gwynedd map 7

▲ Castle Cottage

Pen Llech, Harlech LL46 2YL
TEL/FAX: (01766) 780479

COOKING **2**
MODERN WELSH
£32–£38

Standing practically in the shadow of Harlech's thirteenth-century castle, this white-painted stone cottage is run as a down-to-earth restaurant-with-rooms by husband-and-wife team Glyn and Jacqueline Roberts: he in the kitchen, she front-of-house. The dining room has a comfortably homely feel, with lots of piggy ornaments. Given the decorative theme, one reporter was surprised to see no pork on the menu, but there is plenty that will appeal among the varied options, and, despite an apparent lack of sophistication in the style, the cooking is successful thanks to sensitive treatment of quality materials: for starters, duck liver and Cointreau parfait with red onion marmalade, or a 'breakfast salad' of bacon, black pudding, tomato, fried bread and poached egg. Main courses range from tender and well-flavoured rack of lamb with a herb crust and rich red wine sauce, to a brochette of ginger- and coriander-marinated monkfish on stir-fried noodles with butter sauce. A scouring of the world's wine regions has resulted in a lively mixture of styles old and new, such as a rarely seen Pinot Blanc from Canada. A page of under-£20 recommendations kicks off the compact list, and a final bin-end page is the place to go bargain-hunting. House wines are £10.50.

CHEF: Glyn Roberts PROPRIETORS: Glyn and Jacqueline Roberts OPEN: all week D only 7 to 9.30 CLOSED: 3 weeks Jan to Feb MEALS: Set D £23.75 SERVICE: not inc, card slips closed CARDS: Delta, MasterCard, Switch, Visa DETAILS: 45 seats. Private parties: 45 main room. Vegetarian meals. Children's helpings. No smoking in dining room. Wheelchair access (not WC). Occasional music ACCOMMODATION: 6 rooms, 4 with bath/shower. B&B £29 to £62. Baby facilities (*The Which? Hotel Guide*) (£5)

HAWARDEN Flintshire map 7

The Brasserie

68 The Highway, Hawarden CH5 3DH
TEL: (01244) 536353 FAX: (01244) 520888

COOKING **2**
MODERN EUROPEAN
£25–£44

Since the opening of a new branch in Chester (see entry), Mark Jones has been dividing his time between the two sites, and the consensus is that he may be spreading himself too thinly. The cooking may have lost some of its ambition and sense of adventure, but there have been undoubted successes: among them an assured combination of fresh-tasting pan-fried cod on a bed of Parmesan- and truffle-flavoured mash, accompanied by tomatoes baked on the vine in basil oil. The menu of familiar modern brasserie fare might also provide wild mushrooms on toasted brioche topped with a poached egg, loin of pork on mustard polenta with black pudding fritters, and raspberry ripple cheesecake. The ambience remains informal, service is 'friendly and knowledgeable', and two dozen wines open with house Italian Chardonnay and Merlot at £9.95.

CHEF: Mark Jones PROPRIETORS: Neal Bates and Mark Jones OPEN: Tue to Fri L 12 to 2, Tue to Sat D 6.45 to 9 MEALS: alc (main courses £9 to £15). Set L, and D Tue to Fri 6.45 to 7.30, £25 for 2 people (2 courses) SERVICE: not inc CARDS: Delta, MasterCard, Switch, Visa DETAILS: 40 seats. Private parties: 25 main room. Vegetarian meals. No cigars in dining room. Music. Air-conditioned

LAUGHARNE Carmarthenshire map 4

▲ Cors Restaurant

NEW ENTRY

Newbridge Road, Laugharne SA33 4SH
TEL: (01994) 427219

COOKING **2**
MODERN WELSH
£37–£48

The name of this Victorian country house means 'bog' (it sits between two streams), although that hardly seems an appropriate description of the attractive building or its setting in several acres of mature gardens. The latter are maintained by proprietor Nick Priestland, who also finds time to cook and serve almost single-handedly. Much of what he offers is locally sourced, including meats from a nearby butcher of some repute, and fish caught by a local angler. Freshness and fine timing combine to give zest to the cooking, as in a starter of quickly seared smoked salmon, flash-fried scallops and crisp-skinned sea bass on a bed of beetroot and rocket. Firm textures and impressive flavours are also notable, for example in a main-course rack of organic salt-marsh lamb served with a subtly sweet redcurrant and onion sauce, and an equally pleasing Black beef fillet with a light, creamy peppercorn sauce. Attractively presented desserts might include chocolate fondant with mocha ice cream, or mixed fruit brûlée. Value is excellent throughout the short wine list, which opens with three house wines at £9.50 and offers plenty of choice below £20.

CHEF/PROPRIETOR: Nick Priestland OPEN: Thur to Sat D only 7 to 10 CLOSED: first 2 weeks Oct MEALS: alc (main courses £13 to £17) SERVICE: not inc CARDS: none DETAILS: 24 seats. 12 seats outside. Private parties: 24 main room. Car park. Vegetarian meals. Children's helpings. No smoking in dining room. Wheelchair access (not WC). Music ACCOMMODATION: 2 rooms, both with bath/shower. B&B £35 to £60

LLANARMON DYFFRYN CEIRIOG Wrexham map 7

▲ West Arms £

Llanarmon Dyffryn Ceiriog LL20 7LD
TEL: (01691) 600665 FAX: (01691) 600622
EMAIL: gowestarms@aol.com
WEB SITE: www.hotelwalesuk.com
off A5 LLangollen to Oswestry road at Chirk, then follow B4500 for 11m

COOKING **1**
MODERN BRITISH-PLUS
£22–£40

An idyllic setting in the foothills of the Berwyn Mountains is not the only attraction here. The partly thirteenth-century drovers' inn is also rather attractive, with blackened beams, rough stone walls and inglenooks, and welcoming hosts give it a friendly atmosphere. A short, old-fashioned carte in the bar deals in moules frites, steaks and ploughman's, while the dining room's set menu is more ambitious. Grilled sea bass, crevettes and smoked scallops with lemon and saffron sauce might be followed by pork tenderloin with orange, basil and redcurrants in port sauce, or fillet of Welsh lamb with a parcel of leeks and spinach and a garlic and rosemary sauce. Finish perhaps with Grand Marnier soufflé. There is plenty under £15 on the wine list, starting with three house selections at £11.50.

CHEFS: Grant Williams, Jan Forgeais and Jess Duffield PROPRIETORS: Geoff and Gill Leigh-Ford OPEN: Sun L 12 to 2, all week D 7 to 9 MEALS: alc (main courses £7 to £13). Set L Sun £8.95 (1 course) to £15.35, Set D (Sun to Fri) £19.90 (2 courses) to £24.90 SERVICE: 10% restaurant, not inc bar, card slips closed CARDS: MasterCard, Switch, Visa DETAILS: 60 seats. 30 seats outside. Private parties: 70 main room, 8 and 70 private rooms. Car park. Children's helpings. No smoking in dining room. Wheelchair access (also WC). Music ACCOMMODATION: 16 rooms, all with bath/shower. TV. B&B £52.50 to £118. Rooms for disabled. Baby facilities. Garden. Fishing (*The Which? Hotel Guide*) (£5)

LLANBERIS Gwynedd **map 7**

Y Bistro

43–45 High Street, Llanberis LL55 4EU
TEL/FAX: (01286) 871278
EMAIL: ybistro@fsbdial.co.uk
WEB SITE: www.ybistro.co.uk
off A4086, at foot of Mount Snowdon

COOKING **2**
MODERN WELSH
£29–£50

Housed in a large, tall, corner building in the centre of Llanberis village, this homely, traditional, lace-curtain-bedecked restaurant, now in its third decade, is run by husband and wife team Nerys (chef) and Danny (front-of-house) Roberts. The short, bilingual menu lists seven starters, eight main courses and seven desserts, plus a cheese course. Breads, baked on the premises, are excellent and many of the ingredients are local. 'Nicely timed' fillet of locally landed sea bream and king prawns grilled with wild garlic and lavender butter might start things off, followed by a meaty main course such as best end of Welsh spring lamb served with a redcurrant, port and thyme sauce, or pink roasted Barbary duck accompanied by Seville orange-braised Puy lentils. End with bara brith ice cream, or steamed Snowdon Pudding. The short, mainly French wine list may lack imagination, but there are some reasonably priced bottles, starting at £9.75.

CHEF: Nerys Roberts PROPRIETORS: Danny and Nerys Roberts OPEN: Mon to Sat D only 7.30 to 9.45 (L by prior arrangement; open Sun bank hols) CLOSED: during wintertime phone to check MEALS: alc (main courses £11.50 to £17) SERVICE: not inc, card slips closed CARDS: Delta, MasterCard, Switch, Visa DETAILS: 32 seats. Private parties: 42 main room. Vegetarian meals. Children's helpings. No smoking in dining room. Wheelchair access (not WC). No music

'There was no theoretical reason that carrot and coriander soup, though something of a cliché, should not be adequately prepared. One just knew, however, it was going to have the consistency of baby food, the colour of a secretary returning from a week in Tenerife, and the smell of a motorway café. And so it came to pass.' (On eating in Essex)

LLANDDEINIOLEN Gwynedd map 7

▲ Ty'n Rhos

Seion, Llanddeiniolen LL55 3AE
TEL: (01248) 670489 FAX: (01248) 670079
EMAIL: enquiries@tynrhos.co.uk
WEB SITE: www.tynrhos.co.uk
off B4366, 5m NE of Caernarfon on road signposted Seion

COOKING 2
BRITISH/WELSH
£25–£47

In its rural isolation, this immaculately decorated farmhouse-turned-hotel boasts a well-kept garden, conservatory lounge, and a multi-coloured dining room where the modest cooking style runs from leek and goats' cheese tart, via creamy garlic Port Penrhyn mussels, to a thin tuna steak (cooked through) served with rocket, black olives and green bean salad. Well-sourced fish and meat underpin the operation, best end of Welsh lamb perhaps arriving on a mix of white beans and vegetables with a commercial-tasting mint sauce. Flavourful baked cauliflower, and a variation on ratatouille, seem to be regular main course accompaniments, and Welsh rarebit may appear both as an appetiser (on smoked haddock) and as a savoury. Portions vary from little to large (puddings in the latter category, judging by a wedge of plum and apple tart that failed to win over an inspector). A varied wine list, at fair prices, starts with ten house recommendations at £11.50.

CHEF: Lynda Kettle PROPRIETORS: Lynda and Nigel Kettle OPEN: Sun L 12 to 2, Mon to Sat D 7 to 9 CLOSED: 23 to 30 Dec MEALS: alc (main courses £13.50 to £18). Set L Sun £14.95, Set D £19.50 SERVICE: not inc, card slips closed CARDS: Amex, Delta, MasterCard, Switch, Visa DETAILS: 35 seats. Private parties: 24 main room. Car park. Children's helpings. No children under 6. No smoking in dining room. Wheelchair access (not WC). No music. Air-conditioned ACCOMMODATION: 14 rooms, all with bath/shower. TV. Phone. B&B £55 to £110. Rooms for disabled. No children under 6 (*The Which? Hotel Guide*) (£5)

LLANDEILO Carmarthenshire map 4

▲ Cawdor Arms

72 Rhosmaen Street, Llandeilo SA19 6EN
TEL: (01558) 823500 FAX: (01558) 822399
EMAIL: cawdor.arms@btinternet.com
WEB SITE: www.cawdor-arms.co.uk

COOKING 2
MODERN BRITISH
£22–£42

This fine old coaching inn in the centre of a historical market town is very much a family affair, even more so since John and Sylvia Silver's daughter Jane took over the kitchen. Her cooking is founded on locally sourced produce subjected to a variety of appealing contemporary treatments: grilled mackerel with nasturtium salad and watercress dressing to start, or rillettes of duck with fruit chutney brioche. Meats tend to dominate main courses, perhaps taking in rack of salt-marsh lamb with sauté celeriac and lentil jus, or pan-fried leg and saddle of rabbit with rabbit spring rolls, spinach and couscous. Finish with Welsh cheeses, or a thoroughly modern dessert such as rose bavarois with macerated strawberries. Home-made breads are a highlight: six varieties are usually offered. Service from a young, smartly attired team is overseen by Mr and Mrs

Silver (he is the one in the colourful waistcoat). Wines are divided roughly equally between France and everywhere else and include four Welsh ones. Mark-ups are fair throughout, with three house selections at £10.10.

CHEF: Jane Silver PROPRIETORS: John and Sylvia Silver, and Jane Silver OPEN: all week L 12 to 2, Mon to Sat D 7.30 to 9 MEALS: alc L Mon to Sat (main courses £7.50 to £12.50). Set L Sun £14.50, Set D £17.50 (2 courses) to £21. Light L menu available Mon to Sat SERVICE: not inc, card slips closed CARDS: Amex, Delta, MasterCard, Switch, Visa DETAILS: 90 seats. 20 seats outside. Private parties: 100 main room, 16 and 26 private rooms. Car park. Vegetarian meals. No smoking in dining room. Wheelchair access (also women's WC). Occasional music ACCOMMODATION: 17 rooms, all with bath/shower. TV. Phone. B&B £45 to £75. Baby facilities (*The Which? Hotel Guide*) (£5)

LLANDEWI SKIRRID Monmouthshire map 4

Walnut Tree Inn

Llandewi Skirrid NP7 8AW
TEL: (01873) 852797 FAX: (01873) 859764 COOKING **5**
WEB SITE: www.thewalnuttreeinn.com MEDITERRANEAN/ITALIAN
on B4521, 3m NE of Abergavenny £34–£69

When Ann and Franco Taruschio retired after nigh on 40 distinguished years, visitors wondered what might lie in store under the new regime. Here to replace them was a chef from London who had cooked at Coast and Frith Street in a cosmopolitan style far removed from theirs. In the event, 'our overwhelming sensation was one of relief', confessed one couple. The white-painted, pebble-dash building seems neater, cleaner, trimmer than before, with amalgamation of the old bistro and dining room producing a little more space – these days 'you don't have to balance your bread basket on your knee' – and booking is now the form, so the unseemly rush to get there before opening time, join the scrum and grab a table is a thing of the past.

Stephen Terry is obviously comfortable with the honest, rustic Italian style he chose to inherit, and although the menu is quite a bit shorter than before it still features vincisgrassi Maceratese, brodetto and Lady Llanover's salt-duck. Despite that, it has the makings of its own identity, taking in white bean soup, a wedge of crab tart, and Gressingham duck (roast breast and confit leg) with sweet-and-sour pumpkin. Pasta and risotto dishes come in two sizes: at one meal a dish of simple, freshly made potato gnocchi with beans, asparagus and pesto.

Performance can be uneven, and some dishes still seem to be at the drawing-board stage, while others are highly accomplished: a starter of gently chillied grilled squid 'as tender as can be', with tomato, olives and basil, or well-timed Dover sole fillets served with roast vine tomatoes and lengths of thinly sliced, deep-fried courgette dipped in a light tempura-style batter. Although desserts may be considerably reduced in number nowadays, they are generally well rendered, judging by a wedge of chocolate tart with thin, crisp pastry, and a brace of warm figs with an appealing almondy stuffing. The appetiser – deep-fried pasta triangles filled with spinach and ricotta – is first-class, and followers of Italian wines will be more than content with a list that majors in the country (it also touches down in France, Spain and the New World) and lists specialities such as sparkling Franciacorta, Amarone, and Vin Santo. With very little to be found under £20, however, many characterful wines may be out of reach of ordinary pockets, although house Italian red and white offer lively drinking at £13.50.

CHEFS: Stephen Terry and Rodger Brook PROPRIETORS: Francesco Matioli and Stephen Terry OPEN: Tue to Sun and bank hol Mon L 12 to 3, Tue to Sat D 6.30 to 11 CLOSED: D 23 Dec to L 3 Jan MEALS: alc (main courses £12 to £18) SERVICE: not inc CARDS: MasterCard, Switch, Visa DETAILS: 80 seats. 20 seats outside. Private parties: 40 main room. Car park. Vegetarian meals. Wheelchair access (not WC). No music. Air-conditioned

LLANDRILLO Denbighshire **map 7**

▲ Tyddyn Llan

Llandrillo LL21 0ST
TEL: (01490) 440264 FAX: (01490) 440414
EMAIL: tyddynllanhotel@compuserve.com
WEB SITE: www.tyddynllan.co.uk
on B4401, 4½m S of Corwen

COOKING **6**
MODERN BRITISH
£27–£53

Looking like a Welsh farmhouse, with slate roof and grey-stone walls, Tyddyn Llan is a peaceful rural retreat set against the backdrop of the Berwyn Mountains. Spacious, decorated in yellow and blue, with some of Peter Kindred's paintings on display, it is a friendly and welcoming place. Steve Burnham's attempts to bridge the gap between Wales and the Mediterranean have resulted in a sun-dried tomato terrine with basil-infused goats' cheese, and roasted peppered duck with wild mushroom risotto cake, but loyalties also run to a more native grilled fillet of halibut with samphire, asparagus and a coarse-grain mustard sauce topped with a poached egg.

In the wake of the outbreak of foot-and-mouth disease in early 2001, and the ensuing drop in business as the countryside all but closed down, the Kindreds addressed adversity by coming up with the 'Super Spring Special', a three-course dinner menu for less than the price of a typical main course from the carte. It will be interesting to see whether or not it returns next year. In the meantime the set-price, no-choice, two-course lunch remains. Desserts run from a dark chocolate tart sered with pistachio ice cream, to a champagne jelly set about with summer berries, rhubarb and lavender sorbet, or there may be a savoury of Welsh rarebit with marinated anchovies. A certain repetition, from amuse-gueules to taped music, can beset those who stay several days, but the 70-plus wines promise weeks of enjoyment at affordable prices. Prices start at £13.

CHEF: Steve Burnham PROPRIETORS: Peter and Bridget Kindred OPEN: Tue to Sun L 12.30 to 2, all week D 7 to 9 MEALS: alc (main courses L £7.50 to £13, D £12.50 to £17.50). Set L £10 (2 courses), Set D £27 SERVICE: not inc, card slips closed CARDS: Amex, Delta, Diners, MasterCard, Switch, Visa DETAILS: 60 seats. 15 seats outside. Private parties: 50 main room, 40 and 60 private rooms. Car park. Vegetarian meals. Children's helpings. No smoking in dining room. Wheelchair access (also men's WC). Music ACCOMMODATION: 10 rooms, all with bath/shower. TV. Phone. B&B £67.50 to £140. Baby facilities. Fishing (*The Which? Hotel Guide*) (£5)

'[The chef] takes excellent raw materials, and ruins them thoroughly.'
(On eating in Gloucestershire)

LLANDUDNO Conwy map 7

▲ Bodysgallen Hall

Llandudno LL30 1RS
TEL: (01492) 584466 FAX: (01492) 582519
EMAIL: info@bodysgallen.com
WEB SITE: www.bodysgallen.com
off A470, 2m SE of Llandudno

COOKING **3**
COUNTRY HOUSE
£29–£63

Under the same ownership as Hartwell House and Middlethorpe Hall (see entries, Aylesbury and York), Bodysgallen is stone-built to withstand the worst Welsh weather, and set about with sunken gardens, water features and topiary trees. Beyond the informal lounge and log fires, a more stately dining room with large oil landscapes lays on some typically indulgent and busy country-house cooking, including asparagus salad with soft-poached egg, for example, and brill fillets on crab risotto. Main courses tend towards familiar combinations, such as calf's liver with balsamic onion jus, while a small supplement will bring Welsh Black beef fillet served with horseradish purée, a wild mushroom pancake and morel sauce. Desserts tend to favour traditional ideas too, along the lines of steamed lemon sponge, or apple crumble. The wine list centres on sensible bottles from France but also offers a varied range of styles from the rest of the world, and even Wales gets an entry. An 'ordinary claret' at over £20 indicates the price levels, but two out of the five house recommendations – a southern French red and a Spanish white – come in at £14.50, £3.50 a glass.

CHEF: David Thompson PROPRIETOR: Historic House Hotels Ltd OPEN: all week 12.30 to 1.45, 7.30 to 9.30 MEALS: Set L £15.50 (2 courses) to £19.50, Set D £34.90 SERVICE: net prices, card slips closed CARDS: Delta, MasterCard, Switch, Visa DETAILS: 60 seats. 30 seats outside. Private parties: 40 main room, 40 private room. Car park. Vegetarian meals. No children under 8. Jacket and tie. No smoking in dining room. Wheelchair access (also WC). Occasional music. Air-conditioned ACCOMMODATION: 35 rooms, all with bath/shower. TV. Phone. Room only £104 to £240. Rooms for disabled. No children under 8. Swimming pool (*The Which? Hotel Guide*)

▲ St Tudno Hotel

Promenade, Llandudno LL30 2LP
TEL: (01492) 874411 FAX: (01492) 860407
EMAIL: sttudnohotel@btinternet.com
WEB SITE: www.st-tudno.co.uk

COOKING **4**
MODERN EUROPEAN
£26–£69

This Victorian promenade hotel is the creation of Martin and Janette Bland, its owners since 1972. The Garden Room Restaurant does indeed have an 'indoor garden' atmosphere: summery yellow and green colours, hanging baskets, wicker chairs and trellis wallpaper. David Harding's imaginative dishes are attractively presented and make good use of fine local produce, notably in a fish soup with fennel and herbs, and fillet of Welsh Black beef with globe artichoke, tarragon butter and red wine sauce. A seasonal carte and menu of the day are dotted with luxurious items: foie gras terrine perhaps, Sevruga caviar with smoked salmon, or oysters with poached fillet of sole. Desserts tend to be old-fashioned, taking in baked Alaska, or crispy chocolate tear drop filled with iced cappuccino parfait and Tia Maria cream. Friendly service, excellent canapés and bread rolls, and creative petit fours enhance the meal.

'Hours of exhaustive tastings' have produced a distinctive 36-page list of wine classics and curiosities from across the world that encourages experiment. Starting with Hidalgo sherries by the glass, and especially passionate when the owners have met the winemakers, it offers plenty under £20; special recommendations start at £10.50.

CHEF: David Harding PROPRIETORS: Martin and Janette Bland OPEN: all week 12.30 to 1.45, 7 to 9.30 (9 Sun) MEALS: alc D (main courses £15.50 to £18.50). Set L Mon to Fri £15, Set L Sun £17, Set D Sun to Thur (but not bank hols) £25. Bar menu available Mon to Sat L SERVICE: not inc CARDS: Amex, Delta, Diners, MasterCard, Switch, Visa DETAILS: 60 seats. Private parties: 50 main room (not D). Car park. Vegetarian meals. Children's helpings. No children under 5 at D. No smoking in dining room. Wheelchair access (not WC). Occasional live music. Air-conditioned ACCOMMODATION: 19 rooms, all with bath/shower. TV. Phone. B&B £60 to £250. Baby facilities. Swimming pool (*The Which? Hotel Guide*) (£5)

LLANFRYNACH Powys map 4

White Swan

NEW ENTRY

Llanfrynach LD3 7BZ
TEL: (01874) 665276 FAX: (01874) 665362
WEB SITE: www.the-white-swan.com
3m east of Brecon off the A40, take B4558 and follow signs to Llanfrynach

COOKING **3**
GLOBAL
£24–£49

This white-painted, rough-stone 'very village pub' facing the church has been sympathetically renovated so that it is 'big, generous and uncluttered' inside. Simple décor with heavily beamed ceilings, flagstone floors and a walk-in hearth provide a rustic background for the cooking of Rod Lewis, formerly at Nino's in Hay-on-Wye. Earlier he travelled extensively in South East Asia, and maintains that connection in dishes such as Thai-style wild boar with sticky jasmine rice and ajaad salad. Printed menus offer five options for each course, but these are augmented by blackboard specials that include several fish dishes of the day: well-timed and flavoured seared scallops with red pepper and cumin oil, for example. Among local ingredients are plentiful vegetables: in a starter of Wealden Round (a light cured cheese on Parmesan toast with sauté cherry tomatoes and oregano), or in a main course of courgettes, spring onions and salsa rossa partnering chargrilled Hereford sirloin. Desserts are not a high point, but the 50-strong wine list stays mostly under £20; house Chilean red and white are £11.95.

CHEF: Rod Lewis PROPRIETOR: Richard Griffiths OPEN: Wed to Sun L 12 to 2 (3 Sun), Wed to Sat D 7 to 9.30 MEALS: alc (main courses L £6 to £10, D £9.50 to £16) SERVICE: not inc, card slips closed CARDS: Delta, MasterCard, Switch, Visa DETAILS: 85 seats. 50 seats outside. Private parties: 55 main room, 40 private room. Car park. Vegetarian meals. Children's helpings. No smoking in dining room. Wheelchair access (also WC). Music (£5)

The text of entries is based on unsolicited reports sent in by readers, backed up by inspections conducted anonymously. The factual details under the text are from questionnaires the Guide sends to all restaurants that feature in the book.

LLANGAMMARCH WELLS Powys map 4

▲ Lake Country House

Llangammarch Wells LD4 4BS
TEL: (01591) 620202 FAX: (01591) 620457
EMAIL: info@lakecountryhouse.co.uk
WEB SITE: www.lakecountryhouse.com
off B483 at Garth, 6m W of Builth Wells

COOKING **3**
MODERN BRITISH
£31–£55

Fifty acres of rural Powys (including the lake itself) make a fine setting for this half-timbered black and white Edwardian house whose oak staircase, grandfather clock and oil paintings recall another age. The food is firmly planted in country-house mode: meals generally begin with a soup, followed by a three-way choice (perhaps foie gras terrine, honey-roast duck leg, or roast scallops with basil risotto) before three or four main-course options. Luxuries are evident in, for example, the foie gras, truffles, trompette mushrooms and Sauternes sauce that accompany a fillet of turbot, but local materials, including lamb, beef and venison, are also deployed, the last perhaps served with a sherry vinegar sauce. A citrus tart is not uncommon to follow, or there may be a parcel of banana and white chocolate served with malted vanilla ice cream. The wine list is heavily weighted towards France, with the south presenting some of the best value. House recommendations, selected from the main body of the list and opening at £15.25, are joined at the front by over 30 'specials', more than half under £20. In addition, two house wines, 'French medium red' and 'French medium dry white', are each £13.50 (£3.50 per glass).

CHEF: Sean Cullingford PROPRIETORS: Mr and Mrs J.P. Mifsud OPEN: all week 12.15 to 1.45, 7.15 to 9 MEALS: Set L £18.50, Set D £32.50. Bar menu available L SERVICE: not inc CARDS: Amex, Delta, Diners, MasterCard, Switch, Visa DETAILS: 50 seats. Private parties: 85 main room, 40 private room. Car park. Children's helpings. No children under 7 at D. Jacket and tie. No smoking in dining room. Wheelchair access (also WC). No music ACCOMMODATION: 19 rooms, all with bath/shower. TV. Phone. B&B £95 to £220. Rooms for disabled. Baby facilities. Fishing (*The Which? Hotel Guide*)

LLANSANFFRAID GLAN CONWY Conwy map 7

▲ Old Rectory Country House

Llanrwst Road, Llansanffraid Glan Conwy,
nr Conwy LL28 5LF
TEL: (01492) 580611 FAX: (01492) 584555
EMAIL: info@oldrectorycountryhouse.co.uk
WEB SITE: www.oldrectorycountryhouse.co.uk
on A470, 1m S of junction with A55

COOKING **6**
MODERN BRITISH/FRENCH
£50–£60

The setting is an elegantly furnished Georgian house with a terraced front garden and 'breathtaking' views over the Conwy estuary, and the dining format is a venerable one. Everybody meets in the wood-panelled lounge ('you can hardly move for the Vaughans' accumulated treasures') and sits down together to eat a three-course meal with no choice before dessert. Wendy Vaughan doesn't go in much for excitement or novelty, although not everything is as traditional as, for example, asparagus tart with quail's eggs and hollandaise.

Meals might start with herb-crusted lemon sole served with fennel marmalade and a fennel and parsley soup, and proceed to roast guinea fowl breast with curly kale, plum chutney and sweet potato. And poached roulade of duck with pak choi and celeriac mille-feuille is not exactly out of Elizabeth David either.

The strength is careful, precise, indeed immaculate, cooking in which the principal items are ably supported by those things – such as saucing and pastry – which separate the sheep from the goats. Local materials naturally play a part, perhaps loin of Welsh mountain lamb with cabbage parcels and olive potatoes, and puddings (a choice of two) are considered a highlight, taking in cheesecake 'like I have never tasted before'. Alternatively, there may be a simple home-made ice cream, a selection of Welsh and Celtic farmhouse cheeses, or grilled goats' cheese. The price has gone up a little this year, but Michael Vaughan's meticulous attention to detail is 'top-drawer stuff'. The range of styles and breadth of regional offerings on the wine list are crowned by good value, with plenty of choice under £20. Those seeking mature vintages from good estates around the world will be tempted even more by the fair prices: many come under £40. House red and white are £16.90 and £14.90, respectively.

CHEF: Wendy Vaughan PROPRIETORS: Michael and Wendy Vaughan OPEN: all week D only 7.30 for 8.15 (1 sitting) CLOSED: Dec and Jan MEALS: Set D £34.90 SERVICE: not inc, card slips closed CARDS: Delta, MasterCard, Switch, Visa DETAILS: 14 seats. Private parties: 12 main room. Car park. No children under 5. No smoking in dining room. No music ACCOMMODATION: 6 rooms, all with bath/shower. TV. Phone. B&B £99 to £169. No children under 5 (*The Which? Hotel Guide*)

LLANWRTYD WELLS Powys — map 4

▲ Carlton House

Dolycoed Road, Llanwrtyd Wells LD5 4RA
TEL: (01591) 610248 FAX: (01591) 610242
EMAIL: info@carltonrestaurant.co.uk
WEB SITE: www.carltonrestaurant.co.uk

COOKING **6**
MODERN BRITISH
£32–£51

Near the village crossroads, Carlton House draws the eye with a façade described as 'a forceful shade of pink'. The Gilchrists' recent investment is most evident in the dining room, where up to 14 people may appreciate the Italian dining chairs, French porcelain and stylish wall-lights. Mary Ann Gilchrist's formula is simple: two fixed menus, combinable to offer two selections per course. These appear to change every day, though certain dishes are obviously stalwarts: understandably, given the wholehearted support the place inspires.

Sound principles and fine materials are shown to good effect in a goats' cheese and onion marmalade tart, and in baked smoked haddock with a poached egg, mashed potato and a wholegrain mustard sauce. The higher-priced deal might offer chilli crab with grilled tiger prawns on black tagliolini, before seared beef fillet with rösti, spinach, broccoli and béarnaise. Well-reported dishes have included attractively presented pork tenderloin with a cream sauce, and chicken breast with sauce bois boudran. Lemon posset with raspberry coulis, and poached pear with honey and cinnamon ice cream, are alternatives to a fine selection of Welsh and Irish cheeses. 'Prompt, attentive and polite', Alan Gilchrist runs front-of-house and offers interesting wine styles from around the world (even Wales and Mexico), including some sound rosés. Four house wines at £9.95 and £11.50 give great value, reflecting the general pricing, and 24 half-bottles expand choice further.

Bassets Brasserie (tel: (01591) 610564), under the same ownership, is located at one end of the village's bridge (across from Carlton House) and is decorated in vibrant modern colours. It uses good ingredients, simply transformed into popular snacks, chargrills, pizzas, cakes and pastries.

CHEF: Mary Ann Gilchrist PROPRIETOR: Alan Gilchrist OPEN: Mon to Sat D 7 to 8.30 CLOSED: 10 to 28 Dec MEALS: alc D (main courses - 2 choices – £17 to £19.50). Set D £19.50 (2 courses) to £24 SERVICE: not inc, card slips closed CARDS: Delta, MasterCard, Switch, Visa DETAILS: 14 seats. Private parties: 12 main room. No children under 6. No smoking in dining room. Wheelchair access (not WC). No music ACCOMMODATION: 7 rooms, all with bath/shower. TV. B&B £30 to £75. Baby facilities (*The Which? Hotel Guide*)

MACHYNLLETH Powys **map 4**

▲ Wynnstay

NEW ENTRY

Maengwyn Street, Machynlleth SY20 8AE
TEL: (01654) 702941 FAX: (01654) 703884
EMAIL: info@wynnstay-hotel.com
WEB SITE: www.wynnstay-hotel.com

COOKING **4**
WELSH-PLUS
£19–£36

Change is afoot at this white, gabled eighteenth-century coaching inn on the southern edge of Snowdonia. The Wynnstay celebrated the millennium by recruiting as head chef (in the summer of 2000) Gareth Johns, previously in charge of the stoves at the Red Lion Inn in Llanfihangel-Nant-Melan. As a result, in the view of one reporter, 'it has become a culinary landmark rather than simply a pub in the high street'. There is plenty of space in the oak-beamed dining room, which plays host to an array of locals, tourists and visitors from the nearby Centre for Alternative Technology. The bar, restaurant and bedrooms are getting a lick of paint and a brighter look, and the menu has an impressive new feel too.

A great champion of Welsh produce, Johns seems adept at putting together short (five each, first and main courses), appealing, modern menus. On these you might find starters of warm salad of teriyaki mallard duck, or Penrhyn mussels with leeks and white wine. More local ingredients turn up in roast rump of Welsh lamb with lentils and Carmarthen ham, or Aberdovey sea bass with roasted vegetables and chilli oil. For desserts, 'many a French chef would aspire to the texture of the tarte Tatin', while apple pie with melting pastry and vanilla ice cream shone at inspection; or opt for properly kept Welsh cheeses. The wine list offers a decent choice of New and Old World wines, with a selection of keenly priced bottles; house wines start at £9.75.

CHEFS: Gareth Johns and Justin Robinson PROPRIETORS: Charles Dark and Sheila Simpson OPEN: Sun L 12 to 2, all week D 7 to 9 MEALS: Set L £6.95 (1 course) to £10.95, Set D £18 (2 courses) to £21. Bar meals available SERVICE: not inc, card slips closed CARDS: Amex, Delta, Diners, MasterCard, Switch, Visa DETAILS: 100 seats. 20 seats outside. Private parties: 80 main room, 20 and 10 private rooms. Car park. Vegetarian meals. Children's helpings. No smoking in dining room. Wheelchair access (also WC). Occasional music ACCOMMODATION: 23 rooms, all with bath/shower. TV. Phone. B&B £35 to £50 (£5)

MONTGOMERY Powys map 7

Bricklayers Arms

NEW ENTRY

Chirbury Road, Montgomery SY15 6QQ
TEL: (01686) 668177
on B4836, 1m southwest of Chirbury

COOKING 1
MODERN WELSH
£25–£44

Behind the pale green walls of this long, small building is a 'seriously old' interior done out in bright colours with a 'remarkable array of clutter', including clowns and parrots (not real ones), a huge set of rustic weights, blue mineral water bottles, prints, posters and more. Cooking focuses on local produce, and a single menu might include sirloin of Welsh Black with a port and thyme reduction; and loin of Tywyn lamb stuffed with fruits soaked in damson wine. Blackboards list rare-breed meats such as Red Poll rump steak or Tamworth pork chop, while vegetables are generous in number and portion-size. Fish features too, as in well-flavoured seafood mille-feuille of cod, sea bass and salmon with tiny smoked mussels in Noilly Prat cream reduction under a puff pastry hat. Puddings might include pavlova with strawberries, peach coulis and basil oil; or choose English cheeses served in peak condition. On a short list house wines start at £9.50.

CHEF: Robert Jennings PROPRIETORS: Sara Pezzack and Robert Jennings OPEN: Wed to Sun L 12 to 2, Tues to Sat D 7 to 9 CLOSED: last week Sept, first 2 weeks Feb MEALS: alc (main courses L £7 to £12.50, D £8.50 to £14.50) SERVICE: not inc CARDS: Delta, Diners, MasterCard, Switch, Visa DETAILS: 48 seats. 12 seats outside. Private parties: 30 main room. Car park. Vegetarian meals. No children under 14 after 7pm (unless by prior arrangement). No smoking in dining room. Wheelchair access (also WC). Music (£5)

NANTGAREDIG Carmarthenshire map 4

▲ Four Seasons

Nantgaredig SA32 7NY
TEL: (01267) 290238 FAX: (01267) 290808
EMAIL: jen4seas@aol.com
WEB SITE: www.visit-carmarthenshire.co.uk/4seasons
on B4310, ½m N of Nantgaredig

COOKING 3
MODERN BRITISH
£33–£44

A stroll through well-managed gardens behind the stone-built restaurant leads to fine views over Camarthenshire countryside, but if the setting is rural the food is a shade more cosmopolitan. Service is pleasant and helpful, the atmosphere relaxed, and against a backdrop of white walls, comfortable lounge, conservatory extension, and a high-ceilinged dining room, four-course dinners offer generous choice. Local materials sometimes appear in more or less undiluted form – Black Mountain smoked salmon with laverbread pancakes, for instance – and are sometimes enterprisingly combined, as in a starter of Camarthen ham with tomato and mozzarella crostini, or rack of Welsh lamb with roast pepper and leek couscous. 'This is no nonsense cookery,' complimented one visitor. After cheese come desserts of perhaps warm peach and orange tart, or meringues with berries and cream. Around 50 fairly priced wines start with a quintet of house French and Australian varietals at £10.

CHEFS/PROPRIETORS: Charlotte Pasetti and Maryann Wright OPEN: Tue to Sat D 7.30 to 9.30 CLOSED: Christmas MEALS: Set D £25 SERVICE: not inc, card slips closed CARDS: Delta, MasterCard, Switch, Visa DETAILS: 45 seats. 8 seats outside. Private parties: 50 main room. Car park. Vegetarian meals. Children's helpings. No smoking in dining room. Wheelchair access (not WC). Music ACCOMMODATION: 6 rooms, all with bath/shower. TV. B&B £40 to £65. Rooms for disabled. Baby facilities. Swimming pool (*The Which? Hotel Guide*) (£5)

NEWPORT Pembrokeshire map 4

▲ Cnapan

East Street, Newport SA42 0SY COOKING **2**
TEL: (01239) 820575 TRADITIONAL
WEB SITE: www.online-holidays.net/cnapan £18–£45

The Coopers and Lloyds have run this pale pink town house as a restaurant since 1984: Michael and John work front-of-house efficiently, while Judith runs the kitchen with help from mother Eluned. The welcome is warm and enthusiastic, and there is a 'lived-in feel', with rooms full of family treasures. Lunch is a light affair, taking in spicy salmon fishcakes with tartare sauce, and familiar puddings such as treacle tart with custard. At dinner, when lace tablecloths give the dining room a smarter edge, the menu is more ambitious: roasted peppers with tomatoes, capers, olives and basil, topped with grilled goats' cheese; breast of guinea fowl with a lemon and elderflower sauce; and vanilla crème brûlée with brandied fruits. Presentation is simple, with local ingredients and seasonal organic vegetables to the fore, while the modest wine list, starting at £9.50, features a Welsh Monnow Valley white.

CHEF: Judith Cooper PROPRIETORS: Michael and Judith Cooper, and John and Eluned Lloyd OPEN: Wed to Mon 12 to 2, 6.45 to 9 CLOSED: 25 and 26 Dec, Jan and Feb MEALS: alc (main courses L £6 to £9, D £12.50 to £18.50) SERVICE: not inc, card slips closed CARDS: Delta, MasterCard, Switch, Visa DETAILS: 35 seats. 30 seats outside. Private parties: 35 main room. Car park. Vegetarian meals. Children's helpings. No smoking in dining room. Wheelchair access (also WC). Occasional music ACCOMMODATION: 5 rooms, all with bath/shower. TV. B&B £60 (double room) (*The Which? Hotel Guide*)

PEMBROKE Pembrokeshire map 4

Left Bank

63 Main Street, Pembroke SA71 4DA
TEL/FAX: (01646) 622333 COOKING **2**
EMAIL: emmagriffith@leftbankrestaurant.co.uk FRENCH
WEB SITE: www.leftbankrestaurant.co.uk £22–£51

This light and airy restaurant with stained-glass windows and modern furniture may take its name – and identity – from the rive gauche of the Seine, but this is something of a pun, as the building was formerly a bank of the other sort. 'French-style cooking using the best of local produce, organic meat and vegetables and fresh fish' is what the Griffiths aim to offer, which might mean roast loin of Welsh lamb with chargrilled vegetables and lavender jus, or pan-fried fillets of John Dory with tarragon velouté. First-rate materials and sound execution were evident in one couple's meal of seared scallops, grilled sea bass and 'excellent' fillet steak. The reasonably priced lunch menu might offer grilled mackerel with stewed onion and tomatoes, followed by a tasty and attractively presented hot chocolate fondant with white chocolate ice cream. Service is 'friendly and helpful', though delays are not uncommon. Prices start at £8.60 on the good-value list of over 40 wines.

CHEFS: Andrew Griffith and Sam Strong PROPRIETORS: Emma and Andrew Griffith OPEN: Tue to Sun L 12 to 2.30, Tue to Sat D 7 to 9.30 CLOSED: Sun L in low season, 1 week Oct, 25 Dec, 3 to 4 weeks Jan MEALS: alc Tue to Sat (main courses L £4 to £7, D £13 to £19). Set L Sun £9.95 (2 courses) to £13.95 SERVICE: not inc, card slips closed CARDS: Amex, Delta, MasterCard, Switch, Visa DETAILS: 30 seats. Private parties: 40 main room, 40 private room. Vegetarian meals. Children's helpings. No smoking in dining room. Wheelchair access (not WC). Music (£5)

PONTDOLGOCH Powys map 7

▲ Talkhouse

NEW ENTRY

Pontdolgoch, nr Caersws SY17 5JE COOKING **2**
TEL: (01686) 688919 FAX: (01686) 689134 MODERN BRITISH
on A470, about 1½m NW of Caersws £27–£42

The Talkhouse promises to live up to its name as a conversation piece and at the very least offers something to write home about in this relatively barren area, gastronomically speaking. It looks like an old country inn, with beams, log fire and an informal bar area. The dining room, however, is the focal point of operations: decorated in Laura Ashley fabrics, it has a comfortable, homely feel; while tables on the lawn in the well-tended garden make al fresco dining an appealing possibility in summer. Owners Colin and Melanie Dawson produce a long and varied blackboard menu using the best seasonal local produce they can lay their hands on, although their style shows plenty of Mediterranean influences. A home-made pâté comes with three 'first-rate' spicy chutneys to start, and other well executed dishes run from a Roquefort soufflé to a large portion of tender, tasty salt-marsh lamb on mash and spicy tomato sauce. Bread and butter pudding with wild honey ice cream also comes recommended. Wines are a standard three-dozen selection from Tanners, opening with nine by the glass. Prices start at £10.50.

CHEFS/PROPRIETORS: Colin and Melanie Dawson OPEN: Tue to Sat L 12 to 1.30, Mon to Sat D 6 to 9 CLOSED: 23 to 26 Dec, first week Mar, last week Sept MEALS: alc (main courses £9 to £14). Bar menu available L SERVICE: not inc, card slips closed CARDS: Amex, Delta, MasterCard, Switch, Visa DETAILS: 40 seats. 8 seats outside. Private parties: 30 main room. Car park. Vegetarian meals. No children under 14 at D. No smoking in dining room. Wheelchair access (not WC). Music ACCOMMODATION: 3 rooms, all with bath/shower. TV. B&B £65 to £95. No children (£5)

Several sharp operators have tried to extort money from restaurateurs on the promise of an entry in a guidebook that has never appeared. The Good Food Guide *makes no charge for inclusion.*

PONTFAEN Pembrokeshire map 4

▲ Tregynon Farmhouse

Gwaun Valley, Pontfaen SA65 9TU
TEL: (01239) 820531 FAX: (01239) 820808
EMAIL: tregynon@online-holidays.net
WEB SITE: www.online-holidays.net/tregynon
at junction of Narberth-to-Fishguard B4313 and B4329, take B4313 towards Fishguard, then take first right, and first right again

COOKING **1**
MODERN BRITISH
£32–£50

The old stone farmhouse is surrounded by ten green acres, its outbuildings converted into cottages (now with facilities for self-catering), its innards turned into a small bar, a spacious lounge and a white-walled dining room. To avoid repetition for holiday guests, menus follow a five-day cycle: even canapés, vegetables and petits fours are different each day. A homely streak runs through the cooking, and vegetarian dishes appear in the form of mozzarella bake, mushroom stroganoff, and chickpea patties. Several main courses – such as rack of Pembrokeshire lamb, or tuna steak – carry a supplement; others, such as game pie, are included in the basic price. Desserts are as varied as the rest of the output: lemon meringue roulade, rum and raisin cheesecake, or pears cooked in cider and cinnamon. Wines combine interest (on the main list) with value (in the special selection), starting with house Loires (Sauvignon and Cabernet Franc) at £11.50.

CHEFS: Peter and Jane Heard and Gemma Cox PROPRIETORS: Peter and Jane Heard OPEN: Mon to Wed, Fri and Sat D only 7.30 to 8.30 MEALS: Set D £23.50 (residents £21.50); booking essential SERVICE: not inc CARDS: Delta, MasterCard, Switch, Visa DETAILS: 24 seats. Private parties: 14 main room, 10 private room. Car park. Vegetarian meals. No children under 8. No smoking in dining room. Wheelchair access (also WC). Music ACCOMMODATION: 3 rooms, all with bath/shower. TV. Phone. B&B £70 to £80

PORTHGAIN Pembrokeshire map 4

Harbour Lights

Porthgain, nr St David's SA62 5BL
TEL: (01348) 831549 FAX: (01348) 831193
EMAIL: reception@wales-pembs-art.com
WEB SITE: www.wales-pembs-art.com/pages/restaurant.htm
off A487 at Croesgoch, 4m W of Mathry

COOKING **4**
MODERN WELSH
£35–£43

This unpretentious, family-run restaurant in the tiny fishing harbour of Porthgain is still going strong after 17 years. The long, low building, once three cottages, has a patio area to the side for fine-weather aperitifs and a small art gallery at the other end; paintings by local artists also hang on the walls. Redecoration has given it cheerful appeal, with a white-boarded ceiling and wooden floor, and Anne Marie Davies's compact menu draws predominantly on fruits of the sea: Porthgain crab, mussels, cockles or maybe halibut, though the repertoire also finds a place for organic vegetables and meats (chargrilled sirloin steak topped with garlic and parsley butter, perhaps).

Cooking techniques are simple and straightforward, and presentation is unfussy, allowing main ingredients to do the talking, as emphasised by whole Dover sole simply grilled with parsley-flavoured lemon oil and accompanied by seasonal vegetables that could include a 'delightful white cabbage crumble'. Desserts run on comfortable, familiar lines: perhaps banoffi pie with banana and Jersey cream, or lemon and ginger sorbet 'bursting with taste'. Service is amiable, informal and child-friendly, and the short, predominantly French wine list stays mainly under £20 (with a good number below £15). House red and white are £10.50.

CHEF/PROPRIETOR: Anne Marie Davies OPEN: Thur to Sat D only 7 (6.30 by arrangement) to 9, Sun and Mon bank hols (phone to check) MEALS: Set D £21 (2 courses) to £25 SERVICE: not inc CARDS: Delta, MasterCard, Switch, Visa DETAILS: 35 seats. 20 seats outside. Private parties: 40 main room, 15 private room. Car park. No smoking in dining room. Wheelchair access (not WC). Music

PORTMEIRION Gwynedd map 7

▲ Hotel Portmeirion

Portmeirion LL48 6ET
TEL: (01766) 770000 FAX: (01766) 771331
EMAIL: hotel@portmeirion-village.com
WEB SITE: www.portmeirion.com
off A487, signposted from Minffordd

COOKING **2**
MODERN WELSH–PLUS
£18–£53

Portmeirion shows how buildings can enhance a landscape. The Victorian mansion by the shore, once a literary celebrities' hideaway, is now a smart hotel run by Robin Llywelyn, grandson of the village's visionary designer. Comfortable and tastefully furnished, it has a curvilinear dining room with faux marble pillars and elegantly set tables. Local ingredients play their part, and ideas range far and wide: from venison and apple patties (like large meatballs) to green-lipped mussels with lightly curried hollandaise, from a thick fillet of seared salmon with a mustard and herb crust, to slices of pork tenderloin on an apple and prune compote. Finish with unfussy traditional bread-and-butter pudding, or a light puff-pastry casing filled with a summery red-berry compote and served with a dollop of soft cream cheese. Service is willing and courteous. The well-stocked wine list cuts straight to value, with vibrant, predominantly French house styles at £11, and a page of recommendations under £15 from Europe, South America and elsewhere; try Argentinian Malbec or an aged Navarra red.

Newly opened nearby (too late to report in this edition) is the same owners' brasserie-style Castell Deudraeth Bar and Grill. Open all day, 365 days a year, it serves pasta, shellfish, salads, sandwiches and some more substantial items, such as king prawn and scallop tempura, and braised belly of pork. Reports are welcome.

CHEFS: Billy Taylor and Colin Pritchard PROPRIETOR: Portmeirion Ltd OPEN: Tue to Sun L 12 to 1.45, all week D 6.30 to 9 MEALS: Set L £11 to £15, Set D £35 SERVICE: not inc CARDS: Amex, Delta, Diners, MasterCard, Switch, Visa DETAILS: 100 seats. Private parties: 100 main room, 30 private room. Car park. Children's helpings. No smoking in 1 dining room. No music ACCOMMODATION: 51 rooms, all with bath/shower. TV. Phone. Room only £95 to £230. Rooms for disabled. Baby facilities. Swimming pool (*The Which? Hotel Guide*)

PWLLGLOYW Powys map 4

WALES NEWCOMER OF THE YEAR

▲ Seland Newydd

NEW ENTRY

Pwllgloyw LD3 9PY
TEL/FAX: (01874) 690282
EMAIL: seland@newydd.fsbusiness.co.uk
on B4520, 4m N of Brecon

COOKING 4
MODERN BRITISH/FRENCH
£32–£46

Seland Newydd returns, fighting fit, to the Guide under new ownership, its name unchanged despite the severance of antipodean connections: maybe the Welsh for Nantwich, where the new owners have come from, sounds less romantic. It still functions as both friendly country pub (with a dartboard and games room) and slightly more formal restaurant. The long, confident menu – printed in the restaurant, chalked up on a board in the bar – includes traditional dishes with a modern slant, much of it straightforward. Crisp baguettes, for example, might be stuffed with hot sliced pink beef, onion and horseradish, and spicy fishcakes are served on pesto-flavoured mash. Many dishes in the bar can be ordered as a starter or main course, including lightly cooked chicken livers and 'wonderfully tasty' bacon piled on a generous heap of salad leaves with a sweet-and-sour redcurrant dressing. Among desserts might be a well executed Tia Maria and coffee crème brûlée, or a 'divinely citrussy' glazed lemon tart. A warm and attentive reception is offered to all, including children, and service is knowledgeable and professional. The list of two dozen wines also offers good value, with a pair of house selections from New Zealand at £9.50 a bottle, £1.75 a glass.

CHEF: Paul Thomasson PROPRIETORS: Margaret Thomasson, Paul Thomasson and Tony Savage OPEN: Tue to Sun L 12 to 2, Tue to Sat D 7 to 9.30 (9 Tue and Wed) CLOSED: D 25 Dec MEALS: alc Tue to Sat (main courses £12 to £15). Set L Sun £12.95. SERVICE: not inc, card slips closed CARDS: Delta, Diners, MasterCard, Switch, Visa DETAILS: 40 seats. 25 seats outside. Private parties: 30 main room, 10 private room. Car park. Vegetarian meals. Children's helpings. No smoking in dining room. Wheelchair access (also WC). Music ACCOMMODATION: 3 rooms, all with bath/shower. TV. B&B £37.50 to £50. Rooms for disabled. Baby facilities. Fishing (£5)

PWLLHELI Gwynedd map 7

▲ Plas Bodegroes

Nefyn Road, Pwllheli LL53 5TH
TEL: (01758) 612363 FAX: (01758) 701247
EMAIL: gunna@bodegroes.co.uk
WEB SITE: www.bodegroes.co.uk
on A497, 1m W of Pwllheli

COOKING 7
MODERN WELSH
£26–£53

An ancient beech avenue leads to a Georgian manor house, wisteria and roses covering its verandah and a Japanese-style garden and pond enhancing its 'magically peaceful' atmosphere. Inside, a light, modern feel is created by the dining room's blond wood floor and aquamarine walls hung with contemporary Welsh artworks. Well-spaced tables and comfortable chairs eschew formality in favour of a welcoming, lived-in appeal.

Easy-going professionalism pervades the menu, too. Short and simple, it reflects Chris Chown's culinary confidence and unfrilly approach, starting with a seasonal and flavourful asparagus and lobster risotto for example, or a mushroom tartlet to remember. Strengths are the quality and freshness of supplies, many of them local: Camarthen ham might add its salty tang to a warm salad of chargrilled monkfish in a sweet-sour dressing, or to pan fried foie gras with spiced pear. Fish features prominently, as in one visitor's roast sea bass on a modest pile of fennel, red pepper and tarragon. Local farmers holding to 'traditional' methods are seeing increased demand for their produce; here it may be Black beef, perhaps just chargrilled and served with an oxtail sauce, or equally simple pink lamb cutlets with a Welsh onion cake and rosemary sauce.

Don't expect large portions; this lets the meal end on a high note, maybe with three variations on chocolate (mousse, hot tart, and white chocolate ice cream), or with apple-filled cinnamon biscuits accompanied by an elderflower cream sauce, a rhubarb sorbet and a perfect, almondy langue de chat. Service is friendly, helpful and well-paced, and the wine list thoughtfully groups on the first page bins as diverse as Alsatian Pinot Gris and Argentinian Tempranillo, all well priced, starting at £14.50. After that comes a wide range from around the world; this year Italy's popularity has earned it a larger share.

CHEF: Chris Chown PROPRIETORS: Chris and Gunna Chown OPEN: Sun L 12 to 2, Tue to Sun D 7 to 9 (9.30 in summer) CLOSED: 1 Dec to 11 Feb MEALS: Set L Sun £14.50, alc D (main courses £15 to £18) SERVICE: not inc, card slips closed CARDS: Delta, MasterCard, Switch, Visa DETAILS: 40 seats. Private parties: 40 main room, 16 private room. Car park. No smoking in dining room. Wheelchair access (also WC). Occasional music ACCOMMODATION: 11 rooms, all with bath/shower. TV. Phone. B&B £40 to £120. Baby facilities (*The Which? Hotel Guide*) (£5)

REYNOLDSTON Swansea map 4

▲ Fairyhill

Reynoldston SA3 1BS
TEL: (01792) 390139 FAX: (01792) 391358
EMAIL: postbox@fairyhill.net
WEB SITE: www.fairyhill.net
off B42954

COOKING **4**
MODERN WELSH
£34–£57

An attractive eighteenth-century house set in the heart of the Gower peninsula, Fairyhill boasts orchards, a trout stream and a duck pond. From the compact dining room with its conservatory extension, views of park and woodland add lustre to the experience. The kitchen's unpretentious modern cooking draws on favourite ingredients from the world larder: home-cured bresaola with Parmesan shavings, capers and bruschetta to start, or a more robust griddled venison and juniper sausage with mustard mash and apple sauce. Prawns in tempura batter dressed in chilli and mint have been well reported, as has the signature main course of Welsh Black beef fillet, locally reared meat that may none the less also receive the full Mediterranean treatment, with sun-dried tomato polenta and a black olive and shallot sauce.

Alternatively, fish might be a pairing of lemon sole and John Dory with mussels in a saffron sauce. Pastry work at dessert stage is highly praised, perhaps in the form of pear tart, while zabaglione is made with poached plums and served with cinnamon biscuits. 'Attentive and good-humoured' service leaves nothing to chance. The substantial wine list covers most major regions.

Prices might not be cheap, but an 'under £20 selection' of 11 whites and reds provides good value. Wales has two entries, and two French house wines come in at £13.50.

CHEFS: Adrian Coulthard and Bryony Jones PROPRIETORS: Paul Davies and Andrew Hetherington OPEN: all week 12.30 to 2, 7.30 to 9 (8.15 Sun) CLOSED: D 25 and 26 Dec, 1 to 18 Jan MEALS: alc (main courses £12 to £18.50). Set D £27.50 (2 courses) to £35 SERVICE: not inc, card slips closed CARDS: Amex, Delta, MasterCard, Switch, Visa DETAILS: 60 seats. 20 seats outside. Private parties: 50 main room, 23 to 40 private rooms. Car park. Vegetarian meals. Children's helpings. No children under 8. No smoking in dining room. Music ACCOMMODATION: 8 rooms, all with bath/shower. TV. Phone. B&B £110 to £225. No children under 8 (*The Which? Hotel Guide*) (£5)

ST DAVID'S Pembrokeshire **map 4**

Morgan's Brasserie

20 Nun Street, St David's SA62 6NT
TEL/FAX: (01437) 720508 COOKING **3**
EMAIL: morgans@stdavids.co.uk FISH/MODERN BRITISH
WEB SITE: www.morgans-in-stdavids.co.uk £26–£46

This is a smart stone building with café rail windows, pine panelling, a well-kept air and a 'classy' ambience. The focus is on fish caught off the Pembrokeshire coast and landed at Milford Haven, and its treatment is laudably straightforward. A blackboard menu supplements the regular one, offering perhaps seared fillet of sea bass with Penclawdd cockles, or roast turbot with Menai mussels in a saffron sauce. The simplicity is appreciated, as the kitchen turns out an appetising salad of tiger prawns in filo pastry, well-timed scallops cooked in vermouth with ginger and lime, and Porthgain lobster in a cream sauce. Other tastes are catered for with a filo parcel of ratatouille and goats' cheese, and Welsh Black beef (fillet in a pink peppercorn sauce) or a tasty confit of Welsh lamb. Finish perhaps with Celtic crunch ice cream, or hazelnut pavlova with raspberries and cream. Prices are considered reasonable, and a short but interesting wine list helps to keep it that way, starting with a four-strong French house selection under £15.

CHEF: Ceri Morgan PROPRIETORS: Ceri and Elaine Morgan OPEN: Mon to Sat D only 6.30 to 9 (days open may vary in low season) CLOSED: Jan and Feb MEALS: alc (main courses £9.50 to £16.50) SERVICE: not inc, card slips closed CARDS: Amex, MasterCard, Switch, Visa DETAILS: 32 seats. Private parties: 20 main room. Vegetarian meals. Children's helpings. No smoking in dining room. Occasional music

'To sum up our night in traditional restaurant critic style, I had the choucroute followed by red fruit tart, while my companion had a six-hour wait in casualty followed by eight stitches in her toe after tripping on the stairs. . . . We had enjoyed our meal very much up to that point, so the evening was not a complete disaster.' (On eating in London)

SWANSEA Swansea map 4

La Braseria £

28 Wind Street, Swansea SA1 1DZ — COOKING **1**
TEL: (01792) 469683 FAX: (01792) 470816 — SPANISH
WEB SITE: www.labraseria.co.uk — £24–£50

With all the relaxed conviviality of a bodega, this city-centre restaurant and wine bar is more a party venue than a place for intimate occasions. Rioja labels adorn the pillars and beams, whitewashed walls are covered with stencilled Spanish phrases and wine motifs, and the wooden floor is scattered with sawdust. After being shown your table, head for the bar where meat and fish are displayed in chilled cabinets: various steaks, leg of lamb, and even suckling pig are among the carnivorous offerings, while fish options, depending on the catch, might include anything from halibut and Dover sole to tiger prawns and snapper. Chargrilling is the predominant method of cooking, and there is a choice of baked potato or chips to accompany the protein. Two pages of Spanish wines open the list, and six house selections are £9.95.

CHEF: Ian Wing PROPRIETOR: Manuel Tercero OPEN: Mon to Sat 12 to 2.30, 7 to 11.30 CLOSED: 25 and 31 Dec MEALS: alc (main courses £8 to £19.50). Set L £6.95 (2 courses) SERVICE: not inc, card slips closed CARDS: Amex, Delta, Diners, MasterCard, Switch, Visa DETAILS: 85 seats. Private parties: 100 main room. Vegetarian meals. Wheelchair access (also WC). Music. Air-conditioned

WALES GFG 2002 COMMENDED

Dermott's **NEW ENTRY**

219 High Street, Swansea SA1 1NN — COOKING **5**
TEL/FAX: (01792) 459050 — MODERN EUROPEAN/WELSH
WEB SITE: www.dermotts.org.uk — £37–£52

Providing a splash of colour and style on old Swansea's High Street, this new kid on the block impresses with the sheer quality of its food and modern good looks. A former shop has been converted with flair: cream walls, sepia prints, mirrors and wooden floors provide a smart backdrop for blue gingham-clothed tables and some 'truly imaginative and sophisticated cooking'. Chef/proprietor Dermott Slade shows a sure touch, utilising simple, contemporary flavours and quality ingredients with saucing and presentation high points.

The repertoire, taking in a half-dozen dishes at each course, sparkles with interest: seared king scallops on circles of creamed butternut squash purée topped with flash-fried squid in a light sauce nero, followed by slow-braised boneless shank of lamb on a bed of caramelised parsnips topped with minted pea purée in an intensely flavoured rosemary jus. For dessert there might be iced Welsh honey parfait with rhubarb and ginger compote and crispy tuiles. Appetisers, pre-desserts and home-made sweets with coffee are all of a piece, and pleasant, friendly and helpful service provides support. A compact, worldwide wine list predominantly under £20 (house wines are £11 and £11.95) adds value, while the last Thursday of each month sees a seven-course gourmet evening. Dermott Slade is due to head up the kitchens at Swansea's new Morgan's Hotel, opening spring 2002; reports on his new venture, and on the High Street original (which will remain in his ownership), are most welcome.

CHEF: Dermott Slade PROPRIETORS: Dermott and Wendy Slade OPEN: Tue to Sat D only 7.30 to 9.30 CLOSED: 23 Dec to 14 Jan, 14 July to 1 Aug MEALS: Set D £20.95 (2 courses) to £28.50. Set D last Thur of month £35 (inc wine) SERVICE: not inc, card slips closed CARDS: Delta, MasterCard, Switch, Visa DETAILS: 34 seats. Private parties: 46 main room. Vegetarian meals. Children's helpings. No smoking in dining room. Wheelchair access (not WC). Music

Didier & Stephanie's

NEW ENTRY

56 St Helens Road, Swansea SA1 4BE
TEL: (01792) 655603

COOKING **2**
FRENCH
£20–£34

This converted house is simple and mellow-toned inside, with stripped wood everywhere from the panelling to the window blinds to the chairs (with hymn-book holders on the backs). The eponymous pair – a kitchen as well as a business partnership – produce a version of their native French cooking that is based on clean, clear flavours and sound technique. Lightness characterised an inspection meal that took in goats' cheese soufflé on a pastry base, a modestly proportioned jambonnette of free-range chicken with intensely flavoured wild mushrooms, and an intriguing presentation of sea bream with a jus of fennel and liquorice. The fixed-price format offers broad choice, including such vegetarian options as spinach 'clafoutis'. For pudding a more textbook clafoutis might appear, of plums with a swirl of red fruit coulis and crème anglaise, or apple mousse with Cointreau ice cream. For the savoury-minded, fine French cheeses are imported regularly, including ripe Reblochon, Mignot and creamy blues. The short wine list focuses on France, of course, with the odd bottle from elsewhere; house wine is £8.90, or £2.90 for a large glass.

CHEFS/PROPRIETORS: Stephanie Danvel and Didier Suvé OPEN: Tue to Sat 12 to 2, 7 to 9.30 MEALS: Set L £6.90 (1 course) to £11.90, Set D £9.90 (1 course) to £19.50) SERVICE: not inc, card slips closed CARDS: Amex, Delta, MasterCard, Switch, Visa DETAILS: 30 seats. Private parties: 30 main room, 20 private room. Vegetarian meals. Music

Hanson's

Pilot House Wharf, Trawler Road, Swansea Marina, Swansea SA1 1UN
TEL: (01792) 466200 FAX: (01792) 201774

COOKING **3**
MODERN BRITISH/SEAFOOD
£21–£49

Occupying a bright, cheerful, first-floor room at the end of the lively marina where trawlers unload their catch, Hanson's makes the most of the views and location, not to mention the produce. Daily fish specials are written on a blackboard: perhaps chargrilled sea bass, fresh Gower lobster, or sewin with a well-judged smoked haddock risotto that can be 'confidently recommended'. But there is plenty more besides, including Welsh lamb (chargrilled cutlets) and Black beef (simply grilled sirloin, or fillet with a leek, smoked bacon and cheese gratin). Salady starters run to smoked chicken and mango, and marinated avocado with mozzarella, while desserts might take in white and dark chocolate torte, or lemon and lime bavarois. Although cigarette smoke and 'pop music of near-discotheque loudness' do not endear the place to all comers, service is prompt, efficient, knowledgeable, helpful and pleasant, with good advice on what to choose from the sensibly priced, 30-strong wine list. Three French varietals at £9.95 start the ball rolling.

CHEFS: Andrew Hanson, John Crandon and Ian Bradley PROPRIETORS: Andrew Hanson and Helen Tennant OPEN: all week L 12 to 2, Mon to Sat D 6.30 to 9.30 CLOSED: D 24 Dec, 25 and 26 Dec MEALS: alc (main courses £7.50 to £20). Set L £9.95 (2 courses) to £12.95 SERVICE: not inc, card slips closed CARDS: Delta, MasterCard, Switch, Visa DETAILS: 50 seats. Private parties: 50 main room. Music (£5)

TALSARNAU Gwynedd map 7

▲ Maes-y-Neuadd

Talsarnau LL47 6YA
TEL: (01766) 780200 FAX: (01766) 780211
EMAIL: maes@neuadd.com
WEB SITE: www.neuadd.com
off B4573, 1m S of Talsarnau

COOKING **4**
MODERN WELSH
£23–£53

The fact that several reports in this year's postbag are from repeat visitors – some are almost regulars – is testament to the consistently high standards set by the Slatters and the Jacksons at their luxuriously appointed country-cottage hotel. The formula doesn't change: dinners of up to five courses (plus appetisers and petits fours) and lighter à la carte lunches, using organically grown produce from the walled kitchen gardens and other materials from carefully sourced supply lines.

The modern country-house style of cooking allows room for an inventive streak, mostly in the form of garnishes, dressings and sauces. Thus, a typical menu might turn up attractive-sounding combinations such as white onion soup garnished with fried beetroot leaves, braised veal accompanied by polenta and potato crisps, and collops of venison set off by plum, apple and rosemary. Sensitive portion control means that those who opt for all five courses will have no trouble staying the distance. Finish with fried rice pudding with kumquat compote, perhaps, or the outstanding selection of Welsh cheeses. After efforts to promote German wines, the proprietors have dropped them from the list. The ever-popular claret section, however, has been rejuvenated with some good years, and an increasing number of second wines from big names offers value and excellence. House red comes in at £12.95, white at £11.95.

CHEFS: Peter Jackson and John Owen Jones PROPRIETORS: Mr and Mrs Slatter, and Mr and Mrs Jackson OPEN: all week 12 to 1.45, 7 to 9 MEALS: Set L Sun £14.95, Set D £27 to £34. Bar menu available L Mon to Sat. Cover £3 L in restaurant SERVICE: not inc, card slips closed CARDS: Amex, Delta, Diners, MasterCard, Switch, Visa DETAILS: 60 seats. 16 seats outside. Private parties: 50 main room, 12 private room. Car park. Vegetarian meals. Children's helpings. No children under 7 at D. No smoking in dining room. Wheelchair access (also women's WC). No music ACCOMMODATION: 16 rooms, all with bath/shower. TV. Phone. D,B&B £73 to £233. Rooms for disabled. Baby facilities (*The Which? Hotel Guide*) (£5)

The Guide's longest-serving restaurants are listed near the front of the book.

WHITEBROOK Monmouthshire map 2

▲ Crown at Whitebrook

Whitebrook NP25 4TX
TEL: (01600) 860254 FAX: (01600) 860607
EMAIL: crown@whitebrook.demon.co.uk
WEB SITE: www.crownatwhitebrook.co.uk
leave A466 at Bigsweir bridge, 6m S of Monmouth; follow signs to Whitebrook; hotel is 2m on left

COOKING **4**
MODERN EUROPEAN
£26–£50

A warm family welcome and well-paced service, overseen by the owners, are part of the appeal in this long, narrow, former pub close to the River Wye and Offa's Dyke path south of Monmouth. Swish and cosmopolitan it isn't, but Mark Turton's cooking lifts it out of the ordinary, combining proudly native dishes – warm sewin and laverbread tartlet on roast leeks – with French ones such as soufflé suissesse, and more generally European ideas: seared herring fillet, for example, comes with pickled beetroot and a mustard-based dressing. Fish and game are among the specialities: perhaps turbot with horseradish and sauce vierge, or pigeon breast stuffed with wild mushrooms, then roasted, and served with a pigeon broth and pearl barley risotto. Copious plates of vegetables are served alongside. Meals might end with a rosemary and pear crème brûlée accompanied by a ginger and pear sponge. Thirteen house recommendations set the wine list's tone of value and diversity. A few expensive bins appear but are mostly confined to the 'specials' page. Wales gets a mention too. House wines are £10.95 a bottle, £1.95 a glass.

CHEF: Mark Turton PROPRIETORS: Angela and Elizabeth Barbara OPEN: Tue to Sun L 12 to 1.45, all week D 7 to 8.45 CLOSED: Christmas and New Year MEALS: alc L (main courses £7.50 to £10). Set L Tue to Sat £15.95, Set L Sun £16.95, Set D £29.95 SERVICE: not inc CARDS: Amex, Delta, Diners, MasterCard, Switch, Visa DETAILS: 32 seats. Private parties: 20 main room, 14 private room. Car park. Vegetarian meals. No children under 12. No smoking in dining room. No music ACCOMMODATION: 10 rooms, all with bath/shower. TV. Phone. B&B £52.50 to £85. No children under 12 (*The Which? Hotel Guide*) (£5)

WOLF'S CASTLE Pembrokeshire map 4

▲ The Wolfe

Wolf's Castle SA62 5LS
TEL: (01437) 741662 FAX: (01437) 741676
WEB SITE: www.pembrokeshire-online.co.uk/wolfe/index.htm

NEW CHEF
MODERN BRITISH
£25–£45

The building, with flowers and creepers all over and around it, looks welcoming, its three varied dining areas offering around six choices per course, centring on fish and vegetarian dishes of the day, a choice of fillets (Welsh beef or lamb) and perhaps Gressingham duck breast. Simon Perrin, who used to work here, arrived back too late for us to receive any feedback on performance, so reports are particularly welcome. Some 30 global wines include a handful of interesting Italians, supplemented by a 50-strong list 'from Gianni's personal collection', and ten modestly priced house wines.

CHEF: Simon Perrin PROPRIETOR: Gianni Di Lorenzo OPEN: Tue to Sun L 12 to 2, Tue to Sat D 7 to 9 CLOSED: Mon Nov to Easter MEALS: alc (main courses £10 to £16.50). Bar menu available L and D SERVICE: not inc, card slips closed CARDS: Delta, MasterCard, Switch, Visa DETAILS: 75 seats. 15 seats outside. Private parties: 75 main room. Car park. Vegetarian meals. Children's helpings. No smoking in dining room. Occasional music ACCOMMODATION: 3 rooms, 1 with bath/shower. TV. B&B £35 to £60 (*The Which? Hotel Guide*) (£5)

Channel Islands

BEAUMONT Jersey map 1

Bistro Soleil 🍷 NEW ENTRY

La Route de la Haule, Beaumont,
St Peter JE3 7BA
TEL: (01534) 720249 FAX: (01534) 625621

COOKING **4**
BISTRO/SEAFOOD
£21–£47

Unadorned light wood tables, straight-backed wicker chairs, pale yellow walls and bare wooden floors give a fresh and light feel to the series of connected rooms that make up this bistro in the coastal town hamlet of Beaumont. Not that you will pay much attention to the décor: eyes will inevitably be drawn to the amazing views, straight out to sea – only a low sea wall and the masts of beached yachts stand between the restaurant and the water. The cooking is fittingly bright and modern to go with the setting, and understandably – given the location – there is plenty of seafood: a starter of pan-fried scallops and langoustines on dressed leaves with a herb butter sauce impressed an inspector for artistic presentation with flavours to match, largely thanks to 'amazingly good' materials.

Main courses have made a similarly positive impact, demonstrating that here is a kitchen that knows how to handle fish, whether it's baked cod on a crab cake with ratatouille and balsamic sauce, or 'bright, glossy' pan-fried salmon with a crunchy salty crust, served on crushed potatoes. Pan-fried calf's liver with baked onion compote and crispy pancetta, or roast Gressingham duck breast served with creamed Savoy cabbage and red wine jus demonstrate that meat is taken seriously too. Successful desserts have included glazed lemon tart, and warm chocolate mousse with chocolate ice cream. The wine list is notable for its range of good-value bottles, all bar one priced under £20, with French house red and white at £8.50. French Gewurztraminers, Portuguese red and California Zinfandels are counted among the global-ranging entries.

CHEF: Ian Jones PROPRIETOR: Chris Power OPEN: Tue to Sun L 12 to 2, Tue to Sat D 6.45 to 9.30 MEALS: alc (main courses £14 to £17). Set L £12.75 (2 courses) to £14.75, Set D £25 SERVICE: not inc, 10% for parties of 10 or more CARDS: Amex, Delta, MasterCard, Switch, Visa DETAILS: 55 seats. 40 seats outside. Private parties: 60 main room. Car park. Vegetarian meals. Children's helpings. No music

---

Dining rooms where music, either live or recorded, is never played are signalled by No music *in the details at the end of an entry.*

GOREY Jersey — map 1

Jersey Pottery

Gorey JE3 9EP
TEL: (01534) 851119 FAX: (01534) 856403
EMAIL: jsypot@itl.net
WEB SITE: www.jerseypottery.com

COOKING **1**
MODERN BRITISH/FISH
£22–£64

The glass-roofed Garden Restaurant in the Jersey Pottery is an attractively verdant setting that lives up to its name. Modern seafood cooking is the kitchen's vernacular, which means starters of steamed Jersey mussels with saffron, parsley and cream, followed by cod tempura with chilli aïoli and chips, or pan-fried sea bass with fennel and potato purée. For non-fish eaters there might be rocket, globe artichoke and Parmesan salad among starters, and main courses of mustard-grilled chicken breast with pancetta and thyme, or roast duck breast with herb-crushed Jersey Royals and apple and thyme sauce. Wines range from the pedestrian to the inspired and are fairly priced throughout the list of 60-odd bottles, opening at £11.95.

CHEF: Tony Dorris PROPRIETORS: the Jones family OPEN: Tue to Sun and bank hol Mon L only 12 to 2.30 CLOSED: Tue following bank hol Mon MEALS: alc (main courses £10 to £29.50). Set L £13.50 (2 courses) to £15 SERVICE: net prices, card slips closed CARDS: Amex, Delta, Diners, MasterCard, Switch, Visa DETAILS: 280 seats. 50 seats outside. Private parties: 280 main room, 100 private room. Car park. Vegetarian meals. Children's helpings. No-smoking area. Wheelchair access (also WC). Music

Suma's

JERSEY RESTAURANT OF THE YEAR

Gorey JE3 6ET
TEL: (01534) 853291 FAX: (01534) 851913

COOKING **5**
MODERN EUROPEAN
£21–£49

This harbour-side restaurant, the baby sister to nearby Longueville Manor (see entry, St Saviour), is a bustling and lively place full of young, old and everything in between. The interior is clean and fresh, with wooden floors, white walls and tasteful modern art with pink-grey granite protruding here and there. From the windows you can see Mont Orqueil Castle, and a small terrace at the front has views across Gorey Harbour.

Since it opened in May 1997 there has been a move away from the slightly funky fusion menu; some (but not all) of the offbeat ingredients that were once prevalent have been replaced by more mainstream dishes and combinations. Generally, the move has only served to improve the quality and overall impressiveness. A starter tart of truffle-scented woodland mushrooms with fingerling potatoes and red wine may come overburdened with mushrooms, with a mash of sweet onions in the middle. Some main courses, such as roast Gressingham duck with sesame-scented greens, sweet plum sauce and ginger, have an Eastern feel, while vegetarian options, such as risotto of Roquefort cheese with roast swede and Asian pear, are thoughtfully prepared. Service is swift and friendly, and around 40 wines are arranged by price, favouring France and innovative bottles from the New World. Eight wines are available by the glass, and house selections start at £8.75 (white) or £9 (red).

CHEF: Shaun Rankin PROPRIETORS: Malcom Lewis and Susan Dufty OPEN: all week 12 to 3, 6.30 to 10 CLOSED: 23 Dec, 17 Jan MEALS: alc (main courses £9.50 to £17.50). Set L £11.95 (2 courses) to £15 SERVICE: net prices, card slips closed CARDS: Amex, Delta, Diners, MasterCard, Switch, Visa DETAILS: 45 seats. 12 seats outside. Private parties: 45 main room. Vegetarian meals. Children's helpings. Music. Air-conditioned

Village Bistro

NEW ENTRY

Gorey JE3 9EP | COOKING **4**
TEL: (01534) 853429 | MODERN EUROPEAN
EMAIL: villagebistro@hotmail.com | £20–£46

The Village Bistro was excluded from last year's Guide by virtue of a change of ownership that meant we were unable to inspect before going to press. It makes a welcome return this year under the new regime of proprietor Steven McCormack and chef Alan Mason. Sun, moon and stars are the decorative motifs of the small, informal dining room, reminding one visitor of a New Age gift shop, and the predominantly blue colour scheme is pleasantly restful.

Fresh local produce is the cornerstone of the cooking, used in impressively inventive ways to good effect within the remit of a predominantly classical style. Seared scallops with black pudding, mushy peas and truffle jus impressed at inspection for the inspired combination of sweet yet earthy flavours; also well received was an exemplary risotto of king prawns with woodland mushrooms and Parmesan crisps. At the same meal, main courses did not let the side down: crisp-skinned, succulent pan-fried brill on light, creamy mushroom sauce, and 'melt-in-the-mouth' navarin of lamb on a dark, sweet beetroot sauce containing lots of parsley. And the pace was maintained into desserts, which included vanilla crème brûlée with caramelised bananas, pineapple and passion fruit. Wines are a varied selection, opening at £7.50 and offering plenty more under £20.

CHEFS: Alan F. Mason and John Meyer PROPRIETOR: Steven McCormack OPEN: Wed to Sun L 12 to 2.30, Tue to Sun D 6 to 10 (8.30 Sun) MEALS: alc (main courses £14 to £16.50). Set L Wed to Sat £13.50, Set L Sun £14.95 SERVICE: not inc CARDS: Amex, Delta, MasterCard, Switch, Visa DETAILS: 40 seats. 30 seats outside. Private parties: 40 main room. Vegetarian meals. Children's helpings. No cigars/pipes in dining room. Wheelchair access (also WC). Music

ST SAVIOUR Jersey | **map 1**

▲ Longueville Manor

St Saviour JE2 7WF
TEL: (01534) 725501 FAX: (01534) 731613 | COOKING **5**
EMAIL: longman@itl.net | MODERN EUROPEAN
WEB SITE: www.longuevillemanor.com | £32–£76

This thirteenth-century manor house has comfortable lounges, deep armchairs and log fires; walls are hung with gilt mirrors and pictures, and furnishing is covered in traditional fabrics. But the service isn't as formal as the setting, which puts diners at ease, and Andrew Baird's cooking isn't old-fashioned either. Lunch is a simpler affair than dinner, offering a carte supplemented by two set menus: the 'taste of Jersey' (£47.50), or the 'gourmet menu' (£80 with wine, £57.50 without). Robust flavours show in a warm salad of oven-roast quail with foie gras parfait, glazed figs and ginger to start, or main-course roast best end of lamb with potato gratin, slow roast Mediterranean vegetables and rosemary jus. Desserts can be variable. At inspection the food seemed to miss the heights of previous visits; none the less, it maintains a high standard, with impeccably sourced ingredients. Service, too, is very competent.

Sommeliers are on tap to talk drinkers through the weighty and wide-ranging (but predominantly French) wine list, and this to some extent influences pricing. The Portuguese page offers value and less-often-seen bottles, starting at £15 for a white Bucelas. Enjoy mature vintages of claret or champagne (as old as 1958) if funds allow, or sample the bin-end page at more reasonable prices (from £8.50). Nine house wines start at £12.

CHEF: Andrew Baird PROPRIETORS: Malcolm Lewis and Susan Dufty OPEN: all week 12.30 to 2, 7 to 10 MEALS: alc (main courses L £9.50 to £17, D £24 to £28.50). Set L £17.50 (2 courses) to £22.50, Set D £47.50 to £57.50 SERVICE: net prices, card slips closed CARDS: Amex, Delta, Diners, MasterCard, Switch, Visa DETAILS: 65 seats. 20 seats outside. Private parties: 65 main room, 8 and 20 private rooms. Car park. Vegetarian meals. Children's helpings. No smoking in 1 dining room. Wheelchair access (not WC). No music ACCOMMODATION: 30 rooms, all with bath/shower. TV. Phone. B&B £160 to £300. Rooms for disabled. Swimming pool

Northern Ireland

BALLYCLARE Co Antrim **map 16**

Ginger Tree

29 Ballyrobert Road, Newtownabbey BT39 9RY
TEL: (028) 9084 8176 FAX: (028) 9084 4077

COOKING **4**
JAPANESE
£23–£59

This attractive, authentic Japanese restaurant in a nineteenth-century farmhouse is decorated in completely Japanese style. The chef-patron's faith in fine local produce shows in a menu that eschews tuna but majors on Irish salmon. There are prawns too, and 'outstanding' grilled eel from Lough Neagh is as genuinely local as anything you might find in a Japanese country inn. The seven-course set dinner offers an appetiser, clear soup, skewered chicken, sushi and another dish preceding the main-course beef, tempura prawns, chicken teriyaki or sukiyaki. There are four- and five-course dinners too, and a four-course set lunch. À la carte hors d'oeuvres include gyoza dumplings, chawan mushi (savoury egg custard with prawns, chicken and mushrooms), ohitashi spinach, and (on Fridays and Saturdays) salmon sashimi. A reporter who dined twice in a week commended tempura very highly, and appreciated friendly and efficient service, even on a busy Saturday. Children's meals consist of an appetiser, a main dish of chicken, pork or beef with rice, a dessert and a soft drink for £5.75. Some 40 wines have been selected with a sharp eye for food-matching; house wines are £11.50.

CHEF: Shotaro Obana PROPRIETORS: Elizabeth Wylie and Shotaro Obana OPEN: Mon to Fri L 12 to 2, Mon to Sat D 7 to 8.30 MEALS: alc D (main courses £9 to £14). Set L £13.95, Set D £15.95 to £30 SERVICE: not inc CARDS: Amex, Diners, MasterCard, Visa DETAILS: 60 seats. Private parties: 70 main room. Car park. Vegetarian meals. Children's helpings. No-smoking area. Wheelchair access (also WC). Music. Air-conditioned

BANGOR Co Down **map 16**

Shanks 🍷

The Blackwood Golf Centre,
150 Crawfordsburn Road, Bangor BT19 1GB
TEL: (028) 9185 3313 FAX: (028) 9185 2493

COOKING **6**
MODERN EUROPEAN
£32–£71

Situated within the grounds of the Clandeboye estate, Shanks enjoys ready supplies of game, which ties in with the owners' aim to use only local, seasonal and organic produce; an organic farm in the neighbouring village is the source of much of the meat; and fish and seafood are provided by local fishermen. The materials are put to good use by Robbie Millar in a varied, well-thought-out, menu with a strongly contemporary feel. Meticulous attention to detail and sensitivity to what ingredients go well together ensure that dishes are well-balanced, despite occasionally being rather elaborate. Starters typically include crispy fried squid with rocket salad, roast peppers and lemon aïoli; local lobster with potato purée, asparagus, olive oil and lobster jus; or penne pasta with Gorgonzola, pear and walnuts with a port jus. In a similar vein main courses take in turbot fillet with toasted hazelnuts, black truffles and celeriac purée; monkfish with Toulouse sausage, provençale vegetable puff and rosemary cream; or breast of Barbary duck with spiced Mediterranean vegetables, oregano and couscous. To finish there may be traditional crème brûlée with strawberries, or the intriguingly titled 'marshmallow mango-mango'. The light, airy feel of the two dining rooms – decorated with Hockneys – help to make this a pleasant environment in which to enjoy the fine food on offer, and the experience is enhanced by the 'excellent' value for money which continues into the wine list. Here plenty of global choices are available for under £20, and more exclusive wines, including Cloudy Bay whites, are reasonably priced. Alternatively, choose from the six-strong house wine collection starting at £15 a bottle, £3.75 a glass, for interesting pickings from around the world.

CHEF: Robbie Millar PROPRIETORS: Robbie and Shirley Millar OPEN: Tue to Fri L 12.30 to 2.30, Tue to Sat D 7 to 10 CLOSED: 24 to 26 Dec MEALS: Set L £15.95 (2 courses) to £19.95, Set D £35 SERVICE: not inc, 10% for parties of 6 or more CARDS: Amex, MasterCard, Switch, Visa DETAILS: 60 seats. Private parties: 60 main room, 36 private room. Car park. Vegetarian meals. Children's helpings. No-smoking area. Wheelchair access (also WC). Music. Air-conditioned

BELFAST Co Antrim **map 16**

Alden's

NEW ENTRY

229 Upper Newtownards Road, Belfast BT4 3JF
TEL: (028) 9065 0079 FAX: (028) 9065 0032
WEB SITE: www.aldensrestaurant.co.uk

COOKING **3**
MODERN EUROPEAN
£22–£54

This orange-painted, large-windowed ground-floor restaurant in a former supermarket has the look and feel of a modern brasserie. An up-to-date, minimalist style, starched white tablecloths, abstract paintings and unruffled ambience attract business-people and politicians, arty types and respectable ladies, courting couples and families. The cooking is modern and fashionable, with well-sourced ingredients imaginatively rendered and presented well and without fuss.

Expect to find an eclectic selection of dishes, such as a starter of gratin of oysters, or seared tuna with nori rolls, ginger and wasabi, or main courses of wild boar sausages with mash and onion gravy, or leg of rabbit stuffed with wild mushrooms. Desserts – like a fusion-inspired dish of grilled pineapple with chilli syrup and coconut sorbet, garnished with fresh coriander – are equally beguiling, and service is welcoming and attentive. The wine list, thoughtfully assembled from the more exciting regions of both Old World and New, includes 20 house wines (six available by the glass), ranging from £9.95 to £19.95, that offer interesting, good-value drinking.

CHEF: Cath Gradwell PROPRIETOR: Jonathan Davis OPEN: Mon to Fri L 12 to 2.30, Mon to Sat D 6 to 10 (11 Fri and Sat) CLOSED: public hols, 2 weeks July MEALS: alc (main courses £8 to £16). Set L £7.95 (1 course), Set D Mon to Thur (Fri 6 to 6.45) £14.95 (2 courses) SERVICE: not inc CARDS: Amex, Diners, MasterCard, Switch, Visa DETAILS: 70 seats. Private parties: 70 main room. Vegetarian meals. Children's helpings. No cigars in dining room. Wheelchair access (also WC). Music. Air-conditioned

La Belle Epoque £

61 Dublin Road, Belfast BT2 7HE
TEL: (028) 9032 3244 FAX: (028) 9020 3111

COOKING 2
MODERN FRENCH
£16–£38

Finding French bistro food in what feels more like a trendy city restaurant may seem incongruous, but the accent is most definitely French, right down to the Seurat-style murals. You can lunch on avocat aux crevettes followed by steak entrecôte béarnaise if you wish, or return in the evening for slightly more high-falutin' food, say pigeon breasts with red wine, juniper and redcurrant sauce, with maybe hake meunière to follow. That something as straightforward as a salade niçoise is heartily commended in a reader's report, as is the simple fish cookery, proves the success of the formula. Desserts include mango mousse with crème anglaise, or banana tart with caramel sauce and cream. Service is 'friendly', and the wine list, though omitting vintages, is practical and modestly priced. Eight house wines start at £10.25.

CHEF: A. Rousse PROPRIETORS: A. Rousse, G. Sanchez and J. Delbart OPEN: Mon to Fri L 12 to 5, Mon to Sat D 5.30 to 11.30 CLOSED: 25 and 26 Dec, 12 and 13 July MEALS: alc (main courses L £6.50 to £7.50, D £7 to £12.50). Set L £6.25 (2 courses), Set D Mon to Fri £15 SERVICE: not inc CARDS: Amex, Delta, Diners, MasterCard, Switch, Visa DETAILS: 84 seats. Private parties: 40 main room, 26 private room. Vegetarian meals. Wheelchair access (also WC). Music

Cayenne

7 Ascot House, Shaftesbury Square,
Belfast BT2 7DB
TEL: (028) 9033 1532 FAX: (028) 9026 1575

COOKING 2
GLOBAL
£22–£37

Frosted-glass windows announce this stylishly designed restaurant, a magnet for fun-loving, high-decibel fashionable folk who appreciate its relaxed atmosphere and global style of food. A lively, voguish menu sets out its stall with goats' cheese puff pizza, vegetable sushi rolls, crab and lemon-grass pot-stickers, and Moroccan spiced lamb. Spices come to the fore in dishes from China, Thailand and Japan: a small piece of chargrilled squid is parked on a pile of chilli-dressed rocket and a heap of al dente chickpeas, while light and tasty Thai fishcakes have been served with sweet-and-sour fennel slaw and lime mayo. Chargrilled ribeye of beef, and roast, crisp-skinned fillet of hake come recommended, as do desserts of apple and pear crumble, steamed ginger pudding, and a smooth, creamy coconut pannacotta surrounded by chopped pineapple and served with nutty biscotti. Expect an enthusiastic welcome, and friendly and efficient service, from well-trained young staff. Intelligently chosen and sensibly priced wines (from £12.50) on a varietally arranged list add to the appeal.

CHEFS: Andy Rea and Paul Rankin PROPRIETORS: Paul and Jeanne Rankin OPEN: Mon to Fri L 12 to 2.15, Mon to Sat D 6 to 11.15 CLOSED: 25 and 26 Dec, Easter Mon and Tue, 12 and 13 July MEALS: alc (main courses L £7.50 to £10, D £8.50 to £13). Set L £10 (2 courses) to £13.50 SERVICE: not inc CARDS: Amex, Delta, Diners, MasterCard, Switch, Visa DETAILS: 95 seats. Private parties: 80 main room. Vegetarian meals. Children's helpings. Wheelchair access (also WC). Music. Air-conditioned

▲ Metro Brasserie

13 Lower Crescent, Belfast BT7 1NR
TEL: (028) 9032 3349 FAX: (028) 9032 0646
EMAIL: info@crescenttownhouse.com
WEB SITE: www.crescenttownhouse.co.uk

COOKING **2**
MODERN EUROPEAN
£20–£44

Just south of the city centre, Metro bills itself as a 'modern classic brasserie', aiming to create a 'bright, lively and sophisticated' impression. Menus are certainly promising: penne pasta with chorizo, chicken, leeks and cream; sea bass with red curry risotto and coconut velouté; Barbary duck breast with sweet potato and ginger croquettes; and cod fillet with crunchy bacon and Caesar dressing all appear to be pushing the right contemporary buttons. The décor in the intimate dining room also has a relaxed, modern feel, with marble-topped tables and warm terracotta walls, and soft popular music sets an appropriate tone. The list of two dozen wines is focused principally on the bright, lively flavours of the Antipodes and California, and prices are reasonable throughout, starting at £10.

CHEF: Aaron Loughran PROPRIETOR: Wine Inns Ltd OPEN: Mon to Sat D only 6 to 9.45 (open for bar food L) CLOSED: 25 Dec MEALS: alc (main courses £10 to £14). Set D 6 to 7.15 £9.95 (2 courses) to £12.50 SERVICE: not inc, card slips closed CARDS: Amex, Delta, Diners, MasterCard, Switch, Visa DETAILS: 70 seats. Private parties: 50 main room. Vegetarian meals. Children's helpings. No cigars/pipes in dining room. Wheelchair access (also WC). Music. Air-conditioned ACCOMMODATION: 11 rooms, all with bath/shower. TV. Phone. B&B £50 to £100. Baby facilities (£5)

Nick's Warehouse 🍷

35–39 Hill Street, Belfast BT1 2LB
TEL: (028) 9043 9690 FAX: (028) 9023 0514
WEB SITE: www.nickswarehouse.co.uk

COOKING **5**
MODERN IRISH
£28–£45

'Eclectic dining in Belfast's cathedral quarter' is the promise made by this wine bar and restaurant set in a former whiskey warehouse, considered 'a lively, cheerful place full of character'. On the ground floor is an informal bar, which has its own menu of upmarket contemporary bar food and an animated mood. Up a long flight of stairs is the restaurant, and though somewhat smarter, with white linen on brown tablecloths and assorted prints on the bare brick walls, it is not at all stuffy – the buzz of conversation shows it to be 'a haven of happiness', as one reporter put it.

Nick Price's global cooking style sees French onion soup alongside fried spiced squid with soy and chilli dressing among starters, while main courses range from sausages on champ with rosemary and onion gravy to grilled hake on leek and mushroom risotto with fennel sauce, and Moroccan spiced vegetable casserole on couscous. An inspector was impressed by a lunch of 'perfectly executed and well-balanced' smoked bacon and broccoli tartlet followed by lamb chops in a rich red wine sauce, in which the no-nonsense approach allowed the quality of the raw materials to shine through. Desserts have featured an attractively presented passion fruit cheesecake with blueberry compote and a garnish of fresh fruit and chocolate straws. Value as ever is key on the wine list, and although the 'Fine Wines' section offers more 'exotic' bottles, including Spanish Albariño and Californian Pinot Noir, prices hardly pass the £30 mark, the welcome result of a flat-rate mark-up. The main list kicks off at £10.50 for a choice of nine styles all available by the glass (£2.75).

CHEFS: Nick Price, Alan Montgomery and Gerrard Sands PROPRIETORS: Nick and Kathy Price OPEN: Mon to Fri L 12 to 3, Tue to Sat D 6 to 9.30 (10 Fri and Sat) CLOSED: 24 and 25 Dec, 1 Jan, Easter Mon and Tue, 1 May, 12 July MEALS: alc (main courses £9 to £14.50). Bistro menu available SERVICE: not inc, 10% (optional) for parties of 5 or more CARDS: Amex, Delta, Diners, MasterCard, Switch, Visa DETAILS: 180 seats. Private parties: 90 main room, 50 private room. Vegetarian meals. Children's helpings. Wheelchair access (also WC). Music. Air-conditioned

Restaurant Michael Deane

36–40 Howard Street, Belfast BT16 1YR — COOKING **6**
TEL: (028) 9033 1134 FAX: (028) 9056 0001 — MODERN EUROPEAN-PLUS
£29–£106

As last year's Guide went to press, the restaurant formerly known as Deane's was undergoing major refurbishment. More than just the name has changed: although the main dining room upstairs remains a polished, elegant restaurant in traditional vein – the Restaurant Michael Deane – the ground floor is now Deanes Brasserie. The latter reminded one visitor of a gentlemen's club, with ornate neo-classical decorative features, such as marble columns, heavy chandeliers and enormous cherubs dangling from the ceiling, though cheerful service and a diverse mix of customers help to dispel any sense of formality. Its wide-ranging modern brasserie menu shows plenty of fashionable touches encompassing everything from fish and chips with tartare sauce and omelette Arnold Bennett to penne pasta with chorizo, chilli and coriander, and grilled salmon with Thai spices, coconut and greens.

Upstairs, meanwhile, the style is somewhat more elaborate, blending classical techniques with elements from the prevailing culinary idiom to produce starters of ballottine of chicken with roast sweetbreads and balsamic syrup, and monkfish tortellini in a shiitake broth with baby leeks and lemon grass. Main courses range from breast of duck with hot chorizo risotto and pak choi in a sweet-and-sour sauce, to beef fillet with parsnip mash, carrot confit and black pudding with horseradish. Both restaurant and brasserie have their own imaginative vegetarian menus.

The extensive restaurant wine list focuses on French classics with hefty price tags, though there are a few sub-£20 wines to be found among the New World and rest of Europe sections; house wines range from £13 to £33, and there is a good choice of cognacs and single-malt whiskies. In the brasserie 18 wines are offered, all under £20, again starting at £13.

CHEF/PROPRIETOR: Michael Deane OPEN: restaurant Fri L 12.15 to 2, Wed to Sat D 7 to 9.30; brasserie Mon to Sat L 12 to 2.30 and D 5.30 to 10.30 CLOSED: Christmas, 1 week Jan, Easter, 1 week July MEALS: restaurant Set L £19.50 (2 courses), Set D £29 to £75 (latter for whole table); brasserie alc (main courses £7.50 to 14.50) SERVICE: not inc, 10% for parties of 6 or more CARDS: Amex, Delta, MasterCard, Switch, Visa DETAILS: 35 seats in restaurant, 100 seats in brasserie. Private parties: 35 main room (restaurant), 100 main room (brasserie). Vegetarian meals. Children's helpings in brasserie. No cigars/pipes in restaurant. Wheelchair access (WC) for brasserie. Music. Air-conditioned

Ta Tu

NEW ENTRY

701 Lisburn Road, Belfast BT9 7GU — COOKING **2**
TEL: (028) 9038 0818 FAX: (028) 9038 0828 — MODERN EUROPEAN
WEB SITE: www.ta-tu.com — £20–£45

A glass-and-steel exterior encases this bar/grill/restaurant of minimalist design, bustling atmosphere and fashionable modern cuisine. Inside, Ta Tu (Irish for 'you are') has a high-ceilinged, noisy bar; the dining room beyond has lots of wood and glass, velvet-clad walls and leather chairs. The food is simple, allowing organic local produce to shine. In his modern European menu Neil Bradley – formerly with Paul Rankin at Roscoff (now Cayenne: see entry, Belfast) – reflects many influences: oriental in dishes such as a starter of fried pork with Asian slaw and crispy won tons, or fashionable in seared scallops, crispy fried leeks and curry butter. Among mains, Chinese red braised lamb, soft noodles and pak choi, say, or Italianate veal escalope with Parmesan, gnocchi and parsley jus, sit beside more traditional dishes. Finish with a 'well-executed' lemon meringue pie with fruit coulis. The compact wine list befits the menu, spans the world from £9.95 and offers 16 by the glass.

CHEF: Neil Bradley PROPRIETOR: Bill Wolsey OPEN: all week 12 to 9.45 (8.45 Sun) CLOSED: 24 Dec (D), 25 and 26 Dec, 12 July MEALS: alc (main courses L 12 to 6 £5 to £8, D after 6 £9 to £15). Bar menu also available 6 to 10 (9 Sun) SERVICE: 10% (optional) CARDS: Delta, MasterCard, Switch, Visa DETAILS: 110 seats. 15 seats outside. Private parties: 70 main room. Vegetarian meals. Children's helpings. Music. Air-conditioned (£5)

LIMAVADY Co Londonderry — map 16

Lime Tree £

60 Catherine Street, Limavady BT49 9DB — COOKING **2**
TEL: (028) 7776 4300 — MODERN EUROPEAN
WEB SITE: www.limetreerest.com — £15–£41

'Soothing' and 'friendly' are words that have been used to describe the atmosphere at this family-run restaurant set in a large old house on the high street of this small market town. The kitchen tends to play it safe, sticking largely to tried-and-tested modern-day classics and catering for most tastes. Duck rillettes with plum sauce, and smoked chicken salad with orange and pine nuts sound like attractive ways to start, while the choice of around eight main courses might include seafood thermidor, stir-fried chicken breast with mango and coriander, and pan-fried medallions of halibut with smoked salmon and spring onion sauce. 'Our own home-made desserts' include calorific creations like a choux bun with ice cream, bananas and toffee sauce. Good-value early-bird dinner menus and two-course business lunches are attractive propositions. Wines also represent good value: around a dozen of each colour are offered, the majority weighing in under £15. Those who want to splash out should look in the 'connoisseur's selection' of the list.

CHEF: Stanley Matthews PROPRIETORS: Stanley and Maria Matthews OPEN: Wed to Fri and Sun L 12 to 2, Wed to Sun D 6 to 9 (9.30 Fri and Sat, 8.30 Sun) CLOSED: 1 week Nov, 25 Dec, 1 week Feb to Mar, 1 week mid-July, some bank hols MEALS: alc (main courses L £6 to £7.50, D £10.50 to £15). Set L Wed to Fri £6.50 (2 courses) to £7.50, Set L Sun £13.50, Set D 6 to 7 Wed to Fri and Sun £12.50 (2 courses) to £14.50 SERVICE: not inc CARDS: Amex, Delta, MasterCard, Switch, Visa DETAILS: 30 seats. Private parties: 38 main room. Vegetarian meals. Children's helpings. Wheelchair access (also WC). Music

Republic of Ireland

We have not given marks for cooking for the Republic of Ireland entries because of a shortage of reports; please do give us feedback should you visit. To telephone the Republic from mainland Britain, dial 00 353 followed by the number listed, but dropping the initial 0. Prices are quoted in most cases in Irish punts, though the Republic is due to switch to the euro in early 2002. Where prices are given in euros, this is noted in the entry and the euro symbol (€) is used.

ADARE Co Limerick **map 16**

▲ Adare Manor

Adare
TEL: (061) 396566 FAX: (061) 396124 GLOBAL
EMAIL: reservations@adare.com £54–£91

The palatial proportions of Adare Manor and its setting in 900 acres of magnificent gardens and grounds, incorporating a golf course, belie the modern cooking of its Oak Room restaurant. Chef Thomas Andrews takes a broad world view, embellishing elaborate classical preparations and techniques with elements from the global larder. This philosophy produces starters of rocket salad with vegetable tempura, mozzarella and olive dressing, or rabbit fillet and mushrooms in puff pastry with lentil ragoût and a balsamic jus. Main courses meanwhile run the gamut from pan-fried John Dory on lime-scented new potatoes with tomato beurre fondue, to roast loin of pork accompanied by pistachio and apricot mousse, carrot purée and sage rösti with the roasting juices. Among desserts might be white chocolate and toasted coconut soufflé with rum-flavoured sauce, or warm fig tart with vanilla ice cream and sauce anglaise – or go for a plate of Irish cheeses served with apple, grape and celery chutney. The wine list lives up to the setting, featuring some heavyweight claret with prices to match, but taking in the New World as well as Europe. Fortunately, not everything has a three-figure price tag, and careful searching will reveal a handful of bottles under £30.

CHEF: Thomas Andrews PROPRIETORS: Tom and Judy Kane OPEN: all week, D only 6.30 to 9.30 MEALS: alc (main courses £24 to £28.50). Set D £39.50 SERVICE: not inc CARDS: Amex, Diners, MasterCard, Visa DETAILS: 70 seats. Private parties: 70 main room, 25 to 180 private rooms. Car park. Vegetarian meals. Children's helpings. Jacket and tie. No smoking in 1 dining room. Wheelchair access (also WC). Music ACCOMMODATION: 64 rooms, all with bath/shower. TV. Phone. Room only £155 to £425. Rooms for disabled. Baby facilities. Swimming pool. Fishing

BALLYDEHOB Co Cork **map 16**

Annie's

Main Street, Ballydehob
TEL: (028) 37292

EUROPEAN
£34–£48

Over the winter of 2000 Annie's underwent thorough refurbishment and renovation, including extension of the dining room and installation of a new kitchen. Fans will be pleased to note that these changes have been effected without altering its most important traits: a warm, friendly welcome and excellent service. The format of dinner also remains unchanged, the four courses priced according to choice of main course. Plenty of variety is offered within a classical cooking style, starters ranging from spicy barbecue-style chicken wings to seafood salad. Roughly a dozen main-course options are split evenly between fish and meat; among the former may be scallops in white wine sauce, or fillet of salmon with prawn sauce, the latter taking in perhaps chicken stuffed with blue cheese and wrapped in filo pastry. Raspberry and chocolate tart with crème de cassis custard is a typical dessert. A well-chosen, mostly French wine list opens with six house selections at £12.50.

CHEFS/PROPRIETORS: Dano and Anne Barry OPEN: Tue to Sat D only 6.30 to 9.30 CLOSED: 24 to 27 Dec, Nov MEALS: alc (main courses £15 to £18). Set D £25.50 to £29.50 SERVICE: not inc CARDS: MasterCard, Visa DETAILS: 40 seats. Private parties: 10 main room. Vegetarian meals. Children's helpings. No smoking in 1 dining room. Wheelchair access (also WC). Occasional music. Air-conditioned

BALLYLICKEY Co Cork **map 16**

▲ Ballylickey Manor House

Ballylickey, Bantry Bay
TEL: (027) 50071 FAX: (027) 50124
WEB SITE: www.ballylickeymanorhouse.com

FRENCH
£52–£63

The road to Ballylickey winds through rock escarpments, waterfalls and past a lake, eventually coming out at the head of picturesque Bantry Bay. The attractive Georgian manor is set in charming grounds dotted with immense old trees. Dinner is a largely traditional affair with a strong Gallic accent. Among starters you may well find roast goats' cheese crottin with walnut oil, a platter of lightly smoked Bantry Bay salmon, and terrine of chicken and mushrooms, while main courses take in a duet of black sole and monkfish, roast fillet of spring lamb with rosemary, and turbot with tarragon sauce. Wines, also French (save a handful from Italy), start at £19.

CHEF: Olivier Andermatten PROPRIETORS: George and Christiane Graves OPEN: all week D only 7.30 to 9.30 CLOSED: Nov to March MEALS: Set D £35.50 (2 courses) to £38 SERVICE: not inc CARDS: Amex, MasterCard, Visa DETAILS: 30 seats. 15 seats outside. Private parties: 8 main room. Car park. Vegetarian meals. Children's helpings (residents only). No children under 4. No smoking in dining room. Occasional music ACCOMMODATION: 11 rooms, all with bath/shower. TV. Phone. D,B&B £160 to £280. Swimming pool. Fishing

BALLYVAUGHAN Co Clare map 16

▲ Gregans Castle Hotel

Ballyvaughan
TEL: (065) 7077005 FAX: (065) 7077111
EMAIL: res@gregans.ie
WEB SITE: www.gregans.ie
on N67, 3 ½m S of Ballyvaughan

MODERN IRISH/FRENCH
€60–€80

'New Irish/French with some other influences' is the owners' description of their cuisine, which increasingly looks to organic foods and produce from named local sources. For example, in the six-course set dinner, roast feuilleté of local organic goats' cheese with honey and dill might be preceded by home-made soup and followed by sorbet. The main course might be fresh Doolin turbot fillet baked in coconut milk in a light chorizo sauce, or grilled beef sirloin with wild mushroom sauce; there are also chef's daily specials. Meals appeal to the other senses too, with light piano or harp music, and views of the sunset across Galway Bay and the hills beyond. The long, eclectic wine list follows the same path with more than 20 organic bottles highlighted; it includes some notable mature reds, as well as house wines from €19 per bottle. (They're hot on brandies too.) Note that all prices given are in euros.

CHEF: Régis Herviaux PROPRIETORS: Peter, Moira and Simon Haden OPEN: all week D only 7 to 8.30 CLOSED: 23 Dec to 13 Feb MEALS: alc (main courses €25.50). Set D €33 (2 courses) to €48.50 SERVICE: not inc, card slips closed CARDS: Amex, MasterCard, Visa DETAILS: 50 seats. Private parties: 65 main room, 30 private room. Car park. Children's helpings. No smoking in dining room. Wheelchair access (not WC). Music ACCOMMODATION: 22 rooms, all with bath/shower. Phone. B&B €176 to €400. Rooms for disabled. Baby facilities

BANTRY Co Cork map 16

▲ Larchwood House

Pearsons Bridge, Bantry
TEL: (027) 66181

MODERN IRISH
£37–£46

The compact size of this pretty, creeper-clad stone house is somewhat misleading. Over two dozen diners can fit into the dining room, along with the motley collection of decorative items that includes wooden sculptures, dried flower displays and ornamental lamps. Chef/proprietor Sheila Vaughan cooks in a 'safely modern Irish' style, bringing in plenty of voguish influences to enhance the native produce. Warm salad of duck with ginger, and smoked salmon with citrus salad, are typical starters; then comes an intermediary soup, perhaps nettle and apricot. Menu price is determined by the choice of main course. This could be anything from baked haddock with smoked salmon sauce, to chicken breast with plum sauce, or duckling with kumquats, while desserts take in mango and apple crumble, or steamed rhubarb pudding. Wines are varied and reasonably priced, starting at £14.

CHEF/PROPRIETOR: Sheila Vaughan OPEN: Mon to Sat D 7 to 9.30 CLOSED: Christmas week MEALS: Set D £28 SERVICE: not inc, card slips closed CARDS: Amex, Diners, MasterCard, Visa DETAILS: 25 seats. Private parties: 13 main room. Car park. Vegetarian meals. Children's helpings. No smoking in 1 dining room. Wheelchair access (not WC). Music ACCOMMODATION: 4 rooms, all with bath/shower. B&B £28. Fishing

BLACKLION Co Cavan **map 16**

▲ MacNean Bistro

Main Street, Blacklion
TEL: (072) 53022 FAX: (072) 53404

MODERN IRISH
£23–£60

Hiding its light under a bushel in Blacklion, a modest little town, is this unassuming small hotel in a Victorian house on the main road. 'Modern Irish with Asian and French influences' is how Neven Maguire describes his cooking style, a fair summary of a menu that incorporates starters of chicken and foie gras ravioli with sweet potato mousseline and a ginger and coriander sauce, and seared scallops with crab spring rolls and red pepper salsa. Similarly eclectic main courses encompass loin of lamb in a herb crust with pancetta rösti and rosemary jus, alongside peppered breast of duckling with pak choi, crispy won ton and star anise, and John Dory fillets with organic courgette flowers and cardamom sauce. Vegetarians have their own menu. To finish, the choice is between desserts such as passion fruit pavlova or a selection from the Irish cheeseboard. The wine list is a well-chosen international selection from £12.50, with ten house wines under £17.

CHEF: Neven Maguire PROPRIETORS: Neven and Vera Maguire OPEN: Sun L 12.30 to 3.15, Tue to Sun (Thur to Sun Oct to May) D 6 to 9.30 CLOSED: 1 week Christmas MEALS: Set L Sun £15, Set D £32 to £35 SERVICE: not inc CARDS: Amex, Diners, MasterCard, Switch, Visa DETAILS: 40 seats. Private parties: 40 main room, 14 private room. Car park. Vegetarian meals. Children's helpings. No children after 8. No smoking in dining room. Wheelchair access (not WC). Music ACCOMMODATION: 5 rooms, all with bath/shower. TV. Phone. D,B&B £23 to £26. Baby facilities

CASHEL Co Tipperary **map 16**

Chez Hans

Moor Lane, Cashel
TEL: (062) 61177

MODERN EUROPEAN
£31–£63

Housed in a converted nineteenth-century chapel beneath the Rock of Cashel, this is a veritable family business. The Matthias even list two wines from their German wine estate in the fairly priced list of 70 bins, starting at £13.50. Chef Jason's stated intention is to lighten the food this year, but you can easily defy him by ordering marinated chicken salad with Cashel Blue cheese, new potatoes and crispy bacon, followed by half a honey roast duckling with roast oranges and béarnaise sauce, plus apple tart, caramel ice cream and butterscotch sauce to finish. Or go along with him and choose marinated Knockalara feta cheese with marinated cucumber and plum tomato salad, follow that with grilled lobster with lemon-grass and coriander butter, and end with fresh fruit sorbets accompanied by fresh fruit salad.

CHEF: Jason Matthia PROPRIETORS: Hans Peter and Jason Matthia OPEN: Tue to Sat D only 6 to 10 CLOSED: last 2 weeks Jan, last week Sept MEALS: alc (main courses £14 to £18.50). Set D Tue to Fri 6 to 7.30 £15.50 (2 courses) to £19.50. Set D £30 SERVICE: not inc CARDS: MasterCard, Switch, Visa DETAILS: 80 seats. Private parties: 80 main room. Car park. Vegetarian meals. Children's helpings. No cigars/pipes in dining room. Wheelchair access (not WC)

CASTLEBALDWIN Co Sligo **map 16**

▲ Cromleach Lodge

Castlebaldwin, Via Boyle
TEL: (071) 65155 FAX: (071) 65455
EMAIL: info@cromleach.com
WEB SITE: www.cromleach.com
signposted from Castle Baldwin on the N4

MODERN IRISH
£52–£63

The Carrowkeel Cairns in the background add lushness and splendour to the setting of Christy and Moira Tighe's modern country-house hotel. Moira applies her highly personal style of contemporary Irish cooking to organic produce, parcelling spiced lamb in filo pastry, dressing Parmesan-crusted cod with bacon and balsamic vinegar, and adding sun-dried tomatoes and Gruyère to pappardelle pasta for a vegetarian main course. 'Light portions and intense flavours' are promised in the gourmet tasting menus, which may be built around a fish main course, such as turbot fillet on creamed fennel. Almond and apricot nougat in a honey tuile, or rich chocolate tart with Tia Maria sorbet, are the grander ways to finish. A good number of half-bottles backs up a world-spanning list that ranges from southern French house wines at £14.95 to Mouton-Rothschild at £170.

CHEF: Moira Tighe PROPRIETORS: Christy and Moira Tighe OPEN: all week D only 6.30 to 8.30 CLOSED: Nov to Jan MEALS: Set D £40 SERVICE: not inc CARDS: Amex, Diners, MasterCard, Visa DETAILS: 50 seats. Private parties: 20 main room, 6 to 20 private rooms. Car park. Vegetarian meals. Children's helpings. No smoking in dining room. Wheelchair access (not WC). Occasional music ACCOMMODATION: 10 rooms, all with bath/shower. TV. Phone. B&B £115 to £278. Baby facilities

CORK Co Cork **map 16**

Crawford Gallery Café

Emmet Place, Cork
TEL: (021) 4274415
WEB SITE: www.ballymaloe.ie

IRISH/BRITISH
£21–£35

The gallery itself disappointed one reporter (it was being refurbished at the time) but its café – run by the owners of Ballymaloe in Shanagarry (see entry) – was more impressive. Open for lunches (and for party bookings in the evening), it offers a straightforward, wholesome cooking using locally sourced ingredients. Grilled minute steak with peppercorn sauce and sauté potatoes, or pork 'Valley d'Auge' (sic) with glazed apples, are typical of the style. Starters are likely to feature a soup of the day and something simple like warm salad of bacon, blue cheese and mushrooms, while desserts might include meringue roulade with strawberries and cream. The short menu also includes open sandwiches for those just wanting a snack. A handful of wines opens at £13.

CHEF: Keith Woods PROPRIETORS: Fern and Hazel Allen OPEN: Mon to Sat 12.30 to 2.30 CLOSED: bank hols MEALS: alc (main courses £8.50 to £9). Set L £13 SERVICE: not inc CARDS: MasterCard, Visa DETAILS: 80 seats. Private parties: 80 main room. Children's helpings. No cigars/pipes in dining room. Wheelchair access (also WC). Occasional music

DINGLE Co Kerry map 16

Half Door

3 John Street, Dingle
TEL: (066) 9151600
EMAIL: halfdoor@iol.ie
WEB SITE: www.halfdoor@iol.ie

MODERN IRISH/FISH
£28–£79

'Bain taitneamh as do bheile' is the bidding on the menu at Denis and Teresa O'Connor's town-centre seafood restaurant – it may be a bit of a mouthful for English tongues, but it makes a pleasant change from 'bon appetit'. Fish and seafood, caught off the coast of the Kerry peninsula, are the focal point of the cooking: Cromane mussels steamed with garlic and wine sauce, Dingle oak-smoked salmon, and baked crab au gratin are typical starters. Main courses take a similarly traditional approach, producing lobster thermidor, paupiettes of sole and salmon with prawn sauce, and crispy monkfish fillets with pasta and a tomato and basil sauce. For meat eaters there may be Cajun-style baked chicken with balsamic and honey sauce. Service can be slow at busy times, and the food does not come particularly cheap, but this is a deservedly popular venue none the less. The well-priced wine list offers a range of burgundies and clarets for the traditionally minded, but equally looks towards the lively styles of the southern hemisphere. A wine of the month is chosen for value and character, and the house offerings start prices off at £13 for a brace of Hardy's Australian blends.

CHEFS/PROPRIETORS: Denis and Teresa O'Connor OPEN: Wed to Sat L 12.30 to 2, Mon to Sat D 6 to 10 CLOSED: Jan and Feb MEALS: alc (main courses £9 to £35). Set D 6 to 7 £21 SERVICE: not inc CARDS: Amex, MasterCard, Visa DETAILS: 50 seats. Private parties: 20 main room, 10 to 20 private rooms. Children's helpings. No smoking in 1 dining room. Wheelchair access (not WC). Music. Air-conditioned

DONEGAL Co Donegal map 16

▲ Harvey's Point

Lough Eske, Donegal
TEL: (073) 22208 FAX: (073) 22352
EMAIL: reservations@harveyspoint.com

MODERN EUROPEAN
£26–£58

Standing on the shore of Lough Eske, beneath the magnificent Blue Stack Mountains, Harvey's Point Restaurant and Country Hotel – to give it its full title – resembles a traditional Swiss chalet, which is appropriate considering the nationality of proprietor Marc Gysling. In this serenely peaceful location you are not likely to be disturbed by anything more rowdy than trout leaping about in the water. At the heart of the operation is the Gourmet Restaurant, which has picture windows giving views over the lough. Tartare of smoked salmon and scallops with gazpacho dressing and a quail's egg, and mille-feuille of gingered crab and marinated peppers with orange and cardamom oil are starters that demonstrate the kitchen's liberal-minded modern European approach, while main courses might include roasted cod basted with aïoli and served with herb mash and sun-dried tomato sauce, or lamb cutlets accompanied by gratin dauphinois and summer beans. To finish, try warm crêpes filled with exotic fruit and a honey and yoghurt dressing, or perhaps crunchy chocolate tart with white and dark chocolate sauces. The wine list features a section of 'everyday easy drinking' styles under £20, from crisp French whites to fruit-filled Chilean reds, as well as more up-market and expensive selections from France and elsewhere. House wines are £14.50.

CHEF: Jean-Michel Maquet PROPRIETOR: Marc Gysling OPEN: all week 12.30 to 2.30, 6.30 to 9.30 CLOSED: Sun D, Mon and Tue Nov to Mar MEALS: alc (main courses L £8.50 to £12, D £18.50 to £22). Set L £14.95, Set D £33 SERVICE: not inc, card slips closed CARDS: Amex, Diners, MasterCard, Visa DETAILS: 100 seats. Private parties: 60 main room, 80 and 300 private rooms. Car park. Vegetarian meals. Jacket and tie. No smoking in dining room. Music. Air-conditioned ACCOMMODATION: 20 rooms, all with bath/shower. TV. Phone. B&B £70 to £120

DOOLIN Co Clare **map 16**

▲ Ballinalacken Castle

Coast Road, Doolin
TEL/FAX: (065) 7074025 MODERN IRISH
WEB SITE: www.ballinalackencastle.com £28–£50

Dating from 1840, Ballinalacken Castle is really a grand country house in the Victorian fashion. It still scores highly for dramatic impact, given its clifftop location with impressive sea views and the twisting road that leads here through sensational scenery. Textbook contemporary cooking – founded on local produce embroidered with global flavours – is the order of the day in the contrastingly old-fashioned dining room. Starters of local black pudding and scallops on a potato cake with garlic aïoli and basil oil, or warm polenta and goats' cheese tartlet with fennel, onion and red pepper purée and a gazpacho sauce are followed by a soup course (perhaps seafood chowder), before moving on to mains of cod with a mushroom and herb crust and grain mustard sauce, roast loin of lamb with red onion marmalade and a tarragon and cranberry jus, or perhaps seared pork fillet with rosemary, garlic, celeriac mash and smoky bacon gravy. To finish, there may be individual baked Alaska with blueberry compote. Wines open at £12 and remain fair value throughout the selection of around 30 bottles.

CHEF: Frank Sheedy PROPRIETORS: Denis and Mary O'Callaghan OPEN: Wed to Mon D only 6.45 to 9 CLOSED: early Oct to late Apr MEALS: alc (main courses £12 to £18.50) SERVICE: not inc CARDS: Amex, MasterCard, Visa DETAILS: 40 seats. Private parties: 40 main room. Car park. Vegetarian meals. No smoking in dining room. Occasional music ACCOMMODATION: 13 rooms, all with bath/shower. TV. Phone. B&B £78 to £109 (double room). Baby facilities

DOUGLAS Co Cork map 16

Lovetts

Churchyard Lane, Well Road, Douglas
TEL: (021) 4294909 FAX: (021) 4294024 MODERN EUROPEAN
EMAIL: lovetts@indigo.ie £33–£64

Modern touches in the generally classic menu in the brasserie include filo parcels enclosing black pudding; onion and poppy seed tarte Tatin; and chicken teriyaki with buttered noodles. Similarly in the restaurant, where starters include wild mushroom and sage ravioli with poppy-seed butter, and a hot three-crab starter ('a little bake', crab claws and crab in filo). Main dishes use filo again, to wrap loin of lamb in spinach, which comes with stuffed lamb's kidney, while the vegetarian menu takes in asparagus croissant with wild garlic sauce and deep-fried couscous crackers with tomato and almond mojo. The daily selection of five fresh fish dishes might include wild river salmon with garlic sauce, more conventional black sole meunière or scallops with beurre blanc. The menu listing of local suppliers confirms the serious approach to superior ingredients. Wines favour the Old World over the New on a list that has variety and good depth of range, and some bottles under £20 can be found in each. House French starts at £14. Renovation, planned for late summer 2001, will be completed too late for us to comment on.

CHEF: Marie Harding PROPRIETORS: the Lovett family OPEN: Tue to Sat D 5.30 to 9.30 CLOSED: 1 week Christmas MEALS: alc (main courses £14 to £24). Set D £30 to £40. Brasserie menu available SERVICE: card slips closed, 10% for parties of 5 or more CARDS: Amex, Delta, Diners, MasterCard, Switch, Visa DETAILS: 80 seats. Private parties: 45 main room, 24 private room. Car park. Vegetarian meals. Children's helpings. No smoking in 1 dining room. Wheelchair access (not WC). Music

DUBLIN Co Dublin map 16

▲ Clarence Hotel, Tea Room

6–8 Wellington Quay, Dublin 2
TEL: (01) 407 0800 FAX: (01) 407 0818
EMAIL: reservations@theclarence.ie MODERN IRISH/EUROPEAN
WEB SITE: www.theclarence.ie £27–£78

'Tea Room' is a somewhat misleading moniker for the spacious, high-ceilinged dining room of the Clarence Hotel. This is no coffee and cake joint. Antony Ely's cooking displays impeccably modern credentials, and the classic brasserie-style menu offers plenty of bold flavours and inventive combinations. Gratinated Rossmore oysters with black pudding, Cashel Blue cheese and soda bread is a starter with a homespun feel, while beer-battered salmon nuggets with lime and caper mayonnaise and chips show a more cosmopolitan streak. Main courses are along similar lines, taking in caramelised halibut with cockle risotto and confit tomato, and duck breast on fondant butternut squash with beetroot jus. Finish perhaps with warm chocolate blini on a gratin of berries and Grand Marnier with mint ice cream. Staff are 'friendly and willing, if unco-ordinated'. A page of house wines, which sees eleven whites and eight reds offered by the small and large glass from £3.55, provides an accessible entry into the heavyweight wine list. It comprises serious American and European names dotted with more approachable styles, mainly from the southern Hemisphere. Bottle prices start around £18.

CHEF: Antony Ely PROPRIETOR: Clarence Hotel OPEN: Sun to Fri L 12.30 to 2.30 (11.30 to 3.30 Sun), all week D 6.30 to 10.30 CLOSED: 23 to 27 Dec MEALS: alc L (main courses £15 to £18). Set L £12.50 (2 courses) to £15, Set D £31 to £50 SERVICE: not inc CARDS: Amex, Delta, Diners, MasterCard, Visa DETAILS: 80 seats. Private parties: 16 main room. Vegetarian meals. No children under 10. No-smoking area. Wheelchair access (also WC). Music ACCOMMODATION: 50 rooms, all with bath/shower. TV. Phone. B&B £210 to £1,500

Commons

Newman House, 85–86 St Stephen's Green,
Dublin 2
TEL: (01) 478 0530 FAX: (01) 478 0551
EMAIL: sales@thecommonsrestaurant.ie
WEB SITE: www.thecommonsrestaurant.ie

MODERN IRISH/FRENCH
£37–£107

For a basement dining room this is an 'extremely pleasant place', the bar and dining room displaying an interesting collection of modern paintings and enjoying views over a pretty rear garden and patio. The grand Georgian building that houses the restaurant on St Stephen's Green is fairly difficult to find, even for taxi drivers, but perseverance will be rewarded with some fine cooking in a modern Franco-Irish style. House specialities include stuffed sea bass with crab and basil sauce, and Pyrenees milk-fed lamb with sweet garlic purée, which give some idea of the kitchen's scope. The long carte (around ten choices per course) might also turn up starters of roast scallops with leek boudin and salt-cod purée, baked squab pigeon with broad beans and truffles, or roast foie gras with pear and vanilla purée. Main courses typically encompass boulangère-style baked turbot fillet with garlic confit, pig's trotter stuffed with morels and sweetbreads, and roast ribeye of Irish beef with artichokes, ceps and foie gras parfait. Prices tend to reflect the luxurious nature of the cooking, though the set-price lunch is considered a bargain. The wine list opens with a dozen house selections from £17. Beyond that, prices soon rise into hefty sums, but the range is varied and well chosen.

CHEF: Aiden Byrne PROPRIETOR: Mike Fitzgerald OPEN: Mon to Fri L 12.30 to 2.15, Mon to Sat D 7 to 10.15 CLOSED: 25 Dec, Good Fri, 2 weeks Aug, bank hols MEALS: alc (main courses £23.50 to £30). Set L £18 (2 courses) to £25, Set D £60 SERVICE: not inc CARDS: Amex, Diners, MasterCard, Visa DETAILS: 74 seats. 30 seats outside. Private parties: 74 main room, 26 to 90 private rooms. Vegetarian meals. No-smoking area. Music

L'Ecrivan

109A Lower Baggot Street, Dublin 2
TEL: (01) 661 1919 FAX: (01) 661 0617
EMAIL: enquiries@lecrivain.com
WEB SITE: www.lecrivain.com

MODERN IRISH/FRENCH
£31–£77

Busy and lively even on a Monday evening, L'Ecrivan makes the most of what space it has by squeezing in plenty of tables, though the dining room retains an airy feel. The crowds are attracted by Derry Clarke's creative flair in the kitchen, manifested in a cooking style that combines inventiveness with the virtues of classical French training and the best of Irish produce. Among the many dishes to receive praise, a couple have a habit of cropping up in correspondence: scallops roasted *à point* and accompanied by a spring roll stuffed with the corals, and Dublin Bay prawns wrapped Middle East-style in pastry, served on one occasion with lime mayonnaise, on another with sweet chilli jam and lemon aïoli. A terrine of black pudding has also impressed for its light, crumbly texture, and well-flavoured rack of lamb cooked 'pink and juicy' went down well with its reporter. Service is 'attentive and courteous without being at all stiff'. An ever-improving wine list features star names from around the world, but the focus is still very much the usual French suspects, which are treated in fair depth. Chilean and French country wines, including house reds and whites at £18 (£3.75 a glass), help provide value to a list that can seem dauntingly priced.

CHEF: Derry Clarke PROPRIETORS: Sally-Anne and Derry Clarke OPEN: Mon to Fri L 12.30 to 2, Mon to Sat D 7 to 11 CLOSED: 24 Dec to 4 Jan, bank hols MEALS: alc (main courses £23 to £25). Set L £17.50 (2 courses) to £20, Set D £35 to £50 SERVICE: 10% on food only CARDS: Amex, Diners, MasterCard, Visa DETAILS: 105 seats. 22 seats outside. Private parties: 105 main room, 20 private room. Vegetarian meals. No smoking in 1 dining room. Music. Air-conditioned

Les Frères Jacques

74 Dame Street, Dublin 2
TEL: (01) 679 4555 FAX: (01) 679 4725
EMAIL: info@lesfreresjacques.com
WEB SITE: www.lesfreresjacques.com

FRENCH
£25–£73

Combining the virtues of fine Irish produce and traditional French cooking, Jean-Jacques Caillabet's city-centre restaurant has been going strong for 15 years. Fish and shellfish, bought daily at Dublin's markets, feature prominently on both the carte and set-price menu: typically attractive-sounding main courses might include roasted turbot with mussel and lemon-grass risotto, and pan-fried sea bass with spinach and a shellfish ragoût. If meat and game are more your thing, then pork shank and root vegetable pie with truffle juices, or trio of lamb with gratin dauphinoise ought to appeal. Service and ambience are unreservedly Gallic, as, in the main, is the wine list, which opens with red and white house Côtes du Rhône at £12.50.

CHEF: Daragh Kavanagh PROPRIETOR: Jean-Jacques Caillabet OPEN: Mon to Fri L 12.30 to 2.30, Mon to Sat D 7.15 to 10.30 (11 Fri and Sat) CLOSED: 24 Dec to 2 Jan, bank hols MEALS: alc D (main courses £18.50 to £25). Set L £14.50, Set D £24 SERVICE: 12.5% CARDS: Amex, Delta, MasterCard, Visa DETAILS: 65 seats. Private parties: 40 main room. No smoking in 1 dining room. Music. Air-conditioned (£5)

Restaurateurs justifiably resent no-shows. If you quote a credit card number when booking, you may be liable for the restaurant's lost profit margin if you don't turn up. Always phone to cancel.

Jacob's Ladder

4–5 Nassau Street, Dublin 2
TEL: (01) 670 3865 FAX: (01) 670 3868 MODERN IRISH
WEB SITE: www.jacobsladder.ie £26–£63

This particular ladder does not lead all the way up to heaven, just to a small first-floor dining room where the approach to décor verges on the puritanical, with a wooden floor and unadorned tables. Pleasant views over the hallowed lawns of Trinity College may offer some distraction for the eyes, but Adrian Roche's resourceful cooking is certain to grab the attention of the taste buds. Though dishes are described in a style as straightforward as the décor, it is clear that there is no shortage of imagination and flair at work in the kitchen: a typical menu might include artichoke and hazelnut soup with chicken and tarragon tortellini, roast rump of lamb with turnip and cumin purée, champ and caper dressing, and fillet of pork with Clonakilty pudding, fondant potato, and sage and apple butter. To finish, there might be rice pudding mousse with glazed oranges. Incidentals are highly rated, from the eight varieties of home-made bread offered at the start to the 'real' espresso at the end. The wine list is short and offers hardly anything under £20, except for eight house selections at £13 a bottle, £3.75 a glass.

CHEF: Adrian Roche PROPRIETORS: Adrian and Bernie Roche OPEN: Tue to Sat 12.30 to 2.30 (2 Sat), 6 (7 Sat) to 10 CLOSED: 2 weeks Christmas, 17 Mar, 1 week Aug, bank hols MEALS: alc (main courses L £8 to £10, D £14.50 to £21). Set D Mon to Fri 6 to 7 £14.95 (2 courses) to £18.95, Set D £25 SERVICE: not inc CARDS: Amex, Diners, MasterCard, Visa DETAILS: 80 seats. Private parties: 55 main room, 45 private room. Vegetarian meals. Children's helpings. Music

Mermaid Café

69–70 Dame Street, Dublin 2
TEL: (01) 670 8236 FAX: (01) 670 8205
EMAIL: info@mermaid.ie MODERN EUROPEAN
WEB SITE: www.mermaid.ie £25–£59

The décor is 'contemporarily austere' at this popular, centrally located café close to the Olympia Theatre. Primary sources of inspiration on the carte are the USA and Italy, starters featuring New England crab cakes with piquant mayonnaise on the one hand, and a summer salad of cucumber, beetroot, radish and Gorgonzola dressing on the other. Main courses follow a similar route, taking in thin, crisp Florentine pizza, and pan-fried prosciutto and rosemary chicken breast with grilled polenta and chilli-tossed broccoli, as well as introducing oriental flavours, as in seafood casserole with Thai aromatics. To finish, choose between gooseberry fool with pistachio biscotti, and pecan pie with maple ice cream, or something similar. Service is friendly and attentive, and wines are a concise but well-chosen bunch, prices starting at £13.95.

CHEF: Temple Garner PROPRIETORS: Benedict Gorman and Mark Harrell OPEN: all week 12.30 to 2.30 (12 to 3.30 Sun), 6 to 11 (9 Sun) CLOSED: 24 to 26 and 30 to 31 Dec, 1 Jan MEALS: alc (main courses L £7.50 to £10, D £12 to £22) SERVICE: not inc, 10% Sun L, 12.5% for parties of 5 or more CARDS: MasterCard, Visa DETAILS: 47 seats. Private parties: 25 main room, 28 private room. No children after 7.30pm. No-smoking area. Wheelchair access (also WC). Music. Air-conditioned

▲ Merrion Hotel, Mornington's

NEW ENTRY

Upper Merrion Street, Dublin 2
TEL: (01) 603 0600 FAX: (01) 603 0700
EMAIL: info@merrionhotel.com
WEB SITE: www.merrionhotel.com

MODERN IRISH
£31–£63

The second restaurant to be opened in the Merrion Hotel offers a contrasting – and complementary – style to its illustrious neighbour, Restaurant Patrick Guilbaud (see entry below). A cheerful, animated crowd is drawn to the brick-walled cellar bar in what used to be Lord Mornington's wine vaults; the brasserie itself, upstairs from the bar, is decorated more in keeping with the hotel's age, with Regency chairs and tables, classical prints on the walls, and enormous pillars. Fashionable ideas abound on the menus, and the results on the plate live up to the billing, demonstrating flair in presentation and technique, as well as good-quality raw materials: risotto of red peppers, broad beans and Gruyère, and ravioli of crab and salmon with tomato and herb oil have been impressive starters, while inventive main courses have included lamb carpaccio with a rocket and endive salad and saffron aïoli, and pan-fried fillet of sea bass with salsify and wild mushroom fricassee and a beetroot essence. Among desserts, a rich, creamy lemon parfait has been endorsed. The wine list is short and predominantly French, prices starting at £18.

CHEF: Ed Cooney PROPRIETORS: Lochlann Quinn and Mr Naughton OPEN: Mon to Fri L 12.30 to 2, all week D 6 to 10 MEALS: alc D (main courses £12.50 to £18). Set L £16 (2 courses) to £19 SERVICE: not inc CARDS: Amex, Delta, Diners, MasterCard, Visa DETAILS: 60 seats. Private parties: 14 main room, 6 private room. Vegetarian meals. Children's helpings. Wheelchair access (also WC). Music. Air-conditioned ACCOMMODATION: 145 rooms, all with bath/shower. TV. Phone. Room only £220 to £780. Rooms for disabled. Baby facilities. Swimming pool

Patrick Guilbaud

21 Upper Merrion Street, Dublin 2
TEL: (01) 676 4192 FAX: (01) 661 0052

MODERN IRISH/FRENCH
£51–£112

Set in the lower reaches of a smart Georgian terrace, this has long been one of the bastions of Dublin fine dining. Impressive modern paintings adorn the lounge, service is 'smooth, welcoming and relaxed', and the dining room is a haven of informal elegance. 'People come here for a good time,' observed one reporter, 'not to eat in hushed reverence.' Guillaume Lebrun specialises in seafood, which means ultra-fresh langoustines in balsamic dressing, filling crab and scallop soup, and main courses such as sea bass with caramelised endive and fennel and truffle juices. But the showcase meat dishes also show up well, like the daube of Wicklow deer that stood on a croûton surrounded by a fine red wine reduction and a serving of creamy mash hot with horseradish. Well-kept French cheeses offer an alternative to the rich offerings on the dessert menu. Wines start at £22 a bottle, £3.50 a glass.

CHEF: Guillaume Lebrun PROPRIETOR: Patrick Guilbaud OPEN: Tue to Sat 12.30 to 2.15, 7.30 to 10.15 CLOSED: 25 Dec, 1 week after Christmas, 17 Mar, Good Fri MEALS: alc (main courses £28 to £34). Set L (2 courses) £22 SERVICE: not inc CARDS: Amex, Diners, MasterCard, Visa DETAILS: 85 seats. 20 seats outside. Private parties: 85 main room, 25 private room. No-smoking area. No music. Air-conditioned

Peacock Alley

St Stephen's Green, Dublin 2
TEL: (01) 478 7015 FAX: (01) 478 7043
EMAIL: reservations@
restaurantpeacockalley.com
WEB SITE: www.restaurantpeacockalley.com

MODERN IRISH
£42–£118

The stylish Conran-designed dining room overlooking St Stephen's Green is a fitting venue for Conrad Gallagher's ambitious, cosmopolitan restaurant. Modern abstract paintings, brown-russet carpet, pale green chairs and impeccably set tables give the place a restrained elegance. In the kitchen changes are afoot with the opening by Conrad Gallagher of an eponymous restaurant in London's Shaftesbury Avenue (tel: (020) 7836 3111) just as the Guide went to press. David Cavalier – whose own highly rated London restaurant, Cavaliers, featured in the Guide in the early '90s – has taken over the day-to-day running of the kitchen at St Stephen's Green. If his cooking continues in similar mode to that already established here, it will be expressive, confident, delivering bold, modern flavours aplenty. These were evidenced at an inspection in 2001, where rillettes of chicken with curry oil, and 'fresh-tasting and robust' confit of sea trout heavily crusted with marinated herbs were attractively presented starters, followed by 'perfectly cooked' medallions of beef on a bed of artichoke hearts, fennel and spinach and surrounded by a richly flavoured reduction. 'Baby Alaska' is an update on the classic dessert: a hedgehog-like heap of marshmallow with a vanilla ice cream core. The wine list aims to befit the grandeur of the restaurant in terms of both content and prices, with several bottles achieving four-figure sums. Those with less money to burn should look to the sommelier's selection of ten wines, starting at £23.

CHEFS: Conrad Gallagher and David Cavalier PROPRIETOR: Conrad Gallagher OPEN: all week 12.30 to 2.30, 6 to 12 MEALS: alc D (main courses £26 to £29). Set L £18.95 (2 courses) to £24, Set D 6 to 7 £27.50 (2 courses), Set D 10 to 12 £37.50 (2 courses), Set D £55 to £75 SERVICE: not inc CARDS: Amex, Diners, MasterCard, Visa DETAILS: 100 seats. Private parties: 120 main room, 18 private room. Vegetarian meals. Wheelchair access (also WC). Music. Air-conditioned

Roly's Bistro

7 Ballsbridge Terrace, Dublin 4
TEL: (01) 668 2611 FAX: (01) 660 8535

IRISH/FRENCH
£21–£54

A 26-strong kitchen team and an in-house bakery might seem to be stretching the bistro concept to the limit, but don't worry unduly about the terminology, for this popular Ballsbridge venue, with its maroon frontage, succeeds with a mixture of traditional comfort food and more modern cuisine. That means you might take your cod in beer batter with chips, or with a pea and sweetcorn fritter and apricot salsa. A seafood terrine with saffron aïoli and deep-fried capers is one way of starting, as is Caesar salad, and then there are langoustines Newburg with tarragon-scented rice, chicken breast with a corned-beef stuffing, and duck with polenta, spinach and port among the mains. Finish with Jaffa cake torte with mango and orange sauce, or pancakes filled with apple and cinnamon compote. A short wine list is sensibly priced, with ten house selections all coming in at £13.50.

CHEFS: Colin O'Daly and Paul Cartwright PROPRIETORS: John and Angela O'Sullivan OPEN: all week 12 to 3, 6 to 10 CLOSED: 25 to 27 Dec MEALS: alc D (main courses £11.50 to £17). Set L £12.95, Set D Mon to Thur 6 to 6.45 £12.95 (2 courses) to £14.95 SERVICE: 10% CARDS: Amex, Diners, MasterCard, Visa DETAILS: 170 seats. Private parties: 30 main room. Vegetarian meals. No-smoking area. No pipes in dining room. Wheelchair access (also WC). Music. Air-conditioned

Thornton's

1 Portobello Road, Dublin 8
TEL: (01) 454 9067 FAX: (01) 453 2947 — MODERN IRISH
EMAIL: thornton.m@iolfree.ie — £36–£101

Despite being located away from the main area of Dublin for restaurants and bars, Thornton's has built up such a reputation that pretty much anyone will be able to give you directions. It is on a quiet corner site on the Portobello Road, and the spacious bar area combines knocked-through rooms decorated in an elegantly understated style. Upstairs in the dining area, solid blocks of strong colours set the tone – deep-red carpet, blue sofas and sage-green walls – and the atmosphere is calm but not staid.

The menus include a no-choice set-price lunch and a lengthy carte in the evenings, supplemented by a 'surprise' menu and a separate list of vegetarian choices. Ingredients like lobster, truffles and foie gras are used abundantly to embellish a classic yet contemporary Franco-Irish cooking style with a strong sense of luxury. Among starters, roast scallops with pea sauce, and marinated salmon with cucumber jelly and beluga caviar epitomise Kevin Thornton's approach. Main courses continue on similar lines, with fillets of John Dory with baby fennel, sugar snap peas and samphire sauce, braised suckling pig and its trotter with Maxim potatoes, glazed turnip and poitin (Irish schnapps) sauce, and turbot with girolles, baby courgettes, herb risotto and squid ink sauce. As that last colourful combination suggests, presentation is a strong point, not least in desserts, which may feature poached pear with blueberries and blancmange, or passion fruit and mango mousse with orange segments and chocolate ice cream. Kicking off with a lengthy champagne entry, the wine list features classy bins from France, where it manages to pick out interest from outside the classical range, through to Australia. Dessert wine lovers will be pleased by the succinct range of international sweet styles and impressed by the Ch. d'Yquem vintages ranging back to 1945. A pair of Côtes du Rhône start off the house wines at £18.

CHEF: Kevin Thornton PROPRIETORS: Muriel O'Connor and Kevin Thornton OPEN: Fri L 12.15 to 2, Tue to Sat D 6.30 to 10.30 CLOSED: 1 week Christmas, 1 week Aug MEALS: alc (main courses £28 to £29). Set L £25, Set D £69 SERVICE: not inc CARDS: Amex, Delta, Diners, MasterCard, Switch, Visa DETAILS: 45 seats. Private parties: 14 main room. Vegetarian meals. Children's helpings. No smoking in 1 dining room. No music. Air-conditioned

GOREY Co Wexford **map 16**

▲ Marlfield House

Courtown Road, Gorey
TEL: (055) 21124 FAX: (055) 21572
EMAIL: info@marlfieldhouse.ie MODERN FRENCH
WEB SITE: www.marlfieldhouse.com €52–€90

This magnificent country house may appear as a symbol of the past, but it is embracing the future by pricing its menus and wine list in euros. It is set in vast grounds that incorporate woodland walks and a rose garden, as well as kitchen gardens, which provide all the herbs, salad leaves, vegetables and fruit used by chef Henry Stone. His cooking style is based on classical yet simple techniques with a strong Mediterranean influence. This typically produces starters of pesto crostini with a ragoût of mushrooms, rocket and Parmesan; pan-fried foie gras on champ with a Madeira jus; or chicken liver parfait with asparagus, a beetroot and balsamic reduction and toasted brioche. Roast pork belly with potato galette, buttered spinach, roast garlic and shallots is the house speciality, though choice extends to pan-fried breast of guinea fowl with grilled aubergine, courgettes, roast pepper and basil mash, and fillet of turbot with leek, spring onion, fennel and tomato risotto. Finish on a comforting note with rhubarb crumble and vanilla ice cream. It is easy to mistake vintages and prices on the heavyweight wine list, but outside the French classics a few more modest bottles can be found. Prices start at €23.

CHEF: Henry Stone PROPRIETORS: Mary and Ray Bowe OPEN: Sun L 12.30 to 1.45, all week D 7 to 9 (9.30 Sat) CLOSED: mid-Dec to 1 Feb MEALS: Set L €33, Set D €51. Light L menu available Mon to Sat SERVICE: not inc CARDS: Amex, Diners, MasterCard, Visa DETAILS: 65 seats. Private parties: 20 main room, 20 private room. Car park. Vegetarian meals. Children's helpings. No children under 10 at D. Jacket and tie. No smoking in dining room. Wheelchair access (also WC). No music. Air-conditioned ACCOMMODATION: 20 rooms, all with bath/shower. TV. Phone. B&B €108 to €698. Rooms for disabled. Baby facilities

HOWTH Co Dublin **map 16**

▲ King Sitric

East Pier, Howth
TEL: (01) 832 5235 FAX: (01) 839 2442
EMAIL: info@kingsitric.ie SEAFOOD
WEB SITE: www.kingsitric.ie £28–£95

The approach across the picturesque harbour should help to get diners in the right frame of mind for the sophisticated fish cookery that King Sitric offers. The kitchen's philosophy is to take the best of what the sea can provide and emphasise its natural virtues with straightforward treatments such as grilling, poaching or stir-frying. Baked hake, for example, is served on a bed of dulse seaweed with a fennel and anchovy dressing, turbot steak comes with citrus salsa, and tuna is simply grilled and served with pepper sauce and fried spring onions. The menu also takes in platters of seafood and oysters either *au naturel* or cooked one of three ways: perhaps topped with bacon, parsley and breadcrumbs. The dining room is a pleasant environment, with large, well-spaced tables adding to the comfort, and service is helpful and friendly. The wine list remains centred around France, with an ever-impressive focus on the varied styles of Chablis and particular attention to the rising stars from the south. A pursuit of excellence is evident, carrying through to other world regions, and value is to be found, particularly among the house recommendations starting at £13.50.

CHEF: Aidan MacManus PROPRIETORS: Aidan and Joan MacManus OPEN: Mon to Fri L 12.30 to 2.15, Mon to Sat D 6.30 to 10.30 CLOSED: 2 days for Christmas, last 2 weeks Jan, bank hols MEALS: alc (main courses £16.50 to £42). Set L £15 (2 courses) to £18.50, Set D £34 SERVICE: not inc CARDS: Amex, MasterCard, Switch, Visa DETAILS: 70 seats. Private parties: 80 main room, 30 private room. Children's helpings. No smoking in 1 dining room. No music. Air-conditioned ACCOMMODATION: 8 rooms, all with bath/shower. TV. Phone. B&B £65 to £150. Baby facilities (£5)

KANTURK Co Cork **map 16**

▲ Assolas Country House

Kanturk
TEL: (029) 50015 FAX: (029) 50795
EMAIL: assolas@eircom.net
WEB SITE: www.assolas.com
signposted from N72, NE of Kanturk, 8m W of Mallow

MODERN IRISH
£39–£45

The passion felt towards the use of local suppliers is almost tangible when you study the menu at this handsome manor house, which has as close a relationship as you will find between the source and the plate. Once in the hands of Hazel Bourke, these fine local ingredients might appear as potato and lovage soup for a starter, and roast boned loin of Kanturk lamb with mint jelly, or baked plaice fillet with chanterelle cream sauce as main courses. Then there is dessert and farmhouse cheese from some of the six named makers. Dinner is a three-course affair, with two choices at each stage. There is good news and good sense in the wine list, too: prices carry no service charge and gratuities are not expected. Sensibly, the Bourkes feel unable to represent the wines of the world in their small dining room, so they concentrate on Europe, mainly France, with Guigal's Côtes du Rhône as house wine at £15.

CHEF: Hazel Bourke PROPRIETORS: the Bourke family OPEN: all week D only 7 to 8 CLOSED: 1 Nov to Mar 16 MEALS: Set D £30 SERVICE: none, card slips closed CARDS: MasterCard, Visa DETAILS: 20 seats. Private parties: 24 main room. Car park. Vegetarian meals. Children's helpings. No children under 8. No smoking in dining room. No music ACCOMMODATION: 9 rooms, all with bath/shower. Phone. B&B £63 to £95. Baby facilities. Fishing

Several sharp operators have tried to extort money from restaurateurs on the promise of an entry in a guidebook that has never appeared. The Good Food Guide *makes no charge for inclusion.*

KENMARE Co Kerry map 16

▲ Park Hotel Kenmare

Kenmare
TEL: (064) 41200 FAX: (064) 41402
EMAIL: info@parkkenmare.com
WEB SITE: www.parkkenmare.com

MODERN IRISH
£60–£87

The grand limestone building, now into its second century, stands proud amid the glowering mountains of the south-west, looking out over unruffled Kenmare Bay. Crammed with antiques and the accoutrements of lush living, it is the kind of place where you might expect equally rich cooking. Joe Ryan looks after guests in more ways than one, though, deploying some asterisked health-conscious dishes among the more lavish fare. Pursue this route with a mille-feuille of wild mushrooms, then a lime and champagne sorbet, followed by grilled salmon on a crab and potato cushion with a warm vinaigrette. But such resolutions may be severely tested by desserts such as a brioche box of caramelised fruits and amaretto ice cream, not to mention an assiette gourmande of chocolate things.

The meticulously catalogued wine list takes the whole wine world as seriously as others take only Bordeaux and Burgundy, listing areas such as Australia's Barossa Valley and leading the knowledgeable swiftly to luminaries like Henschke and Grange. For those confused by such choice, a 'Cellar Selection' of house wines starts with classic Bordeaux at £19.50.

CHEF: Joe Ryan PROPRIETOR: Francis Brennan OPEN: all week D 7 to 9 CLOSED: 30 Oct to 23 Dec MEALS: alc D (main courses £21 to £25). Set D £44 SERVICE: not inc, card slips closed CARDS: Amex, Diners, MasterCard, Visa DETAILS: 80 seats. 30 seats outside. Private parties: 50 main room. Car park. Vegetarian meals. Children's helpings. No children under 8. No smoking in dining room. Wheelchair access (not WC). Music ACCOMMODATION: 49 rooms, all with bath/shower. TV. Phone. B&B £149 to £378. Rooms for disabled. Baby facilities

▲ Sheen Falls Lodge, La Cascade

Kenmare
TEL: (064) 41600 FAX: (064) 41386
EMAIL: info@sheenfallslodge.ie
WEB SITE: www.sheenfallslodge.ie
follow signs for Glengarriff from Kenmare; hotel signposted after about ½m

MODERN IRISH
£60–£72

The restaurant at Sheen Falls Lodge – a modern hotel and leisure complex set in lush, verdant countryside – takes its name from the view of a waterfall, though the star attractions are undoubtedly the food and wine. 'We like to describe our cooking as "progressive Irish",' they tell us, which in practice means that they use predominantly local, organic produce prepared in a largely traditional style but with plenty of modern global influences and a sprinkling of luxury ingredients. Among starters, for example, might be local crab scented with coconut, ginger and spring onion and served on avocado cream and red grapefruit, or a salad of air-dried beef with Jerusalem artichoke, foie gras, and a Madeira and truffle dressing. Main courses tend to be earthy-sounding dishes like roast loin of venison with Puy lentils, spinach, onion marmalade and black truffle dressing, or seared John Dory with fennel confit, plum tomatoes, wild mushrooms and citrus cream. Desserts embrace things like prune and armagnac soufflé, or warm rhubarb gratin with ginger sabayon and ice cream. The 950-plus wine list offers a veritable world wine tour, with maps of the 50 or so regions whose bottles feature to help navigate the drinker through its pages. For a lighter read, try the sommeliers' selection, ranging from exciting Italian bottles to lesser-known French styles, or, for less cost, the house offerings, which start off with a French duo at £19.

CHEF: Chris Farrell PROPRIETOR: Bent Hoyer OPEN: all week D only 7.15 to 9.30 CLOSED: Sun to Thur Dec except Christmas and New Year, Jan MEALS: Set D £42.50 SERVICE: not inc, card slips closed CARDS: Amex, Diners, MasterCard, Visa DETAILS: 120 seats. 20 seats outside. Private parties: 120 main room, 20 and 55 private rooms. Car park. Vegetarian meals. Children's helpings. No smoking in 1 dining room. Wheelchair access (also WC). Music ACCOMMODATION: 61 rooms, all with bath/shower. TV. Phone. B&B £180 to £285. Rooms for disabled. Baby facilities. Swimming pool. Fishing

KILKENNY Co Kilkenny **map 16**

▲ Lacken House

Dublin Road, Kilkenny
TEL: (056) 61085 FAX: (056) 62435
EMAIL: info@lackenhouse.ie
WEB SITE: www.lackenhouse.ie

MODERN IRISH
£37–£56

Chef Nicola O'Brien continues to cook in a modern Irish style that blends traditional modes with imaginative modern variations. Thus, starters might include oak-smoked salmon with home-made brown bread, or crab salad with Cajun dressing, while main courses have featured crisp-skinned roast duckling with parsnip purée, alongside chicken breast stuffed with roast peppers, goats' cheese and wild mushrooms, and the speciality of the house: beef fillet with black pudding mash and whole-grain mustard sauce. Finish with raspberry crème brûlée and white chocolate ice cream, or summer fruit tartlet with vanilla ice cream. Prices start at £13 on the short, varied wine list.

CHEF: Nicola O'Brien PROPRIETORS: Jackie and Trevor Toner OPEN: Tue to Sat and bank hol Sun D only 7 to 10.30 CLOSED: 23 to 28 Dec, 7 to 28 Jan MEALS: alc (main courses £18). Set D £27.50 SERVICE: not inc CARDS: MasterCard, Visa DETAILS: 45 seats. Private parties: 50 main room, 25 private room. Car park. Vegetarian meals. Children's helpings. No cigars/pipes in dining room. Occasional music ACCOMMODATION: 11 rooms, all with bath/shower. TV. Phone. B&B £35 to £90. Rooms for disabled. Baby facilities

Net prices *in the details at the end of an entry indicates that the prices given on a menu and on a bill are inclusive of VAT and service charge, and that this practice is clearly stated on menu and bill.*

LISDOONVARNA Co Clare **map 16**

▲ Sheedy's Country House Hotel

Lisdoonvarna
TEL: (065) 7074026 FAX: (065) 7074555 MODERN IRISH
EMAIL: enquiries@sheedyscountryhouse.com £33–£60

This eighteenth-century former farmhouse has been skilfully restored and updated in a tasteful modern style that retains the spirit of its original state. The blending of traditional ideas with the latest fashions is a philosophy that obtains in all areas, including John Sheedy's cooking, which is based on top-quality local, seasonal produce, much of which is organic – and frequent deliveries ensure freshness. The local St Tola goats' cheese, for example, is employed in a tart with onion, served with a tomato salad and lemon dressing. Other starter choices run to duck liver pâté with apple and raisin chutney, and smoked salmon and potato cakes with spring onion crème fraîche. Tradition prevails in main courses, such as fillet steak with oyster mushrooms and red wine sauce, black sole with garlic butter, or slow-roasted crispy duck with sage and onion stuffing and apple sauce. An appealing bar menu deals in the likes of hot crab claws in garlic butter, seafood platters and various open sandwiches, and a short international wine list opens with house French at £13.

CHEF: John Sheedy PROPRIETORS: John and Martina Sheedy OPEN: all week D only 6.30 to 8.30 CLOSED: mid-Oct to Easter MEALS: alc (main courses £14 to £23.50). Bar menu available D SERVICE: not inc, card slips closed CARDS: Amex, MasterCard, Visa DETAILS: 30 seats. Private parties: 30 main room. Car park. Vegetarian meals. Children's helpings. No children after 7.30pm. No smoking in dining room. Wheelchair access (also WC). Music ACCOMMODATION: 11 rooms, all with bath/shower. TV. Phone. B&B £45 to £135. Rooms for disabled

MALLOW Co Cork **map 16**

▲ Longueville House

Mallow
TEL: (022) 47156 FAX: (022) 47459
EMAIL: info@longuevillehouse.ie
WEB SITE: www.longuevillehouse.ie MODERN IRISH/FRENCH
3m W of Mallow on N72 Killarney road £50–£76

Longueville is a sumptuous country house in 500 acres of its own land, enviably incorporating a farm, kitchen gardens, orchards and a stretch of the Blackwater River. These supply much of the produce used in the grandiosely named Presidents' Restaurant, including wild salmon 'of the highest quality' and lamb, the loin of which might be stuffed with a confit of the leg – a dish with 'terrific flavour and texture'. Cooking stays for the most part in classical French mode, as in roast breast of duck with braised red cabbage and prunes, though ravioli of herbs and oyster mushrooms with lime sauce shows that the kitchen is not afraid of more modern ideas. Value is good, considering the nature of the setting, and service is friendly, willing and generally competent. The major French regions are the focal point of the wine list, and prices are mostly over £20. House selections are £16 a bottle, £3.50 a glass.

CHEF: William O'Callaghan PROPRIETORS: the O'Callaghan family OPEN: all week D only 6.30 to 9.30 CLOSED: mid-Nov to mid-Mar MEALS: Set D £37 to £48. Bar menu available 1 to 5 SERVICE: not inc CARDS: Amex, Diners, MasterCard, Visa DETAILS: 70 seats. Private parties: 40 main room, 18 to 20 private rooms. Car park. Vegetarian meals. Children's helpings. No smoking in dining room. Occasional music ACCOMMODATION: 20 rooms, all with bath/shower. TV. Phone. B&B £65 to £285. Baby facilities. Fishing

NEWPORT Co Mayo **map 16**

▲ Newport House

Newport
TEL: (098) 41222 FAX: (098) 41613
EMAIL: info@newporthouse.ie
WEB SITE: www.newporthouse.ie

IRISH/FRENCH
£48–£69

The Thompsons have been running this distinguished Georgian pile since the mid-1980s, and a classy operation it is too. Local beef and lamb, fish from nearby Clew Bay, and exclusively wild salmon, some of which is smoked in-house, are the mainstays of John Gavin's extensive fixed-price menus. An escalope of monkfish is sauced with white wine, tomatoes, chives and cream, while goujons of brill are given a home-made tartare. After a pause for soup or sorbet it's on to turbot with creamed leeks and champagne sauce, or roast rack of lamb in red wine, rosemary and garlic, before finishing with Dutch apple tart with banana and rum ice cream, or mocha vacherin with crème anglaise. The classicist's wine list offers up claret vintages back to the fabulous 1961 and features the established stars from the rest of Europe and the world. Prices are not generally that low, but a range of youthful French reds and whites as well as Alsatian and German Rieslings and a smattering of rosés come in under £20, with house wines starting at £16.

CHEF: John Gavin PROPRIETORS: Kieran and Thelma Thompson OPEN: all week D only 7 to 9.30 (light L 12 to 2.30) CLOSED: 6 Oct to 18 Mar MEALS: Set D £36. Light L menu available SERVICE: not inc, card slips closed CARDS: Amex, Diners, MasterCard, Visa DETAILS: 35 seats. Private parties: 12 main room. Car park. Vegetarian meals. Children's helpings. No smoking in dining room. No music ACCOMMODATION: 18 rooms, all with bath/shower. Phone. B&B £93 to £198. Baby facilities. Fishing

OUGHTERARD Co Galway **map 16**

▲ Currarevagh House

Oughterard, Connemara
TEL: (091) 552312 FAX: (091) 552731
EMAIL: currarevagh@ireland.com
4m NW of Oughterard on Hill of Doon lakeshore road

IRISH COUNTRY-HOUSE
£33–£40

'After so many years it becomes increasingly difficult to tell you anything new,' say the owners of this family-run country-house hotel, beautifully situated overlooking the lough. They also say, 'our formula may be in or out of fashion', but we don't take this implied conservatism too seriously, since a few modern invasions are noticeable in the traditional five-course, no-choice dinner menus.

Roast goose with potato stuffing, and roast beef or roast lamb with the time-honoured accompaniments are certainly conventional. Less predictable are turf-smoked kassler with pineapple gravy, or duck breast marinated in honey and ginger, which might be preceded by Chinese spiced broth, or monkfish with red pepper relish. Soup is occasionally omitted as the second course and replaced by a savoury to precede the final Irish cheese. Five house wines start at £12. Reds, notably clarets, are of reassuring maturity, as are the seven vintage ports.

CHEF: June Hodgson PROPRIETORS: Harry and June Hodgson OPEN: all week D only 8pm (1 sitting) CLOSED: 21 Oct to Apr MEALS: Set D £24 SERVICE: 10%, card slips closed CARDS: MasterCard, Visa DETAILS: 30 seats. Private parties: 15 main room. Car park. Children's helpings. No children under 6. No smoking in dining room. No music ACCOMMODATION: 15 rooms, all with bath/shower. B&B £55 to £125. Baby facilities. Fishing

SHANAGARRY Co Cork map 16

▲ Ballymaloe House

Shanagarry, Midleton
TEL: (021) 4652531 FAX: (021) 4652021
EMAIL: res@ballymaloe.ie
WEB SITE: www.ballymaloe.com
2m outside Cloyne on Ballycotton road

IRISH/INTERNATIONAL
£34–£59

The fame of Ballymaloe owes as much to the warm welcome extended by a family to its home as to the willingness to bring new ideas to its menus (provided they are good ideas). It is not always easy to distinguish the new from the traditional: one day's menu starters ranged from radish leaf soup with chervil cream, via warm salad of Gubbeen bacon with poached egg and Caesar dressing, to asparagus on toast with hollandaise sauce. Main dishes might include tarragon-baked summer turkey baked with spring carrots, or glazed loin of bacon with Irish Mist sauce and spring vegetable purée; the vegetarian dish, spring vegetable pakoras with sweet pepper and banana relish, is surely new. Another innovation is the 'spicy, but not overpowering' chilli salsa that a reporter enjoyed with perfectly cooked fillet of John Dory. Classic French red wines, and enterprising choices from Spain, Italy and the New World, offer a parade of mature vintages, and white wines are equally distinguished. Eight house wines start at £14.

CHEF: Rory O'Connell PROPRIETORS: the Allen family OPEN: all week 1 to 1.30 (1 sitting), 7.30 to 9 CLOSED: 22 to 26 Dec MEALS: Set L £24, Set D £37.50 SERVICE: not inc, card slips closed CARDS: Amex, Diners, MasterCard, Visa DETAILS: 120 seats. Private parties: 30 main room. Car park. Vegetarian meals. No smoking in 1 dining room. Wheelchair access (not WC). No music ACCOMMODATION: 33 rooms, all with bath/shower. Phone. B&B £85 to £200. Rooms for disabled. Baby facilities. Swimming pool

Occasional music *in the details at the end of an entry means live or recorded music is played in the dining room only rarely or for special events.* No music *means it is never played.*

WATERFORD Co Waterford map 16

Dwyers

8 Mary Street, Waterford
TEL: (051) 877478 FAX: (051) 877480
EMAIL: info@dwyersrestaurant.com
WEB SITE: www.dwyersrestaurant.com

FRENCH/IRISH
£26–£49

Having been in business for a number of years now, Martin Dwyer is proud to have built up a good relationship with a range of suppliers who he believes provide him with the best materials available. It is a good starting point for any kitchen, and provides a solid foundation for Martin Dwyer's imaginative approach to cooking. He offers a short set-price early-evening menu and a longer carte, both with plenty to tempt. Spring roll of summer vegetables with harissa and crème fraîche is an appealingly unusual way to start; there might also be potted crab with toasted brioche, or stir-fried scallops with pak choi. Main courses, meanwhile, typically range from roast noisettes of lamb with thyme stuffing, to red onion and cherry tomato tart with mozzarella and black olive dressing, or monkfish with Moroccan spices and couscous. Finish with Baileys and white chocolate tart, or chocolate meringue with praline cream. Around half the three dozen wines are French, the rest a mixed bunch. Prices start at around £10.

CHEFS: Martin Dwyer and Declan Coughlan PROPRIETORS: Martin and Sile Dwyer OPEN: Mon to Sat D only 6 to 10 CLOSED: 4 days Christmas, bank hol Mons MEALS: alc (main courses £12.50 to £17.50). Set D 6 to 7 £17.50 SERVICE: not inc CARDS: Amex, Diners, MasterCard, Visa DETAILS: 36 seats. Private parties: 24 main room, 8 private room. Vegetarian meals. Children's helpings. No smoking in 1 dining room. No cigars/pipes while others eat. Wheelchair access (also WC). Music (£5)

Round-ups

Looking for a suitable place to eat can be a lottery, especially if you are travelling around the country with no set plans in mind. The Round-up section is intended to provide some interesting gastronomic possibilities, whether you find yourself in an unfamiliar city centre or a rural outpost. Pubs are becoming increasingly valuable as sources of high-quality food, but the listings also include modest family-run enterprises in country towns, racy café/bars and ethnic restaurants in big cities, and a sprinkling of hotel dining rooms in all parts of the land. Dip into this section and you are almost bound to find somewhere that suits your needs and pocket. Entries are based mainly on readers' recommendations, supported where appropriate by inspectors' reports. Sometimes restaurants appear in the Round-ups instead of the main entry section because seasonal closures or weekly openings limit their usefulness, or because changes in the kitchen or to ownership have occurred, or because feedback this year has been thin on the ground. Reports on these places are especially welcome, as they help to broaden our coverage of good eating places in Britain. Round-up entries (outside London) are arranged alphabetically by locality within England, Scotland, Wales, Channel Islands and Northern Ireland.

England

• **ALDEBURGH** (Suffolk)
Café 152 152 High Street, (01728) 454152. Bringing a flash of Mediterranean colour and sunshine to the East Anglian coast, this 'seasidey' café with 'flexible' service has now expanded to include a deli. Local seafood gets a good airing in the shape of Aldeburgh cod with white bean mash, or fillet of sea bass on tomato and fennel risotto. Thai-style tomato and coconut soup has been a fiery winner, likewise 'fine' chocolate roulade. In between there could be steamed mushroom pudding with Puy lentils, or roast rump of lamb with grilled polenta. Sit outside in summer. Wines are from Adnams. Open Wed to Mon L and D.

• **AMERSHAM** (Buckinghamshire)
Gilbey's 1 Market Square, (01494) 727242. The 50 French wines are interesting and, as Gilbey's is also a wine merchant, many are significantly cheaper than you would find them elsewhere; prices start at £8.70, six are offered by the glass, and there are 12 half-bottles. On the food front, the set-price lunch menu might propose mussels with a pepper, chilli and dill crust, followed by minted lamb sausage toad-in-the-hole. À la carte dishes embrace red mullet and leek terrine, grilled black pudding and mushroom crostini, fried sea bass fillet with mild curry sauce, or liver and bacon with mash and caramelised sweet corn. Open all week. There is a branch in Ealing (see London Round-ups).
Kings Arms 30 High Street, (01494) 726333. This timbered inn lies as comfortably as a warming pan amid the many antique shops, but its food looks to both the twenty-first and twentieth centuries. Chargrilled radicchio with mozzarella and pancetta might sit alongside salmis of quail on roasted root vegetables as à la carte starters, while pan-fried mackerel with spicy potato and cucumber tzatziki, and lambs' kidneys Turbigo are typical set menu options. Service, and kitchen, may wilt under pressure at busy times. Wines, many under £20, start at £10.20. Closed Mon, and Sun D.

• **ARDINGTON** (Oxfordshire)
Boar's Head Church Street, (01235) 833254. Chef/patron Bruce Buchan (formerly of the Bear & Ragged Staff,

Cumnor) offers a home-grown style of cooking at this pleasant old pub. Seasonal, local produce is used imaginatively, delivering starters of salmon tartare with seared scallops, kipper ravioli with samphire and lettuce coulis, and main dishes such as veal kidney and oyster pudding, plaice fillets with minted peas and bacon, or tournedos with morels, onion confit and foie gras hash. Wines, half of them French, and many classic, start at £9.50. Open Tue to Sun.

• **Barham** (Kent)

Old Coach House Dover Road, (01227) 831218. You can fortify yourself luxuriously for the coach (or any other) journey in Claude Rozard's restaurant-with-rooms. Blackboard specials major on game and fish. They might include venison terrine, asparagus and crab soufflé, or scrambled duck egg with truffles to start, then proceed to monkfish with lobster and salmon sauce, or grilled lobster béarnaise. Less Gallic desserts take in Eton mess and pavlova, but the many cheeses are decidedly Française. Open all week D only.

• **Barnard Castle** (Co Durham)

Blagraves House The Bank, (01833) 637668. This historic North Country house, dating back to the seventeenth century, has been run as a restaurant since 1988 by Elizabeth and Kenneth Marley – who also do the cooking. Their menus change monthly. On the carte you might encounter casserole of seafood with chilli and coriander, or locally smoked duck breast with hazelnut dressing, before roast fillet of salmon on a mussel and saffron sauce, or grilled loin of lamb with minted gravy. Open Tue to Sat D only.

• **Barnstaple** (Devon)

Lynwood House Bishop's Tawton Road, (01271) 343695. The Robertses' restaurant-with-rooms in a Victorian house offers English food with the occasional modern touch. Novelties include chicken biryani in their lighter meal menu, and stir-fried beef as a starter; and there is no English restraint about the garlic in a garlic mushroom tartlet. 'Rich, strongly flavoured' scallops and bacon come with tomato salsa; more classical sauces are rich red wine with local venison, lobster with poached brill; and sage, onion and apple with crisp roast duck. Open Mon to Fri and (D only) Sat.

• **Barton upon Humber** (North Lincolnshire)

Elio's 11 Market Place, (01652) 635147. Elio Grossi has been fronting this cheery old Humberside favourite since 1983 with an all-Italian brigade. The cooking is a cut above your average trattoria, although the menu works its way through pizzas, chicken cacciatore, veal parmigiana, and fettucini with wild mushrooms. The real stars are the fresh fish dishes on the blackboard: baby halibut with a pepper sauce, and monkfish in leek sauce have both been given the thumbs-up. Expect generous vegetables, and simple sweets. Eat al fresco in the summer surrounded by geraniums. Open Tue to Fri L and Mon to Sat D.

• **Bath** (Bath & N.E. Somerset)

Firehouse Rotisserie 2 John Street, (01225) 482070. 'Honest food from the fire' is the daily business at this 'plain and unpretentious' venue with a cooking area at the back. The focus is on good-quality 'succulent' meats, notably 'mouthwatering' lemon thyme chicken with smooth aïoli on the side, or pork loin in a 'subtle, glutinous' ancho Cabernet sauce with apple and shallot chutney, stewed dried apricots and red onion. Bowls of garlic mash have 'punch'. Caesar salad to start, perhaps strawberry shortcake with mascarpone to finish. Service is 'most solicitous'. Open all week. A second branch is at Anchor Square, Bristol; tel (0117) 9157 323.

Woods 9–13 Alfred Street, (01225) 314812. Long-serving brasserie in a Georgian house opposite the Assembly Rooms. Fixed-price lunch and dinner menus are bolstered by a carte and specials 'from the world's markets'. Warm salad of smoked chicken and bacon; loin of pork with red onions and Madeira jus; lemon tartlet with wild berries; and 'excellent' bread-and-butter pudding have all featured in recent reports. Other pluses are prompt, efficient service, an informal atmosphere, and drinkable wines, including many by the glass. Open all week.

• **Birkenhead** (Merseyside)

The Station Hamilton Square, (0151) 647 1047. This little sister of Liverpool's Ziba (see main entry) has it all: it's a small hotel, deli, bakery, and bistro-brasserie at lunch, restaurant in the evening. The daily lunch à la carte offers a choice of soups to start, while Mediterranean notes in main dishes include tagliatelle with Parma ham and salami, chilli glazed sardines, and duck leg with couscous. The shorter evening menu, supplemented by daily specials, might offer mussels with garlic tomato and basil, tian of mango and crab, Thai green vegetable curry, and Toulouse sausage and bean casserole. Wines start at £11.50, and there is good choice by the glass. Open all week.

• **Birmingham** (West Midlands)

Berlioz Burlington Arcade, New Street, (0121) 633 1737. Although Berlioz was established in 1881, its menus are full of modern ideas. Seared sea bass with lemon oil, roast monkfish with herbs and tapénade, and garlic marinated beef strips might feature on the summer version of the seasonally changing salad menu, while à la carte starters have included warm tartlet of chicken livers, and parcel of smoked haddock with caper hollandaise. Continue perhaps with guinea fowl with vegetable couscous, glazed cod with black noodles, or braised root vegetables in red pepper and basil with a crumble topping. Closed Sun L.

Hyatt Regency Hotel Court Café, (0121) 643 1234. The constant commotion on the mezzanine floor of a business-oriented hotel makes this a far from restful refuge. The three-course lunch menu rapide is good value at £13.50, offering a cold buffet starter then perhaps roast turbot, or Thai stir-fried beef, vegetables and egg fried rice. More expensive lunch starter or snack includes burgers, duck pâté with pork rillettes, and main courses ranging from pasta to Scotch entrecôte and shallot fondue. Among desserts praised by an inspector were banoffi pie and cassis ice cream on a tuile. Open all week L and D.

Café Ikon Brindley Place, (0121) 248 3226. Spain reigns at this café attached to a contemporary art gallery near the city centre. It's mostly tapas and raciones, along the lines of guindillas (smoked peppers with chilli), Serrano ham with Manchego cheese, patatas bravas, and albondigas. For something more substantial try one of the five versions of paella, or Spanish black pudding (morcilla) in bean stew. Finish with bizcocho borracho (sponge roll with chestnuts and cream) or lemon tart. Drink Spanish wines, sherries and beers. Closed all day Mon and Sun D.

Maharaja 23–25 Hurst Street, (0121) 622 2641. This long-established restaurant's main menu contains no surprises but might offer a few in the dish of the day. It could be a starter of chicken shahi kebab, or lamb barra kebab, or a main dish such as chicken Samarkand, or king prawn mughlai. But an inspector's daily special produced the high point of his meal in the form of 'absolutely tremendous' tandoori mackerel with a very minty yoghurt. European wines just outnumber New World in the short, low-priced list, with house selections at £8.25. Closed Sun.

San Carlo 4 Temple Street, (0121) 633 0251. The Birmingham original of a small Italian chain (branches in Leicester and Bristol), with cooking a cut above what you might expect from a modern city-centre ristorante/pizzeria. The menu is a long run through pizzas, pasta and trattoria classics like saltimbocca alla romana. Also look out for the blackboard of fish specials. Excellent service, well-chosen wines, 'perfect' coffee. Open all week.

• **Bishop's Stortford** (Hertfordshire)

Lemon Tree Water Lane, (01279) 757788. Bright, warm colours and 'friendly, attentive' service contribute to the Lemon Tree's relaxed ambience, while chef/patron Luke Fishpool serves up attractively multi-flavoured menus. Duck and pork rillettes, and goujons of smoked haddock are among the commended starters. Main courses to please reporters have included roast partridge with braised lettuce and rösti potatoes, and roast skate with Savoy cabbage and beurre rouge, while satisfying desserts have been rich steamed ginger pudding, and baked cheesecake. More exotic flavours appear in Cajun-spiced red snapper, and Szechuan peppered duck with pak choi and rice. Open Tue to Sun L and Tue to Sat D.

• **Bishop's Waltham** (Hampshire)
Wine Bar 6–8 High Street, (01489) 894476. Set in a row of shops on the high street, the place is – despite its name – about equally given over to bar and dining areas. The menus change twice daily, but are built around robust and gutsy dishes such as a hefty crab cake containing potato and spring onion and served with suitably sharp lemon-grass syrup. Roaming far and wide for ideas, the kitchen may well also turn up Moroccan-style skewered lamb with spiced aubergine; Cajun-spiced chicken with tsatsiki; and a slab of dark, fudge-textured chocolate praline, incorporating halved hazelnuts. Open Mon to Sat L and D.

• **Blackpool** (Lancashire)
Kwizeen 49 King Street, (01253) 290045. Marco Calle-Calatayod 'insists on being called a cook rather than a chef', observed a reporter, 'and he produces clean-tasting food'. Find oilcloths at lunchtime, when the set menu is a snip, while in the evening it's all linen and a carte listing starters, mains and desserts ('with impressive spun-sugar work'). A typical meal might begin with carpaccio of salmon with potato and chive salad, followed by honey-glazed duck breast with date and Marsala sauce, finishing with strawberry and cracked pepper tart. Home-made ice creams might be flavoured with anything from basil to Benedictine. Open Mon to Sat.

• **Blewbury** (Oxfordshire)
Blewbury Inn London Road, (01235) 850496. This is more restaurant than country pub, despite the name and the rural setting. Franck Peigne scours the globe for inspiration and his dinner menus pull together all manner of influences. Tartlet of goats' cheese and red onion marmalade comes with a salad of pan-fried haggis, apple and lamb's lettuce in pumpkin oil, while kassler (smoked loin of pork) is served with a pancetta cake, winter vegetables in honey and a tarragon jus. Completing the elaborate picture, there might be a Caribbean 'delice' of coconut frangipane, pineapple and Malibu compote topped with mango sorbet. Light lunches available. Closed Sun D and all day Mon.

• **Brighouse** (West Yorkshire)
Brook's 6–8 Bradford Road, (01484) 715284. All tastes are indulged here. Rump steak or simply grilled fish of the day will gratify conservative tastes, while starters of smoked ostrich with parsnip salsa, or artichokes stuffed with pesto, endive and pink grapefruit salad, are for the adventurous. Italy is a fruitful source of ideas: grilled blue ling fillets with tagliatelle, lime and chilli oil, for example, while India contributes beef-joint Madras. Open D only Mon to Sat.

• **Brighton** (East Sussex)
Bushby's Brasserie 24 Ship Street, (01273) 321233. Take a dip into the global melting-pot at this shop conversion in the Lanes area of the town. Croquettes of Serrano ham come with roasted red peppers, while a 'melange' of king prawns, avocado and asparagus is 'tinged' with lemon-grass dressing. To follow, there might be anything from roast marinated rack of lamb with couscous and green salsa to timbale of lemon sole and spinach on pan-fried garlic and pak choi. Closed Sun D.

Moshi Moshi Sushi Bartholomew Square, (01273) 719195. The first Moshi Moshi outside of London (see main entries) has found an ideal location in a striking new bespoke building tucked away in a square between the Lanes and the sea. The relaxed style should appeal to many among the city's cosmopolitan population, and the many visiting Japanese, who can sit alongside the kaiten (conveyor belt) and choose from the passing nigiri, maki and sashimi, or order 'Japanese tapas' such as 'excellent, light and crisp' tempura. Open all week.

• **BRINKWORTH** (Wiltshire)
Three Crowns Brinkworth, (01666) 510366. In the light and immensely spacious conservatory of this dining pub, the blackboard must be, and is, enormous, to proclaim its long menu of elaborately conceived and described main dishes. With no starters, portions are appropriately gargantuan. One of the simpler dishes was locally produced veal in a pie with a sweet cider, tarragon and white wine sauce accompanied by notably fresh vegetables. Calorie-laden puddings also range from homely to exotic. A well-balanced wine list, some 80-strong, starts with house bottles from £10.95. Closed Sun L.

• **BRISTOL** (Bristol)
Glass Boat Welsh Back, (0117) 929 0704. This converted barge is praised for its décor and ambience, and especially for its views of new waterside developments and swans in the river. The new chef's style is modern and ambitious, though may tend to be over-elaborate and under-sized for some tastes. Ingredients, though, are good, as in 'fresh, juicy, pinkish' peppered loin of lamb with creamed salsify and lemon thyme butter, and 'soft, strong, smooth' chocolate terrine served with a slice of poached pear. Otherwise, there might be salmon carpaccio with wasabi dressing and crisp potatoes, followed by grilled smoked pork belly with choucroute and swede quesadilla. Cheeses come with pine nut baklava. There's a good choice of wines under £20, with house selections from £11. Closed Sat L and all day Sun.
Tico Tico 24 Alma Vale Road, (0117) 923 8700. 'Modern rustic cooking' with a global theme defines this yellow-walled shop conversion off Whiteladies Road. A special 'East West Tapas and Dim Sum Menu' promises basmati sushi rolls stuffed with Irish Cashel Blue cheese, and chargrilled Moroccan lamb meatballs on spiced pumpkin couscous. Alternatively, dip into the main repertoire, where you might find Japanese marinated smoked chicken salad, Jamaican jerk pork fillet with tamarind rice, coconut-crusted fillet of sole with sweet-and-sour leek and shallot confit, or caramelised pineapple with Harvey Wallbanger sorbet. Open Tue to Sat D only.

• **BROADWAY** (Worcestershire)
Oliver's High Street, (01386) 854418. Behind Cotswold stone walls in Broadway's main street is an ancient (and music-free) room with prints of Oliver Cromwell, after whom this brasserie outpost of the Lygon Arms is named. Vegetables, and particularly risottos, are recommended from a menu incorporating a few oriental ideas in a mainly Mediterranean repertoire. Typical are smoked pigeon breast with radicchio, pink grapefruit and chestnuts, and sauté lamb's liver on bacon and onion fondue with Israeli couscous. Eleven wines by the glass, all under £20, start with south-western French red and white at £11.95. Open all week.

• **BROCKENHURST** (Hampshire)
Thatched Cottage 16 Brookley Road, (01590) 623090. This thatched roofed, timber-framed cottage is a hotel with five luxurious rooms, and heavy embroidered lace tablecloths in the sumptuous restaurant. Expensive food, largely organic, can be well prepared and interestingly presented. Dinner menus start at £35, and the £15 'light lunch' includes salade niçoise, feuilleté of beef with wild mushrooms, and cheese or dessert. The high-flying wine list includes some good bottles under £20, with house wines £12.50 white, £14 red. Open Tue to Sun L, Tue to Sat D.

• **BROMFIELD** (Shropshire)
Cookhouse Bromfield, (01584) 856565. This low-lit bistro in a large brick building offers reasonably priced, simply presented dishes. Starters range from crab and pork spring rolls with chilli and coconut milk sauce, to whole Mediterranean prawns with aïoli; and there are house salads served in two sizes. Main dishes include bangers and mash, croque-monsieur (with chips and salad), and chilli con carne with guacamole and tortillas. There is a

separate dining room, where guinea fowl with mushrooms, shallots and a 'good old-fashioned sauce' was found to be 'straightforward' and 'satisfying'. Open 11 to 11 Mon to Sat, and Sun L.

• **BROXTON** (Cheshire)
Frogg Manor Nantwich Road, (01829) 782629. Christened after a girlfriend nicknamed 'Froggy', John Sykes's lavishly furnished hotel in a fine Georgian house is nothing if not idiosyncratic. Away from the quirkiness of it all (menu priced at 30 guineas and numerous frogs in straw, ceramic, wood and brass), the cooking is built around good local supplies. Anything goes, from 'toad not in the hole' (up-market bangers and mash'), to Long John Silver's Jamaican Gunpowder beef with a sauce laced with rum and black treacle. Closed Sat L.

• **BURGH le MARSH** (Lincolnshire)
Windmill 46 High Street, (01754) 810281. The windmill across the car park provides flour for the home-made bread baked in this agreeable roadside restaurant. Herbs are home-grown, fish comes from Grimsby, and there is local game in season. The menu might offer queen scallops in garlic, white wine and coriander; grilled sirloin of Lincoln Red beef with pepper sauce; or roast duckling with black cherry sauce. Desserts run to warm apricot and almond tart and home-made ice creams. 'Personal service, plenty of hospitality from the owners,' remarked one visitor. Open Tue to Sat D and Sun L.

• **BURPHAM** (West Sussex)
George and Dragon Burpham, (01903) 883131. A road through rolling English countryside leads to this village pub on the edge of the South Downs. A rustic bar offers up-market pub food, while in the cottagey, low-ceilinged dining room alongside, Nick Markey's menu is 'a gem'. Top-notch goats' cheese tartlet, pavé of sea bass with creamed leeks, and hot chocolate fondant have impressed. Ideas can be complex: witness oven-baked quail filled with foie gras and cep farce with lentil compote, juniper and game sauce. Service is attentive and unhurried. Closed Sun D only.

• **BURY ST EDMUNDS** (Suffolk)
Angel Hotel, Abbeygate Restaurant Angel Hill, (01284) 714000. The main dining room of this imposing creeper-clad, fifteenth-century building, across the square from the Abbeygate, has been given a makeover: bright, strong colours now contrast with the oil paintings and luxury drapes. The food looks to France for its main inspiration, and reporters have been delighted by seared scallops with cauliflower and white truffle purée, as well as fillet of veal with creamed winter vegetables and delicate mustard sauce. 'Pleasant' desserts have included tarte Tatin with strawberry ice cream, and caramel terrine with apple and calvados sorbet. Smart, professional, friendly service. Open all week L and D.

Priory Hotel Tollgate, (01284) 766181. This carpeted restaurant in 'comfortable hotel' style is found in a fine Georgian building behind a high flint wall. Friendly staff serve set lunches (£19.95 for three courses) and dinners (£23.95) with supplementary 'classic choices'. The menu mixes traditional and modern styles, so sweet potato and coconut chowder might precede seared salmon with spring onion mash and chive and cheese sauce. A reporter's chargrilled beef fillet topped with horseradish bread-and-butter pudding and chanterelles was 'full of lovely fresh flavours'. Half-bottles of wine are listed, but none by the glass. Closed Sat L.

• **BUXTON** (Derbyshire)
Columbine 7 Hall Bank, (01298) 78752. A restaurant set in three cosy rooms (two no-smoking) of a small family house. Light lunch dishes range from avocado on watercress and walnuts served with herb bread, to poached salmon salad with herb mayonnaise and new potatoes. The early-evening three-course Festivals menu will get you to the opera house on time, even after herrings marinated with dill and limes, followed by sauté chicken on saffron risotto and basil sauce. À la carte choices are mostly classical European with occasional oriental influences; specials and desserts are listed on blackboards.

Cheerful, prompt service. Open Mon to Sat D and Fri and Sat L; winter closed for L and Tue D.

• **CAMBRIDGE** (Cambridgeshire)
Loch Fyne The Little Rose, (01223) 362433. Converted city pub, now an East Anglian sibling of the original in Cairndow (see main entry, Scotland). Loch Fyne oysters and pots of Scottish rope-grown mussels top the bill, but the repertoire extends to smoked haddock chowder, deep-fried Kintyre king scallops with tomato dip, and baked sea bass with fennel butter sauce. The company's own kippers and smoked salmon (including hot-smoked braden rost), plus ribeye steaks and Scottish cheeses, complete the picture. You can buy from the adjoining shop. Open all week L and D.
Sala Thong 35 Newnham Road, (01223) 323178. Take a chauffeured punt along the Backs and you can while away the time with some Thai food, courtesy of this restaurant. Alternatively, stay on terra firma where the atmosphere is congenial, decoration modest and the menu holds few daring surprises. There are curries of different colours, stir-fries (prawns with Chinese white asparagus, or pork with chilli and basil, for example), spicy salads and noodle dishes. Start with spring rolls, mung bean toast, or fish 'pattles', and round things off with steamed banana or tapioca pudding. Closed Mon.

• **CHEAM** (Surrey)
Bay Tree 22 Ewell Road, (020) 8643 8838. White linen tablecloths and napkins and warmly welcoming staff await at this converted shop. Of six starters and main dishes on the carte, three are offered in the £10 lunch, or early-evening two-course menu (not Friday or Saturday evenings). East meets West in Mexican spiced meatballs with couscous and raita, but most dishes are as European as rabbit with roasted Mediterranean vegetables, or calf's liver with braised chicory and Marsala sauce. Portions are generous. Ten of the 80 wines come by the glass, with house wines from £9.75. Closed Mon.

• **CHELTENHAM** (Gloucestershire)
Beaujolais 15 Rotunda Terrace, (01242) 525230. In this self-styled 'restaurant Française', located in a Regency shopping parade, the cooking shows as much in the way of modern British influences as a traditional Gallic style. The three-course set-price menu might start with duck liver pâté with cucumber relish and Melba toast, or smoked salmon pieces in a marinated seafood medley. Follow perhaps with poached salmon on wilted spinach with hollandaise, or lamb steak on pea and mint mash with béarnaise sauce, and finally hot apple pie and vanilla ice cream. Closed Mon and Sun.

• **CHETTLE** (Dorset)
Castleman Hotel Chettle, (01258) 830096. Once the Dower House belonging to the estate village of Chettle, the Castlemain is now an unpretentious, pleasing hotel. Sunday lunch has been 'excellent value' for seafood chowder, 'huge' helpings of local roast beef from Sixpenny Handley, and enjoyable puddings. Coffee is served in the pretty blue lounge or the library. The extensive dinner menu promises home-cured gravlax and quails' eggs with cucumber and dill salad; lambs' kidneys with Dijon mustard, pink peppercorns, cider and cream; and bread-and-butter pudding with poached apricots and clotted cream. Open Sun L and all week D.

• **CHICHESTER** (West Sussex)
Comme Ça 67 Broyle Road, (01243) 788724. Once a pub (the Wellington) facing the Chichester Theatre, this is now an ultra-Gallic restaurant ('we had to get our own back,' said one of the French staff). The rooms inside are formal, even luxurious, while its splendid, flowery, heated and canopied courtyard is more *comme il faut* than *ça*. Excellent service is French too, and so is the long, wide-ranging menu which gives helpful translations for such dishes as 'perfectly judged' sauté de crevettes royales au lait de coco et la crème de gingembre, and 'well-hung, tender' filet de boeuf sauce Madère. The wine list, unsurprisingly, is

mainly French. Closed Sun D and all day Mon.

• **Chipping Campden** (Gloucestershire)
Cotswold House The Square, (01386) 840330. Elegantly furnished Georgian hotel offering the prospect of 'leisurely' dining backed up by pleasant, attentive service. Menus in the Garden Room restaurant deal in elaborate ideas based around luxury ingredients: for example pan-fried escalope of foie gras with French bean salad with an orange Muscat sauce; grilled scallops with marinated new potatoes, served with home-made herb pasta, red pepper sauce and scallop soufflé; and crisp pastry layered with vanilla crème brûlée, marinated red fruits and basil sauce. Simpler dishes, salads and grills are served in the separate Hicks Brasserie. Open all week D and Sun L.

• **Clifford's Mesne** (Gloucestershire)
Yew Tree Inn Clifford's Mesne, (01531) 820719. Converted 400-year-old cider press in remote countryside on the fringes of the Forest of Dean. Downstairs is the traditional bar, upstairs is the 'delightful' restaurant offering a menu of ambitious modern dishes. Paul Hackett's fixed-price dinners might kick off with chilled tomato soup with spring onion, coriander and crème fraîche, before fillet of sea bass with champagne and basil cream, while rice pudding and local raspberries is a typical finale. 'Friendly professional service, excellent selection of wines'; good local beers too. Closed Mon.

• **Clipsham** (Rutland)
Olive Branch Main Street, (01780) 410355. Impressively revitalised village pub two miles from the A1. Its traditional virtues remain, but there's now an obvious passion for good food, wines and, of course, beer. Blackboards all around advertise what is on offer. You can have anything from a massive sandwich of locally baked bread to a full meal. The three-course lunch is a snip for perhaps mushroom soup, pork chop with Savoy cabbage and mash, then sticky toffee pudding. Top-drawer honey-glazed duck confit with onion marmalade, braised fillet of herb-crusted turbot with red wine sauce, and spiced pineapple carpaccio with coconut ice demonstrate the serious intent of the kitchen. Closed Sun D. More reports, please.

• **Constantine** (Cornwall)
Trengilly Wartha Nancenoy, (01326) 340332. This pub-restaurant in greenest Cornwall lists 250 wines as well as real ales. Like the food, they are served in a friendly, efficient way which evokes praise. Menus use local ingredients imaginatively in dishes like pork and prawn Chinese dumplings, Thai vegetable lasagne (with mustard pasta), and poached lobster with coriander broth and olive couscous. Stay-at-homes might prefer smoked Cornish lamb fillet with baby broad beans and rosemary, and home-made desserts such as healthy white peach sorbet, or creamy banana mousse with toffee sauce. Open all week L and D.

• **Coppull Moor** (Lancashire)
Coppull Moor 311 Preston Road, (01257) 792222. This little restaurant in a converted roadside pub offers fixed-price dinners that run to six courses. A typical starter might be smoked haddock fishcakes on beansprouts, then perhaps plum tomato and basil soup, before baked salmon with hollandaise. Mains could include chargrilled beef fillet with Madeira sauce, or deep-fried stuffed aubergine. Vegetables are many and varied, while desserts could feature pineapple and kiwi crumble. 'No gratuities, please – service is with our compliments,' states the menu. Open Tue to Sat D.

• **Corbridge** (Northumberland)
Valley Old Station House, (01434) 633434 /633923. 'Passage to India' deals bring customers by train from Newcastle to this novel Indian restaurant in an old station house. The extensive menu meanders through tandooris, biryanis and dhansaks stopping off for a few rarities including salmon bahja (fried with herbs, garlic, ginger and onion). Open Mon to Sat D only. Two related destinations are now up and running: Valley Junction 397 (a

converted signal box and carriage at Old Jesmond Station, Archbold Terrace, Jesmond, tel (0191) 281 6397; and Valley Connection 301, by the abbey at 19 Market Place, Hexham, Northumberland, tel (01434) 601234. Reports, please.

• **DENMEAD** (Hampshire)
Barnard's Hambledon Road, (023) 9225 7788. In this family-run restaurant in a main-road shopping parade you'll find accomplished modern British cooking. Smooth chicken liver parfait, followed by chive omelette filled with tomatoes and sauté potatoes, is a typically simple, traditional idea from the light lunch menu. On the carte, crab and fresh mango tower is dressed with passion fruit vinaigrette, and grilled swordfish steak comes with a spicy salsa and noodles. Modestly priced wines start at £9.95. Open Tue to Fri L and Tue to Sat D.

• **DODDISCOMBSLEIGH** (Devon)
Nobody Inn Doddiscombsleigh, (01647) 252394. 'Hansel-and-Gretel-style, fifteenth-century country pub' famed for its breathtaking selection of more than 50 West Country cheeses and its spectacular 700-strong wine list. The food is robust country cooking without pretensions: wholesome Nobody soup, pâté, and pies in the bar. In the restaurant you might find a touch more elaboration in the shape of melon with Denhay air-dried ham, steak in red wine and mushroom sauce, and raspberry frangipane tart with 'amazing' local clotted cream. Ever-changing real ales and around 200 whiskies, too. Open all week L and D; restaurant closed Sun and Mon

• **EMSWORTH** (Hampshire)
Fat Olives 30 South Street, (01243) 377914. This converted fisherman's terrace cottage, close to the sea, houses a simple restaurant whose motto is 'friendly food, tasty people'. Reporters have enjoyed choices from the three-course menu at £14.50 including a starter of salmon mousse followed by mackerel on a bed of mushrooms and olives. Meaty options include griddled chicken with peppercorn sauce, or pan-fried pork, apples and cider sauce. More adventurous à la carte dishes are poached brill with red wine butter sauce, and duck with kumquat and star anise sauce. Open L and D Tue to Sat.

• **EVERSHOT** (Dorset)
Acorn Inn Fore Street, (01935) 83228. Beamed, four centuries old, and famed as 'The Sow and Acorn' in Thomas Hardy's *Tess of the d'Urbervilles*, this village pub is under the same ownership as The Fox, Corscombe (see England, main entry). Extensive blackboard menus feature a host of dishes, from red mullet with Thai dressing, and pan-fried skate with capers and lime, to smoked chicken with red pepper mayonnaise, and venison casserole with chestnuts. Finish with apple crumble, or chocolate terrine with cappuccino sauce. Sandwiches and traditional pub dishes are also served in the bar. Open all week. Accommodation available.

• **EVESHAM** (Worcester)
Evesham Hotel Coopers Lane, (01386) 765566. The Jenkinson family have been in residence here since 1975 and little seems to change. Menus still have their share of jokey comments, although 'Fresh as a Daisy' specials bring new seasonal treats: cold Cornish lobster with mango and asparagus, for example. Otherwise expect dishes with curious names and long descriptions: Mayle's Delight is slices of roast aubergine with grilled peppers and baked onions; Lamb Neluska consists of grilled cutlets with Chilean red wine and rosemary sauce; while the Bees Knees is a dessert featuring honey ice cream. Lengthy, fascinating wine list. Open all week.

Riverside The Parks, (01386) 446200. Elegant, but homely hotel set high above the River Avon in Evesham Abbey's ancient deer park. Rosemary Willmott uses as much local produce as possible for her regularly changing dinner menus. Her cooking is comforting (mushroom and Parmesan risotto, or eggs from her own hens baked with cream) but also in touch with the trends (seared scallops and sea bass with lime, coriander and baby capers, or rack of lamb with courgette fritters, tomato and basil salsa). Meringues with Chantilly cream or mango ice cream to finish. Closed Sun D and all day Mon.

• **EXETER** Devon

Carved Angel Café 21A Cathedral Yard, (01392) 210303. Facing the Cathedral green, with a pleasingly elegant and welcoming interior, this sister of the Dartmouth Carved Angel Café (see main entry) has not yet quite equalled its sibling's skilful service and cooking. It opens 9 to 5 plus evenings every day for breakfast, morning coffee (in exhilarating varieties), light lunches, teas and dinner. Daily specials complement regular menus offering baked haddock and spinach cannelloni to start, and guinea fowl; Tuscan beef stew and pancetta; or steamed salmon with mushroom and courgette spaghetti to follow. A few wines are listed from £11.95. Open all week.

Galley 41 Fore Street, Topsham, (01392) 876078. Fish cookery with a difference is Paul Da-Costa-Greaves's avowed aim in this converted 300-year-old cottage in a town just outside Exeter. There's no doubting the freshness of the raw materials: mussels with herbs and tomatoes have been outstanding as a starter. Simple dishes tend to work best, but inspiration comes from far and wide. Squid is jazzed up with Szechuan spices, while mahi-mahi is given the balti treatment; otherwise look for grilled brill with herb and lemon butter, or exemplary Brixham sole. Desserts might run to chocolate and Grand Marnier bavarois. Open all week D and Thur to Sun L.

• **FLETCHING** (East Sussex)

Griffin Inn Fletching, (01825) 722890. Children are welcomed at this old inn standing in two acres of gardens with a covered terrace for outdoor dining. The ever-changing ambitious carte offers modern dishes, with a few oriental flourishes, and more Mediterranean influences. Local new season's lamb, organic veal, pheasant, and venison appear in season. Newhaven fish is always featured and Thursday's 'fishtastic' menu might include marinated anchovy salad with feta and pecan nuts, and sushi-grade blue fin tuna with ginger and soy vegetables and green lentils. House wines from £9.80 per bottle are among 12 by the glass in the 90-strong list. Open all week.

• **FLITWICK** (Bedfordshire)

Flitwick Manor Church Road, (01525) 712242. This stately Queen Anne house in expansive grounds complete with a ha-ha and croquet lawn saw the arrival of a new chef in 2001, and early reports have been encouraging. An 'excellent, freshly cooked meal, friendly warm welcome', noted one visitor returning after a ten-year absence. You might begin with ballottine of salmon with salad of cucumber, lemon and vanilla oil, move on to fillet of Angus beef with ragoût of artichokes, wild mushrooms and cep reduction, and finish off with iced prune and Armagnac parfait. Wine prices are 'high'. Closed Sat and Sun D.

• **FOLKESTONE** (Kent)

Pauls 2A Bouverie Road West, (01303) 259697. In addition to its main carte, Pauls bids three clubs for quick-meal-eaters, none requiring membership. The supper club (at £11.95) offers any two starters from the menu (one as a main course with vegetables) plus dessert; the summer lunch club (£5.95) offers lighter food; and the popular lunch club buffet provides six dishes plus coffee (also for £5.95). Starters include mussels and prawns baked in cream, and haggis in filo pastry with whisky cream, while typical main dishes are steak with Stilton butter, or pigeon breasts with wild mushroom sauce. Open all week L and D.

• **FORTON** (Lancashire)

Bay Horse Inn Bay Horse, (01524) 791204. Once the post office in the hamlet of Bay Horse, now a pub-restaurant delivering contemporary food. Soups, such as pea with truffle oil, are 'reliably excellent'. The décor is salmon pink, and *Salmo salar* appears in abundance. Reporters have endorsed salad of seared scallops and smoked salmon with coriander and chilli; and pan-fried sea bass with roast smoked salmon risotto. Away from fish, the 'gradually changing' menu might offer smoked duck with carrot remoulade, balsamic syrup and hazelnut oil, and pineapple crème brûlée. Open Tue to Sun L and D.

El Nido Whinney Brow Lane, (01524) 791254. Early diners get a £10.95 three-course menu of time-honoured restaurant dishes, some with a gentle twist: like rocket leaves and cucumber in the prawn cocktail; tomato with baked egg on spinach; and apricot sour sauce with a bacon joint. The £14.95 menu, served later, offers things like baked mushroom pancakes, or zarzuela de marisco, 'a treasure trove of seafood' in a creamy sauce. The carte also offers gazpacho and paella. Open Sun L and Tue to Sun D.

• **FRESSINGFIELD** (Suffolk)

Fox and Goose Fressingfield, (01379) 586247. A glass of champagne and a saucer of olives in the bar is one way to kick off a meal at this sixteenth-century beamed restaurant. Have a steak sandwich or order from the full menu. Starters of carpaccio of Scotch sirloin, or smoked salmon with toasted muffin, might precede salmon and tiger prawns in Thai broth, or loin of pork with wholegrain mustard sauce and apple fritters. Finish in comforting fashion with Bakewell tart, or rice pudding with raspberry jam. Sunday lunch is a roast, and there are menus for children and vegetarians. Open all week (booking advisable).

• **GEDNEY DYKE** (Lincolnshire)

Chequers Main Street, (01406) 362666. 'An asset to a scattered rural community' is one verdict on the Rattrays' Fenland country pub east of Holbeach. Local ingredients, plenty of fish and some meat from rare breeds flesh out the all-round menu. Reporters have praised chickpea rissoles, and roast cod with scallops ('a distinct success'), while home-baked herb and cheese bread has been deemed 'excellent'. Reasonable wines, real ales and real pub décor. Open all week.

• **GILLAN** (Cornwall)

Tregildry Hotel Gillan, (01326) 231378. 'The real splendours are the views,' observes a reporter. This 'quiet, graciously run' hotel stands high on the cliffs overlooking Falmouth Bay. It feeds its visitors well; dinner menus change daily, but you might find mushroom and sherry soup, or seared scallops with lime and ginger butter to start, and the world tour continues with roast cod with avocado and chilli compote, or breast of duck with spring onion pancakes and Chinese vegetables. To finish, it's back home for West Country cheeses, locally made ice creams or rhubarb trifle. Open all week D only.

• **GRAMPOUND** (Cornwall)

Eastern Promise 1 Moor View, (01726) 883033. 'The promise has been fulfilled!' exclaimed one reporter. China comes to Cornwall in the shape of this lively, often crowded roadside restaurant. Dim sum show up among the long list of appetisers, and the kitchen is fond of fish. Salmon might be stir-fried with black bean sauce, monkfish is cooked with chilli and coriander, squid comes sizzling with ginger and spring onion, while oysters are deep-fried. Alternatively, look for crispy aromatic duck, Szechuan lamb and twice-cooked pork. First-rate very attentive service, with the owner much in evidence. No service charge, no tips accepted. Open Thur to Tue D only.

• **GREAT WHITTINGTON** (Northumberland)

Queens Head Great Whittington, (01434) 672267. Out-of-the-way seventeenth-century village pub, serving twenty-first-century food. 'It can make guinea fowl taste of something, and the lamb's liver is first-rate,' noted a fan from north of the border. Deep-fried black pudding with beetroot relish is a lively-sounding starter, while main courses might encompass honey-glazed chicken on buttered noodles with ginger and marmalade sauce, or herb-crusted cod on tomato fondue. Finish with a liqueur-laced duo of white and dark chocolate mousses. Closed Mon, except bank hols.

• **GREAT YARMOUTH** (Norfolk)

Seafood Restaurant 85 North Quay, (01493) 856009. Enthusiastic reports of the friendly welcome and attentive service in this converted pub are matched by praise for the cooking. The displayed fresh fish can be grilled or poached and might embrace lemon sole with blue cheese sauce, skate with black butter, and turbot with a herb butter sauce that for one reporter was 'a miracle in a ramekin'. Beforehand there are simple luxuries such as cold prawns, or lobster, Loch Fyne oysters, gravadlax, avocado and feta, whitebait, or monkfish in curry sauce. House wines in the long list are £10.95. Closed Sun L, and Sat and Sun D.

• **GUILDFORD** (Surrey)
The Gate 3 Milkhouse Gate, (01483) 576300. The address is a reminder that this restaurant in the old part of town was originally a milking shed. Reporters have endorsed red pepper soup, and Thai salad to start, along with a main course of pork accompanied by 'excellent' potato and onion mash. To finish there's Italian lemon tart, or home-made ice creams with 'interesting flavours'. Dinner is a modern carte, along the lines of pan-fried foie gras with pear and chillies; fillets of red mullet with pak choi plus sweetcorn and coriander salsa; and terrine of summer fruits in red wine jelly on a fruit coulis. Closed Sun and Mon.

• **HARROGATE** (North Yorkshire)
Bettys 1 Parliament Street, (01423) 502746. This is the original branch of the successful mini-chain of tea-shops, with a great line in cakes and pastries, and a menu that extends to sandwiches, soups, and more substantial dishes of the day. It is an ideal venue for weary travellers to re-charge their batteries, and for foreign tourists to get a taste of something traditional. Open all week.

• **HARVINGTON** (Worcestershire)
Mill at Harvington Anchor Lane, (01386) 870688. This converted eighteenth-century malting mill, by the banks of the River Avon, and just outside the village, is now a handsome restaurant-with-rooms. Specialities from the restaurant menu might include warm cheese beignets with tomato salsa, or bouillabaisse to start, then braised lamb shank with lentils and thyme, or fricassee of salmon and mussels. Home-made chocolate brownie ice cream is one possible finale. Less formal meals are served in the Chestnut Tree bar (Mon to Sat), which offers the likes of potted duck with orange and apple chutney, braised rabbit with rice, and seafood pancakes. Open all week.

• **HELSTON** (Cornwall)
Nansloe Manor Meneage Road, (01326) 574691. A long tree-lined driveway through well-manicured grounds leads to the Ridden family's fine-looking Georgian manor. Dinners are keenly priced and the kitchen has global aspirations. You might begin with tempura of red mullet with toasted sesame seed dipping sauce, then move on to crostini of lime-leafed crusted chicken with spiced tapénade, or braised lamb shank with chilli, coriander seeds and lemon grass served with champ. To finish, try tarragon and red berry crème brûlée with lemon polenta biscuit. Open all week D and Mon to Fri bar lunches.

• **HEREFORD** (Herefordshire)
Café @ All Saints All Saints Church, (01432) 370415. As the Café is 'the fund-raising engine' for a medieval church with twentieth-century improvements, 'celebrating human creativity in all its forms' is the message, and it extends to the staff of life baked each day on the premises. Local supplies are at the heart of the daily menus, which might promise anything from Dorothy Goodbody's stout and field mushroom casserole, to Hereford flan with Dunkertons cider. Soups, ploughman's and salads complete the picture, along with organic apple juice, regional beers and home-made lemonade to drink. Closed Sun.

• **HEYTESBURY** (Wiltshire)
Angel High Street, (01985) 840330. This seventeenth-century coaching inn's dining room overlooks a tiny enclosed courtyard where you can dine in summer under a central post topped by a giant cartwheel. The carte is supplemented by three daily specials such as 'rack on black': lamb on black pudding with roasted shallots, garlic and a thyme jus. Other main dishes run from saddle of venison to fillet steak with lambs' kidneys and red onions. Seven wines are served by the

glass, and house wines are £10.50 a bottle. Accommodation available. Open all week.

• **Hockley Heath** (West Midlands)
Nuthurst Grange Nuthurst Grange Lane, (01564) 783972. Staff at this long-established, comfortably furnished country-house hotel cosseted a reporter with 'congenial efficiency and expertise'. New chef Ben Davies's menus range from a two-course express lunch at £12.95 to the £49.50 four-course dinner. Coffee is included, and appreciated 'befores and afters' have been pork satay, cheese balls, and 'minute chocolate cup cakes'. Spinach and nutmeg soup with caviar, and fillet of ling with aubergine caviar and ouzo dressing are in the top menus, while chicken breast with pearl barley is a slightly simpler notion. Closed Sat L.

• **Houghton Conquest**
(Bedfordshire)
Knife & Cleaver The Grove, (01234) 740387. A few miles south of Bedford and more restaurant than pub, the Knife & Cleaver offers a daily choice of fish from the market, which might include Loch Fyne oysters, lobsters, and grilled fillets of sea bass served with wild mushrooms and pesto vinaigrette. Otherwise expect terrine of guinea fowl and summer vegetables, or ribeye steak with sun-dried tomato and black olive butter, plus desserts like lemon and ground almond tart, or crème brûlée with apricots. There's a pleasant terrace with a fountain and orchard garden. Closed Sat L and Sun D.

• **Hovingham** (North Yorkshire)
Worsley Arms Hovingham, (01653) 628234. Master sommelier and co-owner Anthony Finn's passion is wine, and on his list you will find 70 (many below £20) starting from £11.50. Traditional fare supports them well. Starters take in salmon fishcake with tomato and chive butter sauce, or wild mushroom and horseradish risotto with wilted spinach, followed perhaps by braised chicken with leeks, wild mushroom and truffle mash, or pan-roast monkfish with braised fennel, crispy local ham and red wine sauce. But one Worsley Arms special – pressed ham hock and root vegetable terrine with fried quail's egg and chutney – might challenge wine-matchers. Open all week.

• **Ilkley** (West Yorkshire)
Bettys 34 The Grove, (01943) 608029. There is more to Bettys than just tea and cakes, but don't let that stop you from popping in for a brew and a pastry. Like the sister restaurants in the mini-chain (see Round-up entries in Harrogate, Northallerton and York), the menu extends to traditional soups and sandwiches, joined by slightly more ambitious specials of the day. It may not reach great culinary heights, but the homely style offers comfort to locals and travellers alike. Open all week.

• **Ipswich** (Suffolk)
Il Punto Neptune Quay, (01473) 289748. A 'floating brasserie' aboard a 102-year-old former Belgian gunboat and hospital ship, moored next to the Old Customs House. Light dishes are served in the bar on the upper deck, while varnished floorboards and brass railings set the mood in the main restaurant. Dishes have a French accent: 'unctuous' gâteau of duck foie gras with toasted brioche, grilled fillet of beef with mixed peppercorn sauce, and slow-cooked shank of lamb in Mâcon have all impressed. Desserts might include iced pistachio and almond nougat with redcurrant coulis. Open Mon to Fri L and Mon to Sat D.

Scott's Brasserie 4A Orwell Place, (01473) 230254. This brasserie on three levels, close to the town centre, gets the ball rolling with Caesar salad topped with smoked salmon, or chicken and vegetable parfait en croûte, before main courses like confit of Barbary duck on sauté baby leeks with Madeira jus, or grilled fillet of sea bass with warm potato and watercress salad. The printed menu is fleshed out with a few specials, such as baked local cod fillet on puttanesca sauce. Desserts might include tarte Tatin with clotted cream, or bread-and-butter pudding with whisky and caramel sauce. The modest wine list is fairly priced. Closed Sat L and all day Sun.

• **Kibworth Beauchamp** (Leicestershire)
Firenze 9 Station Street, (0116) 2796260. 'Traditional Italian dishes often given a modern twist' sums up the cooking at Sarah and Lino Poli's village restaurant. The décor has a sunny aspect, with Florentine pictures on the walls, and the mood is cheery. Menus might call into play vitello tonnata (veal with tuna); red mullet with basil; and roast quail with sage and garlic. Desserts include hot chocolate pudding, and there's vin santo with cantuccini biscuits. One-plate lunches for £10 offer a chance to try out new dishes. 'Reasonably priced', mostly Italian wines. Open Tue to Fri L and Tue to Sat D.

• **King's Lynn** (Norfolk)
Riverside King's Lynn Arts Centre, (01553) 773134. The views over the River Ouse from the first-floor restaurant are a big attraction at this 500-year-old timbered building that houses the Arts Centre. Light lunch dishes (lamb and apricot casserole) are good value, while the dinner menu expands the theme of honest, unflashy cooking. Fish gets a good billing: you might kick off with home-made lobster soup, or penne with smoked haddock and bacon, before braised fillet of sea bass with fennel sauce, or confit of duck with mash and a red wine and lime sauce. Open Mon to Sat L and D.

• **Kintbury** (Berkshire)
Dundas Arms 53 Station Road, (01488) 658263. Famed for its lovely setting on a little island by the River Kennet, the canal, and for David Dalzell-Piper's mighty 200-strong wine list. He has been at the tiller of this pub-restaurant for more than 30 years and continues to steer a course between traditionalism and fashion. There's spiced potted shrimps and honey-roast ham hock with grain mustard sauce on the one hand; grilled scallops with black pasta and saffron, or roast duck breast with lemon grass on the other. Round things off with apricot crème brûlée, or treacle tart. Closed all Sun and Mon D.

• **Leeds** (West Yorkshire)
Brio 40 Great George Street, (0113) 246 5225. This appropriately named busy bistro speedily serves lively food from its Italian menu, with antipasti such as involtino di granchio (spring roll filled with spider crab and vegetables), or smoked duck salad. Pasta takes in vegetarian temptations such as fussili with chargrilled zucchini and artichokes, while carnivores appreciate tortiglioni alla salsciccia in a ragù of sausage with black olives, red onions and tomato. 'Secondi piatti' run to rack of lamb with minted poached pear, and grilled steak with fruit mostarda di Cremona. There are dishes of the day too. Closed Sun.
Bryans 9 Weetwood Lane, (0113) 278 5679. They've been dispensing incomparable fish and chips, cooked in beef dripping, since John Bryan set up shop in 1934. Eat in or take away from a menu that promises haddock (choose your own size), plaice, hake and halibut with a few detours for Thai fishcakes or grilled Cajun chicken. There are business lunches, senior citizen special deals, and occasional Jazz evenings on Saturdays. Drink tea or champagne. A separate bistro menu casts its net far and wide for things like seafood and mango salad with noodles, vegetable couscous, and grilled tuna with black peppercorns. Open all week.
Cactus Lounge St Peter's Square, (0113) 243 6553. This is not a bar but a Mexican restaurant, artfully sited behind the Leeds Playhouse and alongside the Yorkshire Dance Studio and Leeds College of Music. A two-course lunch is £5.95 and the pre-theatre special offers two courses plus a half-bottle of wine for £9.95. Nachos may be standard, special or de luxe, while burritos, chimichangas, tostadas and enchiladas are some of the tortilla variations which can be filled or topped with chicken, beef, spiced pork, cheese or bean stew with mushrooms. A wide choice of bottled beers includes Cuban, while low-priced, mainly New World wines start at £8.45. Closed Sat L.
Mill Race 2–4 Commercial Road, (0113) 275 7555. Modern-looking organic restaurant in a parade of shops some three miles north of Leeds' city centre. Tables

are beech, and the lights are fashioned from salvaged wood and metal. The fixed-price menu changes daily, the carte every couple of months. Early reports have praised olive tapénade with pan-fried garlic bread, and smoked salmon blinis with fennel and crème fraîche; also fricassee of chicken and sun-dried tomatoes with Gruyère crust and herbed lentils, plus an 'extremely rich' brown bread and chocolate pudding with cinnamon ice cream. Coffee is served in the upstairs lounge. Totally organic wine list. Open Tue to Sat. More reports, please.

Olive Tree Oaklands, (0113) 256 9283. A cookery slot on Cypriot TV is George Psarias' latest claim to fame. His high-profile restaurant a few miles from Leeds city centre is rarely out of the news, and reporters continue to sing its praises. The Greek-Cypriot food 'gets better and better', thanks largely to good-quality ingredients (locally sourced lamb for kleftiko and moussaka, for example), and the meze is as popular as ever. Service is 'most attentive'. Bazouki dancing on Friday and Saturday night. Open all week.

Paris Calverley Lane, Rodley, (0113) 258 1885. This sister restaurant to Leodis (see main entry, Leeds) offers a long à la carte menu, as well as lunch and early-bird deals (the most expensive of which is £15.95 for three courses including wine). The latter are more conservative than the carte, which is modern and inventive without going to extremes. Start perhaps with beef and ale broth with horseradish dumplings, and follow with lemon sole stuffed with crab, ginger and lemon grass, or charred tuna with samphire, shallots and saffron oil. The 150 modestly priced wines start at £10.95. Closed Sat L.

• **LEYBURN** (North Yorkshire)

Sandpiper Inn Market Place, (01969) 622206. Reputedly the town's oldest pub, this is a substantial stone-built house in the market square. Jonathan Harrison is the chef and Jo Harrison leads 'attentive and cheerful' service of food listed on blackboard menus, including daily specials. Recommendations have included game terrine, white bean and celeriac soup with truffle oil, 'perfectly cooked' crispy duck with fried potatoes and oriental sauce, and a special starter of roast salmon with cream and chives sauce. A reporter's 'wonderfully creamy-custardy' crème brulée 'deserved a prize'. Accommodation is available in two rooms, and the pretty garden is an attraction in fine weather. Open Tue to Sun L and D.

• **LICHFIELD** (Staffordshire)

Chandlers Corn Exchange, (01543) 416 688. Up-to-the-minute brasserie cooking in a converted Victorian corn exchange, complete with a circular gallery and stained-glass windows. Menus fizz with modern ideas garnered from around the globe: haddock risotto, poached egg and Parmesan crisps; green tomato tarte Tatin; and chargrilled pork cutlet with Dijon hash, apple and ginger are typical. Daily fish specials show up on the blackboard, while set lunch and supper menus bring further delights in the shape of seared salmon with pak choi and coriander; and bread-and-butter pudding with custard sauce. Open all week.

• **LITTLE ECCLESTON** (Lancashire)

The Smithy Cartford Lane, (01995) 670485. The Gibson family's converted Victorian smithy stands in a village south of Preston, close to the M6. International cooking, with some North Country touches and a few modern flourishes, is the style. Expect dishes such as Caesar salad, herb-crusted cod with leek and watercress sauce, duck with Grand Marnier sauce, and fruit pancakes with glazed fruit. Early-evening menus (Tue to Fri 5.30 to 7) offer excellent value, with reduced prices for children. Open Tue to Sat D, also Sun L.

• **LOWER ODDINGTON** (Gloucestershire)

Fox Inn Lower Oddington, (01451) 870555. Quintessential, but sympathetically extended Cotswold stone pub with several eating areas and lawns beyond. Menus use local and seasonal produce in dishes such as goats' cheese and roasted pepper tart; salmon fishcakes with chive cream sauce; and compote of rhubarb with crème fraîche. Blackboard specials extend the range to seared scallops with tomato vinaigrette; and roast whole sea bass with creamed leeks. Round off with, say, plum and frangipane tart. Owners Kirk and Sally Ritchie (ex-Lygon Arms, Broadway) keep a good wine cellar. Open all week. Accommodation available.

• **LUDLOW** (Shropshire)

Courtyard 2 Quality Square, (01584) 878080. As we go to press this straightforward little place is open for lunch only (Mon to Sat), when it offers an à la carte list of dishes running from soups at £2.50 (courgette and rosemary, perhaps, or butternut squash, ginger and coconut), via Stilton and port pâté, or baked crab with lime and ginger, to warm marinated duck breast salad. Pickles, pastries and cakes are home-made, salads and herbs often home-grown or – in the case of nettles, wild garlic and elderflowers – harvested from local hedgerows. House wines are £9.50, and 25 more are fairly priced.

• **MAIDEN NEWTON** (Dorset)

Le Petit Canard Dorchester Road, (01300) 320536. There is no smoking in this pretty, white-fronted cottage restaurant whose £23.50 menu lists five choices at each three courses. Tomato and fennel broth with halibut, hake and prawns, or grilled goats' cheese salad with toasted pine nuts might precede cod fillet with pesto rarebit crust and roasted plum tomatoes, or cannon of lamb on rosemary mash with a red wine reduction. To finish, consider hot steamed apple sponge with vanilla sauce and cinnamon ice cream, passion fruit crème brûlée, or a platter of British cheeses. Open Tue to Sat D and every third Sun for L.

• **MANCHESTER** (Greater Manchester)

Market Restaurant 104 High Street, (0161) 834 3743. 'All the old virtues' remain at this long-serving restaurant just off Piccadilly. Candles in wine bottles, green wicker chairs, and sewing machine tables sum up the décor. The menu takes in coarse chicken liver paté with spicy apricot chutney, alongside rissois (crisp Portuguese prawn pasties served with red pepper sauce). Also noteworthy this year is duck with spicy plum sauce. Otherwise, the bread remains 'very good', puddings maintain their high reputation, beers are 'excellent', and there are some decent wines.

Palmiro 197 Upper Chorlton Road, (0161) 860 7330. The striking modern look and the loud taped Italian music make this twenty-first-century trattoria a place for the young at heart. It rises above standard 'Britalian' in its careful, concerned service, and in its short menu, with just half a dozen each of imaginative starters and main dishes, and no reliance on pasta. The kitchen has produced deep-fried risotto with mozzarella and a fresh tomato and chilli salsa, and pork medallions with bilberry sauce and a sprig of thyme as main courses. Over 40 Italian wines, from £10, make an interesting list. Open Tue to Sun D only, Sun brunch only.

Pearl City 33 George Street, (0161) 228 7683. Although it is a Cantonese restaurant, it also offers half a dozen Szechuan 'spicy hot' or 'fairly hot' dishes, as well as Cantonese barbecued meats, and chef's specials on request. Thirty dim sum are available even in the evening. The main menu lists few surprises, but set meals include Combination Lobster Banquet, £29.50 per head (minimum two people) that takes in soup, hors d'oeuvres, baked lobster with ginger and spring onion, aromatic crispy duck, plus a choice of decent main dishes. Open all week.

Zinc Bar & Grill Unit 12A, (0870) 333 4333. The northern outpost of the Conran West End original (see Round-up entry, London) is set in the rejuvenated Corn Exchange, now the Triangle Centre. The cooking is 'rough-and-ready, but real,' noted one correspondent. It's also relaxed and flexible, so you can come in for a drink or a full meal. Fish figures strongly, although reporters have mentioned Turkish bread with a trio of dips, Goliath-sized brochette of yoghurt-marinated lamb with couscous, and confit of duck ('with crisp skin and lubricated flesh') on globe artichoke mash. Good-value wine list with many by the glass. Open all week.

• **MELMERBY** (Cumbria)
Village Bakery Melmerby, (01768) 881515. Everything here is organic. They bake their own bread, of course, using the UK's allegedly first computer-controlled wood-fired oven. Their breakfast porridge can be raspberry, or apple and cinnamon, and full fried breakfasts include one for vegetarians. Pasties, quiche and sandwiches are served from 11 to 4.30, while lunch includes mushroom pâté, potato pie, pork with ginger beer sauce, and sea bass in tomato sauce. Finish with home-made ice cream, fruit pie or fool, and drink organic beer, cider or wine from £8.50. Open all week for breakfast and lunch.

• **MERLEY** (Dorset)
Les Bouviers Oakley Hill, (01202) 889555. This restaurant's ambitions can be measured by the encyclopaedic wine list with prices ranging from £11 per bottle to £5,400 for the double magnum of Dom Pérignon 1993. Menus run from a £9.95 two-course lunch to the £49 menu surprise. Although service has come in for criticism, presentation of food is a strong point, and coming in for praise have been dishes such as 'juicy' scallops with ginger and chives served with beans shoots, a main course of 'tender' chargrilled lamb cutlets, and, for dessert, a fine cardamom and orange crème brûlée. Or you might try cream of celery soup topped with basil oil, followed by duck served on carrot fettuccini encircled by Parma ham and capers, and then home-made ice cream or sorbet. Closed all day Mon, Sat L and Sun D.

• **MOUSEHOLE** (Cornwall)
Cornish Range Chapel Street, (01736) 731488. The art collection continues to grow at Andrew Ryan's restaurant in a Cornish harbourside village. Menus draw on the local catch for dressed Newlyn crab with guacamole and pickled cucumber salad, medallions of monkfish with king prawns served with vine tomato and black olive salsa, or pan-fried whole lemon sole. Non-piscine alternatives might be crispy duck won tons, spinach and Ricotta roulade, or chargrilled local fillet steak. Finish with raspberry brûlée, or lemon tart. There are three letting rooms. Open all week D. Closed Jan and Mon, Tue and Wed in winter.

• **NEWARK** (Nottinghamshire)
Café Bleu 14 Castle Gate, (01636) 610141. Live music (anything from jazz to gypsy reels) plays most evenings, vibrant modern canvases line the 'artistically distressed' walls, and contemporary flower arrangements set the mood. This buzzy place, close to the castle ruins, is brasserie by day and restaurant by night. Lunchtime visitors have approved of modern Anglo-European offerings such as seared hand-dived scallops with saffron linguine, roast aubergine and sauce vierge, and warm blueberry tart with Mascarpone and candied lemon. Dinner has brought tuna loin on a bed of couscous, and braised beef with Savoy cabbage on a rösti with morels. Closed Sun D.

• **NEWCASTLE UPON TYNE** (Tyne & Wear)
Leela's 20 Dean Street, (0191) 230 1261. Leela Paul's presence dominates proceedings in this family-run restaurant. The cooking focuses on her native Kerala: the menu is part vegetarian, part meat and part fish. Sauces and chutneys are 'intensely flavoured' and what is delivered to the plate has 'a lightness of touch'. Packavadas (vegetables in herb batter with mint dipping sauce) have been commended, likewise chat poori and creamy vegetable papas with appam (a kind of 'Asian crumpet'). Meaty alternatives might be batham kozhi (marinated chicken in almond sauce garnished with orange slices), or kerala mean (baked trout fillet with tomato and tamarind sauce). Closed Sun.

• **NEWENT** (Gloucestershire)
Three Choirs Restaurant Newent, (01531) 890223. The full output of the nearby Three Choirs vineyard is available at this pleasing restaurant-with-rooms, although reporters have been surprised by the high prices by the glass. On the food front everything is well, with dishes such as twice-baked cheese soufflé, fillets of red

mullet with garlic mash and basil dressing, and elderflower brûlée on offer. Chef Tony Warburton's one-day cookery courses are a sideline. Closed Sun D and all day Mon.

• **NEWMILLERDAM** (West Yorkshire)
On the Edge Newmillerdam, (01924) 253310. This stone cottage, 'on the edge' of Newmillerdam Country Park (a local reservoir) and simply decorated in a café-style with college artwork on the walls, offers a fairly short menu bolstered by blackboard specials. These might feature Roquefort and pear salad with grapes and spiced pecans, then sauté red snapper with creamy tarragon sauce on vegetable couscous, before desserts such as blueberry bread-and-butter pudding with custard. Fixed-price lunch and early-evening menus are a fair deal. Closed Sat L.

• **NORTHALLERTON** (North Yorkshire)
Bettys 188 High Street, (01609) 775154. Bettys may not reach great culinary heights, but the homely style offers comfort to locals and travellers alike. Tea, cakes, sandwiches and soup are the mainstay of the menu, joined by slightly more ambitious specials of the day. The sister restaurants in this mini-chain (see Round-up entries in Harrogate, Ilkley and York), spread the simple philosophy throughout Yorkshire. Open all week.

• **NORTH BOVEY** (Devon)
Blackaller Hotel North Bovey, (01647) 440322. Beautiful gardens and countryside surround this seventeenth-century converted woollen mill, and the friendly welcome from the proprietors is another attraction. The dinner menu, changed daily, is £24 for four courses and coffee. Starters might include warm fennel, onion and cheese tart, and smoked salmon parcels enclosing fresh salmon and prawn mousse. Next comes chilled avocado soup or mango sorbet before perhaps grilled brochette of monkfish and salmon on couscous, or honey and soy marinated Gressingham duck breast. Finish with caramelised banana, chocolate chip meringue cake, or West Country cheeses. Open Tue to Sat D only.

• **NORTON** (Wiltshire)
Vine Tree Foxley Road, Norton, (01666) 837654. In rolling Cotswold country, some belonging to the pub, this former mill house offers a variety of drinking and eating spaces in colourfully decorated open-plan ground and first floors. The light from many big, fat candles adds to the relaxed ambience, and discreetly illuminates nooks and crannies, as well as tables, and their occupants. Daily specials supplement a long, ambitious, à la carte menu of modern British cuisine including the chef's unusual vegetable signature dish of pommes ecrassé (crushed potatoes). House wines are from £9.45, with eight of the 30 bottles listed also offered by the glass. Open all week.

• **NORWICH** (Norfolk)
The Aquarium 22 Tombland, (01603) 630090. Located on the edge of a quay, the restaurant overlooks a dockful of boats, and if you eat on the terrace, 'yachts graze past your table.' The new chef's menu contains some complicated notions, including perhaps warm chive fritters layered with aubergine purée, sliced Brie and mushroom; or shellfish consommé with crab filled won tons and spring onion. Chicken pastry parcels are filled with hazelnut and sage stuffing, and an aromatic dessert is lemon and cardamom parfait with orange sauce. Open Mon to Sat L and D.

By Appointment 25–29 St Georges Street, (01603) 630730. A gilt-framed blackboard displays the menu in this pink, sixteenth-century restaurant-with-rooms. Meals are served in several comfortable dining rooms with antiques and theatrical drapes. A typical dinner might begin with parsnip and lemon soup, or home-smoked duck breast with mango and Chinese leaf coleslaw, before main courses of salmon with a red onion confit crust served on a bed of kale, or roast loin of lamb with sun-dried tomato and basil stuffing. Desserts range from steamed lemon and honey sponge pudding to exotic fruit, ginger and cardamom sorbet. Open Tue to Sat D only.

• **NOTTINGHAM** (Nottinghamshire)
Hotel Des Clos Old Lenton Lane, (0115) 986 6566. The Ralley family, who took over in 1999, have resurrected this previously run-down small 'country house' hotel on the bank of the Trent, easily reached from the city centre. There is a four-course set dinner at £35 and a menu dégustation of seven small courses at £37.50. Some dishes verge on the over-elaborate, but home-made bread, oatcakes, and tiramisù are minor pleasures that indicate the kitchen's high standards. Lunch might start with braised oxtail, followed by a risotto of ceps, finishing with a ravioli of pineapple with a rhubarb confit. A long, splendid wine list includes house selections from £11. More reports please. Open Mon to Fri L and Mon to Sat D.

• **ODIHAM** (Hampshire)
Grapevine 121 High Street, (01256) 701122. This attractive high street bistro is noted for its excellent-value fixed-price lunches and early-evening menus. The full repertoire offers a clutch of modern-sounding European dishes: crostini of charred asparagus with black olive and aubergine salsa; roast fillets of sea bass with saffron potato, vanilla and crab cream; pot-roast rabbit with pancetta, tarragon and Puy lentils. As a finale, try something showy like marbled sorbet terrine with summer berries and caramel spears, or white chocolate mousse with strawberry and champagne compote. A delicatessen is attached. Closed Sat L and all day Sun.

• **ORFORD** (Suffolk)
Butley-Orford Oysterage Market Hill, (01394) 450277. Locally bred oysters and smoked fish from the attached smokehouse are the attractions at this long-running, no-frills Suffolk venue. Cooked dishes aren't a strength, but smoked salmon out of the top drawer, 'superlative' hot-smoked sardines with a honey and mustard dressing, and smoked eel on toast save the day. Expect crowds and queues during the Aldeburgh Festival and summer. Open all week.

• **OXFORD** (Oxfordshire)
Fishers 36–38 St Clements Street, (01865) 243003. 'A supporter of the RNLI and sustainable fishing,' declares a note on the menu, suggesting that this restaurant really does live up to its name. Menus follow the market, and the choice is wide: haddock and chips shares the bill with roast red snapper with smoked salmon, spinach and balsamic dressing. Oysters are Irish, lobsters Scottish. Meat eaters might be offered roast Barbary duck breast with orange butter sauce, and vegetarians could opt for an Italian omelette with roasted vegetables. Useful for pre-theatre meals. Closed Mon L

• **PENRITH** (Cumbria)
A Bit on the Side Brunswick Square, (01768) 892526. This is a useful destination in a notable Lakeland market town. Starters on the shortish menu might feature leek and potato soup with truffle oil, or smoked chicken with onion pickle and mixed leaves, while main courses could range from pan-fried salmon with sweet potato purée, asparagus, pak choi and basil butter, to chargrilled chicken breast with grilled bacon and wild mushroom sauce. A 'Grand Bit on the Side' is a selection of puddings, or else try cherry and brandy flan with raspberry sauce and peach sorbet. Open Tue to Sat D only.

• **POLPERRO** (Cornwall)
Kitchen The Coombes, (01503) 272780. In this simple, informal, rather cramped restaurant the hanging sign 'beware of the cook' at the kitchen entrance may be needed by staff, but not by customers who admire his cosmopolitan ways of preparing good local ingredients, particularly fish. Confit of duck with Chinese-style salad garnish and plum sauce was 'a mixture of cuisines that worked well'. Mussels with cider and saffron, and chargrilled fillet steak with Exmoor blue cheese sauce were other successes. International influences extend to desserts which include Turkish delight ice cream with its 'instantly recognizable flavour'. Opening hours vary; phone to check.

• **Richmond** (Surrey)

Canyon The Tow Path, (020) 8948 2944. A mid-summer day's dream is a terrace table outside this riverside restaurant with a buzzy Californian décor. The brunch menu runs past expected English and American breakfast dishes to soft taco wrap of scrambled eggs with spicy peppers and soured cream, and on to roasts with traditional trimmings. The dinner carte may offer poached langoustines or sweet chilli chicken, followed by Cajun spiced red bream, seared lamb steak, or sesame crusted pork fillet. Wines are fully priced, few under £20, with many Californian. House wines are £12. Open Mon to Fri L, Sat and Sun brunch and all week D.

Ocean 100 Kew Road, (020) 8948 8008. All shades of aquatic blue, plus 'illuminated alcoves containing bottles of tomato ketchup', set the tone in this visually impressive newcomer. A plate of mixed starters has produced a triangular royal blue (of course) dish with 'interesting' sushi, a spring roll, top-notch king prawn tempura, and breaded squid rings. Main courses might range from seared Thai-spiced sea bass with lemon grass and coriander, to roast cod with mash and roast parsnips. A short, well-chosen wine list provides the back-up. Service is 'chatty, informed and welcoming'. Open Mon to Sat D only. More reports, please.

Petersham Hotel, Nightingales Nightingale Lane, (020) 8940 7471. The hotel is a flamboyant Victorian mansion with a spectacular Thames-side setting ('one of the loveliest sights in London'), and its restaurant, Nightingales, is beginning to find its feet. Chef Andy Johns takes a modern view of things, and among dishes commended by reporters is one featuring a single roast scallop topped with caviar on strips of leek, and another of juniper and herb-crusted loin of venison on fondant potato. To finish, caramelised lemon rice pudding with a skewer of marinated fruits has also found favour. Closed Sun D, except for residents.

• **Rock** (Cornwall)

Alwyn's Pavilion Rock, (01208) 862 622. Converted shop housing a bistro-style restaurant where Alwyn Evans cooks and wife Jenny is out front. The bedrock of the menu is classic French – snails, carre d'agneau ('a masterpiece'), chicken with tarragon – but the real interest is the daily blackboard, where fish comes into its own. Dover sole with anchovy butter has been grilled to perfection, and the kitchen also tries its hand at monkfish niçoise and turbot with sun-dried tomatoes and thyme. Portions are extremely generous, puddings are rich: Bakewell tart, kiwi Pavlova, brioche bread-and-butter pudding. Open Mon to Sat D only.

• **Rockbeare** (Devon)

Jack in the Green London Road, (01404) 822240. This well-established gastro-pub some five miles from Exeter is close enough to the M5 to make it a useful stop for motorway travellers. Eat in the bar from a menu that runs all the way from braised faggots to deep-fried prawns with plum sauce. From the fixed-price restaurant menus, reporters have endorsed 'very pleasant' salad of smoked eel with pancetta, duck breast with apricot and ginger sauce, and chicken with West Country cider risotto. Sweets include treacle tart with clotted cream: 'one of the nicest I've had for a while,' noted a traveller in a hurry along the old A30. Good real ales and an impressive choice of wines. Open all week.

• **Roydhouse** (West Yorkshire)

Three Acres Inn Roydhouse, (01484) 602606. It's a big place, this restaurant, hotel and food shop in an over-sized coaching inn, and so are the portions. The menu takes inspiration from far and wide, offering crispy Japanese duck breast, stir-fried monk fish with peppers and pak choi, and fresh Cornish fish. Local items in the £17.95 lunch are Yorkshire cheeses, and Yorkshire pudding with onion gravy (and that's a starter). The fairly priced, 80-strong wine list kicks off with house wines at £10.95. Open all week.

• **SAFFRON WALDEN** (Essex)
Old Hoops 15 King Street, (01799) 522813. Ray and Sue Morrison's oak-beamed first-floor restaurant stands at the heart of historic Saffron Walden. Set lunches remain outstanding value. In the evening set dinner competes with a more ambitious carte that may list mussel and watercress soup, poached halibut with caper and herb sauce, confit of duck on red cabbage, and classic fillet steak with wild mushrooms flamed in brandy. Kentish cherry tart with hot lemon sauce, or chocolate and Seville orange mousse round off proceedings. Closed Sun and Mon.

• **ST ALBANS** (Hertfordshire)
Sukiyaki 6 Spencer Street, (01727) 865009. Just off the market place, this very Japanese little place, looking like a teahouse, has calligraphy on the walls, carefully arranged plants, and quiet, soothing background koto music. Praise for not offering raw fish comes from an inspector, not because he doesn't like it, but because they can't guarantee the absolute freshness of the available fish. He added skewers of chicken yakitori, and grilled gyoza, to the beef shoga lunch (served on a black lacquered tray), which also included 'good domestic-style' miso soup. Green tea is free; otherwise it's beer or saké. Open Tue to Sat L and D.

• **SEAVIEW** (Isle of Wight)
Seaview Hotel High Street, (01983) 612711. This 'truly excellent small hotel' has been cruising along with Nick and Nicky Hayward at the helm since 1980. Two restaurants – one with crisp linen, flowers and clocks, the other boasting a nautical theme – both make good use of ingredients judiciously sourced from the island. 'We had an absolutely stunning meal,' raved one reporter, who mentioned fresh crab salad, scallops, roasted cod, roast spring lamb, plus superb vegetables and puddings. The wine list is 'quite outstanding' and staff are 'charming and helpful'. Closed Sun D (exc bank hols).

• **SHEFFIELD** (South Yorkshire)
Greenhead House 84 Burncross Road, (0114) 246 9004. Small-scale, family-run enterprise with a cottagey feel and limited opening times. Four-course dinner menus are priced according to the main course, and the repertoire is ever-changing. Proceedings kick off with, say, risotto of spring vegetables, or lobster and salmon terrine, before perhaps cold asparagus with tarragon dressing, or a sorbet. Centrepieces range from fillets of sea bass with fennel bubble and squeak, to noisettes of lamb with ratatouille. To finish, maybe choose a plate of chocolate puddings or cheese. Light lunches available. Open Thur and Fri L, Wed to Sat D.
Mediterranean 271 Sharrowvale Road, (0114) 266 1069. Med by name and Med by nature, this converted shop away from the city centre covers a lot of gastronomic ground in a small space. Zarzuela (a classic fish stew) has a Spanish accent, while Italy might be represented by whole roast sea bass with pancetta, olive oil and thyme, or chargrilled salmon with pesto, while North Africa shows up in spicy merguez sausages, or Moroccan chicken with cinnamon, ginger and honey on couscous. Start with creamy clam chowder and finish with sticky baklava. Closed Sun.

• **SHEPTON MALLET** (Somerset)
Blostin's 29 Waterloo Road, (01749) 343648. 'Gone are the Laura Ashley wallpaper and brown tablecloths, in come terracotta rag rolled walls and gold ceilings,' say Nick and Lynne Reed. Their long-established restaurant has a faithful following, so menus don't change much, although seasonal specials add variety. Reporters have praised the fish soup with 'all the trimmings' and salmon fishcakes with prawn, celery and apple salad. Beef is 'well hung' and 'first-class' venison steaks are served with a 'pungent' jus. There's 'admirable' treacle tart or fresh figs to finish. Open Tue to Sat D only.

• **SINNINGTON** (North Yorkshire)
Fox and Hounds Sinnington, (01751) 431577. This is still a local pub with a comfortable, no-smoking restaurant. The long à la carte menu ranges from the simplicity of steak or mixed grill with chips to such 'now' dishes as linguine with

squid, smoked mussels and a basil and dill cream; grilled lemon sole with orange and fennel seed butter; or ostrich fillet on rosemary mash with mushrooms and bacon. Traditionally healthy Yorkshire appetites will enjoy the generous portions. Open all week.

• **SOUTHALL** (Greater London)
Gifto's Lahore Karahi 162–164 The Broadway, (020) 8574 8602. This Pakistani restaurant stands out among the throng on the Broadway, and has now been completely refurbished. The menu, however, is unchanged, delivering skewered tikkas and kebabs barbecued on charcoal, and tandoori specials cooked in the karahi. The list also extends to tawa specials cooked on hot plates, conventional curries, as well as bhel puri and other vegetarian chaat snacks. Service is fast and friendly, and you are welcome to take your own drinks. Open all week.

• **STANDLAKE** (Oxfordshire)
Bell 21 High Street, (01865) 300784. This pub in the centre of the village has a handkerchief of lawn outside, and a pleasant interior with bright modern foodie prints and decorative plates. Ingredients used in the restaurant are of good quality: Scottish mussels with leeks, bacon, garlic, wine and cream; home-made duck confit; or chargrilled lamb leg steak marinated with lemon, garlic and thyme with baba ganoush. In a short list house wines are £9.95; only two others exceed £16. Restaurant open Tue to Sat D and Sun L.

• **STOKE HOLY CROSS** (Norfolk)
Wildebeest Arms 82–86 Norwich Road, (01508) 492497. 'Our best local eatery,' enthused a reporter from the Norwich area. African spears, masks and hanging carpets define the mood in the open-plan dining room, although the menu stays with the Anglo-French and modern Mediterranean repertoire. New chef Daniel Smith came from Morston Hall (see main entry, Morston) and his cooking has prompted praise. Seared tuna with wild rocket and sauce antiboise is a typical starter; while mains range from pesto-baked chicken with goats' cheese mash to herb-crusted best end of lamb with fondant potatoes and niçoise jus. Finish with 'excellent' lemon tart. Open all week.

• **STRATFORD UPON AVON** (Warwickshire)
Desports 13–14 Meer Street, (01789) 269304. In this half-timbered Elizabethan first-floor dining room the modern European menu is surely unique. Most dishes are dual-priced, small portions less than half the price of full ones. The four sections, each offering three dishes, are 'from the earth' (vegetarian options: perhaps cashew nut and herb risotto), 'from the land' (meat, such as home-tea-smoked and confit of duck); and 'from the sea' (garlic grilled brill with stuffed squid, for example). And, tempting fate, one reporter confirmed that pot au chocolat with Cointreau and nutmeg ice cream did indeed come 'from Heaven'. Bourgency house wines are £10.50. Closed Sun and Mon.
Margaux 6 Union Street, (01789) 269106. This ground- and first-floor town bistro dramatically uses deep blue paint against dark wood panelling and furniture, while owner Maggie adds to the cheerful ambience. The new chef's à la carte menu takes in exotic colours too, as in pot roast belly pork with Basmati and guava on macadamia nut coulis, but simpler starters have included mackerel fillet with piccalilli. Main courses, such as red snapper fillet with scallop and prawn won ton, are equally imaginative. Short, well-varied, fairly priced wine list, with house selections £11.75. Closed Sun and Mon.

• **SUDBURY** (Suffolk)
Brasserie Four Seven 47 Gainsborough Street, (01787) 374298. Next to the Gainsborough house and museum in the town centre, the smoke-free restaurant has a European menu, apart from perhaps prawn tempura with hoi sin sauce. More typical are chicken liver pâté with orange and redcurrant sauce; baked cod with leeks; and confit of lamb with rosemary sauce. To wind things up are pear and almond tart, or perhaps roast bananas.

Three courses are priced at £15.50, and the good value is underlined by the short list of wines from £7.95, with only two exceeding £15. Open Tue to Sun L and D.

• **SWANAGE** (Dorset)
Cauldron Bistro 5 High Street, (01929) 422671. Terry Flenley's proud boast is that he has cooked in his bistro every day since it opened in 1990. Local fish – bought in daily – is the star turn, and specials are handwritten on cards: steamed mussels; mackerel with lemon, garlic and chips; fillet of brill with olive oil, capers and anchovies. Haunch of roe deer might be chargrilled, while king scallops are given the wok treatment and, if you want to splash out, £30 will buy you 30 grams of sevruga caviar and a shot of iced vodka. Open Thur to Sun L, Tue to Sun D.

• **TADCASTER** (North Yorkshire)
Hazlewood Castle Paradise Lane, (01937) 535353. The castle appears in the Domesday Book. Its menu of 'cuisine fabriqué en Angleterre' asks diners to 'ne fumer pas', then retreats to English, offering, say, 'posh fried free range egg with luxury caviar and walnut cream (ideal for bread dunking)' to start; main courses of 'braised dinky sexy vegetables with mushroom scented pasta', and 'slither of confited salmon with crisp leeks and a groovy blue potato and langoustine hotpot, indeed'. Finishers number honey-roast pineapple with an iced coconut truffle, and exotic fruit soup, or a 'visit from the Hazlecheese Board'. Closed Sun D and Mon.

• **TADPOLE BRIDGE** (Oxfordshire)
Trout at Tadpole Bridge Buckland Marsh, Faringdon, (01367) 870382. A dyed-in-the-wool village pub on the Thames. Inside décor is traditional, although the non-smoking dining room and Neil Hougardy's cooking strike contemporary notes. Goats' cheese, rolled in poppy seeds, is served with poached pear and chive oil; roast loin of lamb comes with a timbale of couscous, sun-dried tomato farce and mint jus; while grilled fillets of sea bass are served on a rösti with braised red cabbage. There's strawberry vacherin, or apricot and passion fruit beignet, to finish. Decent wines by the glass. Closed Sun D. Accommodation and campsite available.

• **TETBURY** (Gloucestershire)
Calcot Manor (01666) 890391. A fine Georgian manor in rolling Cotswold countryside, with the Gumstool Inn (open all day) overlooking the formal gardens and taking a flexible, modern brasserie view of things. Here you will find potted haddock, devilled lamb's kidneys, shepherd's pie and so on. The formal conservatory restaurant, meanwhile, promises more complex-sounding dishes such as curried mussels with tagliatelle, coriander and tomato; breast of Gressingham duck with roasted fennel, orange and cumin; and chargrilled Dover sole with sea salt and lime. Round it all off with caramelised fig tarte Tatin with mascarpone and honey. Open all week.
Close Hotel Long Street, (01666) 502272. Inside this sixteenth-century, 'rather squat', grey-stone building, the eye-catching painted décor includes a trompe l'oeil ceiling, authentic white plasterwork and an impressive fireplace. An inspector found superb ingredients – in dishes of Cornish sea bass, and Gressingham duck with tiny beetroot dice, broad beans and roasted shallots – though was less impressed with sauces and garnishing. A praiseworthy dessert has been apricot strudel with chocolate and cardamom ice cream and vanilla froth. Service is 'caring, observant, intelligent and friendly'. Open all week.

• **TORQUAY** (Devon)
Mulberry House 1 Scarborough Road, (01803) 213639. Since 1985 Lesley Cooper has been pleasing locals and holidaymakers alike with her distinctive version of home cooking. Ingredients are fresh, prices modest and her dining room 'immaculate'. A host of dishes from her daily blackboard has been heartily endorsed, among them melon compote topped with lemon balm; bouillabaisse; toad in the hole; chicken breast wrapped in bacon and stuffed with fruit; aubergine charlotte – not to mention chocolate truffle torte and 'fantastic' banoffi bread-

and-butter pudding. A short, well-chosen wine list. Open Wed to Sat D and Fri to Sun L (residents only Mon and Tue D).

• **Tresco** (Isles of Scilly)
Island Hotel Tresco, (01720) 422883. Expect wonderful views and a glorious setting on the Island of Flowers. Local Tresco lobsters (done four ways), Bryher crab, and Devon beef make their seasonal presence felt on the menu, along with salad of Barbary duck with 'island leaves' and parsnip crisps; chargrilled swordfish with red pepper dressing; and medallions of marinated venison with sauté sweet potatoes and a juniper and 'garden rosemary' jus. West Country cheeses are alternatives to home-made iced parfaits or blackcurrant délice. Open all week. Hotel closed 28 Oct to March.

• **Tunbridge Wells** (Kent)
Sankey's 39 Mount Ephraim, (01892) 511422. Billed as a 'fish house', Guy Sankey's long-runner in a Victorian villa comprises a restaurant, oyster bar and cellar wine bar. Seafood is the business of the day and supplies are patriotically British: crabs, lobsters and langoustines from Loch Fyne, and oysters from Whitstable. Wild sea bass comes with Caerphilly and leek mash and sweet peppers; Shetland haddock fillet is poached and served with white wine and mushroom sauce, while Welsh sewin appears with samphire. Meat eaters might choose braised pheasant or steak and kidney pudding. Closed Sun.

• **Twickenham** (Greater London)
Brula 43 Crown Road, (020) 8892 0602. This popular medium-priced bistro is close to St Margaret's Station. Within, a few ecclesiastical elements, including uncushioned church chairs and pews in the main area, and stained glass windows, add to the ambience. Set lunches are £8 for two courses, £10 for three, and in the evening the à la carte offers four choices at each stage. Starters might include red pepper soup, or leek vinaigrette with pickled anchovies and focaccia, while a typical main dish is chicken basquaise. Or perhaps choose a daily fish special such as sea bream with Jerusalem artichoke and peas. No credit cards but Switch accepted. Open Mon to Sat.

Loch Fyne Restaurant 175 Hampton Road, (020) 8255 6222. The original in Cairndow (see main entry, Scotland) continues to spawn offshoots in England. This spic-and-span branch is in a converted pub; the atmosphere is relaxed and informal, and staff are polite and friendly. Loch Fyne oysters and smoked salmon in various forms are the obvious stars, but the kitchen can also cook. 'Wonderfully fresh' tranche of halibut has been served with pesto sauce, while roast monkfish has come with a spicy mussel sauce. Crème brûlée has finished off proceedings acceptably. Open all week.

• **Warwick** (Warwickshire)
Cellar 5–6 The Knibbs, (01926) 400809. This cellar is a livelier, and lovelier, venue than the name suggests, with its sunny, colourful Mediterranean décor and blue chairs, tablecloths and even wine glasses evoking memories of sea and sky (although some of this may change, as it was closed for refurbishment as the Guide went to press). The three-course menu at £15 might include rabbit and chicken liver parfait with gooseberry compote followed by suprème of chicken au poivre and carrot crisps. The food emanating from the tiny kitchen does not always live up to its French connections, but fine ingredients commended by reporters include mussels, venison and rump of lamb. Open Tue to Sat.

• **Westfield** (East Sussex)
Wild Mushroom Westfield Lane, (01424) 751137. Noted for its 'fresh bread,' 'local ingredients and smooth presentation,' this simply decorated Victorian house run by Paul and Rebecca Webbe as a family business is set back from the A28. Recommended lunch dishes have included duck and pistachio terrine with black plum sauce; 'superb' carpaccio of beef with tapénade and Parmesan; and pink roast duck breast with rösti, caramelised pears and Cassis sauce. To finish, iced black fruit parfait has been 'a revelation'. Very welcoming, efficient

service. Closed Sat L, Sun D and all day Mon.

• **WEYBOURNE** (Norfolk)

Gasche's The Street, (01263) 588220. Thirty years ago, this tidy thatched restaurant was 'famously the place to eat on the North Norfolk coast', recalls a well-travelled reporter. Since 1994, John Fountain and Deryk Riches have given it a new lease of life. Weekly-changing lunch and dinner menus are a blend of old and new: avocado with prawns, entrecote steak garni, and lemon meringues on the one hand; warm Thai chicken salad, brill with roasted chilli and sweet onion sauce, and marzipan and prune tart on the other. Outside is a patio garden for al fresco eating. Closed Mon, Tue and Sun D.

• **WEYMOUTH** (Dorset)

Abbotsbury Seafood Bar Abbotsbury Oyster Farm, (01305) 788867. Informal seafood restaurant attached to Abbotsbury Oyster Farm, located on the Fleet Lagoon (Britain's oldest water reserve) close to Portland Bill. No surprises here: oysters top the bill, but other fish is delivered from a local 'day boat' – bad weather sometimes means no supplies. Anything from potted shrimps with Dorset knobs (hard biscuits/bread), or a crab sandwich, to scallop and monkfish kebabs, jambalaya, or the full seafood feast. Steaks for meat eaters. Bottles of stout go down well; otherwise drink wine, coffee or tea. Open Tue to Sun L, Thur to Sat D.

Perry's 4 Trinity Road, (01305) 785799. Old-fashioned harbourside restaurant with 'patient, polite waitresses in black and white' and a dedication to fish. Blackboards advertise shellfish soup with Parmesan, fillet of turbot with olive oil and citrus dressing, and plenty more besides. The printed menu accommodates all comers with chilled tomato mousse, duck pâté on marinated beetroot, and roast fillet of pork with apples and calvados. 'Generous portions' and 'beautifully served' desserts such as passion fruit soufflé, or apple sorbet in a brandy-snap basket with apple crisps. Open Tue to Fri and Sun L, and all week D.

• **WHITSTABLE** (Kent)

Whitstable Oyster Fishery Company Royal Native Oyster Stores, (01227) 276856. The location, practically on the beach, is the ideal setting in which to enjoy fresh fish and seafood. The menu is listed on large blackboards and has included bivalves, moules marinière, skate with black butter and capers, pan-fried scallops with balsamic vinegar, and chargrilled mackerel with apple sauce. The short, predominantly white wine list opens at £10.95. Closed Mon (exc bank hols), and Sun (exc summer).

• **WOBURN** (Bedfordshire)

Paris House Woburn Park, (01525) 290692. A 'unique' timbered house that really did once have an address in Paris. It was transplanted to these shores – bit by bit – in 1878 and now stands imposingly in the grounds of Woburn Park: an apt setting for Peter Chandler's interpretations of classic French cooking. The main menu runs along the lines of terrine of foie gras with walnut salad; roast brill with Noilly Prat sauce; and braised belly pork; with chocolate and orange truffle cake for afters. Sunday lunch has yielded one of the best plates of roast beef that one reporter could remember. Closed Sun D and all Mon.

• **WRIGHTINGTON** (Lancashire)

High Moor High Moor Lane, (01257) 252364. The moor is very high, and the old coaching inn with views over open countryside draws diners from Manchester, Wigan, Liverpool and beyond. 'Good robust filling food' ranges from standard roasts and grills, including 'seriously good' ribeye steak, to more subtle 'genuine' terrine of smoked salmon, wild mushroom soup, or lamb shank on potato and spinach. A reporter's American friend happily plumbed the mystery of mushy peas, served on a glass plate, accompanying haddock and chips that were presented in an edition of the *Financial Times* printed on food wrapping paper. Closed Mon and Tue and Sat L.

• **YORK** (North Yorkshire)

Bettys 6–8 St Helen's Square, (01904) 659142. The York branch of this homely

chain of tea-shops is the perfect place for weary tourists to re-charge their batteries with traditional tea and cakes. More substantial dishes include sandwiches, soups and daily specials. The sister restaurants in this mini-chain (see Round-up entries in Harrogate, Ilkley and Northallerton) spread the simple philosophy throughout Yorkshire. Open all week.
Blue Bicycle 34 Fossgate, (01904) 673990. 'Passionate about food' proclaims the titillating blurb about this up-and-coming restaurant on the site of a Victorian brothel. 'Impeccable' fish might include Thai-style mussels; baked cod with niçoise salad; or spiced monkfish on seafood boulangère with spring cabbage. Otherwise consider chicory tarte Tatin with baked goats' cheese; Gressingham duck with herb pasta; fig and Parma ham salad; or sauté chicken breast with Bombay potato. 'Exceptionally good' desserts have included sticky toffee pudding, and chocolate and walnut marquise. 'Great atmosphere, very good service and a good wine list.' Open all week.

Scotland

• **Archiestown** (Moray)
Archiestown Hotel Archiestown, (01340) 810218. Philip and Rosalind Lewis took over in May 2001. Philip's lunch and dinner menus provide an overview of 50 years of gastronomic history, from half-avocado with prawns, to grilled herring fillets on roasted peppers and onions with tomato sauce, or to poached duck's egg on black pudding and spinach leaves with sauce Mornay. Franco-Italians will specially appreciate bresaola, and Lyons saucisson with baked pepper and focaccia. Simpler seafood dishes might include grilled halibut with grain mustard sauce, west coast scallops meunière, or lobster (cold or grilled with garlic). More reports please. Open all week.

• **Bowmore** (Argyll & Bute, Isley)
Harbour Inn The Square, (01496) 810330. Indigenous ingredients are the cornerstone of a menu which besides local mussels and langoustines, takes in fresh Islay crabmeat with an Islay cheese soufflé topping, and Loch Gruinart oysters either simply with lemon and wholemeal bread, or baked with creamed leeks. And all that is just for starters. Also from the island are beef, lamb and game, to say nothing of Islay malt whiskies. Wines at remarkably low prices, nearly all under £20, start with house selections at £9.95 and come from vineyards world-wide (though none on Islay). Closed Sun L.

• **Crieff** (Perthshire & Kinross)
Bank Restaurant 32 High Street, (01764) 656575. 'Crieff is lucky to have such a good atmospheric place to dine,' writes a fan of Bill and Lilias McGuigan's town-centre bistro. He cooks, she runs front-of house and doubles as pastry chef. Local supplies show up well in the shape of heather-fed lamb, Tibbermore beef, salad leaves 'from a chap in Crieff', and boxes of Crannog seafood. Praise has been heaped on pork, sage and onion terrine studded with black pudding, and sea bream on courgette and herb risotto with champagne and chive beurre blanc. As a finale, burnt Glayva cream continues to win votes. Accommodation is planned. Open all week.

• **Dervaig** (Argyll & Bute, Mull)
Druimard Country House Dervaig, (01688) 400345/291. This small country-house hotel in a restored Victorian granite-faced manse has fine views over the glen and River Bellart. It is next to the Mull little theatre, and dinner times are arranged to suit the rise and fall of the theatre's curtains. Mrs Hubbard's menu now offers a choice at all courses, and local ingredients include herbs and salads from their own gardens. House wines from the Côtes de Duras are £9.50; another 30 are modestly priced. Open all week D only.

• **EDINBURGH** (Edinburgh)
Howie's 208 Bruntsfield Place, (0131) 221 1777. One of a growing band of good-value restaurants making an impact on Scotland's east coast. Fixed-priced menus are peppered with appealing ideas. Salad of grilled black pudding is served with apple and ginger dressing; pan-seared chicken is accompanied by slow-roast cherry tomatoes, while steamed cod comes with buttered Savoy cabbage and mussel and dill cream. Puddings range from rhubarb crème brûlée to plum and frangipane tart. Licensed but you can also BYO. Three other branches in Edinburgh, at 4–6 Granville Place, 29 Waterloo Place, and 63 Dalry Road; also one at 50 Chapel Street, Aberdeen; more are planned. Open all week.
Rhodes & Co 3–15 Rose Street, (0131) 220 9190. This northern outpost of the Rhodes brand, consisting of a ground-floor bar and first-floor dining room at one end of Jenners department store, deals in modern fare along the lines of grilled sardines on courgette linguine, roast loin of pork with a white pudding sausage, and warm chocolate mousse with stewed kumquats. Snacks are available all day from 11.30 to 5. As the Guide was about to go to press, we learned of the temporary appointment of Wayne Tapsfield, an executive chef with the group; he will run the kitchen until a replacement is found. Closed Sun D.

• **GATTONSIDE** (Borders)
Hoebridge Inn Gattonside, (01896) 823082. One reporter described this converted coaching inn by the banks of the Tweed as 'an oasis in the desert between Newcastle and Edinburgh'. Tony and Maureen Rennie deal in 'modern Scottish food' based resolutely on local and seasonal produce: 'She cooks, he shoots.' Specials from the monthly menus show the style: chargrilled salmon fillet with langoustine vinaigrette; or rare roasted saddle of venison with beetroot, red wine jus, stir-fried baby beets and pak choi, for example. 'Divine' home-baked bread to start, and home-made sweets, ices and sorbets to finish. Service is 'excellent', and there is an enthusiastically assembled wine list. Open Tue to Sun D only.

• **GLASGOW** (Glasgow)
Air Organic 36 Kelvingrove Street, (0141) 564 5200. Air is actually a mixture of inorganic chemicals, albeit with a lot of organic microbes swirling about in it, but let that go. The fare in this bright, airy (ah, so that's it) place is a mixture too, with Japanese as the prime influence, others including Thai and Italian. You might eat king prawn tempura wraps with tzatziki and sweet chilli; tomato, or spinach pizza; or Air fruit salad with mango, avocado tomato and organic green leaves. The three-course set lunch is £12.95, and there are some organic wines. Open all week L and D.
Lux 1051 Great Western Road, (0141) 576 7576. In the building that was once Kelvinside Railway station is now a bar/brasserie and – above it – a dimly lit, bare-walled restaurant, Lux. (Each has a different chef.) Fixed-price menus in the restaurant mix modern ideas with some 'Flower of Scotland' gestures: collops of monkfish with chunky cucumber, tomato and lime relish on the one hand; and mignons of Highland venison with game haggis and a pickled nut jus on the other. Desserts range from crème brûlée with home-made shortbread, to strawberries glazed with lavender sabayon and served with vanilla ice cream. Open Mon to Sat D only.
Rococo 202 West George Street, (0141) 221 5004. Bold colours and loud music set the mood in this airy basement café/bar. A new chef arrived in 2001 and his fixed-price dinner menus promise such things as roast loin of rabbit with crispy bacon, shallot and tarragon cream; steamed halibut with herb mousse and creamed leek and oyster fumet; and poached corn-fed chicken with confit of cabbage and café au lait sauce – with iced raspberry and pistachio parfait bringing up the rear. Lunch and early-evening menus follow the same style. Open Mon to Sat.

• **KINFAUNS** (Perthshire & Kinross)
Kinfauns Castle Hotel Kinfauns, by Perth, (01738) 620777. This is a country-house hotel ' on a grand scale', complete with stained-glass coats-of-arms, tartans aplenty, and an ornately carved fireplace. Scottish produce and a global outlook define business in the Library Restaurant, where sensibly short fixed-price dinners might involve roast quail with winter chanterelles; loin of lamb with Savoy cabbage, strudel potato and red onion marmalade; then glazed lemon tart with a compote of berries and blueberry coulis. Open all week.

• **MELROSE** (Borders)
Burt's Hotel The Square, (01896) 822285. Owned and run by the Henderson family for more than three decades, the hotel is still very much at the heart of town life. The building dates from the eighteenth century, but the food strikes a more modern note: roasted goats' cheese with chargrilled vegetables; breast of maize-fed chicken on butternut squash and capsicum risotto, as well as fillet steak with béarnaise sauce. Lunches in the bar are simpler affairs, rounded off by some exotic desserts such as mango cheesecake with a ragoût of paw-paw and passion fruit water ice. Open all week.

• **NEWTON STEWART** (Dumfries & Galloway)
Kirroughtree Hotel Newton Stewart, (01671) 402141. Cheerful, formal service matches the ambience of this traditionally decorated eighteenth-century country house whose dining room enjoys attractive views from tall windows. A new chef arrived in summer 2001. His lunch might include 'fresh-tasting' baked goats' cheese wrapped in filo pastry set on sweet pepper relish, followed by roast loin of Kirroughtree venison with fondant potatoes, creamed cabbage and Grand Veneur sauce (a dish that was 'full-flavoured and elegantly presented'). In the £30, four-course dinner menu non-meat eaters will find carrot and coriander soup and grande assiette vegetarienne. Open all week L and D.

• **OBAN** (Argyll & Bute)
Ee-Usk – The Fish Cafe 104 George Street, (01631) 565666. 'Ee-usk' is Gaelic for fish, so there's no doubting the main theme in this converted bank building with high ceilings and stone walls. The MacLeod family used to run The Pierhouse (see main entry, Port Appin) and have immediately created a place with a comfortable, relaxed atmosphere. The printed menu is bolstered by specials depending on the catch: 'really excellent' langoustines, local mussels done three ways, oysters, Thai fish cakes, pan-fried lemon sole, and sea bass with creamed leeks are just some of the options. Around 30 appropriate wines. Open all week. More reports, please.

• **PLOCKTON** (Highland)
Plockton Inn Innes Street, (01599) 544222. Thriving village pub/restaurant-with-rooms run by a local family. The harbour is 100 yards away, and fish is the focus; in fact, the owners have their own smokehouse for prawns, mussels, sprats, and more, and gravlax is cured on the premises. Lunch brings light dishes in starter or main-course sizes. Dinners take in Plockton prawns (a.k.a. langoustines), queenies with bacon, and collops of venison with bramble and port sauce. Daily specials run to crab cakes with aïoli, and monkfish with fennel and Pernod. There's honey and whisky ice cream, or Scottish cheeses, to finish. Open all week.

• **STROMNESS** (Orkney)
Hamnavoe 35 Graham Place, (01856) 850606. Stromness fishermen provide the seafood that dominates this homely little restaurant's short menu. Chris Thomas offers grilled queen scallops wrapped in bacon on a skewer of lemon grass, or grilled halibut with herb and lemon butter, and more. Steaks of Orkney beef also feature, along with gâteau of haggis, neeps and tatties with whisky and chive sauce, or roast chicken breast marinated in garlic and thyme on a bed of egg noodles. Orkney cheeses and caramelised apple tart to round things off with. No credit cards. Open Mon to Sat D only.

• **Walls** (Shetland)
Burrastow House Burrastow, (01595) 809307. Sea fishing in the hotel's own boat is one of the attractions at this eighteenth-century house right by the water's edge. The short menu (normally three options per course) changes daily, with simple pan-frying a regular technique, applied to anything from locally caught monkfish and scallops, to the hotel's home-produced beef fillet. The hotel was up for sale as the Guide went to press.

• **West Linton** (Borders)
Old Bakehouse Main Street, (01968) 660830. The original bakery ovens are built into the walls of this 'delightful' restaurant, which boasts 'eclectic and interesting' décor. Traditional Danish smorgasbord is the star attraction, featuring a selection of seafood, fish, meat, cheese and salad for two people. Away from the renowned Scandinavian delights, reporters have also endorsed 'fragrant' mushroom soup, duck breast with parsley mash, and grilled wild boar loin steak with fennel confit. Successful puddings have included 'sinful but light' raspberry pannacotta. Open Wed to Sun L and D.

Wales

• **Aberystwyth** (Ceredigion)
Conrah Country House Chancery, (01970) 617941. The white-painted house was the mansion house of the surrounding 22-acre estate. Its dignified non-smoking restaurant with discrete, well-informed service, offers lunch à la carte while a three-course set dinner (at £27) features regional produce in, for example, starters of gâteau of locally smoked salmon and trout, or a salad of smoked pork loin and prawns with lime and basil yoghurt. Main dishes feature Welsh lamb and beef, and, for a lighter lunch, wild mushroom, asparagus and smoked cheese omelette. Rhubarb from Conrah's garden comes with pistachio sauce. Open all week L and D.

• **Cardiff** (Cardiff)
Buffs 8 Mount Stuart Square, (029) 2046 4628. Choose a wine-bar lunch from blackboard specials, such as a salad of smoked duck with pears and walnuts, or mixed Italian meats with pasta. Hot parcels may be spicy vegetables with curry sauce, salmon with spinach sauce, or chicken and Chinese vegetables with sweet-and-sour sauce. Some of these dishes also appear as starters on the restaurant menu, and may be followed by lamb chops with blackcurrant and raspberry sauce, herb-crusted baked cod, or duck breast with honey, orange and ginger sauce on red cabbage and apple. Open Mon to Fri L only.

De Courcey's Tyla Morris Avenue, (029) 2089 2232. This stylish restaurant is set in three acres of grounds within striking distance of the city centre. Choose from the fixed-price 'house' menu or the 'gourmet' carte. Starters might include warm crab and chive mousse with mussels and cream sauce, while main courses follow suit with fillets of lemon sole with chorizo, asparagus and courgette ribbons in caper butter sauce, or chicken with leek and artichoke ravioli and saffron sauce. Conclude with, say, hot rhubarb soufflé, or seasonal fruits in lemon-grass jelly with peach sorbet. Open Sun L and Wed to Sat D.

Metropolis 60 Charles Street, (029) 2034 4300. Downstairs is the bar, above it the restaurant. This metropolitan venue lives up to its name with contemporary, Med-influenced food including a starter of buffalo Mozzarella with plum tomatoes and a sea salt, basil and balsamic syrup. Main courses might run to seared tuna niçoise, and red pepper risotto with a red onion, caper and oregano dressing, although it's back home for smoked haddock with bubble and squeak, and chilled summer fruit pudding. Express lunches bring fish and chips with mushy peas, lamb and leek pie with garlic mash, and medallions of pork with calvados. Closed Sun.

Le Monde 60 St Mary Street, (029) 2038 7376. A 'fun and original' venue with sawdust on the floors and a unique modus operandi. There are no bookings (apart from large parties), so queue and choose your meat or fish from the display counters. Decide how you want it cooked, check out the salad bar, then find a table. Expect anything from deep-fried hake, or sea bass baked in rock salt, via breast of chicken with lemon, to beef kebabs. Closed Sun. Under the same ownership and under the same roof are La Brasserie, tel (029) 2037 2164; and Champers, tel (029) 207 3363.

• **CHEPSTOW** (Monmouthshire)

Wye Knot 18A The Back, (01291) 622929. 'A very pleasant, homely sort of place', hard by the Wye riverbank. Consider the carte and you might find warm Thai salad of fish and shellfish, roast rump of Welsh lamb with a gâteau of roast Mediterranean vegetables, and chilled crème brûlée with marinated sun-dried cherries glazed with praline. Sunday lunch has produced 'excellent-quality' rib of beef and 'top-notch' peach soufflé. Cheap and cheerful wines, and 'absurdly low prices' in the opinion of those who frequent the metropolis. Open Tue to Sun L (booking advisable), Tue to Sat D.

• **CHURCH BAY** (Isle of Anglesey)

Lobster Pot Church Bay, (01407) 730588/730398. As the name hints, this is very much a seafood restaurant, from the boiled winkles on the bar to lobsters kept in tanks in the garden and brought to your table prepared in seven different ways. Meat eaters are not overlooked, and can opt for duckling with a choice of orange, gooseberry or blackcurrant sauce, or steak, chicken or pork. But to dive back into the sea, starters include dressed crab, sweetcured herring, moules marinières, scallops Mornay (or in herb butter), lobster bisque, and Anglesey oysters. Open Tue to Sun.

• **GLANWYDDEN** (Conwy)

Queen's Head Glanwydden, (01492) 546570. This welcoming country pub offers daily specials and printed menus. Lunchtime open sandwiches are replaced at dinner by steaks and grills. 'Chef's specials' show an inventive mind in the fresh plum and port sauce accompanying Welsh lamb cutlets, or the vegetarian Welsh smoked mushrooms with hollandaise sauce with smoked Caerphilly cheese and grilled almonds. Interesting starters have included potted crab, and smoked goose breast with peach and apple chutney, while home-made desserts take in oranges in Cointreau, pecan pie with ice cream, or chocolate nut fudge pie. Open all week.

• **LLANFYLLIN** (Powys)

Seeds 5 Penybryn Cottages, (01691) 648604. Mementoes from Mark and Felicity Seager's travels (including from Indonesia) add to the atmosphere in their 'delightful' Welsh cottage. She runs front-of-house with 'unfailing charm and efficiency', while he takes charge of the kitchen. Regulars have endorsed 'simply cooked' mussels, rack of Welsh lamb with Dijon and herb crust, and roast Barbary duck breast. Vegetables are 'ample', and lemon posset is a popular sweet. Better-than-average house wine offering 'outstanding value'. Closed Sun and all day Mon.

• **LLANRHIDIAN** (Swansea)

Welcome to Town Llanrhidian, (01792) 390015. This 300-year-old whitewashed country inn is set in an area of outstanding natural beauty overlooking the Bury estuary. New owners Ian and Jay Bennett (ex- Kirroughtree Hotel, Newton Stewart; see entry, Scotland Round-ups) arrived as the Guide was going to press. The menu promises up-market bistro cooking along the lines of seared scallops with vegetable relish, breast of Gressingham duck with Cassis sauce, and roast peaches in nutty caramel sauce. Fixed price lunches are fair value. Closed Sun D and all day Mon. More reports, please.

• **LLANWDDYN** (Powys)

Lake Vyrnwy Hotel Lake Vyrnwy, (01691) 870692. Situated high on the hillside of the Berwyn mountain range, the hotel boasts views of mountains, moorland and forest from its restaurant and many of its bedrooms. One reporter's enjoyable three-course lunch at £15.95 (offering a choice of three dishes at each stage) turned up 'very good' bresaola with generous shavings of Parmesan, followed by 'tender and tasty' roast lamb, then – instead of pudding – 'very pungent' warm goats' cheese on thin bread with salad and chutney to finish. Choice is extended to four options per stage on the £27.50 evening menu, where sweet lovers might want to sample the chef's mini assiette of desserts. Competent and efficient service. Open all week.

• **PENMACHNO** (Conwy)
Penmachno Hall Penmachno, (01690) 760207. Martin James and Jan Williams, formerly of Martins in Llandudno, have moved to this country house in Snowdonia. Here Martin plans to prepare 'more elaborate and exquisite dishes' than he could in a popular seaside restaurant. We look forward to your feedback on the £29.50 dinner that might include wild mushroom consommé in puff pastry, lobster gâteau with crab ravioli and a saffron and chive sauce, roast rack of lamb on a compote of red cabbage, and sabayon glazed strawberries on brioche. Reports please.

• **PENMAENPOOL** (Gwynedd)
Penmaenuchaf Hall Penmaenpool, (01341) 422129. Lorraine Fielding and Mark Watson remain at the helm of this elegant hotel, although yet another new chef, Tim Rogers, arrived in February 2001. The style remains elaborately European: terrine of duck confit, foie gras and lentils comes with truffle cream; rack of lamb is served with garlic potatoes, red pepper fondue and rosemary jus; while fillet of plaice is accompanied by cucumber couscous, red wine and sultana sauce. Desserts range from bitter dark chocolate tart with raspberry sauce to hot syrup sponge with cinnamon custard. Open all week.

• **RUTHIN** (Denbighshire)
Da Vincis 7 Upper Clwyd Street, (01824) 702200. From an inconspicuous door in a mini shopping arcade a narrow staircase leads up to this surprisingly airy, split-level simply furnished restaurant with terracotta washed walls. Despite the Italian name, the food is mainly traditional: witness a starter of black pudding with potato cake and apricot gravy, and a main dish of chicken in herb crust – both served under cloches. Sauces tend to be rich, portions hearty, and Welsh lamb has been commended. The short, reasonably priced wine list starts with house choices at £9.95 per litre. Open Tue to Sat L and D.

• **SOLVA** (Pembrokeshire)
Old Pharmacy 5 Main Street, (01437) 720005. Bistro-style restaurant occupying the ground floor of a defunct chemist's shop. Paintings by local artists line the walls, and the Lawton brothers dispense the likes of Mediterranean fish chowder, chocolate torte and treacle pudding. In between there's a patriotic feel to grilled Welsh lamb steak with basil, onion and tomato chutney; local venison sausages with bubble and squeak; and fillet of Welsh Black beef on celeriac and potato mash; also check the daily list of seafood specials. 'Very acceptable' cappuccino. Open Mon to Sun D only, booking advisable.

• **SWANSEA** (Swansea)
P.A.'s 95 Newton Road, (01792) 367723. A 'lively, cheerful' venue in the commercial centre of Mumbles. The fish board changes daily: reporters have singled out black bream with a salsa dressing, although the repertoire extends to chargrilled swordfish with salsa verde, and baked hake with smoked salmon and basil sauce. Long-serving chef Liz Richards also turns her hand to such things as potted smoked mackerel pâté with cucumber relish, braised rabbit with stuffed cabbage leaves, and chargrilled ostrich steak with wild mushroom and Madeira sauce. To finish, chocolate gâteau is a 'rich' confection. Closed Sun D.

• **TENBY** (Pembrokeshire)
Mews Bistro The Mews, Upper Frog Street, (01834) 844068. Andrew Swales is at the helm of this buzzy bistro, where fish is the main theme. Caldey Sound sea bass

is one of the stars, perhaps 'brick-charred' and served with citrus and green herb butter or simply roasted whole. Mussels are done every which way (Thai, Creole, jalfrezi, etc.), and there are crabs, lobsters, Tenby plaice, and Teifi salmon, too. Away from fish, expect Welsh Black beef steaks, haunch of Welsh lamb with red pepper ragoût, and spinach and ricotta pancakes. Open all week D only.

• **TREDUNNOCK** (Monmouthshire)
Newbridge Inn Tredunnock, (01633) 451000. A great waterside location by the River Usk is one of the assets of this re-styled country pub in the Welsh borderlands. Chef Andrew Reagen used to be at Le Cassoulet (see main entry, Cardiff) and his cooking has serious intentions. Specials show the style: salad of marinated swordfish with an asparagus and lobster vinaigrette, pot-roast brisket of organic beef with truffle mash and baby vegetables, prune tartlet with caramel sauce and Armagnac ice cream. At lunchtime there are also light dishes and sandwiches. Restaurant closed Mon.

• **WELSH HOOK** (Pembrokeshire)
Stone Hall Welsh Hook, (01348) 840212. Centuries-old Welsh manor house with woodland grounds and its fair share of inglenooks, beams and panelling. Here you can relish some nostalgic French cooking of the old school: onion tart, cassoulet a l'ancienne, crème brûlée, for example. Bilingual menus also feature snails in garlic butter, breast of guinea fowl with grapes, and monkfish with grapefruit and cream sauce. There's a short, modestly priced wine list, and friendly, efficient service. Open Wed to Sat D only. Accommodation available.

Channel Islands

• **ST BRELADE** (Jersey)
Sea Crest La Route du Petit Port, (01534) 746353. On the roadside, but within sight of La Pulente headland and a short stroll from the golden sands of St Ouen's Bay, this restaurant saw another change of hands at the stoves in 2001. But the overall style seems intact; fish delivered to the kitchen door is the mainstay, and current menus list scallops with pea, mint and coriander risotto, and fillet of brill with a crab cake, spring greens and mussel chowder. Steak Diane is flambéed at table, as are crêpes suzette. No doubt service will continue to run 'like clockwork'. Closed Mon, also Sun D Jan to Apr and Oct to Dec.

• **ST PETER PORT** (Guernsey)
La Frégate Les Cotils, (01481) 724624. Enchanting views of the harbour are a big plus at this refurbished fixture of the Guernsey scene. Lobster bisque, rack of lamb, and crème brûlée sum up the output of the kitchen and have all been deemed 'excellent'. Otherwise look for classical French dishes along the lines of confit of duck with kumquat sauce, fillet of brill with local mussels and saffron sauce, and chateaubriand with béarnaise and a bourguignon sauce. Chocolate marquise, and crêpes suzette complete the picture. Open all week.

Le Nautique Quay Steps, (01481) 721714. At this long-running harbourside restaurant chef/proprietor Günter Botzenhardt (ex La Frégate, see entry above) and second chef Kevin Gauvain produce a mix of classic and contemporary ideas that make the best of the island's seafood. Mussel soup with saffron and Guernsey cream, and fillet of red mullet with Mediterranean vegetables and red pepper beurre blanc are typical. Otherwise, note pot-roast shank of lamb on creamy mash, or medallions of beef and monkfish with pepper and orange sauce. To finish, consider lemon tart with cassis coulis and lemon sorbet. Closed Sun.

Northern Ireland

• **LONDONDERRY** (Co Londonderry) ***Beech Hill Hotel, Ardmore Restaurant*** 32 Ardmore Road, (028) 7134 9279. Built as a family home in 1729, Beech Hill Hotel now boasts a conservatory with views of the gardens, ponds and waterfalls. The glass-ceilinged Ardmore Restaurant, once the billiard room, is the focus of culinary attention. Luxury ingredients abound: pâté de foie gras with balsamic jelly, ravioli of langoustines with julienne of vegetables, for example. Elsewhere, roast loin of venison comes with beetroot bubble and squeak and Brussels sprout purée, while roast halibut is accompanied by baby leeks, fondant potato and a lemon and lime beurre blanc. Open all week.

The Good Food Club 2001

Many thanks to all the following people who contributed to this year's Guide. . .

Russell and Irene Abrahams
Dr Sidney Abrahams
David Adam
Mr and Mrs J.G. Adams
Jan Adams
Stephen Adams
Mr D.E. Addison
Martin Ainsworth
John and Leslie Aird
Mrs S. Albinson
Mr and Mrs M. and S. Alexander
Dr and Mrs A.A. Alibhai
Alexander Allcock-Rouse
M. Allen
Sir Anthony Alment
Catherine Althaus
Mr and Mrs Kurt Angelrath
Sir Michael Angus
Mr H. Arbuthnott
Cynthia Archer
Michael Armstrong
Dr Sidney Arnott
Brian Ashby
Dr Robert Asher
V. Ashworth
Mr C. Aspin
D. and D. Astle
Mr P.D. Atkins
Nicholas Atkinson
David Atwell
Mr and Mrs D.G. Austin
Mrs C.S. Avery Jones
Mr and Mrs I.M. Bacon
Roger Baggallay
Jane and Martin Bailey
Iain Baillie
Mr W.H. Baily
Audrey Bainbridge
Mr and Mrs J. Baird
Mr R.W. Baker
Richard Balkwill
Dr C.B. Ballinger
Hilary Bammer
John Barker
Glenice Barnard
Mr and Mrs B.J. Barry
Mr M.D. Bartlett
Alan and Lisa Barton
Mr P. Basterra
Mrs M.A. Batchelor
Romney Bathurst
Mrs J.B. Battersby
Lindsay Baugh
Conrad Bayliss
T.H. Beale
Valerie Beck
Ms E. Becker
Mr F.R. Beckett
Prof. John Belchem
C.J. Bell
George Bell
John Bence
John Bennett
Mr and Mrs J. Bentley
Peter Bentley
W.M. Bentsen
Mr C.K. Beresford
Lucy Beresford
Gabriele Berneck
Patrick Best
Paul Betts
P.L. Bevis
Mrs L.M. Bhgelmi
Dr Delia Bickerton
Betty and Chris Birch
Ken Bird
Mr R.G. Birt
Dr J. Bisdee
Mr C.T. Blackburn
Trevor and Ann Blackburn
Mrs V. Blackburn
Mrs J.H. Blake
Mr P. Blake
Mrs J.A. Blanks
Edward Blincoe
Mr and Mrs S. Bliss
C.C. Bonwick
Alistair Booth
Dr Ben Booth
Michel Boulesteix
Canon and Mrs M.A. Bourdeaux
Mr A.J. Bowen
Rosemary Bowen
George and Garnette Bowler
John Boyd
S. Boyd
Simon Boyd
Lorraine Boyle
Anthony Bradbury
Barry Brahams
Beatrice Brandon
Chris Bray
Mr and Mrs Edwin Brew
Alex Bridgeman
Kenneth Brightman
Hazel Broadbent
Bob Broadhead
Mrs P.J. Broadhurst
Andrew Broche
Roy Bromell
Dr David Brooks
Douglas Brooks
Col. J.M. Browell
Dr and Mrs D.G. Brown
Mr and Mrs D. and J. Brown
Graham Brown
Kaye Brown
Mr N. Browne
Mr and Mrs S.G. Brunning
William Bruton
M. Bryden
Mr and Mrs Bryson-Edwards
Mike Buchanan
R.W. Buckle
Alan Buckuz
Jeremy Budden
Alan Bullock
Daphne Bullock
David Bultitude
Michael Bunce
Mr and Mrs A.G.M. Burge
Mr W.W. Burke
Renee and Gareth Burn
Michael Burns
Mr M.H. Burr
T. Burton
Mrs J. Bush
Richard Bush
Paul and Chris Butler
Peter Byworth
Dr Anne Calder
Caro Campbell
Mr J. Campos
Jane Carroll
Dr John Carroll
Mr K. Carslaw
Brian Carson
Tracy Carville
Richard Cashmore
Holger Castenskiold
Dr R.E. Catlow
Mr and Mrs M. Cavaghan-Pack
Susan Chait
Richard Chapman
S. Charles
Mr N. Charnock
Mr B.A. Chatwin
Peter Cheetham
David Cholmondeley
Mr and Mrs K.M. Choy
Mr and Mrs J. Clapham
Mrs A. Colbatch Clark
David Clarke
Mr P.K. Clarke
William Clarke and Myra Drake
K. Cleveland
Doug and Ruth Clunie
Roger Cockbill
Michael Codron
Ann Cohen

Mr and Mrs Cole
K.J. Coleman
Sara Colville
Mr R.T. Combe
Mr W. Combe
Michael Comninos
Michael Connolly
Sean Connolly
Michelle Cook
Ronald Cook
Peter Coombes
Mr B.A. Cooper
Peter Cooper
Prof. Alex Coram
Ron and Sheila Corbett
Brian Cornwell
Mr and Mrs J.I. Corrie Hill
Mr and Mrs A. Cotcher
Stephen Court
N.A. Coussmaker
Mr T. S. Couzens
Pamela Cowen
G. Craig
Gordon Craig
Mr and Mrs Peter Crane
Nigel Crapper
Mr J. Crisp
Mr A. Cross
Neil Croucher
Doreen Cunningham
Dr Stan Da Prato
Mr and Mrs Dalzell
Mr M. Daneshvar
Patricia Darby
Michael Darin
Peter and Jane Davey
Mr and Mrs D.W.M. Davidson
Alun Davies
Beatrix Davies
Brian and Sue Davies
Duncan Davies
John Davies
Margaret Davies
Roger Davies
Brian Davis
D.S. Davis
N. Davis
Roger Davis
Dr and Mrs R.P.R. Dawber
Prof. Alan Day
Mr M.J. Day
Timothy James De Lay
Sarah De Lisle
Mr and Mrs F.C. de Paula
Ms N.C. Dee
James Delahooke
Timothy Delay
Hugh Dempster
Mr and Mrs Dewar
Mrs K. Diamond
Fiona Dick
Ms E. Dickinson and Mr R. Seddon
Alex Dickson
Mellanie Dixon-Peel
Mr G.M. Dobbie
Mr and Mrs James Douglas
Mr A.J. Dourleyn
Fergus Dowding
Hilary and Mike Downes
Barrie Drewitt
Mr D.R. Drucquer
Robin Drummond
Laleh Dubash
John Ducker
Sally Duckham
Mr and Mrs L.S. Dunbar
Prof. John Duncan
Nigel Duncan
Paul Dunmore
Dr Andrew Dunn
Ryan Dutton
Claude Duval
Mr R.S. Eades
John Earthy
Dr and Mrs Lindsay Easton
Mr and Mrs K. Eckett
Mrs N. Eden
Dr S. Eden
Aileen Edwards
Anthony and Beth Edwards
Malcolm Edwards
Mark Edwards
Mr R.C. Edwards
John Elder
G. Elflett
Mrs C.M. Elkington
Derrick and Margaret Elliot
Mr I.R. Elliott
David Ellis
Dr and Mrs R.A. Emmott
D.J. Endersby
Mr H.M. Escolme
Maurice Escow
David Etherington
Mrs A.M. Evans
D. Evans
Mr and Mrs M. Everard
Jed Falby
E.R. Farmer
T. Farrell
Mr and Mrs Farrell
Ann Farrow
Mrs E.A. Faulkner
Dr Philip Feldman
Mr G.A. Fenn
Brian Ferms
Stephanie Fierz
John Finlayson
Julie Fisher
Sir Richard Fitzherbert
Mr A.T.R. Fletcher
Clare Fletcher
G.E. Fletcher
Anthea Forbes
Dr E.A. Foreman
Christopher Forman
Mrs P.L. Forrest
Mr and Mrs R.E. Forrest
G.L. Forster
Mr A. Foster
Mr R.J.N. Fowler
Linda Frain
Daphne Francis
Dr M.L. Franks
G. Franses
R.S. and S. Frapwell
Mr R.L. Fraser
Ann and Don French
Joy French
Mr C.W. Freyer
Mr A. Furness
Mr R. Fuse
Mr Gamitcheson
Paul Gane
R.J. Garlick
Amanda Garrett
Dr Ian Gavin
Mr K. Geenwell
Patricia Gerrard
Mr P. Gibbs
Richard Gibson
Anthony Gilbey
Elizabeth Gilmore
John Glaze
Mrs P.M. Glover
Christopher Godber
Mr and Mrs Jim Godfrey
Maria Goldberg
Dr Lawrence Goldie
Joy and Raymond Goldman
Linda and Susie Goldschmidt
Corinne Golightly
Mr R.F. Gompertz
Tom Gondris
Kate Goodchild
Mrs J. Gooding
Joan Goodrum
Larry and Pauline Goodson
Kate Gordon
Mr R.L. Gorick
Terry Gorman
Mr and Mrs A. Gough
Mr C. Gould
Mrs J.B. Gould
Amanda Gourlay
Mr M.B. Gowers
Mr and Mrs J.W.L. Graham
John Graham
Mr R. Graham
David Grant
Mrs M. Granzon
Jean Gray
Monique Gray
Mr M.C. Green
Mr T.G. Green
Richard Greenwell
Jim Greenwood
Conal Gregory
Mrs J. Gregory
Dr P.R. Gregory
E.J. Gribbon
Mr R.F. Grieve
Edward Griffin
Ffion Griffith
Mr R.F.B Grimble
Mr and Mrs Jim Grimes
Nigel Grimweed
Mr N.M. Grimwood
Richard Grosby
Dr Kerrie Grove
Lieut K.R. Groves
Jayne Guest
Stuart Guntzenbach
Alice Gwinnell
Michelle and Spencer Hagard

Joy Haigh
Dr Bryan Hall
C.J. Hall
Ian Hall
Dr J.M. Hall
Marlene Hall
Prof. Peter Hall
Tom Halsall
Dr B. Hamilton
Matthew Hamlyn
John Hammond
Tony Hampton
Mr C. Hancock
Gordon Hands
Mr F.G. Hankins
Ian Hannah
Mr S. Hanney
David Hansen
Mr J.G. Hanson
Mr F. Hardy
Mr J. Harison
Christopher Harlowe
Tim Harper
Dr and Mrs J.A. Harrington
Raymond Harris
Rita Harris
Dr B.D.W. Harrison
Howard Harrison
Nigel Harte
Mr J.D. Hartley
Ben and Valerie Hartman
C.I. Harvey
Julian Harvey
Peter Harvey
Mr I.H. Haste
Mrs S.D. Hayes
Vivian Hayter
Lydia Heah
T.P. Heavisides
Mr H. Hedworth
A.J.A. Helme
Pat and Roger Hemingway
Mr J.F. Hemmings
Mr P.R. Hemsley
Dr A. Henderson
Dr Anne Henderson
Mr N.F. Henshaw
Dr's Geoffrey and Joselen Heron
Dr Andrew Herxheimer
Mrs V. Heseltine
John Heskell
D. Hew
Allan Hewitt
James Hewlett
John Hicks
Russell Hilborne
Mr A. Hill
D.R. Hill
Jennifer Hill
Wendy Hillary
Hindle Zinkin
Mr E. Hinds
Mr and Mrs P.A. Hoare
Mrs L. Hodge
Ian Hollows
Betty Hooper
Frank Hoppe
Ralph Hopton
Alistair Horne
Chris Horner
Captain Vincent Howard
Mr D.M. Howarth
Lydia and Julian Howarth
Alan Howe
Mr D.P. Howell
Timothy Howram
David Hudson
Katherine Hughes
N. and M. Hull
Mr and Mrs E. Hume
Dr Tim Hunt
Mr T.J. Hypher
Fred Inglis
Mrs H.E. Ingmire
Dr Sheila Innes
K.G. Isaacson
Mrs B.W. Jack
Dr P. Jacques
Sally Jaine
Gareth James
Mrs R.G. James
J.R. Jameson
Bruce Jamieson
Robert Jamieson
Anthony Jay
Brenda Jeeves
M.F. Jeeves
Mary Jefferies
Alan Jefferson
Sarah Jeffery
A.B. Jenkins
Sir Elgar Jenkins
Valerie Jenkins
Col. F.G. Jennings
Kathy Jenson
Paul Jerome
David Jervois
Stephen Jessel
Mr B.M. Joce
Robert John
Ron Johns
Dr Paddy Johnson
R.T. Johnson
Mrs M. Johnston Jones
Alexander Johnstone
Benita and Ian Jones
Douglas Jones
Ian Jones
Mrs J. Jones
L. Jones
Dr Mel Jones
Paul Joslin
Peter Jowitt
Mr M.R Judd
Mr R. Karpinski
Dr Leon Kaufman
Mr M.M. Keir
Allan Kelly
Geoffrey Kemp
Henry Kemp
C.N. Kendall
Rosalind Kent
Mrs J.M. Kenwand
Anne Kerr
Rev Peter Kettle
Elizabeth Key
Mr and Mrs J.H. Kilby
Peter Kilfoyle
John Kimble
Mr and Mrs Michael Kirk
Mr R.N. Kirk
Mr C. Kitchen
Carol Kite
John Kleeman
Sylvia Knapp
Dr E.B. Knight-Jones
R.C.A. Knott
Peter Knowes
Chris Kong
Wendy Kramer
Peter Kromes
Mr W.F. Lahaise
Mr I. Laidlaw-Dickson
Mr S.H. Lait
Christine Lakic
R. Lambert
Michael Launder
Mr and Mrs Kevan Lavender
Dr and Mrs J. Lawrence
Richard Lawrence
Mr A. Lawson
Dr and Mrs L. Leaston
Mr and Mrs G.H. Ledbury
Adrian Lee
Mr M.P. Lee
Patricia Lee
Lt. Col. M.I. Leese
Mrs J.M. Lefeaux
Mike Lefroy
P.L. Leonard
Dr Michael Lerner
Mr D.J. Lethem
O. Levinson
Mike Levy
Alan Lewis
Mr and Mrs E. Lewis
Susan Lewis
Mr and Mrs Leonard Licht
Mr B.N. Liddiard
Mr J.R. Liddiard
Mr and Mrs R.G Lightwood
Mrs Lincoln
Keith and Katherine Lindop
Katherine Lindsay
Prof. P.A. Lindsay
Ian Lipton
Mr V.C.M. Lister
Mrs B. Littlefair
Dr David Lloyd
Andrew Lobbenberg
Mrs Brigitta Lock
Victoria Lodge
Ian Logan
Paul Lomas
Sheila Longbottom
Zara Longlands
Mr and Mrs Lourenco
Deborah Loveluck
M. Lowden
Mr G.S. Lowth
Jeremy Lucas
Mr P.S. Luckin
David Lymer
Dr and Mrs A.J. Macdonald
Dr and Mrs I.S. Macdonald
Robert Macgregor
Mr A.J. Macintosh
C.H.N. Mackey
Mrs A. Mackinnon
Prof. Margaret Maden
Sean Magee

Peter Mair
Mr J.P. Malon
Jan Manning
David Mariano
Dr Charles Markus
J.P. Marland
Philippa Marnham
Christine Marris
June Marsden
Mrs M. Marsh
R.O. Marshall
Mr and Mrs Roger Marshall
Mr and Mrs T.F. Marshall
Mr and Mrs St John Marston
Alex Martin
Mr and Mrs G.D. Martin
Roger and Joan Martin
Donald Massey
Victoria Matthem
Mr J. Maxim
Dr Victor Maxwell
C.J. May
Elspeth May
Ian May
Mr and Mrs Kenneth May
Doug Mayman
Fiona Maynard
J. McArthur
Kevin and Margaret McBrien
Colin McCarty
Thomas McCourt
John McCracken
Michael McEvoy
Charles McFeeters
Colin and Lilian McGhee
Jennifer McIntosh
Mr and Mrs Maurice McKee
Dr John McKenzie
Mr J.A. McKinnell
Barbara McLeish
Mr J.P. McMahon
Anthony Meekin
Sally Melling
A. Melnikoff
Mr and Mrs D. Melzack
Mrs E. Merriam
Harold Michaels
Dr Guy Michell
Robin Middleton
Mr and Mrs J.D. Miles
Jean and Iain Millar
Christine Miller
Mr T.W. Miller-Jones
Mrs S.B. Milne
Chris Milton
Dr Philip Mitchell
Wendy Montague
Mr A.J.R. Moon
Ms R.D. Moon
Barry Moorcroft
Mrs C.M. Moreton
John Morgan
Malcolm and Catherine Morrell
Mr N. Mountjoy
Gillian Moussa
Sandy and Lorna Mulr
Patrick Murphy
Mr G.R. Murray
Sara Nathan
Mr and Mrs Natton
Dr Malcolm Nattrass
Mr C.H. Naylor
Chris and Vicki Naylor
Julia Neuberger
Max Newfeld
Brian Newman
Brian and Tessa Newman
F.S. Newman
Mr J. Newman
Dr John Newton
Mr and Mrs Nichollsen
Mr C.C. Nichols
Frank Nicol
Ann and Edward Nicoll
Brian Norbury
Mr J.G. Norris
Bruce and Kate Nottage
Dr Ian Nussey
David Nutt
Lucy O'Leary
Neal O'Leary
Mr K.P. O'Mahoney
Gregg O'Reilly
Anthony Ogden
Prof. Robert Orledge
Mr and Mrs R.E. Osborne
Dr Elizabeth Owen
Patricia Owers
William Pack
Stephen Page
Dr Kelvin Palmer
Dennis Parker
Mr J.R. Parker
Richard and Andrea Parker
Karly Parrett
John Richard Parry
Owen Parry
Dr C.J. Parsons
Greg Parsons
Mr and Mrs John Parsons
Steven Parsons
N. Partelle
Lt Col H.C. Paterson
Bridget Patterson
Paul Patterson
Michael Pattison
Michael Perkins
Debra Perry
Keith Perry
B. Perryman
P. Peterson
Mr B.W.B. Pettifer
Joanna Phillips
Dr Alex Phipps
A.M. Pickup
Dr A.D. Picton
Richard Pierce
David Pilling
Hugh Pitt
Prof. Peter Plesch
Simon Pollentime
K.W. Prescot
Arthur Price
Mrs L. Price
R.S. Price
Mr R.S. Price
Mr and Mrs Jeremy Prideaux-Jackson
Edwin Prince
M.E.G. Prince
J. Procter
Andrew Putnam
Jack Raeburn
Jim Railton
Anne-Marie Ralston
Alan and Sue Randall and Smith
Julie Randall
T.A. Rankin
Dr and Mrs Raphael
Caroline Raphael
Gerald Ratzin
Phillip Rayner
Mrs A. Redfern
Shirley Redpath
Mrs B. Reedman
Dave and Daphne Reesor
Paul Reeve
Prof. and Mrs G. Reeves
Mr and Mrs J. Reeves
David Reid
Pat and Derek Rendell
John Reuter
Mr B.W. Reynolds
John Reynolds
Anne Rhodes
Mr and Mrs G. Rhodes
Lewis Rich
Mr D.L. Richards
Mr and Mrs W. Richards
Mr C.J. Richardson
Heather Richardson
Mr C. Ridley
Bryan Rigby
Gordon Ringrose
B.J. Ripley
Dr B. Ritson
Mrs L. Roberts
Mark Roberts
Mr A.J. Robertson
Ronald and Rosemary Robertson
Alan Robinson
Mr D.R. Robinson
Harry Robinson
John Robinson
Sarah Robinson
Mr and Mrs M. Roche
Mr J. Rochelle
Sir Frank Rogers
Frank Rogers
Margaret Rogers
Joanne Rose
Maureen Rothstein
Mr P.G. Row
Michael Rowland
Mr and Mrs D. Rowlands
Gill Rowley
Robin Roy
Mr and Mrs Ian Royle
Stephen Rudge
Mr D. Russell
Sally Russell
Mr J.S. Rutter
Ilse Ryder

Penny Ryder
Miss N. Sacchetti
L. and J. Saferoni
Mr L. Saffron
Keith Salway
Peter and Aileen Salway
Mrs K.A.R. Saunders
Mr and Mrs J.A. Savage
Emma Scammell
Christopher Scarles
Michael Schofield
Jeremey Scholes
Howard Schuman
Julian Schwarzenbach
Esme Scott
John Scott
Elenor Sebastian
E.J. Seddon
David Sefton
Paul and Stewart Sempile
Chris Serjeant
Cliff and Ann-Marie Sharp
John Sharpe
Bryan Sharratt
J.D. Sheffield
Mrs E. Silverwood
Giles Sim
Sue Simon
Audrey and David Simpson
Penny Simpson
Paula Sinberg
Mr C.T. Sinclair-Stevenson
Mr T.R.H. Sizer
Mrs J. Skilbeck
Peter Skinnard
Mr D.A. Slade
Kevin Sloane
Gillian Smale
Simon Small
Mark Smee and Fiona Clifton
Mr and Mrs C.M. Smith
F. Smith
John Smith
Julie Smith
Kenneth Smith
Paul and Yvonne Smith
John Smither
Mr A.J. Smithson
Julie Smullen
Mr G. Smyth
Mr and Mrs G.H. Snell
Stephen and Helen Solley
D.J. Solomon
Mr and Mrs W.A. Somers
John Sparrow
Alan Spedding
Dr Lian Spencer
Mrs Stainforth
Gaile Stanley
Mr K.R. Stanley
Mr J. Stanley-Smith
Derek St Clair-Stannard
John Steadman
P.M. Steeples
Mrs G.M. Stein
Mrs Stephens
Mrs J. Stephens
Anthony Stern
Will Stevens
Alastair Stevenson
Dr Andrew Stevenson
John Stevenson
Capt and Mrs J.S. Stewart
Dr and Mrs James Stewart
Mr P.N. Stoakley
Neville Stock
F.M. Stockdale
Lynda Stockdale
Mr David Stoddart and K. Bertrand
Mr and Mrs C.M. Stooke
Dr D.W. Stooke
C.W.R. Storey
J.C. Stot
John Stott
Mary Stow
Alastair Streatfield
Pamela Stringer
Julian Struthers Danskin
Neil Stuart
Mr and Mrs N. Stupple
Diane Summer
Jill Sumner
Michael Sutcliffe
Mrs C.M. Sutton
A.M. Sutton-Scott-Tucker
Margaret Swain
Mrs A.J.G. Swainson
Mr T. Swallow
Ray Sweby
Brenda Symes
Richard Tabor
Anne Tait
Simon Tanlaw
John Tarrant
Mr and Mrs Tate
Evelyn Tawell
Mrs A.C. Taylor
Prof. David Taylor
George Taylor
Mrs J.L. Taylor
Jean Taylor
M.L. Taylor
Peter Taylor
Mrs J.E. Terrington
Peter Terrington
Dr B. Thalayasingam
Russell Thersby
Alan Thomas
Mrs J.M. Thomas
J.E. Thomas
Sue Thompson
Mrs D.M. Thomson
Elaine Thomspon
J.E. Thornell
Mr and Mrs G.N. Thornton
Michael Thrusfield
Mr and Mrs Thurlow
John Tipton
Alison Todd
Mr H. Tomlinson
John Tovey
Elizabeth Towns
Steven Trembath
Sylvia Trench
Dr P.E. Trier
Mr and Mrs J.C.M. Troughton
Mrs B.R. Turnbull
W. Turnbull
Iain Tyson
Charles Ullmann
Adrian Underwood
Roger Utley
Mary Jane Van Meter Johnson
Mr J. Vanderbilt-Sloane
Anthony Verdin
Dr P.J. Verrill
Mrs S. Vicar
Mr M.S. Viner
Mitesh Visaria
Dr A. Voller
Michael Wace
Mr P.H. Wainman
Lilian Wakefield
Mrs A.M. Walden
Ted Walken Hansen
Chris Walker
Drs John and Maureen Walker
Mr and Mrs R. Walker
Val Walker-Dendle
Beryl Waller
Dr Graham Wallis
Inez and Kees Walraven
Capt P.J. Walsh
Mr and Mrs J. Ward
Mrs O.M. Ward
S. Ward
Mr A.J. Wardrop
Mr R.A. Wartnaby
John Warwick
Mr and Mrs J.S. Waters
Frank Watkin
Dr W.P. Watson
Mrs J. Watt
John Weaver
Don Webber
Ethel Webster
Dr I. Webster
Marcia Webster
Roger Weldhen
R. Wells
I.E. West
Mr J.F.M. West
M.J. West
Mr T.J.M. Weston
Mrs M. Weston-Smith
Dr and Mrs E.J. Wharton
Stacey Whatling
Mr and Mrs John Wheeler
Dr G.T. Whitaker
Liz White
Martin White
N.H. White
Mrs S.S. White
John Whiteley
Paul Whiteley
Paul Whittard
Mr and Mrs S. Whittle
Barry Whyman
John Wilkin

Mr J.B. Wilkins
Mr P. Willer
Mrs A. Williams
Mr D. Williams
Mr Dick Williams
Mr and Mrs G. Williams
Mr M.K. Williams
J.W.M. Wilsom
Drs A. and C. Wilson
Kate Wilson
Prof. P.N. Wilson
Lesley and Bernd Wilson-Goellnitz
Paul Windle-Taylor
Stuart Winter
Prof. Richard Wise
G.M. Wisenfeld
Mr G.W. Wood
David Woods
Barbara Wooldridge
J.L. Wormald
Mr and Mrs C. Worth
J.A. Wotley
John and Rachel Wren
Dr A.P. Wright
Dr J.D. Wright
Keith Wright
R.A. Wyld
Mr and Mrs J. Wyndham
Bruce Yardley
John Yeudall
Camilla Youde
John Zimbler

Index of entries

Index of entries

Names in bold are main entries. Names in italics are Round-ups.

Report Form 2002

To the Editor *The Good Food Guide*
FREEPOST, 2 Marylebone Road, London NW1 4DF

Or send your report by electronic mail to: *goodfoodguide@which.net*

From my personal experience the following establishment should/should not be included in the Guide (please print in BLOCK CAPITALS):

____

____

Telephone____________________

I had lunch/dinner/stayed there on (date) ____________________

I would rate this establishment _____ out of ten.

please continue overleaf

My meal for ___ people cost £____________ *attach bill where possible*

☐ Please tick if you would like more report forms

Reports received up to the end of **May 2002** will be used in the research of the 2003 edition.

I am not connected in any way with management or proprietors, and have not been asked by them to write to the Guide.
Name and address (BLOCK CAPITALS, please)

Signed ______________________________

As a result of your sending us this report form, we may send you information on *The Good Food Guide* and *The Which? Hotel Guide* in the future. If you would prefer not to receive such information, please tick this box☐.

Report Form 2002

To the Editor *The Good Food Guide*
FREEPOST, 2 Marylebone Road, London NW1 4DF

Or send your report by electronic mail to: *goodfoodguide@which.net*

From my personal experience the following establishment should/should not be included in the Guide (please print in BLOCK CAPITALS):

____

____

Telephone________________

I had lunch/dinner/stayed there on (date) ________________

I would rate this establishment _____ out of ten.

please continue overleaf

My meal for ___ people cost £_______________ *attach bill where possible*

☐ Please tick if you would like more report forms

Reports received up to the end of **May 2002** will be used in the research of the 2003 edition.

I am not connected in any way with management or proprietors, and have not been asked by them to write to the Guide.
Name and address (BLOCK CAPITALS, please)

____

____

Signed ____

As a result of your sending us this report form, we may send you information on *The Good Food Guide* and *The Which? Hotel Guide* in the future. If you would prefer not to receive such information, please tick this box ☐.

Report Form 2002

To the Editor *The Good Food Guide*
FREEPOST, 2 Marylebone Road, London NW1 4DF

Or send your report by electronic mail to: *goodfoodguide@which.net*

From my personal experience the following establishment should/should not be included in the Guide (please print in BLOCK CAPITALS):

____

____

Telephone____________________

I had lunch/dinner/stayed there on (date) ____________________

I would rate this establishment _____ out of ten.

please continue overleaf

My meal for ___ people cost £__________ *attach bill where possible*

☐ Please tick if you would like more report forms

Reports received up to the end of **May 2002** will be used in the research of the 2003 edition.

I am not connected in any way with management or proprietors, and have not been asked by them to write to the Guide.
Name and address (BLOCK CAPITALS, please)

Signed ______________________________

As a result of your sending us this report form, we may send you information on *The Good Food Guide* and *The Which? Hotel Guide* in the future. If you would prefer not to receive such information, please tick this box☐.

Report Form 2002

To the Editor *The Good Food Guide*
FREEPOST, 2 Marylebone Road, London NW1 4DF

Or send your report by electronic mail to: *goodfoodguide@which.net*

From my personal experience the following establishment should/should not be included in the Guide (please print in BLOCK CAPITALS):

____

____

Telephone____________________

I had lunch/dinner/stayed there on (date) ____________________

I would rate this establishment _____ out of ten.

please continue overleaf

My meal for ___ people cost £______________ *attach bill where possible*

☐ Please tick if you would like more report forms

Reports received up to the end of **May 2002** will be used in the research of the 2003 edition.

I am not connected in any way with management or proprietors, and have not been asked by them to write to the Guide.
Name and address (BLOCK CAPITALS, please)

Signed ______________________________

As a result of your sending us this report form, we may send you information on *The Good Food Guide* and *The Which? Hotel Guide* in the future. If you would prefer not to receive such information, please tick this box ☐.

Report Form 2002

To the Editor *The Good Food Guide*
FREEPOST, 2 Marylebone Road, London NW1 4DF

Or send your report by electronic mail to: *goodfoodguide@which.net*

From my personal experience the following establishment should/should not be included in the Guide (please print in BLOCK CAPITALS):

____

____

Telephone____________________

I had lunch/dinner/stayed there on (date) ____________________

I would rate this establishment ______ out of ten.

please continue overleaf

My meal for ___ people cost £____________ *attach bill where possible*

☐ Please tick if you would like more report forms

Reports received up to the end of **May 2002** will be used in the research of the 2003 edition.

I am not connected in any way with management or proprietors, and have not been asked by them to write to the Guide.
Name and address (BLOCK CAPITALS, please)

Signed ____________________

As a result of your sending us this report form, we may send you information on *The Good Food Guide* and *The Which? Hotel Guide* in the future. If you would prefer not to receive such information, please tick this box ☐.